Golf World Directory

The Ultimate "where to golf guide"
for UK and Irish Golf Clubs and Courses

**Containing over 4,500 Golf Courses,
driving ranges and retail outlets.**

Also available on CD-ROM
Updated daily on www.hccgolfworld.com

The next generation directories

GolfWorld Directory

Publishing Director: Howard Cox

Sales Manager: Neil Stokes

Project Manager: Julian Grattidge

Design & Production Manager: Lucy Hibbert
Design & Production Assistant: Paul Harrison
Design & Production Assistant: Mathew Jennings

Data Research Manager: Claire Thorpe
Researchers: Sarah Martin, Lise Taylor, Sarah Lockett, Angela Evans, Faye Jackson, James Lloyd, Marie Devaney, Michelle Malbon, Sally Webster, Sarah Murray

Editorial Programmer: Matthew Corne
CD programming: Paul Crossley
Website design and programming: Martin Robinson

Publisher: HCC Publishing Ltd

ISBN: 1-903897-01-7

Whilst every effort has been made to ensure the contents of this publication are accurate at the time of publishing, HCC Publishing and those involved in producing the content cannot be held responsible for any errors, omissions or changes in the details of this guide or for the consequences of any reliance on the information provided in the same. We have tried to ensure accuracy in this Directory but things do change and we would be grateful if readers would advise us of any inaccuracies they might encounter.

Cover Photographs:
Main Picture: Glenisla Golf Centre, © David Whyte
Grantown-On-Spey Golf Club

Further Information:

Emails: golfworld@hccpublishing.co.uk
           contactus@hccpublishing.co.uk

Website: www.hccgolfworld.com

Address: Meaford Power Station, Meaford, Stone, Staffordshire, ST15 0UU.

Tel: 0870 7541666 (From outside the UK +441782 371184)
Fax: 0870 7541667 (From outside the UK +441782 371167)

Foreword

Having been a keen golfer for over 25 years, like many others, I am abundantly aware how locating new golfing venues can be fraught with confusion and misinformation. I am a member of a brilliant championship course in Kent designed by the legendary Nick Faldo called Chart Hills. It is an incredible inland golfing experience and certainly tests my "12.6" handicap to the limit. Unfortunately as I get older and the pressures of work continue to mount, I have little time to play as often as I would like but want to find the playing venues that meet my own particular needs.

Many of my golfing friends also reflect on wanting to play different types of courses and often ask questions such as "have you played that course?" or "what is that course like?" We all have to rely so much on hearsay, the golfing press, poorly updated directories and the exploits of professionals seen on TV to select new courses to play. I have played over 150 courses in the UK and Ireland but know there are so many more "gems" out there to savour!

On many society and friendly golfing trips, my friends have always enjoyed the golf but often reflect at the "19th" about visiting new clubs based on what those courses have to offer. These discussions often became heated with questions about new golfing opportunities, choices and locations. Here are some of those discussion points that invariably never get completely answered to complete satisfaction.

- **Where is a course that is easy walking in Yorkshire?**
- **What about playing a course that has 6 par 3's?**
- **Can we find a course that will cost less than £20 each to play?**
- **Need a course that drains well**
- **Must have breakfast, lunch and dining facilities**
- **It would be good if we could stay the night at the course**
- **Where can I take my youngster to get a lesson?**

There were so many questions, requirements and wishes, I could have filled this page and several more. It was patently obvious that no one knew of a way or information source of finding new golf clubs and courses by asking about:

What a course has to offer or what facilities are available?

...But now at last there is Golf World's Directory!

A clear, concise, and informative next-generation directory with details of over 4,500 clubs, courses and related golfing opportunities in the UK and Ireland.

Whatever your fondness, long courses, links courses, tough courses, easy walking courses, or small par 4 courses: Golf World's Directory of UK and Irish Golf Courses provides usable information on name, location, description, facilities, price, and so much more. All the information you could need to help you find the golfing experience you cherish.

With over 3,000 clubs in to this new edition, along with information on golf suppliers, manufacturers and shops, Golf World's Directory remains the most comprehensive work of its kind. As a testament to the quality of this information Golf World, one of the largest selling golf magazines, has agreed to put its prestigious brand name into partnership with HCC Publishing, the directory's creator.

In addition to this hard copy format, The Golf World Directory is also available as a powerful interactive CD-ROM, containing additional venue information, more than 5000 photographs, scorecards even details of the nearest pub!

Purchasing The Golf World Directory in either form also allows membership to the www.hccgolfworld.com website, giving access to a whole host of golfing location information updated on a daily basis. AND most importantly the CD and website give you millions of extra ways to locate the golf club of your choice. Imagine being able to search for a parkland course with green fees under £20, where buggy hire is available and there is a traditional club house which serves bar snacks. Only your imagination will limit the way you use the electronic forms of the Golf World Directory.

Enjoy sifting through this new publication in your armchair and with your friends. We are continually evolving this product on a daily basis, so why not come and enjoy the whole experience and join the website as well. No doubt you will spot some anomalies, even some mistakes, but I guarantee you will not find a better or more comprehensive guide to so many golf courses and clubs for the UK and Ireland.

Keep those scores low.

Howard C Cox
Publishing & Managing Director

Your Involvement

We welcome your input; in fact we positively encourage your comments about any inaccuracies that may be apparent. We also welcome your recommendations about golf courses not currently covered in this directory. So let's hear your constructive criticism. It is our aim to continue to improve the most comprehensive source of information about UK & Irish golf clubs and courses currently available to you. So complete the form located at the back of this book, or write to us about the clubs and courses included or not included in Golf World.

Data issue points to be aware of whilst using the Golf World Directory.

1. Information given by clubs is usually obtained using sophisticated "data collection" questionnaires. If you would like to receive one please contact us by telephone on 0870 754 1666 or you can also email us at: **golfworld@hccpublishing.co.uk**

2. London (Greater) is listed as a county (we know it is not). Sub-areas of London have been recognised as a locality and are entered when they are known (e.g. Camden, Waterloo etc).

3. The Channel Islands are listed under England.

4. Some areas of information are incomplete due to lack of any co-operation by a course representative. That person, for unclear reasoning, prefers that you do not know more than they want to divulge.

5. In certain sections some names have been shortened to enable a uniform layout, but remain recognisable.

6. All telephone numbers have been corrected to the British Telecom recommended layout, including international numbers (any changes to numbers after publication is in the hands of BT). Don't forget that the international code for the UK is +44 and Ireland is +353

7. All prices listed are in UK pounds. Irish Punts and Euros have been converted to UK pounds at the time of publishing.

8. Total Yardage (Yds) and Par displayed refer to playing a course from the 'back' or 'medal' tees. Exceptions to this rule include 9-hole courses to be played twice, therefore making 18-holes. For example; a 9-hole Par 70, at 6512 Yards.

9-Hole courses note:

Some 9-hole courses are part of a 27 or more hole complex
where the 18-hole course played is decided by the club on
any day. For example; Wisley 3 x 9 holes Par 36 making high
quality 18-hole Par 72 courses.

Club/Course names note:

Club/course names beginning with Royal, or County, have
been standardised so that they appear in brackets, for
example; Royal Troon will be listed as; Troon (Royal).

Standard Abbreviations

Ass - Association
Ast - Associates
Ave - Avenue
B9 Yds - Back Nine Yards
Blvd - Boulevard
Cl - Close
Clge - College
Co - Company
Coun - Council
Cres - Crescent
Ctre - Centre
Ctry - Country
Dept - Department
Est - Estate
F9 Yds - Front Nine Yards
Fed - Federation
GB - Great Britain
Gen - General
Grp - Group
Gr - Grove
Gt - Great
Hse - House
Ind - Independent
Ins - Institute
Int - International
Mngmt - Management
Nat - National
Nr - Near
Nrth - North
Org - Organisation
Pk - Park
Pl - Place
Prde - Parade
Rd - Road
Sq - Square
St - Street
St. - Saint
Sv - Service
Svs - Services
Trce - Terrace
UK - United Kingdom

Golf World Top 100

The courses listed on the following pages form the basis of the most recent Golf World Top 100 courses.

Each course in the Top 100 is represented in Section 1 with a ☨ symbol.

Panellists were asked to rate the courses out of 100, using the following criteria; Quality of Test & Design (40pts) Visual Appeal & Enjoyment (30pts) Fairness & Presentation (20pts) Ambiance & History (10pts).

The marks were then averaged out, with the highest and lowest score for each course being discounted to guard against rouge scoring. The course score was then converted to form the top 100 rankings.

Contents

SECTION 1

This is the main section of the directory. It is used to locate a club or course you may know, or one you may have wanted to find by accessing the other sections of this book.

What information can I find?

An alphabetical listing of golf clubs with course names, address details, useful contacts, membership type, size of complex, course profile: (description, green speed, type of ground it is built on, number of holes, par, length of course, who designed it, date it was built, and prevailing wind).

Where applicable, one professional is listed per club, however section 12a and 12b may contain others.

GolfWorld Directory

ABBEY HILL

BURHILL GOLF CENTRES LTD, Monks Way, Two Mile Ash, Milton Keynes, **BUCKINGHAMSHIRE**, MK8 8AA, **ENGLAND**.
(T) 01908 563845

Membership: Public

Contact/s:
● **Professional:** Mr Keith Bond

Course/s:
● **ABBEY HILL**
Description: Parkland, Undulating, Open, Tight, Drains Well
Green Speed: Medium
Built: 1975 **Built On:** Sand
Number of Holes: 18 **Par:** 71
Yds: 5996 **F9 Yds:** 3026 **B9 Yds:** 2970
Designer: Howard Swan
Further Information:
A challenging course

● **THE FAMILY**
Number of Holes: 9

ABBEY HOTEL

ABBEY HOTEL GOLF & COUNTRY CLUB, Dagnall End Rd, Redditch, **WORCESTERSHIRE**, B98 7BD, **ENGLAND**.
(T) 01527 406600

Contact/s:
● **Professional:** Mr Declane Malone

Course/s:
● **ABBEY HOTEL**
Description: Championship, Parkland
Number of Holes: 18 **Par:** 72

ABBEY VIEW

ABBEY VIEW GOLF COURSE, Westminster Lodge Leisure Ctre, Hollywell Hill, St. Albans, **HERTFORDSHIRE**, AL1 2DL, **ENGLAND**.
(T) 01727 868227

Contact/s:
● **Course Manager:** Mr Darren Kilby

Course/s:
● **ABBEY VIEW**
Number of Holes: 9

ABBEYDALE

ABBEYDALE GOLF CLUB, Twentywell Lane, Sheffield, **YORKSHIRE (SOUTH)**, S17 4QA, **ENGLAND**.
(T) 0114 2360763
(E) abbeygolf@compuserve.com
(W) www.abbeydalegolf.co.uk

Contact/s:
● **Club Secretary:** Mr Graham Lord

Course/s:
● **ABBEYDALE**
Number of Holes: 18 **Par:** 72
Yds: 6407 **F9 Yds:** 3508 **B9 Yds:** 2899
Designer: Fowler

ABBEYFEALE

ABBEYFEALE GOLF CENTRE, Dromtrasna, Collins, Abbeyfeale, **COUNTY LIMERICK**, **IRELAND**.
(T) 068 32033
(E) abbeyfealegolf@hotmail.com

Membership: Members & Public

Contact/s:
● **Professional:** Ian Mowbray
● **Book Tee Times:** Elizabeth Riordan

Course/s:

● **ABBEYFEALE**
Description: Parkland, Short, Ideal for the Elderly
Built: 1993
Number of Holes: 9
Designer: Arthur Spring

ABBEYLEIX

ABBEYLEIX GOLF CLUB, Abbeyleix, **COUNTY LAOIS**, **IRELAND**.
(T) 050 231450

Contact/s:
● **Club Secretary:** Mr Michael Martin

Course/s:
● **ABBEYLEIX**
Number of Holes: 18 **Par:** 72
Yds: 6020

ABBEYMOOR

ABBEYMOOR GOLF CLUB, Green Lane, Addlestone, **SURREY**, KT15 2XU, **ENGLAND**.
(T) 01932 570741

Membership: Members & Public

Contact/s:
● **Pro Shop:** Mr R Wiltshire
☎ 01932 570765

Course/s:
● **ABBEYMOOR**
Description: Parkland
Built: 1991
Number of Holes: 9
Yds: 2552
Designer: David Taylor

ABBOTSLEY

AMERICAN GOLF CORPORATION, Eynesbury Hardwicke, St. Neots, Huntingdon, **CAMBRIDGESHIRE**, PE19 4XN, **ENGLAND**.
(T) 01480 474000
(E) abbotsley@americangolf.uk.com
(W) www.americangolf.com

Membership: Members & Public

Contact/s:
● **Professional:** Mr Steve Connolly
● **Pro Shop:**
☎ 01480 477669

Course/s:
● **ABBOTSLEY**
Description: Championship, Parkland, Undulating, Medium Length, Drains Well
Green Speed: Medium
Built: 1981 **Built On:** Soil
Number of Holes: 18 **Par:** 73
Par 3's: 4 **Par 4's:** 9 **Par 5's:** 5
Yds: 6311 **F9 Yds:** 3049 **B9 Yds:** 3262
Designer: V Saunders, D Young

● **CROMWELL**
Description: Open, Medium Length, Drains Well, Ideal for the Elderly
Green Speed: Medium **Built On:** Soil
Number of Holes: 18 **Par:** 70
Par 3's: 3 **Par 4's:** 14 **Par 5's:** 1
Yds: 6087 **F9 Yds:** 2844 **B9 Yds:** 3243

ABERDARE

ABERDARE GOLF CLUB, Golf Rd, Aberdare, **GLAMORGAN (VALE OF)**, CF44 0RY, **WALES**.
(T) 01685 871188

Membership: Members & Public

Contact/s:
● **Professional:** Mr Alan Palmer

Course/s:

● **ABERDARE**
Description: Parkland
Built: 1921
Number of Holes: 18 **Par:** 69
Par 3's: 6 **Par 4's:** 9 **Par 5's:** 3
Yds: 5875 **F9 Yds:** 3003 **B9 Yds:** 2872
Further Information:
Magnificent views of Brecon Beacons.

ABERDEEN (ROYAL)

ROYAL ABERDEEN GOLF CLUB, Links Rd, Bridge Of Don, Aberdeen, **ABERDEEN (CITY OF)**, AB23 8AT, **SCOTLAND**.
(T) 01224 702571
(W) www.royalaberdeengolf.com

Course/s:
● **BALGOWNIE LINKS**
Number of Holes: 18 **Par:** 70
Par 3's: 4 **Par 4's:** 12 **Par 5's:** 2
Yds: 6415 **F9 Yds:** 3385 **B9 Yds:** 3030
Designer: James Braid, Simpson ⚑

● **SILVERBURN**
Number of Holes: 18 **Par:** 64
Par 3's: 8 **Par 4's:** 10
Yds: 4021 **F9 Yds:** 2166 **B9 Yds:** 1855
Designer: James Braid, Simpson

ABERDELGHY

ABERDELGHY GOLF COURSE, Bells Lane, Lisburn, **COUNTY ANTRIM**, BT27 4QH, **NORTHERN IRELAND**.
(T) 028 92662738

Course/s:
● **ABERDELGHY**
Number of Holes: 9
Designer: Alec Blair

ABERDOUR

ABERDOUR GOLF CLUB, Seaside Pl, Aberdour, Burntisland, **FIFE**, KY3 0TX, **SCOTLAND**.
(T) 01383 860080
(W) www.accrington-golf-club.fsnet.co.uk/

Membership: Members & Public

Contact/s:
● **Professional:** Mr Gordon McCalum

Course/s:
● **ABERDOUR**
Description: Wooded, Parkland, Valley, Open, Short, Drains Well, Ideal for the Elderly
Green Speed: Medium
Built: 1896 **Built On:** Soil
Number of Holes: 18 **Record:** 66 (Gordon McCalum)
Prevailing Wind: East
Further Information:
River views from every hole.

ABERDOVEY

ABERDOVEY GOLF CLUB, Station Rd, Aberdovey, **GWYNEDD**, LL35 0RT, **WALES**.
(T) 01654 767493
(W) www.aberdoveygolf.co.uk

Membership: Members & Public

Contact/s:
● **Club Secretary:** Mr John Griffiths
● **Professional:** Mr John Davies
☎ 01654 767602

Course/s:
● **ABERDOVEY**
Number of Holes: 18 **Par:** 71
Yds: 6445 **F9 Yds:** 2919 **B9 Yds:** 3379
Designer: James Braid, Fowler ⚑

ABERFELDY

ABERFELDY GOLF CLUB, Taybridge Rd, Aberfeldy, **PERTH AND KINROSS,** PH15 2BH, **SCOTLAND**.
(T) 01887 820535
(E) abergc@support.co.uk
(W) www.aberfeldygolf.co.uk

Contact/s:
● **Manager:** Mr D Dolzanski

Course/s:
⛳ **ABERFELDY**
Number of Holes: 18 **Par:** 68
Par 3's: 5 **Par 4's:** 12 **Par 5's:** 1
Yds: 5283 **F9 Yds:** 2889 **B9 Yds:** 2394
Designer: Soutars

ABERFOYLE

ABERFOYLE GOLF CLUB, Braeval, Aberfoyle, Stirling, **STIRLING,** FK8 3UY, **SCOTLAND**.
(T) 01877 382809

Contact/s:
● **Club Secretary:** Mr R Steale
● **Book Tee Times:** Mr Duncan Brown
  ☎ 01877 382493

Course/s:
⛳ **ABERFOYLE**
Description: Wooded, Parkland
Built: 1890
Number of Holes: 18 **Par:** 67
Further Information:
Superb view of Ben Lomond from 6th tee.

ABERGELE

ABERGELE GOLF CLUB, Tan-Y-Goppa, Abergele, **CONWY,** LL22 8DS, **WALES**.
(T) 01745 824034

Contact/s:
● **Club Secretary:** Mrs C Langdon
● **Professional:** Mr Iain Runcie

Course/s:
⛳ **ABERGELE**
Description: Links, Parkland
Built: 1910
Number of Holes: 18 **Par:** 72
Designer: Hawtree
Further Information:
Attractive coastal course.

ABERNETHY

ABERNETHY GOLF CLUB, Nethy Bridge, **HIGHLANDS,** PH25 3EB, **SCOTLAND**.
(T) 01479 821305
(E) abernethy-golfclub@lineonet.net
(W) www.nethybridge.com/golfclub.htm

Contact/s:
● **Club Secretary:** Mr R H Robbie

Course/s:
⛳ **ABERNETHY**
Number of Holes: 9 **Par:** 33
Par 3's: 3 **Par 4's:** 6
Yds: 2519
Further Information:
9 hole course can be played as an 18 hole course

ABERSOCH

ABERSOCH GOLF CLUB, Golf Rd, Abersoch, Pwllheli, **GWYNEDD,** LL53 7EY, **WALES**.
(T) 01758 712636
(E) admin@abersochgolf.co.uk
(W) www.abersochgolf.co.uk

Contact/s:

● **Professional:** Mr A Jones
  ☎ 01758 712622

Course/s:
⛳ **ABERSOCH**
Description: Links, Parkland
Built: 1907
Number of Holes: 18 **Par:** 68
Yds: 5362 **F9 Yds:** 2354 **B9 Yds:** 3008
Designer: Harry Vardon
Further Information:
Views of Cardigan Bay and Snowdonia Mountain.

ABERYSTWYTH

ABERYSTWYTH GOLF CLUB, Brynmor Rd, Aberystwyth, **CEREDIGION,** SY23 2HY, **WALES**.
(T) 01970 615104
(E) aberystwythgolf@talk21.com

Contact/s:
● **Professional:** Mr Jim McCloud

Course/s:
⛳ **ABERYSTWYTH**
Description: Undulating
Built: 1911
Number of Holes: 18 **Par:** 70
Yds: 6119 **F9 Yds:** 3018 **B9 Yds:** 3101
Designer: Harry Vardon
Further Information:
Views of Cardigan Bay.

ABOYNE

ABOYNE GOLF CLUB, Formeston Pk, Aboyne, **ABERDEENSHIRE,** AB34 5HP, **SCOTLAND**.
(T) 01339 886328
(W) www.geocities.com/aboynegolf

Contact/s:
● **Club Secretary:** Mrs Mairi Maclean
  ☎ 01339 887078
● **Professional:** Mr Innes Wright

Course/s:
⛳ **ABOYNE**
Description: Parkland, Medium Length
Green Speed: Medium
Built: 1883 **Built On:** Soil
Number of Holes: 18 **Par:** 67
Par 3's: 6 **Par 4's:** 10 **Par 5's:** 2
Yds: 5944 **F9 Yds:** 2933 **B9 Yds:** 3011
Further Information:
2 Lochs on course.

ABRIDGE

ABRIDGE GOLF & COUNTRY CLUB, Epping Lane, Stapleford Tawney, Romford, **ESSEX,** RM4 1ST, **ENGLAND**.
(T) 01708 688396
(E) info@abridgegolfclub.co.uk
(W) www.abridgegolfclub.co.uk

Membership: Members & Public
Size of Complex: 240 Acres

Contact/s:
● **Club Secretary:** Miss Lynn Payne
● **Professional:** Mr Stuart Leyton

Course/s:
⛳ **ABRIDGE GOLF AND COUNTRY CLUB**
Description: Championship, Parkland, Undulating, Open, Medium Length, Drains Well, Ideal for the Elderly
Green Speed: Medium **Built On:** Clay
Number of Holes: 18 **Par:** 72
Par 3's: 4 **Par 4's:** 9 **Par 5's:** 5
Yds: 6493 **F9 Yds:** 3168 **B9 Yds:** 3325
Prevailing Wind: East
Designer: Henry Cotton
Further Information:
Beautiful parkland with views of the Essex

countryside. Offers a challenging game.

ACCRINGTON & DISTRICT

ACCRINGTON & DISTRICT GOLF CLUB, Devon Ave, Oswaldtwistle, Accrington, **LANCASHIRE,** BB5 4LS, **ENGLAND**.
(T) 01254 232734
(E) info@accrington-golf-club.fsnet.co.uk
(W) www.accrington-golf-club.fsnet.co.uk

Membership: Members & Public

Contact/s:
● **Club Secretary:** Mr Les McGray
● **Professional:** Mr William Harling
● **Pro Shop:**
  ☎ 01254 231091

Course/s:
⛳ **ACCRINGTON**
Description: Moorland, Undulating, Open, Medium Length, Drains Well
Green Speed: Fast
Built: 1893 **Built On:** Clay
Number of Holes: 18 **Par:** 70
Prevailing Wind: West
Designer: James Braid
Further Information:
Thinking man's course which looks easy but is deceptive.

ACHILL ISLAND

ACHILL ISLAND GOLF CLUB, Keel, Achill, Achill Island, **COUNTY MAYO,** **IRELAND**.
(T) 098 43456
(W) www.golfeurope.com/clubs/achill/index.htm

Contact/s:
● **Club Secretary:** Mr P Lavelle

Course/s:
⛳ **ACHILL**
Number of Holes: 9
Yds: 2942

ACREGATE

ACREGATE GOLF CLUB, Penny Bridge Lane, Urmston, Manchester, **MANCHESTER (GREATER),** M41 5DX, **ENGLAND**.
(T) 0161 7481226

Contact/s:
● **Chairman:** Mr C Brown

Course/s:
⛳ **ACREGATE**
Number of Holes: 18 **Par:** 64
Yds: 4395

ADARE MANOR

ADARE MANOR GOLF CLUB, Adare, **COUNTY LIMERICK,** **IRELAND**.
(T) 061 396204

Course/s:
⛳ **ADARE MANOR**
Number of Holes: 18
Designer: Edward Hackett, Ben Sayers

ADDINGTON

ADDINGTON GOLF CLUB, Shirley Church Rd, Croydon, **SURREY,** CR0 5AB, **ENGLAND**.
(T) 02087 771055
(E) theaddgc@dialstart.net

Membership: Members & Public

Contact/s:
● **Club Secretary:** Mr Bob Hill
  ☎ 020 87776057

Course/s:

⛳ **THE ADDINGTON**
Description: Parkland, Heath Land
Number of Holes: 18 Par: 71
Yds: 6335
Designer: J F Abercromby

ADDINGTON COURT GOLF CLUB

AMERICAN GOLF CORPORATION,
Featherbed Lane, Croydon, **SURREY**, CR0 9AA, **ENGLAND**.
(T) 020 8651 5270
(W) www.americangolf.com

Membership: Members & Public

Contact/s:
● Professional: Mr John Good
● Pro Shop:
  ☎ 020 8657 0281

Course/s:
⛳ **ADDINGTON 9 HOLE**
Number of Holes: 9 Par: 31
Designer: Hawtree

⛳ **CHAMPIONSHIP**
Description: Parkland, Undulating, Drains Well
Built: 1930
Number of Holes: 18 Par: 68
Yds: 5577
Designer: Hawtree, Taylor

⛳ **FALCONWOOD**
Description: Parkland, Undulating
Number of Holes: 18 Par: 68
Yds: 5472
Designer: Hawtree

⛳ **THE ACADEMY**
Description: Championship, Parkland, Medium Length, Drains Well, Ideal for the Elderly
Green Speed: Fast
Built: 1961 Built On: Chalk/Sand
Number of Holes: 18
Designer: Neil Carter

ADDINGTON PALACE

ADDINGTON PALACE GOLF CLUB LTD,
Addington Pk, Gravel Hill, Croydon, **SURREY**, CR0 5BB, **ENGLAND**.
(T) 02086 543061

Membership: Members & Public

Contact/s:
● Club Secretary: Mrs Pat Argent
● Professional: Mr Roger Williams
  ☎ 020 86541786

Course/s:
⛳ **ADDINGTON PALACE**
Description: Wooded, Parkland, Hilltop, Undulating, Medium Length, Tends to Flood
Built: 1920 Built On: Clay
Number of Holes: 18 Par: 71
Par 3's: 4 Par 4's: 11 Par 5's: 3
Yds: 6339
Designer: J H Taylor

ADDLETHORPE

ADDLETHORPE GOLF & COUNTRY CLUB,
Chapel Lane, Addlethorpe, Skegness, **LINCOLNSHIRE**, PE24 4TG, **ENGLAND**.
(T) 01754 871020

Membership: Members & Public

Contact/s:
● Part Owner: Mr R Barclay

Course/s:
⛳ **CAESARS PARK**
Description: Parkland
Green Speed: Fast

Built: 1994
Number of Holes: 9

ADLINGTON

ADLINGTON GOLF CENTRE, Sandy Hey Farm, London Rd, Adlington, Macclesfield, **CHESHIRE**, SK10 4NG, **ENGLAND**.
(T) 01625 850660

Membership: Public

Contact/s:
● Owner: Mr David Moss
  ☎ 01625 878468

Course/s:
⛳ **ACADEMY**
Description: Short
Green Speed: Medium
Built: 1995
Number of Holes: 9
Designer: Hawtree

AIGAS

AIGAS GOLF COURSE, Mains of Aigas, Aigas, Beauly, **HIGHLANDS**, IVA 7AD, **SCOTLAND**.
(T) 01463 782423

Contact/s:
● Owner: Mr P J Masheter

Course/s:
⛳ **AIGAS**
Number of Holes: 9 Par: 33
Yds: 2439

AINTREE

AINTREE GOLF CENTRE, AINTREE RACECOURSE CO LTD, Melling Rd, Aintree, Liverpool, **MERSEYSIDE**, L9 5AS, **ENGLAND**.
(T) 0151 5235157

Membership: Members & Public

Contact/s:
● Professional: Mr Scot Duffy
● Book Lessons: Mr Geoff Jones

Course/s:
⛳ **AINTREE GOLF CENTRE**
Description: Heath Land, Open, Long, Drains Well, Ideal for the Elderly
Green Speed: Medium
Built: 1994 Built On: Sand
Number of Holes: 9 Par: 35
Par 3's: 3 Par 4's: 4 Par 5's: 2
Yds: 3200
Designer: Mike Slater

AIRDRIE

AIRDRIE GOLF CLUB, Glenmavis Rd, Glenmavis, Airdrie, **LANARKSHIRE (NORTH)**, ML6 0PQ, **SCOTLAND**.
(T) 01236 762195

Contact/s:
● Club Secretary: Mr D Hardie

Course/s:
⛳ **AIRDRIE**
Number of Holes: 18

AIRLINKS

AIRLINKS GOLF CLUB, Southall Lane, Hounslow, **LONDON (GREATER)**, TW5 9PE, **ENGLAND**.
(T) 020 85611418

Contact/s:
● General Manager: Mr Stefan Brewster

Course/s:
⛳ **AIRLINKS**

Number of Holes: 18

ALDEBURGH

ALDEBURGH GOLF CLUB, Saxmundham Rd, Aldeburgh, **SUFFOLK**, IP15 5PE, **ENGLAND**.
(T) 01728 452890

Contact/s:
● Club Secretary: Mr Ian M Simpson
● Pro Shop: Mr Keith Preston
  ☎ 01728 453309

Course/s:
⛳ **ALDEBURGH**
Description: Links, Heath Land, Drains Well
Green Speed: Fast Built On: Sand
Number of Holes: 18 Par: 68
Yds: 6349 F9 Yds: 3165 B9 Yds: 3184
Designer: William Fernie, Thompson ⚑

⛳ **RIVER**
Description: Links, Heath Land, Drains Well
Green Speed: Fast Built On: Sand
Number of Holes: 9 Par: 32
Yds: 2114 F9 Yds: 2114

ALDENHAM

ALDENHAM GOLF & COUNTRY CLUB,
Church Lane, Aldenham, Watford, **HERTFORDSHIRE**, WD2 8AL, **ENGLAND**.
(T) 01923 857889

Contact/s:
● Club Secretary: Mrs Stephanie Taylor

Course/s:
⛳ **NEW**
Number of Holes: 9

⛳ **OLD**
Number of Holes: 18

ALDER ROOT

ALDER ROOT GOLF CLUB, Alder Root Lane, Winwick, Warrington, **CHESHIRE**, WA2 8RZ, **ENGLAND**.
(T) 01925 291932

Membership: Members & Public

Contact/s:
● Club Secretary: Mrs Karen Sykes
● Book Tee Times: Mr Chris McKevitt

Course/s:
⛳ **ALDER ROOT**
Description: Parkland
Built: 1993 Built On: Soil
Number of Holes: 10 Par: 69
Par 3's: 4 Par 4's: 5 Par 5's: 1
Yds: 5837 F9 Yds: 2841 B9 Yds: 2996
Designer: Lander, Millington
Further Information:
10 hole course can be played as a 9 or 18 hole course

ALDERLEY EDGE

ALDERLEY EDGE GOLF CLUB LTD, Brook Lane, Alderley Edge, **CHESHIRE**, SK9 7RU, **ENGLAND**.
(T) 01625 585583
(W) www.aegc.co.uk
Size of Complex: 53 Acres

Contact/s:
● Club Secretary: Mr Barry Page
● Professional: Mr Peter Bowring
  ☎ 01625 584493

Course/s:
⛳ **ALDERLEY EDGE**
Description: Undulating

Green Speed: Medium
Built: 1907 Built On: Soil
Number of Holes: 9 Par: 68 Record: 63 (Mike Slater)
Par 3's: 3 Par 4's: 5 Par 5's: 1
Yds: 5823 F9 Yds: 2920 B9 Yds: 2909
Prevailing Wind: West
Designer: Renouf
Further Information:
Challenging course which can be played as an 18 hole course.

ALDERNEY

ALDERNEY GOLF CLUB, Route des Carrieres, Alderney, **CHANNEL ISLANDS**, GY9 3YD, **ENGLAND**.
(T) 01481 822835
Course/s:
● ALDERNEY
   Number of Holes: 9 Par: 64
   Yds: 5006
   Further Information:
   9 hole course can be played as an 18 hole course

ALDERSEY GREEN

ALDERSEY GREEN GOLF CLUB, Aldersey Green, Aldersey Lane, Tattenhall, Chester, **CHESHIRE**, CH3 9EH, **ENGLAND**.
Membership: Members & Public
Contact/s:
● Professional: Mr Steven Bradbury
● Book Tee Times:
   ☎ 01829 782157
Course/s:
● ALDERSEY GREEN
   Description: Wooded, Parkland, Medium Length, Tight, Tends to Flood
   Green Speed: Medium
   Built: 1993 Built On: Clay
   Number of Holes: 18

ALDWARK MANOR

ALDWARK MANOR HOTEL GOLF & COUNTRY CLUB, Aldwark, Alne, York, **YORKSHIRE (NORTH)**, YO6 1UF, **ENGLAND**.
(T) 01347 838353
(W) www.aldwarkmanor.co.uk
Membership: Members & Public
Size of Complex: 170 Acres
Contact/s:
● Professional: Mr Geoff Platt
Course/s:
● ALDWARK MANOR
   Description: Championship, Wooded, Parkland, Sheltered, Drains Well, Tends to Flood, Ideal for the Elderly
   Green Speed: Medium
   Built: 1978 Built On: Clay
   Number of Holes: 18

ALDWICKBURY PARK

ALDWICKBURY PARK GOLF CLUB LTD, Piggottshill Lane, Harpenden, **HERTFORDSHIRE**, AL5 1AB, **ENGLAND**.
(T) 01582 760112
(E) enquiries@aldwickburyparkgolfclub.com
(W) www.aldwickburyparkgolfclub.com
Membership: Members & Public
Contact/s:
● Club Secretary: Mr Allan Knott
   ☎ 01582 765112
● Professional: Mr Steve Plumb
Course/s:

● ALDWICKBURY PARK
   Description: Wooded, Parkland, Undulating, Medium Length, Drains Well
   Green Speed: Fast
   Built: 1995 Built On: Soil
   Number of Holes: 18 Par: 71
   Par 3's: 4 Par 4's: 11 Par 5's: 3
   Yds: 6331 F9 Yds: 3248 B9 Yds: 3083
   Designer: K Brown, Martin Gillett
   Further Information:
   Superb course with copses of mature woodland. Spectacular views across Lea valley with lakes on two holes.

ALDWICKBURY PARK

ALDWICKBURY PARK GOLF CLUB LTD, Pro Shop, .
(T) 01582 766463
Membership: Members & Public
Contact/s:
● Club Secretary: Mr Allan Knott
   ☎ 01582 765112
● Professional: Mr Steve Plumb
   ☎ 01582 760112
Course/s:
● ALDWICKBURY PARK
   Description: Wooded, Parkland, Undulating, Medium Length, Drains Well
   Green Speed: Fast
   Built: 1995 Built On: Soil
   Number of Holes: 18 Par: 71
   Par 3's: 4 Par 4's: 11 Par 5's: 3
   Yds: 6331 F9 Yds: 3248 B9 Yds: 3083
   Designer: K Brown, Martin Gillett
   Further Information:
   Superb course with copses of mature woodland. Spectacular views across Lea valley with lakes on two holes.

ALEXANDRA

ALEXANDRA GOLF COURSE, Alexandra Prde, Glasgow, **GLASGOW (CITY OF)**, G31 3BS, **SCOTLAND**.
(T) 0141 5561294
Membership: Members & Public
Contact/s:
● Club Secretary: Mr G Campbell
Course/s:
● ALEXANDRA
   Description: Parkland, Undulating, Open, Short, Drains Well, Ideal for the Elderly
   Number of Holes: 9 Par: 30
   Par 3's: 6 Par 4's: 3
   Yds: 2008

ALFORD

ALFORD GOLF CLUB, Montgarrie Rd, Alford, **ABERDEENSHIRE**, AB33 8AE, **SCOTLAND**.
(T) 01975 562178
(E) golf@alford.co.uk
(W) www.golf.alford.co.uk
Contact/s:
● Book Tee Times: Mr John Pennet
Course/s:
● ALFORD
   Description: Parkland
   Built: 1982
   Number of Holes: 18 Par: 69
   Further Information:
   Challenging without being physically demanding.

ALFRETON

ALFRETON GOLF CLUB, Wingfield Rd, Alfreton, **DERBYSHIRE**, DE55 7LH, **ENGLAND**.

(T) 01773 832070
Contact/s:
● Treasurer: Mr Eric Brown
Course/s:
● ALFRETON
   Description: Parkland, Tight
   Built: 1892
   Number of Holes: 11 Par: 67
   Further Information:
   Can be played as an 18 hole course by playing the round twice, missing out the first 2 holes on the second round

ALICE SPRINGS

ALICE SPRINGS GOLF CLUB, Court Windermere, Bettws Newydd, Usk, **MONMOUTHSHIRE**, NP15 1JY, **WALES**.
(T) 01873 880914
Membership: Members & Public
Contact/s:
● Club Secretary: Mr Keith Morgan
● Professional: Mr Michael Davies
Course/s:
● KINGS
   Number of Holes: 18
   Designer: Keith Morgan

● QUEENS
   Description: Parkland, Undulating, Sheltered, Open, Medium Length, Drains Well
   Green Speed: Medium
   Built: 1989 Built On: Soil
   Number of Holes: 18
   Designer: Keith Morgan
   Further Information:
   Wind direction on the course is unpredictable.

ALLEN PARK

ALLEN PARK GOLF CENTRE, 45 Castle Rd, Off Randalstown Rd, Antrim, **COUNTY ANTRIM**, BT41 4NA, **NORTHERN IRELAND**.
(T) 028 94429001
Membership: Members & Public
Size of Complex: 142 Acres
Contact/s:
● Club Secretary: Mr John McGarry
● Professional: Mr Stephen Hamill
Course/s:
● ALLEN PARK
   Description: Parkland, Heath Land, Sheltered, Long, Tight, Drains Well, Ideal for the Elderly
   Green Speed: Medium
   Built: 1995 Built On: Clay/Sand/Soil
   Number of Holes: 18 Par: 72
   Par 3's: 4 Par 4's: 10 Par 5's: 4
   Yds: 6683 F9 Yds: 3486 B9 Yds: 3197
   Designer: J J Macauley
   Further Information:
   The course offers a challenging game for any standard of golfer.

ALLENDALE

ALLENDALE GOLF CLUB, High Studdon, Allenheads Rd, Allendale, Hexham, **NORTHUMBERLAND**, NE47 9DH, **ENGLAND**.
(T) 01434 683926
Course/s:
● ALLENDALE
   Number of Holes: 16 Par: 66
   Yds: 4541

ALLERTHORPE

ALLERTHORPE PARK GOLF, Allerthorpe, York, **YORKSHIRE (NORTH)**, YO42 4RL, **ENGLAND**.
(T) 01759 306686
Course/s:
- **ALLERTHORPE**
  Number of Holes: 13 **Par:** 68
  Yds: 5634
  Further Information:
  Course can be played as an 18 hole.

ALLERTON

ALLERTON GOLF COURSE, Allerton Rd, Mossley Hill, Liverpool, **MERSEYSIDE**, L18 3JT, **ENGLAND**.
(T) 0151 4287490
Membership: Public
Contact/s:
- **Professional:** Mr Barry Large
Course/s:
- **ALLERTON 18 HOLE**
  Description: Parkland, Undulating, Sheltered, Short, Drains Well, Ideal for the Elderly
  Green Speed: Medium
  Built: 1920
  Number of Holes: 18 **Par:** 67
  Par 3's: 5 **Par 4's:** 13
  Yds: 5494
  Prevailing Wind: North/West
- **ALLERTON 9 HOLE**
  Number of Holes: 9 **Par:** 34
  Par 3's: 3 **Par 4's:** 5 **Par 5's:** 1
  Yds: 1841

ALLESTREE

ALLESTREE PARK GOLF COURSE,
Allestree Hall, Duffield Rd, Allestree, Derby, **DERBYSHIRE**, DE22 2EU, **ENGLAND**.
(T) 01332 550616
Membership: Members & Public
Contact/s:
- **Club Secretary:** Ms Ann Wright
  ☎ 01332 552971
- **Book Tee Times:** Mr Ian Hague
- **Book Lessons:** Mr Leigh Woodward
Course/s:
- **ALLESTREE PARK**
  Description: Parkland, Undulating, Open, Short, Drains Well
  Green Speed: Slow
  Built: 1948
  Number of Holes: 18 **Par:** 68
  Record: 66 (Leigh Woodward)
  Par 3's: 5 **Par 4's:** 12 **Par 5's:** 1
  Yds: 5806 **F9 Yds:** 2837 **B9 Yds:** 2969
  Prevailing Wind: North
  Further Information:
  The course contains many challenging Par 3's.

ALLHALLOWS

ALLHALLOWS GOLF COURSE, Avery Way, Allhallows, Rochester, **KENT**, ME3 9QJ, **ENGLAND**.
(T) 01634 271414
(W) www.kingsmead.co.uk
Membership: Members & Public
Size of Complex: 19 Acres
Contact/s:
- **Club Secretary:** Mr Matt Wheatley
Course/s:
- **ALLHALLOWS**

Description: Links, Parkland, Undulating, Open, Short, Drains Well
Green Speed: Medium
Built: 1998 **Built On:** Soil
Number of Holes: 9 **Par:** 55
Par 3's: 8 **Par 4's:** 1
Yds: 2702 **F9 Yds:** 1502 **B9 Yds:** 1200
Prevailing Wind: North
Designer: W B Hales
Further Information:
9 hole course can be played as an 18 hole course. there are 18 separate tees

ALLOA

ALLOA GOLF CLUB, Schaw Pk, Sauchie, Alloa, **CLACKMANNANSHIRE**, FK10 3AX, **SCOTLAND**.
(T) 01259 724476
Membership: Members & Public
Size of Complex: 137 Acres
Contact/s:
- **Club Secretary:** Mr Peter Ramage
  ☎ 01259 722745
- **Professional:** Mr Bill Bennett
- **Book Lessons:** Mr David Herd
Course/s:
- **ALLOA (SHAW PARK)**
  Description: Parkland, Medium Length
  Green Speed: Medium
  Built: 1946 **Built On:** Soil
  Number of Holes: 18 **Par:** 69
  Record: 71 (John Wither, Ian Collins)
  Par 3's: 4 **Par 4's:** 13 **Par 5's:** 1
  Yds: 6229
  Prevailing Wind: West
  Designer: James Braid
  Further Information:
  Panoramic views of Ochills. Good testing course for all standard of golfers. Course is always in excellent condition and has tree lined fairways.

ALLT-GYMBYD

ALLT-GWMBYD 9-HOLE GOLF COURSE, Allt Gymbyd, Llanormon-yn-Ial, Mold, **FLINTSHIRE**, CH7 4QU, **WALES**.
(T) 01824 780647
Membership: Members & Public
Size of Complex: 51 Acres
Contact/s:
- **Club Secretary:** Ms Brenda McKensie
Course/s:
- **ALLT-GWMBYD 9 HOLE**
  Description: Championship, Links, Wooded, Parkland, Valley, Undulating, Sheltered, Open, Medium Length, Tight, Drains Well, Ideal for the Elderly
  Green Speed: Medium
  Built: 1996 **Built On:** Clay/Soil
  Number of Holes: 9
  Prevailing Wind: South/West
  Designer: W Adamson

ALLT-Y-GRABAN

ALLT-Y-GRABAN GOLF CLUB, Allt-Y-Graban Rd, Pontlliw, Swansea, **SWANSEA**, SA4 1DT, **WALES**.
(T) 01792 885757
Course/s:
- **ALLT-Y-GRABAN**
  Description: Parkland
  Built: 1993
  Number of Holes: 9 **Par:** 33
  Designer: F G Thomas
  Further Information:
  The course boasts excellent views of Gower Peninsula.

ALNESBOURNE PRIORY

ALNESBOURNE PRIORY GOLF COURSE, Priory Pk, Ipswich, **SUFFOLK**, IP10 0JT, **ENGLAND**.
(T) 01473 727393
(W) www.golfcourses.org/courses/showclub.asp?i=534&s=d
Course/s:
- **ALNESBOURNE PRIORY**
  Description: Wooded
  Number of Holes: 9 **Par:** 29
  Yds: 1700

ALNESS

ALNESS GOLF CLUB, Ardross Rd, Alness, **HIGHLANDS**, IV17 0QA, **SCOTLAND**.
(T) 01349 883877
(E) info@alnessgolfclub.co.uk
(W) www.alness.com
Contact/s:
- **Club Secretary:** Mrs M Rogers
Course/s:
- **ALNESS**
  Description: Parkland, Tight
  Built: 1904
  Number of Holes: 18 **Par:** 67
  Par 3's: 6 **Par 4's:** 11 **Par 5's:** 1
  Yds: 4886 **F9 Yds:** 2787 **B9 Yds:** 2099
  Further Information:
  Overlooks the Cromarty Firth and surrounding Easter Ross hills. Four of the courses holes run parallel to the gorge of the River Averon.

ALNMOUTH

ALNMOUTH GOLF CLUB, Foxton Hall, Foxton, Alnmouth, Alnwick, **NORTHUMBERLAND**, NE66 3BE, **ENGLAND**.
(T) 01665 830231
Contact/s:
- **Club Secretary:** Mr Michael Tait
Course/s:
- **ALNMOUTH**
  Number of Holes: 18
  Designer: Harry Shapland Colt

ALNMOUTH VILLAGE

ALNMOUTH VILLAGE GOLF CLUB LTD, Marine Rd, Alnmouth, Alnwick, **NORTHUMBERLAND**, NE66 2RZ, **ENGLAND**.
(T) 01665 830370
(E) secretary@alnmouthgolfclub.com
(W) www.alnmouthgolfclub.com
Contact/s:
- **Club Secretary:** Mr W Maclean
Course/s:
- **ALNMOUTH VILLAGE**
  Number of Holes: 9

ALNWICK

ALNWICK GOLF CLUB, Swansfield Pk Rd, Alnwick, **NORTHUMBERLAND**, NE66 1AB, **ENGLAND**.
(T) 01665 602632
(E) post@alnwickgolfclub.co.uk
(W) www.alnwickgolfclub.co.uk
Contact/s:
- **Club Secretary:** Mr L E Stewart
  ☎ 01665 602499
Course/s:
- **ALNWICK**
  Description: Parkland

Built: 1907
Number of Holes: 18 **Par:** 70
Yds: 6250 **F9 Yds:** 3203 **B9 Yds:** 3047
Designer: Rochester

ALRESFORD

ALRESFORD GOLF CLUB, Cheriton Rd,
Alresford, **HAMPSHIRE**, SO24 0PN,
ENGLAND.
(T) 01962 733746
(E) alresford-golf@demon.co.uk
(W) www.alresfordgolf.com
Contact/s:
● **Professional:** Mr Malcolm Scott
  ☎ 01962 733998
Course/s:
● ALRESFORD
  Number of Holes: 18
  Designer: Scott Webb Young

ALSAGER

ALSAGER GOLF & COUNTRY CLUB,
Audley Rd, Alsager, Stoke-on-Trent,
STAFFORDSHIRE, ST7 2UR, **ENGLAND**.
(T) 01270 875700
Contact/s:
● **Professional:** Mr Richard Brown
● **Book Tee Times:**
  ☎ 01270 877432
Course/s:
● ALSAGER
  Description: Parkland
  Built: 1976
  Number of Holes: 18 **Par:** 70

ALSTON MOOR

ALSTON MOOR GOLF CLUB, The
Hermitage, Middleton In Teesdale Rd, Alston,
CUMBRIA, CA9 3DB, **ENGLAND**.
(T) 01434 381675
Contact/s:
● **Hon Secretary:** Mr H Robinson
  ☎ 01434 381354
Course/s:
● ALSTON MOOR
  Built: 1969
  Number of Holes: 10 **Par:** 68
  Par 3's: 4 **Par 4's:** 4 **Par 5's:** 2
  Yds: 5518 **F9 Yds:** 2761 **B9 Yds:** 2757
  Further Information:
  This testing 10 hole course is located high
  in the Pennines. There are double tees on
  various holes, therefore it can be played
  as an 18 hole course.

ALTON

ALTON GOLF CLUB, Old Odiham Rd, Alton,
HAMPSHIRE, GU34 4BU, **ENGLAND**.
(T) 01420 82042
Membership: Members & Public
Size of Complex: 55 Acres
Contact/s:
● **Club Secretary:** Mr Paul Brown
● **Pro Shop:**
  ☎ 01420 86518
Course/s:
● ALTON
  Description: Parkland, Undulating,
  Medium Length, Tight, Drains Well, Ideal
  for the Elderly
  Green Speed: Medium
  Built: 1908 **Built On:** Chalk
  Number of Holes: 9 **Record:** 62 (R
  Edwards)
  Prevailing Wind: South

Designer: James Braid

ALTRINCHAM

ALTRINCHAM GOLF COURSE, Stockport
Rd, Timperley, Altrincham, **CHESHIRE**,
WA15 7LP, **ENGLAND**.
(T) 0161 9280761
Course/s:
● ALTRINCHAM
  Number of Holes: 18 **Par:** 72
  Yds: 6162

ALVA

ALVA GOLF CLUB, Beauclerc St, Alva,
CLACKMANNANSHIRE, FK12 5LD,
SCOTLAND.
(T) 01259 760431
Course/s:
● ALVA
  Number of Holes: 9
  Further Information:
  Record Par 63

ALVASTON HALL

ALVASTON HALL GOLF COURSE, Alvaston
Hall Hotel, Middlewich Rd, Nantwich,
CHESHIRE, CW5 6PE, **ENGLAND**.
(T) 01270 629444
Contact/s:
● **Professional:** Mr Kevin Valentine
Course/s:
● ALVASTON
  Built: 1989
  Number of Holes: 9 **Par:** 32
  Further Information:
  A challenging EGU standard course that
  follows the meandering flow of the River
  Weaver.

ALWOODLEY

ALWOODLEY GOLF CLUB, Wigton Lane,
Leeds, **YORKSHIRE (WEST)**, LS17 8SA,
ENGLAND.
(T) 0113 2681680
(W) www.alwoodley.co.uk
Membership: Members & Public
Contact/s:
● **Club Secretary:** Mr Chris Wiltshire
● **Professional:** Mr John Green
● **Pro Shop:**
  ☎ 0113 2689603
Course/s:
● ALWOODLEY
  Description: Championship, Heath Land,
  Sheltered, Open, Long, Drains Well
  Green Speed: Medium
  Built: 1907 **Built On:** Soil
  Number of Holes: 18 **Par:** 71
  Par 3's: 4 **Par 4's:** 5 **Par 5's:** 1
  Yds: 6785 **F9 Yds:** 3194 **B9 Yds:** 3108
  Prevailing Wind: West
  Designer: Harry Shapland Colt
  Further Information:
  The McKenzie course is among one of the
  top 500 toughest championship courses
  in Britain. ☂

ALYTH

ALYTH GOLF CLUB, Pitcrocknie, Alyth,
Blairgowrie, **PERTH AND KINROSS**, PH11
8HF, **SCOTLAND**.
(T) 01828 633490
Contact/s:
● **Managing Secretary:** Mr James
  Docherty

Course/s:
● THE ALYTH 1894
  Number of Holes: 18
  Designer: James Braid

AMPFIELD PAR-THREE

**AMPFIELD PAR-THREE GOLF &
COUNTRY CLUB LTD,** Winchester Rd,
Ampfield, Romsey, **HAMPSHIRE**, SO51
9BQ, **ENGLAND**.
(T) 01794 368480
Contact/s:
● **Managing Director:** Mrs P Cockshott
Course/s:
● AMPFIELD PAR THREE
  Number of Holes: 18
  Designer: Henry Cotton

ANDOVER

ANDOVER GOLF CLUB, 51 Winchester Rd,
Andover, **HAMPSHIRE**, SP10 2EF,
ENGLAND.
(T) 01264 323980
Contact/s:
● **Club Secretary:** Mr David Dunn
Course/s:
● ANDOVER
  Number of Holes: 9
  Designer: Taylor

ANGLESEY

ANGLESEY GOLF CLUB, Station Rd,
Rhosneigr, **ISLE OF ANGLESEY**, LL64 5QX,
WALES.
(T) 01407 811202
Contact/s:
● **Professional:** Mr Paul Lovell
Course/s:
● ANGLESEY
  Description: Links, Heath Land
  Built: 1914
  Number of Holes: 18 **Par:** 68
  Designer: H Hilton
  Further Information:
  The River Crigyll runs through the course.

ANNANHILL

ANNANHILL GOLF CLUB, Irvine Rd,
Kilmarnock, **AYRSHIRE (EAST)**, KA1 2RT,
SCOTLAND.
(T) 01563 521644
Contact/s:
● **Recreation Manager:** Mr D Spence
  ☎ 01563 576703
Course/s:
● ANNANHILL
  Number of Holes: 18
  Designer: Jack McLean

ANSTRUTHER

ANSTRUTHER GOLF CLUB, Marsfield,
Shore Rd, Anstruther, **FIFE**, KY10 3DZ,
SCOTLAND.
(T) 01333 310956
(W) www.eastneukwide.co.uk/anstergolf
Membership: Members & Public
Contact/s:
● **Club Secretary:** Mr Graham Simpson
  ☎ 01333 312283
Course/s:
● ANSTRUTHER
  Description: Links, Parkland, Open,
  Short, Drains Well, Ideal for the Elderly

Green Speed: Medium
Built: 1890 Built On: Sand/Soil
Number of Holes: 9 Par: 31
Par 3's: 5 Par 4's: 4
Yds: 2397 F9 Yds: 2397
Prevailing Wind: North/West
Further Information:
The course has a reputation for its fine par
3. It hosts seaside links and is always in
good conditon. It can be played as an 18
hole course.

ANSTY GOLF CTRE

ANSTY GOLF CENTRE, Brinklow Rd, Ansty,
Coventry, **MIDLANDS (WEST)**, CV7 9JN,
ENGLAND.
(T) 024 76621341
Course/s:
🏌 **ANSTY GOLF CTRE**
Number of Holes: 18
Designer: David Morgan

ANTROBUS

ANTROBUS GOLF CLUB, Foggs Lane,
Antrobus, Northwich, **CHESHIRE**, CW9 6JQ,
ENGLAND.
(T) 01925 730890
(W) www.antrobusgolfclub.co.uk
Membership: Members & Public
Contact/s:
● Club Secretary: Miss Celia Axford
● Professional: Mr Paul Farrance
  ☎ 01925 730900
Course/s:
🏌 **ANTROBUS**
Description: Wooded, Parkland,
Undulating
Green Speed: Medium
Built: 1994 Built On: Clay/Soil
Number of Holes: 18 Par: 71
Par 3's: 5 Par 4's: 9 Par 5's: 4
Yds: 6204 F9 Yds: 3024 B9 Yds: 3180

APPLEBY

APPLEBY GOLF CLUB, Brackenber,
Appleby-In-Westmorland, **CUMBRIA**, CA16
6LP, **ENGLAND**.
(T) 01768 351432
Membership: Members & Public
Contact/s:
● Club Secretary: Mr Malcolm Doig
● Professional: Mr Gary Key
● Pro Shop:
  ☎ 01768 352922
● Book Lessons: Mr James Taylor
Course/s:
🏌 **APPLEBY**
Description: Championship, Moorland,
Undulating, Open, Medium Length,
Drains Well, Ideal for the Elderly
Green Speed: Fast Built On: Sand
Number of Holes: 18 Par: 68
Record: 62
Par 3's: 4 Par 4's: 14
Yds: 5755 F9 Yds: 2963 B9 Yds: 2792
Prevailing Wind: West
Designer: William Fernie
Further Information:
River on the 15th hole.

APPROACH

APPROACH GOLF COURSE, Royal Victoria
Pk, Bath, **BATH & SOMERSET (NORTH
EAST)**, BA1 2NR, **ENGLAND**.
(T) 01225 331162
Course/s:

🏌 **APPROACH GOLF COURSE**
Number of Holes: 18

AQUARIUS

AQUARIUS GOLF CLUB, Marmora Rd,
Forest Hill, London, **LONDON (GREATER)**,
SE22 0RY, **ENGLAND**.
(T) 020 86931626
Membership: Members & Public
Size of Complex: 25 Acres
Contact/s:
● Club Secretary: Mr H Brown
● Professional: Mr Fred Private
Course/s:
🏌 **AQUARIUS**
Description: Parkland, Hilltop, Open,
Medium Length, Drains Well
Green Speed: Medium
Built: 1913 Built On: Clay
Number of Holes: 9 Par: 70 Record: 66
(Andrew Gooden)
Par 3's: 3 Par 4's: 5 Par 5's: 1
Yds: 5767 F9 Yds: 2888 B9 Yds: 2879
Prevailing Wind: South/East
Further Information:
9 hole course can be played as an 18
hole course, With Views of the London
Eye and Westminster.

ARBROATH

ARBROATH GOLF COURSE, Elliot,
Arbroath, **ANGUS**, DD11 2PE, **SCOTLAND**.
(T) 01241 875837
Membership: Members & Public
Contact/s:
● Club Secretary: Mr Scott Milne
● Professional: Mr Linsey Ewart
Course/s:
🏌 **ARBROATH**
Description: Links, Open, Medium
Length, Drains Well
Green Speed: Fast
Built: 1903 Built On: Sand
Number of Holes: 18 Par: 68
Yds: 6185 F9 Yds: 3046 B9 Yds: 3139
Prevailing Wind: North
Designer: James Braid
Further Information:
The course is situated by the coast.

ARCOT HALL

ARCOT HALL GOLF CLUB LTD, Dudley,
Cramlington, **NORTHUMBERLAND**, NE23
7QP, **ENGLAND**.
(T) 0191 2362794
Contact/s:
● Club Secretary: Mr Frank Elliot
Course/s:
🏌 **ARCOT HALL**
Number of Holes: 18
Designer: James Braid

ARDEE

ARDEE GOLF CLUB, Townparks, Ardee,
COUNTY LOUTH, **IRELAND**.
(T) 041 6853227
Course/s:
🏌 **ARDEE**
Number of Holes: 18

ARDEER

ARDEER GOLF COURSE, Greenhead Ave,
Stevenston, **AYRSHIRE (NORTH)**, KA20
4JX, **SCOTLAND**.

(T) 01294 465316
Size of Complex: 120 Acres
Contact/s:
● Club Secretary: Mr Peter Watson
● Pro Shop: Mr R Summerfield
  ☎ 01294 601327
Course/s:
🏌 **ARDEER**
Description: Parkland, Hilltop, Long,
Tends to Flood
Green Speed: Fast
Built: 1965 Built On: Clay
Number of Holes: 18 Record: 67 (D
McLellan)
Designer: Stutt
Further Information:
British Open winners Jamie Anderson
(1877, 1878, 1879) and Willie Fernie
(1883) were club members.

ARDGLASS

ARDGLASS GOLF CLUB, Castle Pl,
Ardglass, Downpatrick, **COUNTY DOWN**,
BT30 7TP, **NORTHERN IRELAND**.
(T) 028 44841219
(W) www.ardglass.force9.co.uk
Membership: Members & Public
Contact/s:
● Club Secretary: Miss Debbie Polly
● Professional: Mr Phillip Farrell
  ☎ 028 44841422
● Pro Shop:
  ☎ 028 44811422
Course/s:
🏌 **ARDGLASS**
Description: Parkland, Cliff Top, Open,
Medium Length, Drains Well, Ideal for the
Elderly
Green Speed: Medium Built On: Soil
Number of Holes: 18 Par: 70
Par 3's: 5 Par 4's: 10 Par 5's: 3
Yds: 6043 F9 Yds: 2937 B9 Yds: 3106
Designer: David Jones

ARDMINNAN

ARDMINNAN GOLF COURSE, 15
Ardminnan Rd, Portaferry, Newtownards,
COUNTY DOWN, BT22 1QJ, **NORTHERN
IRELAND**.
(T) 028 42771321
Size of Complex: 50 Acres
Contact/s:
● Owner: Mrs Iris Gowan
Course/s:
🏌 **ARDMINNAN**
Description: Parkland
Number of Holes: 9 Par: 70

ARKLEY

ARKLEY GOLF CLUB, Rowley Green Rd,
Barnet, **HERTFORDSHIRE**, EN5 3HL,
ENGLAND.
(T) 020 84490394
(E) secretary@arkleygolfclub.co.uk
(W) www.arkleygolfclub.co.uk
Membership: Members & Public
Size of Complex: 67 Acres
Contact/s:
● Club Secretary: Mr Dennis Reed
● Professional: Mr Martin Porter
  ☎ 020 84408473
Course/s:
🏌 **ARKLEY**
Description: Parkland, Valley, Undulating,
Sheltered, Medium Length, Tight, Drains
Well, Ideal for the Elderly

Green Speed: Fast
Built: 1909　Built On: Soil
Number of Holes: 9　Par: 69
Yds: 6106　F9 Yds: 2998　B9 Yds: 3108
Prevailing Wind: South/West
Designer: James Braid
Further Information:
This challenging course is laid out so that
there are in fact 18 holes. The back nine
being greatly different from the front nine!

ARKLOW

ARKLOW GOLF CLUB, Arklow, **COUNTY
WICKLOW, IRELAND**.
(T) 040 232492
Course/s:
- ARKLOW
  Number of Holes: 18
  Designer: Hawtree, Taylor

ARMAGH (COUNTY)

COUNTY ARMAGH GOLF CLUB, 7 Newry
Rd, Armagh, **COUNTY ARMAGH**, BT60 1EN,
NORTHERN IRELAND.
(T) 028 37511720
Contact/s:
- Manageress: Mrs A Knight
Course/s:
- ARMAGH
  Number of Holes: 18

ARMY

ARMY GOLF CLUB, Laffans Rd, Aldershot,
HAMPSHIRE, GU11 2HF, **ENGLAND**.
(T) 01252 337272
Size of Complex: 150 Acres
Contact/s:
- Club Secretary: Major John Douglas
- Professional: Mr G Conley
  ☎ 01252 336722
Course/s:
- ARMY
  Description: Wooded, Heath Land,
  Sheltered, Long, Tight, Tends to Flood,
  Ideal for the Elderly
  Green Speed: Medium Built On: Clay
  Number of Holes: 18　Par: 71
  Record: 67 (Ian Benson)
  Par 3's: 3　Par 4's: 13　Par 5's: 2
  Yds: 6550
  Prevailing Wind: West
  Further Information:
  Well established and maintained course.

ARROWE PARK

ARROWE PARK GOLF COURSE, Arrowe Pk
Rd, Wirral, **MERSEYSIDE**, L49 5LW,
ENGLAND.
(T) 0151 6771527
Membership: Public
Contact/s:
- Club Secretary: Mr Cliff Jones
- Professional: Mr Colin Disbury
Course/s:
- LONG
  Description: Parkland, Sheltered, Long,
  Tends to Flood, Ideal for the Elderly
  Green Speed: Medium Built On: Clay
  Number of Holes: 18　Par: 71
  Par 3's: 5　Par 4's: 9　Par 5's: 4
  Yds: 6387　F9 Yds: 3050　B9 Yds: 3337
- SHORT
  Number of Holes: 9　Par: 68
  Par 3's: 2　Par 4's: 6　Par 5's: 1

Yds: 5873　F9 Yds: 2868　B9 Yds: 3005
Further Information:
9 hole course can be played as an 18 hole
course

ARSCOTT

ARSCOTT GOLF CLUB, Arscott, Pontesbury,
Shrewsbury, **SHROPSHIRE**, SY5 0XP,
ENGLAND.
(T) 01743 860114
(W) www.arscottgolfclub.co.uk
Membership: Members & Public
Size of Complex: 100 Acres
Contact/s:
- Club Secretary: Mr Tony Peterson
- Professional: Mr Ian Dovan
  ☎ 01743 860881
Course/s:
- ARSCOTT
  Description: Parkland, Undulating, Tight,
  Drains Well, Ideal for the Elderly
  Green Speed: Medium
  Built: 1992　Built On: Clay/Soil
  Number of Holes: 18　Record: 66
  Yds: 6100
  Designer: Martin Hamer

ASCOT (ROYAL)

ROYAL ASCOT GOLF CLUB, Winkfield Rd,
Ascot, **BERKSHIRE**, SL5 7LJ, **ENGLAND**.
(T) 01344 625175
Membership: Members & Public
Contact/s:
- Club Secretary: Mrs S Thompson
- Professional: Mr Alistair White
  ☎ 01344 624656
Course/s:
- ROYAL ASCOT
  Description: Heath Land, Open, Medium
  Length, Tight, Drains Well, Ideal for the
  Elderly
  Green Speed: Medium
  Built: 1889　Built On: Sand/Soil
  Number of Holes: 18　Par: 69
  Record: 67 (Barry Lane)
  Yds: 5716　F9 Yds: 2815　B9 Yds: 2901
  Designer: Taylor
  Further Information:
  Built on Ascot Race Course, the Royal
  Ascot is the oldest golf club in Berkshire.

ASH VALLEY GOLF CLUB

MUCH HADHAM GOLF PAY & PLAY, Much
Hadham Golf Course, Much Hadham Lane,
Much Hadham, **HERTFORDSHIRE**, SG10
6HD, **ENGLAND**.
(T) 01279 843253
Membership: Members & Public
Contact/s:
- Employee: Mr M McGeoch
Course/s:
- ASH VALLEY
  Description: Hilltop, Undulating, Open,
  Long
  Green Speed: Medium
  Built: 1994
  Number of Holes: 18
  Designer: Martin Gillett

ASHBOURNE

ASHBOURNE GOLF CLUB, Archerstown,
Ashbourne, **COUNTY MEATH**, **IRELAND**.
(T) 01 8352005
(E) ashgc@iol.ie
(W) www.ashbournegolfclub.ie

Course/s:
- ASHBOURNE
  Number of Holes: 18　Par: 68
  Yds: 6141

ASHBOURNE

ASHBOURNE GOLF CLUB, Wyaston Rd,
Ashbourne, **DERBYSHIRE**, DE6 1NB,
ENGLAND.
(T) 01335 342078
Membership: Members & Public
Size of Complex: 130 Acres
Contact/s:
- Professional: Mr Andrew Smith
  ☎ 01335 347960
Course/s:
- ASHBOURNE
  Description: Championship, Parkland,
  Moorland, Undulating, Open, Medium
  Length, Tight, Drains Well, Ideal for the
  Elderly
  Green Speed: Medium
  Built: 1998　Built On: Clay/Sand
  Number of Holes: 18　Par: 71
  Par 3's: 5　Par 4's: 9　Par 5's: 4
  Yds: 6365
  Prevailing Wind: South/West
  Designer: D Hemstock
  Further Information:
  USPGA specification greens with 3 water
  features. Course was previously in 1886
  as a 9 hole course but was upgraded in
  1998 to an 18 hole course.

ASHBURNHAM

ASHBURNHAM GOLF CLUB, Cliffe Trce,
Burry Port, **CARMARTHENSHIRE**, SA16
0HN, **WALES**.
(T) 01554 832269
Contact/s:
- Club Secretary: Mr D K Williams
- Pro Shop: Mr R Ryder
Course/s:
- ASHBURNHAM
  Number of Holes: 18
  Designer: Taylor

ASHBURY

ASHBURY GOLF HOTEL, Higher Maddaford,
Southcott, Okehampton, **DEVON**, EX20 4NL,
ENGLAND.
(T) 01837 55453
(W) www.ashburygolfhotel.co.uk
Membership: Members & Public
Size of Complex: 240 Acres
Contact/s:
- Club Secretary: Mr Paul Ratenbury
- Professional: Mr Reg Cade
Course/s:
- ACORNS PAR 3
  Number of Holes: 18
- BEECHES AND WILLOWS
  Number of Holes: 18　Par: 66
  Yds: 4954
- OAKWOOD
  Description: Wooded, Parkland, Valley,
  Undulating, Sheltered, Open, Short, Tight,
  Drains Well, Ideal for the Elderly
  Green Speed: Medium
  Built: 1991　Built On: Sand/Soil
  Number of Holes: 18　Par: 68
  Yds: 5343
  Designer: David Fenson
- PINES AND BEECHES
  Number of Holes: 18　Par: 70

WILLOWS AND PINES
Number of Holes: 18 **Par:** 68
Yds: 5316

ASHBY DECOY

ASHBY DECOY GOLF CLUB, Burringham Rd, Scunthorpe, **LINCOLNSHIRE (NORTH),** DN17 2AB, **ENGLAND.**
(T) 01724 866561
(W) www.ashbydecoy.co.uk
Membership: Members & Public

Contact/s:
- **Club Secretary:** Ms Jane Harrison
- **Professional:** Mr Andrew Miller
  ☎ 01724 868972

Course/s:
ASHBY DECOY
Description: Parkland, Undulating, Sheltered, Open, Medium Length, Tight, Drains Well, Ideal for the Elderly
Green Speed: Medium
Built: 1936 **Built On:** Sand
Number of Holes: 18 **Par:** 71
Par 3's: 5 **Par 4's:** 9 **Par 5's:** 4
Yds: 6250 **F9 Yds:** 3022 **B9 Yds:** 3228

ASHDOWN FOREST

ASHDOWN FOREST GOLF HOTEL, Chapel Lane, Forest Row, **SUSSEX (EAST),** RH18 5BB, **ENGLAND.**
(T) 01342 824866

Course/s:
WEST
Number of Holes: 18

ASHDOWN FOREST (ROYAL)

ROYAL ASHDOWN FOREST GOLF CLUB, Chapel Lane, Forest Row, **SUSSEX (EAST),** RH18 5LR, **ENGLAND.**
(T) 01342 822018

Contact/s:
- **Club Secretary:** Mr D Scrivens
- **Professional:** Mr Martyn Landsborough
  ☎ 01342 822247

Course/s:
OLD
Description: Heath Land, Undulating
Green Speed: Medium
Built: 1888 **Built On:** Clay/Sand
Number of Holes: 18 **Par:** 72
Par 3's: 4 **Par 4's:** 10 **Par 5's:** 4
Yds: 6477 **F9 Yds:** 3062 **B9 Yds:** 3415
Further Information:
The course has panoramic views and no bunkers. ♈

ASHFORD

ASHFORD GOLF CLUB, Sandyhurst Lane, Ashford, **KENT,** TN25 4NT, **ENGLAND.**
(T) 01233 620180
Size of Complex: 105 Acres

Contact/s:
- **Club Secretary:** Mr Anthony Story
  ☎ 01233 622655
- **Professional:** Mr Hugh Sherman
  ☎ 01233 629644

Course/s:
ASHFORD
Description: Parkland, Medium Length, Drains Well
Green Speed: Medium
Built: 1925 **Built On:** Sand
Number of Holes: 18 **Par:** 71
Par 3's: 4 **Par 4's:** 11 **Par 5's:** 3
Yds: 6255 **F9 Yds:** 3093 **B9 Yds:** 3162
Designer: C K Cotton

Further Information:
Challenging course.

ASHFORD

ASHFORD GOLF COMPLEX, Bears Lane, Great Chart, Ashford, **KENT,** TN23 3BZ, **ENGLAND.**
(T) 01233 645858
Membership: Members & Public
Size of Complex: 20 Acres

Contact/s:
- **Professional:** Mr Cameron Cowie
- **Pro Shop:** Mr Dominic Collins

Course/s:
ASHFORD
Description: Wooded, Parkland, Open, Medium Length, Drains Well, Ideal for the Elderly
Green Speed: Medium
Built: 1992 **Built On:** Clay/Soil
Number of Holes: 9 **Par:** 64
Yds: 4887 **F9 Yds:** 2407 **B9 Yds:** 2480
Prevailing Wind: South/West
Designer: Kay
Further Information:
9 hole course can be played as an 18 hole course

ASHFORD MANOR

ASHFORD MANOR GOLF CLUB, Fordbridge Rd, Ashford, **SURREY,** TW15 3RT, **ENGLAND.**
(T) 01784 424644

Contact/s:
- **Club Secretary:** Mr David Seward
- **Professional:** M Finney
  ☎ 01784 255940

Course/s:
ASHFORD MANOR
Description: Parkland
Number of Holes: 18
Yds: 6352

ASHLEY WOOD

ASHLEY WOOD GOLF CLUB, Wimborne Rd, Blandford Forum, **DORSET,** DT11 9HN, **ENGLAND.**
(T) 01258 452253
Membership: Members & Public

Contact/s:
- **Club Secretary:** Miss C Joyce
  ☎ 01258 450590

Course/s:
THE ASHLEY WOOD
Description: Wooded, Parkland, Undulating, Medium Length, Drains Well, Ideal for the Elderly
Green Speed: Medium/Fast
Built: 1896 **Built On:** Chalk
Number of Holes: 18 **Par:** 70
Par 3's: 4 **Par 4's:** 12 **Par 5's:** 2
Yds: 6281 **F9 Yds:** 3036 **B9 Yds:** 3245
Designer: P Tallack

ASHRIDGE

ASHRIDGE GOLF CLUB, Golf Club Rd, Little Gaddesden, Berkhamsted, **HERTFORDSHIRE,** HP4 1LY, **ENGLAND.**
(T) 01442 842379
(W) www.ashridgegolfclub.ltd.uk
Membership: Members & Public
Size of Complex: 350 Acres

Contact/s:
- **Club Secretary:** Mr M Silver
  ☎ 01442 842244

- **Professional:** Mr Andrew Ainsworth
  ☎ 01442 842307

Course/s:
ASHRIDGE
Description: Wooded, Parkland, Sheltered, Medium Length, Tight, Drains Well
Green Speed: Medium/Fast
Built: 1932
Number of Holes: 18 **Par:** 72
Par 3's: 5 **Par 4's:** 8 **Par 5's:** 5
Yds: 6547 **F9 Yds:** 3103 **B9 Yds:** 3444
Designer: Campbell, C Hutchinson, N Hutchinson

ASHTON

ASHTON GOLF CENTRE, Ashton With Stodday, Lancaster, **LANCASHIRE,** LA2 0AJ, **ENGLAND.**
(T) 01524 752221
Membership: Members & Public

Contact/s:
- **Professional:** Mr Andrew Pye
- **Pro Shop:** Mr David Bonehill

Course/s:
ASHTON 9 HOLE
Description: Open, Short, Tight, Drains Well
Green Speed: Slow
Built: 1993 **Built On:** Soil
Number of Holes: 9
Prevailing Wind: South/West

ASHTON & LEA

ASHTON & LEA GOLF CLUB, Tudor Ave, Off Blackpool Rd, Lea, Preston, **LANCASHIRE,** PR4 0XA, **ENGLAND.**
(T) 01772 735282
Membership: Members & Public

Contact/s:
- **Club Secretary:** Mr Trevor Ashton
  ☎ 01772 732107
- **Professional:** Mr Mike Greenough
  ☎ 01772 720374

Course/s:
ASHTON & LEA
Description: Parkland
Green Speed: Medium
Built: 1913 **Built On:** Clay
Number of Holes: 18 **Par:** 71
Record: 66 (John Hawksworth)
Par 3's: 3 **Par 4's:** 13 **Par 5's:** 2
Yds: 6334 **F9 Yds:** 3114 **B9 Yds:** 3220
Prevailing Wind: West
Designer: J Steel

ASHTON COURT

ASHTON COURT GOLF COURSE, Ashton Court, Long Ashton, Bristol, **BRISTOL,** BS41 9JN, **ENGLAND.**
(T) 01179 738508

Contact/s:
- **General Manager:** Mr Richard Roose

Course/s:
LODGE COURSE
Number of Holes: 18

PLATEAU
Number of Holes: 18

ASHTON IN MAKERFIELD

ASHTON IN MAKERFIELD GOLF CLUB, Garswood Pk, Liverpool Rd, Ashton-In-Makerfield, Wigan, **LANCASHIRE,** WN4 0YT, **ENGLAND.**
(T) 01942 719330

Contact/s:
● Club Secretary: Mr Jim Hey

Course/s:
🏌 **ASHTON-IN-MAKERFIELD**
Number of Holes: 18

ASHTON-ON-MERSEY

ASHTON-ON-MERSEY GOLF CLUB,
Church Lane, Sale, **CHESHIRE**, M33 5QQ,
ENGLAND.
(T) 0161 9623727

Contact/s:
● Professional: Mr Michael Williams

Course/s:
🏌 **ASHTON ON MERSEY**
Description: Wooded, Parkland, Tight
Built: 1897
Number of Holes: 9　Par: 71

ASHTON-UNDER-LYNE

ASHTON-UNDER-LYNE GOLF CLUB,
Gorsey Way, Kings Rd, Ashton-under-Lyne,
LANCASHIRE, OL6 9HT, **ENGLAND.**
(T) 0161 3301537
(W) www.astonwoodgolfclub.co.uk

Membership: Members & Public

Contact/s:
● Club Secretary: Mr Alan Jackson
● Professional: Mr Colin Boyle

Course/s:
🏌 **ASHTON-UNDER-LYNE**
Description: Championship, Wooded,
Parkland, Sheltered, Long, Ideal for the
Elderly
Green Speed: Medium
Built: 1913　Built On: Clay
Number of Holes: 18
Prevailing Wind: West
Further Information:
Demanding course.

ASHWOODS

ASHWOODS GOLF CENTRE, Sligo Rd,
Enniskillen, **COUNTY FERMANAGH**, BT74
7JZ, **NORTHERN IRELAND.**
(T) 028 6632 5321

Membership: Members & Public
Size of Complex: 29 Acres

Contact/s:
● Club Secretary: Mr Michael O'Dolan
● Professional: Mr Patrick Trainor
● Pro Shop: Mr Thomas Laughran

Course/s:
🏌 **ASHWOODS**
Description: Wooded, Sheltered,
Medium Length, Tight, Drains Well, Ideal
for the Elderly
Green Speed: Fast
Built: 1995　Built On: Soil
Number of Holes: 14
Prevailing Wind: West
Designer: O'Dolan
Further Information:
Ideal for casual golfers.

ASKERNISH

ASKERNISH GOLF CLUB, Askernish,
Lochboisdale, **WESTERN ISLES**, PA81 5SY,
SCOTLAND.

Course/s:
🏌 **ASKERNISH**
Number of Holes: 9
Designer: Tom Morris

ASPECT PARK

ASPECT PARK GOLF CLUB, Remenham
Hill, Henley-on-Thames, **OXFORDSHIRE**,
RG9 3EH, **ENGLAND.**
(T) 01491 577562

Contact/s:
● Professional: Mr Terry Notley

Course/s:
🏌 **ASPECT PARK GOLF CENTRE**
Description: Parkland, Undulating, Drains
Well
Built: 1989
Number of Holes: 18　Par: 72
Yds: 6595
Designer: Tim Winsland

ASPLEY GUISE & WOBURN SANDS

**ASPLEY GUISE & WOBURN SANDS GOLF
CLUB LTD,** West Hill, Aspley Guise, Milton
Keynes, **BUCKINGHAMSHIRE**, MK17 8DX,
ENGLAND.
(T) 01908 583596

Contact/s:
● Manager: Mr R Lally

Course/s:
🏌 **ASPLEY GUISE & WOBURN SANDS**
Description: Heath Land, Undulating
Number of Holes: 18　Par: 71
Yds: 6079
Designer: S Herd

ASTBURY

ASTBURY GOLF CLUB, Professional Shop,
Peel Lane, Astbury, Congleton, **CHESHIRE**,
CW12 4RE, **ENGLAND.**
(T) 01260 298663

Contact/s:
● Manager: Mr S Leach

Course/s:
🏌 **ASTBURY**
Number of Holes: 18

ASTON WOOD

ASTON WOOD GOLF CLUB, Blake St, Little
Aston, Sutton Coldfield, **MIDLANDS
(WEST)**, B74 4EU, **ENGLAND.**
(T) 0121 5807803
(E) enquiries@astonwoodgolfclub.co.uk
(W) www.astonwoodgolfclub.co.uk

Membership: Members & Public

Contact/s:
● Club Secretary: Mr Ken Heathcote
　☎ 0121 580 7807
● Professional: Mr Simon Smith
　☎ 0121 580 7801

Course/s:
🏌 **ASTON WOOD**
Description: Parkland, Open, Medium
Length, Drains Well, Ideal for the Elderly
Green Speed: Medium
Built: 1994
Number of Holes: 18
Designer: Peter Alliss, Clive Clarke

ATHENRY

ATHENRY GOLF CLUB, Palmerstown,
Athenry, Oranmore, **COUNTY GALWAY**,
IRELAND.
(T) 091 794466

Membership: Members & Public
Size of Complex: 110 Acres

Contact/s:
● Club Secretary: Mr Padraig Flattery

● Pro Shop: Mr Raymond Ryan
　☎ 09179 0599
● Book Tee Times: Ms Linda Madden

Course/s:
🏌 **ATHENRY**
Description: Wooded, Parkland, Heath
Land, Medium Length, Drains Well, Ideal
for the Elderly
Green Speed: Medium
Built: 1978　Built On: Sand/Soil
Number of Holes: 18　Par: 70
Yds: 6246　F9 Yds: 3128　B9 Yds: 3118
Prevailing Wind: West
Designer: Edward Hackett

ATHERSTONE

ATHERSTONE GOLF CLUB, The Outwoods,
Atherstone, Nuneaton, **WARWICKSHIRE**,
CV9 2RL, **ENGLAND.**
(T) 01827 715419

Membership: Members & Public
Size of Complex: 120 Acres

Contact/s:
● Club Secretary: Val Walton
　☎ 01827 713110

Course/s:
🏌 **ATHERSTONE**
Description: Parkland, Hilltop,
Undulating, Medium Length, Tight
Green Speed: Medium
Built: 1894　Built On: Soil
Number of Holes: 18　Par: 72
Record: 68
Par 3's: 4　Par 4's: 10　Par 5's: 4
Yds: 6012　F9 Yds: 2721　B9 Yds: 3291
Prevailing Wind: South/West
Designer: Hawtree
Further Information:
Challenging course.

ATHLONE

ATHLONE GOLF CLUB, Hodson Bay,
Athlone, **COUNTY ROSCOMMON**,
IRELAND.
(T) 090 292073

Contact/s:
● Professional: Mr Martin Quinn

Course/s:
🏌 **ATHLONE**
Number of Holes: 18　Par: 71
Yds: 6381　F9 Yds: 3273　B9 Yds: 3108

ATHY

ATHY GOLF CLUB, Geraldine, Athy,
COUNTY KILDARE, **IRELAND.**
(T) 050 731729
(E) info@athygolfclub.com
(W) www.athygolfclub.com

Contact/s:
● Office Manager: Mrs Kathleen Grey

Course/s:
🏌 **ATHY**
Number of Holes: 18　Par: 71
Yds: 6340　F9 Yds: 3013　B9 Yds: 3327

AUCHENBLAE

AUCHENBLAE GOLF COURSE,
Auchenblae, Laurencekirk,
ABERDEENSHIRE, AB30 1TX, **SCOTLAND.**
(T) 01561 320002

Course/s:
🏌 **AUCHENBLAE**
Number of Holes: 9

AUCHENHARVIE

AUCHENHARVIE GOLF COMPLEX,
Moorpark Rd West, Stevenston, **AYRSHIRE (NORTH)**, KA20 3HU, **SCOTLAND**.
(T) 01294 603103

Membership: Members & Public

Contact/s:
● **Professional:** Mr Bob Rodgers

Course/s:
● AUCHENHARVIE
  Description: Parkland, Medium Length, Tight, Ideal for the Elderly
  Green Speed: Medium
  Built: 1981 **Built On:** Sand/Soil
  Number of Holes: 9 **Par:** 66 **Record:** 62 (Paul Rodgers)
  Par 3's: 3 **Par 4's:** 6
  Yds: 5203
  Further Information:
  There is a large group of swans on the course. 9 hole course can be played as an 18 hole course

AUCHMILL

AUCHMILL GOLF COURSE, Bonnyview Rd, Aberdeen, **ABERDEEN (CITY OF)**, AB16 7FQ, **SCOTLAND**.
(T) 01224 655419

Contact/s:
● **Manager:** Mr N Tennant

Course/s:
● AUCHMILL
  Number of Holes: 18
  Designer: Neil Coles, Brian Huggett

AUCHTERARDER

AUCHTERARDER GOLF CLUB, Orchil Rd, Auchterarder, **PERTH AND KINROSS**, PH3 1LS, **SCOTLAND**.
(T) 01764 662804

Contact/s:
● **Club Secretary:** Mr W M Campbell
● **Professional:** Mr Gavin Baker
  ☎ 01764 663711

Course/s:
● AUCHTERARDER
  Number of Holes: 18 **Par:** 69
  Yds: 5775 **F9 Yds:** 3044 **B9 Yds:** 2731

AUCHTERDERRAN

AUCHTERDERRAN GOLF CLUB, Woodend Rd, Cardenden, Lochgelly, **FIFE**, KY5 0NH, **SCOTLAND**.
(T) 01592 721519

Membership: Members & Public

Contact/s:
● **Club Secretary:** Mr Charlie Taylor

Course/s:
● AUCHTERDERRAN
  Description: Parkland, Hilltop, Valley, Undulating, Open, Short, Drains Well
  Green Speed: Slow
  Built: 1904 **Built On:** Clay
  Number of Holes: 9
  Prevailing Wind: West
  Designer: Reverend Delvlin
  Further Information:
  9 hole course can be played as an 18 hole course

AUSTERFIELD

AUSTERFIELD GOLF CLUB, Cross Lane, Austerfield, Doncaster, **YORKSHIRE (SOUTH)**, DN10 6RF, **ENGLAND**.

(T) 01302 710841

Contact/s:
● **Joint Director:** Mr Leonard Bradley

Course/s:
● AUSTERFIELD PARK
  Number of Holes: 18

AUSTIN LODGE

AUSTIN LODGE GOLF CLUB, Upper Austin Lodge Rd, Eynsford, Dartford, **KENT**, DA4 0HU, **ENGLAND**.
(T) 01322 863000

Contact/s:
● **Professional:** Mr Paul Edwards

Course/s:
● AUSTIN LODGE
  Description: Parkland, Valley
  Built: 1991
  Number of Holes: 18 **Par:** 73
  Yds: 6575
  Designer: P Bevan, Mike Walsh
  Further Information:
  Challenging course.

AVISFORD PARK

AVISFORD PARK GOLF COURSE, Yapton Lane, Walberton, Arundel, **SUSSEX (WEST)**, BN18 0LS, **ENGLAND**.
(T) 01243 554611

Membership: Members & Public

Contact/s:
● **Club Secretary:** Mr Nick Upjohn
● **Professional:** Mr Richard Beech

Course/s:
● AVISFORD PARK
  Description: Parkland, Valley, Open, Short, Tends to Flood
  Green Speed: Medium **Built On:** Clay
  Number of Holes: 18 **Par:** 67
  Par 3's: 6 **Par 4's:** 11 **Par 5's:** 1
  Yds: 5255
  Prevailing Wind: South
  Designer: R Moore
  Further Information:
  Pleasant, not too demanding course.

AVRO

AVRO GOLF CLUB, Old Hall Lane, Off Chester Rd, Woodford, Stockport, **CHESHIRE**, SK7 1RN, **ENGLAND**.
(T) 0161 4392709

Course/s:
● AVRO
  Number of Holes: 9

AXE CLIFF

AXE CLIFF GOLF CLUB, Axmouth, Seaton, **DEVON**, EX12 4AB, **ENGLAND**.
(T) 01297 24371

Contact/s:
● **Club Secretary:** Mr John Davies

Course/s:
● AXE CLIFF
  Number of Holes: 18 **Par:** 70
  Yds: 5969 **F9 Yds:** 3143 **B9 Yds:** 2826

AYCLIFFE

AYCLIFFE GOLF CLUB, School Aycliffe Lane, Newton Aycliffe, **COUNTY DURHAM**, DL5 4EF, **ENGLAND**.
(T) 01325 312994

Course/s:
● AYCLIFFE

AYLESBURY

AYLESBURY GOLF CENTRE, Hulcott Lane, Bierton, Aylesbury, **BUCKINGHAMSHIRE**, HP22 5GA, **ENGLAND**.
(T) 01296 393644

Membership: Members & Public
Size of Complex: 120 Acres

Contact/s:
● **Professional:** Mr Alex Saary

Course/s:
● AYLESBURY
  Description: Parkland, Open, Medium Length, Tends to Flood, Ideal for the Elderly
  Built: 1991 **Built On:** Clay
  Number of Holes: 18 **Par:** 71
  Par 3's: 6 **Par 4's:** 7 **Par 5's:** 5
  Yds: 5965
  Designer: T S Benwell

AYLESBURY PARK

AYLESBURY PARK GOLF CLUB, Oxford Rd, Hartwell, Aylesbury, **BUCKINGHAMSHIRE**, HP17 8QQ, **ENGLAND**.
(T) 01296 399196
(E) staff@aylesburypark.fsnet.co.uk
(W) www.aylesburyparkgolf.com

Membership: Members & Public

Contact/s:
● **Manager:** Mr M Lee

Course/s:
● AYLESBURY PARK
  Description: Parkland, Open, Medium Length, Drains Well, Ideal for the Elderly
  Green Speed: Slow
  Built: 1995
  Number of Holes: 18
  Designer: Hawtree

AYLESBURY VALE

AYLESBURY VALE GOLF CLUB, Stewkley Rd, Wing, Leighton Buzzard, **BEDFORDSHIRE**, LU7 0UJ, **ENGLAND**.
(T) 01525 240196

Contact/s:
● **Professional:** Mr Guy Goble
  ☎ 01525 240197

Course/s:
● AYLESBURY VALE
  Description: Undulating
  Built: 1991
  Number of Holes: 18 **Par:** 72
  Designer: D Wright
  Further Information:
  Generous Fairways.

BABERTON

BABERTON GOLF CLUB, 50 Baberton Ave, Edinburgh, **EDINBURGH (CITY OF)**, EH14 5DU, **SCOTLAND**.
(T) 0131 4534911

Contact/s:
● **Club Secretary:** Mr A Boe

Course/s:
● BABERTON
  Number of Holes: 18
  Designer: William Park

BACKWORTH

BACKWORTH GOLF CLUB, The Hall, Backworth, Shiremoor, Newcastle Upon Tyne, **TYNE AND WEAR**, NE27 0AH, **ENGLAND**.

(T) 0191 2681048

Course/s:

BACKWORTH
Number of Holes: 9

BACUP

BACUP GOLF CLUB, Golf Hse, Maden Rd, Bacup, **LANCASHIRE**, OL13 8HY, **ENGLAND**.
(T) 01706 873170

Membership: Members & Public

Contact/s:
● Club Secretary: Mr Tom Leyland

Course/s:

BACUP
Description: Wooded, Moorland, Hilltop, Open, Short, Drains Well
Green Speed: Fast
Built: 1945 Built On: Soil
Number of Holes: 9
Prevailing Wind: South/West
Further Information:
Small challenging course.

BAGDEN HALL

BAGDEN HALL HOTEL & GOLF COURSE, Wakefield Rd, Scissett, Huddersfield, **YORKSHIRE (WEST)**, HD8 9LE, **ENGLAND**.
(T) 01484 865330
(E) bagdenhallinfo@bagdenhall.demon.co.uk
(W) www.bagdenhall.demon.co.uk

Membership: Public
Size of Complex: 40 Acres

Contact/s:
● General Manager: Mr R Gill

Course/s:

BAGDEN HALL
Description: Parkland
Number of Holes: 9

BAILDON

BAILDON GOLF CLUB, Moorgate, Baildon, Shipley, Bradford, **YORKSHIRE (WEST)**, BD17 5PP, **ENGLAND**.
(T) 01274 584266
(W) www.baildongolfclub.com

Membership: Members & Public
Size of Complex: 600 Acres

Contact/s:
● Club Secretary: Mr John Cooley
● Professional: Mr Richard Masters
  ☎ 01274 595162

Course/s:

BAILDON
Description: Moorland, Open, Medium Length, Drains Well
Green Speed: Medium
Built: 1896 Built On: Clay
Number of Holes: 18 Par: 69
Par 3's: 5 Par 4's: 11 Par 5's: 2
Yds: 6231 F9 Yds: 2660 B9 Yds: 3035
Prevailing Wind: West
Designer: James Braid, Tom Morris
Further Information:
With no trees or sand, the main hazard of the course is the encircling rough.

BAKEWELL

BAKEWELL GOLF CLUB, Station Rd, Bakewell, **DERBYSHIRE**, DE45 1GB, **ENGLAND**.
(T) 01629 812307

Contact/s:

● Club Secretary: Mr Frank Parker

Course/s:

BAKEWELL
Number of Holes: 9 Par: 34
Yds: 2620 F9 Yds: 2620

BALA

BALA GOLF CLUB, Penlan, Bala, **GWYNEDD**, LL23 7YD, **WALES**.
(T) 01678 520359

Contact/s:
● Club Secretary: Mr G Rhys Jones

Course/s:

BALA
Description: Drains Well
Built: 1972
Number of Holes: 10 Par: 66
Yds: 4980 F9 Yds: 2552 B9 Yds: 2428

BALBIRNIE PARK

BALBIRNIE PARK GOLF CLUB, Balbirnie Pk, Markinch, Glenrothes, **FIFE**, KY7 6DD, **SCOTLAND**.
(T) 01592 612095
(E) bpgcgolf@aol.com

Membership: Members & Public

Contact/s:
● Club Secretary: Mr Stephen Oliver
● Professional: Mr Steven Craig
● Pro Shop: Mr Craig Donnelly

Course/s:

BALBIRNIE PARK
Description: Championship, Wooded, Parkland, Valley, Sheltered, Medium Length, Tight, Drains Well, Ideal for the Elderly
Green Speed: Medium/Fast
Built: 1983 Built On: Clay
Number of Holes: 18 Record: 67 (Craig Donnelly)
Designer: Fraser Middleton

BALBRIGGAN

BALBRIGGAN GOLF CLUB, Balbriggan, **COUNTY DUBLIN**, **IRELAND**.
(T) 01 8412173

Contact/s:
● Club Secretary: Mr Michael O'Halloran

Course/s:

BALBRIGGAN
Number of Holes: 18 Par: 71
Par 3's: 4 Par 4's: 11 Par 5's: 3
Yds: 6455 F9 Yds: 3249 B9 Yds: 3110
Designer: Paramoir

BALCARRICK

BALCARRICK GOLF CLUB, Corballis, Donabate, **COUNTY DUBLIN**, **IRELAND**.
(T) 01 8436957

Course/s:

BALCARRICK
Number of Holes: 18
Designer: Barry Langan

BALLA

BALLA GOLF CLUB, Balla, **COUNTY MAYO**, **IRELAND**.
(T) 094 65470
(E) ba.golf@mayo-ireland.ie

Course/s:

BALLA GOLF COURSE
Number of Holes: 18 Par: 54
Par 3's: 18

BALLAGHADERREEN

BALLAGHADERREEN GOLF CLUB, Ballaghaderreen, **COUNTY ROSCOMMON**, **IRELAND**.
(T) 090 760295

Course/s:

BALLAGHADERREEN
Number of Holes: 9
Designer: P Skerritt

BALLARDS GORE

BALLARDS GORE GOLF CLUB, Gore Rd, Stambridge, Rochford, **ESSEX**, SS4 2DA, **ENGLAND**.
(T) 01702 258917

Contact/s:
● Owner: Mr J Caton

Course/s:

BALLARDS GORE
Number of Holes: 18

BALLATER

BALLATER GOLF CLUB, Victoria Rd, Ballater, **ABERDEENSHIRE**, AB35 5QX, **SCOTLAND**.
(T) 01339 755567
(W) www.ballatergolfclub.co.uk

Membership: Public

Contact/s:
● Club Secretary: Mr Sandy Barclay
● Professional: Mr Bill Yule
  ☎ 01339 755658

Course/s:

BALLATER
Description: Heath Land, Undulating, Medium Length
Built: 1892
Number of Holes: 18

Yds: 6112 F9 Yds: 3144 B9 Yds: 2968

BALLINA

BALLINA GOLF CLUB, Mossgrove, Shanaghy, Ballina, **COUNTY MAYO**, **IRELAND**.
(T) 096 21050
(E) ballinagc@eircom.net
(W) www.ballinagolfclub.com

Membership: Members & Public
Size of Complex: 120 Acres

Contact/s:
● Book Tee Times: Ms Marguerite Martin

Course/s:

BALLINA
Description: Parkland, Medium Length
Green Speed: Medium
Built: 1924 Built On: Soil
Number of Holes: 18 Par: 71
Par 3's: 4 Par 4's: 11 Par 5's: 3
Yds: 6103 F9 Yds: 3034 B9 Yds: 3069
Designer: Edward Hackett

BALLINAMORE

BALLINAMORE GOLF CLUB, Ballinamore, Carrick-on-Shannon, **COUNTY LEITRIM**, **IRELAND**.
(T) 078 44346

Course/s:

BALLINAMORE
Number of Holes: 9
Designer: A Spring

BALLINASCORNEY

BALLINASCORNEY GOLF CLUB, Ballinascorney, **COUNTY DUBLIN, IRELAND.**
(T) 01 4516430
(E) ballinascorney@globalgolf.com
(W) www.globalgolf.com
Course/s:
🏌 **BALLINASCORNEY**
   Number of Holes: 18
   Designer: Edward Hackett

BALLINASLOE

BALLINASLOE GOLF CLUB, Ballinasloe, **COUNTY GALWAY, IRELAND.**
(T) 090 542126
Course/s:
🏌 **BALLINASLOE**
   Description: Parkland
   Built: 1894
   Number of Holes: 18   Par: 72
   Further Information:
   Testing course.

BALLINROBE

BALLINROBE GOLF CLUB, Clooncastle, Ballinrobe, **COUNTY MAYO, IRELAND.**
(T) 092 41118
Course/s:
🏌 **BALLINROBE**
   Built: 1895
   Number of Holes: 18   Par: 73
   Yds: 6817
   Designer: Edward Hackett

BALLINTESKIN PAR 3

BALLINTESKIN PAR 3, New Ross, Ballinteskin, **COUNTY WEXFORD, IRELAND.**
(T) 051 422779
Course/s:
🏌 **BALLINTESKIN**
   Number of Holes: 9   Par: 27

BALLOCHMYLE

BALLOCHMYLE GOLF CLUB, Catrine Rd, Mauchline, **AYRSHIRE (EAST),** KA5 6LE, **SCOTLAND.**
(T) 01290 550469
Contact/s:
● Club Secretary: Mr R L Crawford
Course/s:
🏌 **BALLOCHMYLE**
   Description: Wooded, Parkland, Undulating, Medium Length, Ideal for the Elderly
   Green Speed: Medium
   Built: 1937 Built On: Clay
   Number of Holes: 18   Record: 64
   Further Information:
   9 hole course can be played as an 18 hole course

BALLYBOFEY & STRANORLAR

BALLYBOFEY & STRANORLAR GOLF CLUB, Ballybofey, **COUNTY DONEGAL, IRELAND.**
(T) 074 31093
Course/s:
🏌 **BALLYBOFEY & STRANORLAR**
   Number of Holes: 18

BALLYBUNION

BALLYBUNION GOLF CLUB, Ballybunion, **COUNTY KERRY, IRELAND.**
(T) 068 27146
(E) bbgolfc@iol.ie
(W) www.ballybuniongolfclub.ie
Membership: Members & Public
Contact/s:
● Club Secretary: Mr Jim McKenna
● Professional: Mr Brian O'Callaghan
   ☎ 068 27842
Course/s:
🏌 **CASHEN**
   Description: Links, Undulating
   Number of Holes: 18   Par: 72
   Par 3's: 5   Par 4's: 8   Par 5's: 5
   Yds: 5997 F9 Yds: 3164 B9 Yds: 2833
🏌 **OLD**
   Description: Links, Undulating
   Number of Holes: 18   Par: 72
   Par 3's: 5   Par 4's: 9   Par 5's: 4
   Yds: 6175 F9 Yds: 2893 B9 Yds: 2959
   Designer: P Murphy, T Simpson 🏆

BALLYCASTLE

BALLYCASTLE GOLF CLUB, 2 Cushendall Rd, Ballycastle, **COUNTY ANTRIM,** BT54 6QP, **NORTHERN IRELAND.**
(T) 028 20762536
Membership: Members & Public
Contact/s:
● Club Secretary: Mrs Noelle Boyle
● Professional: Mr Ian McLaughlin
Course/s:
🏌 **BALLYCASTLE**
   Description: Parkland, Cliff Top, Undulating, Open, Short, Drains Well, Ideal for the Elderly
   Green Speed: Medium
   Built: 1890 Built On: Chalk/Sand
   Number of Holes: 18   Par: 71
   Par 3's: 4   Par 4's: 11   Par 5's: 3
   Yds: 5927 F9 Yds: 3072 B9 Yds: 2855
   Further Information:
   There are views of Mull of Kintyre from the course. The first five holes of the course are situated around an 18th century Friary.

BALLYCLARE

BALLYCLARE GOLF CLUB, 25 Springvale Rd, Ballyclare, **COUNTY ANTRIM,** BT39 9JW, **NORTHERN IRELAND.**
(T) 028 93322696
Contact/s:
● Manager: Mr Harry McConnell
Course/s:
🏌 **BALLYCLARE**
   Number of Holes: 18
   Designer: T McCauley

BALLYHAUNIS

BALLYHAUNIS GOLF CLUB, Ballyhaunis, **COUNTY MAYO, IRELAND.**
(T) 090 730014
Course/s:
🏌 **BALLYHAUNIS**
   Number of Holes: 9

BALLYHEIGUE CASTLE

BALLYHEIGUE CASTLE GOLF COURSE, Ballyheigue, **COUNTY KERRY, IRELAND.**
(T) 066 7133555
Membership: Members & Public

Contact/s:
● Club Secretary: Mr Michael Dowling
Course/s:
🏌 **BALLYHEIGUE CASTLE**
   Description: Wooded, Parkland, Long
   Built: 1995
   Number of Holes: 9
   Designer: Roger Jones

BALLYKISTEEN

BALLYKISTEEN GOLF & COUNTRY CLUB, Monard, Limerick Junction, **COUNTY TIPPERARY, IRELAND.**
(T) 062 33333
(E) ballykisteen@eircom.net
(W) www.tipp.ie/ballykgc.htm
Contact/s:
● Club Secretary: Ms Josephine Ryan
● Professional: Mr James McBride
   ☎ 086 3502202
Course/s:
🏌 **BALLYKISTEEN**
   Description: Parkland
   Green Speed: Fast
   Built: 1991
   Number of Holes: 18
   Designer: D Smyth

BALLYLIFFIN

BALLYLIFFIN GOLF CLUB, Ballyliffin, Cardonagh, **COUNTY DONEGAL, IRELAND.**
(T) 077 76119
Membership: Members & Public
Contact/s:
● Course Manager: Mr Cecil Doherty
Course/s:
🏌 **GLASHEDY LINKS**
   Description: Links
   Built: 1995 Built On: Sand
   Number of Holes: 18   Par: 72
   Yds: 7135
   Designer: Tom Craddock, Pat Ruddy 🏆
🏌 **OLD LINKS**
   Description: Links
   Number of Holes: 18
   Designer: Tom Craddock, Pat Ruddy
   Further Information:
   Nick Faldo described the course as 'the most natural golf links... a hidden gem.' while Fred Daly described it as 'a real jewel.'

BALLYMASCANLON HOUSE

BALLYMASCANLON HOUSE HOTEL GOLF COURSE, Dundalk, **COUNTY LOUTH, IRELAND.**
(T) 04271 124
Course/s:
🏌 **BALLYMASCANLON HOUSE**
   Number of Holes: 18

BALLYMENA

BALLYMENA GOLF CLUB, 128 Raceview Rd, Ballymena, **COUNTY ANTRIM,** BT42 4HY, **NORTHERN IRELAND.**
(T) 028 25861487
Membership: Members & Public
Size of Complex: 97 Acres
Contact/s:
● Club Secretary: Mr Carl McAuley
● Professional: Mr Ken Revie
Course/s:
🏌 **BALLYMENA**
   Description: Parkland, Heath Land,

Open, Tight, Drains Well, Ideal for the Elderly
Green Speed: Medium
Built: 1903 **Built On:** Sand
Number of Holes: 18 **Par:** 68
Record: 63 (David Graham)
Par 3's: 6 **Par 4's:** 10 **Par 5's:** 2
Yds: 5299 **F9 Yds:** 2673 **B9 Yds:** 2626
Prevailing Wind: North
Further Information:
This challenging course provides mountain views close to Broughshane Village.

BALLYMONEY

BALLYMONEY GOLF CLUB, Ballymoney, Gorey, **COUNTY WEXFORD**, **IRELAND**.
Membership: Public
Contact/s:
● Club Secretary: Shalga Breen
Course/s:
🏌 **BALLYMONEY**
Description: Parkland
Green Speed: Medium
Built: 1993
Number of Holes: 18
Designer: P Suttle

BALLYMOTE

BALLYMOTE GOLF CLUB, Ballinascarrow, Ballymote, **COUNTY SLIGO**, **IRELAND**.
(T) 071 89059
Course/s:
🏌 **BALLYMOTE**
Number of Holes: 9
Designer: Edward Hackett

BALLYREAGH

BALLYREAGH GOLF COURSE, 2 Glen Rd, Portrush, **COUNTY ANTRIM**, BT56 8LX, **NORTHERN IRELAND**.
(T) 028 70822028
Contact/s:
● Manager: Mr B Cockromb
Course/s:
🏌 **BALLYREAGH**
Number of Holes: 9
Designer: V Lathery

BALMORAL

BALMORAL GOLF CLUB LTD, 518 Lisburn Rd, Belfast, **COUNTY ANTRIM**, BT9 6GX, **NORTHERN IRELAND**.
(T) 028 90381514
Contact/s:
● General Manager: Mr R McConkey
Course/s:
🏌 **BALMORAL**
Number of Holes: 18 **Par:** 69
Yds: 6276 **F9 Yds:** 3006 **B9 Yds:** 3270

BALMORE

BALMORE GOLF CLUB, Golf Course Rd, Balmore, Torrance, Glasgow, **GLASGOW (CITY OF)**, G64 4AW, **SCOTLAND**.
(T) 01360 620284
Contact/s:
● Club Secretary: Mr Stewart Keir
Course/s:
🏌 **BALMORE**
Number of Holes: 18 **Par:** 66
Yds: 5542 **F9 Yds:** 2954 **B9 Yds:** 2588
Designer: James Braid

BALNAGASK

BALNAGASK GOLF COURSE, St. Fitticks Rd, Aberdeen, **ABERDEEN (CITY OF)**, AB11 8TN, **SCOTLAND**.
(T) 01224 876407
Course/s:
🏌 **BALNAGASK**
Number of Holes: 18

BALTINGLASS

BALTINGLASS GOLF CLUB, Baltinglass, **COUNTY WICKLOW**, **IRELAND**.
(T) 050 881350
Course/s:
🏌 **BALTINGLASS**
Number of Holes: 9

BAMBURGH CASTLE

BAMBURGH CASTLE GOLF CLUB, Bamburgh, **NORTHUMBERLAND**, NE69 7DE, **ENGLAND**.
(T) 01668 214321
Contact/s:
● Club Secretary: Mr Alan Patterson
Course/s:
🏌 **BAMBURGH CASTLE**
Number of Holes: 18
Designer: George Rochester

BANBRIDGE

BANBRIDGE GOLF CLUB, 116 Huntly Rd, Banbridge, **COUNTY DOWN**, BT32 3UR, **NORTHERN IRELAND**.
(T) 028 40662211
(E) info@banbridge-golf.freeserve.co.uk
(W) www.banbridge-golf.freeserve.co.uk
Contact/s:
● Club Secretary: Mrs J Anketell
● Pro Shop: Mr Derek Brown
Course/s:
🏌 **BANBRIDGE**
Description: Parkland
Built: 1912
Number of Holes: 18 **Par:** 69
Yds: 5590 **F9 Yds:** 2539 **B9 Yds:** 3051
Further Information:
Challenging, but not intimidating course.

BANBURY GOLF CTRE

BANBURY GOLF CENTRE, Aynho Rd, Adderbury, Banbury, **OXFORDSHIRE**, OX17 3NT, **ENGLAND**.
(T) 01295 810419
(W) www.banburygolfcentre.co.uk
Membership: Members & Public
Size of Complex: 230 Acres
Contact/s:
● Club Secretary: Mr Barrie Fowler
● Professional: Mr Peter Kingsley PGA
☎ 01295 812880
● Pro Shop: Mr Stuart Kier
Course/s:
🏌 **BLUE**
Description: Wooded, Parkland, Valley, Undulating, Sheltered, Medium Length, Ideal for the Elderly
Green Speed: Medium
Built: 1994 **Built On:** Sand
Number of Holes: 9 **Par:** 36
Par 3's: 1 **Par 4's:** 7 **Par 5's:** 1
Yds: 3354
Designer: Jon Payn, Mike Reed
🏌 **RED**

Description: Parkland, Valley, Undulating, Sheltered, Medium Length, Ideal for the Elderly
Green Speed: Medium
Built: 1994 **Built On:** Sand
Number of Holes: 9 **Par:** 36
Par 3's: 2 **Par 4's:** 5 **Par 5's:** 2
Yds: 3330
Designer: Jon Payn, Mike Reed
🏌 **YELLOW**
Description: Parkland, Valley, Undulating, Sheltered, Medium Length, Ideal for the Elderly
Green Speed: Medium
Built: 1994 **Built On:** Sand
Number of Holes: 9 **Par:** 35
Par 3's: 2 **Par 4's:** 6 **Par 5's:** 1
Yds: 3227
Designer: Jon Payn, Mike Reed

BANCHORY

BANCHORY GOLF CLUB, Kinneskie Rd, Banchory, **ABERDEENSHIRE**, AB31 5TA, **SCOTLAND**.
(T) 01330 822365
Size of Complex: 90 Acres
Contact/s:
● Professional: Mr David Naylor
☎ 01330 822447
Course/s:
🏌 **BANCHORY**
Description: Parkland, Valley, Sheltered, Medium Length, Drains Well, Ideal for the Elderly
Green Speed: Medium
Built: 1905 **Built On:** Sand
Number of Holes: 18 **Par:** 69
Record: 67 (Craig Ronald)
Par 3's: 6 **Par 4's:** 9 **Par 5's:** 3
Yds: 5781 **F9 Yds:** 2616 **B9 Yds:** 3165

BANDON

BANDON GOLF CLUB, Castle Bernard, Bandon, **COUNTY CORK**, **IRELAND**.
(T) 023 41111
(E) bandongolfclub@eircom.net
Course/s:
🏌 **BANDON**
Number of Holes: 18

BANGOR

BANGOR GOLF CLUB, Broadway, Bangor, **COUNTY DOWN**, BT20 4RH, **NORTHERN IRELAND**.
(T) 028 91270922
Contact/s:
● Manager: Mr D J Ryan
Course/s:
🏌 **BANGOR**
Number of Holes: 18
Designer: James Braid

BANK HOUSE

BANK HOUSE HOTEL GOLF & COUNTRY CLUB, Bransford, Worcester, **WORCESTERSHIRE**, WR6 5JD, **ENGLAND**.
(T) 01886 833545
(E) info@bankhousehotel.co.uk
Contact/s:
● Golf Secretary: Mr Patrick Holmes
Course/s:
🏌 **PINE LAKES**
Description: Parkland
Green Speed: Medium
Built: 1990
Number of Holes: 18 **Par:** 72

Par 3's: 6   Par 4's: 6   Par 5's: 6
Yds: 6204   F9 Yds: 3118   B9 Yds: 3086
Designer: Robert Sandow
Further Information:
The course has 14 lakes and 2 island greens.

BANSTEAD DOWNS

BANSTEAD DOWNS GOLF CLUB, Burdon Lane, Belmont, Sutton, **SURREY**, SM2 7DD, **ENGLAND**.
(T) 020 86422284
(E) bdgc@ukonline.co.uk
Membership: Members & Public
Size of Complex: 104 Acres
Contact/s:
● **Professional:** Mr Roger Dickman
  ☎ 020 86426884
Course/s:
● **BANSTEAD DOWNS**
  Description: Links, Downland, Medium Length, Tight, Drains Well, Ideal for the Elderly
  Green Speed: Medium
  Built: 1890   **Built On:** Chalk
  Number of Holes: 18   **Par:** 69
  Record: 64 (Mark Wheeler)
  Par 3's: 5   **Par 4's:** 11   **Par 5's:** 2
  Yds: 6194   **F9 Yds:** 3104   **B9 Yds:** 3090
  Prevailing Wind: North
  Designer: James Braid, J H Taylor
  Further Information:
  Site of special and scientific interest for chalkland flora and fauna. Heritage site registered with English Heritage.

BANTRY BAY

BANTRY BAY GOLF CLUB, Bantry Bay, Bantry, **COUNTY CORK**, **IRELAND**.
(T) 027 50579
(E) info@bantrygolf.com
(W) www.bantrygolf.com
Size of Complex: 170 Acres
Course/s:
● **BANTRY BAY**
  Description: Championship, Cliff Top
  Built: 1975
  Number of Holes: 18   **Par:** 71
  Designer: Christy O'Connor, Edward Hackett

BARGOED

BARGOED GOLF CLUB, Bargoed, **CAERPHILLY**, CF81 9GF, **WALES**.
(T) 01443 830608
Contact/s:
● **Company Secretary:** Mr G Williams
Course/s:
● **BARGOED**
  Number of Holes: 18

BARKWAY PARK

BARKWAY PARK GOLF CLUB,
Nuthampstead Rd, Barkway, Royston, **HERTFORDSHIRE**, SG8 8EN, **ENGLAND**.
(T) 01763 848215
Membership: Members & Public
Size of Complex: 200 Acres
Contact/s:
● **Professional:** Mr Jamie Bates
Course/s:
● **BARKWAY GOLF**
  Description: Parkland, Undulating, Open, Long, Drains Well
  Green Speed: Medium

Built: 1992   **Built On:** Chalk/Clay
Number of Holes: 18   **Record:** 68
Prevailing Wind: South/West
Designer: V Saunders
Further Information:
Barkway plays similar to an inland links course.

BARLASTON

BARLASTON GOLF CLUB, Meaford Rd, Meaford, Stone, **STAFFORDSHIRE**, ST12 9EB, **ENGLAND**.
(T) 01782 372795
Contact/s:
● **Professional:** Mr Ian Rogers
Course/s:
● **BARLASTON**
  Description: Parkland, Short
  Built: 1978
  Number of Holes: 18   **Par:** 69
  Yds: 5800
  Designer: Peter Alliss
  Further Information:
  The River Trent runs alongside the course. It also contains other water features throughout.

BARLBOROUGH LINKS

BARLBOROUGH LINKS GOLF CLUB,
Oxcroft Way, Barlborough, Chesterfield, **DERBYSHIRE**, S43 4WN, **ENGLAND**.
(T) 01246 813111
Membership: Members & Public
Contact/s:
● **Club Secretary:** Mr W Weights
● **Professional:** Mr J Carnall
Course/s:
● **BARLBOROUGH LINKS GOLF**
  Description: Championship, Parkland, Open, Medium Length, Tends to Flood
  Green Speed: Medium/Fast
  Built: 1998   **Built On:** Clay
  Number of Holes: 9   **Record:** 64 (Haden Selby-Green)
  Designer: D Hemstock

BARNARD CASTLE

BARNARD CASTLE GOLF CLUB, Harmire Rd, Barnard Castle, **COUNTY DURHAM**, DL12 8QN, **ENGLAND**.
(T) 01833 638355
(E) christine.sec@talk21.com
(W) www.barnardcastlegolfclub.org.uk
Membership: Members & Public
Size of Complex: 117 Acres
Contact/s:
● **Club Secretary:** Mrs Christine Wright
● **Professional:** Mr Darren Pearce
  ☎ 01833 631980
Course/s:
● **BARNARD CASTLE**
  Description: Wooded, Heath Land, Open, Medium Length, Drains Well, Ideal for the Elderly
  Green Speed: Medium
  Built: 1898   **Built On:** Soil
  Number of Holes: 18   **Par:** 73
  Par 3's: 4   **Par 4's:** 9   **Par 5's:** 5
  Yds: 6406   **F9 Yds:** 3253   **B9 Yds:** 3153
  Prevailing Wind: West
  Further Information:
  A challenging course.

BARNEHURST

BARNEHURST GOLF COURSE, Mayplace Rd East, Bexleyheath, **KENT**, DA7 6JU,

ENGLAND.
(T) 01322 552952
Contact/s:
● **Club Secretary:** Ms Natalie Huntley
  ☎ 01322 523746
● **Professional:** Mr David Lewis
Course/s:
● **BARNEHURST PUBLIC PAY & PLAY**
  Built: 1904
  Number of Holes: 9
  Yds: 2737
  Designer: James Braid

BARNHAM BROOM

BARNHAM BROOM, Honingham Rd, Barnham Broom, Norwich, **NORFOLK**, NR9 4DD, **ENGLAND**.
(T) 01603 759393
(W) www.barnham-broom.co.uk
Membership: Members & Public
Contact/s:
● **General Manager:** Mr Robin Brooks
Course/s:
● **HILL**
  Number of Holes: 18   **Par:** 71
  Yds: 6495
  Designer: Frank Pennink, Donald Steel
  Further Information:
  The course has wide fairways.
● **VALLEY**
  Description: Wooded, Parkland, Valley
  Number of Holes: 18   **Par:** 72
  Yds: 6603
  Designer: Frank Pennink

BARNSLEY

BARNSLEY GOLF CLUB, Clubhouse, Wakefield Rd, Staincross, Barnsley, **YORKSHIRE (SOUTH)**, S75 6JZ, **ENGLAND**.
(T) 01226 382856
Contact/s:
● **Manager:** Mr Mel Gillett
Course/s:
● **BARNSLEY**
  Number of Holes: 18

BARON & BARONESS

BEADLOW MANOR GOLF & COUNTRY CLUB, Beadlow, Shefford, **BEDFORDSHIRE**, SG17 5PH, **ENGLAND**.
(T) 01525 860800
Membership: Members & Public
Size of Complex: 150 Acres
Contact/s:
● **Club Secretary:** Mr Mike Davies
● **Professional:** Mr Geoff Swain
Course/s:
● **BARON MANHATTAN**
  Description: Championship, Parkland, Undulating, Medium Length, Drains Well, Ideal for the Elderly
  Green Speed: Fast
  Built: 1961   **Built On:** Clay
  Number of Holes: 18   **Par:** 73
  Par 3's: 4   **Par 4's:** 9   **Par 5's:** 5
  Yds: 6342   **F9 Yds:** 3150   **B9 Yds:** 3192
  Prevailing Wind: South/West
  Further Information:
  A challenging course.
● **BARONESS MANHATTAN**
  Description: Championship, Parkland, Undulating, Medium Length
  Green Speed: Medium
  Built: 1971   **Built On:** Clay
  Number of Holes: 18   **Par:** 71

Par 3's: 4   Par 4's: 11   Par 5's: 3
Yds: 5763   F9 Yds: 2988   B9 Yds: 2775
Prevailing Wind: South/West

BARON HILL

BARON HILL GOLF CLUB, Baron Hill,
Beaumaris, **ISLE OF ANGLESEY**, LL58 8YW,
WALES.
(T) 01248 810231
(E) golf@baronhill.co.uk
(W) www.baronhill.co.uk

Contact/s:
● Club Secretary: Mr Alwyn Pleming

Course/s:
🏌 **BARON HILL**
Description: Parkland
Built: 1895
Number of Holes: 9   Par: 68
Further Information:
Views of Menai Straits and Snowdonia.

BARROW

BARROW GOLF CLUB, Rakesmoor Lane,
Hawcoat, Barrow-In-Furness, **CUMBRIA**,
LA14 4QB, **ENGLAND**.
(T) 01229 825444

Membership: Members & Public

Contact/s:
● Club Secretary: Mr J Slater
  ☎ 01229 826968
● Professional: A Whitehall
  ☎ 01229 832121
● Book Tee Times: Mr Eddie Payne

Course/s:
🏌 **BARROW**
Description: Parkland, Medium Length
Green Speed: Medium
Built: 1922
Number of Holes: 18

BARROW HILLS

BARROW HILLS GOLF CLUB, Longcross,
Chertsey, **SURREY**, KT16 0DS, **ENGLAND**.
(T) 01344 635770

Course/s:
🏌 **BARROW HILLS**
Number of Holes: 18

BARSHAW

BARSHAW GOLF CLUB, Barshaw Pk,
Paisley, **RENFREWSHIRE**, PA1 3TJ,
SCOTLAND.
(T) 0141 8892908

Course/s:
🏌 **BARSHAW**
Number of Holes: 18

BARTON-ON-SEA

BARTON-ON-SEA GOLF CLUB, Milford Rd,
New Milton, **HAMPSHIRE**, BH25 5PP,
ENGLAND.
(T) 01425 615308
(W) www.barton-on-sea-golf.co.uk

Contact/s:
● Professional: Mr Peter Rodgers
  ☎ 01425 611210

Course/s:
🏌 **BECTON**
Description: Links, Cliff Top, Open, Long,
Ideal for the Elderly
Green Speed: Medium Built On: Clay
Number of Holes: 9   Record: 65 (John
Le'roux)
Prevailing Wind: South

🏌 **NEEDLES**
Number of Holes: 9

🏌 **STROLLER**
Number of Holes: 9

BASILDON

BASILDON GOLF COURSES, Clayhill Lane,
Basildon, **ESSEX**, SS16 5JP, **ENGLAND**.
(T) 01268 294194

Contact/s:
● Manager: Mr Nick Sears

Course/s:
🏌 **BASILDON**
Number of Holes: 18
Designer: Cotton

BASINGSTOKE

BASINGSTOKE GOLF CLUB, Kempshott Pk,
Basingstoke, **HAMPSHIRE**, RG23 7LL,
ENGLAND.
(T) 01256 465990

Contact/s:
● Manager: Mr W A Jefford

Course/s:
🏌 **BASINGSTOKE**
Number of Holes: 18
Designer: James Braid

BASINGSTOKE

BASINGSTOKE GOLF CENTRE, Worting Rd,
West Ham, Basingstoke, **HAMPSHIRE**,
RG23 0TY, **ENGLAND**.
(T) 01256 350054

Contact/s:
● Professional: Mr Scott Watson

Course/s:
🏌 **BASINGSTOKE**
Description: Parkland, Undulating, Short,
Drains Well, Ideal for the Elderly
Green Speed: Fast Built On: Soil
Number of Holes: 9
Further Information:
An ideal course for beginners with a
variety of par 3 holes.

BATCHWOOD

BATCHWOOD GOLF & TENNIS CENTRE,
Batchwood Dr, St. Albans,
HERTFORDSHIRE, AL3 5SA, **ENGLAND**.
(T) 01727 844250

Contact/s:
● Manager: Mr C Rolfe

Course/s:
🏌 **BATCHWOOD HALL**
Number of Holes: 18

BATCHWORTH PARK

BATCHWORTH PARK GOLF CLUB, London
Rd, Rickmansworth, **HERTFORDSHIRE**,
WD3 1JS, **ENGLAND**.
(T) 01923 711400
(E) bpgc@crownsportsplc.com
(W) www.crownsportsplc.com

Membership: Members & Public

Contact/s:
● Professional: Mr Stephen Proudfoot
  ☎ 01927 714922

Course/s:
🏌 **BATCHWORTH PARK**
Description: Links, Medium Length,
Drains Well
Green Speed: Medium
Built: 1996

Number of Holes: 18
Designer: Dave Thomas Designs Ltd

BATH

BATH GOLF CLUB, Sham Castle North Rd,
Bath, **BATH & SOMERSET (NORTH EAST)**,
BA2 6JG, **ENGLAND**.
(T) 01225 463834
(E) enquiries@bathgolfclub.org.uk

Contact/s:
● Club Secretary: Mr Paul Ware

Course/s:
🏌 **BATH**
Number of Holes: 18   Par: 71
Yds: 6442   F9 Yds: 3287   B9 Yds: 3155
Designer: Charles Hugh Alison, Harry
Shapland Colt

BATHGATE

BATHGATE GOLF CLUB, Edinburgh Rd,
Bathgate, **LOTHIAN (WEST)**, EH48 1BA,
SCOTLAND.
(T) 01506 652232
(E) bathgate.golfclub@lineone.net

Contact/s:
● Club Secretary: Mr W A Osbourne
● Professional: Mr S Strachan
  ☎ 01506 630505

Course/s:
🏌 **BATHGATE**
Number of Holes: 18   Par: 71
Yds: 6328   F9 Yds: 3218   B9 Yds: 3110
Designer: William Park

BATTLE

BATTLE GOLF CLUB, Netherfield Hill, Battle,
SUSSEX (EAST), TN33 0LH, **ENGLAND**.
(T) 01424 775677

Membership: Members & Public
Size of Complex: 100 Acres

Contact/s:
● Club Secretary: Miss C Lyons
● Professional: Mr Sean Creasey
  ☎ 01424 777497

Course/s:
🏌 **BATTLE**
Description: Parkland, Undulating,
Medium Length, Drains Well
Green Speed: Fast
Built: 1994   Built On: Clay/Sand
Number of Holes: 9
Prevailing Wind: South/West
Designer: John Daley

BAWBURGH

GLEN LODGE & BAWBURGH GOLF CLUB,
Marlingford Rd, Bawburgh, Norwich,
NORFOLK, NR9 3LU, **ENGLAND**.
(T) 01603 740404
(E) info@bawburgh.com
(W) www.bawburgh.com
Size of Complex: 130 Acres

Contact/s:
● Professional: Mr Chris Potter
  ☎ 01603 742323

Course/s:
🏌 **GLEN LODGE**
Description: Parkland, Heath Land,
Undulating, Medium Length, Drains Well
Green Speed: Medium
Built: 1979   Built On: Sand/Soil
Number of Holes: 18   Par: 70
Record: 65 (Andrew Collison)
Yds: 6231   F9 Yds: 3341   B9 Yds: 2890

BAXENDEN & DISTRICT

BAXENDEN & DISTRICT GOLF CLUB LTD,
Wooley Lane, Baxenden, Accrington,
LANCASHIRE, BB5 2EA, **ENGLAND**.
(T) 01254 234555

Contact/s:
- Club Secretary: Mr D Bottomley

Course/s:
- BAXENDEN & DISTRICT
  Number of Holes: 9

BEACON PARK

BEACON PARK GOLF COURSE, Beacon
Lane, Dalton, Wigan, **LANCASHIRE**, WN8
7RU, **ENGLAND**.
(T) 01695 622700

Contact/s:
- Owner: Mr R Peters

Course/s:
- BEACON PARK PUBLIC GOLF CENTRE
  Number of Holes: 18
  Designer: Donald Steel

BEACONSFIELD

BEACONSFIELD GOLF CLUB, Seer Green,
Beaconsfield, **BUCKINGHAMSHIRE**, HP9
2UR, **ENGLAND**.
(T) 01494 676545

Contact/s:
- Club Secretary: Mr R E Thomas

Course/s:
- BEACONSFIELD
  Number of Holes: 18
  Designer: Harry Shapland Colt

BEAMISH PARK

BEAMISH PARK GOLF CLUB, Beamish,
Stanley, **COUNTY DURHAM**, DH9 0RH,
ENGLAND.
(T) 0191 3701382

Membership: Members & Public
Size of Complex: 100 Acres

Contact/s:
- Professional: Mr Chris Cole
  ☎ 0191 3701984

Course/s:
- BEAMISH PARK
  Description: Wooded, Parkland, Medium
  Length
  Green Speed: Medium/Fast
  Built: 1964   Built On: Soil
  Number of Holes: 18
  Designer: Henry Cotton

BEARNA

BEARNA GOLF & COUNTRY CLUB,
Corboley, Bearna, **COUNTY GALWAY**,
IRELAND.
(T) 091 592677
(E) bearnagc@eircom.net

Membership: Members & Public

Contact/s:
- Club Secretary: Mr Gerry Davy

Course/s:
- BEARNA
  Description: Championship, Moorland,
  Drains Well
  Green Speed: Medium
  Built: 1996
  Number of Holes: 18
  Designer: R Browne

BEARSDEN

BEARSDEN GOLF CLUB, Thorn Rd,
Bearsden, Glasgow, **GLASGOW (CITY OF)**,
G61 4BP, **SCOTLAND**.
(T) 0141 9422351

Membership: Members & Public

Contact/s:
- Club Secretary: Mr O J McComish

Course/s:
- BEARSDEN
  Description: Parkland, Undulating,
  Medium Length, Drains Well
  Green Speed: Fast
  Built: 1994   Built On: Clay/Sand
  Number of Holes: 9
  Prevailing Wind: South/West
  Designer: John Daley

BEARSTED

BEARSTED GOLF CLUB, Ware St, Bearsted,
Maidstone, **KENT**, ME14 4PQ, **ENGLAND**.
(T) 01622 738389

Membership: Members & Public

Contact/s:
- Club Secretary: Mrs Linda Seems
  ☎ 01622 738198
- Professional: Mr Tim Simpson
  ☎ 01622 738024

Course/s:
- BEARSTED
  Description: Championship, Parkland,
  Undulating, Open, Medium Length
  Green Speed: Medium
  Built: 1895   Built On: Clay
  Number of Holes: 18   Par: 71
  Par 3's: 4   Par 4's: 11   Par 5's: 3
  Yds: 6452

BEARWOOD

BEARWOOD GOLF CLUB, Mole Rd,
Sindlesham, **BERKSHIRE**, RG41 5DB,
ENGLAND.
(T) 0118 9760060

Contact/s:
- Manager: Mr Barry Tustin

Course/s:
- BEARWOOD
  Number of Holes: 9
  Designer: Barry Tustin

BEARWOOD LAKES

BEARWOOD LAKES GOLF CLUB, The
Cottage, Bearwood Rd, Wokingham,
BERKSHIRE, RG41 4SJ, **ENGLAND**.
(T) 0118 9797900
(E) golf@bearwoodlakes.co.uk
(W) www.bearwoodlakes.co.uk

Membership: Members & Public

Contact/s:
- Professional: Mr Euan Ingus
  ☎ 0118 9783030

Course/s:
- BEARWOOD LAKES
  Description: Championship, Wooded,
  Parkland, Undulating, Sheltered, Long,
  Drains Well
  Green Speed: Fast
  Built: 1996
  Number of Holes: 18
  Designer: Hawtree

BEAU DESERT

BEAU DESERT GOLF CLUB LTD, Rugeley
Rd, Hazel Slade, Cannock,
STAFFORDSHIRE, WS12 5PJ, **ENGLAND**.
(T) 01543 422773

Contact/s:
- Club Secretary: Mrs P Mason

Course/s:
- BEAU DESERT
  Number of Holes: 18
  Designer: Fowler

BEAUCHIEF MUNICIPAL

BEAUCHIEF MUNICIPAL GOLF CLUB,
Abbey Lane, Sheffield, **YORKSHIRE
(SOUTH)**, S8 0DB, **ENGLAND**.
(T) 0114 2367274

Membership: Public

Contact/s:
- Manager: Mr Mark Trippett

Course/s:
- BEAUCHIEF MUNICIPAL GOLF
  Number of Holes: 18

BEAUFORT

BEAUFORT GOLF COURSE, Churchtown,
Beaufort, Killarney, **COUNTY KERRY**,
IRELAND.
(T) 064 44440
(E) beaufort@eircorn.net

Course/s:
- BEAUFORT
  Number of Holes: 18
  Designer: Arthur Spring

BEAVERSTOWN

BEAVERSTOWN GOLF CLUB, Donabate,
COUNTY DUBLIN, **IRELAND**.
(T) 01 8436721
(E) bgc@iol.ie

Course/s:
- BEAVERSTOWN
  Number of Holes: 18

BECCLES

BECCLES GOLF CLUB, Common Lane,
Beccles, **SUFFOLK**, NR34 9BX, **ENGLAND**.
(T) 01502 712244

Contact/s:
- Manager: Mr Tunks

Course/s:
- BECCLES
  Number of Holes: 9

BECKENHAM PLACE PARK

BECKENHAM PLACE PARK GOLF CLUB,
Beckenham Hill, Beckenham, **KENT**, BR3
5BP, **ENGLAND**.
(T) 020 86502292

Membership: Members & Public
Size of Complex: 214 Acres

Contact/s:
- Club Secretary: Mr Trevor Moorcroft
- Professional: Mr John Denham

Course/s:
- BECKENHAM PLACE PARK
  Description: Championship, Parkland,
  Undulating, Sheltered, Short, Tight, Tends
  to Flood, Ideal for the Elderly
  Green Speed: Fast
  Built: 1898   Built On: Soil
  Number of Holes: 18   Par: 69
  Par 3's: 4   Par 4's: 13   Par 5's: 1
  Yds: 5722

BECKSIDE

BECKSIDE GOLF CLUB, Ellerbeck Farm, Crook, Kendal, **CUMBRIA**, LA8 8LE, **ENGLAND**.
(T) 01539 821415
Membership: Members & Public
Contact/s:
● **Club Secretary:** Ms Kathleen Jackson
Course/s:
🏌 **BECKSIDE**
  Description: Undulating
  Green Speed: Medium
  Built: 1990
  Number of Holes: 9
  Designer: Michael Jackson

BEDALE

BEDALE GOLF CLUB LTD, Leyburn Rd, Bedale, **YORKSHIRE (NORTH)**, DL8 1EZ, **ENGLAND**.
(T) 01677 422451
(E) bedalegolfclub@aol.com
(W) www.bedalegolfclub.com
Contact/s:
● **Club Secretary:** Mrs G Brown
Course/s:
🏌 **BEDALE**
  Number of Holes: 18 **Par:** 72
  Yds: 6610 **F9 Yds:** 3415 **B9 Yds:** 3195

BEDFORD

BEDFORD GOLF CLUB (THE), Great Denham Golf Village, Biddenham, Bedford, **BEDFORDSHIRE**, MK40 4BF, **ENGLAND**.
(T) 01234 320022
(W) www.kolvengolf.com
Membership: Members & Public
Size of Complex: 165 Acres
Contact/s:
● **Professional:** Mr Zac Thompson
Course/s:
🏌 **THE BEDFORD**
  Description: Championship, Links, Open, Long, Drains Well, Ideal for the Elderly
  Green Speed: Fast
  Built: 1998 **Built On:** Gravel/Sand
  Number of Holes: 18 **Par:** 72
  Par 3's: 4 **Par 4's:** 10 **Par 5's:** 4
  Yds: 6264 **F9 Yds:** 3166 **B9 Yds:** 3098
  Prevailing Wind: West
  Designer: David Pottage
  Further Information:
  The greens are in superb condition.

BEDFORD & COUNTY

BEDFORD & COUNTY GOLF CLUB, Green Lane, Clapham, Bedford, **BEDFORDSHIRE**, MK41 6ET, **ENGLAND**.
(T) 01234 352617
(W) www.bedfordandcountygolfclub.co.uk
Contact/s:
● **Professional:** Mr Roger Tattersall
● **Book Tee Times:**
  ☎ 01234 359189
Course/s:
🏌 **BEDFORD & COUNTY**
  Description: Parkland
  Built: 1912
  Number of Holes: 18 **Par:** 70
  Yds: 6399 **F9 Yds:** 3017 **B9 Yds:** 3382
  Further Information:
  The course provides a challenging and relaxing game.

BEDFORDSHIRE

BEDFORDSHIRE GOLF CLUB, Bromham Rd, Biddenham, Bedford, **BEDFORDSHIRE**, MK40 4AF, **ENGLAND**.
(T) 01234 261669
Course/s:
🏌 **BEDFORDSHIRE**
  Description: Parkland, Ideal for the Elderly
  Number of Holes: 18 **Par:** 70
  Yds: 6305

BEDLINGTONSHIRE

BEDLINGTONSHIRE GOLF CLUB, Acorn Bank, Bedlington, **NORTHUMBERLAND**, NE22 6AA, **ENGLAND**.
(T) 01670 822457
Contact/s:
● **Club Secretary:** F M Hanson
● **Professional:** M Webb
Course/s:
🏌 **BEDLINGTONSHIRE**
  Number of Holes: 18 **Par:** 73
  Designer: Frank Pennink

BEECH PARK

BEECH PARK GOLF CLUB, Johnstown, Rathcoole, **COUNTY DUBLIN**, **IRELAND**.
(T) 01 4580522
Contact/s:
● **General Manager:** Mr Paul Muldowney
Course/s:
🏌 **BEECH PARK**
  Number of Holes: 18 **Par:** 72
  Yds: 6271 **F9 Yds:** 3168 **B9 Yds:** 3103

BEEDLES LAKE

BEEDLES LAKE GOLF CENTRE, 170 Broome Lane, East Goscote, Leicester, **LEICESTERSHIRE**, LE7 3WQ, **ENGLAND**.
(T) 0116 2606759
Membership: Members & Public
Size of Complex: 140 Acres
Contact/s:
● **Club Secretary:** Mr David Lilley
  ☎ 0116 2661541
● **Professional:** Mr Sean Byrne
Course/s:
🏌 **BEEDLES LAKE**
  Description: Open, Medium Length, Drains Well, Ideal for the Elderly
  Green Speed: Medium
  Built: 1993 **Built On:** Clay
  Number of Holes: 18 **Par:** 72
  Record: 67 (Sean Byrne *Unofficial*)
  Par 3's: 3 **Par 4's:** 12 **Par 5's:** 3
  Yds: 6732 **F9 Yds:** 3442 **B9 Yds:** 3290
  Designer: David Tucker

BEESTON FIELDS

BEESTON FIELDS GOLF CLUB, Beeston Fields Drive, Beeston, Nottingham, **NOTTINGHAMSHIRE**, NG9 3DD, **ENGLAND**.
(T) 0115 9257062
(W) www.beestonfields.co.uk
Contact/s:
● **Professional:** Mr Alan Wardle
  ☎ 0115 9220872
Course/s:
🏌 **BEESTON FIELDS**
  Number of Holes: 18 **Par:** 71
  Par 3's: 4 **Par 4's:** 11 **Par 5's:** 3

  Yds: 6404 **F9 Yds:** 3021 **B9 Yds:** 3383
  Designer: Tom Williamson

BEITH

BEITH GOLF CLUB, Threepwood Rd, Beith, **AYRSHIRE (NORTH)**, KA15 2JR, **SCOTLAND**.
(T) 01505 503166
Contact/s:
● **Club Secretary:** Mrs Margaret Murphy
  ☎ 01505 506814
● **Book Tee Times:** Mrs L Guffie
Course/s:
🏌 **BEITH**
  Description: Parkland, Moorland, Undulating, Open, Short
  Built: 1896
  Number of Holes: 18 **Par:** 68
  Par 3's: 5 **Par 4's:** 12 **Par 5's:** 1
  Yds: 5629 **F9 Yds:** 2754 **B9 Yds:** 2875
  Further Information:
  Views over 7 counties.

BELFAIRS PARK

BELFAIRS PARK GOLF COURSE, Eastwood Rd North, Leigh-on-Sea, **ESSEX**, SS9 4LR, **ENGLAND**.
(T) 01702 525345
Course/s:
🏌 **BELFAIR MUNICIPAL**
  Description: Parkland, Undulating, Medium Length, Tight, Drains Well, Ideal for the Elderly
  Green Speed: Medium
  Built: 1960 **Built On:** Clay
  Number of Holes: 18
  Prevailing Wind: South/West

BELFAST

CITY OF BELFAST GOLF COURSE, Antrim Rd, Newtownabbey, **COUNTY ANTRIM**, BT36 5DA, **NORTHERN IRELAND**.
(T) 028 90843799
Membership: Public
Contact/s:
● **Club Secretary:** Mr John Patterson
Course/s:
🏌 **CITY OF BELFAST**
  Description: Parkland, Undulating, Sheltered, Short, Tight, Drains Well, Ideal for the Elderly
  Green Speed: Medium
  Built: 1985 **Built On:** Clay
  Number of Holes: 9
  Yds: 2343
  Prevailing Wind: North

BELFAST (ROYAL)

ROYAL BELFAST GOLF CLUB, Pro Shop, Station Rd, Holywood, **COUNTY DOWN**, BT18 0BP, **NORTHERN IRELAND**.
(T) 028 90428586
Course/s:
🏌 **THE ROYAL BELFAST**
  Number of Holes: 18
  Designer: Harry Shapland Colt

BELFORD

BELFORD GOLF CLUB, South Rd, Belford, **NORTHUMBERLAND**, NE70 7DP, **ENGLAND**.
(T) 01668 213433
(W) www.belfordgolfclub.co.uk
Size of Complex: 70 Acres
Contact/s:

- Club Secretary: Mr A M Gilhome

Course/s:

🏌 **BELFORD**
Description: Parkland
Green Speed: Fast
Built: 1993 Built On: Soil
Number of Holes: 9 Par: 72
Par 3's: 2 Par 4's: 5 Par 5's: 2
Yds: 6304 F9 Yds: 3152 B9 Yds: 3152
Designer: N Williams
Further Information:
9 hole course can be played as an 18 hole course

BELFRY

BELFRY (THE), Wishaw, Sutton Coldfield, **MIDLANDS (WEST)**, B76 9PR, **ENGLAND**.
(T) 01675 470301
(E) enquiries@thebelfry.com
(W) www.thebelfry.com

Membership: Members & Public

Contact/s:

- Golf Operations Manager: Mr Simon Wordsworth

Course/s:

🏌 **BRABAZON**
Built: 1998
Number of Holes: 18 Par: 72
Yds: 7118 F9 Yds: 3611 B9 Yds: 3507
Designer: P Alliss, D Thomas

🏌 **DERBY**
Built: 1977
Number of Holes: 18
Yds: 6009 F9 Yds: 2765 B9 Yds: 3244
Designer: Peter Alliss, David Thomas

🏌 **PGA NATIONAL**
Built: 1997
Number of Holes: 18
Yds: 7053 F9 Yds: 3593 B9 Yds: 3460
Designer: Peter Alliss, D Thomas

BELHUS PARK

BELHUS PARK GOLF CLUB, Belhus Pk Leisure Complex, Aveley, South Ockendon, **ESSEX**, RM15 4QR, **ENGLAND**.
(T) 01708 852907

Membership: Members & Public

Contact/s:

- Manageress: Ms A Stevens

Course/s:

🏌 **BELHUS PARK**
Description: Wooded, Undulating, Open, Short, Drains Well, Ideal for the Elderly
Green Speed: Medium
Built: 1972
Number of Holes: 18 Par: 68
Par 3's: 5 Par 4's: 12 Par 5's: 1
Yds: 5589
Prevailing Wind: North
Designer: Thurrock Council
Further Information:
A challenging course offering an interesting game.

BELLEISLE & SEAFIELD

BELLEISLE & SEAFIELD GOLF COURSES, Doonfoot Rd, Ayr, **AYRSHIRE (SOUTH)**, KA7 4DU, **SCOTLAND**.
(T) 01292 441258

Membership: Public

Contact/s:

- Professional: Mr Richard Gordon
  ☎ 01292 441314
- Pro Shop: Mr David Gemmil
- Book Tee Times: Mr Alan Thomson

Course/s:

🏌 **BELLEISLE**
Description: Championship, Wooded, Parkland, Undulating, Long
Green Speed: Medium
Built: 1927 Built On: Clay
Number of Holes: 18 Par: 71
Record: 64 (J Farmer)
Par 3's: 5 Par 4's: 9 Par 5's: 4
Yds: 6040 F9 Yds: 2990 B9 Yds: 3050
Designer: James Braid
Further Information:
The course is deep in the heart of 'Burns Country'. Belleisle offers panoramic views from alll around the course.

🏌 **SEAFIELD**
Description: Links, Wooded, Parkland, Undulating, Sheltered, Open, Medium Length, Drains Well
Green Speed: Medium/Fast
Built: 1904 Built On: Clay/Sand
Number of Holes: 18 Par: 68
Par 3's: 4 Par 4's: 14
Yds: 5481 F9 Yds: 2695 B9 Yds: 2786
Further Information:
Along with the sister course 'Belleisle', Seafield enjoys panoramic views within 'Burns country'.

BELLINGHAM

BELLINGHAM GOLF CLUB, Boggle Hole Farm, Bellingham, Hexham, **NORTHUMBERLAND**, NE48 2DT, **ENGLAND**.
(T) 01434 220530

Membership: Members & Public
Size of Complex: 105 Acres

Contact/s:

- Club Secretary: Mr Peter Cordiner
- Book Tee Times: Mrs V Roberts
  ☎ 01434 220152

Course/s:

🏌 **BOOGLE HOLE**
Description: Parkland, Undulating, Medium Length
Green Speed: Medium
Built: 1893 Built On: Clay
Number of Holes: 18 Par: 70
Par 3's: 4 Par 4's: 12 Par 5's: 2
Yds: 6077 F9 Yds: 2950 B9 Yds: 3127
Prevailing Wind: West
Designer: E Johnson, I Wilson
Further Information:
With a highly regarded course design, Boogle Hole became a regular county venue since the 18 holes were completed. Very attractive tourist area between Hadrians Wall and Scottish border.

BELLSHILL

BELLSHILL GOLF CLUB, Community Rd, Orbiston, Bellshill, **LANARKSHIRE (NORTH)**, ML4 2RZ, **SCOTLAND**.
(T) 01698 745124

Contact/s:

- Captain: Mr David Miller

Course/s:

🏌 **BELLSHILL**
Number of Holes: 18

BELMONT

BELMONT GOLF COURSE, Belmont Hse, Belmont, Hereford, **HEREFORDSHIRE**, HR2 9SA, **ENGLAND**.
(T) 01432 352717

Contact/s:

- Manager: Mr M Welsh

Course/s:

🏌 **BELMONT**
Number of Holes: 18
Designer: Robert Sandow

BELTON PARK

BELTON PARK GOLF CLUB, Londonthorpe Rd, Grantham, **LINCOLNSHIRE**, NG31 9SH, **ENGLAND**.
(T) 01476 567399
(E) greatgolf@beltonpark.co.uk
(W) www.beltonpark.co.uk

Membership: Members & Public

Contact/s:

- Club Secretary: Mr Trevor Ireland
- Professional: Mr Brian McKee
  ☎ 01476 563911

Course/s:

🏌 **ANCASTER**
Description: Wooded, Parkland
Built: 1890
Number of Holes: 9 Par: 70
Par 3's: 2 Par 4's: 5 Par 5's: 2
Yds: 6305 F9 Yds: 3341 B9 Yds: 2964
Designer: Peter Alliss, John P Williams
Further Information:
Ancaster can be combined with either Browlow or Belmont in order to create an 18 hole course.

🏌 **BELMONT**
Number of Holes: 9 Par: 69
Par 3's: 2 Par 4's: 6 Par 5's: 1
Yds: 6075 F9 Yds: 3111 B9 Yds: 2964
Designer: Peter Alliss, John P Williams
Further Information:
Belmont course can be combined with either Ancaster or Brownlow in order to create an 18 hole round

🏌 **BROWNLOW**
Description: Wooded, Parkland, Sheltered, Medium Length, Drains Well, Ideal for the Elderly
Green Speed: Medium
Built: 1890
Number of Holes: 9 Par: 71
Par 3's: 2 Par 4's: 5 Par 5's: 2
Yds: 6452 F9 Yds: 3341 B9 Yds: 3111
Designer: Tom Williamson
Further Information:
Brownlow course can be combined with either Ancaster or Belmont in order to create an 18 hole round. Wildlife in abundance - especially fallow deer.

BELTON WOODS

DE VERE BELTON WOODS HOTEL & COUNTRY CLUB, Belton, Grantham, **LINCOLNSHIRE**, NG32 2LN, **ENGLAND**.
(T) 01476 593200

Contact/s:

- Professional: Mr Steve Sayers

Course/s:

🏌 **THE LAKES**
Built: 1991
Number of Holes: 18 Par: 72
Further Information:
The 9th hole is exceptionally long.

🏌 **THE WOODSIDE**
Description: Wooded
Built: 1991
Number of Holes: 18 Par: 73

BELTURBET

BELTURBET GOLF CLUB, Erne Hill, Belturbet, **COUNTY CAVAN**, **IRELAND**.
(T) 049 9522287

Course/s:
- BELTURBET
  Number of Holes: 9

BELVOIR PARK

BELVOIR PARK GOLF CLUB, 73 Church Rd, Newtownbreda, Belfast, **COUNTY ANTRIM**, BT8 7AN, **NORTHERN IRELAND**.
(T) 028 90491693

Contact/s:
- Professional: Mr Maurice Kelly

Course/s:
- THE BELVOIR PARK
  Number of Holes: 18
  Designer: Harry Shapland Colt

BEN RHYDDING

BEN RHYDDING GOLF CLUB, Ilkley, **YORKSHIRE (WEST)**, LS29 8SB, **ENGLAND**.
(T) 01943 608759

Course/s:
- BEN RHYDDING
  Number of Holes: 9

BENBURB VALLEY

BENBURB VALLEY GOLF COURSE, Maydown Rd, Benburb, Dungannon, **COUNTY TYRONE**, BT71 7LJ, **NORTHERN IRELAND**.
(T) 028 37549868
(W) www.benburbvalley.co.uk

Contact/s:
- Owner: Mr R Erwyn

Course/s:
- BENBURB VALLEY
  Number of Holes: 9 Par: 72
  Yds: 6404
  Further Information:
  This 9 hole course can be played as an 18 hole.

BENFIELD VALLEY

BENFIELD VALLEY GOLF COURSE, Hangleton Lane, Hove, **SUSSEX (EAST)**, BN3 8AU, **ENGLAND**.
(T) 01273 411358

Contact/s:
- Club Secretary: Susan Callow
- Professional: Mr Simon Martin

Course/s:
- BENFIELD VALLEY
  Number of Holes: 9 Par: 31
  Yds: 2166

BENONE

BENONE GOLF COURSE, 53 Benone Ave, Limavady, **COUNTY LONDONDERRY**, BT49 0LQ, **NORTHERN IRELAND**.
(T) 028 77750555

Course/s:
- BENONE
  Number of Holes: 9

BENTHAM

BENTHAM GOLF CLUB, Robin Lane, High Bentham, Lancaster, **LANCASHIRE**, LA2 7AG, **ENGLAND**.
(T) 01524 262455

Membership: Members & Public

Contact/s:
- Club Secretary: Mr Trevor Tudor

Course/s:
- BENTHAM
  Description: Parkland, Open, Medium Length, Tends to Flood, Ideal for the Elderly
  Green Speed: Fast
  Built: 1921 Built On: Clay
  Number of Holes: 9 Par: 70
  Prevailing Wind: West
  Further Information:
  Very challenging course.

BENTLEY

BENTLEY GOLF & COUNTRY CLUB LTD, Ongar Rd, Brentwood, **ESSEX**, CM15 9SS, **ENGLAND**.
(T) 01277 373179

Contact/s:
- Club Secretary: Mr J A Vivers

Course/s:
- BENTLEY
  Number of Holes: 18
  Designer: Alec Swann

BENTON HALL

BENTON HALL GOLF CLUB, Wickham Hill, Witham, **ESSEX**, CM8 3LH, **ENGLAND**.
(T) 01376 502454
(W) www.clubhaus.com

Membership: Members & Public

Contact/s:
- Professional: Mr Colin Fairweather
- Pro Shop: Mr Richard Kingston

Course/s:
- BENTON HALL
  Description: Championship, Parkland, Undulating, Sheltered, Medium Length, Tight, Drains Well
  Green Speed: Medium
  Built: 1990 Built On: Clay/Soil
  Number of Holes: 18 Par: 72
  Par 3's: 3 Par 4's: 12 Par 5's: 3
  Yds: 6046 F9 Yds: 2843 B9 Yds: 3203
  Designer: Charlie Cox, Alan Walker
  Further Information:
  Course offers championship golf to all players.

BENTRA MUNICIPAL

BENTRA MUNICIPAL GOLF CLUB, 1 Slaughterford Rd, Whitehead, Carrickfergus, **COUNTY ANTRIM**, BT38 9TG, **NORTHERN IRELAND**.
(T) 028 93378996

Membership: Public
Size of Complex: 47 Acres

Contact/s:
- Greenkeeper: Mr Cecil Knox

Course/s:
- BENTRA MUNICIPAL
  Description: Parkland, Valley, Sheltered, Long, Drains Well, Ideal for the Elderly
  Green Speed: Medium
  Built: 1850 Built On: Soil
  Number of Holes: 9 Par: 36
  Par 3's: 2 Par 4's: 5 Par 5's: 2
  Yds: 3042 F9 Yds: 3042
  Prevailing Wind: North/West
  Further Information:
  This is one of the longest 9 hole courses in Europe.

BEREHAVEN

BEREHAVEN GOLF CLUB & AMENITY PARK, Castletownbere, **COUNTY CORK**, **IRELAND**.

(T) 027 70700

Course/s:
- BEREHAVEN
  Description: Links, Ideal for the Elderly
  Built: 1906
  Number of Holes: 9 Par: 68
  Further Information:
  The course is close to the sea and is surrounded by mountains.

BERKHAMSTED

BERKHAMSTED GOLF CLUB, The Common, Berkhamsted, **HERTFORDSHIRE**, HP4 2QB, **ENGLAND**.
(T) 01442 865832
(W) www.golfagent.com/clubsites/Berkhamsted/

Membership: Members & Public

Contact/s:
- Professional: Mr Basil Proudfoot
  ☎ 01442 865851
- Pro Shop: Mr J Clarke

Course/s:
- BERKHAMSTED
  Description: Wooded, Heath Land, Sheltered, Medium Length, Tight, Drains Well
  Green Speed: Medium
  Built: 1890 Built On: Clay
  Number of Holes: 18 Par: 71
  Par 3's: 4 Par 4's: 11 Par 5's: 3
  Yds: 6610 F9 Yds: 3243 B9 Yds: 3367
  Designer: James Braid, Taylor
  Further Information:
  This course is famous for having no sand bunkers, only grass mounds and hollows. It is not suitable for novice or high handicap golfers.

BERKSHIRE

BERKSHIRE GOLF CLUB LTD (THE), Swinley Rd, Ascot, **BERKSHIRE**, SL5 8AY, **ENGLAND**.
(T) 01344 622351

Membership: Members & Public

Contact/s:
- Club Secretary: Lt. Col. J C F Hunt
  ☎ 01344 621496
- Professional: Mr P Anderson

Course/s:
- BLUE
  Description: Heath Land
  Number of Holes: 18 Par: 71
  Par 3's: 4 Par 4's: 11 Par 5's: 3
  Yds: 6260 F9 Yds: 3073 B9 Yds: 3187
  Designer: Herbert Fowler ♈
- RED
  Description: Heath Land
  Number of Holes: 18 Par: 72
  Yds: 6379
  Designer: Herbert Fowler ♈

BERWICK

BERWICK-UPON-TWEED GOLF CLUB, Goswick, Berwick-upon-Tweed, **NORTHUMBERLAND**, TD15 2RW, **ENGLAND**.
(T) 01289 387256

Membership: Members & Public

Contact/s:
- Club Secretary: Mr D Wilkinson
- Professional: Mr Paul Terras

Course/s:
- BERWICK-UPON-TWEED (GOSWICK)
  Description: Links, Undulating, Open,

Long, Drains Well, Ideal for the Elderly
Green Speed: Fast
Built: 1890　**Built On:** Sand
Number of Holes: 18　**Par:** 72
Par 3's: 4　**Par 4's:** 10　**Par 5's:** 4
Yds: 6452　**F9 Yds:** 3330　**B9 Yds:** 3122
Prevailing Wind: West
Designer: James Braid
Further Information:
The course has a seaside view.

BETCHWORTH PARK

BETCHWORTH PARK GOLF CLUB, Reigate Rd, Dorking, **SURREY**, RH4 1NZ, **ENGLAND**.
(T) 01306 882052

Contact/s:
- **Club Secretary:** Mr John Holton
- **Professional:** Mr Andy Tocher

Course/s:
🏌 **BETCHWORTH PARK**
　Number of Holes: 18　**Par:** 69
　Yds: 6266　**F9 Yds:** 3108　**B9 Yds:** 3158
　Designer: Harry Shapland Colt

BETHUNE PARK

BETHUNE PARK GOLF COURSE, Manor Drive, London, **LONDON (GREATER)**, N11 1NE, **ENGLAND**.
(T) 020 83688153

Membership: Members & Public

Contact/s:
- **General Manager:** Mr Peter Proto

Course/s:
🏌 **CALDERFIELDS**
　Description: Parkland, Breckland, Hilltop, Undulating, Open, Medium Length, Tends to Flood
　Green Speed: Medium
　Built: 1930　**Built On:** Clay/Soil
　Number of Holes: 9　**Par:** 73
　Yds: 6509　**F9 Yds:** 3066　**B9 Yds:** 2648
　Designer: Colin Andrews
　Further Information:
　A challenging course near to the coast.

BETWS-Y-COED

BETWS-Y-COED GOLF CLUB LTD, Golf Clubhouse, Ffordd Hen Eglwys, Betws-Y-Coed, **CONWY**, LL24 0AL, **WALES**.
(T) 01690 710556

Membership: Members & Public

Contact/s:
- **Club Secretary:** Mrs Pat Rowley

Course/s:
🏌 **BETWS-Y-COED**
　Description: Championship, Wooded, Parkland, Tight, Ideal for the Elderly
　Green Speed: Medium
　Built: 1977　**Built On:** Clay
　Number of Holes: 9　**Par:** 64
　Yds: 4998　**F9 Yds:** 2455　**B9 Yds:** 2543
　Prevailing Wind: South/West
　Further Information:
　The course is located in the middle of Conway Valley.

BEVERLEY & EAST RIDING

BEVERLEY & EAST RIDING GOLF CLUB, The Westwood, Beverley, **YORKSHIRE (EAST)**, HU17 8RG, **ENGLAND**.
(T) 01482 869519

Contact/s:
- **Club Secretary:** Mr M E Drew
　☎ 01482 868757
- **Professional:** Mr Alex Ashby

Course/s:
🏌 **WESTWOOD**
　Number of Holes: 18　**Par:** 69
　Yds: 6017　**F9 Yds:** 3064　**B9 Yds:** 2953

BEWDLEY PINES

BEWDLEY PINES GOLF CLUB, Habberley Rd, Bewdley, **WORCESTERSHIRE**, DY12 1LY, **ENGLAND**.
(T) 01299 404744

Contact/s:
- **Joint Owner:** Mr Alan Hobday

Course/s:
🏌 **BEWDLEY PINES**
　Number of Holes: 18　**Par:** 69
　Yds: 5618

BEXLEYHEATH

BEXLEYHEATH GOLF CLUB, Mount Rd, Bexleyheath, **KENT**, DA6 8JS, **ENGLAND**.
(T) 020 83034232

Contact/s:
- **Club Secretary:** Mr S Squires

Course/s:
🏌 **BEXLEYHEATH**
　Number of Holes: 9

BICESTER GOLF & COUNRTY CLUB

BICESTER GOLF & COUNTRY CLUB, Chesterton, Bicester, **OXFORDSHIRE**, OX6 8TE, **ENGLAND**.
(T) 01869 241204
(E) bicestergolf@ukonline.co.uk

Contact/s:
- **General Manager:** Mr Paul Fox

Course/s:
🏌 **BICESTER GOLF & COUNRTY CLUB**
　Number of Holes: 18　**Par:** 72
　Yds: 6700　**F9 Yds:** 3400　**B9 Yds:** 3300
　Designer: R Stagg

BIDFORD GRANGE

BIDFORD GRANGE GOLF CLUB, Bidford Grange, Bidford-on-Avon, Alcester, **WARWICKSHIRE**, B50 4LY, **ENGLAND**.
(T) 01789 490319

Contact/s:
- **Owner:** Mr Broadhurst

Course/s:
🏌 **BIDFORD GRANGE**
　Description: Parkland
　Number of Holes: 18　**Par:** 72
　Yds: 7233
　Designer: Howard Swan, Paul Tillman
　Further Information:
　The last 4 holes have views of the River Avon.

BIDSTON

BIDSTON GOLF CLUB, Bidston Link Rd, Wallasey, **MERSEYSIDE**, L44 2HR, **ENGLAND**.
(T) 0151 6383412

Contact/s:
- **Club Secretary:** Mr Frank Taylor
- **Professional:** Mr Neil MacFarlane
　☎ 0151 6306650

Course/s:
🏌 **BIDSTON**
　Description: Undulating, Open, Medium Length, Drains Well, Ideal for the Elderly
　Green Speed: Fast
　Built: 1913　**Built On:** Clay

Number of Holes: 18　**Par:** 70
Par 3's: 4　**Par 4's:** 12　**Par 5's:** 2
Yds: 6153
Prevailing Wind: West

BIGBURY

BIGBURY GOLF CLUB LTD, Bigbury on Sea, Kingsbridge, **DEVON**, TQ7 4BB, **ENGLAND**.
(T) 01548 810557

Contact/s:
- **Club Secretary:** Mr M Lowry

Course/s:
🏌 **BIGBURY**
　Number of Holes: 18　**Par:** 70
　Yds: 5896
　Designer: Taylor

BIGGAR

BIGGAR GOLF CLUB, Broughton Rd, Biggar, **LANARKSHIRE (SOUTH)**, ML12 6HA, **SCOTLAND**.
(T) 01899 220319

Contact/s:
- **Club Secretary:** Mr Tom Rodgers

Course/s:
🏌 **BIGGAR**
　Number of Holes: 18
　Designer: William Park

BILLINGBEAR PARK

BILLINGBEAR PARK GOLF COURSE, The Straight Mile, Wokingham, **BERKSHIRE**, RG40 5SJ, **ENGLAND**.
(T) 01344 869259

Membership: Public

Contact/s:
- **Club Secretary:** Mrs Jackie Blainey
- **Professional:** Mr M Blainey

Course/s:
🏌 **THE NEW**
　Number of Holes: 9　**Par:** 54
　Par 3's: 9
　Yds: 1238　**F9 Yds:** 1238

🏌 **THE OLD**
　Description: Wooded, Undulating, Sheltered, Medium Length, Drains Well
　Green Speed: Medium
　Built: 1990　**Built On:** Clay
　Number of Holes: 9　**Par:** 68
　Par 3's: 3　**Par 4's:** 5　**Par 5's:** 1
　Yds: 5761　**F9 Yds:** 2875　**B9 Yds:** 2886
　Further Information:
　The Old Course can be played as 18 holes. It also has 4 lakes throughout the course.

BILLINGHAM

BILLINGHAM GOLF CLUB, Sandy Lane, Billingham, **CLEVELAND**, TS22 5NA, **ENGLAND**.
(T) 01642 533816

Membership: Members & Public

Contact/s:
- **Club Secretary:** Mr E I Douglas
- **Professional:** Mr Michael Ure
- **Pro Shop:**
　☎ 01642 557060

Course/s:
🏌 **BOGGLE HOLE**
　Description: Parkland, Sheltered, Medium Length, Tends to Flood
　Green Speed: Medium
　Built: 1967　**Built On:** Clay
　Number of Holes: 18　**Par:** 73

Record: 63 (Marcus Maith)
Par 3's: 4 Par 4's: 9 Par 5's: 5
Yds: 6404 F9 Yds: 3119 B9 Yds: 3285

BINGLEY ST IVES

BINGLEY ST IVES GOLF CLUB LTD, St. Ives Est, Harden, Bingley, **YORKSHIRE (WEST)**, BD16 1AT, **ENGLAND**.
(T) 01274 511788

Contact/s:
• **Professional:** Mr Ray Firth
• **Book Tee Times:**
  ☎ 01274 562506

Course/s:
🏌 **BINGLEY ST IVES**
  Description: Wooded, Parkland, Moorland
  Built: 1932
  Number of Holes: 18 **Par:** 71
  Designer: Alistair MacKenzie
  Further Information:
  Sandy Lyle and Nick Faldo have won PGA tour events which have been staged here.

BIRCH GROVE

BIRCH GROVE GOLF CLUB, Layer Rd, Kingsford, Colchester, **ESSEX**, CO2 0HS, **ENGLAND**.
(T) 01206 734276

Membership: Members & Public
Size of Complex: 40 Acres

Contact/s:
• **Club Secretary:** Mr E Goldsmith
• **Professional:** Mr C Laitt

Course/s:
🏌 **BIRCH GROVE**
  Description: Wooded, Undulating, Sheltered, Medium Length, Tight, Drains Well, Ideal for the Elderly
  Green Speed: Medium
  Built: 1970 **Built On:** Sand/Soil
  Number of Holes: 9 **Par:** 33
  Par 3's: 4 **Par 4's:** 4 **Par 5's:** 1
  Yds: 2266 **F9 Yds:** 2266
  Prevailing Wind: South/West
  Designer: Lawrie Marston
  Further Information:
  This challenging 9 hole course can be played as an 18 hole course.

BIRCH HALL

BIRCH HALL GOLF CLUB, Sheffield Rd, Unstone, Dronfield, **DERBYSHIRE**, S18 4DB, **ENGLAND**.
(T) 01246 291979

Contact/s:
• **Manager:** Mr R Cheetham

Course/s:
🏌 **BIRCH HALL**
  Number of Holes: 18
  Designer: D Tucker

BIRCHWOOD

BIRCHWOOD GOLF CLUB, Kelvin Cl, Birchwood, Warrington, **CHESHIRE**, WA3 7PB, **ENGLAND**.
(T) 01925 818819

Contact/s:
• **Manager:** Mr J Hilton

Course/s:
🏌 **BIRCHWOOD**
  Number of Holes: 18
  Designer: T McCauley

BIRCHWOOD PARK

BIRCHWOOD PARK GOLF CENTRE, Birchwood Rd, Wilmington, Dartford, **KENT**, DA2 7HJ, **ENGLAND**.
(T) 01322 660554/ 662038

Course/s:
🏌 **BIRCHWOOD PARK GOLF CENTRE LTD**
  Description: Parkland, Undulating, Open
  Built: 1992
  Number of Holes: 18 **Par:** 71
  Yds: 6364 **F9 Yds:** 3222 **B9 Yds:** 3142
  Designer: Howard Swan

BIRD HILLS

BIRD HILLS GOLF CLUB, Drift Rd, Hawthorn Hill, Maidenhead, **BERKSHIRE**, SL6 3ST, **ENGLAND**.
(T) 01628 771030
(E) info@birdhills.co.uk
(W) www.birdhills.co.uk

Contact/s:
• **General Manager:** Mr Steve Farrin

Course/s:
🏌 **BIRD HILLS**
  Number of Holes: 18 **Par:** 72
  Par 3's: 4 **Par 4's:** 10 **Par 5's:** 4
  Yds: 6212 **F9 Yds:** 3165 **B9 Yds:** 3047

BIRKDALE (ROYAL)

ROYAL BIRKDALE GOLF CLUB, Waterloo Rd, Birkdale, Southport, **MERSEYSIDE**, PR8 2LX, **ENGLAND**.
(T) 01704 567920
(E) royalbirkdale@ukgolfer.org
(W) www.ukgolfer.org/clubs/royalbirkdale

Membership: Members & Public

Contact/s:
• **Club Secretary:** Mr M C Gilyeat
• **Professional:** Mr Brian Hodgkinson

Course/s:
🏌 **ROYAL BIRKDALE**
  Description: Championship, Links
  Built On: Sand
  Number of Holes: 18 **Par:** 71
  Par 3's: 4 **Par 4's:** 11 **Par 5's:** 3
  Yds: 6305
  Designer: Hawtree, Lowe 🏆

BIRLEY WOOD

BIRLEY WOOD GOLF CLUB, Birley Lane, Sheffield, **YORKSHIRE (SOUTH)**, S12 3BP, **ENGLAND**.
(T) 0114 2647262
(W) www.birleywood.free-online.co.uk

Contact/s:
• **Club Secretary:** Mr Philip Renshaw
  ☎ 0114 2653784
• **Professional:** Mr Pete Ball

Course/s:
🏌 **THE FAIRWAY**
  Number of Holes: 18 **Par:** 68
  Yds: 5647 **F9 Yds:** 3037 **B9 Yds:** 2610

BIRR

BIRR GOLF CLUB, The Glens, Birr, **COUNTY OFFALY**, **IRELAND**.
(T) 050 920082

Course/s:
🏌 **BIRR**
  Number of Holes: 18

BIRSTALL

BIRSTALL GOLF CLUB, Station Rd, Birstall, Leicester, **LEICESTERSHIRE**, LE4 3BB, **ENGLAND**.
(T) 0116 2674450

Contact/s:
• **Club Secretary:** Mrs Sue Chilton
  ☎ 0116 2674322
• **Professional:** Mr Dave Clark
  ☎ 0116 2675245

Course/s:
🏌 **BIRSTALL**
  Description: Parkland
  Built: 1901
  Number of Holes: 18 **Par:** 70
  Yds: 6230 **F9 Yds:** 3003 **B9 Yds:** 3227
  Further Information:
  An attractive and testing course.

BIRTLEY

BIRTLEY GOLF CLUB, Birtley Lane, Birtley, Chester Le Street, **COUNTY DURHAM**, DH3 2LR, **ENGLAND**.
(T) 0191 4102207

Contact/s:
• **Treasurer:** Mr Malcolm Wakefield

Course/s:
🏌 **BIRTLEY**
  Number of Holes: 9

BISHOP AUCKLAND

BISHOP AUCKLAND GOLF CLUB, High Plains, Durham Rd, Bishop Auckland, **COUNTY DURHAM**, DL14 8DL, **ENGLAND**.
(T) 01388 602198
(E) enquiries@bagc.co.uk
(W) www.bagc.co.uk

Membership: Members & Public
Size of Complex: 150 Acres

Contact/s:
• **Club Secretary:** Mr Allan Milne
  ☎ 01388 663648
• **Professional:** Mr David Skiffington
  ☎ 01388 661618

Course/s:
🏌 **BISHOP AUCKLAND**
  Description: Parkland, Open, Medium Length, Drains Well, Ideal for the Elderly
  Green Speed: Medium
  Built: 1894 **Built On:** Soil
  Number of Holes: 18 **Par:** 72
  Yds: 6124 **F9 Yds:** 3120 **B9 Yds:** 3004
  Designer: James Kay

BISHOPBRIGGS

BISHOPBRIGGS GOLF CLUB (THE), Brackenbrae Rd, Bishopbriggs, Glasgow, **GLASGOW (CITY OF)**, G64 2DX, **SCOTLAND**.
(T) 0141 7721810
(E) bgcsecretary@dial.pipex.com
(W) www.thebishopbriggsgolfclub.com

Contact/s:
• **Club Secretary:** Mr Andrew Smith
  ☎ 0141 7728938

Course/s:
🏌 **THE BISHOPBRIGGS**
  Number of Holes: 18 **Par:** 69
  Yds: 6056

BISHOPS STORTFORD

BISHOPS STORTFORD GOLF CLUB, Dunmow Rd, Bishop's Stortford, **HERTFORDSHIRE**, CM23 5HP, **ENGLAND**.
(T) 01279 654715
(E) bishopstortfordgc@hotmail.com
(W) www.bsgc.co.uk

Membership: Members & Public

Contact/s:
- **Professional:** Mr Stephen M Bryan
- **Pro Shop:**
  ☎ 01279 651324

Course/s:

🏌 **BISHOP'S STORTFORD**
  Description: Wooded, Parkland, Undulating, Medium Length, Ideal for the Elderly
  Green Speed: Medium
  Built: 1910
  Number of Holes: 18 **Par:** 71
  Yds: 6404 **F9 Yds:** 3052 **B9 Yds:** 3352
  Designer: James Braid

BISHOPSWOOD

BISHOPSWOOD GOLF COURSE, The Clubhouse, Bishopswood Lane, Tadley, **HAMPSHIRE**, RG26 4AT, **ENGLAND**.
(T) 0118 9812200

Contact/s:
- **Professional:** Mr S Ward

Course/s:

🏌 **BISHOPSWOOD**
  Number of Holes: 9 **Par:** 36
  Par 3's: 2 **Par 4's:** 5 **Par 5's:** 2
  Yds: 3237
  Designer: G Blake, M Phillips

BLACK BUSH

BLACK BUSH GOLF CLUB, Thomastown, Dunshaughlin, **COUNTY MEATH**, **IRELAND**.
(T) 01 8250021

Course/s:

🏌 **COURSE 1**
  Number of Holes: 18
  Designer: R Browne

🏌 **COURSE 2**
  Number of Holes: 9
  Designer: R Browne

BLACKBURN

BLACKBURN GOLF CLUB, Beardwood Brow, Revidge Rd, Blackburn, **LANCASHIRE**, BB2 7AX, **ENGLAND**.
(T) 01254 51122

Contact/s:
- **Professional:** Mr Alan Rodwell

Course/s:

🏌 **BLACKBURN**
  Number of Holes: 18

BLACKBURN

BLACKBURN GOLF CLUB,

Contact/s:
- **Professional:** Mr Alan Rodwell

Course/s:

🏌 **BLACKBURN**
  Number of Holes: 18

BLACKHEATH (ROYAL)

ROYAL BLACKHEATH GOLF CLUB, Court Rd, Eltham, London, **LONDON (GREATER)**, SE9 5AF, **ENGLAND**.
(T) 020 8850 1795
(E) info@rbgc.com
(W) www.rbgc.com

Membership: Members & Public
Size of Complex: 110 Acres

Contact/s:
- **Club Secretary:** Mr A Dunlop

Course/s:

🏌 **ROYAL BLACKHEATH**
  Description: Parkland, Sheltered, Drains Well
  Green Speed: Medium **Built On:** Clay
  Number of Holes: 18 **Par:** 70
  Par 3's: 4 **Par 4's:** 12 **Par 5's:** 2
  Yds: 6219 **F9 Yds:** 3226 **B9 Yds:** 2993
  Prevailing Wind: West
  Designer: James Braid

BLACKLEY

BLACKLEY GOLF CENTRE, Victoria Ave East, Blackley, Manchester, **MANCHESTER (GREATER)**, M9 7HW, **ENGLAND**.
(T) 0161 6547770

Membership: Members & Public
Size of Complex: 80 Acres

Contact/s:
- **Club Secretary:** Mr Chris Leggett
- **Professional:** Mr Craig Gould
  ☎ 0161 6433912

Course/s:

🏌 **BLACKLEY**
  Description: Parkland, Moorland, Undulating, Medium Length, Drains Well, Ideal for the Elderly
  Green Speed: Fast
  Built: 1907 **Built On:** Soil
  Number of Holes: 18 **Record:** 70 (Craig Gould)
  Prevailing Wind: North/West
  Further Information:
  A challenging course.

BLACKLION

BLACKLION GOLF CLUB, Toam, Blacklion, **COUNTY CAVAN**, **IRELAND**.
(T) 072 53024

Course/s:

🏌 **BLACKLION**
  Number of Holes: 9
  Designer: Edward Hackett

BLACKMOOR

BLACKMOOR GOLF CLUB, Golf Lane, Whitehill, Bordon, **HAMPSHIRE**, GU35 9EH, **ENGLAND**.
(T) 01420 472775

Membership: Members & Public

Contact/s:
- **Professional:** Mr Stephen Clay
  ☎ 01420 472345

Course/s:

🏌 **BLACKMOOR**
  Description: Championship, Parkland, Moorland, Medium Length, Tight
  Green Speed: Medium
  Built: 1913 **Built On:** Sand
  Number of Holes: 18 **Record:** 64 (R Dickman)
  Prevailing Wind: North
  Designer: Harry Shapland Colt
  Further Information:
  A challenging course.

BLACKNEST

BLACKNEST GOLF CLUB, Blacknest Rd, Blacknest, Alton, **HAMPSHIRE**, GU34 4QL, **ENGLAND**.
(T) 01420 22888

Contact/s:
- **Professional:** Mr Ian Benson

Course/s:

🏌 **BLACKNEST**

Description: Parkland
Built: 1992
Number of Holes: 18 **Par:** 69
Designer: Nicholson
Further Information:
A testing course for any golfer.

BLACKPOOL NORTH SHORE

BLACKPOOL NORTH SHORE GOLF CLUB, Devonshire Rd, Blackpool, **LANCASHIRE**, FY2 0RD, **ENGLAND**.
(T) 01253 352054

Membership: Members & Public
Size of Complex: 95 Acres

Contact/s:
- **Club Secretary:** Mr Michael Ogden
- **Professional:** Mr Brenden Ward

Course/s:

🏌 **BLACKPOOL NORTH SHORE**
  Description: Links, Parkland, Undulating, Open, Medium Length, Drains Well, Ideal for the Elderly
  Green Speed: Medium
  Built: 1904 **Built On:** Clay
  Number of Holes: 18
  Prevailing Wind: West

BLACKPOOL PARK

BLACKPOOL PARK GOLF CLUB, North Pk Drive, Blackpool, **LANCASHIRE**, FY3 8LS, **ENGLAND**.
(T) 01253 391004

Contact/s:
- **Club Secretary:** Mr D Stones
- **Professional:** Mr Brian Purdie

Course/s:

🏌 **STANLEY PARK MUNICIPAL**
  Number of Holes: 18 **Par:** 70
  Yds: 6687 **F9 Yds:** 3875 **B9 Yds:** 2812
  Designer: Alistair MacKenzie

BLACKTHORN WOOD

BLACKTHORN WOOD GOLF COMPLEX, Corby Rd, Cottingham, Market Harborough, **LEICESTERSHIRE**, LE16 8XL, **ENGLAND**.
(T) 01536 403119

Membership: Members & Public

Contact/s:
- **Professional:** Mr Bryn Morriss

Course/s:

🏌 **BLACKTHORN WOOD**
  Description: Parkland, Undulating, Short, Tends to Flood, Ideal for the Elderly
  Green Speed: Medium
  Built: 1996
  Number of Holes: 9

BLACKWATER VALLEY

BLACKWATER VALLEY GOLF CLUB, Fox Lane, Eversley, Hook, **HAMPSHIRE**, RG27 0RA, **ENGLAND**.
(T) 01252 874725

Contact/s:
- **Manager:** Mr H Alanby

Course/s:

🏌 **BLACKWATER VALLEY**
  Number of Holes: 9

BLACKWELL

BLACKWELL GOLF CLUB LTD, Agmore Rd, Blackwell, Bromsgrove, **WORCESTERSHIRE**, B60 1PY, **ENGLAND**.
(T) 0121 4451994
(W) www.blackwell-golf-club.co.uk

Contact/s:
- Club Secretary: J T Meas
- Pro Shop: Mr N Blake
- ☎ 0121 4453113

Course/s:
- **THE BLACKWELL**
  Description: Parkland
  Number of Holes: 18 Par: 70
  Yds: 6260 F9 Yds: 3017 B9 Yds: 3243
  Designer: Herbert Fowler, T Simpson

BLACKWELL GRANGE

BLACKWELL GRANGE GOLF CLUB, Briar Cl, Darlington, **COUNTY DURHAM**, DL3 8QX, **ENGLAND**.
(T) 01325 464458
(E) secretary@blackwell-grange.co.uk

Contact/s:
- Honorary Secretary: Mr Peter Brian Burkhill

Course/s:
- **BLACKWELL GRANGE**
  Number of Holes: 18 Par: 68
  Par 3's: 7 Par 4's: 8 Par 5's: 3
  Yds: 5584 F9 Yds: 2828 B9 Yds: 2756
  Designer: Frank Pennink

BLACKWOOD

BLACKWOOD GOLF CLUB, Cwmgelli, Blackwood, **CAERPHILLY**, NP2 1EL, **WALES**.
(T) 01495 222121

Course/s:
- **BLACKWOOD**
  Number of Holes: 9 Par: 66
  Yds: 5322 F9 Yds: 2671 B9 Yds: 2661

BLACKWOOD GOLF CTRE

BLACKWOOD GOLF CENTRE, 150 Crawfordsburn Rd, Bangor, **COUNTY DOWN**, BT19 1GB, **NORTHERN IRELAND**.
(T) 028 91852706

Contact/s:
- Professional: Ms Debbie Hanna

Course/s:
- **HAMILTON**
  Built: 1994
  Number of Holes: 18 Par: 71
  Yds: 6392 F9 Yds: 3211 B9 Yds: 3181
  Designer: Simon Gidman
- **TEMPLE**
  Built: 1994
  Number of Holes: 18 Par: 54
  Par 3's: 18
  Designer: Simon Gidman

BLAINROE

BLAINROE GOLF CLUB, Blainroe, **COUNTY WICKLOW**, **IRELAND**.
(T) 040 468168

Course/s:
- **BLAINROE**
  Number of Holes: 18
  Designer: Hawtree

BLAIR ATHOLL

BLAIR ATHOLL GOLF CLUB, Invertilt Rd, Bridge Of Tilt, Pitlochry, **PERTH AND KINROSS**, PH18 5TE, **SCOTLAND**.
(T) 01796 481407

Contact/s:
- Club Secretary: Mr Tony Boon

Course/s:

- **BLAIR ATHOLL**
  Number of Holes: 9
  Designer: Morris

BLAIRBETH

BLAIRBETH GOLF CLUB, Fernbrae Ave, Rutherglen, Glasgow, **GLASGOW (CITY OF)**, G73 4SF, **SCOTLAND**.
(T) 0141 6343355

Contact/s:
- Club Secretary: Mr Fred Henderson
- Book Tee Times: Mr Ian Whyte
  ☎ 0141 6343325

Course/s:
- **BLAIRBETH**
  Description: Parkland
  Built: 1910
  Number of Holes: 18 Par: 70
  Further Information:
  A challenging course with panoramic views.

BLAIRGOWRIE

BLAIRGOWRIE GOLF CLUB, Golf Course Rd, Blairgowrie, **PERTH AND KINROSS**, PH10 6LG, **SCOTLAND**.
(T) 01250 872594

Membership: Members & Public

Contact/s:
- Club Secretary: Mr John Simpson
- Professional: Mr Charles Dernie
  ☎ 01250 873116

Course/s:
- **LANSDOWNE**
  Number of Holes: 18
  Designer: Peter Alliss, James Braid, Tom Morris, David Thomas
- **ROSEMOUNT**
  Number of Holes: 18 Par: 72
  Yds: 6590
  Designer: Peter Alliss, James Braid, Tom Morris, David Thomas 🏆
- **WEE**
  Number of Holes: 9
  Designer: Peter Alliss, James Braid, Tom Morris, David Thomas

BLANKNEY

BLANKNEY GOLF CLUB, Clubhouse, Lincoln Rd, Blankney, Lincoln, **LINCOLNSHIRE**, LN4 3AZ, **ENGLAND**.
(T) 01526 320202

Contact/s:
- General Manager: Mr David Priest

Course/s:
- **BLANKNEY**
  Number of Holes: 18 Par: 72
  Yds: 6638 F9 Yds: 3437 B9 Yds: 3201
  Designer: C Sinclair

BLARNEY

BLARNEY GOLF COURSE, Stoneview, Blarney, **COUNTY CORK**, **IRELAND**.
(T) 021 4382455
(E) blarneygolf@esatbiz.com

Membership: Public
Size of Complex: 110 Acres

Contact/s:
- Club Secretary: Mr Dan Quill
- Pro Shop: Ms Deborah Murphy

Course/s:
- **BLARNEY**
  Description: Parkland, Undulating, Short, Drains Well, Ideal for the Elderly

Green Speed: Medium
Built: 1996 Built On: Clay/Soil
Number of Holes: 18 Par: 70
Par 3's: 4 Par 4's: 12 Par 5's: 2
Yds: 5748 F9 Yds: 2963 B9 Yds: 2785
Prevailing Wind: South/West
Designer: P Suttle
Further Information:
Views of Blarney Castle and Blarney Stone.

BLETCHINGLEY

BLETCHINGLEY GOLF CLUB, Church Lane, Bletchingley, Redhill, **SURREY**, RH1 4LP, **ENGLAND**.
(T) 01883 744848

Course/s:
- **BLETCHINGLEY**
  Number of Holes: 18 Par: 72
  Yds: 6531 F9 Yds: 3441 B9 Yds: 3090

BLOXWICH

BLOXWICH GOLF CLUB, Stafford Rd, Walsall, **MIDLANDS (WEST)**, WS3 3PQ, **ENGLAND**.
(T) 01922 476593

Contact/s:
- Club Secretary: Mr Dennis Frost
- Professional: Mr Richard J Dance

Course/s:
- **BLOXWICH**
  Number of Holes: 18 Par: 71
  Par 3's: 5 Par 4's: 9 Par 5's: 4
  Yds: 6294 F9 Yds: 3100 B9 Yds: 3194

BLUE MOUNTAIN GOLF CENTRE

AMERICAN GOLF CORPORATION, Wood Lane, Binfield, Bracknell, **BERKSHIRE**, RG42 4EX, **ENGLAND**.
(T) 01344 300200
(W) www.americangolf.com

Membership: Members & Public

Contact/s:
- Professional: Mr Ian Looms
- Pro Shop:
  ☎ 01344 300220

Course/s:
- **BLUE MOUNTAIN**
  Description: Parkland, Undulating, Short, Tight, Drains Well, Ideal for the Elderly
  Green Speed: Medium Built On: Clay
  Number of Holes: 18 Par: 70
  Yds: 6097 F9 Yds: 3337 B9 Yds: 2760
  Further Information:
  Water features throughout the course

BLUNDELLS HILL

BLUNDELLS HILL GOLF CLUB, Blundells Lane, Rainhill, Prescot, **MERSEYSIDE**, L35 6NA, **ENGLAND**.
(T) 0151 4300100
(E) info@blundellshill.co.uk
(W) www.blundellshill.co.uk

Membership: Members & Public

Contact/s:
- Club Secretary: Mr Andy Roberts
  ☎ 0151 4309551
- Professional: Mr Richard Burbidge

Course/s:
- **BLUNDELL'S HILL**
  Description: Parkland, Hilltop, Undulating, Open, Medium Length, Drains Well Built: 1994 Built On: Sand
  Number of Holes: 18
  Designer: Steve Marnoch

BLYTH

BLYTH GOLF CLUB, New Delaval, Newsham, Blyth, **NORTHUMBERLAND**, NE24 4DB, **ENGLAND**.
(T) 01670 540110
(E) blythgc@lineone.net
(W) www.blythgolf.co.uk

Contact/s:
● **Professional:** Mr Andrew Brown

Course/s:
⛳ **BLYTH**
    Number of Holes: 18 **Par:** 72
    Yds: 6456 **F9 Yds:** 3287 **B9 Yds:** 3169
    Designer: J Hamilton-Stutt

BOARS HEAD

BOARS HEAD GOLF CENTRE, Boars Head Farm, Boars Head, Crowborough, **SUSSEX (EAST)**, TN6 3HD, **ENGLAND**.
(T) 01892 664545

Membership: Members & Public
Size of Complex: 66 Acres

Contact/s:
● **Professional:** Mr David Edwards

Course/s:
⛳ **BOAR'S HEAD**
    Description: Parkland, Undulating, Sheltered, Short, Drains Well
    Green Speed: Medium
    Built: 1997 **Built On:** Clay
    Number of Holes: 9 **Par:** 35
    Par 3's: 2 **Par 4's:** 6 **Par 5's:** 1
    Yds: 2802
    Designer: Martin Gillett
    Further Information:
    This Par 35 course can be played as 18 holes.

BOAT OF GARTEN

BOAT OF GARTEN GOLF & TENNIS CLUB, Nethybridge Rd, Boat Of Garten, **HIGHLANDS**, PH24 3BQ, **SCOTLAND**.
(T) 01479 831282
(E) boatgolf@enterprise.net
(W) www.boatgolf.com

Contact/s:
● **Club Secretary:** Mr Paddy Symth
● **Professional:** Mr James Ingram

Course/s:
⛳ **BOAT OF GARTEN**
    Description: Heath Land, Undulating, Short, Tight, Drains Well
    Green Speed: Medium **Built On:** Sand
    Number of Holes: 18
    Prevailing Wind: South/West
    Designer: James Braid
    Further Information:
    The course provides superb Highland views and a challenging game of golf.

BODENSTOWN

BODENSTOWN GOLF CLUB, Ladyhill, Bodenstown, **COUNTY KILDARE**, **IRELAND**.
(T) 045 897096

Contact/s:
● **Club Secretary:** Mrs Rita Mather

Course/s:
⛳ **BODENSTOWN**
    Number of Holes: 18 **Par:** 71
    Yds: 6708
    Designer: Richard Mather

⛳ **LADYHILL**
    Number of Holes: 18 **Par:** 68
    Yds: 5774

Designer: Richard Mather

BOGNOR REGIS

BOGNOR REGIS GOLF CLUB, Downview Rd, Felpham, Bognor Regis, **SUSSEX (WEST)**, PO22 8JD, **ENGLAND**.
(T) 01243 865209

Membership: Members & Public

Contact/s:
● **Professional:** Mr Steve Bassil

Course/s:
⛳ **BOGNOR REGIS**
    Description: Wooded, Parkland, Sheltered, Medium Length, Tends to Flood, Ideal for the Elderly
    Green Speed: Medium
    Built: 1892 **Built On:** Soil
    Number of Holes: 18 **Par:** 70
    Par 3's: 4 **Par 4's:** 12 **Par 5's:** 2
    Yds: 6238 **F9 Yds:** 3200 **B9 Yds:** 3038
    Prevailing Wind: West
    Designer: James Braid
    Further Information:
    Views of South Downs.

BOLDMERE

BOLDMERE GOLF COURSE, Monmouth Drive, Sutton Coldfield, **MIDLANDS (WEST)**, B73 6JL, **ENGLAND**.
(T) 0121 3543379

Membership: Members & Public

Contact/s:
● **Professional:** Mr Trevor Short

Course/s:
⛳ **BOLDMERE**
    Description: Parkland, Short, Ideal for the Elderly
    Green Speed: Medium
    Built: 1936 **Built On:** Soil
    Number of Holes: 18 **Par:** 62
    Record: 57 (Phil Weaver)
    Yds: 4474
    Further Information:
    A flat course which is ideal for ladies.

BOLDON

BOLDON GOLF CLUB LTD, Dipe Lane, East Boldon, **TYNE AND WEAR**, NE36 0PQ, **ENGLAND**.
(T) 0191 5364182
(E) info@boldongolfclub.co.uk
(W) www.boldongolfclub.co.uk

Contact/s:
● **Club Secretary:** Mr R Benton
    ☎ 0191 5365360
● **Professional:** Mr Sean Richardson

Course/s:
⛳ **BOLDON**
    Number of Holes: 18 **Par:** 72
    Par 3's: 4 **Par 4's:** 10 **Par 5's:** 4
    Yds: 6338 **F9 Yds:** 3027 **B9 Yds:** 3311
    Designer: Harry Vardon

BOLTON

BOLTON GOLF & LEISURE LTD, Longsight Pk, Longsight Lane, Harwood, Bolton, **LANCASHIRE**, BL2 4JX, **ENGLAND**.
(T) 01204 597659

Membership: Members & Public

Contact/s:
● **Professional:** Mr Andrew Duncan

Course/s:
⛳ **BOLTON OPEN**
    Description: Wooded, Parkland, Undulating, Sheltered, Short, Tight, Drains Well
    Green Speed: Medium
    Built: 1992 **Built On:** Soil
    Number of Holes: 18 **Par:** 70
    Par 3's: 5 **Par 4's:** 10 **Par 5's:** 3
    Yds: 5710 **F9 Yds:** 2757 **B9 Yds:** 2953
    Prevailing Wind: West

BOLTON

BOLTON GOLF CLUB LTD, Lostock Pk, Chorley New Rd, Lostock, Bolton, **LANCASHIRE**, BL6 4AJ, **ENGLAND**.
(T) 01204 843067

Contact/s:
● **Pro Shop:** Mr Bob Longworth
    ☎ 01204 843073

Course/s:
⛳ **BOLTON**
    Number of Holes: 18 **Par:** 70
    Yds: 6213 **F9 Yds:** 3052 **B9 Yds:** 3161

BON-ACCORD

BON-ACCORD GOLF CLUB, 19 Golf Rd, Aberdeen, **ABERDEEN (CITY OF)**, AB24 5QB, **SCOTLAND**.
(T) 01224 633464

Course/s:
⛳ **KINGS LINKS**
    Number of Holes: 18 **Par:** 69
    Yds: 6270

BONAR BRIDGE/ARDGAY

BONAR BRIDGE/ARDGAY GOLF CLUB, Migdale Rd, Ardgay, **HIGHLANDS**, IV24 3EJ, **SCOTLAND**.
(T) 01863 766375

Course/s:
⛳ **BONAR BRIDGE/ARDGAY**
    Number of Holes: 9 **Par:** 34
    Yds: 2602 **F9 Yds:** 2602

BONDHAY GOLF & FISHING CLUB

BONDHAY GOLF & FISHING CLUB, Bondhay Lane, Whitwell Common, Worksop, **NOTTINGHAMSHIRE**, S80 3EH, **ENGLAND**.
(T) 01909 723608

Contact/s:
● **Managing Director:** Mr Alan Hardisty

Course/s:
⛳ **DEVONSHIRE**
    Number of Holes: 18 **Par:** 72
    Yds: 6720
    Designer: Donald Steel

⛳ **FAMILY**
    Number of Holes: 9 **Par:** 27
    Yds: 1690
    Designer: Donald Steel

BONNYBRIDGE

BONNYBRIDGE GOLF CLUB, Larbert Rd, Bonnybridge, **FALKIRK**, FK4 1NY, **SCOTLAND**.
(T) 01324 812822
(E) bonnybridgegolfclub@hotmail.com

Membership: Members & Public

Contact/s:
● **Club Secretary:** Mr James Mullen

Course/s:
⛳ **BONNYBRIDGE**
    Description: Parkland, Heath Land, Medium Length, Tight, Drains Well
    Built: 1925
    Number of Holes: 9
    Yds: 3029

Designer: Richard Mather

BONNYTON

BONNYTON GOLF CLUB, Eaglesham, Glasgow, **GLASGOW (CITY OF)**, G76 0QA, **SCOTLAND**.
(T) 01355 302781

Contact/s:
● **Club Secretary:** Mrs Anne Hughes
● **Professional:** Mr K McWade

Course/s:
🌑 **BONNYTON**
  Number of Holes: 18   **Par:** 72
  Yds: 6255   **F9 Yds:** 3178   **B9 Yds:** 3077

BOOTHFERRY PARK

BOOTHFERRY PARK GOLF CLUB,
Spaldington Lane, Howden, Goole,
YORKSHIRE (EAST), DN14 7NG,
ENGLAND.
(T) 01430 430364

Contact/s:
● **Professional:** Mr Nigel Bundy
  ☎ 01430 430634

Course/s:
🌑 **BOOTHFERRY PARK**
  Description: Open
  Green Speed: Medium
  Built: 1982   **Built On:** Clay
  Number of Holes: 18   **Par:** 73
  Par 3's: 4   **Par 4's:** 9   **Par 5's:** 5
  Yds: 6651   **F9 Yds:** 3368   **B9 Yds:** 3283
  Designer: Donald Steel
  Further Information:
  Natural dykes requiring concentration of club selection on a number of holes.

BOOTLE

BOOTLE GOLF CLUB, Dunnings Bridge Rd, Bootle, **MERSEYSIDE**, L30 2PP, **ENGLAND**.
(T) 0151 9281371

Membership: Public

Contact/s:
● **Club Secretary:** Mr John Morgan
● **Professional:** Mr Alan Bradshaw

Course/s:
🌑 **BOOTLE**
  Number of Holes: 9   **Par:** 35
  Yds: 3005

BORRIS

BORRIS GOLF CLUB, Deer Pk, Borris, **COUNTY CARLOW**, **IRELAND**.
(T) 050 373310
(E) borrisgolfclub@eircom.net

Contact/s:
● **Club Secretary:** Nollaig Lucas

Course/s:
🌑 **BORRIS**
  Number of Holes: 9   **Par:** 70
  Yds: 5680   **F9 Yds:** 2835   **B9 Yds:** 2845

BORTH & YNYSLAS

BORTH & YNYSLAS GOLF CLUB LTD, Aer Y Mor, Borth, **CEREDIGION**, SY24 5JS, **WALES**.
(T) 01970 871202
(E) secretary@borthgolf.co.uk
(W) www.borthgolf.co.uk

Membership: Members & Public

Contact/s:
● **Club Secretary:** Mr Gareth Pritchard
● **Professional:** Mr John Lewis
● **Pro Shop:**
  ☎ 01970 871557

Course/s:
🌑 **BORTH & YNYSLAS**
  Description: Links, Open, Medium Length, Tight, Drains Well, Ideal for the Elderly
  Green Speed: Medium/Fast
  Built: 1885   **Built On:** Sand
  Number of Holes: 18   **Par:** 70
  Par 3's: 5   **Par 4's:** 10   **Par 5's:** 3
  Yds: 6116   **F9 Yds:** 3291   **B9 Yds:** 2825
  Designer: Harry Shapland Colt
  Further Information:
  The course offers a challenging game for its members and holiday golfers.

BOSCOMBE LADIES

BOSCOMBE LADIES GOLF CLUB, Queens Pk West Drive, Bournemouth, **DORSET**, BH8 9BY, **ENGLAND**.
(T) 01202 303927

Membership: Members & Public

Contact/s:
● **Club Secretary:** Mrs V J Goodwin
● **Professional:** Mr Richard Hill
  ☎ 01202 396198

Course/s:
🌑 **QUEENS PARK**
  Description: Wooded, Parkland, Medium Length, Tight, Drains Well
  Green Speed: Medium
  Built: 1900
  Number of Holes: 18
  Designer: Taylor

BOSTON

BOSTON GOLF CLUB, Horncastle Rd, Cowbridge, Boston, **LINCOLNSHIRE**, PE22 7EL, **ENGLAND**.
(T) 01205 362306

Membership: Members & Public
Size of Complex: 130 Acres

Contact/s:
● **Professional:** Mr T Squires
● **Book Tee Times:** Mr S P Shaw

Course/s:
🌑 **BOSTON**
  Description: Parkland, Open, Medium Length, Tight
  Green Speed: Fast   **Built On:** Soil
  Number of Holes: 18   **Par:** 72
  Par 3's: 3   **Par 4's:** 12   **Par 5's:** 3
  Yds: 6561   **F9 Yds:** 3209   **B9 Yds:** 3352
  Prevailing Wind: South/West
  Designer: Members

BOTHWELL CASTLE

BOTHWELL CASTLE GOLF CLUB, Blantyre Rd, Bothwell, Glasgow, **GLASGOW (CITY OF)**, G71 8PJ, **SCOTLAND**.
(T) 01698 853177

Contact/s:
● **Club Secretary:** Mr D McNaught
  ☎ 01698 854052
● **Pro Shop:** Mr A McCloskey
  ☎ 01698 852052

Course/s:
🌑 **BOTHWELL CASTLE**
  Number of Holes: 18   **Par:** 70
  Yds: 6225   **F9 Yds:** 3022   **B9 Yds:** 3203

BOTLEY PARK

BOTLEY PARK HOTEL GOLF & COUNTRY CLUB, Winchester Rd, Boorley Green, Botley, Southampton, **HAMPSHIRE**, SO32 2UA, **ENGLAND**.
(T) 01489 796000

(E) info@botleypark.macdonald-hotels.co.uk
(W) www.macdonaldhotels.co.uk/botley-park-hotel/

Membership: Members & Public

Contact/s:
● **Club Secretary:** Mrs A Johnson
● **Professional:** Mr Tim Barter
  ☎ 01489 789771

Course/s:
🌑 **BOTLEY PARK**
  Description: Parkland, Undulating, Open, Medium Length, Drains Well, Ideal for the Elderly
  Green Speed: Fast
  Built: 1989   **Built On:** Clay
  Number of Holes: 18   **Par:** 70
  Par 3's: 5   **Par 4's:** 10   **Par 5's:** 3
  Yds: 6341
  Prevailing Wind: South/West

BOUGHTON

BOUGHTON GOLF COURSE, Brickfield Lane, Boughton-under-Blean, Faversham, **KENT**, ME13 9AJ, **ENGLAND**.
(T) 01227 752277

Membership: Members & Public
Size of Complex: 190 Acres

Contact/s:
● **Professional:** Mr Trevor Dungate
  ☎ 01227 751112

Course/s:
🌑 **BOUGHTON 18 HOLE**
  Description: Parkland, Undulating, Open, Medium Length, Drains Well, Ideal for the Elderly
  Green Speed: Fast
  Number of Holes: 18   **Par:** 72
  Par 3's: 4   **Par 4's:** 10   **Par 5's:** 4
  Yds: 6469
  Designer: P Sparks

BOURN

BOURN GOLF CLUB, Toft Rd, Bourn, Cambridge, **CAMBRIDGESHIRE**, CB3 7TT, **ENGLAND**.
(T) 01954 718057
(E) proshop@bourn-golf-club.co.uk
(W) www.bourn-golf-club.co.uk

Membership: Members & Public

Contact/s:
● **Professional:** Mr Craig Watson
  ☎ 01954 718958

Course/s:
🌑 **BOURN**
  Description: Parkland, Undulating, Open, Drains Well
  Green Speed: Medium
  Built: 1991   **Built On:** Clay
  Number of Holes: 18
  Designer: J Hull
  Further Information:
  The course contains 3 lakes.

BOURNEMOUTH & MEYRICK

BOURNEMOUTH & MEYRICK PARK GOLF CLUB, Meyrick Pk, Bournemouth, **DORSET**, BH2 6LH, **ENGLAND**.
(T) 01202 786040

Membership: Members & Public

Contact/s:
● **Club Secretary:** Ms Margaret Rocks
  ☎ 01202 786000
● **Professional:** Mr David Miles
● **Pro Shop:** Mr Jason Cooke

Course/s:

⛳ **BOURNEMOUTH & MEYRICK PARK**
Description: Wooded, Undulating, Sheltered, Medium Length, Drains Well, Ideal for the Elderly
Green Speed: Fast **Built On:** Sand
Number of Holes: 18 **Par:** 69
Par 3's: 5 **Par 4's:** 11 **Par 5's:** 2
Yds: 5802 **F9 Yds:** 2916 **B9 Yds:** 2886
Designer: Harry Shapland Colt, Tom Dunn

BOWENHURST

BOWENHURST GOLF CENTRE, Mill Lane, Crondall, Farnham, **SURREY**, GU10 5RP, **ENGLAND**.
(T) 01252 851344

Membership: Members & Public

Contact/s:
● **Club Secretary:** Mr G Corbey
● **Professional:** Mr Adrian Carter

Course/s:
⛳ **BOWENHURST**
Description: Wooded, Parkland, Short, Tight
Green Speed: Medium
Built: 1992 **Built On:** Clay
Number of Holes: 9 **Par:** 31
Yds: 2023 **F9 Yds:** 2023
Designer: Finn
Further Information:
A reasonably flat course.

BOWOOD

BOWOOD GOLF CLUB, Lanteglos, Camelford, **CORNWALL**, PL32 9RF, **ENGLAND**.
(T) 01840 213017

Membership: Members & Public
Size of Complex: 230 Acres

Contact/s:
● **Professional:** Mr Rob Page

Course/s:
⛳ **BOWOOD**
Description: Championship
Built: 1991
Number of Holes: 18 **Par:** 72
Designer: Robert Sandow

BOWOOD

BOWOOD GOLF & COUNTRY CLUB, Bowood, Calne, **WILTSHIRE**, SN11 9PQ, **ENGLAND**.
(T) 01249 822228
(E) golfclub@bowood.org
(W) www.bowood.org
Size of Complex: 200 Acres

Contact/s:
● **Sales & Marketing Manager:** Mrs Karen Elson

Course/s:
⛳ **BOWOOD**
Description: Championship, Wooded, Undulating, Drains Well
Built: 1992 **Built On:** Sand
Number of Holes: 18 **Par:** 72
Par 3's: 4 **Par 4's:** 10 **Par 5's:** 4
Yds: 6890 **F9 Yds:** 3488 **B9 Yds:** 3402
Designer: Peter Alliss
Further Information:
The course is suitable for golfers of any ability.

BOWRING PARK

BOWRING PARK GOLF CLUB, Roby Rd, Huyton, Liverpool, **MERSEYSIDE**, L36 4HD, **ENGLAND**.

(T) 0151 4810509

Contact/s:
● **Manager:** Mrs E Goodwin

Course/s:
⛳ **BOWRING**
Number of Holes: 18

BOXMOOR

BOXMOOR GOLF CLUB, Box Lane, Hemel Hempstead, **HERTFORDSHIRE**, HP3 0DJ, **ENGLAND**.
(T) 01442 242434

Contact/s:
● **Manager:** Mrs Helen Spear

Course/s:
⛳ **BOXMOOR**
Number of Holes: 9 **Par:** 32
Yds: 4812 **F9 Yds:** 4812

BOYCE HILL

BOYCE HILL GOLF & COUNTRY CLUB, Vicarage Hill, Benfleet, **ESSEX**, SS7 1PD, **ENGLAND**.
(T) 01268 793625

Membership: Members & Public
Size of Complex: 95 Acres

Contact/s:
● **Club Secretary:** Mrs Sue Walker
● **Professional:** Mr Graham Burrows

Course/s:
⛳ **BOYCE HILL**
Description: Parkland, Hilltop, Undulating, Sheltered, Short, Tight, Drains Well
Green Speed: Medium/Fast
Built: 1922 **Built On:** Clay
Number of Holes: 18 **Par:** 68
Par 3's: 5 **Par 4's:** 12 **Par 5's:** 1
Yds: 5988 **F9 Yds:** 3088 **B9 Yds:** 2900
Prevailing Wind: South/West
Designer: James Braid
Further Information:
A challenging course.

BOYLE

BOYLE GOLF CLUB, Knockadoobrusna, Boyle, **COUNTY ROSCOMMON**, **IRELAND**.
(T) 079 62594

Contact/s:
● **Club Secretary:** Mr P Nagal

Course/s:
⛳ **BOYLE**
Number of Holes: 9 **Par:** 65
Yds: 5423
Designer: Edward Hackett

BOYSNOPE PARK

BOYSNOPE PARK GOLF COURSE, Liverpool Rd, Eccles, Manchester, **MANCHESTER (GREATER)**, M30 7RJ, **ENGLAND**.
(T) 0161 7076125
(W) www.boysnopegolfclub.co.uk

Membership: Members & Public
Size of Complex: 125 Acres

Contact/s:
● **Club Secretary:** Mrs Jean Stringer
● **Professional:** Mr Scott Currie

Course/s:
⛳ **BOYSNOPE PARK**
Description: Wooded, Parkland, Undulating, Open, Long, Drains Well
Green Speed: Medium
Built: 1997 **Built On:** Soil

Number of Holes: 18
Prevailing Wind: North/East
Designer: Tony Holmes

BOYSTOWN

BOYSTOWN GOLF COURSE, Baltyboys, Blessington, **COUNTY WICKLOW**, **IRELAND**.
(T) 045 867146

Contact/s:
● **Club Secretary:** Vincent Balfe

Course/s:
⛳ **BOYSTOWN GOLF COURSE**
Number of Holes: 9 **Par:** 36
Yds: 3476
Further Information:
Can be played as an 18 hole course

BRACKEN GHYLL

BRACKEN GHYLL GOLF CLUB, Skipton Rd, Addingham, Ilkley, **YORKSHIRE (WEST)**, LS29 0SL, **ENGLAND**.
(T) 01943 831207
(E) office@brackenghyll.com

Membership: Members & Public

Contact/s:
● **Club Secretary:** Mr A Thompson

Course/s:
⛳ **BRACKEN GHYLL**
Description: Parkland, Medium Length, Tight
Green Speed: Medium
Built: 1993
Number of Holes: 18

BRACKENWOOD

BRACKENWOOD GOLF CLUB, Bracken Lane, Wirral, **MERSEYSIDE**, CH63 2LY, **ENGLAND**.
(T) 0151 6085394

Contact/s:
● **Professional:** Mr C Bisbury

Course/s:
⛳ **BRACKENWOOD**
Number of Holes: 18 **Par:** 69
Yds: 6131

BRACKENWOOD MUNICIPAL

BRACKENWOOD MUNICIPAL GOLF COURSE, Bracken Lane, Wirral, **MERSEYSIDE**, CH63 2LY, **ENGLAND**.
(T) 0151 6083093

Membership: Public

Contact/s:
● **Head Professional:** Mr Ken Lamb

Course/s:
⛳ **BRACKENWOOD**
Number of Holes: 18 **Par:** 70
Yds: 6285 **F9 Yds:** 3120 **B9 Yds:** 3165

BRACKLEY

BRACKLEY GOLF COURSE, Bullows Rd, Little Hulton, Manchester, **MANCHESTER (GREATER)**, M38 9TR, **ENGLAND**.
(T) 0161 7906076

Contact/s:
● **Professional:** Mr S Lomax

Course/s:
⛳ **BRACKLEY MUNICIPAL**
Number of Holes: 9 **Par:** 36
Yds: 3003

BRADFORD

BRADFORD GOLF CLUB LTD, Hawksworth Lane, Guiseley, Leeds, **YORKSHIRE (WEST)**, LS20 8NP, **ENGLAND**.
(T) 01943 873817

Contact/s:
● **Manager:** Mr T Eagle

Course/s:
🏌 **BRADFORD**
　Number of Holes: 18　**Par:** 71
　Par 3's: 3　**Par 4's:** 13　**Par 5's:** 2
　Yds: 6303　**F9 Yds:** 3279　**B9 Yds:** 3024
　Designer: W Herbert Fowler

BRADFORD MOOR

BRADFORD MOOR GOLF CLUB, Scarr Hall, Pollard Lane, Bradford, **YORKSHIRE (WEST)**, BD2 4RW, **ENGLAND**.
(T) 01274 771693

Contact/s:
● **Club Secretary:** Mr C Bedford

Course/s:
🏌 **BRADFORD MOOR**
　Number of Holes: 9　**Par:** 70　**Record:** 65
　Yds: 5900　**F9 Yds:** 2950　**B9 Yds:** 2950
　Further Information:
　9 hole course can be played as an 18 hole course

BRADFORD-ON-AVON

BRADFORD-ON-AVON GOLF COURSE, Avon Cl, Off Trowbridge Rd, Bradford-on-Avon, **WILTSHIRE**, BA15 1JJ, **ENGLAND**.
(T) 01225 868268

Membership: Public
Size of Complex: 32 Acres

Contact/s:
● **Professional:** Mr G Sawyer

Course/s:
🏌 **BRADFORD ON AVON**
　Description: Parkland, Undulating, Open, Short, Tight, Drains Well
　Green Speed: Fast
　Built: 1989　**Built On:** Soil
　Number of Holes: 9　**Par:** 33
　Par 3's: 3　**Par 4's:** 6
　Yds: 2109
　Further Information:
　The course is adjacent to the River Avon.

BRADLEY HALL

BRADLEY HALL GOLF CLUB, Holywell Green, Halifax, **YORKSHIRE (WEST)**, HX4 9AN, **ENGLAND**.
(T) 01422 374108

Membership: Members & Public

Contact/s:
● **Club Secretary:** Mr Brian Cresswell
● **Professional:** Mr Peter Wood
　☎ 01422 370231

Course/s:
🏌 **HALIFAX BRADLEY HALL**
　Description: Parkland, Undulating, Sheltered, Open, Medium Length, Drains Well
　Green Speed: Fast
　Built: 1907　**Built On:** Clay
　Number of Holes: 18　**Par:** 70
　Par 3's: 4　**Par 4's:** 12　**Par 5's:** 2
　Yds: 6138　**F9 Yds:** 2875　**B9 Yds:** 3263
　Prevailing Wind: West

BRADLEY PARK

BRADLEY PARK GOLF COURSE &

DRIVING RANGE, Bradley Rd, Huddersfield, **YORKSHIRE (WEST)**, HD2 1PZ, **ENGLAND**.
(T) 01484 223772

Membership: Members & Public
Size of Complex: 125 Acres

Contact/s:
● **Club Secretary:** Ms Dennise Bird

Course/s:
🏌 **BRADLEY PARK**
　Description: Parkland, Undulating, Sheltered, Medium Length, Tends to Flood
　Green Speed: Medium
　Built: 1977　**Built On:** Clay
　Number of Holes: 18　**Par:** 70
　Record: 68 (Parnell Reilly)
　Par 3's: 4　**Par 4's:** 12　**Par 5's:** 2
　Yds: 6068　**F9 Yds:** 3061　**B9 Yds:** 3007
　Prevailing Wind: West
　Designer: Donald Steel

BRAEHEAD

BRAEHEAD GOLF CLUB, Alloa Rd, Cambus, Alloa, **CLACKMANNANSHIRE**, FK10 2NT, **SCOTLAND**.
(T) 01259 725766

Membership: Members & Public

Contact/s:
● **Club Secretary:** Mr Paul MacMichael
● **Professional:** Mr David Boyce
　☎ 01259 722078

Course/s:
🏌 **BRAEHEAD**
　Description: Wooded, Parkland, Undulating, Medium Length, Drains Well
　Green Speed: Fast
　Built: 1891　**Built On:** Clay
　Number of Holes: 18　**Par:** 70
　Par 3's: 4　**Par 4's:** 12　**Par 5's:** 2
　Yds: 6052　**F9 Yds:** 2778　**B9 Yds:** 3274
　Designer: Robert Tait
　Further Information:
　Splendid scenic views from many parts of the course. Plenty of variety to test your game to your full ability.

BRAEMAR

BRAEMAR GOLF CLUB, Braemar, Ballater, **ABERDEENSHIRE**, AB35 5XX, **SCOTLAND**.
(T) 01339 741618

Contact/s:
● **Professional:** Mr John Pennet

Course/s:
🏌 **BRAEMAR**
　Built: 1902
　Number of Holes: 18　**Par:** 65
　Yds: 4916
　Designer: Joe Anderson
　Further Information:
　This is Scotland's highest 18 hole course which is easy walking. The River Clunie splits the course in two, with water being a main feature on 13 of the holes.

BRAID HILLS

BRAID HILLS GOLF COURSE, 22 Braid Hills Approach, Edinburgh, **EDINBURGH (CITY OF)**, EH10 6JY, **SCOTLAND**.
(T) 0131 4476666/5575457

Contact/s:
● **Manager:** Mr W Winkler

Course/s:
🏌 **BRAIDS NO 1**
　Built: 1893
　Number of Holes: 18　**Par:** 72

🏌 **BRAIDS NO 2**
　Built: 1893
　Number of Holes: 18　**Par:** 69
　Further Information:
　A challenging course with great views over the city.

BRAILES

BRAILES GOLF CLUB, Sutton Lane, Lower Brailes, Banbury, **OXFORDSHIRE**, OX15 5BB, **ENGLAND**.
(T) 01608 685611
(E) office@brailes-golf-club.co.uk
(W) www.brailes-golf-club.co.uk

Contact/s:
● **Professional:** Mr Alistair Brown
● **Book Tee Times:** Mr Hamish Ritchie
　☎ 01608 685633

Course/s:
🏌 **BRAILES**
　Description: Undulating
　Built: 1992
　Number of Holes: 18　**Par:** 71
　Par 3's: 4　**Par 4's:** 11　**Par 5's:** 3
　Yds: 6311　**F9 Yds:** 3159　**B9 Yds:** 3152
　Designer: B A Hull
　Further Information:
　The Sutton Brook comes into play at strategic points across 5 of the holes.

BRAILSFORD

BRAILSFORD GOLF COURSE, Pauls Head Lane, Brailsford, Ashbourne, **DERBYSHIRE**, DE6 3BU, **ENGLAND**.
(T) 01335 360096

Membership: Members & Public

Contact/s:
● **Club Secretary:** Mr Ken Wilson
● **Professional:** Mr D McArthy

Course/s:
🏌 **BRAILSFORD**
　Description: Parkland, Undulating, Open, Medium Length, Drains Well
　Green Speed: Medium
　Built: 1994　**Built On:** Soil
　Number of Holes: 9　**Record:** 66 (David McArthy)
　Yds: 6219

BRAINTREE

BRAINTREE GOLF CLUB, Kings Lane, Stistead, Braintree, **ESSEX**, CM7 8DA, **ENGLAND**.
(T) 01376 346079

Contact/s:
● **Club Secretary:** Mr D. W. B. Hart
● **Professional:** Mr Tony Parcell
● **Book Tee Times:**
　☎ 01376 343465

Course/s:
🏌 **BRAINTREE**
　Description: Wooded, Parkland
　Built: 1971
　Number of Holes: 18　**Par:** 70
　Designer: Hawtree
　Further Information:
　The 14th has a reputation as one of the best par 3's in Essex.

BRAMALL PARK

BRAMALL PARK GOLF CLUB, 20 Manor Rd, Bramhall, Stockport, **CHESHIRE**, SK7 3LY, **ENGLAND**.
(T) 0161 4853119

Contact/s:
● **Club Secretary:** Mr D McNeil

Course/s:

● **BRAMALL PARK**
Number of Holes: 18   Par: 70
Yds: 6214

BRAMCOTE HILLS

BRAMCOTE HILLS GOLF COURSE,
Thoresby Rd, Bramcote, Nottingham,
NOTTINGHAMSHIRE, NG9 3EP, **ENGLAND**.
(T) 0115 9281880

Membership: Public

Contact/s:
● General Manager: Mr D Savage

Course/s:

● **BRAMCOTE HILLS**
Description: Parkland, Hilltop, Open,
Short
Green Speed: Medium
Number of Holes: 18   Par: 54
Yds: 1500

BRAMCOTE WATERS

BRAMCOTE WATERS GOLF COURSE,
Bazzard Rd, Bramcote, Nuneaton,
WARWICKSHIRE, CV11 6QJ, **ENGLAND**.
(T) 01455 220807

Membership: Members & Public

Contact/s:
● Professional: Mr Nicholas Gilks

Course/s:

● **BRAMCOTE WATERS**
Description: Wooded, Parkland,
Undulating, Sheltered, Open, Short, Tight,
Drains Well, Ideal for the Elderly
Green Speed: Medium
Built: 1995   Built On: Clay
Number of Holes: 9   Par: 33
Par 3's: 3   Par 4's: 6
Yds: 2491
Prevailing Wind: East/West
Designer: David Snell
Further Information:
This tricky course can also be played as
18 holes.

BRAMHALL

BRAMHALL GOLF CLUB LTD, Ladythorn
Rd, Bramhall, Stockport, **CHESHIRE**, SK7
2EY, **ENGLAND**.
(T) 0161 4394057

Contact/s:
● Honorary Secretary: Mr Barry Hill

Course/s:

● **BRAMHALL**
Number of Holes: 18   Par: 70
Yds: 6136   F9 Yds: 3112   B9 Yds: 3024

BRAMLEY

BRAMLEY GOLF CLUB, Links Rd, Bramley,
Guildford, **SURREY**, GU5 0AL, **ENGLAND**.
(T) 01483 892696

Membership: Members & Public

Contact/s:
● Club Secretary: Mrs M Lambert
● Professional: Mr G Peddie
● Pro Shop:
  ☎ 01483 893685

Course/s:

● **BRAMLEY**
Description: Wooded, Undulating,
Sheltered, Short, Tight, Drains Well
Built: 1913
Number of Holes: 18   Par: 69
Yds: 5990

Designer: James Braid

BRAMPTON

BRAMPTON GOLF CLUB, Tarn Rd,
Brampton, **CUMBRIA**, CA8 1HN, **ENGLAND**.
(T) 01697 72000

Membership: Members & Public

Contact/s:
● Club Secretary: Mr Ian Meldrum
  ☎ 01697 72255
● Professional: Mr Stewart Wilkinson

Course/s:

● **BRAMPTON**
Description: Hilltop, Undulating, Open,
Medium Length, Drains Well, Ideal for the
Elderly
Green Speed: Medium
Built: 1900   Built On: Sand
Number of Holes: 18   Par: 72
Yds: 6407   F9 Yds: 3270   B9 Yds: 3137
Prevailing Wind: North/East
Designer: James Braid

BRAMPTON GOLF

BRAMPTON GOLF COURSE, Little
Brampton, Brampton Rd, Madley, Hereford,
HEREFORDSHIRE, HR2 9LX, **ENGLAND**.
(T) 01981 251308
(E) bramptonhols@tinyworld.co.uk
(W) www.bramptonhols.co.uk

Membership: Public

Contact/s:
● Professional: Mr James Stokes

Course/s:

● **BRAMPTON GOLF**
Description: Parkland, Short, Tight,
Drains Well, Ideal for the Elderly
Green Speed: Medium
Built: 1989
Number of Holes: 9
Designer: Stokes & Sons International

BRAMPTON HEATH

BRAMPTON HEATH GOLF CENTRE, Sandy
Lane, Church Brampton, Northampton,
NORTHAMPTONSHIRE, NN6 8AX,
ENGLAND.
(T) 01604 843939
(W) www.bhgc.co.uk

Membership: Members & Public
Size of Complex: 150 Acres

Contact/s:
● Professional: Mr Richard Hudson
● Pro Shop: Mr Carl Sainsbury

Course/s:

● **MAIN**
Description: Parkland, Valley, Open,
Medium Length, Drains Well, Ideal for the
Elderly
Green Speed: Medium
Built: 1995   Built On: Sand
Number of Holes: 18   Record: 69
(Shane Rose, Andy Garth)
Prevailing Wind: North/East
Designer: D Snell

● **SHORT**
Built: 1995
Number of Holes: 9

BRAMPTON PARK

BRAMPTON PARK GOLF CLUB, Buckden
Rd, Brampton, Huntingdon,
CAMBRIDGESHIRE, PE28 4NF, **ENGLAND**.
(T) 01480 434705

Contact/s:

● Professional: Mr Alisdair Currie

Course/s:

● **BRAMPTON PARK**
Description: Championship, Wooded,
Sheltered
Built: 1991
Number of Holes: 18   Par: 71
Designer: Simon Gidman

BRAMSHAW

BRAMSHAW GOLF CLUB LTD, Brook,
Lyndhurst, **HAMPSHIRE**, SO43 7HE,
ENGLAND.
(T) 023 80813433
(E) golf@bramshaw.co.uk
(W) www.bramshaw.co.uk

Contact/s:
● General Manager: Mr M Tingey

Course/s:

● **FOREST**
Number of Holes: 18   Par: 69
Yds: 5774   F9 Yds: 2914   B9 Yds: 2860

● **MANOR**
Number of Holes: 18   Par: 71
Yds: 6517   F9 Yds: 3258   B9 Yds: 3259

BRAMSHOTT HILL

BRAMSHOTT HILL GOLF CLUB, Main Rd,
Dibden, Southampton, **HAMPSHIRE**, SO45
5TB, **ENGLAND**.
(T) 023 80843943

Course/s:

● **BRAMSHOTT HILL**
Number of Holes: 18   Par: 70
Yds: 5931   F9 Yds: 3354   B9 Yds: 2577

BRANCEPETH CASTLE

BRANCEPETH CASTLE GOLF CLUB,
Brancepeth, Durham, **COUNTY DURHAM**,
DH7 8EA, **ENGLAND**.
(T) 0191 3780183

Course/s:

● **BRANCEPETH CASTLE**
Number of Holes: 18   Par: 70
Yds: 6300
Designer: Harry Shapland Colt

BRANDHALL

BRANDHALL GOLF CLUB, Heron Rd,
Warley, **MIDLANDS (WEST)**, B68 8AQ,
ENGLAND.
(T) 0121 5522195

Course/s:

● **BRANDHALL**
Number of Holes: 18   Par: 70
Yds: 5734

BRANDON

BRANDON GOLF COURSE, Holywell Lane,
Shadwell, Leeds, **YORKSHIRE (WEST)**,
LS17 8EZ, **ENGLAND**.
(T) 0113 2737471

Contact/s:
● Owner: Mr John Binner

Course/s:

● **BRANDON**
Number of Holes: 18   Par: 68
Yds: 4800

BRANDON WOOD MUNICIPAL

BRANDON WOOD MUNICIPAL GOLF COURSE, Brandon Lane, Wolston, Coventry, **MIDLANDS (WEST)**, CV8 3GQ, **ENGLAND**.
(T) 024 76543141

Membership: Members & Public

Contact/s:
• **Professional:** Mr Chris Gledhill

Course/s:
🏌 **BRANDON WOOD**
  Description: Wooded, Parkland, Undulating, Medium Length, Tends to Flood
  Green Speed: Medium
  Built: 1977
  Number of Holes: 18

BRANSHAW

BRANSHAW GOLF CLUB, Sykes Head, Oakworth, Keighley, **YORKSHIRE (WEST)**, BD22 7ES, **ENGLAND**.
(T) 01535 643235

Course/s:
🏌 **BRANSHAW**
  Number of Holes: 18 **Par:** 69
  Yds: 6000
  Designer: James Braid

BRANSTON

BRANSTON GOLF & COUNTRY CLUB, Burton Rd, Branston, Burton-on-Trent, **STAFFORDSHIRE**, DE14 3DP, **ENGLAND**.
(T) 01283 512211
(W) www.branston-golf-club.co.uk
Size of Complex: 160 Acres

Contact/s:
• **Professional:** Mr Richard Odell
• **Book Tee Times:**
  ☎ 01283 543207

Course/s:
🏌 **ACADEMY**
  Built: 2001
  Number of Holes: 9

🏌 **BRANSTON**
  Description: Championship, Parkland, Valley, Medium Length, Drains Well, Tends to Flood, Ideal for the Elderly
  Green Speed: Medium
  Built: 1975 **Built On:** Soil
  Number of Holes: 18
  Further Information:
  The course tends to drain well but can flood when the river next to it rises.

BRAXTED PARK

BRAXTED PARK GOLF CLUB, Braxted Pk, Witham, **ESSEX**, CM8 3EN, **ENGLAND**.
(T) 01376 572372

Membership: Members & Public

Contact/s:
• **Club Secretary:** Ms Judy Taylor
• **Professional:** Mr John Hudson

Course/s:
🏌 **BRAXTED PARK**
  Description: Parkland, Undulating, Open, Short, Tight, Drains Well, Ideal for the Elderly
  Green Speed: Fast
  Built: 1953 **Built On:** Clay
  Number of Holes: 9 **Par:** 35
  Yds: 2940
  Designer: A Clark

BRAY

BRAY GOLF CLUB, Ravenswell Rd, Bray, **COUNTY WICKLOW**, **IRELAND**.
(T) 01 2862092

Course/s:
🏌 **BRAY**
  Number of Holes: 9 **Par:** 70
  Yds: 6279
  Further Information:
  Course can be played as 18 holes.

BREADSALL PRIORY

MARRIOTT BREADSALL PRIORY HOTEL & COUNTRY CLUB, Moor Rd, Morley, Ilkeston, **DERBYSHIRE**, DE7 6DL, **ENGLAND**.
(T) 01332 836007
(W) www.marriotthotels.com
Size of Complex: 400 Acres

Contact/s:
• **Professional:** Mr Damon Steels
  ☎ 01332 836016

Course/s:
🏌 **MOORLAND**
  Description: Moorland
  Number of Holes: 18
  Designer: Brian Pierson

🏌 **PRIORY**
  Description: Wooded, Parkland
  Number of Holes: 18
  Par 3's: 4 **Par 4's:** 12 **Par 5's:** 2
  Yds: 5875 **F9 Yds:** 2876 **B9 Yds:** 2999

BREAN

BREAN GOLF CLUB, Coast Rd, Brean, Burnham-on-Sea, **SOMERSET**, TA8 2QY, **ENGLAND**.
(T) 01278 752111

Membership: Members & Public
Size of Complex: 300 Acres

Contact/s:
• **Professional:** Mr David Haynes

Course/s:
🏌 **BREAN**
  Description: Wooded, Parkland, Open, Short, Tight, Drains Well
  Green Speed: Medium
  Built: 1970 **Built On:** Soil
  Number of Holes: 18
  Prevailing Wind: East

BRECHIN GOLF & SQUASH CLUB

BRECHIN GOLF & SQUASH CLUB, Trinity, Brechin, **ANGUS**, CC9 7PD, **SCOTLAND**.
(T) 01356 622383

Membership: Members & Public

Contact/s:
• **Club Secretary:** Mr Ian Jardine
• **Professional:** Mr Stephen Rennie
• **Book Tee Times:**
  ☎ 01356 625270

Course/s:
🏌 **BRECHIN GOLF & SQUASH CLUB**
  Description: Wooded, Parkland, Sheltered, Open, Short, Tends to Flood
  Green Speed: Fast
  Built: 1893 **Built On:** Soil
  Number of Holes: 18 **Par:** 69
  Par 3's: 6 **Par 4's:** 9 **Par 5's:** 3
  Yds: 6096 **F9 Yds:** 3164 **B9 Yds:** 2932
  Prevailing Wind: North
  Designer: James Braid

BRECON

BRECON GOLF CLUB, Newton Pk, Brecon, **POWYS**, LD3 8PA, **WALES**.
(T) 01874 622004

Contact/s:
• **Club Secretary:** Mr D Rodrick

Course/s:
🏌 **BRECON**
  Number of Holes: 9 **Par:** 66
  Yds: 5256
  Designer: James Braid
  Further Information:
  9 hole course can be played as an 18 hole course

BREEDON PRIORY

BREEDON PRIORY GOLFING CENTRE, Green Lane, Wilson, Melbourne, Derby, **DERBYSHIRE**, DE73 1LG, **ENGLAND**.
(T) 01332 863081

Contact/s:
• **Manager:** Mr Matthew Mayfield

Course/s:
🏌 **BREEDON PRIORY GOLF CENTRE**
  Number of Holes: 18 **Par:** 70
  Yds: 5532
  Designer: David Snell

BREIGHTMET

BREIGHTMET GOLF CLUB LTD, Red Bridge, Red Lane, Bolton, **LANCASHIRE**, BL2 5PA, **ENGLAND**.
(T) 01204 527381

Membership: Members & Public
Size of Complex: 60 Acres

Contact/s:
• **Club Secretary:** Mr S P Griffiths

Course/s:
🏌 **BREIGHTMET**
  Description: Parkland, Undulating, Long, Drains Well
  Green Speed: Medium
  Built: 1912 **Built On:** Soil
  Number of Holes: 9 **Par:** 72 **Record:** 66 (P Alliss)
  Par 3's: 1 **Par 4's:** 7 **Par 5's:** 1
  Yds: 6416 **F9 Yds:** 3246 **B9 Yds:** 3170
  Further Information:
  The course has a justified reputation for its permanent good condition. The course is due to be extended to 18 holes in the spring of 2003. At present, this 9 hole course has 18 tees and can therefore be played as an 18 hole course.

BRENT VALLEY

BRENT VALLEY GOLF CLUB, 138 Church Rd, London, **LONDON (GREATER)**, W7 3BE, **ENGLAND**.
(T) 020 85674230

Course/s:
🏌 **BRENT VALLEY**
  Number of Holes: 18

BRENT VALLEY PUBLIC

BRENT VALLEY PUBLIC GOLF COURSE, Church Rd, London, **LONDON (GREATER)**, W7 3BE, **ENGLAND**.
(T) 020 8567 1287

Membership: Members & Public

Contact/s:
• **Club Secretary:** Miss Marge Griffin
• **Professional:** Mr Peter Bryant
• **Pro Shop:** Mr Victor Santos

Course/s:

BRENT VALLEY PUBLIC
Description: Championship, Wooded, Parkland, Hilltop, Valley, Undulating, Open, Medium Length, Drains Well, Ideal for the Elderly
Green Speed: Slow/Medium/Fast
Built: 1938 **Built On:** Clay/Sand/Soil
Number of Holes: 18 **Par:** 72
Yds: 6165 **F9 Yds:** 3149 **B9 Yds:** 3016
Prevailing Wind: North/West
Designer: Neil Coles
Further Information:
The River Brent runs through the course.

BRETTVALE

BRETT VALE GOLF CLUB, Noakes Rd, Raydon, Ipswich, **SUFFOLK**, IP7 5LR, **ENGLAND**.
(T) 01473 310718

Membership: Members & Public
Size of Complex: 182 Acres

Contact/s:
- **Professional:** Mr Robert Taylor
- **Pro Shop:** Mr Tony Norton

Course/s:

BRETTVALE
Description: Wooded, Undulating, Open, Short, Drains Well, Ideal for the Elderly
Green Speed: Medium
Built: 1993 **Built On:** Sand
Number of Holes: 18 **Par:** 70
Record: 70 (Tony Norton)
Yds: 6000
Prevailing Wind: North
Designer: Howard Swan
Further Information:
Testing Course.

BRICKENDON GRANGE

BRICKENDON GRANGE GOLF CLUB, Pembridge Lane, Brickendon, Hertford, **HERTFORDSHIRE**, SG13 8PD, **ENGLAND**.
(T) 01992 511228
(E) genman@brickendongrangegc.co.uk
(W) www.brickendongrangegc.co.uk

Contact/s:
- **Book Tee Times:** Mr Graham Tippett
  ☎ 01992 511218

Course/s:

BRICKENDON GRANGE
Description: Parkland, Undulating
Built: 1965
Number of Holes: 18 **Par:** 71
Yds: 6315
Designer: Cotton
Further Information:
The course has a variety of specimen trees.

BRICKHAMPTON COURT

BRICKHAMPTON COURT GOLF COMPLEX, Cheltenham Rd, Church Down, **GLOUCESTERSHIRE**, GL2 9QP, **ENGLAND**.
(T) 01452 859444
(W) www.brickhampton.co.uk

Membership: Members & Public

Contact/s:
- **Manager:** Mr R East

Course/s:

GLEVUM
Built: 1994
Number of Holes: 9 **Par:** 31
Designer: Simon Gidman
Further Information:
Laid out along the banks of Hatherley Brook

SPA
Description: Parkland, Undulating, Ideal for the Elderly
Green Speed: Medium
Built: 1994
Number of Holes: 18 **Par:** 71
Yds: 6449
Designer: Simon Gidman

BRIDGE OF ALLAN

BRIDGE OF ALLAN GOLF CLUB, Pendreigh Rd, Bridge of Allan, **CLACKMANNANSHIRE**, FK9 4LY, **SCOTLAND**.
(T) 01786 832332

Course/s:

BRIDGE OF ALLAN
Number of Holes: 9 **Par:** 66
Yds: 4932
Designer: Tom Morris

BRIDGECASTLE

BRIDGECASTLE GOLF CLUB, North St, Armadale, Bathgate, **LOTHIAN (WEST)**, EH48 3NX, **SCOTLAND**.
(T) 01501 734806

Membership: Members & Public

Contact/s:
- **Club Secretary:** Miss M O'Connor
- **Professional:** Andy Marshall

Course/s:

THE MONSTER
Description: Parkland, Valley, Undulating, Long, Tight
Green Speed: Medium
Built: 1996
Number of Holes: 9
Designer: Kevin Keane, John Slattery

BRIDGEDOWN

BRIDGEDOWN GOLF CLUB, St. Albans Rd, Barnet, **HERTFORDSHIRE**, EN5 4RE, **ENGLAND**.
(T) 020 84417649

Course/s:

BRIDGEDOWN
Number of Holes: 18 **Par:** 72
Yds: 6626

BRIDGEND

BRIDGEND & DISTRICT GOLF CLUB, Willowdean, Bridgend, Linlithgow, **LOTHIAN (WEST)**, EH49 6NW, **SCOTLAND**.
(T) 01506 834140

Membership: Members & Public

Contact/s:
- **Club Secretary:** Mr D Williamson

Course/s:

HAUGHBORN
Description: Heath Land, Short, Tight, Drains Well
Green Speed: Medium
Built: 1998 **Built On:** Sand/Soil
Number of Holes: 9
Further Information:
The course was built with lottery aid.

BRIDGNORTH

BRIDGNORTH GOLF CLUB, Stanley Lane, Bridgnorth, **SHROPSHIRE**, WV16 4SF, **ENGLAND**.
(T) 01746 763315
(E) bridgnorth-golf@supanet.com

Membership: Members & Public

Size of Complex: 250 Acres

Contact/s:
- **Club Secretary:** Mr K D Cole
- **Professional:** Mr Paul Hinton
  ☎ 01746 762045

Course/s:

BRIDGNORTH
Description: Wooded, Parkland, Tends to Flood
Green Speed: Medium
Built: 1925 **Built On:** Sand
Number of Holes: 18 **Par:** 73
Record: 65 (Paul Hitchen)
Yds: 6673
Designer: M Cooksey
Further Information:
The course is generally parkland but divided into three distinct zones, with hundreds of deciduous and evergreen trees.

BRIDLINGTON

BRIDLINGTON GOLF CLUB, Belvedere Rd, Bridlington, **YORKSHIRE (EAST)**, YO15 3NA, **ENGLAND**.
(T) 01262 401690

Contact/s:
- **Manager:** Mr A Howarth

Course/s:

BRIDLINGTON
Number of Holes: 18 **Par:** 72
Yds: 6638

BRIDLINGTON

BRIDLINGTON LINKS GOLF CLUB, Flamborough Rd, Sewerby, Bridlington, **YORKSHIRE (EAST)**, YO15 1DW, **ENGLAND**.
(T) 01262 401584

Membership: Members & Public
Size of Complex: 120 Acres

Contact/s:
- **Club Secretary:** Mr Colin Greenwood
  ☎ 01262 606367
- **Professional:** Mr Anthony Howarth

Course/s:

BRIDLINGTON
Description: Wooded, Parkland, Open, Medium Length, Drains Well, Ideal for the Elderly
Green Speed: Medium
Built: 1905 **Built On:** Clay
Number of Holes: 18
Prevailing Wind: South/West
Designer: James Braid

BRIDPORT & WEST DORSET

BRIDPORT & WEST DORSET GOLF CLUB, East Cliff, West Bay, Bridport, **DORSET**, DT6 4EP, **ENGLAND**.
(T) 01308 421095

Membership: Members & Public

Contact/s:
- **Club Secretary:** Mr Peter Ridler
- **Professional:** Mr David Parsons
  ☎ 01308 421491

Course/s:

BRIDPORT & WEST DORSET
Description: Links, Cliff Top
Built: 1891
Number of Holes: 18 **Par:** 73
Yds: 6028 **F9 Yds:** 3163 **B9 Yds:** 2865
Designer: Hawtree
Further Information:
The course offers views of Lyme Bay and the Dorset countryside.

BRIERLEY FOREST

BRIERLEY FOREST GOLF CLUB, Hilltop Farm, Main St, Huthwaite, Sutton-In-Ashfield, **NOTTINGHAMSHIRE**, NG17 2LG, **ENGLAND**.
(T) 01623 550761

Membership: Members & Public

Contact/s:
- **Club Secretary:** Mr D Crafts

Course/s:
🏌 **DAVCOLM**
Description: Parkland, Open
Green Speed: Medium
Built: 1993 **Built On:** Clay/Soil
Number of Holes: 18 **Par:** 72
Par 3's: 4 **Par 4's:** 10 **Par 5's:** 4
Yds: 6008 **F9 Yds:** 2960 **B9 Yds:** 3048
Designer: Hibbert, Walsh
Further Information:
There are 2 ponds on the course.

BRIGGENS HOUSE

BRIGGENS HOUSE HOTEL GOLF COURSE, Briggens Pk, Stanstead Rd, Stanstead Abbotts, Ware, **HERTFORDSHIRE**, SG12 8LD, **ENGLAND**.
(T) 01279 793742

Course/s:
🏌 **BRIGGENS PARK**
Description: Parkland
Built: 1988
Number of Holes: 9 **Par:** 36
Yds: 2793
Further Information:
A challenging 9 hole course.

BRIGHOUSE BAY

BRIGHOUSE BAY GOLF COURSE, Borge, Kirkcudbright, **DUMFRIES AND GALLOWAY**, DG6 4TS, **SCOTLAND**.
(T) 01557 870409
(E) complex@gillespie-leisure.fsnet.co.uk
(W) www.brighousebay-golfclub.co.uk

Contact/s:
- **Manager:** Mrs Alison Prevett-Stanfield

Course/s:
🏌 **BRIGHOUSE BAY**
Description: Cliff Top, Undulating, Drains Well
Built: 1999
Number of Holes: 18 **Par:** 73
Yds: 6366 **F9 Yds:** 3015 **B9 Yds:** 3351
Further Information:
Beautifully situated offering glorious clifftop views. Combines natural costal undulations and contours with several water hazards.

BRIGHT CASTLE

BRIGHT CASTLE GOLF CLUB, 14 Coniamstown Rd, Downpatrick, **COUNTY DOWN**, BT30 8LU, **NORTHERN IRELAND**.
(T) 028 44841319

Course/s:
🏌 **BRIGHT CASTLE**
Number of Holes: 18 **Par:** 74
Yds: 7143
Designer: Ennis

BRIGHTON & HOVE

BRIGHTON & HOVE GOLF CLUB, Devils Dyke Rd, Brighton, **SUSSEX (EAST)**, BN1 8YJ, **ENGLAND**.
(T) 01273 556482

Contact/s:
- **Club Secretary:** Mr Michael Harrity
- **Professional:** Mr Phil Bonsall
- **Book Tee Times:**
  ☎ 01273 540560

Course/s:
🏌 **BRIGHTON & HOVE**
Built: 1887
Number of Holes: 9 **Par:** 68
Par 3's: 3 **Par 4's:** 5 **Par 5's:** 1
Yds: 5710 **F9 Yds:** 2834 **B9 Yds:** 2876
Designer: James Braid
Further Information:
9 hole course can be played as an 18 hole course

BRINKWORTH

BRINKWORTH GOLF COURSE, Longmans Farm, Brinkworth, Chippenham, **WILTSHIRE**, SN15 5DG, **ENGLAND**.
(T) 01666 510277

Membership: Members & Public

Contact/s:
- **Professional:** Mr C Pears

Course/s:
🏌 **BRINKWORTH**
Description: Parkland, Undulating, Medium Length, Drains Well
Green Speed: Fast
Built: 1983 **Built On:** Clay
Number of Holes: 18 **Par:** 70
Par 3's: 5 **Par 4's:** 10 **Par 5's:** 3
Yds: 5954 **F9 Yds:** 3102 **B9 Yds:** 2852
Designer: Julian Sheppard
Further Information:
There are hedges & ditches throughout holes 1 to 9.

BRISTOL & CLIFTON

BRISTOL & CLIFTON GOLF CLUB, Beggar Bush Lane, Failand, Bristol, **BRISTOL**, BS8 3TH, **ENGLAND**.
(T) 01275 393474
(W) www.bristolgolf.co.uk

Membership: Members & Public
Size of Complex: 180 Acres

Contact/s:
- **Club Secretary:** Ms Pauline Lions
- **Professional:** Mr Paul Mitchell
- **Book Lessons:** Mr Peter Manson

Course/s:
🏌 **BRISTOL AND CLIFTON**
Description: Parkland, Hilltop, Undulating, Medium Length, Drains Well
Green Speed: Fast
Built: 1891
Number of Holes: 18
Prevailing Wind: South/West
Designer: Alistair MacKenzie

BRITISH STEEL PORT TALBOT

BRITISH STEEL PORT TALBOT GOLF COURSE, Sports & Social Club, Margam, Port Talbot, **NEATH PORT TALBOT**, SA13 2NF, **WALES**.
(T) 01639 814182 & 871111

Course/s:
🏌 **BRITISH STEEL PORT TALBOT**
Number of Holes: 9

BROADSTONE

BROADSTONE (DORSET) GOLF CLUB, Wentworth Drive, Broadstone, **DORSET**, BH18 8DQ, **ENGLAND**.
(T) 01202 842416

(E) admin@broadstonegolfclub.com
Size of Complex: 250 Acres

Contact/s:
- **Professional:** Mr Nigel Tokely
  ☎ 01202 692835
- **Book Tee Times:**
  ☎ 01202 692595

Course/s:
🏌 **BROADSTONE**
Description: Championship, Heath Land, Undulating, Medium Length, Tight, Drains Well
Green Speed: Fast **Built On:** Sand
Number of Holes: 18 **Par:** 70
Record: 63 (Gary Emerson, Stuart Little)
Par 3's: 4 **Par 4's:** 12 **Par 5's:** 2
Yds: 6323
Prevailing Wind: South/West
Designer: Harry Shapland Colt, Tom Dunn

BROADWATER PARK

BROADWATER PARK GOLF CLUB, Guildford Rd, Farncombe, Godalming, **SURREY**, GU7 3BU, **ENGLAND**.
(T) 01483 429955

Membership: Public

Contact/s:
- **Club Secretary:** Mr Rob Ashby
- **Professional:** Mr K Milton

Course/s:
🏌 **BROADWATER PARK**
Description: Parkland, Sheltered, Short, Tight, Drains Well, Ideal for the Elderly
Green Speed: Fast
Built: 1989 **Built On:** Soil
Number of Holes: 9
Designer: Kevin Milton
Further Information:
This is a reasonably flat course.

BROADWAY

BROADWAY GOLF CLUB, Willersey, Broadway, **WORCESTERSHIRE**, WR12 7LG, **ENGLAND**.
(T) 01386 853275

Contact/s:
- **Professional:** Mr Martyn Freeman
  ☎ 01386 853683

Course/s:
🏌 **BROADWAY**
Number of Holes: 18 **Par:** 72
Yds: 6228 **F9 Yds:** 3134 **B9 Yds:** 3094
Designer: James Braid

BROCKET HALL

BROCKET HALL GOLF CLUB, Brocket Hall, Welwyn Garden City, **HERTFORDSHIRE**, AL8 7XG, **ENGLAND**.
(T) 01707 335241

Membership: Members & Public
Size of Complex: 543 Acres

Contact/s:
- **Professional:** Mr Keith Wood

Course/s:
🏌 **MELBOURNE**
Description: Championship, Parkland, Medium Length, Drains Well
Green Speed: Medium/Fast
Built: 1992
Number of Holes: 18 **Par:** 72
Record: 65 (Stephen Ames)
Par 3's: 4 **Par 4's:** 10 **Par 5's:** 4
Yds: 6173 **F9 Yds:** 2795 **B9 Yds:** 3378
Prevailing Wind: South
Designer: Peter Alliss, Clive Clark

PALMERSTON
Description: Championship, Wooded, Undulating, Sheltered, Long, Tight, Drains Well
Green Speed: Fast
Built: 1999
Number of Holes: 18 **Par:** 73
Par 3's: 4 **Par 4's:** 9 **Par 5's:** 5
Yds: 6823 **F9 Yds:** 3283 **B9 Yds:** 3540
Designer: Donald Steel

BROCKINGTON

BROCKINGTON GOLF CLUB, Bodenham, Hereford, **HEREFORDSHIRE**, HR1 3HX, **ENGLAND**.
(T) 01568 797877

Membership: Members & Public
Contact/s:
- **Club Secretary:** Mr F D Powell
- **Book Tee Times:** Pat Bartup

Course/s:
BROCKINGTON
Description: Sheltered, Drains Well, Ideal for the Elderly
Green Speed: Medium
Built: 1992 **Built On:** Gravel
Number of Holes: 9 **Par:** 66
Par 3's: 4 **Par 4's:** 4 **Par 5's:** 1
Yds: 4688 **F9 Yds:** 2344 **B9 Yds:** 2344
Further Information:
A Brook runs through this 9 hole course which can be played as an 18 hole course.

BROCTON HALL

BROCTON HALL GOLF CLUB, Brocton, Stafford, **STAFFORDSHIRE**, ST17 0TH, **ENGLAND**.
(T) 01785 661901

Membership: Members & Public
Contact/s:
- **Club Secretary:** Mr Graham Ashley
- **Professional:** Mr Bob Johnson
  ☎ 01785 661485

Course/s:
BROCTON HALL
Description: Parkland, Undulating, Open, Drains Well, Ideal for the Elderly
Green Speed: Fast
Built: 1884 **Built On:** Gravel
Number of Holes: 18
Designer: Harry Vardon

BRODICK

BRODICK GOLF CLUB, Main St, Brodick, **AYRSHIRE (NORTH)**, KA27 8DL, **SCOTLAND**.
(T) 01770 302349

Contact/s:
- **Club Secretary:** Mr H McRea
- **Professional:** Mr P McCalle

Course/s:
BRODICK
Number of Holes: 18

BROKE HILL

BROKE HILL GOLF CLUB LTD, Sevenoaks Rd, Halstead, Sevenoaks, **KENT**, TN14 7HR, **ENGLAND**.
(T) 01959 533225

Course/s:
BROKE HILL
Number of Holes: 18 **Par:** 72
Yds: 6374 **F9 Yds:** 3268 **B9 Yds:** 3106

BROKENHURST MANOR

BROKENHURST MANOR GOLF CLUB, Sway Rd, Brockenhurst, **HAMPSHIRE**, SO42 7SG, **ENGLAND**.
(T) 01590 623332

Contact/s:
- **Manager:** Mr P Clifford

Course/s:
BROKENHURST MANOR
Number of Holes: 18
Designer: Harry Shapland Colt

BROMBOROUGH

BROMBOROUGH GOLF CLUB, Raby Hall Rd, Wirral, **MERSEYSIDE**, CH63 0NW, **ENGLAND**.
(T) 0151 3342155

Membership: Members & Public
Contact/s:
- **Club Secretary:** Mr J T Baraclough
- **Professional:** Mr Geoff Berry
  ☎ 0151 3344499

Course/s:
BROMBOROUGH
Description: Parkland, Undulating, Open, Long, Ideal for the Elderly
Green Speed: Medium
Built: 1904 **Built On:** Clay
Number of Holes: 18
Designer: J Hassall

BROMLEY

BROMLEY GOLF CLUB, Magpie Hall Lane, Bromley, **KENT**, BR2 8JF, **ENGLAND**.
(T) 020 8462 7014

Membership: Public
Contact/s:
- **Professional:** Mr Alan Hodgeson

Course/s:
BROMLEY
Description: Open, Short
Number of Holes: 9
Yds: 2745

BROMSGROVE

BROMSGROVE GOLF CENTRE, Stratford Rd, Bromsgrove, **WORCESTERSHIRE**, B60 1LD, **ENGLAND**.
(T) 01527 579179
(W) www.bromsgrovegolfcentre.co.uk

Membership: Members & Public
Contact/s:
- **Club Secretary:** Mr Dave Went
- **Professional:** Mr Graeme Long
- **Pro Shop:** Mr Terry Matthews

Course/s:
BROMSGROVE
Description: Parkland, Undulating, Sheltered, Open, Medium Length, Drains Well, Ideal for the Elderly
Green Speed: Medium
Built: 1992 **Built On:** Sand
Number of Holes: 18 **Par:** 68
Par 3's: 5 **Par 4's:** 12 **Par 5's:** 1
Yds: 5880
Designer: Hawtree

BROOKDALE

BROOKDALE GOLF CLUB, Medlock Rd, Failsworth, Manchester, **MANCHESTER (GREATER)**, M35 9WQ, **ENGLAND**.
(T) 0161 6812655
(W) www.brookdalegolfclub.co.uk

Membership: Members & Public
Contact/s:
- **Club Secretary:** Mr Joseph Chadwick
- **Professional:** Mr Tony Cuppello

Course/s:
BROOKDALE
Description: Parkland, Undulating, Open, Short, Tends to Flood
Green Speed: Medium
Built: 1896 **Built On:** Clay
Number of Holes: 18
Prevailing Wind: East

BROOKLANDS PARK

BROOKLANDS PARK GOLF CENTRE, Brighton Rd, Worthing, **SUSSEX (WEST)**, BN11 2HP, **ENGLAND**.
(T) 01903 232270

Membership: Public
Contact/s:
- **Professional:** Mr Simon Blanshard

Course/s:
BROOKLANDS
Description: Short, Drains Well, Ideal for the Elderly
Green Speed: Medium
Built: 1996
Number of Holes: 9
Designer: Peter Alliss

BROOKMANS PARK

BROOKMANS PARK GOLF CLUB, Brookmans Pk, Hatfield, **HERTFORDSHIRE**, AL9 7AT, **ENGLAND**.
(T) 01707 652459

Membership: Members & Public
Size of Complex: 100 Acres
Contact/s:
- **Club Secretary:** Mr Peter Gill
- **Professional:** Mr Ian Jelley
  ☎ 01707 652468
- **Book Tee Times:** Mr Ian Jelly

Course/s:
BROOKMANS PARK
Description: Parkland, Undulating, Long, Drains Well
Green Speed: Medium
Built: 1933 **Built On:** Clay
Number of Holes: 18
Designer: Hawtree, Taylor

BROOME MANOR

BROOME MANOR GOLF COMPLEX, Pipers Way, Swindon, **WILTSHIRE**, SN3 1RG, **ENGLAND**.
(T) 01793 532403
(W) www.bmgc.co.uk

Membership: Public
Contact/s:
- **Professional:** Mr B Sandry

Course/s:
BROOME MANOR
Description: Parkland, Undulating, Long, Drains Well
Green Speed: Medium
Built: 1976
Built On: Chalk/Clay/Sand/Soil
Number of Holes: 18
Designer: Hawtree
Further Information:
A challenging course with ponds throughout.

BROOME PARK

BROOME PARK GOLF & COUNTRY CLUB,
Broome Pk, Barham, Canterbury, **KENT**, CT4
6QX, **ENGLAND**.
(T) 01227 831126
(E) broomeparkgolf@compuserve.com
(W) www.broomepark.co.uk

Contact/s:
- **Professional:** Mr Tienie Britz
- **Book Tee Times:** Mr Neil Morris

Course/s:
- **BROOME PARK**
  Description: Championship, Parkland,
  Undulating, Medium Length, Tends to
  Flood, Ideal for the Elderly
  Green Speed: Medium
  Built: 1980
  Number of Holes: 18 **Par:** 72
  Record: 66 (Brian Impett)
  Par 3's: 4 **Par 4's:** 10 **Par 5's:** 4
  Yds: 6610
  Designer: Donald Steel

BROOMIEKNOWE

BROOMIEKNOWE GOLF CLUB LTD, 36
Golf Course Rd, Bonnyrigg, **LOTHIAN (MID)**,
EH19 2HZ, **SCOTLAND**.
(T) 0131 669317
(E) administrator@broomieknowe.com
(W) www.broomieknowe.com

Contact/s:
- **Hon Secretary:** Mr John Fisher

Course/s:
- **BROOMIEKNOWE**
  Number of Holes: 18 **Par:** 70
  Yds: 6150
  Designer: Hawtree, Ben Sayers

BRORA

BRORA GOLF CLUB, Golf Rd, Brora,
HIGHLANDS, KW9 6QS, **SCOTLAND**.
(T) 01408 621417

Membership: Members & Public
Size of Complex: 248 Acres

Contact/s:
- **Club Secretary:** Mr James Fraser
- **Pro Shop:** Mr I D Hamilton
  ☎ 01408 621473

Course/s:
- **BRORA**
  Description: Links, Undulating, Medium
  Length, Tight, Drains Well
  Green Speed: Fast
  Built: 1891 **Built On:** Sand
  Number of Holes: 18 **Par:** 69
  Record: 67 (David Huish)
  Yds: 6110 **F9 Yds:** 3028 **B9 Yds:** 3082
  Prevailing Wind: South/East
  Designer: James Braid

BROUGH

BROUGH GOLF CLUB, Cave Rd, Brough,
YORKSHIRE (EAST), HU15 1HB,
ENGLAND.
(T) 01482 667291

Course/s:
- **BROUGH**
  Number of Holes: 18 **Par:** 68
  Par 3's: 5 **Par 4's:** 12 **Par 5's:** 1
  Yds: 6075 **F9 Yds:** 3094 **B9 Yds:** 2981

BROUGHTON HEATH

BROUGHTON HEATH GOLF COURSE, Bent
Lane, Church Broughton, Derby,

DERBYSHIRE, DE65 5BA, **ENGLAND**.
(T) 01283 521235

Membership: Members & Public
Size of Complex: 44 Acres

Contact/s:
- **Club Secretary:** Mr Jim Bentley
- **Professional:** Mr Sean Stiff

Course/s:
- **BROUGHTON HEATH**
  Description: Parkland, Short, Drains Well,
  Ideal for the Elderly
  Green Speed: Medium
  Built: 1998
  Number of Holes: 18 **Par:** 54
  Record: 51 (Mike Gallagher)
  Par 3's: 18
  Yds: 3087 **F9 Yds:** 1565 **B9 Yds:** 1522
  Prevailing Wind: West
  Designer: Ken Tunnicliffe
  Further Information: This is one of the
  longest Par 3 courses in the UK with
  bunkers throughout the course.

BROW

BROW GOLF CLUB (THE), The Brow,
Ellesmere, **SHROPSHIRE**, SY12 9HW,
ENGLAND.
(T) 01691 622628
(E) browgolf@btinternet.com

Membership: Members & Public

Contact/s:
- **Club Secretary:** Mr David Davies
- **Professional:** Mr Alan Strange

Course/s:
- **BROW**
  Number of Holes: 9

BROWN TROUT

BROWN TROUT GOLF & COUNTRY INN,
209 Agivey Rd, Aghadowey, Coleraine,
COUNTY LONDONDERRY, BT51 4AD,
NORTHERN IRELAND.
(T) 028 70868209

Contact/s:
- **Professional:** Mr Ken Revie

Course/s:
- **BROWN TROUT**
  Description: Wooded
  Built: 1973
  Number of Holes: 9 **Par:** 70
  Designer: Bill O'Hara
  Further Information:
  There are several water hazards on the
  course. 9 hole course can be played as
  an 18 hole course

BRUNSHAW

BRUNSHAW GOLF COURSE, Deerpark Rd,
Burnley, **LANCASHIRE**, BB10 4SD,
ENGLAND.
(T) 01282 421517

Membership: Public

Contact/s:
- **Pro Shop:** Mr Derek Garside

Course/s:
- **BRUNSHAW**
  Description: Wooded, Parkland,
  Sheltered, Open, Short, Tends to Flood,
  Ideal for the Elderly
  Green Speed: Slow
  Built: 1983 **Built On:** Clay
  Number of Holes: 9
  Further Information:
  A cheap and enjoyable course in good
  condition.

BRUNSTON CASTLE

BRUNSTON CASTLE GOLF CLUB, Brunston
Castle, Dailly, **AYRSHIRE (SOUTH)**, KA26
9GD, **SCOTLAND**.
(T) 01465 811471

Membership: Members & Public
Size of Complex: 250 Acres

Contact/s:
- **Club Secretary:** Ms Jenny Brady
- **Professional:** Mr Steven Forbes

Course/s:
- **BRUNSTON CASTLE**
  Description: Parkland, Valley, Long
  Green Speed: Fast
  Built: 1992
  Number of Holes: 18 **Par:** 72
  Record: 67 (Ross Drummond)
  Par 3's: 4 **Par 4's:** 12 **Par 5's:** 3
  Yds: 6662
  Designer: Donald Steel

BRUNTSFIELD GOLF CLUB

**BRUNTSFIELD LINKS GOLFING SOCIETY
LTD,** The Clubhouse, 32 Barnton Ave,
Edinburgh, **EDINBURGH (CITY OF)**, EH4
6JH, **SCOTLAND**.
(T) 0131 3361479

Membership: Members & Public
Size of Complex: 150 Acres

Contact/s:
- **Professional:** Mr Brian Mackenzie
  ☎ 0131 3364050
- **Book Tee Times:** Mr David Sandford

Course/s:
- **BRUNTSFIELD**
  Description: Parkland
  Green Speed: Medium **Built On:** Soil
  Number of Holes: 18 **Par:** 70
  Par 3's: 4 **Par 4's:** 12 **Par 5's:** 2
  Yds: 6407
  Prevailing Wind: South/West
  Designer: Hawtree, Alistair MacKenzie,
  William Park
  Further Information:
  The course offers stunning views over
  Firth of Forth and has a wonderful variety
  of mature trees along the greens.

BRYN MEADOWS

**BRYN MEADOWS GOLF & COUNTRY
CLUB,** Maesycwmmer, Nr Ystrad Mynach,
Hengoed, **CAERPHILLY**, CF82 7SN,
WALES.
(T) 01495 225590
(E) information@brynmeadows.co.uk
(W) www.brynmeadows.co.uk

Contact/s:
- **Director:** Mr G Mayo

Course/s:
- **BRYN MEADOWS GOLF & COUNTRY HOTEL**
  Number of Holes: 18 **Par:** 72
  Yds: 6156 **F9 Yds:** 2963 **B9 Yds:** 3193
  Designer: Defoy, Mayo

BRYN MORFYDD

BRYN MORFYDD HOTEL GOLF CLUB,
Llanrhaedr, Denbigh, **DENBIGHSHIRE**, LL16
4NP, **WALES**.
(T) 01745 890280

Course/s:
- **DUCHESS**
  Built: 1992
  Number of Holes: 9 **Par:** 27
  Designer: Peter Alliss, Duncan Muirhead

DUKES
Description: Parkland
Built: 1992
Number of Holes: 18 **Par:** 70
Designer: Peter Alliss, Duncan Muirhead
Further Information:
A testing course.

BRYNHILL

BRYNHILL GOLF CLUB, The Bungalow,
Brynhill Golf Club, Little Brynhill Lane, Barry,
GLAMORGAN (VALE OF), CF62 8PN,
WALES.
(T) 01446 720277

Contact/s:
● **Club Secretary:** Mr Phil Gershenton

Course/s:
BRYNHILL
Number of Holes: 18

BUCHANAN CASTLE

BUCHANAN CASTLE GOLF CLUB, Drymen,
STIRLING, G63 0HY, **SCOTLAND.**
(T) 01360 660330

Contact/s:
● **Professional:** Mr Keith Baxter

Course/s:
BUCHANAN CASTLE
Description: Wooded, Parkland
Built: 1936
Number of Holes: 18 **Par:** 70
Designer: James Braid
Further Information:
The course is situated less than a mile
from Loch Lomond in the heavily forested
Buchanan Castle Estate. One of the least
known gems of Scottish golf.

BUCKINGHAM

BUCKINGHAM GOLF CLUB, Tingewick Rd,
Tingewick, **BUCKINGHAMSHIRE**, MK18
4AE, **ENGLAND.**
(T) 01280 815566

Membership: Members & Public

Contact/s:
● **Club Secretary:** Mr Tom Gates
● **Pro Shop:** Mr Greg Hannah
☎ 01280 815210

Course/s:
BUCKINGHAM
Description: Wooded, Tends to Flood
Built: 1921
Number of Holes: 18

BUCKINGHAMSHIRE

BUCKINGHAMSHIRE GOLF CLUB,
Denham Court Drive, Denham, **LONDON
(GREATER)**, UB9 5BG, **ENGLAND.**
(T) 01895 835777
(W) www.buckinghamshire-golfclub.co.uk

Contact/s:
● **Club Secretary:** Mr Mucha Murapa
☎ 01895 836800

Course/s:
BUCKINGHAMSHIRE
Number of Holes: 18 **Par:** 72
Yds: 6880 **F9 Yds:** 3316 **B9 Yds:** 3564
Designer: John Jacobs

BUCKPOOL

BUCKPOOL GOLF CLUB, Barhill Rd, Buckie,
MORAY, AB56 1DU, **SCOTLAND.**
(T) 01542 832236

Membership: Members & Public

Contact/s:
● **Club Secretary:** Ms M Coull

Course/s:
BUCKPOOL
Description: Links, Ideal for the Elderly
Built: 1930 **Built On:** Sand
Number of Holes: 18 **Par:** 70
Par 3's: 4 **Par 4's:** 12 **Par 5's:** 2
Yds: 6257

BUDE & NORTH CORNWALL

BUDE NORTH CORNWALL GOLF CLUB,
Burn View, Bude, **CORNWALL**, EX23 8DA,
ENGLAND.
(T) 01288 353635
(E) secretary@budegolf.co.uk
(W) www.budegolf.co.uk

Membership: Members & Public

Contact/s:
● **Club Secretary:** Ms Pauline Ralph
● **Professional:** Mr John Yeo
☎ 01288 363635
● **Book Tee Times:**
☎ 01288 352006

Course/s:
BUDE & NORTH CORNWALL
Description: Links, Drains Well
Green Speed: Fast **Built On:** Sand
Number of Holes: 18 **Par:** 71
Par 3's: 4 **Par 4's:** 11 **Par 5's:** 3
Yds: 6057 **F9 Yds:** 2866 **B9 Yds:** 3191
Prevailing Wind: West
Designer: Dunn

BUDOCK VEAN

**BUDOCK VEAN THE HOTEL ON THE
RIVER,** Helford River, Mawnan Smith,
Falmouth, **CORNWALL**, TR11 5LG,
ENGLAND.
(T) 01326 250288
(E) relax@budockvean.co.uk
(W) www.budockvean.co.uk

Contact/s:
● **Director:** Mr M Barlow

Course/s:
BUDOCK VEAN
Number of Holes: 18 **Par:** 68
Yds: 5255 **F9 Yds:** 2602 **B9 Yds:** 2653
Designer: James Braid

BUILTH WELLS

BUILTH WELLS GOLF CLUB LTD, The
Clubhouse, Golf Links Rd, Builth Wells,
POWYS, LD2 3NF, **WALES.**
(T) 01982 553296
(E) builthwellsgolfclub1@btinternet.com
(W) www.builthwellsgolfclub.com

Membership: Members & Public
Size of Complex: 130 Acres

Contact/s:
● **Club Secretary:** Mr John Jones
● **Professional:** Mr Simon Edwards
☎ 01982 551155

Course/s:
BUILTH WELLS
Description: Wooded, Parkland,
Undulating, Short, Ideal for the Elderly
Green Speed: Medium
Built: 1923 **Built On:** Soil
Number of Holes: 18 **Par:** 66
Par 3's: 6 **Par 4's:** 12
Yds: 5376 **F9 Yds:** 2816 **B9 Yds:** 2560
Prevailing Wind: West
Further Information:
The course boasts small, guarded, well
maintained greens.

BULBURY

BULBURY GOLF CLUB, Bulbury Lane,
Lytchett Matravers, Poole, **DORSET**, BH16
6HR, **ENGLAND.**
(T) 01929 459574

Course/s:
BULBURY
Number of Holes: 18

BULL BAY

BULL BAY GOLF CLUB, Amlwch, **ISLE OF
ANGLESEY**, LL68 9RY, **WALES.**
(T) 01407 830960

Contact/s:
● **Professional:** Mr John Burns

Course/s:
BULL BAY
Description: Heath Land
Built: 1913
Number of Holes: 18 **Par:** 70
Yds: 6276 **F9 Yds:** 3095 **B9 Yds:** 3178
Designer: W Herbert Fowler
Further Information:
An attractive coastal course. For those
who do not wish to play 18 holes, it is
possible to play shorter rounds and still
finish on the 18th.

BULLPITS

BULLPITS GOLF COURSE, Bourton,
Gillingham, **DORSET**, SP8 5AX, **ENGLAND.**
(T) 01747 840084

Contact/s:
● **Owner:** Mr John Freeman

Course/s:
BULLPITS
Description: Short
Number of Holes: 9 **Par:** 60
Yds: 3362 **F9 Yds:** 1532 **B9 Yds:** 1830
Further Information:
This 9 hole course can be played as an 18
hole.

BULWELL FOREST

BULWELL FOREST GOLF CLUB, Hucknall
Rd, Nottingham, **NOTTINGHAMSHIRE**, NG6
9LQ, **ENGLAND.**
(T) 0115 9770576

Membership: Members & Public

Contact/s:
● **Club Secretary:** Mr D Waddilove
● **Professional:** Mr Lee Rawlings
☎ 0115 9763172

Course/s:
BULWELL FOREST
Description: Heath Land, Undulating,
Sheltered, Short, Tight, Drains Well
Green Speed: Medium/Fast
Built: 1894 **Built On:** Sand/Soil
Number of Holes: 18 **Par:** 68
Record: 64 (Robert Smth)
Par 3's: 5 **Par 4's:** 12 **Par 5's:** 1
Yds: 5616 **F9 Yds:** 2824 **B9 Yds:** 2792
Further Information:
This challenging course has very
demanding par 3's on the 3rd, 10th, 12th
and 17th holes.

BUNCRANA

BUNCRANA GOLF CLUB, Ballymacarry,
Buncrana, **COUNTY DONEGAL**, **IRELAND.**
(T) 077 62279
(E) buncranagc@eircom.net

Contact/s:
- Club Secretary: Mr F McGray
- ☎ 077 20749

Course/s:
- **BUNCRANA**
  Number of Holes: 9 Par: 62
  Yds: 4250 F9 Yds: 2125 B9 Yds: 2125

BUNDORAN

BUNDORAN GOLF CLUB, Bundoran,
COUNTY DONEGAL, IRELAND.
(T) 072 41302
(W) www.bundorangolfclub.com

Contact/s:
- Club Secretary: Mr John McGagh
- Professional: Mr David T Robinson

Course/s:
- **BUNDORAN**
  Number of Holes: 18 Par: 70
  Par 3's: 4 Par 4's: 12 Par 5's: 2
  Yds: 6200 F9 Yds: 2972 B9 Yds: 3227

BUNGAY & WAVENEY VALLEY

**BUNGAY & WAVENEY VALLEY GOLF
CLUB,** Outney Common, Bungay, **SUFFOLK,**
NR35 1DS, **ENGLAND.**
(T) 01986 892337

Contact/s:
- Club Secretary: Mr R W Stacey

Course/s:
- **BUNGAY & WAVENEY VALLEY**
  Number of Holes: 18

BUNSAY DOWNS

BUNSAY DOWNS GOLF CLUB, Little
Baddow Rd, Woodham Walter, Maldon,
ESSEX, CM9 6RP, **ENGLAND.**
(T) 01245 223258
(W) www.warrengolfclub.co.uk

Membership: Members & Public
Size of Complex: 80 Acres

Contact/s:
- Club Secretary: Mr Jamie Durham
- Professional: Mr Henry Roblin

Course/s:
- **BUNSAY DOWNS**
  Description: Parkland, Hilltop, Sheltered,
  Open, Long, Drains Well, Ideal for the
  Elderly
  Green Speed: Medium
  Built: 1982 Built On: Soil
  Number of Holes: 9
  Prevailing Wind: South/West
  Designer: John Durham
- **PAR 3**
  Description: Parkland, Hilltop, Sheltered,
  Open, Low, Tight, Drains Well
  Green Speed: Medium
  Built: 1989 Built On: Soil
  Number of Holes: 9
  Prevailing Wind: South/West
  Designer: John Durham

BURFORD

BURFORD GOLF CLUB, New Clubhouse,
Burford, **OXFORDSHIRE,** OX18 4JG,
ENGLAND.
(T) 01993 822583

Contact/s:
- Club Secretary: Mr Robin Thompson

Course/s:
- **BURFORD**
  Number of Holes: 18 Par: 71
  Yds: 6432 F9 Yds: 3314 B9 Yds: 3118

Designer: John Turner

BURGESS (ROYAL)

ROYAL BURGESS GOLFING SOCIETY, 181
Whitehouse Rd, Edinburgh, **EDINBURGH
(CITY OF),** EH4 6ND, **SCOTLAND.**
(T) 0131 3392012

Contact/s:
- Club Secretary: Mr J P Audis

Course/s:
- **ROYAL BURGESS GOLFING SOCIETY OF
  EDINBURGH**
  Number of Holes: 18
  Designer: Tom Morris

BURGESS HILL

BURGESS HILL GOLF COURSE, Cuckfield
Rd, Burgess Hill, **SUSSEX (WEST),** RH15
8RF, **ENGLAND.**
(T) 01444 258585
(E) info@burgesshillgolfcentre.co.uk
(W) www.burgesshillgolfcentre.co.uk

Contact/s:
- Managing Director: Mr C Collins

Course/s:
- **BURGESS HILL & ACADEMY**
  Number of Holes: 9 Par: 27
  Yds: 1250 F9 Yds: 1250
  Designer: Donald Steel

BURGHAM

BURGHAM PARK GOLF CLUB, Felton,
Morpeth, **NORTHUMBERLAND,** NE65 8QP,
ENGLAND.
(T) 01670 787898

Membership: Members & Public
Size of Complex: 200 Acres

Contact/s:
- Club Secretary: Mr Jim Carr
- Professional: Mr Steve McNally
  ☎ 01670 787978

Course/s:
- **BURGHAM PARK**
  Description: Open, Long, Drains Well,
  Ideal for the Elderly
  Green Speed: Medium
  Built: 1994 Built On: Clay
  Number of Holes: 18 Par: 72
  Par 3's: 4 Par 4's: 10 Par 5's: 4
  Yds: 6751 F9 Yds: 3323 B9 Yds: 3428
  Prevailing Wind: West
  Designer: Mark James, Andrew Mair
  Further Information:
  The course is played around a farm and
  has wonderful sea views.

BURGHILL VALLEY

BURGHILL VALLEY GOLF CLUB, Tillington
Rd, Burghill, Hereford, **HEREFORDSHIRE,**
HR4 7RW, **ENGLAND.**
(T) 01432 760808

Contact/s:
- Owner: Mrs P Barnet

Course/s:
- **BURGHILL VALLEY**
  Number of Holes: 18
  Designer: M Barnett

BURGHLEY PARK

BURGHLEY PARK GOLF CLUB, Burghley
Pk, St. Martins Without, Stamford,
LINCOLNSHIRE, PE9 3JX, **ENGLAND.**
(T) 01780 753789
(E) burghley.golf@lineone.net

Contact/s:
- Club Secretary: Mr H Mulligan
- Professional: Mr Glenn Davies

Course/s:
- **BURGHLEY PARK**
  Number of Holes: 18 Par: 70
  Par 3's: 4 Par 4's: 12 Par 5's: 2
  Yds: 6230 F9 Yds: 3024 B9 Yds: 3206
  Designer: Reverend J Day

BURHILL

BURHILL GOLF CLUB, Burwood Rd,
Walton-on-Thames, **SURREY,** KT12 4BL,
ENGLAND.
(T) 01932 227345

Membership: Members & Public
Size of Complex: 300 Acres

Contact/s:
- Professional: Mr L Johnson
- Pro Shop:
  ☎ 01932 221729
- Book Tee Times: Ms. Sally Ives

Course/s:
- **BURHILL (NEW)**
  Description: Parkland, Long, Drains Well,
  Ideal for the Elderly
  Built: 2001
  Number of Holes: 18
  Prevailing Wind: North
  Designer: Simon Gidman
- **BURHILL (OLD)**
  Description: Parkland, Long, Drains Well,
  Ideal for the Elderly
  Green Speed: Medium
  Built: 1907 Built On: Clay
  Number of Holes: 18 Par: 70
  Par 3's: 4 Par 4's: 12 Par 5's: 2
  Yds: 6479
  Prevailing Wind: North/East
  Designer: William Park

BURLEY

BURLEY GOLF CLUB, Cott Lane, Burley,
Ringwood, **HAMPSHIRE,** BH24 4BB,
ENGLAND.
(T) 01425 402431

Contact/s:
- Professional: Mr W P Tye
- Book Tee Times:
  ☎ 01282 455266

Course/s:
- **BURLEY**
  Description: Moorland, Undulating
  Built: 1905
  Number of Holes: 9 Par: 69

BURNFIELD HOUSE

BURNFIELD HOUSE GOLF CLUB, 10
Cullyburn Rd, Newtownabbey, **COUNTY
ANTRIM,** BT36 5BN, **NORTHERN IRELAND.**
(T) 028 90838737
(W) www.burnfieldhousegolfclub.co.uk

Contact/s:
- Owner: Mr D Cahill

Course/s:
- **BURNFIELD HOUSE**
  Number of Holes: 9 Par: 70
  Yds: 5500
  Further Information: This 9 hole course
  can be played as an 18 hole.

BURNHAM & BERROW

BURNHAM & BERROW GOLF CLUB, St.
Christophers Way, Burnham-on-Sea,
SOMERSET, TA8 2PE, **ENGLAND.**

(T) 01278 783137

(W) www.burnhamandberrowgc.2-golf.com

Contact/s:
- **Club Secretary:** Mrs E L Sloman
  ☎ 01278 785760
- **Professional:** Mr Mark Crowther Smith

Course/s:

🏌 **CHAMPIONSHIP**
Number of Holes: 18   Par: 71
Par 3's: 4   Par 4's: 11   Par 5's: 3
Yds: 6606   F9 Yds: 3300   B9 Yds: 3306
🏆

🏌 **CHANNEL**
Number of Holes: 9   Par: 35
Par 3's: 2   Par 4's: 6   Par 5's: 1
Yds: 3060   F9 Yds: 3060
Further Information:
9 hole course can be played as an 18 hole course

BURNHAM BEECHES

BURNHAM BEECHES GOLF CLUB, Green Lane, Burnham, Slough, **BERKSHIRE**, SL1 8EG, **ENGLAND**.
(T) 01628 661448
(E) enquries@bbgc.co.uk
(W) www.bbgc.co.uk

Contact/s:
- **Professional:** Mr R Bolton

Course/s:

🏌 **BURNHAM BEECHES**
Number of Holes: 18   Par: 70
Yds: 6449   F9 Yds: 3255   B9 Yds: 3214

BURNHAM-ON-CROUCH

BURNHAM-ON-CROUCH GOLF CLUB LTD, Ferry Rd, Burnham-on-Crouch, **ESSEX**, CM0 8PQ, **ENGLAND**.
(T) 01621 782282
(E) burnhamgolf@hotmail.com
Membership: Members & Public
Size of Complex: 130 Acres

Contact/s:
- **Professional:** Mr Steven Cardy

Course/s:

🏌 **BURNHAM ON CROUCH**
Description: Parkland, Undulating
Green Speed: Medium
Built: 1923   Built On: Clay
Number of Holes: 18   Par: 70
Par 3's: 4   Par 4's: 12   Par 5's: 2
Yds: 6056   F9 Yds: 2732   B9 Yds: 3324
Prevailing Wind: West
Designer: Howard
Further Information:
The course has a Riverside location.

BURNLEY

BURNLEY GOLF CLUB, Glen View Rd, Burnley, **LANCASHIRE**, BB11 3RW, **ENGLAND**.
(T) 01282 451281
(E) burnleygolfclub@onthegreen.co.uk

Contact/s:
- **Club Secretary:** Mr Malcolm Wills

Course/s:

🏌 **BURNLEY**
Number of Holes: 18   Par: 69
Yds: 5939   F9 Yds: 3078   B9 Yds: 2861

BURNTISLAND

BURNTISLAND GOLF HOUSE CLUB, Dodhead, Burntisland, **FIFE**, KY3 9LQ, **SCOTLAND**.
(T) 01592 874093

- **Manager:** Mrs Wendy Taylor

Course/s:

🏌 **BURNTISLAND**
Number of Holes: 18
Designer: William Park

BURROW

BURROW (THE), Stepaside, **COUNTY DUBLIN**, **IRELAND**.
(T) 01 2954281

Contact/s:
- **Owner:** Mr Douglas Richardson

Course/s:

🏌 **BURROW PAR 3 GOLF COURSE**
Number of Holes: 18

BURSLEM

BURSLEM GOLF CLUB LTD, Wood Farm, High Lane, Burselm, Stoke-on-Trent, **STAFFORDSHIRE**, ST1 6JT, **ENGLAND**.
(T) 01782 837006

Course/s:

🏌 **BURSLEM**
Number of Holes: 9

BURSTEAD

BURSTEAD GOLF CLUB (THE), Tye Common Rd, Little Burstead, Billericay, **ESSEX**, CM12 9SS, **ENGLAND**.
(T) 01277 631171

Contact/s:
- **Accountant:** Mr Richard Lawford Duncan Tucker

Course/s:

🏌 **THE BURSTEAD**
Number of Holes: 18
Designer: P Tallack

BURTON ON TRENT

BURTON ON TRENT GOLF CLUB, 43 Ashby Rd East, Burton-on-Trent, **STAFFORDSHIRE**, DE15 0PS, **ENGLAND**.
(T) 01283 568708

Contact/s:
- **Professional:** Mr Gary Stafford

Course/s:

🏌 **BURTON UPON TRENT**
Number of Holes: 18
Designer: Harry Shapland Colt

BURY

BURY GOLF CLUB, Unsworth Hall, Blackford Bridge, Bury, **LANCASHIRE**, BL9 9TJ, **ENGLAND**.
(T) 0161 7664897
(W) www.burygolfclub.com

Contact/s:
- **Club Secretary:** Mr R Adams

Course/s:

🏌 **BURY**
Number of Holes: 18   Par: 69
Yds: 5927   F9 Yds: 3289   B9 Yds: 2638
Designer: Alistair MacKenzie

BURY ST EDMUNDS

BURY ST EDMUNDS GOLF CLUB, Tut Hill, Fornham All Saints, Bury St. Edmunds, **SUFFOLK**, IP28 6LG, **ENGLAND**.
(T) 01284 755979
(E) bury.golf@talk21.com
Membership: Members & Public

Size of Complex: 150 Acres

Contact/s:
- **Professional:** Mr Mark Jillings
  ☎ 01284 755978

Course/s:

🏌 **BURY ST EDMUNDS**
Description: Wooded, Parkland, Sheltered, Long, Ideal for the Elderly
Green Speed: Medium
Built: 1924   Built On: Chalk
Number of Holes: 18   Par: 72
Par 3's: 4   Par 4's: 10   Par 5's: 4
Yds: 6669   F9 Yds: 3225   B9 Yds: 3444
Prevailing Wind: West
Designer: Ted Ray

🏌 **BURY ST EDMUNDS 9 HOLE**
Description: Wooded, Parkland, Ideal for the Elderly
Built: 1992   Built On: Chalk
Number of Holes: 9   Par: 31
Par 3's: 5   Par 4's: 4
Yds: 2217
Prevailing Wind: South/West
Designer: Hawtree

BUSH HILL PARK

BUSH HILL PARK GOLF CLUB, Winchmore Hill, London, **LONDON (GREATER)**, N21 2BU, **ENGLAND**.
(T) 020 83605738
(W) www.bushhillparkgolfclub.co.uk
Membership: Members & Public

Contact/s:
- **Professional:** Mr Adrian Andrews

Course/s:

🏌 **BUSH HILL PARK**
Description: Wooded, Parkland, Undulating, Sheltered, Short, Tight
Green Speed: Medium
Built: 1895   Built On: Clay
Number of Holes: 18   Par: 70
Record: 58
Yds: 5767   F9 Yds: 2888   B9 Yds: 2879
Prevailing Wind: South/West
Further Information:
The course contains 6 long Par 3's.

BUSHEY GOLF COURSE

BUSHEY COUNTRY CLUB, High St, Bushey, Watford, **HERTFORDSHIRE**, WD23 1TT, **ENGLAND**.
(T) 020 89502283
Membership: Members & Public
Size of Complex: 105 Acres

Contact/s:
- **Professional:** Mr Graham Atkinson
  ☎ 020 89502215

Course/s:

🏌 **BUSHEY**
Description: Parkland, Undulating, Open, Medium Length, Tends to Flood
Green Speed: Medium/Fast
Built: 1979   Built On: Clay
Number of Holes: 9   Par: 35   Record: 67
(Robert Green)
Par 3's: 2   Par 4's: 6   Par 5's: 1
Yds: 2716   F9 Yds: 2716
Prevailing Wind: West
Designer: Donald Steel
Further Information: 9 hole course can be played as an 18 hole course

BUSHEY HALL

BUSHEY HALL GOLF CLUB, Bushey Hall Drive, Bushey, **HERTFORDSHIRE**, WD23 2EP, **ENGLAND**.

(T) 01923 222253
(W) www.golf-guide.com

Membership: Members & Public

Contact/s:
● **General Manager:** Mr R B Penman

Course/s:
◐ **BUSHEY HALL**
Description: Wooded, Parkland
Built: 1890
Number of Holes: 18 **Par:** 70
Yds: 6055 **F9 Yds:** 2986 **B9 Yds:** 3069

BUSHFOOT

BUSHFOOT GOLF CLUB, 50 Bushfoot Rd, Portballintrae, Bushmills, **COUNTY ANTRIM,** BT57 8RR, **NORTHERN IRELAND.**
(T) 028 20731317

Course/s:
◐ **BUSHFOOT**
Number of Holes: 9

BUTE

BUTE GOLF CLUB, Kingarth, Rothesay, **ARGYLL AND BUTE,** PA20 9HN, **SCOTLAND.**
(T) 01700 504369

Contact/s:
● **Honary Secretary:** Mr Ian McDougall

Course/s:
◐ **BUTE**
Number of Holes: 9 **Par:** 66
Yds: 5147 **F9 Yds:** 2573 **B9 Yds:** 2573

BUXTON & HIGH PEAK

BUXTON & HIGH PEAK GOLF CLUB, Waterswallows Rd, Fairfield, Buxton, **DERBYSHIRE,** SK17 7EN, **ENGLAND.**
(T) 01298 23453
(W) www.buxtonandhighpeakgolfclub.co.uk

Contact/s:
● **Professional:** Mr Gary Brown
　☎ 01298 26263
● **Pro Shop:**
　☎ 01298 23112
● **Book Tee Times:** Mrs Jane Dobson

Course/s:
◐ **BUXTON AND HIGH PEAK**
Description: Moorland, Undulating, Open, Medium Length, Drains Well
Green Speed: Medium
Built: 1887 **Built On:** Soil
Number of Holes: 18 **Par:** 69
Record: 63 (David Russell)
Par 3's: 5 **Par 4's:** 11 **Par 5's:** 2
Yds: 5966 **F9 Yds:** 2814 **B9 Yds:** 3152
Designer: J Morris
Further Information:
The course is built on limestone. There is also a quarry hole on the course.

C & L

C & L GOLF & COUNTRY CLUB, Westend Rd, Northolt, **LONDON (GREATER),** UB5 6RD, **ENGLAND.**
(T) 01818 455662

Course/s:
◐ **C & L**
Number of Holes: 9 **Par:** 33
Par 3's: 3 **Par 4's:** 6
Yds: 2107 **F9 Yds:** 2107
Designer: P Tallack
Further Information:
9 hole course can be played as an 18 hole course

CADMORE LODGE

CADMORE LODGE HOTEL, GOLF & COUNTRY CLUB, Berrington Green, St. Michaels, Tenbury Wells, **WORCESTERSHIRE,** WR15 8TQ, **ENGLAND.**
(T) 01584 810044

Course/s:
◐ **CADMORE LODGE HOTEL & COUNTRY CLUB**
Description: Valley
Built: 1990
Number of Holes: 9 **Par:** 68
Further Information:
The course has a lake which is a central feature and can be played as an 18 hole course

CAERLEON

CAERLEON GOLF COURSE, Broadway, Caerleon, Newport, **NEWPORT,** NP18 1AY, **WALES.**
(T) 01633 420342

Membership: Members & Public

Contact/s:
● **Club Secretary:** Mr Paul Inker
　☎ 07968 092233
● **Professional:** Mr Jim Lynch

Course/s:
◐ **CAERLEON**
Description: Wooded, Parkland, Breckland, Open, Medium Length, Tends to Flood, Ideal for the Elderly
Green Speed: Medium **Built On:** Clay
Number of Holes: 9
Prevailing Wind: West
Designer: Donald Steel

CAERNARFON (ROYAL TOWN OF)

ROYAL TOWN OF CAERNARFON GOLF CLUB, Aber Foreshore Rd, Caernarfon, **GWYNEDD,** LL54 5RP, **WALES.**
(T) 01286 678359
(E) caerngc@talk21.com
(W) www.northwales.uk.com

Membership: Members & Public

Contact/s:
● **Club Secretary:** Mr Grenville Jones
● **Professional:** Mr Aled Owen

Course/s:
◐ **ROYAL TOWN OF CAERNARFON**
Description: Parkland, Undulating, Open, Short, Ideal for the Elderly
Green Speed: Medium
Built: 1907 **Built On:** Clay
Number of Holes: 18 **Par:** 69
Yds: 5891
Further Information:
Views of Snowdonia and Anglesey.

CAERPHILLY

CAERPHILLY GOLF CLUB, Mountain Rd, Caerphilly, **CAERPHILLY,** CF83 1HJ, **WALES.**
(T) 029 2086 3441

Contact/s:
● **Captain:** Mr G P Howells

Course/s:
◐ **CAERPHILLY**
Number of Holes: 13 **Par:** 71
Yds: 5944 **F9 Yds:** 2967 **B9 Yds:** 2977
Further Information:
The course is due to be increased to an 18 hole course in 2003.

CAERWYS NINE OF CLUBS

CAERWYS NINE OF CLUBS GOLF COURSE, Coed Farm, Coed Farm Rd, Caerwys, Mold, **FLINTSHIRE,** CH7 5AQ, **WALES.**
(T) 01352 720692

Contact/s:
● **Owner:** Mr T P Evans

Course/s:
◐ **CAERWYS NINE OF CLUBS**
Number of Holes: 9
Designer: Eleanor Barlow

CAHIR PARK

CAHIR PARK GOLF CLUB, Kilcommon, Cahir, **COUNTY TIPPERARY,** IRELAND.
(T) 052 41474

Contact/s:
● **Honary Secretary:** Mr John Costigan
　☎ 052 41146

Course/s:
◐ **CAHIR PARK**
Number of Holes: 18 **Par:** 71
Yds: 6351 **F9 Yds:** 2901 **B9 Yds:** 3449
Designer: Edward Hackett

CAIRD PARK

CAIRD PARK GOLF CLUB, Mains Loan, Dundee, **ANGUS,** DD4 9BX, **SCOTLAND.**
(T) 01382 453606

Contact/s:
● **Club Secretary:** Mr Gregg Martin

Course/s:
◐ **CAIRD PARK**
Number of Holes: 18

CAIRNDHU

CAIRNDHU GOLF CLUB LTD, 192 Coast Rd, Ballygally, Larne, **COUNTY ANTRIM,** BT40 2QG, **NORTHERN IRELAND.**
(T) 028 28583248
(E) cairndhu@globalgolf.com
(W) www.globalgolf.com

Membership: Members & Public
Size of Complex: 250 Acres

Contact/s:
● **Club Secretary:** Mr P R Stinston
● **Professional:** Mr Bob Walker

Course/s:
◐ **CAIRNDHU**
Description: Championship, Parkland, Undulating, Sheltered, Open, Long, Tight, Drains Well, Ideal for the Elderly
Green Speed: Fast
Built: 1958 **Built On:** Soil
Number of Holes: 18 **Par:** 70
Par 3's: 4 **Par 4's:** 12 **Par 5's:** 2
Yds: 5945 **F9 Yds:** 2777 **B9 Yds:** 3168
Prevailing Wind: South/West
Designer: Morrison
Further Information:
Typical Irish parkland course with the second hole being 5 ft above sea level.

CALCOT PARK

CALCOT PARK GOLF CLUB, Calcot Pk, Bath Rd, Calcot, Reading, **BERKSHIRE,** RG31 7RN, **ENGLAND.**
(T) 0118 9427124
(E) info@calcotpark.fsworld.co.uk
(W) www.calcotpark.fsworld.co.uk

Membership: Members & Public
Size of Complex: 218 Acres

Contact/s:
- Club Secretary: Mr John Cox
- Professional: Mr Ian Campbell
  ☎ 01189 427797

Course/s:
🌑 **CALCOT PARK**
Description: Wooded, Parkland, Undulating, Medium Length, Drains Well
Green Speed: Slow
Built: 1930 Built On: Clay
Number of Holes: 18 Par: 70
Par 3's: 4 Par 4's: 12 Par 5's: 2
Yds: 6283 F9 Yds: 3113 B9 Yds: 3170
Designer: Harry Shapland Colt

CALDECOTT HALL

CALDECOTT HALL GOLF & LEISURE,
Beccles Rd, Fritton, Great Yarmouth,
NORFOLK, NR31 9EY, **ENGLAND**.
(T) 01493 488488

Contact/s:
- Club Secretary: Mr Roger Beales
- Professional: Mr Syer Schulver

Course/s:
🌑 **CALDECOTT HALL**
Description: Parkland, Undulating, Sheltered, Long, Drains Well
Built: 1998 Built On: Sand
Number of Holes: 18
Further Information:
There is a pond on the course.

CALDERBRAES

CALDERBRAES GOLF CLUB, 57
Roundknowe Rd, Uddingston, Glasgow,
GLASGOW (CITY OF), G71 6NG,
SCOTLAND.
(T) 01698 813425

Contact/s:
- Club Secretary: Mr Seamus McGuigain
  ☎ 07967 050511

Course/s:
🌑 **CALDERBRAES**
Number of Holes: 9 Par: 66
Yds: 5046 F9 Yds: 2523 B9 Yds: 2523
Further Information:
9 hole course can be played as an 18 hole course

CALDERFIELDS

CALDERFIELDS GOLF CLUB, Aldridge Rd,
Walsall, **MIDLANDS (WEST)**, WS4 2JS,
ENGLAND.
(T) 01922 632243

Membership: Members & Public

Contact/s:
- Owner: Mr C Andrews

Course/s:
🌑 **CALDERFIELDS**
Number of Holes: 18
Designer: R Winter

CALDWELL

CALDWELL GOLF CLUB LTD, Lugton Rd,
Uplawmoor, Glasgow, **GLASGOW (CITY OF)**, G78 4AU, **SCOTLAND**.
(T) 01505 850366
(E) caldwellgolfclub@aol.com

Contact/s:
- Club Secretary: Mr H I F Harper

Course/s:
🌑 **CALDWELL**
Number of Holes: 18 Par: 71
Yds: 6195 F9 Yds: 2952 B9 Yds: 3243

CALDY

CALDY GOLF CLUB LTD, Links Hey Rd,
Wirral, **MERSEYSIDE**, CH48 1NB,
ENGLAND.
(T) 0151 6255660
(W) www.caldygolfclub.co.uk

Membership: Members & Public

Contact/s:
- Club Secretary: Ms Gail Copple
- Book Lessons: Mr Alan Gibbons

Course/s:
🌑 **CALDY**
Description: Championship, Links, Parkland, Undulating, Open, Long, Drains Well, Ideal for the Elderly
Green Speed: Medium
Built: 1906 Built On: Clay
Number of Holes: 18 Par: 72
Yds: 6668 F9 Yds: 3344 B9 Yds: 3324

CALEDONIAN

CALEDONIAN GOLF CLUB, 20 Golf Rd,
Aberdeen, **ABERDEEN (CITY OF)**, AB24
50B, **SCOTLAND**.
(T) 01224 632443

Membership: Members & Public

Contact/s:
- Club Secretary: Mr D Essan
- Pro Shop: Mr David McDonell

Course/s:
🌑 **CALEDONIAN**
Description: Links Built On: Sand
Number of Holes: 18

CALLAN

CALLAN GOLF CLUB, Geraldine, Callan,
COUNTY KILKENNY, **IRELAND**.
(T) 056 25136

Course/s:
🌑 **CALLAN**
Number of Holes: 18

CALLANDER

CALLANDER GOLF CLUB, Aveland Rd,
Callander, **PERTH AND KINROSS**, FK17
8EN, **SCOTLAND**.
(T) 01877 330090
(E) callandergc@netcall.net

Contact/s:
- Club Secretary: Mrs S Smart

Course/s:
🌑 **CALLANDER**
Number of Holes: 18 Par: 63
Yds: 5116 F9 Yds: 2238 B9 Yds: 2209
Designer: William Fernie, George Morris

CALVERLEY

CALVERLEY GOLF CLUB, Woodhall Lane,
Calverley, Pudsey, **YORKSHIRE (WEST)**,
LS28 5QY, **ENGLAND**.
(T) 0113 2569244

Membership: Members & Public

Contact/s:
- Club Secretary: Mr Phil Dyson
- Pro Shop: Mr Neil Wendel-Jones

Course/s:
🌑 **CALVERLEY**
Description: Parkland, Sheltered, Medium Length, Tends to Flood
Green Speed: Medium
Built: 1980 Built On: Soil
Number of Holes: 18 Par: 68
Record: 63 (C Hustwit)

Yds: 5590 F9 Yds: 2795 B9 Yds: 2795
Prevailing Wind: North

CAMBERLEY HEATH

CAMBERLEY HEATH GOLF CLUB, Golf
Drive, Camberley, **SURREY**, GU15 1JG,
ENGLAND.
(T) 01276 23258

Contact/s:
- Professional: Mr Glenn Ralph
- Pro Shop:
  ☎ 01276 27905
- Book Tee Times: Ms Rita Deakin

Course/s:
🌑 **CAMBERLEY HEATH**
Description: Heath Land, Undulating, Sheltered, Medium Length, Tight, Drains Well
Built: 1913
Number of Holes: 18 Par: 72
Par 3's: 4 Par 4's: 10 Par 5's: 4
Yds: 6147 F9 Yds: 3168 B9 Yds: 2979
Designer: Harry Shapland Colt

CAMBRIDGE

CAMBRIDGE GOLF CLUB, Station Rd,
Longstanton, Cambridge,
CAMBRIDGESHIRE CB4 5DS, **ENGLAND**.
(T) 01954 789388

Membership: Members & Public
Size of Complex: 210 Acres

Contact/s:
- Club Secretary: Ms Linda Green
  ☎ 01954 739388
- Professional: Mr Adrienne Engelman
- Pro Shop: Mr Geoff Huggett

Course/s:
🌑 **CAMBRIDGE**
Description: Parkland, Undulating, Open, Long, Drains Well, Ideal for the Elderly
Green Speed: Medium/Fast
Built: 1990 Built On: Sand
Number of Holes: 18 Par: 72
Yds: 6818 F9 Yds: 3397 B9 Yds: 3421
Prevailing Wind: East
Further Information:
The course is predominantly for the 12 - 28 handicap golfer.

CAMBRIDGE LAKES

CAMBRIDGE LAKES GOLF COURSE,
Trumpington Rd, Cambridge,
CAMBRIDGESHIRE, CB2 2AJ, **ENGLAND**.
(T) 01223 324242
(W) www.cambridgelakes.co.uk

Membership: Public

Contact/s:
- Book Lessons: Mr Bob Barnes

Course/s:
🌑 **CAMBRIDGE LAKES**
Description: Parkland, Open, Short, Drains Well, Ideal for the Elderly
Green Speed: Medium
Built: 1995
Number of Holes: 9
Designer: Vicenzo Castiglia

CAMBRIDGE MERIDIAN

CAMBRIDGE MERIDIAN GOLF CLUB,
Comberton Rd, Toft, Cambridge,
CAMBRIDGESHIRE, CB3 7RY, **ENGLAND**.
(T) 01223 264700
(E) meridian@golfsocieties.com
(W) www.golfsocieties.com

Membership: Members & Public
Size of Complex: 200 Acres

Contact/s:
- **Professional:** Mr Michael Clemons
  ☎ 01223 264702

Course/s:
- **CAMBRIDGE MERIDIAN**
  Description: Championship, Long
  Built: 1994
  Number of Holes: 18 **Par:** 73
  Yds: 6707 **F9 Yds:** 3279 **B9 Yds:** 3428
  Designer: Peter Alliss, Clive Clark
  Further Information:
  Challenging for experienced golfers.

CAMBRIDGESHIRE MOAT HOUSE

CAMBRIDGESHIRE MOAT HOUSE HOTEL GOLF CLUB, Bar Hill, Bar Hill, Cambridge, **CAMBRIDGESHIRE**, CB3 8EU, **ENGLAND**.
(T) 01954 780098

Contact/s:
- **Manager:** Mr J MacDonald

Course/s:
- **CAMBRIDGESHIRE MOAT HOUSE**
  Number of Holes: 18

CAMBUSLANG

CAMBUSLANG GOLF CLUB, 30 Westburn Drive, Cambuslang, Glasgow, **GLASGOW (CITY OF)**, G72 7NA, **SCOTLAND**.
(T) 0141 6413130

Contact/s:
- **Club Secretary:** Mr R M Dunlop

Course/s:
- **CAMBUSLANG**
  Number of Holes: 9 **Par:** 35
  Yds: 2971

CAME DOWN

CAME DOWN GOLF CLUB, Higher Carne, Dorchester, **DORSET**, DT2 8NR, **ENGLAND**.
(T) 01305 813494

Membership: Members & Public

Contact/s:
- **Professional:** Mr Nick Rogers
  ☎ 01305 812670

Course/s:
- **CAME DOWN**
  Description: Downland, Hilltop, Undulating, Open, Medium Length, Drains Well
  Green Speed: Medium
  Built: 1896 **Built On:** Chalk
  Number of Holes: 18 **Par:** 70
  Yds: 6255 **F9 Yds:** 3246 **B9 Yds:** 3009
  Designer: Taylor
  Further Information:
  There are about 10 Ancient Burial Mines (Tumuli) on the course.

CAMPERDOWN

CAMPERDOWN GOLF CLUB, Camperdown House, Camperdown Pk, Dundee, **ANGUS**, DD2 4TF, **SCOTLAND**.
(T) 01382 623398

Contact/s:
- **Club Secretary:** Mrs J Lettuce

Course/s:
- **CAMPERDOWN**
  Number of Holes: 18

CAMPSIE

CAMPSIE GOLF CLUB, Crow Rd, Lennoxtown, Glasgow, **GLASGOW (CITY OF)**, G66 7HX, **SCOTLAND**.
(T) 01360 310244

Contact/s:
- **Professional:** Mr Mark Brennan
- **Book Tee Times:**
  ☎ 01360 310920

Course/s:
- **CAMPSIE**
  Built: 1897
  Number of Holes: 18 **Par:** 70
  Designer: William Auchterlonie
  Further Information:
  Great views and testing qualities complement this hillside course.

CAMS HALL ESTATE GOLF CLUB

AMERICAN GOLF CORPORATION, Cams Hall, Fareham, **HAMPSHIRE**, PO16 8UP, **ENGLAND**.
(T) 01329 827222
(W) www.americangolf.com

Membership: Members & Public

Contact/s:
- **Professional:** Mr Jason Neve
- **Pro Shop:**
  ☎ 01329 827732
- **Book Tee Times:** Mr Justin Sandler

Course/s:
- **CREEK**
  Description: Championship, Links, Parkland, Open, Medium Length, Drains Well, Ideal for the Elderly
  Green Speed: Medium
  Built: 1992 **Built On:** Sand
  Number of Holes: 18 **Par:** 71
  Par 3's: 4 **Par 4's:** 11 **Par 5's:** 3
  Yds: 6222 **F9 Yds:** 2977 **B9 Yds:** 3245
  Designer: Peter Alliss, Clive Clark
  Further Information:
  The course runs by saltwater lakes.

- **PARK**
  Description: Parkland, Open, Medium Length, Drains Well, Ideal for the Elderly
  Green Speed: Medium
  Built: 1992
  Number of Holes: 9 **Par:** 36
  Par 3's: 2 **Par 4's:** 5 **Par 5's:** 2
  Yds: 3197
  Designer: Peter Alliss, Clive Clark
  Further Information:
  The course runs by the sea saltwater lakes.

CANFORD MAGNA

CANFORD MAGNA GOLF CLUB, Knighton Lane, Wimborne, **DORSET**, BH21 3AS, **ENGLAND**.
(T) 01202 592552
(W) www.canfordmagnagc.co.uk

Membership: Members & Public

Contact/s:
- **Club Secretary:** Mr Trevor Smith
- **Professional:** Mr Roger Tuddenham
  ☎ 01202 591212

Course/s:
- **CANFORD MAGNA**
  Built: 1994
  Number of Holes: 18
  Designer: Howard Swan

CANMORE

CANMORE GOLF CLUB, Venturefair, Dunfermline, **FIFE**, KY12 0PE, **SCOTLAND**.
(T) 01383 724969

Membership: Members & Public

Contact/s:
- **Club Secretary:** Mr Charlie Stuart
- **Professional:** Mr David Gemmell

- **Book Tee Times:**
  ☎ 01383 728416

Course/s:
- **CANMORE**
  Description: Wooded, Parkland, Hilltop, Open, Short, Drains Well, Ideal for the Elderly
  Green Speed: Medium
  Built: 1897 **Built On:** Soil
  Number of Holes: 18 **Par:** 67
  Record: 65 (Thomas Bjorn)
  Yds: 5134 **F9 Yds:** 2630 **B9 Yds:** 2504
  Prevailing Wind: South/West

CANNINGTON

CANNINGTON GOLF COURSE, Cannington College, Cannington, Bridgwater, **SOMERSET**, TA5 2LS, **ENGLAND**.
(T) 01278 655050
(W) www.cannington.co.uk

Membership: Members & Public

Contact/s:
- **Club Secretary:** Mr Ron McCrow

Course/s:
- **CANNINGTON**
  Description: Links, Parkland, Undulating, Open, Medium Length, Ideal for the Elderly
  Green Speed: Fast
  Built: 1993 **Built On:** Soil
  Number of Holes: 9 **Par:** 68
  Par 3's: 3 **Par 4's:** 5 **Par 5's:** 1
  Yds: 6092 **F9 Yds:** 3055 **B9 Yds:** 3037
  Prevailing Wind: North/West
  Designer: Hawtree
  Further Information:
  The course is at the base of sea level and offers views of Quantock Hills, River Parrot Estuary and The Bristol Channel. This 9 hole course has 18 tees and therefore, can be played as 18 holes.

CANNOCK PARK

CANNOCK PARK GOLF CLUB, Stafford Rd, Cannock, **STAFFORDSHIRE**, WS11 2AL, **ENGLAND**.
(T) 01543 578850

Membership: Members & Public

Contact/s:
- **Professional:** Mr David Dunk

Course/s:
- **CANNOCK PARK**
  Description: Parkland, Undulating, Sheltered, Short, Tight, Drains Well, Ideal for the Elderly
  Green Speed: Medium/Fast
  Built: 1989 **Built On:** Sand
  Number of Holes: 18 **Record:** 61 (David Dunk)
  Designer: John Mainland

CANNONS COURT

CANNONS COURT GOLF CLUB, Bradley Green, Wotton-under-Edge, **GLOUCESTERSHIRE**, GL12 7PN, **ENGLAND**.
(T) 01453 843128

Contact/s:
- **Club Secretary:** Mr Adam Bennett
- **Professional:** Mr Ian Watts

Course/s:
- **CANNONS COURT**
  Number of Holes: 9 **Par:** 68
  Yds: 5323
  Further Information: This 9 hole course can be played as an 18 hole.

CANONS BROOK

CANONS BROOK GOLF CLUB LTD,
Elizabeth Way, Harlow, **ESSEX**, CM19 5BE, **ENGLAND**.
(T) 01279 425142

Membership: Members & Public
Size of Complex: 150 Acres

Contact/s:
- **Club Secretary:** Mrs Sandra Langton
- **Professional:** Mr Alan McGinn

Course/s:
- **CANONS BROOK**
  Description: Championship, Parkland, Hilltop, Undulating, Open, Long, Drains Well, Ideal for the Elderly
  Green Speed: Medium/Fast
  Built: 1964 **Built On:** Clay
  Number of Holes: 18 **Par:** 73
  Record: 66 (David Jones)
  Par 3's: 4 **Par 4's:** 9 **Par 5's:** 5
  Yds: 6569 **F9 Yds:** 3206 **B9 Yds:** 3363
  Prevailing Wind: West
  Designer: Henry Cotton
  Further Information:
  A championship course welcoming all types of golfers.

CANTERBURY

CANTERBURY GOLF CLUB, Scotland Hills, Littlebourne Rd, Canterbury, **KENT**, CT1 1TW, **ENGLAND**.
(T) 01227 453532

Contact/s:
- **Club Secretary:** Mr John Morgan
- **Professional:** Mr Paul Everard
  ☎ 01227 462865

Course/s:
- **CANTERBURY**
  Description: Parkland, Undulating, Sheltered, Medium Length, Tight, Drains Well
  Green Speed: Medium
  Built: 1927 **Built On:** Chalk
  Number of Holes: 18
  Prevailing Wind: West
  Designer: Harry Shapland Colt

CANWICK PARK

CANWICK PARK GOLF CLUB, Canwick Pk, Washingborough Rd, Lincoln, **LINCOLNSHIRE**, LN4 1EF, **ENGLAND**.
(T) 01522 542912

Contact/s:
- **Club Secretary:** Mr D J Dixon
- **Professional:** Mr S J Williamson
- **Book Tee Times:**
  ☎ 01522 536870

Course/s:
- **CANWICK PARK**
  Description: Parkland
  Built: 1975
  Number of Holes: 18 **Par:** 70
  Designer: Hawtree
  Further Information:
  The course offers views of Lincoln Cathedral.

CAPE CORNWALL

CAPE CORNWALL GOLF & COUNTRY CLUB, Nanpean Farm, Cape Cornwall, St. Just, Penzance, **CORNWALL**, TR19 7NL, **ENGLAND**.
(T) 01736 788611
(E) capecornwall@hotmail.com
(W) www.capecornwall.com

Contact/s:

- **Manager:** Mr N Paine

Course/s:
- **CAPE CORNWALL**
  Number of Holes: 18 **Par:** 69
  Yds: 5632 **F9 Yds:** 2771 **B9 Yds:** 2861
  Designer: Bob Hamilton

CAPEL BANGOR

CAPEL BANGOR GOLF & COUNTRY CLUB, Capel Bangor, Aberystwyth, **CEREDIGION**, SY23 3LL, **WALES**.
(T) 01970 880741

Membership: Members & Public
Size of Complex: 40 Acres

Contact/s:
- **Pro Shop:** Mr Adam Baker

Course/s:
- **CAPEL BANGOR**
  Description: Wooded, Parkland, Undulating, Sheltered, Short, Tight, Drains Well, Ideal for the Elderly
  Green Speed: Fast
  Built: 1992 **Built On:** Sand/Soil
  Number of Holes: 9 **Par:** 29
  Par 3's: 7 **Par 4's:** 2
  Yds: 1656 **F9 Yds:** 1656
  Prevailing Wind: West
  Designer: W Evans
  Further Information:
  A challenging 9 hole course for all types of golfers which can also be played as 18 holes.

CAPRINGTON

CAPRINGTON GOLF CLUB, Ayr Rd, Caprington, Kilmarnock, **AYRSHIRE (EAST)**, KA1 4UW, **SCOTLAND**.
(T) 01563 523702

Course/s:
- **CAPRINGTON**
  Number of Holes: 18 **Par:** 68
  Yds: 5810 **F9 Yds:** 2851 **B9 Yds:** 2959

CARDEN PARK

CARDEN PARK GOLF CLUB, Carden Pk, Chester, **CHESHIRE**, CH3 9DQ, **ENGLAND**.
(T) 01829 731000
(W) www.carden-park.co.uk

Membership: Members & Public
Size of Complex: 750 Acres

Contact/s:
- **Book Lessons:** Mr Richard Edwards
  ☎ 01829 731500

Course/s:
- **THE CHESHIRE**
  Built: 1993
  Number of Holes: 18 **Par:** 72
  Par 3's: 4 **Par 4's:** 10 **Par 5's:** 4
  Yds: 6653 **F9 Yds:** 3508 **B9 Yds:** 3145
  Designer: Nicklaus
- **THE NICKLAUS**
  Built: 1999
  Number of Holes: 18 **Par:** 72
  Yds: 6302 **F9 Yds:** 3165 **B9 Yds:** 3137
  Designer: Nicklaus

CARDIFF

CARDIFF GOLF CLUB, Sherborne Ave, Cardiff, **GLAMORGAN (VALE OF)**, CF23 6SJ, **WALES**.
(T) 029 20754772
(E) cardiffgolfclub@virgin.net

Contact/s:
- **Professional:** Mr Terry Hanson
  ☎ 02920 752272

Course/s:
- **CARDIFF**
  Number of Holes: 18 **Par:** 70
  Yds: 6016 **F9 Yds:** 3027 **B9 Yds:** 2989

CARDIGAN

CARDIGAN GOLF CLUB, Gwbert, Cardigan, **CEREDIGION**, SA43 1PR, **WALES**.
(T) 01239 615359

Membership: Members & Public
Size of Complex: 120 Acres

Contact/s:
- **Club Secretary:** Mr John Jones
- **Professional:** Mr Colin Parsons

Course/s:
- **CARDIGAN**
  Description: Championship, Links, Cliff Top, Open, Medium Length, Drains Well
  Green Speed: Fast
  Built: 1895 **Built On:** Sand
  Number of Holes: 18 **Par:** 72
  Par 3's: 4 **Par 4's:** 10 **Par 5's:** 4
  Yds: 6426 **F9 Yds:** 3182 **B9 Yds:** 3244
  Prevailing Wind: South/West
  Designer: Hawtree
  Further Information:
  A picturesque, challenging championship course.

CARDRONA

CARDRONA GOLF & COUNTRY CLUB, Cardrona, Cardrona, Peebles, **SCOTTISH BORDERS**, EH45 9HX, **SCOTLAND**.
(T) 01896 831971

Membership: Members & Public

Contact/s:
- **Manager:** Mr L Hogarth
  ☎ 01896 831660

Course/s:
- **CARDRONA**
  Description: Championship, Wooded, Parkland, Sheltered, Long, Ideal for the Elderly
  Green Speed: Fast
  Built: 1998
  Number of Holes: 18
  Designer: Peter Alliss

CARDROSS

CARDROSS GOLF CLUB, Main Rd, Cardross, Dumbarton, **ARGYLL AND BUTE**, G82 5LB, **SCOTLAND**.
(T) 01389 841754
(E) golf@cardross.com
(W) www.cardross.com

Membership: Members & Public

Contact/s:
- **Club Secretary:** Mr Iain Waugh
- **Professional:** Mr Robert Farrell
  ☎ 01389 841350

Course/s:
- **CARDROSS**
  Description: Championship, Parkland, Undulating, Sheltered, Long, Drains Well
  Green Speed: Fast
  Built: 1895 **Built On:** Sand
  Number of Holes: 18 **Par:** 71
  Par 3's: 3 **Par 4's:** 13 **Par 5's:** 2
  Yds: 6469 **F9 Yds:** 3063 **B9 Yds:** 3406
  Designer: James Braid

CARHOLME

CARHOLME GOLF CLUB, Carholme Rd, Lincoln, **LINCOLNSHIRE**, LN1 1SE, **ENGLAND**.

(T) 01522 523725
(E) info@carholme-golf-club.co.uk
(W) www.carholme-golf-club.co.uk

Membership: Members & Public

Contact/s:
- **Club Secretary:** Mr James Lammin
- **Professional:** Mr Richard Hunter
  ☎ 01522 536811
- **Book Lessons:**
  ☎ 01522 536211

Course/s:

CARHOLME
Description: Parkland
Built: 1906
Number of Holes: 18 Par: 71
Yds: 6215 F9 Yds: 2931 B9 Yds: 3284
Prevailing Wind: West
Further Information:
The course offers superb views of Lincoln Cathedral and surrounding area.

CARLISLE

CARLISLE GOLF CLUB, Aglionby, Carlisle, **CUMBRIA**, CA4 8AG, **ENGLAND**.
(T) 01228 513029

Membership: Members & Public

Contact/s:
- **Club Secretary:** Mrs H Rowell
- **Professional:** Mr Martin Heggie
  ☎ 01228 513241
- **Book Tee Times:** Mr Michael Rudduck
  ☎ 01228 510164

Course/s:

CARLISLE
Description: Parkland, Undulating, Sheltered, Medium Length, Drains Well, Ideal for the Elderly
Green Speed: Fast
Built: 1908
Number of Holes: 18 Par: 71
Yds: 6223 F9 Yds: 2999 B9 Yds: 3224
Prevailing Wind: South/West
Designer: Alistair MacKenzie, L Ross

CARLOW

CARLOW GOLF CLUB, Deer Pk, Carlow, **COUNTY CARLOW**, **IRELAND**.
(T) 050 331695
(E) info@carlowgolfclub.com
(W) www.carlowgolfclub.com

Contact/s:
- **Professional:** Andrew Gilbert

Course/s:

CARLOW
Number of Holes: 18 Par: 70
Yds: 6512 F9 Yds: 3285 B9 Yds: 3226
Designer: Simpson

CARLUKE

CARLUKE GOLF CLUB, Mauldslie Rd, Carluke, **LANARKSHIRE (SOUTH)**, ML8 5HG, **SCOTLAND**.
(T) 01555 771070

Contact/s:
- **Club Secretary:** Mr T Pheely
  ☎ 01555 770574

Course/s:

CARLUKE
Number of Holes: 18 Par: 70
Yds: 5136 F9 Yds: 2724 B9 Yds: 2412

CARLYON BAY

CARLYON BAY HOTEL & GOLF CLUB, Beach Rd, Carlyon Bay, St. Austell, **CORNWALL**, PL25 3RG, **ENGLAND**.

(T) 01726 814250

Membership: Members & Public

Contact/s:
- **Professional:** Mr Mark Rowe
  ☎ 01726 814228

Course/s:

CARLYON BAY
Description: Championship, Parkland, Cliff Top, Medium Length
Green Speed: Medium
Built: 1926
Number of Holes: 18

CARMARTHEN

CARMARTHEN GOLF CLUB, Blaenycoed Rd, Carmarthen, **CARMARTHENSHIRE**, SA33 6EH, **WALES**.
(T) 01267 281493

Membership: Members & Public
Size of Complex: 125 Acres

Contact/s:
- **Club Secretary:** Mr Jonathan Coe
- **Professional:** Mr Pat Gillis

Course/s:

CARMARTHEN
Description: Wooded, Heath Land, Medium Length, Drains Well
Green Speed: Medium
Built: 1910
Number of Holes: 18 Par: 71
Par 3's: 4 Par 4's: 11 Par 5's: 3
Yds: 6245 F9 Yds: 3230 B9 Yds: 3015
Prevailing Wind: South/West
Designer: Taylor
Further Information:
A challenging course with spectacular views.

CARNALEA

CARNALEA GOLF CLUB, Station Rd, Bangor, **COUNTY DOWN**, BT19 1EZ, **NORTHERN IRELAND**.
(T) 028 91270368

Membership: Members & Public
Size of Complex: 88.1 Acres

Contact/s:
- **Club Secretary:** Mr Gary Y Steele
- **Professional:** Mr Thomas Loughran
  ☎ 028 91270122
- **Book Tee Times:** Mr Gary Steele

Course/s:

CARNALEA
Description: Links, Parkland, Undulating, Open, Medium Length, Drains Well, Ideal for the Elderly
Green Speed: Medium
Built: 1927 Built On: Soil
Number of Holes: 18 Par: 69
Par 3's: 5 Par 4's: 11 Par 5's: 2
Yds: 5647 F9 Yds: 2949 B9 Yds: 2698
Prevailing Wind: North/East

CARNBEG

CARNBEG GOLF COURSE, Carnbeg, Dundalk, Kilcurry, **COUNTY LOUTH**, **IRELAND**.
(T) 042 9332518

Course/s:

CARNBEG
Number of Holes: 18 Par: 72
Yds: 6321

CARNE

CARNE GOLF COURSE, Carne, Belmullet, **COUNTY MAYO**, **IRELAND**.

(T) 097 82292
(E) carngolf@iol.ie

Contact/s:
- **Club Secretary:** Mr Liam McAndrew

Course/s:

CARNE GOLF LINKS
Description: Links, Valley
Number of Holes: 18 Par: 72
Yds: 6608
Designer: Edward Hackett

CARNEGIE

CARNEGIE CLUB (THE), Skibo Castle, Dornoch, **HIGHLANDS**, IV25 3RQ, **SCOTLAND**.
(T) 01862 894600
(E) info@carnegieclubs.com
(W) www.carnegieclub.co.uk

Membership: Members & Public

Contact/s:
- **Professional:** Mr David Thomson

Course/s:

CARNEGIE CLUB
Description: Championship, Links, Drains Well
Built: 1898
Number of Holes: 18 Par: 71
Par 3's: 5 Par 4's: 9 Par 5's: 4
Yds: 6184 F9 Yds: 3025 B9 Yds: 3159
Designer: Donald Steel, J Sutherland
Further Information:
Views of Struie Hill

CARNOUSTIE

CARNOUSTIE GOLF LINKS (THE), 3 Links Prde, Carnoustie, **ANGUS**, DD7 7JE, **SCOTLAND**.
(T) 01241 852480
(W) www.carnoustie.co.uk

Membership: Members & Public

Contact/s:
- **Club Secretary:** Mr David Curtis

Course/s:

BUDDON LINKS
Description: Links, Short, Drains Well
Built On: Sand
Number of Holes: 18 Par: 66
Par 3's: 7 Par 4's: 10 Par 5's: 1
Yds: 5420 F9 Yds: 2703 B9 Yds: 2717
Designer: James Braid

BURNSIDE
Description: Links, Drains Well
Built On: Sand
Number of Holes: 18 Par: 68
Par 3's: 5 Par 4's: 12 Par 5's: 1
Yds: 6020 F9 Yds: 2870 B9 Yds: 3150
Designer: James Braid

CHAMPIONSHIP
Description: Championship, Links, Long, Drains Well Built On: Sand
Number of Holes: 18 Par: 72
Par 3's: 3 Par 4's: 12 Par 5's: 3
Yds: 7368 F9 Yds: 3671 B9 Yds: 3697
Designer: James Braid, Tom Morris, William Park, A Robertson

CARNWATH

CARNWATH GOLF CLUB, 1 Main St, Carnwath, Lanark, **LANARKSHIRE (SOUTH)**, ML11 8JX, **SCOTLAND**.
(T) 01555 840251

Membership: Members & Public

Contact/s:
- **Club Secretary:** Mrs Linda McPate

Course/s:

CARNWATH

Description: Parkland, Open, Long, Drains Well
Built: 1907
Number of Holes: 18   **Par:** 69
Yds: 5632   **F9 Yds:** 2854   **B9 Yds:** 2778

CARRADALE

CARRADALE GOLF CLUB, Carradale, Campbeltown, **ARGYLL AND BUTE**, PA28 6SG, **SCOTLAND**.
(T) 01583 431321

Contact/s:
- Club Secretary: Mr R J Abernethy
- Book Tee Times:
  ☎ 01583 431378

Course/s:
⛳ **CARRADALE**
Description: Valley, Short
Built: 1906
Number of Holes: 9   **Par:** 63
Yds: 4694   **F9 Yds:** 2358   **B9 Yds:** 2336
Further Information:
Beautifully scenic 9 holes bordering the Clyde Estuary, but not links. Relatively short but very tricky, with most greens elevated and set into the hillside. 9 hole course can be played as an 18 hole course.

CARRBRIDGE

CARRBRIDGE GOLF CLUB, Inverness Rd, Carrbridge, **HIGHLANDS**, PH23 3AU, **SCOTLAND**.
(T) 01479 841623
(E) enquiries@carrbridgegolf.com
(W) www.carrbridgegolf.com

Contact/s:
- Club Secretary: Mrs A Baird
  ☎ 01479 841506

Course/s:
⛳ **CARRBRIDGE**
Description: Parkland, Heath Land
Built: 1980
Number of Holes: 9   **Par:** 71
Par 3's: 2   **Par 4's:** 6   **Par 5's:** 1
Yds: 2682
Further Information:
The course can be played as an 18 hole course using different coloured markers. It has magnificent views of the Cairngorm mountains.

CARRICK KNOWE

CARRICK KNOWE GOLF COURSE, Balgreen Rd, Edinburgh, **EDINBURGH (CITY OF)**, EH12 5TY, **SCOTLAND**.
(T) 0131 3371096

Contact/s:
- Manager: Mr A Smeaton

Course/s:
⛳ **CARRICK KNOWE**
Number of Holes: 18

CARRICK KNOWE

CARRICK KNOWE GOLF CLUB, 27 Glendevon Pk, Edinburgh, **EDINBURGH (CITY OF)**, EH12 5XA, **SCOTLAND**.
(T) 0131 3372217

Course/s:
⛳ **CARRICK KNOWE**
Number of Holes: 18   **Par:** 70
Yds: 6150

CARRICKFERGUS

CARRICKFERGUS GOLF CLUB, 35 North Rd, Carrickfergus, **COUNTY ANTRIM**, BT38 8LP, **NORTHERN IRELAND**.
(T) 028 93363713

Contact/s:
- Manager: Mr John Thomson

Course/s:
⛳ **CARRICKFERGUS**
Number of Holes: 18   **Par:** 68
Yds: 5623   **F9 Yds:** 2549   **B9 Yds:** 3074

CARRICKMINES

CARRICKMINES GOLF CLUB, Carrickmines, Dublin, **COUNTY DUBLIN**, **IRELAND**.
(T) 01 2955972

Contact/s:
- Honorary Secretary: T J B Webb

Course/s:
⛳ **CARRICKMINES**
Number of Holes: 9   **Par:** 71
Yds: 6063   **F9 Yds:** 3085   **B9 Yds:** 2978
Further Information:
9 hole course can be played as an 18 hole course.

CARRICK-ON-SHANNON

CARRICK-ON-SHANNON GOLF CLUB, Woodbrook, Carrick-on-Shannon, **COUNTY LEITRIM**, **IRELAND**.
(T) 079 67015

Contact/s:
- Captain: Mr A Hynes
  ☎ 078 35009

Course/s:
⛳ **CARRICK-ON-SHANNON**
Number of Holes: 9   **Par:** 70
Yds: 6072   **F9 Yds:** 3047   **B9 Yds:** 3026
Designer: Edward Hackett
Further Information:
Can be played as an 18 hole course.

CARRICK-ON-SUIR

CARRICK-ON-SUIR GOLF CLUB, Garravoone, Carrick-On-Suir, **COUNTY TIPPERARY**, **IRELAND**.
(T) 051 640047

Course/s:
⛳ **CARRICK-ON-SUIR**
Number of Holes: 18
Designer: Edward Hackett

CARRICKVALE

CARRICKVALE GOLF CLUB, 29 Glendevon Pk, Edinburgh, **EDINBURGH (CITY OF)**, EH12 5UZ, **SCOTLAND**.
(T) 0131 3371932

Contact/s:
- Club Secretary: Mr Tom Wooton

Course/s:
⛳ **CARRICKVALE**
Number of Holes: 18   **Par:** 70
Yds: 6055

CARRIGLEADE

CARRIGLEADE GOLF COURSE, Carrigleade Cross, Graiguenamanagh, **COUNTY KILKENNY**, **IRELAND**.
(T) 050 324370/087 2569012
Membership: Public

Contact/s:

- Club Secretary: Bridie Galavan

Course/s:
⛳ **CARRIGLEADE**
Description: Wooded, Parkland, Sheltered, Medium Length, Drains Well, Ideal for the Elderly
Green Speed: Medium
Built: 1995
Number of Holes: 18
Designer: Dan Galavan

CARSWELL

CARSWELL GOLF & COUNTRY CLUB, Carswell Home Farm, Carswell, Faringdon, **OXFORDSHIRE**, SN7 8PU, **ENGLAND**.
(T) 01367 870422

Membership: Members & Public

Contact/s:
- Professional: Mr Steve Parker

Course/s:
⛳ **CARSWELL**
Description: Parkland, Open, Medium Length, Drains Well, Ideal for the Elderly
Green Speed: Slow
Built: 1994   **Built On:** Sand
Number of Holes: 18

CARUS GREEN

CARUS GREEN GOLF COURSE, Burneside Rd, Kendal, **CUMBRIA**, LA9 6EB, **ENGLAND**.
(T) 01539 721097

Course/s:
- Professional: Mr D Turner

Course/s:
⛳ **CARUS GREEN**
Description: Parkland, Open, Medium Length, Drains Well, Ideal for the Elderly
Green Speed: Medium
Built: 1995   **Built On:** Sand/Soil
Number of Holes: 18   **Par:** 70
Yds: 5716   **F9 Yds:** 2832   **B9 Yds:** 2884
Prevailing Wind: West
Designer: W Adamson
Further Information:
The River Kent runs through 5 holes.

CASHEL GOLF RANGE

CASHEL GOLF RANGE & COURSE, Ballyknock, Cashel, **COUNTY TIPPERARY**, **IRELAND**.
(T) 062 62111

Contact/s:
- Professional: Mr Dominic Foran

Course/s:
⛳ **CASHEL**
Number of Holes: 18   **Par:** 54
Par 3's: 18

CASTELL HEIGHTS

CASTELL HEIGHTS & MOUNTAIN LAKES GOLF CLUB, Blaengwynlais, Caerphilly, **CAERPHILLY**, CF83 1NG, **WALES**.
(T) 029 208861128

Contact/s:
- Professional: Sion Bebb

Course/s:
⛳ **CASTELL HEIGHTS**
Description: Parkland
Built: 1989
Number of Holes: 9
Designer: Robert Sandow

⛳ **MOUNTAIN LAKES**
Description: Championship

Built: 1989
Number of Holes: 18 Par: 72
Designer: Robert Sandow

CASTERTON

CASTERTON GOLF COURSE, Sedbergh Rd, Casterton, Kirkby Lonsdale, **CUMBRIA**, LA6 2LA, **ENGLAND**.
(T) 01524 271592
(E) castertongc@hotmail.com

Membership: Members & Public
Size of Complex: 70 Acres

Contact/s:
● Professional: Mr Roy Williamson
☎ 01524 272740

Course/s:
🏌 CASTERTON
Description: Parkland, Undulating, Sheltered, Medium Length, Drains Well
Green Speed: Medium
Built: 1992 Built On: Soil
Number of Holes: 9 Par: 70
Par 3's: 2 Par 4's: 6 Par 5's: 1
Yds: 5726 F9 Yds: 2863 B9 Yds: 2863
Prevailing Wind: West
Designer: W Adamson
Further Information:
9 hole course can be played as an 18 hole course

CASTLE

CASTLE GOLF CLUB LTD, Woodside Drive, Rathfarnham, **COUNTY DUBLIN**, **IRELAND**.
(T) 01 4904207

Contact/s:
● Club Secretary: Leslie Blackburne
● Professional: Mr D Kinsella
☎ 01 4920272

Course/s:
🏌 CASTLE
Number of Holes: 18 Par: 69
Yds: 6748

CASTLE BARNA

CASTLE BARNA GOLF CLUB, Daingean, **COUNTY OFFALY**, **IRELAND**.
(T) 0506 53384
(E) info@castlebarna.ie
Size of Complex: 150 Acres

Contact/s:
● Club Secretary: Ms Evelyn Mangan
● Book Tee Times: Ms Dorothy Kilmurray

Course/s:
🏌 CASTLE BARNA
Description: Parkland, Medium Length, Drains Well, Ideal for the Elderly
Green Speed: Medium
Built: 1992 Built On: Soil
Number of Holes: 18 Par: 72
Yds: 6200
Designer: Alan Duggan
Further Information:
The course is built on the very best of mature parkland with natural streams flowing through, and an abundance of wildlife. The first green is built inside the foundation walls of the castle which was plundered more than 300 years ago.

CASTLE DOUGLAS

CASTLE DOUGLAS GOLF CLUB, Abercromby Rd, Castle Douglas, **DUMFRIES AND GALLOWAY**, DG7 1BB, **SCOTLAND**.
(T) 01556 502801

Contact/s:
● Club Secretary: A D Millar

☎ 01556 502099

Course/s:
🏌 CASTLE DOUGLAS
Number of Holes: 9 Par: 68
Yds: 5408 F9 Yds: 2704 B9 Yds: 2734
Further Information:
Can be played as an 18 hole course.

CASTLE EDEN

CASTLE EDEN GOLF CLUB, Castle Eden, Hartlepool, **CLEVELAND**, TS27 4SS, **ENGLAND**.
(T) 01429 836510
(W) www.ceden-golf.co.uk

Contact/s:
● Professional: Mr Peter Jackson
☎ 01429 836689

Course/s:
🏌 CASTLE EDEN
Description: Parkland, Undulating
Green Speed: Medium
Number of Holes: 18 Par: 70
Yds: 6272 F9 Yds: 2987 B9 Yds: 3285

CASTLE HAWK

CASTLE HAWK GOLF CLUB, Chadwick Lane, Rochdale, **LANCASHIRE**, OL11 3BY, **ENGLAND**.
(T) 01706 659995

Membership: Members & Public

Contact/s:
● Club Secretary: Mrs Louise Entwistle
● Professional: Mr Craig Bowring

Course/s:
🏌 NEW
Number of Holes: 9
Designer: T Wilson

🏌 OLD
Description: Championship, Parkland, Open, Medium Length, Drains Well
Green Speed: Medium
Built: 1960 Built On: Clay
Number of Holes: 18
Prevailing Wind: North
Designer: T Wilson

CASTLE HUME

CASTLE HUME GOLF CLUB, Belleek Rd, Enniskillen, **COUNTY FERMANAGH**, BT93 7ED, **NORTHERN IRELAND**.
(T) 028 66327077
(W) www.castlehumegolf.com

Membership: Members & Public
Size of Complex: 125 Acres

Contact/s:
● President: Mr Jimmy Sharpe

Course/s:
🏌 CASTLE HUME
Description: Championship, Parkland, Open, Long, Tight, Drains Well, Ideal for the Elderly
Green Speed: Medium/Fast
Built: 1991 Built On: Chalk/Sand
Number of Holes: 18 Par: 72
Par 3's: 4 Par 4's: 10 Par 5's: 4
Yds: 6310 F9 Yds: 3238 B9 Yds: 3072
Prevailing Wind: North
Designer: R Browne
Further Information:
A challenging championship course situated on the edge of Castle Hume Lake.

CASTLE PARK

CASTLE PARK GOLF CLUB, Gifford,

Haddington, **LOTHIAN (EAST)**, EH41 4PL, **SCOTLAND**.
(T) 01620 810733
(W) www.castleparkgolfclub.co.uk

Membership: Members & Public
Size of Complex: 145 Acres

Contact/s:
● Club Secretary: Mr Stuart Fortune
● Professional: Mr Derek Small
☎ 01368 862872

Course/s:
🏌 CASTLE PARK
Description: Parkland, Undulating, Medium Length, Tight, Drains Well
Green Speed: Fast
Built: 1994 Built On: Soil
Number of Holes: 9 Par: 34 Record: 70 (David Drysdale)
Par 3's: 2 Par 4's: 7
Yds: 2837
Further Information:
The course is located close to Lammermuir Hills, surrounded by mature woodlands. It will be extended to 18 holes in the Spring of 2002. The 9 hole course can be played as an 18 hole course, with three different tees on the second 9.

CASTLE POINT

CASTLE POINT GOLF CLUB, Somnes Ave, Canvey Island, **ESSEX**, SS8 9FG, **ENGLAND**.
(T) 01268 696298

Membership: Public

Contact/s:
● Club Secretary: Mrs D Archer
☎ 01268 754676
● Professional: Mr M Utteridge
☎ 01268 510830

Course/s:
🏌 CASTLE POINT
Description: Links
Number of Holes: 18 Par: 71
Yds: 6176

CASTLE ROYLE

CASTLE ROYLE GOLF & COUNTRY CLUB, Bath Rd, Knowl Hill, Reading, **BERKSHIRE**, RG10 9XA, **ENGLAND**.
(T) 01628 820700
(W) www.clubhaus.com
Size of Complex: 180 Acres

Contact/s:
● Club Secretary: Mr Gordon Jones
● Professional: Mr Jason Brant
● Pro Shop: Mr David Stobie

Course/s:
🏌 CASTLE ROYLE
Description: Championship, Links, Parkland, Open, Long, Drains Well
Green Speed: Medium/Fast
Built: 1994 Built On: Sand
Number of Holes: 18 Par: 72
Record: 62
Par 3's: 4 Par 4's: 10 Par 5's: 4
Yds: 6828
Designer: Neil Coles
Further Information:
USGA Course. Views of Windsor Castle from the 18th hole.

CASTLEBAR

CASTLEBAR GOLF CLUB, Hawthorn Lodge, Castlebar, **COUNTY MAYO**, **IRELAND**.
(T) 094 21649

Contact/s:
● Club Secretary: Angus Ryan

☎ 094 32232

Course/s:

🌑 **CASTLEBAR**
Number of Holes: 18
Yds: 6229

CASTLEBLAYNEY

CASTLEBLAYNEY GOLF CLUB,
Castleblayney, **COUNTY MONAGHAN,**
IRELAND.
(T) 042 9749485

Contact/s:
● Club Secretary: D McGlynn
  ☎ 042 1401907

Course/s:

🌑 **CASTLEBLAYNEY**
Number of Holes: 9 Par: 68
Yds: 5356 F9 Yds: 2678 B9 Yds: 2678
Designer: R Browne
Further Information:
Can be played as an 18 hole course

CASTLECOCH

CASTLECOCH GOLF CLUB, Castle Rd,
Tongwynlais, Cardiff, **GLAMORGAN (VALE**
OF), CF15 7JQ, **WALES.**
(T) 029 20813370

Membership: Public

Contact/s:
● Book Tee Times: Mr E Fears

Course/s:

🌑 **CASTLECOCH**
Description: Parkland, Undulating, Open,
Short, Drains Well
Green Speed: Fast
Built: 1988 Built On: Clay
Number of Holes: 9
Further Information:
Castlecoch overlooks the whole course.

CASTLECOMER

CASTLECOMER GOLF CLUB, Drumgoole,
Castlecomer, **COUNTY KILKENNY,**
IRELAND.
(T) 056 41139
(E) info@castlecomergolf.com
(W) www.castlecomergolf.com

Membership: Members & Public

Contact/s:
● Club Secretary: Mr Matt Dooley

Course/s:

🌑 **CASTLECOMER**
Description: Wooded, Undulating
Number of Holes: 9 Par: 71
Yds: 6477
Further Information:
Junior Golfers welcome up to 4p.m.

CASTLEGREGORY

CASTLEGREGORY GOLF & FISHING
CLUB, Stradbally, Castlegregory, **COUNTY**
KERRY, IRELAND.
(T) 066 7139444

Contact/s:
● Club Secretary: Mr Martin Lynch

Course/s:

🌑 **CASTLEGREGORY**
Description: Links
Number of Holes: 9 Par: 34
Yds: 5057 F9 Yds: 2528 B9 Yds: 2529
Designer: A Spring
Further Information:
Can be played as an 18 hole course.
Home to numerous species of wildlife

both flora and fauna, including a
manmade lake on the ninth, breeding
ground for the Natterjack Toad, unique to
this location.

CASTLEREA

CASTLEREA GOLF CLUB, Clonalis,
Castlerea, **COUNTY ROSCOMMON,**
IRELAND.
(T) 090 720068

Contact/s:
● Club Secretary: W Gannon

Course/s:

🌑 **CASTLEREA**
Description: Parkland
Green Speed: Fast
Number of Holes: 9 Par: 68
Yds: 5466
Further Information:
A good challenge for the high
handicappers.

CASTLEROSSE

CASTLEROSSE GOLF CLUB, Castlefosse
Hotel, Killorglin Rd, Killarney, **COUNTY**
KERRY, IRELAND.
(T) 064 31144
(E) castle@iol.ie
(W) www.castlerossegolf.com

Membership: Members & Public

Contact/s:
● Club Secretary: Ms Con Horgan
● Book Tee Times: Ms Dagmar Williams

Course/s:

🌑 **CASTLEROSSE**
Description: Wooded, Parkland, Short,
Drains Well
Green Speed: Medium
Number of Holes: 9 Par: 36
Yds: 3020
Designer: Harry Wallace

CASTLETOWN GOLF LINKS

CASTLETOWN GOLF LINKS, Fort Island,
Derbyhaven, Castletown, **ISLE OF MAN,** IM9
1VA, **ENGLAND.**
(T) 01624 822201

Membership: Members & Public

Contact/s:
● Professional: Mr Murray Crowe

Course/s:

🌑 **CASTLETOWN GOLF LINKS**
Description: Championship, Links,
Undulating, Drains Well Built On: Sand
Number of Holes: 18 Par: 72
Yds: 6711 F9 Yds: 3484 B9 Yds: 3227
Designer: Alistair MacKenzie, L Ross ⚐

CASTLETROY

CASTLETROY GOLF CLUB, Castletroy,
Limerick, **COUNTY LIMERICK, IRELAND.**
(T) 061 335753
(E) cgc@iol.ie

Contact/s:
● Club Secretary: Mr Laurence Hayes
● Professional: Mr Noel Cassidy
  ☎ 061 338283

Course/s:

🌑 **CASTLETROY**
Description: Parkland
Number of Holes: 18 Par: 71
Yds: 6447

CASTLEWARDEN

CASTLEWARDEN GOLF & COUNTRY
CLUB, Castlewarden, Straffan, **COUNTY**
KILDARE, IRELAND.
(T) 01 4589254
(E) castlewarden@clubi.ie
(W) www.castlewardengolfclub.com

Contact/s:
● Professional: Mr Gerry Egan

Course/s:

🌑 **CASTLEWARDEN**
Description: Undulating, Ideal for the
Elderly
Number of Holes: 18 Par: 71
Par 3's: 3 Par 4's: 12 Par 5's: 3
Yds: 6690 F9 Yds: 3562 B9 Yds: 3128
Designer: Tommy Halpin and Tom
Craddock

CATHCART CASTLE

CATHCART CASTLE GOLF CLUB, Old
Mearns Rd, Clarkston, Glasgow, **GLASGOW**
(CITY OF), G76 7YL, **SCOTLAND.**
(T) 0141 6383436

Membership: Members & Public
Size of Complex: 95 Acres

Contact/s:
● Manager: Mr J Adams

Course/s:

🌑 **CATHCART CASTLE**
Description: Wooded, Parkland
Number of Holes: 18 Par: 68
Yds: 5832
Further Information:
A fair test to players of all standards.

CATHKIN BRAES

CATHKIN BRAES GOLF CLUB, Cathkin Rd,
Rutherglen, Glasgow, **GLASGOW (CITY OF),**
G73 4SE, **SCOTLAND.**
(T) 0141 6346605
(E) golf@cathkinbraes.freeserve.co.uk

Contact/s:
● Club Secretary: Mr Hugh Millar

Course/s:

🌑 **CATHKIN BRAES**
Number of Holes: 18 Par: 71
Yds: 6208 F9 Yds: 3021 B9 Yds: 3187
Designer: James Braid

CATTERICK

CATTERICK GOLF CLUB LTD, Leyburn Rd,
Catterick Garrison, **YORKSHIRE (NORTH),**
DL9 3QE, **ENGLAND.**
(T) 01748 833268
(W) www.catterickgolfclub.co.uk

Contact/s:
● Club Secretary: Mrs Diane Hopkins
● Professional: Mr Andy Marshall
  ☎ 01748 833671

Course/s:

🌑 **CATTERICK**
Number of Holes: 18 Par: 71
Par 3's: 3 Par 4's: 13 Par 5's: 2
Yds: 6329 F9 Yds: 3154 B9 Yds: 3175
Designer: Arthur Day

CAVAN (COUNTY)

COUNTY CAVAN GOLF CLUB, Aranmore
Hse, Drumelis, Cavan, **COUNTY CAVAN,**
IRELAND.
(T) 049 4331541
(W) www.cavangolf.ie

Membership: Members & Public

Course/s:

CAVAN
Description: Wooded, Parkland, Undulating
Number of Holes: 18 **Par:** 70
Yds: 5519
Designer: Edward Hackett
Further Information:
A good challenge to mid to high handicappers.

CAVE CASTLE

CAVE CASTLE GOLF CLUB, South Cave, Brough, **YORKSHIRE (EAST)**, HU15 2EU, **ENGLAND**.
(T) 01430 421286
Size of Complex: 160 Acres

Contact/s:
● **Professional:** Mr Steve Mackinder

Course/s:

CAVE CASTLE GOLF HOTEL
Description: Parkland, Undulating, Medium Length
Green Speed: Medium
Built: 1989 **Built On:** Clay/Soil
Number of Holes: 18 **Par:** 72
Yds: 6524 **F9 Yds:** 3428 **B9 Yds:** 3096

CAVENDISH

CAVENDISH GOLF CLUB, Gadley Lane, Watford Rd, Buxton, **DERBYSHIRE**, SK17 6XD, **ENGLAND**.
(T) 01298 79708
Membership: Members & Public

Contact/s:
● **Club Secretary:** Mr J D Rushton

Course/s:

CAVENDISH
Description: Parkland, Moorland, Open
Number of Holes: 18 **Par:** 68
Yds: 5833
Designer: Alistair MacKenzie
Further Information:
The wind causes many tests for players of all standards. The course is noted for excellent greens which are very well maintained.

CAVERSHAM HEATH

CAVERSHAM HEATH GOLF CLUB LTD, Mapledurham Village, Reading, **BERKSHIRE**, RG4 7TR, **ENGLAND**.
(T) 0118 9478600
(E) info@caversham.co.uk
(W) www.cavershamgolf.co.uk

Contact/s:
● **Professional:** Mr Carl Rutherford
☎ 0118 9479400

Course/s:

CAVERSHAM HEATH
Description: Heath Land
Green Speed: Medium
Built: 2000
Number of Holes: 18

CAWDER

CAWDER GOLF CLUB, Cadder Rd, Bishopbriggs, Glasgow, **GLASGOW (CITY OF)**, G64 3QD, **SCOTLAND**.
(T) 0141 7727101

Contact/s:
● **Club Secretary:** G T Stoddart
● **Professional:** K Stevely
☎ 0141 7727102

Course/s:

CAWDER
Number of Holes: 18 **Par:** 70
Yds: 6295
Further Information:
Hilly and challenging.

KEIR
Number of Holes: 18 **Par:** 68
Yds: 5877
Further Information:
Less challenging than the Cawder course.

CEANN SIBEAL

CEANN SIBEAL GOLF CLUB, Dingle Golf Club, Ceann Sibeal, Ballyferriter, **COUNTY KERRY**, **IRELAND**.
(T) 066 9156255
(E) dinglegc@iol.ie
(W) www.dingle-golf.com

Contact/s:
● **Club Secretary:** Mr Steve Fahy
● **Professional:** Mr Dermot O'Connor

Course/s:

CEANN SIBEAL
Number of Holes: 18 **Par:** 72
Par 3's: 4 **Par 4's:** 10 **Par 5's:** 4
Yds: 6689 **F9 Yds:** 3339 **B9 Yds:** 3350
Designer: Edward Hackett, O'Connor

CELBRIDGE ELM HALL

CELBRIDGE ELM HALL GOLF COURSE, Elm Hall, Celbridge, **COUNTY KILDARE**, **IRELAND**.
(T) 01 6288208
Membership: Members & Public

Contact/s:
● **Owner:** Mr Seamus Lawless

Course/s:

CELBRIDGE ELM HALL
Description: Parkland, Medium Length, Drains Well
Green Speed: Medium
Built: 1996
Number of Holes: 9

CELTIC MANOR

CELTIC MANOR RESORT (THE), Coldra Woods, Catash Rd, Newport, **NEWPORT**, NP18 1HQ, **WALES**.
(T) 01633 413000
(E) postbox@celtic-manor.com
(W) www.celtic-manor.com
Membership: Members & Public

Contact/s:
● **Club Secretary:** Mr Shane Weeson
● **Professional:** Mr Scott Patience
☎ 01633 410312
● **Pro Shop:** Mr Mark Smith
● **Book Tee Times:** Mr Stewart Evans
☎ 01633 410263
● **Book Lessons:** Mr Carl Johnson

Course/s:

COLDRA WOODS
Description: Short
Built: 1996
Number of Holes: 18 **Par:** 59
Yds: 4001
Designer: Robert Trent Jones (Jnr)

ROMAN ROAD
Built: 1995
Number of Holes: 18 **Par:** 69
Yds: 6685
Designer: Robert Trent Jones (Jnr)

WENTWOOD HILLS
Description: Championship
Built: 1999
Number of Holes: 18 **Par:** 72
Yds: 7403
Designer: Robert Trent Jones (Jnr)

CENTRAL LONDON

CENTRAL LONDON GOLF CENTRE, Burntwood Lane, London, **LONDON (GREATER)**, SW17 0AT, **ENGLAND**.
(T) 020 88712468
(W) www.clgc.co.uk
Membership: Public
Size of Complex: 29 Acres

Contact/s:
● **Professional:** Mr John Woodroffe
● **Pro Shop:** Mr Martin Rathbone
● **Book Lessons:** Mr Kevin Whale

Course/s:

CENTRAL LONDON
Description: Wooded, Parkland, Open, Short, Tight, Drains Well, Ideal for the Elderly
Green Speed: Medium
Built: 1992 **Built On:** Clay
Number of Holes: 9 **Par:** 31
Yds: 2332
Designer: P Tallack
Further Information:
The course has a narrow fairway.

CENTRAL PARK

CENTRAL PARK GOLF CLUB, Central Pk Ave, Plymouth, **DEVON**, PL4 6NW, **ENGLAND**.
(T) 01752 509391
Membership: Public

Contact/s:
● **Owner:** Mr Pete Mehigan

Course/s:

CENTRAL PARK
Description: Parkland, Ideal for the Elderly
Green Speed: Slow
Number of Holes: 9

CHADWELL SPRINGS

CHADWELL SPRINGS GOLF CLUB, Hartford Rd, Ware, **HERTFORDSHIRE**, SG12 9LE, **ENGLAND**.
(T) 01920 461447
Membership: Members & Public

Contact/s:
● **Club Secretary:** Mr D J Evans
● **Professional:** Mr M Wall

Course/s:

CHADWELL SPRINGS
Description: Parkland, Undulating, Open, Long, Drains Well
Green Speed: Fast
Built: 1900 **Built On:** Chalk
Number of Holes: 9 **Par:** 72 **Record:** 69 (Mark Linton)
Yds: 6418
Further Information:
Can be played as an 18 hole course.

CHALGRAVE MANOR

CHALGRAVE MANOR GOLF CLUB, Dunstable Rd, Toddington, Dunstable, **BEDFORDSHIRE**, LU5 6JN, **ENGLAND**.
(T) 01525 876556
Membership: Members & Public
Size of Complex: 150 Acres

Contact/s:
● **Club Secretary:** Mr Steve Rumball
● **Professional:** Mr Terry Bunyan

Course/s:

CHALGRAVE MANOR
Description: Parkland, Undulating, Medium Length, Drains Well, Ideal for the Elderly
Green Speed: Medium
Built: 1992 Built On: Clay
Number of Holes: 18 Par: 72
Par 3's: 5 Par 4's: 8 Par 5's: 5
Yds: 6398 F9 Yds: 3449 B9 Yds: 2949
Prevailing Wind: South/West
Designer: Mike Palmer
Further Information:
The course offers a good test for all standards of golfers.

CHANNELS

CHANNELS GOLF CLUB LTD, Belsteads Farm Lane, Little Waltham, Chelmsford, **ESSEX**, CM3 3PT, **ENGLAND**.
(T) 01245 440005
(E) info@channelsgolf.co.uk
(W) www.channelsgolf.co.uk
Membership: Members & Public

Contact/s:
- Club Secretary: Mr Tony Squire
- Professional: Mr Ian Sinclair
  ☎ 01245 441056

Course/s:

BELSTEAD
Description: Parkland, Undulating, Drains Well
Green Speed: Fast
Built: 1995 Built On: Soil
Number of Holes: 18 Par: 67
Par 3's: 6 Par 4's: 11 Par 5's: 1
Yds: 4779 F9 Yds: 2467 B9 Yds: 2312
Prevailing Wind: West
Designer: Michael Shattocks

CHANNELS
Description: Parkland, Undulating, Sheltered, Open, Medium Length, Tight, Drains Well, Ideal for the Elderly
Green Speed: Fast
Built: 1974 Built On: Clay/Soil
Number of Holes: 18 Par: 71
Par 3's: 4 Par 4's: 11 Par 5's: 3
Yds: 6402 F9 Yds: 3442 B9 Yds: 2960
Prevailing Wind: West
Designer: Henry Cotton

CHAPEL-EN-LE-FRITH

CHAPEL-EN-LE-FRITH GOLF CLUB LTD, The Cockyard, Manchester Rd, Chapel-en-le-Frith, High Peak, **DERBYSHIRE**, SK23 9UH, **ENGLAND**.
(T) 01298 813943
(E) info@chapelgolf.co.uk
(W) www.chapelgolf.co.uk
Membership: Members & Public

Contact/s:
- Club Secretary: Mr John Hilton
- Professional: Mr David Cullen

Course/s:

CHAPEL-EN-LE-FRITH
Description: Parkland, Medium Length
Built: 1905 Built On: Clay
Number of Holes: 18 Par: 70
Par 3's: 4 Par 4's: 12 Par 5's: 2
Yds: 6054 F9 Yds: 2745 B9 Yds: 3309
Designer: David Williams

CHARLESLAND

CHARLESLAND GOLF & COUNTRY CLUB HOTEL, Greystones, **COUNTY WICKLOW**, **IRELAND**.
(T) 01 2874360

(E) teetimes@charlesland.com
(W) www.charlesland.com

Contact/s:
- Professional: Mr Peter Duignan

Course/s:

CHARLESLAND
Description: Championship, Parkland, Open
Built: 1992
Number of Holes: 18 Par: 72
Par 3's: 4 Par 4's: 10 Par 5's: 4
Yds: 6439 F9 Yds: 3079 B9 Yds: 3360
Designer: Edward Hackett
Further Information:
The course offers spectacular views of the mountains and the Irish Sea.

CHARLETON

CHARLETON GOLF COURSE, Charleton, Colinsburgh, **FIFE**, KY9 1HG, **SCOTLAND**.
(T) 01333 340505
(W) www.charleton.co.uk
Membership: Members & Public
Size of Complex: 160 Acres

Contact/s:
- Club Secretary: Mr Jonathan Pattisson
- Professional: Mr Andy Hutton

Course/s:

CHARLETON
Description: Parkland, Undulating, Sheltered, Medium Length, Drains Well
Green Speed: Medium
Built: 1992 Built On: Soil
Number of Holes: 18 Par: 72
Par 3's: 2 Par 4's: 14 Par 5's: 2
Yds: 6152 F9 Yds: 2902 B9 Yds: 3250
Prevailing Wind: West
Designer: John Salverson
Further Information:
The course offers views over the Firth of Forth. Acclaimed to be the most attractive course in Fife with the most testing greens.

CHARLETON 9 HOLE
Built: 1994
Number of Holes: 9

CHARLEVILLE

CHARLEVILLE GOLF CLUB, Charleville, Cork, **COUNTY CORK**, **IRELAND**.
(T) 063 81257
(E) charlevillegolf@eircom.net
(W) www.charlevillegolf.com

Contact/s:
- Club Secretary: Mr Pat Nagle

Course/s:

CHARLEVILLE
Number of Holes: 18 Par: 71
Yds: 6467 F9 Yds: 3004 B9 Yds: 3463

CHARLEVILLE 9 HOLE
Number of Holes: 9 F9 Yds: 3451
Further Information:
9 hole course can be played as an 18 hole course

CHARNOCK RICHARD

CHARNOCK RICHARD GOLF CLUB, Preston Rd, Charnock Richard, Chorley, **LANCASHIRE**, PR7 5LE, **ENGLAND**.
(T) 01257 470707
(W) www.charnockrichardgolfclub.co.uk
Membership: Members & Public

Contact/s:
- Club Secretary: Mr Lee Taylor
- Professional: Mr Gareth Roper

Course/s:

CHARNOCK RICHARD
Description: Parkland, Sheltered, Open, Medium Length, Tight, Drains Well
Green Speed: Medium
Built: 1994 Built On: Soil
Number of Holes: 18 Par: 71
Prevailing Wind: West

CHARNWOOD FOREST

CHARNWOOD FOREST GOLF CLUB, Breakback Rd, Woodhouse Eaves, Loughborough, **LEICESTERSHIRE**, LE12 8TA, **ENGLAND**.
(T) 01509 890259
Membership: Members & Public

Contact/s:
- Club Secretary: Mrs Julie Bowler

Course/s:

CHARNWOOD FOREST
Description: Wooded, Heath Land, Sheltered, Open, Short, Drains Well, Ideal for the Elderly
Green Speed: Medium
Built: 1890 Built On: Clay
Number of Holes: 9 Par: 69
Par 3's: 2 Par 4's: 7
Yds: 5970 F9 Yds: 2935 B9 Yds: 3035
Prevailing Wind: West
Further Information:
This 9 hole course has 16 different tees, therefore it can be played as an 18 hole course, playing the 1st and 9th tee twice. It also offers oustanding, beautiful scenery.

CHART HILLS

CHART HILLS GOLF CLUB, Weeks Lane, Biddenden, Ashford, **KENT**, TN27 8JX, **ENGLAND**.
(T) 01580 292222
(E) info@charthills.co.uk
(W) www.charthills.co.uk
Membership: Members & Public

Contact/s:
- Professional: Mr Danny French
- Book Tee Times: Ms Mary Millen

Course/s:

CHART HILLS
Description: Championship, Parkland, Drains Well, Ideal for the Elderly
Green Speed: Fast
Built: 1993 Built On: Clay
Number of Holes: 18 Par: 72
Record: 66 (John Pierre-Cixaux)
Par 3's: 4 Par 4's: 10 Par 5's: 4
Yds: 6449 F9 Yds: 3188 B9 Yds: 3261
Designer: Nick Faldo ♟

CHARTHAM PARK

CHARTHAM PARK GOLF CLUB, Felcourt Rd, East Grinstead, **SUSSEX (WEST)**, RH19 2JT, **ENGLAND**.
(T) 01342 870340
Membership: Members & Public
Size of Complex: 300 Acres

Contact/s:
- Club Secretary: Ms Jan Lane
- Professional: Mr David Hobbs

Course/s:

CHARTHAM PARK
Description: Championship, Wooded, Parkland, Undulating, Sheltered, Long, Tight, Drains Well, Ideal for the Elderly
Green Speed: Fast
Built: 1993 Built On: Sand

Number of Holes: 18   Par: 72
Record: 72 (Carl Richard)
Yds: 6680
Prevailing Wind: West
Designer: Neil Coles
Further Information:
Rather a testing course.

CHARTRIDGE PARK

CHARTRIDGE PARK GOLF CLUB,
Chartridge Lane, Chartridge, Chesham,
BUCKINGHAMSHIRE, HP5 2TF, **ENGLAND**.
(T) 01494 791772
(E) peter.gibbins@tinyworld.co.uk
(W) www.cpgc.net

Contact/s:
● Professional: Mr Peter Gibbins

Course/s:

● CHARTRIDGE PARK
Built: 1989
Number of Holes: 18   Par: 69
Yds: 5580   F9 Yds: 2606   B9 Yds: 2974
Designer: John Jacobs
Further Information:
An easy walking course with water
hazards.

CHASE

CHASE GOLF CLUB (THE), Pottal Pool Rd,
Penkridge, Stafford, **STAFFORDSHIRE**,
ST19 5RN, **ENGLAND**.
(T) 01785 712191
(W) www.crownsportsplc.com

Membership: Members & Public

Contact/s:
● Book Tee Times: Mr James Green
● Book Lessons: Mr Andrew Preston

Course/s:

● THE CHASE
Description: Parkland, Open, Long,
Drains Well, Ideal for the Elderly
Green Speed: Medium
Built: 1993
Number of Holes: 18   Par: 73
Par 3's: 5   Par 4's: 7   Par 5's: 6
Yds: 6707   F9 Yds: 3492   B9 Yds: 3215

CHEADLE

CHEADLE GOLF CLUB, Cheadle Rd,
Cheadle, **CHESHIRE**, SK8 1HW, **ENGLAND**.
(T) 0161 4282160

Contact/s:
● Club Secretary: Mr Barry Woodhouse

Course/s:

● CHEADLE
Number of Holes: 9   Par: 64
Yds: 5006
Designer: Renouf
Further Information:
Good test of golf for all levels.

CHEDINGTON COURT

CHEDINGTON COURT GOLF CLUB, Holts
Farm, South Perrott, Beaminster, **DORSET**,
DT8 3HU, **ENGLAND**.
(T) 01935 891413

Membership: Members & Public

Contact/s:
● General Manager: Mr David Astell
  ☎ 01935 981217

Course/s:

● CHEDINGTON COURT
Description: Wooded, Parkland,
Undulating, Sheltered, Drains Well, Ideal
for the Elderly

Green Speed: Medium
Built: 1991
Number of Holes: 18   Record: 70
(Stewart Cronin)
Designer: D Hemstock

CHELMSFORD

CHELMSFORD GOLF CLUB, Widford Rd,
Chelmsford, **ESSEX**, CM2 9AP, **ENGLAND**.
(T) 01245 256483
(E) office@chelmsfordgc.sagehost.co.uk
(W) www.chelmsfordgc.co.uk

Membership: Members & Public
Size of Complex: 100 Acres

Contact/s:
● Club Secretary: Mr G Winckless
● Professional: Mr Mark Welch
  ☎ 01245 257079

Course/s:

● CHELMSFORD
Description: Parkland, Undulating, Open,
Medium Length, Tight, Drains Well
Green Speed: Fast
Built: 1911   Built On: Clay
Number of Holes: 18   Par: 68
Record: 63 (Lee Fickling)
Par 3's: 5   Par 4's: 12   Par 5's: 1
Yds: 5981   F9 Yds: 2992   B9 Yds: 2989
Prevailing Wind: West
Designer: Harry Shapland Colt

CHELSFIELD LAKES GOLF CTRE

AMERICAN GOLF CORPORATION, Court
Rd, Orpington, **KENT**, BR6 9BX, **ENGLAND**.
(T) 01689 896266
(W) www.chelsfieldgolf.co.uk

Membership: Members & Public

Contact/s:
● General Manager: Mr Neil Munro
● Professional: Ms Jane Fernley

Course/s:

● CHELSFIELD DOWNS
Description: Parkland, Sheltered,
Medium Length, Drains Well, Ideal for the
Elderly
Number of Holes: 18   Par: 71
Par 3's: 4   Par 4's: 11   Par 5's: 3
Yds: 6110   F9 Yds: 3137   B9 Yds: 2973
Designer: Robert Sandow

● THE WARREN
Description: Parkland, Open, Drains Well
Built On: Chalk
Number of Holes: 9   Par: 27
Par 3's: 9
Yds: 1188
Designer: Robert Sandow
Further Information:
A very interesting course with excellent
greens.

CHERRY BURTON

CHERRY BURTON GOLF CLUB, Leaconfield
Lane, Cherry Burton, Beverley, **YORKSHIRE
(EAST)**, HU17 7RB, **ENGLAND**.
(T) 01964 550924

Membership: Members & Public
Size of Complex: 62 Acres

Contact/s:
● Club Secretary: Mr Andrew Kelly
● Professional: Mr James Calum

Course/s:

● CHERRY BURTON
Description: Parkland, Undulating, Open,
Long, Drains Well
Green Speed: Medium
Built: 1993   Built On: Soil

Number of Holes: 9
Prevailing Wind: North
Designer: W Adamson

CHERRY LODGE

CHERRY LODGE GOLF CLUB, Jail Lane,
Biggin Hill, Westerham, **KENT**, TN16 3AX,
ENGLAND.
(T) 01959 572250
(W) www.cherrylodge.dabsol.co.uk

Membership: Members & Public

Contact/s:
● Club Secretary: Mr A Kemsley
● Professional: Mr Nigel Child
  ☎ 01959 572989

Course/s:

● CHERRY LODGE
Description: Championship, Parkland,
Undulating, Open, Long
Green Speed: Medium
Built: 1969   Built On: Chalk/Clay
Number of Holes: 18   Par: 72
Record: 66 (Fraser Scott)
Yds: 6653
Designer: John Day
Further Information:
Some hard walking and very testing holes
that will challenge all standards of players.

CHERWELL EDGE

CHERWELL EDGE GOLF COURSE,
Chacombe, Banbury, **OXFORDSHIRE**, OX17
2EN, **ENGLAND**.
(T) 01295 711591
(E) cegc@sagehost.co.uk

Membership: Members & Public
Size of Complex: 120 Acres

Contact/s:
● Club Secretary: Mr Bob Bear
● Professional: Mr Joe Kingston

Course/s:

● CHERWELL EDGE
Description: Parkland, Undulating,
Sheltered, Open, Medium Length, Drains
Well, Ideal for the Elderly
Green Speed: Medium
Built: 1980   Built On: Clay
Number of Holes: 18   Record: 64 (Mark
Booth)
Designer: R Davies

CHESFIELD DOWNS

CHESFIELD DOWNS GOLF CLUB, Jacks
Hill, Graveley, Hitchin, **HERTFORDSHIRE**,
SG4 7EQ, **ENGLAND**.
(T) 01462 482332
(W) www.clubhaus.com

Contact/s:
● Professional: Ms Jane Fernley
● Pro Shop: Mr Jason Cretton

Course/s:

● CHESFIELD DOWNS
Description: Championship, Drains Well
Built: 1991   Built On: Chalk
Number of Holes: 18   Par: 71
Designer: J Gaunt

CHESHAM & LEY HILL

CHESHAM & LEY HILL GOLF CLUB, Ley
Hill, Chesham, **BUCKINGHAMSHIRE**, HP5
1UZ, **ENGLAND**.
(T) 01494 784541

Course/s:

● CHESHAM & LEY HILL
Number of Holes: 9

CHESHUNT PARK GOLF COURSE

CHESHUNT PARK GOLF COURSE, Park Lane, Cheshunt, Waltham Cross, **HERTFORDSHIRE**, EN7 6QD, **ENGLAND**.
(T) 01992 624009

Contact/s:
● **Club Secretary:** Mr Robin Wilbourn

Course/s:
⛳ **CHESHUNT PARK**
Number of Holes: 18 **Par:** 72
Yds: 6692 **F9 Yds:** 3400 **B9 Yds:** 3292

CHESSINGTON

CHESSINGTON GOLF CENTRE, Garrison Lane, Chessington, **SURREY**, KT9 2LW, **ENGLAND**.
(T) 020 83910948

Membership: Members & Public
Size of Complex: 27 Acres

Contact/s:
● **Club Secretary:** Mr J Barton
● **Professional:** Mr M Janes

Course/s:
⛳ **CHESSINGTON**
Description: Parkland, Short, Drains Well, Ideal for the Elderly
Green Speed: Medium
Built: 1983 **Built On:** Soil
Number of Holes: 9 **Par:** 30
Par 3's: 6 **Par 4's:** 3
Yds: 1761 **F9 Yds:** 1761
Prevailing Wind: North
Designer: P Tallack
Further Information:
The course is ideal for beginners and the elderly. Wonderful panoramic views over Surrey Downs. The course can be played as 18 holes.

CHESTER

CHESTER GOLF CLUB, Curzon Pk North, Chester, **CHESHIRE**, CH4 8AR, **ENGLAND**.
(T) 01244 675130

Course/s:
⛳ **CHESTER**
Number of Holes: 18

CHESTERFIELD

CHESTERFIELD GOLF CLUB, Matlock Rd, Walton, Chesterfield, **DERBYSHIRE**, S42 7LA, **ENGLAND**.
(T) 01246 279256

Contact/s:
● **Club Secretary:** Mr B G Broughton
● **Professional:** Mr Mike McLean

Course/s:
⛳ **CHESTERFIELD**
Description: Parkland, Undulating, Sheltered, Medium Length
Green Speed: Medium
Built: 1903 **Built On:** Clay
Number of Holes: 18 **Par:** 71
Par 3's: 4 **Par 4's:** 11 **Par 5's:** 3
Yds: 6261
Prevailing Wind: South/West
Further Information:
Mature trees throughout course.

CHESTER-LE-STREET

CHESTER-LE-STREET GOLF CLUB, Lumley Links, Chester Le Street, **COUNTY DURHAM**, DH3 4NS, **ENGLAND**.
(T) 0191 3883218

Contact/s:
● **Club Secretary:** Mr B Forster
● **Professional:** Mr David Fletcher
☎ 0191 3890157

Course/s:
⛳ **CHESTER-LE-STREET**
Description: Wooded, Parkland, Open, Tends to Flood, Ideal for the Elderly
Built: 1908
Number of Holes: 18 **Record:** 65
Designer: Taylor

CHESTERTON VALLEY

CHESTERTON VALLEY GOLF CLUB, Worfield Rd, Chesterton, Bridgnorth, **SHROPSHIRE**, WV15 5NX, **ENGLAND**.
(T) 01746 783682

Contact/s:
● **Owner:** Mr P Hinton

Course/s:
⛳ **CHESTERTON VALLEY**
Number of Holes: 18 **Par:** 69
Yds: 5671 **F9 Yds:** 2960 **B9 Yds:** 2711

CHESTFIELD

CHESTFIELD GOLF CLUB, 103 Chestfield Rd, Chestfield, Whitstable, **KENT**, CT5 3LU, **ENGLAND**.
(T) 01227 792243
(W) www.chestfield-golfclub.co.uk

Membership: Members & Public

Contact/s:
● **Club Secretary:** Mr Charles Maxted
☎ 01227 794411
● **Professional:** Mr John Brotherton
☎ 01227 793563
● **Book Tee Times:** Ms Valerie Jennings

Course/s:
⛳ **CHESTFIELD**
Description: Parkland, Undulating, Open, Medium Length, Ideal for the Elderly
Green Speed: Medium/Fast
Built: 1925 **Built On:** Clay
Number of Holes: 18 **Par:** 70
Par 3's: 4 **Par 4's:** 12 **Par 5's:** 2
Yds: 6208 **F9 Yds:** 3195 **B9 Yds:** 3013
Prevailing Wind: North/West
Designer: A Mitchell
Further Information:
A 4 lane highway runs underneath the course.

CHEVIN

CHEVIN GOLF CLUB, Golf Lane, Duffield, Belper, **DERBYSHIRE**, DE56 4EE, **ENGLAND**.
(T) 01332 841864

Membership: Members & Public
Size of Complex: 104 Acres

Contact/s:
● **Club Secretary:** Mr J A Milner
● **Professional:** Mr Willie Bird
☎ 01332 841112

Course/s:
⛳ **CHEVIN**
Description: Parkland, Moorland, Hilltop, Open, Medium Length, Tight, Drains Well
Green Speed: Medium/Fast
Built: 1894 **Built On:** Clay/Sand
Number of Holes: 18 **Par:** 69
Record: 64 (Andrew Hare)
Par 3's: 5 **Par 4's:** 11 **Par 5's:** 2
Yds: 6057
Designer: James Braid
Further Information:
The 8th hole (Tribulation) has a testing tee shot.

CHEWTON GLEN

CHEWTON GLEN HOTEL & GOLF COURSE, Christchurch Rd, New Milton, **HAMPSHIRE**, BH25 6QS, **ENGLAND**.
(T) 01425 275341

Course/s:
⛳ **CHEWTON GLEN HOTEL**
Number of Holes: 9

CHICHESTER

CHICHESTER GOLF CLUB, Hunston, Chichester, **SUSSEX (WEST)**, PO20 6AX, **ENGLAND**.
(T) 01243 536666
(E) enquiries@chichestergolf.com
(W) www.chichestergolf.com

Membership: Members & Public
Size of Complex: 287 Acres

Contact/s:
● **Professional:** Mr John Slinger
● **Pro Shop:** Mr Carl Smith

Course/s:
⛳ **CATHEDRAL**
Number of Holes: 18
Designer: P Saunders

⛳ **CHICHESTER**
Description: Wooded, Parkland, Undulating, Open, Medium Length, Tight, Drains Well, Ideal for the Elderly
Green Speed: Medium
Built: 1990 **Built On:** Soil
Number of Holes: 18 **Par:** 72
Yds: 6442 **F9 Yds:** 3502 **B9 Yds:** 2940
Prevailing Wind: South/West
Designer: P Saunders
Further Information:
Nice mixture of tricky holes.

CHIDDINGFOLD

CHIDDINGFOLD GOLF CLUB, Petworth Rd, Chiddingfold, Godalming, **SURREY**, GU8 4SL, **ENGLAND**.
(T) 01428 685888
(W) www.chiddingfoldgc.co.uk

Membership: Members & Public

Contact/s:
● **Club Secretary:** Mrs C Mentz
● **Professional:** Mr Gary Wallis

Course/s:
⛳ **CHIDDINGFOLD**
Description: Wooded, Parkland, Undulating, Medium Length, Tight, Tends to Flood
Green Speed: Medium
Built: 1994 **Built On:** Clay
Number of Holes: 18 **Par:** 70
Par 3's: 4 **Par 4's:** 12 **Par 5's:** 2
Yds: 5568 **F9 Yds:** 2692 **B9 Yds:** 2876
Designer: Jonathan Gaunt

CHIGWELL

CHIGWELL GOLF CLUB, The High Rd, Chigwell, **ESSEX**, IG7 5BH, **ENGLAND**.
(T) 020 85002059

Membership: Members & Public
Size of Complex: 99 Acres

Contact/s:
● **Club Secretary:** Mr Richard Danzey
● **Professional:** Mr Ray Board

Course/s:
⛳ **CHIGWELL**
Description: Parkland, Undulating, Open, Medium Length, Drains Well, Ideal for the Elderly

Built: 1925
Number of Holes: 18 **Par:** 71
Par 3's: 4 **Par 4's:** 11 **Par 5's:** 3
Yds: 6279 **F9 Yds:** 3149 **B9 Yds:** 3130
Designer: Hawtree, Taylor

CHILDWALL

CHILDWALL GOLF CLUB, Naylors Rd,
Gateacre, Liverpool, **MERSEYSIDE,** L27
2YB, **ENGLAND.**
(T) 0151 4879982

Membership: Members & Public

Contact/s:
● **Club Secretary:** Mr J Tully
● **Professional:** Mr Nigel Parr
  ☎ 0151 4879971

Course/s:
● **CHIDWALL**
  Description: Parkland, Open, Medium
  Length, Tends to Flood, Ideal for the
  Elderly
  Green Speed: Medium
  Built: 1939 **Built On:** Soil
  Number of Holes: 18 **Par:** 72
  Par 3's: 4 **Par 4's:** 10 **Par 5's:** 4
  Yds: 6470 **F9 Yds:** 3212 **B9 Yds:** 3258
  Prevailing Wind: East
  Designer: James Braid

CHILTERN FOREST

CHILTERN FOREST GOLF CLUB, Aston
Hill, Halton, Aylesbury,
BUCKINGHAMSHIRE, HP22 5NQ,
ENGLAND.
(T) 01296 631817
(W) www.chilternforest.co.uk

Contact/s:
● **Club Secretary:** Ms Susan Short
● **Pro Shop:** Mr Andy Lavers

Course/s:
● **CHILTERN FOREST**
  Description: Wooded, Valley, Undulating,
  Medium Length
  Number of Holes: 18 **Par:** 70
  Par 3's: 4 **Par 4's:** 12 **Par 5's:** 2
  Yds: 5760

CHILWELL MANOR

CHILWELL MANOR GOLF CLUB, Meadow
Lane, Chilwell, Nottingham,
NOTTINGHAMSHIRE, NG9 5AE, **ENGLAND.**
(T) 0115 9258958
(E) chilwellmanorgolfclub@barbox.net

Membership: Members & Public
Size of Complex: 120 Acres

Contact/s:
● **Club Secretary:** Mr R Wescott
● **Professional:** Mr Paul Wilson
● **Pro Shop:**
  ☎ 0115 9258993

Course/s:
● **CHILWELL MANOR**
  Description: Wooded, Parkland,
  Sheltered, Medium Length, Tight, Tends to
  Flood
  Green Speed: Medium
  Built: 1906 **Built On:** Soil
  Number of Holes: 18 **Par:** 70
  Par 3's: 4 **Par 4's:** 12 **Par 5's:** 2
  Yds: 6255 **F9 Yds:** 3247 **B9 Yds:** 3008
  Designer: Tom Williamson
  Further Information:
  A flat course with 2 ponds and dykes
  throughout the course.

CHILWORTH

CHILWORTH GOLF CLUB, Main Rd,
Chilworth, Southampton, **HAMPSHIRE,**
SO16 7JP, **ENGLAND.**
(T) 023 80740544

Course/s:
● **MANOR**
  Number of Holes: 18
  Designer: J Garner

CHINA FLEET

CHINA FLEET GOLF & COUNTRY CLUB,
Pill, Saltash, **CORNWALL,** PL12 6LJ,
ENGLAND.
(T) 01752 848668

Course/s:
● **CHINA FLEET COUNTRY CLUB**
  Number of Holes: 18
  Designer: Hawtree

CHINGFORD

CHINGFORD GOLF CLUB, 158 Station Rd,
Chingford, London, **LONDON (GREATER),**
E4 6AN, **ENGLAND.**
(T) 020 8529 2107

Membership: Public
Size of Complex: 120 Acres

Contact/s:
● **Club Secretary:** Mr Bryan Sinden
● **Professional:** Mr Andrew Taynor

Course/s:
● **CHINGFORD**
  Description: Wooded, Short, Tight
  Green Speed: Medium
  Built: 1899
  Number of Holes: 18
  Yds: 6342
  Prevailing Wind: East
  Further Information:
  The course is set in Epping Forest.

CHIPPENHAM

CHIPPENHAM GOLF CLUB, Malmesbury
Rd, Langley Burrell, Chippenham,
WILTSHIRE, SN15 5LT, **ENGLAND.**
(T) 01249 655519

Course/s:
● **CHIPPENHAM**
  Number of Holes: 18

CHIPPING NORTON

CHIPPING NORTON GOLF CLUB,
Southcombe, Chipping Norton,
OXFORDSHIRE, OX7 5QH, **ENGLAND.**
(T) 01608 642383

Contact/s:
● **Club Secretary:** Mr Simon Chislett

Course/s:
● **CHIPPING NORTON**
  Number of Holes: 18 **Par:** 71
  Yds: 6241 **F9 Yds:** 3148 **B9 Yds:** 3093

CHIPPING SODBURY

CHIPPING SODBURY GOLF CLUB, Horton
Rd, Chipping Sodbury, Bristol, **BRISTOL,**
BS37 6PU, **ENGLAND.**
(T) 01454 315822

Contact/s:
● **Club Secretary:** Mr D Bird

Course/s:
● **NEW**
  Number of Holes: 18

Designer: Hawtree
● **OLD**
  Number of Holes: 9
  Designer: Hawtree

CHIPSTEAD

CHIPSTEAD GOLF CLUB, How Lane,
Coulsdon, **SURREY,** CR5 3LN, **ENGLAND.**
(T) 01737 555019
(E) office@chipsteadgolf.freeserve.co.uk
(W) www.chipsteadgolf.co.uk

Contact/s:
● **Professional:** Mr Gary Torbett
  ☎ 01737 555781

Course/s:
● **CHIPSTEAD**
  Description: Wooded
  Built: 1905
  Number of Holes: 18 **Par:** 68
  Yds: 5504 **F9 Yds:** 2882 **B9 Yds:** 2622
  Further Information:
  A testing course.

CHIRK

CHIRK GOLF CLUB, Chirk, Wrexham,
WREXHAM, LL14 5AD, **WALES.**
(T) 01691 774407

Contact/s:
● **Professional:** Mr Mark Maddison

Course/s:
● **CHIRK**
  Description: Championship
  Built: 1990
  Number of Holes: 18 **Par:** 72
  Par 3's: 4 **Par 4's:** 10 **Par 5's:** 4
  Yds: 7045 **F9 Yds:** 3530 **B9 Yds:** 3515
  Further Information:
  The course is overlooked by Chirk Castle
  and Chirk Marina.

● **CHIRK 9 HOLE**
  Number of Holes: 9 **Par:** 27
  Par 3's: 9
  Yds: 1141

CHISLEHURST

CHISLEHURST GOLF CLUB, Camden Pl,
Camden Pk Rd, Chislehurst, **KENT,** BR7 5HJ,
ENGLAND.
(T) 020 84673055

Course/s:
● **CHISLEHURST**
  Number of Holes: 18
  Designer: William Park

CHOBHAM

CHOBHAM GOLF CLUB, Chobham Rd,
Knaphill, Woking, **SURREY,** GU21 2TZ,
ENGLAND.
(T) 01276 855584
(W) www.chobhamgolfclub.co.uk

Contact/s:
● **Professional:** Mr Tim Coombes
  ☎ 01276 855748

Course/s:
● **CHOBHAM**
  Description: Championship, Wooded,
  Parkland
  Built: 1993
  Number of Holes: 18 **Par:** 69
  Yds: 5959 **F9 Yds:** 2989 **B9 Yds:** 2970
  Designer: Peter Alliss, Clive Clark
  Further Information:
  USGA specification greens and tees.

CHORLEY

CHORLEY GOLF CLUB, Hall O'the Hill, Chorley Rd, Heath Charnock, Chorley, **LANCASHIRE**, PR6 9HX, **ENGLAND**.
(T) 01257 480263

Contact/s:
● Club Secretary: Mrs A Allen

Course/s:
🏌 **CHORLEY**
Number of Holes: 18
Designer: J A Steer

CHORLEYWOOD

CHORLEYWOOD GOLF CLUB, Common Rd, Chorleywood, Rickmansworth, **HERTFORDSHIRE**, WD3 5LN, **ENGLAND**.
(T) 01923 282009

Contact/s:
● Club Secretary: Mr B Cable

Course/s:
🏌 **CHORLEYWOOD**
Description: Wooded, Heath Land, Sheltered, Short, Drains Well
Green Speed: Medium
Built: 1890 Built On: Soil
Number of Holes: 9 Par: 34
Par 3's: 3 Par 4's: 5 Par 5's: 1
Yds: 2856
Designer: James Braid
Further Information:
A testing flat course with small greens and natural hazards.

CHORLTON-CUM-HARDY

CHORLTON-CUM-HARDY GOLF CLUB, Barlow Hall, Barlow Hall Rd, Manchester, **MANCHESTER (GREATER)**, M21 7JJ, **ENGLAND**.
(T) 0161 8815830

Membership: Members & Public
Size of Complex: 90 Acres

Contact/s:
● Club Secretary: Ms Kay Poole
● Professional: Mr David Valentine
  ☎ 0161 8819911

Course/s:
🏌 **CHORLTON-CUM-HARDY**
Description: Wooded, Parkland, Sheltered, Medium Length, Tight, Drains Well, Ideal for the Elderly
Green Speed: Medium
Built: 1901 Built On: Soil
Number of Holes: 18
Prevailing Wind: South/West
Further Information:
Tight course.

CHRISTY O'CONNOR

CHRISTY O'CONNOR GOLF CLUB, Holytown, Dublin, **COUNTY DUBLIN**, **IRELAND**.
(T) 01 8226302

Contact/s:
● Club Secretary: Dennis Darcey
● Professional: Christy O'Connor

Course/s:
🏌 **CHRISTY O'CONNOR**
Number of Holes: 18 Par: 70
Yds: 6700

CHULMLEIGH

CHULMLEIGH GOLF COURSE, Leigh Rd, Chulmleigh, **DEVON**, EX18 7BL, **ENGLAND**.
(T) 01769 580519

(E) howard@chulmleighgolf.co.uk
(W) www.chulmleighgolf.co.uk

Membership: Members & Public

Contact/s:
● Club Secretary: Mr Howard Meadows

Course/s:
🏌 **SUMMER**
Number of Holes: 18 Par: 54
Yds: 1450 F9 Yds: 722 B9 Yds: 728
Designer: John Goodban

🏌 **WINTER SHORT**
Built: 1975
Number of Holes: 9 Par: 27
Yds: 1155 F9 Yds: 1155
Designer: John Goodban
Further Information:
A challenging course.

CHURCH STRETTON

CHURCH STRETTON GOLF CLUB, Trevor Hill, Church Stretton, **SHROPSHIRE**, SY6 6JH, **ENGLAND**.
(T) 01694 722281

Contact/s:
● Professional: Mr James Townsend
  ☎ 01694 720001

Course/s:
🏌 **CHURCH STRETTON**
Description: Hilltop
Built: 1898
Number of Holes: 18 Par: 66
Yds: 5020 F9 Yds: 2309 B9 Yds: 2711
Designer: James Braid
Further Information:
Tricky approaches to greens.

CHURCHILL & BLAKEDOWN

CHURCHILL & BLAKEDOWN GOLF CLUB, Churchill Lane, Blakedown, Kidderminster, **WORCESTERSHIRE**, DY10 3NB, **ENGLAND**.
(T) 01562 700018

Membership: Members & Public

Contact/s:
● Pro Shop: Mr Graham Wright
  ☎ 01562 700454

Course/s:
🏌 **CHURCHILL AND BLAKEDOWN**
Description: Undulating, Sheltered, Drains Well, Ideal for the Elderly
Green Speed: Fast Built On: Sand
Number of Holes: 9 F9 Yds: 3253
Prevailing Wind: East

CHURSTON

CHURSTON GOLF CLUB, Dartmouth Rd, Churston Ferrers, Brixham, **DEVON**, TQ5 0LA, **ENGLAND**.
(T) 01803 842751
(E) manager@churstongc.fsnet.co.uk
(W) www.churstongolfclublimited.co.uk
Size of Complex: 70 Acres

Contact/s:
● Professional: Mr Neil Holman
  ☎ 01803 843442

Course/s:
🏌 **CHURSTON**
Description: Hilltop, Cliff Top, Medium Length, Tight, Drains Well
Green Speed: Medium
Built: 1890 Built On: Chalk
Number of Holes: 18 Par: 70
Record: 65 (J Langmead)
Yds: 6208 F9 Yds: 3159 B9 Yds: 3049
Prevailing Wind: South/West

Designer: Harry Shapland Colt
Further Information:
The course is always in good condition and it offers spectacular views across the bay.

CILGWYN

CILGWYN GOLF CLUB LTD, Llangybi, Lampeter, **CARMARTHENSHIRE**, SA48 8NN, **WALES**.
(T) 01570 493286

Membership: Members & Public
Size of Complex: 49 Acres

Contact/s:
● Club Secretary: Mr John Morgan
● Pro Shop: Mr Brian Hankey

Course/s:
🏌 **CILGWYN**
Description: Parkland, Valley, Sheltered, Medium Length, Tends to Flood, Ideal for the Elderly
Green Speed: Slow
Built: 1974 Built On: Soil
Number of Holes: 9
Prevailing Wind: South/West

CILL-DARA

CILL-DARA GOLF CLUB, Little Curragh, Llandeilo, **COUNTY KILDARE**, **IRELAND**.
(T) 045 521433

Course/s:
🏌 **CILL DARA**
Number of Holes: 9

CINQUE PORTS (ROYAL)

ROYAL CINQUE PORTS, Golf Rd, Deal, **KENT**, CT14 6RF, **ENGLAND**.
(T) 01304 374328
(W) www.royalcinqueports.com

Membership: Members & Public

Contact/s:
● Club Secretary: Mr C Hammond
  ☎ 01304 374007
● Professional: Mr Andrew Reynolds
  ☎ 01304 374170

Course/s:
🏌 **ROYAL CINQUE PORTS**
Description: Undulating
Green Speed: Fast
Number of Holes: 18 Par: 72
Yds: 6754
Prevailing Wind: South/West
Designer: James Braid 🏆

CIRENCESTER

CIRENCESTER GOLF CLUB, Cheltenham Rd, Bagendon, Cirencester, **GLOUCESTERSHIRE**, GL7 7BH, **ENGLAND**.
(T) 01285 653939
(E) cirencestergolf@compuserve.com
(W) www.cirencestergolfclub.co.uk

Contact/s:
● Professional: Mr Peter Garratt
  ☎ 01285 656124

Course/s:
🏌 **CIRENCESTER**
Description: Drains Well
Built: 1910
Number of Holes: 18 Par: 70
Yds: 6055 F9 Yds: 2885 B9 Yds: 3170
Designer: James Braid
Further Information:
A suitable course for golfers of all standards.

CITYWEST

CITYWEST GOLF CLUB, Saggart, **COUNTY KILDARE, IRELAND**.
(T) 01 4588566

Course/s:
● **CITYWEST**
  Number of Holes: 18 Par: 70
  Yds: 6314

CLACTON

CLACTON GOLF CLUB, West Rd, Clacton-on-Sea, **ESSEX**, CO15 1AJ, **ENGLAND**.
(T) 01255 421919
(E) clactongolfclub@btclick.com
(W) www.clactongolfclub.com

Membership: Members & Public
Size of Complex: 110 Acres

Contact/s:
● **Club Secretary:** Mr Jim Wiggam
● **Professional:** Mr Stuart Levermore
  ☎ 01255 426304

Course/s:
● **CLACTON**
  Description: Wooded, Open, Tends to Flood
  Built: 1892
  Number of Holes: 18 Par: 71
  Par 3's: 5 Par 4's: 9 Par 5's: 4
  Yds: 6532 F9 Yds: 3395 B9 Yds: 3137

CLANDEBOYE

CLANDEBOYE GOLF CLUB, Tower Rd, Conlig, Newtownards, **COUNTY DOWN**, BT23 7PN, **NORTHERN IRELAND**.
(T) 028 9127 1767
(E) contact@cgc-ni.com
(W) www.cgc-ni.com

Contact/s:
● **Administration:** Mrs R Eddis

Course/s:
● **AVA**
  Number of Holes: 18 Par: 70
  Yds: 5465 F9 Yds: 2840 B9 Yds: 2625
  Designer: W Robinson
● **DUFFERIN**
  Number of Holes: 18 Par: 71
  Yds: 6335 F9 Yds: 3173 B9 Yds: 3162
  Designer: W Robinson

CLANDON REGIS

CLANDON REGIS GOLF CLUB, Epsom Rd, West Clandon, Guildford, **SURREY**, GU4 7TT, **ENGLAND**.
(T) 01483 224888

Contact/s:
● **Manager:** Mrs Wendy Savage

Course/s:
● **CLANDON REGIS**
  Number of Holes: 18

CLARE COUNTRY

CLARE COUNTRY GOLF COURSE, 260C Drumnakilly Rd, Sixmilecross, Omagh, **COUNTY TYRONE**, BT79 9PU, **NORTHERN IRELAND**.
(T) 028 08761667

Course/s:
● **CLARE COUNTRY**
  Number of Holes: 18 Par: 54

CLARE PARK LAKE

CLARE PARK LAKE & GOLF COURSE,
Stoke Rd, Clare, Sudbury, **SUFFOLK**, CO10 8HG, **ENGLAND**.
(T) 01787 278693

Membership: Members & Public

Contact/s:
● **Owner:** Mrs S M Moore

Course/s:
● **CLARE PARK LANE AND**
  Description: Parkland, Valley, Undulating, Sheltered, Open, Short, Tight, Drains Well, Tends to Flood, Ideal for the Elderly
  Green Speed: Slow
  Built: 1954 Built On: Sand/Soil
  Number of Holes: 9 Par: 31
  Yds: 1268 F9 Yds: 1268 B9 Yds: 1268
  Prevailing Wind: South/West
  Further Information:
  Clare is a tricky little par three course particularly suited to beginners, those who don't have alot of time, ladies, those who play infrequently, seniors and couples. While the course is on a flood plane it tends to floods regularly but when the water subsides, the course drains quickly.

CLAREMORRIS

CLAREMORRIS GOLF CLUB, Castlemagarrett, Claremorris, **COUNTY MAYO, IRELAND**.
(T) 094 71527
(E) claremorrisgc@ebookireland.com
(W) www.ebookireland.com

Contact/s:
● **Administrator:** Ms Chris Rush
  ☎ 087 6441204/094 71527

Course/s:
● **CLAREMORRIS**
  Number of Holes: 18
  Designer: T Craddock

CLAYS GOLF CTRE

CLAYS GOLF CENTRE LTD, Bryn Estyn Rd, Wrexham, **WREXHAM**, LL13 9UB, **WALES**.
(T) 01978 661406

Membership: Members & Public
Size of Complex: 130 Acres

Contact/s:
● **Club Secretary:** Mr Fred Court
● **Professional:** Mr David Larkin

Course/s:
● **CLAYS**
  Description: Parkland, Open, Medium Length, Drains Well, Ideal for the Elderly
  Green Speed: Fast
  Built: 1993 Built On: Clay
  Number of Holes: 18
  Designer: Roger Jones

CLAYTON

CLAYTON GOLF CLUB, Thornton View Farm, Thornton View Rd, Clayton, Bradford, **YORKSHIRE (WEST)**, BD14 6JX, **ENGLAND**.
(T) 01274 880047

Course/s:
● **CLAYTON**
  Number of Holes: 9 Par: 70
  Yds: 5504 F9 Yds: 2752 B9 Yds: 2752

CLECKHEATON & DISTRICT

CLECKHEATON & DISTRICT GOLF CLUB, 483 Bradford Rd, Chain Bar, Cleckheaton, **YORKSHIRE (WEST)**, BD19 6BU, **ENGLAND**.
(T) 01274 851266
(E) info@cleckheatongolf.fsnet.co.uk
(W) www.cleckheatongolfclub.fsnet.co.uk

Contact/s:
● **Assistant Secretary:** Mrs Rona Newsholme

Course/s:
● **CLECKHEATON & DISTRICT**
  Number of Holes: 18 Par: 71
  Yds: 5769 F9 Yds: 3006 B9 Yds: 2763

CLEETHORPES

CLEETHORPES GOLF CLUB LTD, Kings Rd, Cleethorpes, **LINCOLNSHIRE (NORTH EAST)**, DN35 0PN, **ENGLAND**.
(T) 01472 812059

Contact/s:
● **Club Secretary:** Mr Harry Long

Course/s:
● **CLEETHORPES**
  Number of Holes: 18

CLEEVE HILL

CLEEVE HILL GOLF CLUB, Cleeve Hill, Cheltenham, **GLOUCESTERSHIRE**, GL52 3PW, **ENGLAND**.
(T) 01242 672025

Course/s:
● **CLEEVE HILL**
  Number of Holes: 18

CLEOBURY MORTIMER

CLEOBURY MORTIMER GOLF CLUB, The Clubhouse, Wyre Common, Cleobury Mortimer, **SHROPSHIRE**, DY14 8HQ, **ENGLAND**.
(T) 01299 271112
(W) www.cleoburygolfclub.com

Membership: Members & Public
Size of Complex: 200 Acres

Contact/s:
● **Club Secretary:** Mr Nigel Smith
● **Professional:** Mr Martin Payne
● **Book Tee Times:** Mrs Ingrid Barton

Course/s:
● **BADGERS SET**
  Number of Holes: 9 Par: 36
  Par 3's: 2 Par 4's: 5 Par 5's: 2
  Yds: 3271
● **DEER PARK**
  Description: Wooded, Parkland, Hilltop, Medium Length, Ideal for the Elderly
  Green Speed: Medium Built On: Soil
  Number of Holes: 9 Par: 35 Record: 71 (Neil Turley)
  Par 3's: 2 Par 4's: 6 Par 5's: 1
  Yds: 3167
  Prevailing Wind: West
  Designer: Ray Baldwin
● **FOXES RUN**
  Description: Wooded, Parkland, Hilltop, Medium Length, Ideal for the Elderly
  Green Speed: Medium Built On: Soil
  Number of Holes: 9 Par: 34 Record: 64 (Neil Turley)
  Par 3's: 3 Par 4's: 5 Par 5's: 1
  Yds: 2980
  Prevailing Wind: West
  Designer: Ray Baldwin

CLEVEDON

CLEVEDON GOLF CLUB, Castle Rd, Clevedon, **SOMERSET (NORTH)**, BS21 7AA, **ENGLAND**.
(T) 01275 874057

Contact/s:
- Manager: Mr J Cunning

Course/s:

⛳ **CLEVEDON**
Number of Holes: 18   Par: 72
Yds: 6557   F9 Yds: 3343   B9 Yds: 3005
Designer: S Herd

CLEVELAND

CLEVELAND GOLF CLUB, Queen St, Redcar, **CLEVELAND,** TS10 1BT, **ENGLAND.**
(T) 01642 471798
(W) www.clevelandgolfclub.co.uk

Membership: Members & Public

Contact/s:
- Club Secretary: Mr Peter Fletcher
- Professional: Mr Craig Donaldson
  ☎ 01642 483462

Course/s:

⛳ **CLEVELAND**
Description: Links, Open
Built: 1887   Built On: Sand
Number of Holes: 18   Par: 72
Yds: 6746   F9 Yds: 3490   B9 Yds: 3256

CLEWBAY

CLEWBAY GOLF CLUB, Claggan, Kilmenna, Westport, **COUNTY MAYO, IRELAND.**
(T) 098 41730
(W) www.clewbayhotel.com

Course/s:

⛳ **CLEWBAY**
Number of Holes: 9   Par: 35
Yds: 2725

CLIFF HOTEL

CLIFF HOTEL GOLF COURSE, Gwbert-on-Sea, Cardigan, **CEREDIGION,** SA43 1PP, **WALES.**
(T) 01239 613241

Course/s:

⛳ **CARDIGAN**
Description: Championship, Links, Cliff Top, Open, Medium Length, Drains Well
Green Speed: Fast
Built: 1895   Built On: Sand
Number of Holes: 18   Par: 72
Yds: 6426   F9 Yds: 3182   B9 Yds: 3244
Prevailing Wind: South/West
Designer: Hawtree
Further Information:
A challenging and picturesque course.

CLIFTONVILLE

CLIFTONVILLE GOLF CLUB LTD, 44 Westland Rd, Belfast, **COUNTY ANTRIM,** BT14 6NH, **NORTHERN IRELAND.**
(T) 028 90744158

Membership: Members & Public
Size of Complex: 70 Acres

Contact/s:
- Professional: Mr Robert Hutton

Course/s:

⛳ **CLIFTONVILLE**
Description: Parkland, Hilltop, Open, Long, Tight, Drains Well, Ideal for the Elderly
Green Speed: Medium
Built: 1910   Built On: Clay/Soil
Number of Holes: 9   Par: 35
Par 3's: 2   Par 4's: 6   Par 5's: 1
Yds: 3116   F9 Yds: 3116
Prevailing Wind: West
Further Information:
The course offers views over Belfast City.

CLITHEROE

CLITHEROE GOLF CLUB LTD, Whalley Rd, Pendleton, Clitheroe, **LANCASHIRE,** BB7 1PP, **ENGLAND.**
(T) 01200 422292
(W) www.clitheroegolfclub.com

Membership: Members & Public
Size of Complex: 120 Acres

Contact/s:
- Club Secretary: Mr T Ashton
- Professional: Mr J Twissell
  ☎ 01200 424242

Course/s:

⛳ **CLITHEROE**
Description: Championship, Parkland, Valley, Medium Length, Ideal for the Elderly
Green Speed: Medium
Built: 1932   Built On: Clay
Number of Holes: 18   Par: 71
Par 3's: 4   Par 4's: 11   Par 5's: 3
Yds: 6323   F9 Yds: 3035   B9 Yds: 3288
Prevailing Wind: West
Designer: James Braid
Further Information:
A superb inland course.

CLOBER

CLOBER GOLF CLUB, Clubhouse, Milngavie, Glasgow, **GLASGOW (CITY OF),** G62 7HP, **SCOTLAND.**
(T) 0141 9561685

Contact/s:
- Club Secretary: Mr T Arthur
- Pro Shop:
  ☎ 0141 9566963

Course/s:

⛳ **CLOBER**
Number of Holes: 18

CLONES

CLONES GOLF CLUB, Hilton Pk, Clones, Clones, **COUNTY MONAGHAN, IRELAND.**
(T) 353 04756017
(W) www.clonesgolf.com

Membership: Members & Public
Size of Complex: 140 Acres

Contact/s:
- Club Secretary: Mr Martin Taylor

Course/s:

⛳ **CLONES**
Description: Parkland, Medium Length, Drains Well
Built: 1913
Number of Holes: 9   Par: 34
Par 3's: 3   Par 4's: 5   Par 5's: 1
Yds: 2824
Further Information:
9 hole course can be played as an 18 hole course

CLONLARA GOLF & LEISURE

CLONLARA GOLF & LEISURE, Clonlara, **COUNTY CLARE, IRELAND.**
(T) 061 354141

Course/s:

⛳ **CLONLARA GOLF & LEISURE**
Number of Holes: 12
Designer: Noel Cassidy

CLONMEL

CLONMEL GOLF CLUB, Mountain Rd, Clonmel, **COUNTY TIPPERARY, IRELAND.**
(T) 052 24050

(E) cgc@indigo.ie

Contact/s:
- Club Secretary: Ms Aine Myles-Keating

Course/s:

⛳ **CLONMEL**
Number of Holes: 18   Par: 72
Yds: 6347   F9 Yds: 3101   B9 Yds: 3246
Designer: Edward Hackett

CLONTARF

CLONTARF GOLF CLUB AND BOWLING CLUB, Donnycarney Hse, Malahide Rd, Dublin, **COUNTY DUBLIN, IRELAND.**
(T) 01 8331892
(W) www.clontarf-online.com

Membership: Members & Public

Contact/s:
- Club Secretary: Mr Arthur Cahill
- Professional: Mr Mark Callan

Course/s:

⛳ **CLONTARF**
Description: Parkland, Valley, Sheltered, Medium Length, Tight, Drains Well
Green Speed: Medium
Built: 1912   Built On: Clay
Number of Holes: 18
Designer: Harry Shapland Colt

CLOUGHANEELY

CLOUGHANEELY GOLF CLUB, Ballyconnell, Falcarragh, **COUNTY DONEGAL, IRELAND.**
(T) 074 65416

Membership: Members & Public

Contact/s:
- Club Secretary: Mr Simon McGinley
  ☎ 074 65336

Course/s:

⛳ **CLOUGHANEELY**
Description: Wooded, Parkland, Sheltered, Short
Green Speed: Slow
Built: 1994
Number of Holes: 9

CLOVERHILL

CLOVERHILL GOLF COURSE, Lough Rd, Mullaghbawn, Newry, **COUNTY DOWN,** BT35 9XP, **NORTHERN IRELAND.**
(T) 028 30889374
(E) info@cloverhillgc.com
(W) www.cloverhillgc.com

Membership: Members & Public

Contact/s:
- Club Secretary: Mr Joe Pilkington
  ☎ 028 30861825
- Book Tee Times: Mr Pat Smyth

Course/s:

⛳ **CLOVERHILL**
Description: Parkland, Open, Medium Length, Drains Well, Ideal for the Elderly
Green Speed: Medium
Built: 1999   Built On: Clay
Number of Holes: 9   Par: 36
Par 3's: 2   Par 4's: 6   Par 5's: 1
Yds: 2771
Prevailing Wind: North

CLYDEBANK & DISTRICT

CLYDEBANK & DISTRICT GOLF CLUB, Clydebank, **ARGYLL AND BUTE,** G81 5QY, **SCOTLAND.**
(T) 01389 383831

Contact/s:
- Chairman: Mr P Greenleas

Course/s:

CLYDEBANK & DISTRICT
Number of Holes: 18

CLYNE

CLYNE GOLF CLUB, 118 - 120 Owls Lodge Lane, Mayals, Swansea, **SWANSEA**, SA3 5DP, **WALES**.
(T) 01792 401989
(E) clynegolfclub@supanet.com

Membership: Members & Public

Contact/s:
* **Professional:** Mr J Clewett
* **Pro Shop:**
  ☎ 01792 402094

Course/s:

CLYNE
Description: Moorland, Hilltop, Undulating, Open, Medium Length
Green Speed: Fast
Built: 1920 Built On: Soil
Number of Holes: 18 Par: 70
Yds: 6334 F9 Yds: 3161 B9 Yds: 3173
Designer: Harry Shapland Colt, Harris
Further Information:
A challenging course.

COATBRIDGE

COATBRIDGE GOLF COURSE & DRIVING RANGE, Townhead Rd, Coatbridge, **LANARKSHIRE (NORTH)**, ML5 2HX, **SCOTLAND**.
(T) 01236 421492

Course/s:

COATBRIDGE
Number of Holes: 18 Par: 70
Yds: 6020

COBH

COBH GOLF CLUB, Ballywilliam, Cobh, **COUNTY CORK**, **IRELAND**.
(T) 021 4812399

Membership: Members & Public

Contact/s:
* **Club Secretary:** Mr Barry Lynch
* **Book Tee Times:** Mr Henry Cunningham

Course/s:

COBH
Description: Parkland, Undulating, Medium Length, Tight, Drains Well
Green Speed: Fast
Built: 1987
Number of Holes: 9
Designer: Edward Hackett

COBTREE MANOR PARK

COBTREE MANOR PARK GOLF COURSE, Chatham Rd, Sandling, Maidstone, **KENT**, ME14 3AZ, **ENGLAND**.
(T) 01622 753276
(W) www.medwaygolf.co.uk

Membership: Public

Contact/s:
* **Club Secretary:** Mr Steve Mattingly
* **Professional:** Mr Paul Foston

Course/s:

COBTREE MANOR PARK
Description: Parkland, Undulating, Sheltered, Short, Tight, Tends to Flood, Ideal for the Elderly
Green Speed: Medium
Built: 1984 Built On: Clay
Number of Holes: 18
Prevailing Wind: South

COCHRANE CASTLE

COCHRANE CASTLE GOLF CLUB, Scott Ave, Craigston, Johnstone, **RENFREWSHIRE**, PA5 0HF, **SCOTLAND**.
(T) 01505 320146

Contact/s:
* **Club Secretary:** Mrs Patricia Quin
* **Professional:** Mr Alan J Logan
* **Book Tee Times:**
  ☎ 01505 328465

Course/s:

COCHRANE CASTLE
Description: Wooded, Parkland, Undulating
Built: 1895
Number of Holes: 18 Par: 71
Yds: 6194 F9 Yds: 3117 B9 Yds: 3077
Designer: J Hunter

COCKERMOUTH

COCKERMOUTH GOLF CLUB, Embleton, Cockermouth, **CUMBRIA**, CA13 9SG, **ENGLAND**.
(T) 01768 776223

Membership: Members & Public

Contact/s:
* **Club Secretary:** Mr David Pollard

Course/s:

COCKERMOUTH
Description: Heath Land, Hilltop, Open, Medium Length, Drains Well, Ideal for the Elderly
Green Speed: Medium
Built: 1896 Built On: Clay
Number of Holes: 18 Par: 69
Yds: 5496 F9 Yds: 2635 B9 Yds: 2861
Designer: James Braid
Further Information:
The course offers picturesque views.

COCKS MOORS WOODS

COCKS MOORS WOODS MUNICIPAL GOLF CLUB, Alcester Rd South, Kings Heath, Birmingham, **MIDLANDS (WEST)**, B14 4ER, **ENGLAND**.
(T) 0121 4443584

Membership: Public

Course/s:

COCKS MOORS WOODS
Number of Holes: 18

COCKSFORD

COCKSFORD GOLF CLUB LTD, Stutton, Tadcaster, **YORKSHIRE (NORTH)**, LS24 9NG, **ENGLAND**.
(T) 01937 834253
(E) enquiries@cocksfordgolfclub.freeserve.co.uk
(W) www.cocksfordgolfclub.freeserve.co.uk

Membership: Members & Public

Contact/s:
* **Club Secretary:** Mrs F Judson
* **Professional:** Mr Graham Thompson

Course/s:

COCKSFORD
Description: Wooded, Parkland, Valley, Undulating, Sheltered, Medium Length, Tight, Drains Well, Ideal for the Elderly
Green Speed: Medium
Built: 1992
Number of Holes: 18 Par: 70
Par 3's: 4 Par 4's: 12 Par 5's: 2
Yds: 5679 F9 Yds: 2572 B9 Yds: 3107
Prevailing Wind: South/West
Designer: Bill Brodigan

COLCHESTER

COLCHESTER GOLF CLUB, Clubhouse, 21 Braiswick, Colchester, **ESSEX**, CO4 5AU, **ENGLAND**.
(T) 01206 853396

Membership: Members & Public

Contact/s:
* **Club Secretary:** Mr Terry Peck
* **Professional:** Mr Mark Angel

Course/s:

COLCHESTER
Description: Parkland, Undulating, Sheltered, Medium Length, Drains Well, Ideal for the Elderly
Green Speed: Medium
Built: 1907 Built On: Clay
Number of Holes: 18
Designer: James Braid

COLD ASHBY

COLD ASHBY GOLF CLUB, Stanford Rd, Cold Ashby, Northampton, **NORTHAMPTONSHIRE**, NN6 6EP, **ENGLAND**.
(T) 01604 740548
(E) coldashbygolfclub@virgin.net
(W) www.coldashbygolfclub.com

Membership: Members & Public
Size of Complex: 200 Acres

Contact/s:
* **Club Secretary:** Mrs Carole Oliver
* **Professional:** Mr Shane Rose
  ☎ 01604 740099

Course/s:

WINWICK/ASHBY
Description: Championship, Parkland, Undulating, Medium Length, Drains Well
Green Speed: Medium
Built: 1974 Built On: Soil
Number of Holes: 18 Par: 70
Par 3's: 5 Par 4's: 10 Par 5's: 3
Yds: 5693 F9 Yds: 2800 B9 Yds: 2893
Designer: David Croxton
Further Information:
A natural terrain gives a great variety in the type of holes.

COLLEGE PINES

COLLEGE PINES GOLF CLUB, Worksop College Drive, Worksop, **NOTTINGHAMSHIRE**, S80 3AP, **ENGLAND**.
(T) 01909 501431
(W) www.collegepinesgolfclub.co.uk

Membership: Members & Public

Contact/s:
* **Club Secretary:** Mr C Snell

Course/s:

COLLEGE PINES
Description: Heath Land, Medium Length, Drains Well
Green Speed: Medium
Built: 1994
Number of Holes: 18
Designer: David Snell

COLLINGTREE PARK

COLLINGTREE PARK GOLF COURSE, 90 Windingbrook Lane, Northampton, **NORTHAMPTONSHIRE**, NN4 0XN, **ENGLAND**.
(T) 01604 701202
(W) www.collingtreeparkgolf.com

Membership: Members & Public

Contact/s:
* **Club Secretary:** Mr Geoff Pook

- **Professional:**
  ☎ 01604 700000
- **Book Tee Times:** Booking Office

Course/s:

COLLINGTREE PARK
Description: Championship, Parkland, Open, Long, Drains Well, Ideal for the Elderly
Green Speed: Medium
Built: 1990 **Built On:** Clay
Number of Holes: 18 **Par:** 72
Par 3's: 4 **Par 4's:** 10 **Par 5's:** 4
Yds: 6776
Prevailing Wind: West
Designer: J Miller

COLMWORTH & NORTH BEDFORDSHIRE

COLMWORTH & NORTH BEDFORDSHIRE GOLF CLUB, New Rd, Colmworth, Bedford, **BEDFORDSHIRE**, MK44 2NN, **ENGLAND**.
(T) 01234 378181
(E) golf@colmworthgc.fsbusiness.co.uk

Membership: Members & Public

Contact/s:

- **Club Secretary:** Mr Alan Willis

Course/s:

COLMWORTH & NORTH BEDFORDSHIRE
Description: Open, Long, Drains Well, Ideal for the Elderly
Green Speed: Medium
Built: 1992 **Built On:** Clay
Record: 70 (Craig Gould)
Number of Holes: 18 **Par:** 72
Par 3's: 4 **Par 4's:** 10 **Par 5's:** 4
Yds: 6435 **F9 Yds:** 3114 **B9 Yds:** 3321
Designer: John Glasson
Further Information:
A challenging course.

COLNE

COLNE GOLF CLUB, Law Farm, Skipton Old Rd, Colne, **LANCASHIRE**, BB8 7EB, **ENGLAND**.
(T) 01282 863391

Membership: Members & Public
Size of Complex: 45 Acres

Contact/s:

- **Club Secretary:** Mr Alan Turpin
  ☎ 01282 691412

Course/s:

COLNE
Description: Wooded, Parkland, Valley, Undulating, Open, Medium Length, Drains Well, Ideal for the Elderly
Green Speed: Fast
Built: 1901 **Built On:** Soil
Number of Holes: 9
Prevailing Wind: North/West

COLNE VALLEY

COLNE VALLEY GOLF CLUB, Station Rd, Earls Colne, Colchester, **ESSEX**, CO6 2LT, **ENGLAND**.
(T) 01787 224343

Membership: Members & Public
Size of Complex: 110 Acres

Contact/s:

- **Professional:** Mr Robert Taylor

Course/s:

COLNE VALLEY
Description: Parkland, Valley, Sheltered, Medium Length, Tight, Drains Well
Green Speed: Fast
Built: 1991 **Built On:** Clay
Number of Holes: 18 **Par:** 70
Record: 63 (Paul Curry)

Par 3's: 6 **Par 4's:** 8 **Par 5's:** 4
Yds: 6303 **F9 Yds:** 3096 **B9 Yds:** 3207
Prevailing Wind: West
Designer: Howard Swan
Further Information:
Buggies are recommended for the elderly.

COLONSAY

COLONSAY GOLF CLUB, Isle of Colonsay, **ARGYLL AND BUTE**, PA61 7YP, **SCOTLAND**.
(T) 01951 200316

Course/s:

COLONSAY
Number of Holes: 18

COLVEND

COLVEND GOLF CLUB, Sandyhills, Colvend, Dalbeattie, **DUMFRIES AND GALLOWAY**, DG5 4PY, **SCOTLAND**.
(T) 01556 630398
(E) secretary@colvendgolfclub.co.uk
(W) www.colvendgolfclub.co.uk

Membership: Members & Public
Size of Complex: 120 Acres

Contact/s:

- **Club Secretary:** Mr Jim Henderson
- **Pro Shop:** Mr Graham Sharp

Course/s:

COLVEND
Description: Parkland, Undulating, Sheltered, Open, Short, Drains Well
Green Speed: Medium
Built: 1985 **Built On:** Soil
Number of Holes: 18 **Par:** 68
Designer: Peter Alliss, David Thomas
Further Information:
Beautiful views include Isle of Man & Galloway Hills.

COLVILLE PARK

COLVILLE PARK GOLF CLUB, New Jerviston Hse, Jerviston Est, Merry St, Motherwell, **LANARKSHIRE (NORTH)**, ML1 4UG, **SCOTLAND**.
(T) 01698 265779

Course/s:

COLVILLE PARK
Number of Holes: 18
Designer: James Braid

COMBE GROVE MANOR

COMBE GROVE MANOR HOTEL & COUNTRY CLUB, Brassknocker Hill, Monkton Combe, Bath, **BATH & SOMERSET (NORTH EAST)**, BA2 7HS, **ENGLAND**.
(T) 01225 835533
(W) www.combegrovemanor.com

Membership: Members & Public

Contact/s:

- **Manager:** Mr Jim Tyrie

Course/s:

COMBE GROVE MANOR
Description: Hilltop, Short, Drains Well
Green Speed: Slow
Built: 1985
Number of Holes: 5
Par 3's: 5

COMRIE

COMRIE GOLF CLUB, Comrie Golf Clubhouse, Comrie, Crieff, **PERTH AND KINROSS**, PH6 2LR, **SCOTLAND**.
(T) 01764 670055

Course/s:

COMRIE
Number of Holes: 9 **Par:** 70
Yds: 6040 **F9 Yds:** 3020 **B9 Yds:** 3020
Designer: Colonel Williamson

CONCORD GOLF CTRE

CONCORD GOLF CENTRE, Shiregreen Lane, Sheffield, **YORKSHIRE (SOUTH)**, S5 6AE, **ENGLAND**.
(T) 0114 2577378

Course/s:

CONCORD PARK
Number of Holes: 18

CONGLETON

CONGLETON GOLF CLUB, Biddulph Rd, Congleton, **CHESHIRE**, CW12 3LZ, **ENGLAND**.
(T) 01260 273540

Course/s:

CONGLETON
Number of Holes: 9

CONNEMARA

CONNEMARA GOLF CLUB, Ballyconneely, Clifden, **COUNTY GALWAY**, **IRELAND**.
(T) 095 23502
(E) links@iol.ie
(W) www.westcoastlinks.com

Membership: Members & Public

Contact/s:

- **Club Secretary:** Mr Richard Flaherty
- **Professional:** Mr Hugh O'Neill

Course/s:

CONNEMARA
Description: Championship, Links, Undulating, Open, Long, Drains Well, Ideal for the Elderly
Green Speed: Fast
Built: 1973 **Built On:** Sand
Number of Holes: 18 **Par:** 72
Yds: 6860 **F9 Yds:** 3236
Designer: Edward Hackett

CONNEMARA 9 HOLE
Number of Holes: 9 **Par:** 35
Yds: 3012

CONNEMARA ISLES

CONNEMARA ISLES GOLF CLUB, Annaghvane, Lettermore, **COUNTY GALWAY**, **IRELAND**.
(T) 091 572498

Course/s:

CONNEMARA ISLES
Number of Holes: 9 **Par:** 68
Yds: 5633
Further Information:
This 9 hole course can be played as an 18 hole.

CONSETT & DISTRICT

CONSETT & DISTRICT GOLF CLUB, Elmfield Rd, Consett, **COUNTY DURHAM**, DH8 5NN, **ENGLAND**.
(T) 01207 502186
(W) www.derwentside.org/consettgolfclub

Membership: Members & Public

Contact/s:

- **Club Secretary:** Mr Ian Murray
- **Professional:** Mr Jack Ord
  ☎ 01207 580210
- **Pro Shop:** Mr Stuart Ord

Course/s:

CONSETT & DISTRICT
Description: Parkland, Long, Tends to Flood
Green Speed: Medium
Built: 1911 **Built On:** Clay
Number of Holes: 18
Prevailing Wind: North

CONWY
CONWY (CAERNARVONSHIRE) GOLF CLUB, Beacons Way, Morfa, **CONWY**, LL32 8ER, **WALES**.
(T) 01492 592423

Contact/s:
● Club Secretary: Mr D L Brown
● Professional: Mr Peter Lees

Course/s:
🍂 CONWY
Description: Championship, Links
Built: 1890
Number of Holes: 18 **Par:** 72
Yds: 6647 **F9 Yds:** 3268 **B9 Yds:** 3379
Further Information:
The course offers views of Conwy Bay.

COODEN BEACH
COODEN BEACH GOLF CLUB, Cooden Sea Rd, Cooden, Bexhill-on-Sea, **SUSSEX (EAST)**, TN39 4TR, **ENGLAND**.
(T) 01424 842040

Membership: Members & Public

Contact/s:
● Club Secretary: Mr P Svehlik
● Professional: Mr J Sim
☎ 01424 843938

Course/s:
🍂 COODEN BEACH
Description: Open, Long, Drains Well
Green Speed: Medium
Built: 1912 **Built On:** Soil
Number of Holes: 18 **Par:** 72
Yds: 6500 **F9 Yds:** 3245 **B9 Yds:** 3255
Designer: W Herbert Fowler

COOKRIDGE HALL GOLF CLUB
AMERICAN GOLF CORPORATION, Cookridge Lane, Leeds, **YORKSHIRE (WEST)**, LS16 7NL, **ENGLAND**.
(T) 0113 203 0183
(E) cookridgehall@americangolf.uk.com
(W) www.americangolf.com

Membership: Members & Public

Contact/s:
● Professional: Mr Mark Pearson

Course/s:
🍂 COOKRIDGE HALL GOLF COURSE
Description: Parkland, Undulating, Open, Long, Drains Well
Green Speed: Medium
Built: 1997 **Built On:** Clay
Number of Holes: 18 **Par:** 72
Par 3's: 4 **Par 4's:** 10 **Par 5's:** 4
Yds: 6497 **F9 Yds:** 3286 **B9 Yds:** 3211
Designer: Karl Litten

COOLATTIN
COOLATTIN GOLF CLUB, Shillelagh, Arklow, **COUNTY WICKLOW**, **IRELAND**
(T) 055 29125

Course/s:
🍂 COOLATTIN
Number of Holes: 18 **Par:** 70
F9 Yds: 3000 **B9 Yds:** 2831

COOLATTIN
COOLATTIN GOLF COURSE, Coollattin, Shillelagh, Coollattin, **COUNTY WICKLOW**, **IRELAND**.
(T) 055 29125
(W) www.coollattin.com

Membership: Members & Public

Contact/s:
● Club Secretary: Mr Denis Bryne
☎ 054 77314
● Professional: Mr Peter Jones
☎ 055 25125
● Book Tee Times: Mr Dave Masterson

Course/s:
🍂 COOLLATTIN
Description: Parkland
Green Speed: Medium
Number of Holes: 18
Designer: P McEvoy

COOMBE HILL
COOMBE HILL GOLF CLUB, Golf Club Drive, Kingston Upon Thames, **LONDON (GREATER)**, KT2 7DF, **ENGLAND**.
(T) 020 89422284

Contact/s:
● Club Secretary: Mr C Defoy
● Pro Shop:
☎ 020 83367615

Course/s:
🍂 COOMBE HILL
Description: Parkland, Undulating, Sheltered, Medium Length, Tight, Drains Well **Green Speed:** Fast
Built: 1911 **Built On:** Soil
Number of Holes: 18
Designer: J F Abercromby
Further Information:
Rhododendrons throughout the course.

COOMBE WOOD
COOMBE WOOD GOLF CLUB LTD, George Rd, Kingston Hill, Kingston Upon Thames, **LONDON (GREATER)**, KT2 7NS, **ENGLAND**.
(T) 020 89420388
(E) cwoodgc@ukonline.co.uk
(W) www.coombewoodgolf.com

Membership: Members & Public
Size of Complex: 84 Acres

Contact/s:
● Club Secretary: Mr Peter Urwin
● Professional: Mr David Butler
● Pro Shop:
☎ 020 89426764
● Book Lessons: Mr Phil Wright

Course/s:
🍂 COOMBE WOOD
Description: Wooded, Parkland, Short, Tight, Drains Well, Ideal for the Elderly
Green Speed: Fast
Built: 1903 **Built On:** Clay/Gravel
Number of Holes: 18 **Par:** 66
Record: 60 (David Butler)
Yds: 5266
Further Information:
The course has 7 tricky, par 3 holes.

COOSHEEN GOLF LINKS
COOSHEEN GOLF LINKS, Coosheen, Schull, **COUNTY CORK**, **IRELAND**.
(T) 028 28182

Course/s:
🍂 COOSHEEN
Number of Holes: 9
Yds: 2205

COPT HEATH
COPT HEATH GOLF CLUB LTD, Warwick Rd, Knowle, Solihull, **MIDLANDS (WEST)**, B93 9LN, **ENGLAND**.
(T) 01564 776155

Contact/s:
● Manager: Mr B Barton

Course/s:
🍂 COPT HEATH
Number of Holes: 18 **Par:** 71
Yds: 6517 **F9 Yds:** 3192 **B9 Yds:** 3325
Designer: Harry Vardon

COPTHORNE
COPTHORNE GOLF CLUB, Borers Arms Rd, Copthorne, Crawley, **SUSSEX (WEST)**, RH10 3LL, **ENGLAND**.
(T) 01342 712033
(E) info@copthornegolfclub.co.uk

Contact/s:
● Club Secretary: Mr J Pyne

Course/s:
🍂 COPTHORNE
Number of Holes: 18 **Par:** 71
Yds: 6505
Designer: James Braid

CORBALLIS PUBLIC LINKS
CORBALLIS PUBLIC LINKS GOLF COURSE, Donabate, **COUNTY DUBLIN**, **IRELAND**.
(T) 01 8436583

Course/s:
🍂 CORBALLIS PUBLIC
Number of Holes: 18

CORBY PUBLIC
CORBY PUBLIC GOLF COURSE, Stamford Rd, Weldon, Corby, **NORTHAMPTONSHIRE**, NN17 3JH, **ENGLAND**.
(T) 01536 260756

Membership: Public
Size of Complex: 144 Acres

Contact/s:
● Club Secretary: Mr Terry Arnold
● Professional: Mr Jeff Bradbrook

Course/s:
🍂 CORBY PUBLIC
Description: Parkland, Undulating, Sheltered, Long, Drains Well, Ideal for the Elderly
Green Speed: Medium
Built: 1965 **Built On:** Clay
Number of Holes: 18 **Par:** 72
Yds: 6631 **F9 Yds:** 3238 **B9 Yds:** 3393
Designer: Hawtree

CORHAMPTON
CORHAMPTON GOLF CLUB, Corhampton, Southampton, **HAMPSHIRE**, SO32 3LP, **ENGLAND**.
(T) 01489 877638

Contact/s:
● Club Secretary: Mrs L Collins

Course/s:
🍂 CORHAMPTON
Number of Holes: 18

CORK
CORK GOLF CLUB, Little Island, **COUNTY CORK**, **IRELAND**.

(T) 021 4353451

Contact/s:
● Professional: Mr Peter Hickey

Course/s:
⛳ **CORK**
Number of Holes: 18 Par: 72
Yds: 6731 F9 Yds: 3317 B9 Yds: 3414
Designer: Alistair MacKenzie

CORNGREAVES

CORNGREAVES GOLF COURSE,
Corngreaves Rd, Cradley Heath, **MIDLANDS (WEST)**, B64 7NL, **ENGLAND**.
(T) 01384 567880

Course/s:
⛳ **CORNGREAVES HALL**
Number of Holes: 9

CORRIE

CORRIE GOLF CLUB, Sannox, Brodick,
AYRSHIRE (NORTH), KA27 8JD,
SCOTLAND.
(T) 01770 810223

Course/s:
⛳ **CORRIE**
Number of Holes: 9

CORRSTOWN

CORRSTOWN GOLF CLUB, Kilsallaghan,
COUNTY DUBLIN, **IRELAND**.
(T) 01 8640533/534
(E) corrstowngolfclub@eircom.net
(W) www.corrstown.com

Course/s:
⛳ **ORCHARD**
Number of Holes: 9
Designer: Edward Connaughton

⛳ **RIVER**
Number of Holes: 18 Par: 72
Yds: 6865 F9 Yds: 3254 B9 Yds: 3611
Designer: Edward Connaughton

COSBY

COSBY GOLF CLUB, Chapel Lane, Cosby,
Leicester, **LEICESTERSHIRE**, LE9 1RG,
ENGLAND.
(T) 0116 2848275
(E) secretary@cosby-golf-club.co.uk
(W) www.cosby-golf-club.co.uk

Contact/s:
● Honary Secretary: Mr G T Kirkpatrick

Course/s:
⛳ **COSBY**
Number of Holes: 18 Par: 71
Par 3's: 3 Par 4's: 13 Par 5's: 2
Yds: 6410 F9 Yds: 3245 B9 Yds: 3165
Designer: Hawtree

COSTESSEY PARK

COSTESSEY PARK GOLF COURSE,
Parklands, Costessey, Norwich, **NORFOLK**,
NR8 5AL, **ENGLAND**.
(T) 01603 746333
(W) www.costesseypark.com

Membership: Members & Public

Contact/s:
● Club Secretary: Mr Steve Beckham
● Professional: Mr Andrew Young
● Pro Shop:
  ☎ 01603 747085

Course/s:
⛳ **COSTESSEY PARK**
Description: Parkland, Valley, Undulating,
Short, Tight, Drains Well
Green Speed: Medium
Built: 1984 Built On: Soil
Number of Holes: 18
Further Information:
A challenging course.

COTGRAVE PLACE

AMERICAN GOLF CORPORATION,
Stragglethorpe, Cotgrave, Nottingham,
NOTTINGHAMSHIRE, NG12 3HB,
ENGLAND.
(T) 0115 9333344
(E) cotgrave@americangolf.com
(W) www.americangolf.com

Membership: Members & Public
Size of Complex: 300 Acres

Contact/s:
● Professional: Mr Robert Smith
● Book Lessons: Mr Matt Alls

Course/s:
⛳ **MASTERS**
Description: Championship, Parkland,
Undulating, Open
Green Speed: Medium
Built: 1991 Built On: Clay
Number of Holes: 18 Par: 69
Par 3's: 5 Par 4's: 11 Par 5's: 2
Yds: 5651 F9 Yds: 2609 B9 Yds: 3042
Designer: Peter Alliss

⛳ **OPEN**
Description: Championship, Parkland,
Drains Well
Green Speed: Medium
Built: 1991 Built On: Clay
Number of Holes: 18 Par: 71
Par 3's: 3 Par 4's: 12 Par 5's: 3
Yds: 5847 F9 Yds: 3002 B9 Yds: 2845
Prevailing Wind: North/West
Further Information:
The course has a superb layout, excellent
approaches, quality greens and lots of
water.

COTSWOLD EDGE

COTSWOLD EDGE GOLF CLUB, Upper
Rushmire, Bowcott, Wotton-under-Edge,
GLOUCESTERSHIRE, GL12 7PT, **ENGLAND**.
(T) 01453 844167

Membership: Members & Public

Contact/s:
● Club Secretary: Mr Neil James Newman
● Professional: Mr David Gosling
  ☎ 01453 844398

Course/s:
⛳ **COTSWOLD EDGE**
Description: Parkland, Undulating,
Sheltered, Medium Length, Tight, Tends to
Flood
Green Speed: Medium
Built: 1980 Built On: Clay
Number of Holes: 18 Par: 71
Yds: 6170 F9 Yds: 3306 B9 Yds: 2864
Prevailing Wind: South
Designer: A J & N Newman

COTSWOLD HILLS

COTSWOLD HILLS GOLF CLUB LTD,
Ullenwood, Cheltenham,
GLOUCESTERSHIRE, GL53 9QT, **ENGLAND**.
(T) 01242 515264

Membership: Members & Public
Size of Complex: 171 Acres

Contact/s:
● Professional: Mr Norman Allen
  ☎ 01242 515263

Course/s:
⛳ **COTSWOLD HILLS**
Description: Hilltop, Open, Drains Well
Green Speed: Medium
Built: 1976 Built On: Soil
Number of Holes: 18 Par: 72
Record: 67 (J Loughnane)
Par 3's: 4 Par 4's: 10 Par 5's: 4
Yds: 6565 F9 Yds: 3281 B9 Yds: 3284
Prevailing Wind: West
Designer: M Little

COTTESMORE

AMERICAN GOLF CORPORATION, Buchan
Hill, Pease Pottage, Crawley, **SUSSEX
(WEST)**, RH22 9AT, **ENGLAND**.
(T) 01293 528256
(E) cottesmore@americangolf.uk.com

Membership: Members & Public

Contact/s:
● Professional: Mr Callum Callan
● Pro Shop:
  ☎ 01293 535399

Course/s:
⛳ **GRIFFIN**
Description: Parkland, Sheltered,
Medium Length, Tight, Drains Well
Green Speed: Medium
Number of Holes: 18 Par: 71
Par 3's: 5 Par 4's: 9 Par 5's: 4
Yds: 6248 F9 Yds: 2945 B9 Yds: 3303
Designer: M Rogerson
Further Information: This course is
extremely tight. Drains exepctionally weel.

⛳ **PHOENIX**
Description: Parkland, Sheltered,
Medium Length, Drains Well
Green Speed: Medium Built On: Soil
Number of Holes: 18 Par: 69
Par 3's: 6 Par 4's: 9 Par 5's: 3
Yds: 5482 F9 Yds: 2946 B9 Yds: 2536
Designer: M Rogerson

COTTRELL PARK

COTTRELL PARK GOLF CLUB, St.
Nicholas, Cardiff, **GLAMORGAN (VALE OF)**,
CF5 6JY, **WALES**.
(T) 01446 781781
(W) www.cottrell-park.co.uk

Contact/s:
● Professional: Mr Stephen Birch

Course/s:
⛳ **BUTTON**
Description: Parkland, Valley, Open
Green Speed: Medium
Built: 1996 Built On: Sand
Number of Holes: 9 Par: 35
Par 3's: 2 Par 4's: 6 Par 5's: 1
Yds: 2808
Further Information:
No temporary greens.

⛳ **MACKINTOSH**
Description: Championship, Parkland,
Undulating, Medium Length, Drains Well
Green Speed: Medium
Built: 1996 Built On: Sand
Number of Holes: 18 Par: 72
Par 3's: 4 Par 4's: 10 Par 5's: 4
Yds: 6397 F9 Yds: 3243 B9 Yds: 3154
Designer: Robert Sandow
Further Information:
Greens all year round.

COULSDON MANOR

COULSDON MANOR GOLF CENTRE,
Coulsdon Court Rd, Coulsdon, **SURREY**,
CR5 2LL, **ENGLAND**.

(T) 020 86606083

Course/s:

🔹 **COULSDON MANOR HOTEL**
Number of Holes: 18
Designer: Harry Shapland Colt

COUNTY

COUNTY GOLF CLUB, Botley Rd, West End, Southampton, **HAMPSHIRE**, SO30 3HA, **ENGLAND**.
(T) 023 80471111

Membership: Members & Public
Size of Complex: 152 Acres

Contact/s:
● Professional: Mr Ian Warick

Course/s:

🔹 **COUNTY**
Description: Wooded, Parkland, Undulating, Medium Length, Drains Well, Ideal for the Elderly
Green Speed: Medium
Built: 1994 Built On: Sand
Number of Holes: 9 Record: 70 (Ian Warick)
Prevailing Wind: West
Further Information:
The course is situated on a cricket ground and all greens are USGA specification. There is a computerised irrigation system.

COURTOWN

COURTOWN GOLF CLUB, Kiltennel, Gorey, **COUNTY WEXFORD**, **IRELAND**.
(T) 055 25166
(E) courtown@iol.ie

Contact/s:
● Club Secretary: Mr David Cleere

Course/s:

🔹 **COURTOWN**
Number of Holes: 18 Par: 71
Yds: 6450 F9 Yds: 3124 B9 Yds: 3326
Designer: Harris

COVENTRY

COVENTRY GOLF CLUB LTD, St. Martins Rd, Finham Pk, Coventry, **MIDLANDS (WEST)**, CV3 6RJ, **ENGLAND**.
(T) 024 7641 4152
(E) coventrygolfclub@hotmail.com
(W) www.coventrygolfcourse.co.uk

Contact/s:
● Club Secretary: Mr Brian Fox

Course/s:

🔹 **COVENTRY**
Number of Holes: 18 Par: 73
Yds: 6601 F9 Yds: 3127 B9 Yds: 3474
Designer: Hawtree, Harry Vardon

COWAL

COWAL GOLF CLUB, Ardenslate Rd, Dunoon, **ARGYLL AND BUTE**, PA23 8NN, **SCOTLAND**.
(T) 01369 705673
(E) info@cowalgolfclub.co.uk
(W) www.cowalgolfclub.co.uk

Membership: Members & Public

Contact/s:
● Club Secretary: Mrs Wilma Fraser
● Professional: Mr Russell Weir
☎ 01369 702395

Course/s:

🔹 **COWAL**
Description: Heath Land, Medium Length, Tight

Green Speed: Medium Built On: Soil
Number of Holes: 18 Par: 70
Yds: 6063 F9 Yds: 2869 B9 Yds: 3194
Prevailing Wind: South
Designer: James Braid

COWDENBEATH

COWDENBEATH GOLF CLUB, Seco Pl, Cowdenbeath, **FIFE**, KY4 8PF, **SCOTLAND**.
(T) 01383 511918

Contact/s:
● Club Secretary: Mr C Ingles
☎ 01383 611251

Course/s:

🔹 **DORA**
Number of Holes: 18 Par: 70
Par 3's: 3 Par 4's: 14 Par 5's: 1
Yds: 6201 F9 Yds: 2842 B9 Yds: 3359

COWDRAY PARK

COWDRAY PARK GOLF CLUB, Midhurst, **SUSSEX (WEST)**, GU29 0BB, **ENGLAND**.
(T) 01730 813599

Contact/s:
● General Manager: Mr D J Rodbard

Course/s:

🔹 **COWDRAY PARK**
Number of Holes: 18
Designer: Jack White

COWES

COWES GOLF CLUB, Crossfield Ave, Cowes, **ISLE OF WIGHT**, PO31 8HN, **ENGLAND**.
(T) 01983 292303

Contact/s:
● Club Secretary: Mr David Weaver

Course/s:

🔹 **COWES**
Number of Holes: 9
Par 3's: 2 Par 4's: 6 Par 5's: 1
F9 Yds: 2947
Designer: J Hamilton-Stutt
Further Information:
This 9 hole course can be played as an 18 hole course, with 2 different tees on the second 9.

COWGLEN

COWGLEN GOLF CLUB, 301 Barrhead Rd, Glasgow, **GLASGOW (CITY OF)**, G43 1AU, **SCOTLAND**.
(T) 0141 6320556

Contact/s:
● Manager: Mr G Young

Course/s:

🔹 **COWGLEN**
Number of Holes: 18
Designer: David Adams, James Braid

COXMOOR

COXMOOR GOLF CLUB LTD, Coxmoor Rd, Sutton-In-Ashfield, **NOTTINGHAMSHIRE**, NG17 5LF, **ENGLAND**.
(T) 01623 557359
(E) coxmoor@freeuk.com

Contact/s:
● Club Secretary: Mr Brian Noble
● Professional: Mr David Ridley

Course/s:

🔹 **COXMOOR**
Number of Holes: 18 Par: 73
Par 3's: 4 Par 4's: 9 Par 5's: 5
Yds: 6596 F9 Yds: 3237 B9 Yds: 3359

CRADDOCKSTOWN

CRADDOCKSTOWN GOLF CLUB, Blessington Rd, Naas, **COUNTY KILDARE**, **IRELAND**.
(T) 045 897610

Membership: Members & Public

Contact/s:
● General Manager: Ms Gay Nolan

Course/s:

🔹 **CRADDOCKSTOWN**
Description: Championship, Parkland, Undulating, Open, Ideal for the Elderly
Green Speed: Medium
Built: 1994
Number of Holes: 18
Designer: A Spring

CRAIBSTONE

CRAIBSTONE GOLF CENTRE, Craibstone Est, Bucksburn, Aberdeen, **ABERDEEN (CITY OF)**, AB21 9YA, **SCOTLAND**.
(T) 01224 716777
(E) golf@ab.sac.ac.uk
(W) www.craibstone.com

Membership: Members & Public

Contact/s:
● Club Secretary: Mrs Gwen Bruce
☎ 01224 711011
● Book Tee Times: Mrs Gina Manders

Course/s:

🔹 **CRAIBSTONE**
Description: Wooded, Parkland, Short, Ideal for the Elderly
Green Speed: Fast
Built: 1999 Built On: Sand/Soil
Number of Holes: 18 Par: 69
Par 3's: 5 Par 4's: 11 Par 5's: 2
Yds: 5613
Prevailing Wind: South/West
Designer: Greens of Scotland
Further Information:
The course has very good greens.

CRAIGAVON

CRAIGAVON GOLF & SKI CENTRE, Turmoyra Lane, Silverwood, Lurgan, **COUNTY ARMAGH**, BT66 6NG, **NORTHERN IRELAND**.
(T) 02838 326606

Contact/s:
● Manager: Mr Geoff Coupland

Course/s:

🔹 **CRAIGAVON**
Number of Holes: 18 Par: 72
Yds: 6188 F9 Yds: 3370 B9 Yds: 2818

CRAIGENTINNY

CRAIGENTINNY GOLF COURSE, Fillyside Rd, Edinburgh, **EDINBURGH (CITY OF)**, EH7 6RG, **SCOTLAND**.
(T) 0131 5547501

Contact/s:
● Book Tee Times: Mr Ian Whitewall

Course/s:

🔹 **CRAIGENTINNY**
Description: Parkland, Undulating
Built: 1891
Number of Holes: 18 Par: 67
Further Information:
The course offers superb views of Arthur's Seat which dominates the skyline to the south.

CRAIGIE HILL

CRAIGIE HILL GOLF CLUB, Cherrybank, Perth, **PERTH AND KINROSS**, PH2 0NE, **SCOTLAND**.
(T) 01738 620829
(E) chgc@fairieswell.freeserve.co.uk
(W) www.craigiehill.scottishgolf.com

Contact/s:
● **Professional:** Mr Ian Muir
● **Book Tee Times:**
  ☎ 01738 622644

Course/s:
● **CRAIGIE HILL**
  Description: Parkland, Short
  Built: 1911
  Number of Holes: 18 **Par:** 66
  Par 3's: 6 **Par 4's:** 12
  Yds: 5386 **F9 Yds:** 2756 **B9 Yds:** 2630
  Designer: Jamie Anderson, William Fernie
  Further Information:
  The course offers superb views over Perth.

CRAIGIEKNOWES

CRAIGIEKNOWES GOLF COURSE, Barnbarroch Farm, Barnbarroch, Dalbeattie, **DUMFRIES AND GALLOWAY**, DG5 4QS, **SCOTLAND**.
(T) 01556 620244

Membership: Members & Public

Contact/s:
● **Club Secretary:** Mrs K Roan

Course/s:
● **CRAIGIEKNOWES**
  Description: Breckland, Hilltop, Undulating, Open, Medium Length, Tends to Flood
  Green Speed: Medium
  Built: 1994 **Built On:** Soil
  Number of Holes: 9 **Par:** 54
  Par 3's: 9
  Yds: 2782 **F9 Yds:** 1391 **B9 Yds:** 1391
  Designer: D Gray
  Further Information:
  A challenging course offering beautiful scenery, situated near to the coast. Can be played as an 18 hole course.

CRAIGMILLAR PARK

CRAIGMILLAR PARK GOLF CLUB, 1 Observatory Rd, Edinburgh, **EDINBURGH (CITY OF)**, EH9 3HG, **SCOTLAND**.
(T) 0131 6672837

Membership: Members & Public

Contact/s:
● **Club Secretary:** Mr Tom Lawson
● **Professional:** Mr B McGhee

Course/s:
● **CRAIGMILLAR PARK**
  Description: Parkland, Undulating, Open, Medium Length, Tends to Flood, Ideal for the Elderly
  Green Speed: Medium
  Built: 1925 **Built On:** Clay
  Number of Holes: 18
  Prevailing Wind: South/West
  Designer: James Braid

CRAIGNURE

CRAIGNURE GOLF CLUB, Scallastle, Craignure, Isle of Mull, **ARGYLL AND BUTE**, PA65 6PB, **SCOTLAND**.
(T) 01680 812487&812416

Course/s:

● **CRAIGNURE**
  Number of Holes: 9

CRAIL

CRAIL GOLFING SOCIETY, Balcomie Clubhouse, Crail, Anstruther, **FIFE**, KY10 3XN, **SCOTLAND**.
(T) 01333 450686/450278
(E) crailgolf@aol.com
(W) www.golfagent.com/clubsites/crail

Membership: Members & Public

Contact/s:
● **Professional:** Mr Graeme Lennie
● **Book Tee Times:** Mr Jim Horsfiled
  ☎ 01333 450686

Course/s:
● **BALCOMIE LINKS**
  Description: Links, Open, Medium Length, Drains Well
  Green Speed: Fast **Built On:** Sand/Soil
  Number of Holes: 18 **Par:** 69
  Yds: 5922
  Prevailing Wind: South/West
  Designer: Tom Morris ♟

● **CRAIGHEAD LINKS COURSE**
  Description: Links, Medium Length, Drains Well
  Green Speed: Fast **Built On:** Sand
  Number of Holes: 18 **Par:** 71
  Yds: 6728
  Designer: Gil Hanse

CRANE VALLEY

CRANE VALLEY GOLF CLUB, The Clubhouse, Verwood, **DORSET**, BH31 7LE, **ENGLAND**.
(T) 01202 814088
(E) crane-valley@hoburne.com

Membership: Members & Public
Size of Complex: 180 Acres

Contact/s:
● **Club Secretary:** Mr Andrew Blackwell
● **Professional:** Mr D Ranson
● **Book Lessons:** Mr Darrel Ranson

Course/s:
● **VALLEY 18 HOLE**
  Description: Championship, Parkland, Valley, Undulating, Open, Medium Length, Ideal for the Elderly
  Green Speed: Fast
  Built: 1991 **Built On:** Clay
  Number of Holes: 18 **Par:** 72
  Record: 66 (George Ryall)
  Par 3's: 4 **Par 4's:** 10 **Par 5's:** 4
  Yds: 6425
  Prevailing Wind: West
  Designer: Donald Steel
  Further Information:
  The River Crane meanders through the course.

● **WOODLAND 9 HOLE**
  Number of Holes: 9 **Par:** 66
  Par 3's: 3 **Par 4's:** 6
  Yds: 4120 **F9 Yds:** 2060 **B9 Yds:** 2060
  Further Information:
  Can be played as an 18 hole course.

CRANLEIGH

CRANLEIGH GOLF & COUNTRY CLUB, Barhatch Lane, Cranleigh, **SURREY**, GU6 7NG, **ENGLAND**.
(T) 01483 268855

Membership: Members & Public

Contact/s:
● **Professional:** Mr T Longmuir
● **Pro Shop:**

(T) 01483 277188

Course/s:
● **CRANLEIGH**
  Description: Wooded, Parkland, Undulating, Short, Tight, Drains Well
  Green Speed: Medium
  Built: 1986 **Built On:** Clay
  Number of Holes: 18 **Par:** 68
  Par 3's: 6 **Par 4's:** 10 **Par 5's:** 2
  Yds: 5648 **F9 Yds:** 2966 **B9 Yds:** 2682

CRAY VALLEY

AMERICAN GOLF CORPORATION, Sandy Lane, St. Pauls Cray, Orpington, **KENT**, BR5 3HY, **ENGLAND**.
(T) 01689 831927

Membership: Members & Public

Contact/s:
● **Professional:** Mr Raphael Giannandrea
● **Book Lessons:** Mr Paul Watkins

Course/s:
● **CRAY VALLEY 18 HOLES**
  Description: Parkland, Heath Land, Valley, Open, Medium Length, Drains Well, Ideal for the Elderly
  Green Speed: Medium
  Built: 1976 **Built On:** Clay
  Number of Holes: 18 **Par:** 70
  Yds: 5669 **F9 Yds:** 2802 **B9 Yds:** 2867

● **CRAY VALLEY 9 HOLE**
  Description: Parkland, Undulating, Open, Short, Drains Well
  Green Speed: Medium
  Built: 1976 **Built On:** Chalk
  Number of Holes: 9 **Par:** 32
  Yds: 2140 **F9 Yds:** 2140

CRAYTHORNE

CRAYTHORNE GOLF CLUB (THE), Craythorne Rd, Stretton, Burton-on-Trent, **STAFFORDSHIRE**, DE13 0AZ, **ENGLAND**.
(T) 01283 564329

Membership: Members & Public

Contact/s:
● **Professional:** Mr Steve Hadfield

Course/s:
● **CRAYTHORNE**
  Description: Parkland **Built On:** Clay
  Number of Holes: 18

CREDITON

DOWNES CREDITON GOLF CLUB, Hookway, Crediton, **DEVON**, EX17 3PT, **ENGLAND**.
(T) 01363 773025

Membership: Members & Public
Size of Complex: 180 Acres

Contact/s:
● **Club Secretary:** Mr P Lee
● **Professional:** Mr Howard Finch
● **Pro Shop:** Mr Richard Johns

Course/s:
● **CREDITON**
  Description: Wooded, Parkland, Sheltered, Medium Length, Drains Well
  Green Speed: Medium
  Built: 1973 **Built On:** Soil
  Number of Holes: 18 **Par:** 70
  Record: 70 (Howard Finch)
  Yds: 5934
  Prevailing Wind: North/West
  Designer: Donald Steel

CREIGIAU

CREIGIAU GOLF CLUB, Llanwit Rd, Creigiau, Cardiff, **GLAMORGAN (VALE OF)**, CF15 9NN, **WALES**.
(T) 029 20890263
(W) www.creigiaugolf.co.uk

Membership: Members & Public
Size of Complex: 95 Acres

Contact/s:
- Club Secretary: Mr A J Greedy
  ☎ 029 10890263
- Pro Shop: Mr Iain Luntz
  ☎ 029 20891909

Course/s:
🏌 CREIGIAU
  Description: Wooded, Parkland, Valley, Sheltered, Medium Length, Tight, Drains Well, Ideal for the Elderly
  Green Speed: Medium
  Built: 1921 **Built On:** Chalk/Clay
  Number of Holes: 18
  Further Information:
  A flat course with fountains throughout.

CRETINGHAM

CRETINGHAM GOLF CLUB, Cretingham, Woodbridge, **SUFFOLK**, IP13 7BA, **ENGLAND**.
(T) 01728 685275

Membership: Members & Public

Contact/s:
- Club Secretary: Mrs Kate Jackson
- Professional: Mr N Jackson
- Pro Shop: Mr Matthew Lockwood

Course/s:
🏌 CRETINGHAM
  Description: Wooded, Undulating, Sheltered, Open, Short, Tight, Drains Well, Tends to Flood, Ideal for the Elderly
  Green Speed: Medium
  Built: 1983 **Built On:** Soil
  Number of Holes: 18 **Record:** 64 (John Pelan)
  Prevailing Wind: East
  Designer: Neil Jackson
  Further Information:
  A testing course.

CREWE

CREWE GOLF CLUB LTD, Fields Rd, Haslington, Crewe, **CHESHIRE**, CW1 5TB, **ENGLAND**.
(T) 01270 584227

Contact/s:
- Chairman: Mr G Davies

Course/s:
🏌 CREWE
  Number of Holes: 18

CREWS HILL

CREWS HILL GOLF CLUB, The Clubhouse, Cattlegate Rd, Enfield, **LONDON (GREATER)**, EN2 8AZ, **ENGLAND**.
(T) 020 8363 6674

Contact/s:
- Professional: N Wickelow
- Pro Shop:
  ☎ 020 8366 7422

Course/s:
🏌 CREWS HILL
  Number of Holes: 18
  Designer: Harry Shapland Colt

CRICCIETH

CRICCIETH GOLF CLUB, Criccieth, **GWYNEDD**, LL52 0PH, **WALES**.
(T) 01766 522154

Contact/s:
- Treasurer: Mr D H Williams
  ☎ 01766 523385

Course/s:
🏌 CRICCIETH
  Number of Holes: 18 **Par:** 68
  Yds: 5535 **F9 Yds:** 2486 **B9 Yds:** 3049

CRICHTON

CRICHTON GOLF CLUB, Bankend Rd, Dumfries, **DUMFRIES AND GALLOWAY**, DG1 4TH, **SCOTLAND**.
(T) 01387 247894
(E) admin@crichton.co.uk

Membership: Members & Public

Contact/s:
- Club Secretary: Mr Alan Cathro

Course/s:
🏌 CRICHTON
  Description: Medium Length, Tends to Flood
  Green Speed: Medium
  Built: 1970 **Built On:** Soil
  Number of Holes: 9 **Par:** 70
  Yds: 5952 **F9 Yds:** 2976 **B9 Yds:** 2976
  Further Information:
  9 hole course can be played as an 18 hole course

CRICKLADE

CRICKLADE HOTEL GOLF & COUNTRY CLUB, Common Hill, Cricklade, **WILTSHIRE**, SN6 6HA, **ENGLAND**.
(T) 01793 750751
(W) www.crickladehotel.co.uk

Contact/s:
- Professional: Mr Ian Bolt

Course/s:
🏌 CRICKLADE
  Number of Holes: 9 **Par:** 31
  Yds: 1830
  Designer: Ian Bolt, Colin Smith

CRIEFF

CRIEFF GOLF CLUB LTD, Perth Rd, Crieff, **PERTH AND KINROSS**, PH7 3LR, **SCOTLAND**.
(T) 01764 652909

Contact/s:
- Professional: Mr David Murchie

Course/s:
🏌 DORNOCK
  Description: Parkland, Short
  Number of Holes: 9 **Par:** 64
  Designer: James Braid
  Further Information:
  9 hole course can be played as an 18 hole course. Has excellent views over the Strathearn.

🏌 FERNTOWER
  Description: Parkland, Short
  Number of Holes: 18 **Par:** 71
  Designer: James Braid
  Further Information:
  The course offers magnificent views over the Strathearn Valley and has mostly wide fairways.

CRIMPLE VALLEY

CRIMPLE VALLEY GOLF CLUB, Hookstone Wood Rd, Harrogate, **YORKSHIRE (NORTH)**, HG2 8PN, **ENGLAND**.
(T) 01423 883485

Membership: Members & Public

Contact/s:
- Manager: Mr A Dover

Course/s:
🏌 CRIMPLE VALLEY
  Description: Open, Medium Length, Drains Well
  Built: 1976
  Number of Holes: 9
  Designer: Robin Lumb

CROHAM HURST

CROHAM HURST GOLF CLUB, Croham Rd, South Croydon, **SURREY**, CR2 7HJ, **ENGLAND**.
(T) 020 86575581
(W) www.chgc.co.uk

Contact/s:
- Club Secretary: Mr H Fleming
- Professional: Mr E Stillwell
  ☎ 0208 657 7705

Course/s:
🏌 CROHAM HURST
  Description: Parkland, Undulating, Medium Length, Tight, Drains Well
  Green Speed: Medium
  Built: 1912 **Built On:** Chalk
  Number of Holes: 18 **Par:** 70
  Par 3's: 5 **Par 4's:** 10 **Par 5's:** 3
  Yds: 6290 **F9 Yds:** 3195 **B9 Yds:** 3095
  Prevailing Wind: South/West
  Designer: James Braid

CROMER (ROYAL)

ROYAL CROMER GOLF CLUB, 145 Overstrand Rd, Cromer, **NORFOLK**, NR27 0JH, **ENGLAND**.
(T) 01263 512884
(W) www.royal-cromer.com

Membership: Members & Public
Size of Complex: 130 Acres

Contact/s:
- Professional: Mr L Patterson
- Pro Shop:
  ☎ 01263 512267

Course/s:
🏌 ROYAL CROMER
  Description: Parkland, Cliff Top, Undulating, Open, Long, Drains Well
  Green Speed: Medium
  Built: 1888 **Built On:** Sand
  Number of Holes: 18 **Par:** 72
  Record: 69
  Yds: 6508
  Designer: James Braid, Tom Morris
  Further Information:
  The course offers panoramic views, with strong sea breezes.

CROMPTON & ROYTON

CROMPTON & ROYTON GOLF CLUB, High Barn St, Royton, Oldham, **MANCHESTER (GREATER)**, OL2 6RW, **ENGLAND**.
(T) 0161 6240986

Membership: Members & Public

Contact/s:
- Club Secretary: Mr Brian Lord
- Professional: Mr David Melling

Course/s:
🏌 CROMPTON & ROYTON
  Description: Wooded, Parkland, Undulating, Open, Medium Length,

Drains Well, Ideal for the Elderly
Green Speed: Medium
Built: 1913 **Built On:** Clay
Number of Holes: 18 **Par:** 70
Yds: 6186 **F9 Yds:** 3032 **B9 Yds:** 3154
Further Information:
Tony Jacklin & Nick Faldo have played on
this difficult course.

CRONDON PARK

CRONDON PARK GOLF CLUB, Stock Rd,
Stock, Ingatestone, **ESSEX**, CM4 9DP,
ENGLAND.
(T) 01277 841115
(E) info@crondon.com
(W) www.crondon.com
Membership: Members & Public
Contact/s:
• **Club Secretary:** Mr P Cranwell
• **Professional:** Mr P Barham
• **Pro Shop:** Mr G McCarthy
  ☎ 01277 841887
Course/s:
🦅 **CRONDON PARK**
  Description: Championship, Parkland,
  Valley, Long, Drains Well
  Green Speed: Medium
  Built: 1989
  Number of Holes: 18
  Designer: Martin Gillett

🦅 **PAR 3**
  Number of Holes: 9

CROOK

CROOK GOLF CLUB, The Clubhouse, Low
Jobs Hill, Crook, **COUNTY DURHAM**, DL15
9AA, **ENGLAND.**
(T) 01388 762429/767926
Contact/s:
• **Chairman:** Mr Alan Race
Course/s:
🦅 **CROOK**
  Number of Holes: 18 **Par:** 70
  Yds: 6076 **F9 Yds:** 2833 **B9 Yds:** 3243

CROOKHILL PARK MUNICIPAL

**CROOKHILL PARK MUNICIPAL GOLF
COURSE,** Carr Lane, Conisbrough, Doncaster,
YORKSHIRE (SOUTH), DN12 2AH,
ENGLAND.
(T) 01709 862974
Membership: Public
Course/s:
🦅 **CROOKHILL PARK MUNICIPAL**
  Number of Holes: 18

CROSLAND HEATH

CROSLAND HEATH GOLF CLUB LTD, Felk
Stile Rd, Crosland Hill, Huddersfield,
YORKSHIRE (WEST), HD4 7AF, **ENGLAND.**
(T) 01484 653216
Membership: Members & Public
Contact/s:
• **Club Secretary:** Mr Donald Walker
• **Professional:** Mr Jamie Coverley
  ☎ 01484 653877
Course/s:
🦅 **CROSLAND HEATH**
  Description: Heath Land, Open, Medium
  Length, Drains Well
  Green Speed: Medium
  Built: 1913 **Built On:** Sand
  Number of Holes: 18 **Par:** 70
  Par 3's: 5 **Par 4's:** 10 **Par 5's:** 3

Yds: 6004
Prevailing Wind: West
Further Information:
Crosland Heath is a challenging upland
course. All but a few holes have long
distance views with the 9th & 10th having
a 360 degree panorama. The course is
not long but several holes have a long
carry over thick heather. There are 5 par
3s, 4 of which have carries over former
quarries. The course is generally breezy.

CROW NEST PARK

CROW NEST PARK GOLF CLUB, Coach Rd,
Hove Edge, Brighouse, **YORKSHIRE
(WEST)**, HD6 2LN, **ENGLAND.**
(T) 01484 401121
Membership: Members & Public
Contact/s:
• **Professional:** Mr Paul Everett
Course/s:
🦅 **CROW NEST PARK**
  Description: Wooded, Parkland,
  Undulating, Sheltered, Medium Length,
  Tight, Drains Well
  Green Speed: Fast
  Built: 1995
  Number of Holes: 9 **Par:** 70 **Record:** 66
  (James Burke)
  Yds: 5979 **F9 Yds:** 3003 **B9 Yds:** 2976
  Prevailing Wind: West
  Further Information:
  A good testing course which is built on the
  grounds of an old manor house.

CROW WOOD

CROW WOOD GOLF CLUB, Cumbernauld
Rd, Chryston, Glasgow, **GLASGOW (CITY
OF)**, G69 9JF, **SCOTLAND.**
(T) 0141 7791943
Contact/s:
• **Owner:** Mr Brian Moffat
Course/s:
🦅 **CROW WOOD**
  Number of Holes: 18
  Designer: James Braid

CROWBOROUGH BEACON

CROWBOROUGH BEACON GOLF CLUB,
Beacon Rd, Crowborough, **SUSSEX (EAST)**,
TN6 1UJ, **ENGLAND.**
(T) 01892 661511
Contact/s:
• **Club Secretary:** Ms A Isaacs
• **Professional:** Mr D Newnham
  ☎ 01892 653877
Course/s:
🦅 **CROWBOROUGH BEACON**
  Description: Heath Land, Hilltop,
  Undulating, Sheltered, Open, Long, Tight
  Green Speed: Medium
  Built: 1895 **Built On:** Clay
  Number of Holes: 18 **Par:** 71
  Par 3's: 4 **Par 4's:** 11 **Par 5's:** 3
  Yds: 6273
  Prevailing Wind: South/West
  Further Information:
  The course offers panoramic views and is
  800 feet above sea level.

CRUDEN BAY

CRUDEN BAY GOLF CLUB, Aulton Rd,
Cruden Bay, Peterhead, **ABERDEENSHIRE**,
AB42 0NN, **SCOTLAND.**
(T) 01779 812285
(E) cbaygc@aol.com

(W) www.crudenbaygolfclub.co.uk
Membership: Members & Public
Contact/s:
• **Pro Shop:** Mr Robbie Stewart
  ☎ 01779 812414
• **Book Tee Times:** Mrs Rosemary
  Pittendrigh
Course/s:
🦅 **CRUDEN BAY**
  Description: Links Built On: Sand
  Number of Holes: 18 **Par:** 70
  Par 3's: 4 **Par 4's:** 12 **Par 5's:** 2
  Yds: 6395 **F9 Yds:** 3329 **B9 Yds:** 3066
  Designer: Simpson 🏆

CRUIT ISLAND

CRUIT ISLAND GOLF COURSE,
Kincasslagh, Cruit Island, **COUNTY
DONEGAL**, **IRELAND.**
(T) 075 43296
Course/s:
🦅 **CRUIT ISLAND**
  Number of Holes: 9
  Designer: Michael Doherty

CUCKFIELD

CUCKFIELD GOLF COURSE, Staplefield Rd,
Cuckfield, Haywards Heath, **SUSSEX
(WEST)**, RH17 5HY, **ENGLAND.**
(T) 01444 459999
Membership: Members & Public
Size of Complex: 100 Acres
Contact/s:
• **Professional:** Mr Bernard Firkins
• **Book Tee Times:** Mr Andrew Ponsford
Course/s:
🦅 **CUCKFIELD**
  Description: Parkland, Undulating, Open,
  Long
  Green Speed: Medium **Built On:** Soil
  Number of Holes: 9 **Par:** 36
  Par 3's: 2 **Par 4's:** 5 **Par 5's:** 2
  Yds: 2897
  Designer: D Amer, A J Pomsford

CUDDINGTON

CUDDINGTON GOLF CLUB, Banstead Rd,
Banstead, **SURREY**, SM7 1RD, **ENGLAND.**
(T) 020 83930951
Contact/s:
• **Manager:** Mr D M Scott
Course/s:
🦅 **CUDDINGTON**
  Number of Holes: 18
  Designer: Harry Shapland Colt

CULLEN

CULLEN GOLF CLUB, The Links, Cullen,
Buckie, **MORAY**, AB56 4WB, **SCOTLAND.**
(T) 01542 840685
Membership: Members & Public
Contact/s:
• **Club Secretary:** Mr Ian Findley
  ☎ 01542 840174
Course/s:
🦅 **CULLEN**
  Description: Links, Short
  Built: 1903
  Number of Holes: 18 **Par:** 63
  Par 3's: 10 **Par 4's:** 7 **Par 5's:** 1
  Yds: 4610 **F9 Yds:** 2071 **B9 Yds:** 2539
  Designer: Tom Morris, C Neaves
  Further Information:
  The course has traditional Scottish Links

and is laid out on two levels with rocks and ravines making some of the holes very interesting. The scenery is spectacular.

CUMBERWELL

CUMBERWELL PARK GOLF CLUB, Great Cumberwell, Bradford On Avon, Bath, **WILTSHIRE**, BA15 2PQ, **ENGLAND**.
(T) 01225 863322
(E) reception@cumberwellpark.co.uk
(W) www.cumberwellpark.co.uk
Membership: Members & Public
Contact/s:
● **Book Tee Times:** Mr Michael Craig
● **Book Lessons:** Mr John Jacobs
   ☎ 01225 862332
Course/s:
🌑 **LAKELANDS**
   Number of Holes: 9

🌑 **PARKLANDS**
   Number of Holes: 9

🌑 **WOODLANDS**
   Description: Parkland, Undulating, Medium Length
   Green Speed: Medium
   Built: 1995 **Built On:** Clay
   Number of Holes: 9
   Prevailing Wind: West
   Designer: Adrian Stiff
   Further Information:
   The course has 3 loops of 9 holes, each being distinctly different. There are water features on all 3 nines. The course has a 4 star 'Golf World' rating

CUPAR

CUPAR GOLF CLUB, Hilltarvit, Cupar, **FIFE**, KY15 5NZ, **SCOTLAND**.
(T) 01334 653549
(E) secretary@cupargolfclub.freeserve.co.uk
Membership: Members & Public
Contact/s:
● **Club Secretary:** Mr John Houston
● **Book Tee Times:** Mrs Heather Sharp
Course/s:
🌑 **CUPAR**
   Description: Parkland, Open, Short, Drains Well
   Green Speed: Medium
   Built: 1855 **Built On:** Soil
   Number of Holes: 9 **Par:** 68
   Yds: 5074 **F9 Yds:** 2537 **B9 Yds:** 2537
   Designer: A Robertson
   Further Information:
   The oldest continuous 9-hole club in Britain.

CURRA WEST

CURRA WEST GOLF CLUB, Curra Kylebrack, Loughrea, **COUNTY GALWAY**, **IRELAND**.
(T) 050 945121
Course/s:
🌑 **CURRA WEST**
   Number of Holes: 18 **Par:** 67
   Yds: 4548

CURRAGH

CURRAGH GOLF CLUB, Curragh, **COUNTY KILDARE**, **IRELAND**.
(T) 045 441238
Course/s:
🌑 **THE CURRAGH**
   Number of Holes: 18

CUSHENDALL

CUSHENDALL GOLF CLUB, 21 Shore Rd, Cushendall, Ballymena, **COUNTY ANTRIM**, BT44 0NG, **NORTHERN IRELAND**.
(T) 028 21771318
Contact/s:
● **Honorary Secretary:** Mr Shaun McLaughlin
   ☎ 028 21758366
Course/s:
🌑 **CUSHENDALL**
   Built: 1937
   Number of Holes: 9 **Par:** 66
   Par 3's: 3 **Par 4's:** 6
   Yds: 4384 **F9 Yds:** 2193 **B9 Yds:** 2191
   Designer: D Delargy
   Further Information:
   The course offers views of Mull of Kintyre with picturesque 9 holes on the shores of the Northern Antrim coast. Signature hole 2/11 par 3 - tee shot across River Dall to plateau green . This 9 hole course has 16 separate tees and therefore can be played as an 18 hole course, playing off 2 tees twice.

CWMRHYDNEUADD

CWMRHYDNEUADD GOLF CLUB, Pentregat, Llandysul, **CEREDIGION**, SA44 6HD, **WALES**.
(T) 01239 654933
Membership: Members & Public
Size of Complex: 28 Acres
Contact/s:
● **Club Secretary:** Mr John Curry
● **Professional:** Mr Steve Parsons
Course/s:
🌑 **CWMRHYDNEUADD 9 HOLE**
   Description: Parkland, Valley, Sheltered, Short, Tight, Drains Well, Ideal for the Elderly
   Green Speed: Medium
   Built: 1991 **Built On:** Clay
   Number of Holes: 9 **Par:** 62
   Par 3's: 5 **Par 4's:** 4
   Yds: 4176 **F9 Yds:** 2073 **B9 Yds:** 2103
   Prevailing Wind: South/West
   Designer: Gerwyn Davies
   Further Information:
   9 hole course can be played as an 18 hole course

DAINTON PARK

DAINTON PARK GOLF CLUB LTD, Ipplepen, Newton Abbot, **DEVON**, TQ12 5TN, **ENGLAND**.
(T) 01803 815000
Membership: Members & Public
Size of Complex: 130 Acres
Contact/s:
● **Club Secretary:** Mr Mike Penlington
   ☎ 01803 815004
● **Professional:** Mr Martin Tyson
Course/s:
🌑 **DAINTON PARK**
   Description: Parkland, Undulating, Medium Length
   Green Speed: Medium
   Built: 1993 **Built On:** Sand/Soil
   Number of Holes: 18 **Par:** 71
   Record: 65 (Stuart Little)
   Yds: 6234 **F9 Yds:** 3111 **B9 Yds:** 3096
   Designer: Adrian Stiff
   Further Information:
   The opening 2 holes are tough. There are water features on 6 holes, tree lined

fairways and well protected greens.

DALE HILL

DALE HILL HOTEL & GOLF CLUB, Ticehurst, Wadhurst, **SUSSEX (EAST)**, TN5 7DQ, **ENGLAND**.
(T) 01580 200112
(E) info@dalehill.co.uk
(W) www.dalehill.co.uk
Contact/s:
● **Club Secretary:** Ms Maggie Harris
   ☎ 01580 201800
● **Professional:** Mr Paul Charman
   ☎ 01580 201090
● **Pro Shop:** Mr Richard Hollands
Course/s:
🌑 **THE IAN WOOSNAM**
   Description: Championship, Parkland, Valley, Undulating, Open, Medium Length
   Green Speed: Fast
   Built: 1997
   Number of Holes: 18 **Par:** 71
   Yds: 6512
   Designer: Ian Woosnam

🌑 **THE OLD**
   Description: Wooded, Parkland
   Built: 1973
   Number of Holes: 18 **Par:** 70
   Yds: 6000

DALFABER

DALFABER GOLF & COUNTRY CLUB, Dalfaber Drive, Aviemore, **HIGHLANDS**, PH22 1ST, **SCOTLAND**.
(T) 01479 811244
Contact/s:
● **Manager:** Mr Ivan Frassen
Course/s:
🌑 **DALFABER**
   Number of Holes: 9

DALMAHOY

MARRIOTT DALMAHOY HOTEL & COUNTRY CLUB, Kirknewton, Edinburgh, **EDINBURGH (CITY OF)**, EH27 8EB, **SCOTLAND**.
(T) 0131 3331845
(E) golf.dalmahoy@marriotthotels.co.uk
Contact/s:
● **Director Of Golf:** Mr Iain Burns
Course/s:
🌑 **EAST**
   Description: Undulating, Long
   Built: 1927
   Number of Holes: 18 **Par:** 72
   Yds: 6638 **F9 Yds:** 3202 **B9 Yds:** 3436
   Designer: James Braid

🌑 **WEST**
   Description: Tight
   Built: 1927
   Number of Holes: 18 **Par:** 68
   Yds: 5168
   Designer: James Braid

DALMALLY

DALMALLY GOLF COURSE, Old Saw Mill, Dalmally, **ARGYLL AND BUTE**, PA33 1AE, **SCOTLAND**.
(T) 01838 200370
(E) golfclub@loch-awe.com
(W) www.loch-awe.com/golfclub/default.htm
Contact/s:
● **Club Secretary:** Mr A J Burke
Course/s:

⚫ **DALMALLY**
Number of Holes: 9 Par: 32
Par 3's: 4 Par 4's: 5
Yds: 2264
Designer: Barrow, MacFarlane
Further Information:
9 hole course can be played as an 18 hole course

DALMILLING

DALMILLING GOLF COURSE, Westwood Ave, Whitletts, Ayr, **AYRSHIRE (SOUTH)**, KA8 0QY, **SCOTLAND**.
(T) 01292 263893

Membership: Members & Public

Contact/s:
● Professional: Mr Philip Cheyney

Course/s:
⚫ **DALMILLING**
Description: Parkland, Valley, Medium Length, Tends to Flood, Ideal for the Elderly
Green Speed: Medium
Built: 1960 Built On: Clay
Number of Holes: 18 Par: 69
Par 3's: 5 Par 4's: 11 Par 5's: 2
Yds: 5686

DALMUIR MUNICIPAL

DALMUIR MUNICIPAL GOLF COURSE, Overtoun Rd, Dalmuir, Dumbartonshire, Clydebank, **ARGYLL AND BUTE**, G81 3RE, **SCOTLAND**.
(T) 0141 9526372

Membership: Public

Course/s:
⚫ **DALMUIR MUNICIPAL**
Number of Holes: 18

DALMUNZIE

DALMUNZIE GOLF CLUB, Dalmunzie Estate, Spittal Of Glenshee, Blairgowrie, **PERTH AND KINROSS**, PH10 7QG, **SCOTLAND**.
(T) 01250 885226

Contact/s:
● Owner: Mr Simon Winton

Course/s:
⚫ **DALMUNZIE**
Number of Holes: 9 Par: 30
Yds: 2099

DALZIEL

DALZIEL PARK GOLF & COUNTRY CLUB, Hagen Drive, Motherwell, **LANARKSHIRE (NORTH)**, ML1 5RZ, **SCOTLAND**.
(T) 01698 862444

Course/s:
⚫ **DALZIEL**
Number of Holes: 18 Par: 71
Yds: 6300

DANESBURY PARK

DANESBURY PARK GOLF CLUB, Codicote Rd, Welwyn, **HERTFORDSHIRE**, AL6 9SD, **ENGLAND**.
(T) 01438 840100
(E) ds@snowdongolf.com

Membership: Members & Public

Contact/s:
● Club Secretary: Mr Derek Snowdon
● Professional: Mr Gary Toiley

Course/s:

⚫ **DANESBURY**
Number of Holes: 9

DARENTH VALLEY

DARENTH VALLEY GOLF COURSE, Station Rd, Shoreham, Sevenoaks, **KENT**, TN14 7SA, **ENGLAND**.
(T) 01959 522922

Membership: Public

Contact/s:
● Professional: Mr David Copsey

Course/s:
⚫ **DARENTH VALLEY**
Description: Parkland, Valley, Undulating, Sheltered, Medium Length, Drains Well, Ideal for the Elderly
Green Speed: Medium
Built: 1973 Built On: Chalk
Number of Holes: 18 Par: 72
Par 3's: 4 Par 4's: 10 Par 5's: 4
Yds: 6302 F9 Yds: 3129 B9 Yds: 3173
Further Information:
The course is very picturesque.

DARLINGTON

DARLINGTON GOLF CLUB, Haughton Grange, Darlington, **COUNTY DURHAM**, DL1 3JD, **ENGLAND**.
(T) 01325 355324

Contact/s:
● Professional: Mr Craig Dilley
● Book Tee Times: Mr Mark Rogers
☎ 01325 484198

Course/s:
⚫ **DARLINGTON**
Description: Parkland
Built: 1908
Number of Holes: 18 Par: 70
Yds: 6181 F9 Yds: 3148 B9 Yds: 3033
Designer: Alistair MacKenzie

A MacKenzie

DARTFORD

DARTFORD GOLF CLUB, Heath Lane (Upper), Dartford, **KENT**, DA1 2TN, **ENGLAND**.
(T) 01322 226455
Size of Complex: 60 Acres

Contact/s:
● Professional: Mr John Gregory
☎ 01322 226409

Course/s:
⚫ **DARTFORD**
Description: Parkland, Undulating, Sheltered, Medium Length, Ideal for the Elderly
Green Speed: Slow Built On: Soil
Number of Holes: 18 Par: 69
Record: 61
Yds: 5591 F9 Yds: 2831 B9 Yds: 2760
Designer: James Braid

DARTMOUTH

DARTMOUTH GOLF & COUNTRY CLUB, Blackawton, Totnes, **DEVON**, TQ9 7DE, **ENGLAND**.
(T) 01803 712686
(E) info@dgcc.co.uk
(W) www.dgcc.co.uk

Membership: Members & Public
Size of Complex: 225 Acres

Contact/s:
● Professional: Mr Steven Dougan
● Pro Shop:
☎ 01803 712650

Course/s:
⚫ **CHAMPIONSHIP**
Description: Championship, Parkland, Valley, Undulating, Sheltered, Open, Medium Length, Drains Well, Ideal for the Elderly
Green Speed: Fast
Built: 1992
Number of Holes: 18 Par: 72
Record: 72 (Steven Dougan)
Par 3's: 4 Par 4's: 10 Par 5's: 4
Yds: 6663 F9 Yds: 3126 B9 Yds: 3537
Designer: Jeremy Pern
Further Information:
There are water features on 11 of the course's holes.

⚫ **CLUB**
Number of Holes: 9 Par: 66
Par 3's: 5 Par 4's: 2 Par 5's: 2
Yds: 4791 F9 Yds: 2252 B9 Yds: 2539
Designer: Jeremy Pern
Further Information:
9 hole course can be played as an 18 hole course

DARTMOUTH

DARTMOUTH GOLF CLUB, Vale St, West Bromwich, **MIDLANDS (WEST)**, B71 4DW, **ENGLAND**.
(T) 0121 5882131

Contact/s:
● Professional: Mr Simon Joyce

Course/s:
⚫ **DARTMOUTH**
Description: Parkland, Tight
Built: 1910
Number of Holes: 9 Par: 71
Yds: 6036 F9 Yds: 3086 B9 Yds: 2950
Further Information:
This 9 hole course offers a challenging game. It has a tough opening hole and can be played as 18 holes.

DARWEN

DARWEN GOLF CLUB LTD, Duddon Ave, Darwen, **LANCASHIRE**, BB3 0LB, **ENGLAND**.
(T) 01254 704367

Contact/s:
● Manageress: Ms J Stanley

Course/s:
⚫ **DARWEN**
Number of Holes: 18

DATCHET

DATCHET GOLF CLUB, Buccleuch Rd, Datchet, Slough, **BERKSHIRE**, SL3 9BP, **ENGLAND**.
(T) 01753 543887/541872
(W) www.datchetgolfclub.co.uk

Contact/s:
● Club Secretary: Mr Darren Murphy
● Professional: Mr Ian Godleman
☎ 01753 545222

Course/s:
⚫ **DATCHET**
Description: Parkland, Short, Ideal for the Elderly
Green Speed: Medium/Fast
Built: 1890 Built On: Soil
Number of Holes: 9 Par: 70
Yds: 6087 F9 Yds: 3049 B9 Yds: 3038
Further Information:
The course offers views of Windsor Castle.

DAVENPORT

DAVENPORT GOLF CLUB, Middlewood Rd, Poynton, Stockport, **CHESHIRE**, SK12 1TS, **ENGLAND**.
(T) 01625 876951
Membership: Members & Public
Contact/s:
● **Club Secretary:** Mr T E Bonfield
● **Professional:** Mr Gary Norcott
  ☎ 01625 877319
Course/s:
🌑 **DAVENPORT**
  Description: Parkland, Undulating
  Built: 1973 **Built On:** Clay
  Number of Holes: 18 **Par:** 69
  Par 3's: 5 **Par 4's:** 11 **Par 5's:** 2
  Yds: 6027 **F9 Yds:** 3058 **B9 Yds:** 2969
  Further Information:
  There is a pond on the course.

DAVENTRY & DISTRICT

DAVENTRY & DISTRICT GOLF CLUB, Norton Rd, Daventry, **NORTHAMPTONSHIRE**, NN11 5LS, **ENGLAND**.
(T) 01327 702829
Contact/s:
● **Club Secretary:** Mr E G Smith
Course/s:
🌑 **DAVENTRY & DISTRICT**
  Number of Holes: 9

DAVYHULME PARK

DAVYHULME PARK GOLF CLUB, Gleneagles Rd, Urmston, Manchester, **MANCHESTER (GREATER)**, M41 8SA, **ENGLAND**.
(T) 0161 7482260
Membership: Members & Public
Size of Complex: 95 Acres
Contact/s:
● **Club Secretary:** Mr L B Wright
● **Professional:** Mr Dean Butler
● **Book Tee Times:** Mrs Sandy Rogerson
Course/s:
🌑 **DAVYHULME PARK**
  Description: Wooded, Parkland, Open, Short, Medium Length, Drains Well, Ideal for the Elderly
  Green Speed: Medium
  Built: 1936 **Built On:** Soil
  Number of Holes: 18
  Prevailing Wind: West

DAWLISH APPROACH

DAWLISH APPROACH GOLF COURSE, Sandy Lane, Dawlish, **DEVON**, EX7 0AF, **ENGLAND**.
(T) 01626 888272
Course/s:
🌑 **DAWLISH APPROACH**
  Number of Holes: 9

DAWN 'TIL DUSK

DAWN 'TIL DUSK GOLF COURSE, Bastleford Rd, Rosemarket, Milford Haven, **PEMBROKESHIRE**, SA73 1JY, **WALES**.
(T) 01437 890281
Membership: Members & Public
Size of Complex: 120 Acres
Contact/s:
● **Club Secretary:** Mr W R Young
● **Pro Shop:** Mrs Bridie Young

Course/s:
🌑 **DAWN 'TIL DUSK**
  Description: Parkland, Open, Long, Drains Well, Ideal for the Elderly
  Green Speed: Medium
  Built: 1993 **Built On:** Soil
  Number of Holes: 18 **Par:** 73
  Par 3's: 2 **Par 4's:** 13 **Par 5's:** 3
  Yds: 6373 **F9 Yds:** 3345 **B9 Yds:** 3028
  Prevailing Wind: South/West
  Designer: W R Young
  Further Information:
  This is the longest 9 hole course in Wales.

DEAN FARM

DEAN FARM GOLF CLUB, Main Rd, Kingsley, Bordon, **HAMPSHIRE**, GU35 9NG, **ENGLAND**.
(T) 01420 489478
Contact/s:
● **Owner:** Mr G W Doggrell
Course/s:
🌑 **DEAN FARM**
  Number of Holes: 9

DEAN WOOD

DEAN WOOD GOLF CLUB, Lafford Lane, Upholland, Skelmersdale, **LANCASHIRE**, WN8 0QZ, **ENGLAND**.
(T) 01695 622980
Membership: Members & Public
Size of Complex: 96 Acres
Contact/s:
● **Club Secretary:** Mr A S McGregor
● **Professional:** Mr Stuart Danchin
Course/s:
🌑 **DEAN WOOD**
  Description: Parkland, Hilltop, Undulating, Open, Medium Length, Drains Well
  Green Speed: Medium
  Built: 1922 **Built On:** Clay
  Number of Holes: 18 **Par:** 71
  Yds: 6148 **F9 Yds:** 3318 **B9 Yds:** 2830
  Prevailing Wind: North/West
  Designer: James Braid

DEANE

DEANE GOLF CLUB, Broadford Rd, Bolton, **LANCASHIRE**, BL3 4NS, **ENGLAND**.
(T) 01204 651808
Membership: Members & Public
Size of Complex: 89 Acres
Contact/s:
● **Club Secretary:** Mr Roy Y Hough
● **Professional:** Mr David Martindale
Course/s:
🌑 **DEANE**
  Description: Parkland, Hilltop, Undulating, Sheltered, Open, Short
  Green Speed: Medium
  Built: 1906 **Built On:** Clay
  Number of Holes: 18 **Par:** 68
  Yds: 5652 **F9 Yds:** 2830 **B9 Yds:** 2822
  Prevailing Wind: West
  Further Information:
  A testing course.

DEANGATE RIDGE

DEANGATE RIDGE GOLF COURSE, Dux Court Rd, Hoo, Rochester, **KENT**, ME3 8RZ, **ENGLAND**.
(T) 01634 251180
Membership: Members & Public
Contact/s:

● **Professional:** Mr Richard Fox
Course/s:
🌑 **DEANGATE RIDGE**
  Description: Parkland, Undulating, Open, Medium Length, Tends to Flood, Ideal for the Elderly
  Green Speed: Slow
  Built: 1972 **Built On:** Clay
  Number of Holes: 18 **Record:** 66
🌑 **PAR 3**
  Number of Holes: 18

DEANWOOD PARK

DEANWOOD PARK, Deanwood Farm, Baydon Rd, Stockcross, Newbury, **BERKSHIRE**, RG20 8JS, **ENGLAND**.
(T) 01635 48772
Membership: Public
Size of Complex: 40 Acres
Contact/s:
● **Club Secretary:** Mr John Bowness
  ☎ 01635 72824
● **Professional:** Mr James Purton
Course/s:
🌑 **DEANWOOD**
  Description: Wooded, Parkland, Undulating, Short, Drains Well, Ideal for the Elderly
  Green Speed: Medium
  Built: 1995
  Number of Holes: 9 **Par:** 32
  Par 3's: 4 **Par 4's:** 5
  Yds: 2114
  Further Information:
  This 9 hole course offers views over Donnington Castle. It has many large mature trees along the course and it can be played as 18 holes.

DEER PARK

DEER PARK GOLF & COUNTRY CLUB, Golf Course Rd, Livingston, **LOTHIAN (WEST)**, EH54 8AB, **SCOTLAND**.
(T) 01506 446688
Contact/s:
● **Professional:** Mr Brian Dumber
Course/s:
🌑 **DEER PARK**
  Description: Championship, Parkland, Long
  Built: 1978
  Number of Holes: 18 **Par:** 72
  Designer: Peter Alliss, David Thomas
  Further Information:
  A fairly flat, testing championship course.

DEER PARK HOTEL

DEER PARK HOTEL & GOLF COURSES, Howth, Dublin, **COUNTY DUBLIN**, **IRELAND**.
(T) 01 8322624
(E) sales@deerpark.iol.ie
Course/s:
🌑 **DEER PARK**
  Number of Holes: 18
🌑 **GRACE O'MALLEY**
  Number of Holes: 9
🌑 **SHORT**
  Number of Holes: 9
🌑 **ST FINTANS**
  Number of Holes: 9

DEESIDE

DEESIDE GOLF CLUB, Golf Rd, Bieldside, Aberdeen, **ABERDEEN (CITY OF)**, AB15 9DL, **SCOTLAND**.
(T) 01224 869457

Membership: Members & Public

Contact/s:
- **Pro Shop:** Mr Frank Coutts
  ☎ 01224 861041

Course/s:
- **BLAIRS**
  Number of Holes: 9   **Par:** 71
  Par 3's: 3   **Par 4's:** 4   **Par 5's:** 2
  Yds: 5581   **F9 Yds:** 2769   **B9 Yds:** 2812
  Further Information:
  9 hole course can be played as an 18 hole course

- **HAUGHTON**
  Description: Parkland
  Built: 1903   **Built On:** Soil
  Number of Holes: 18   **Par:** 70
  Par 3's: 5   **Par 4's:** 10   **Par 5's:** 3
  Yds: 6286   **F9 Yds:** 3334   **B9 Yds:** 2952

DELAPRE PARK GOLF COMPLEX

DELAPRE PARK GOLF COMPLEX, Eagle Drive, Northampton, **NORTHAMPTONSHIRE**, NN4 7DU, **ENGLAND**.
(T) 01604 764036

Membership: Members & Public

Contact/s:
- **Club Secretary:** Mr John Corby
- **Pro Shop:** Mr John Cuddihy

Course/s:
- **HARDING STONE**
  Description: Undulating
  Built: 1994
  Number of Holes: 9

- **MAIN**
  Description: Parkland, Sheltered, Open, Medium Length, Tends to Flood, Ideal for the Elderly
  Green Speed: Slow
  Built: 1976   **Built On:** Clay
  Number of Holes: 18

  Prevailing Wind: East
  Designer: John Jacobs, John Corby

DELGANY

DELGANY GOLF CLUB, Delgany, **COUNTY DUBLIN**, **IRELAND**.
(T) 01 2874536
(E) delganygolf@eircom.net

Contact/s:
- **Club Secretary:** Mr Robbie Kelly

Course/s:
- **DELGANY**
  Built: 1908
  Number of Holes: 18   **Par:** 69
  Yds: 6567
  Designer: Harry Vardon

DELVIN CASTLE

DELVIN CASTLE GOLF CLUB, Delvin, **COUNTY WESTMEATH**, **IRELAND**.
(T) 044 64315

Course/s:
- **DELVIN CASTLE**
  Number of Holes: 18
  Designer: John Day

DENBIGH

DENBIGH GOLF CLUB, Henllan Rd, Denbigh, **DENBIGHSHIRE**, LL16 5AA, **WALES**.
(T) 01745 816669

Membership: Members & Public
Size of Complex: 90 Acres

Contact/s:
- **Professional:** Mr Mike Jones
  ☎ 01745 814159

Course/s:
- **DENBIGH**
  Description: Parkland, Undulating, Short, Tight, Drains Well, Ideal for the Elderly
  Green Speed: Medium
  Built: 1922   **Built On:** Soil
  Number of Holes: 18   **Par:** 69
  Par 3's: 4   **Par 4's:** 13   **Par 5's:** 1
  Yds: 5712   **F9 Yds:** 2780   **B9 Yds:** 2932

DENHAM

DENHAM GOLF CLUB, Tilehouse Lane, Denham, Uxbridge, **LONDON (GREATER)**, UB9 5DE, **ENGLAND**.
(T) 01895 832022

Contact/s:
- **Club Secretary:** Mr M Miller

Course/s:
- **DENHAM**
  Number of Holes: 18   **Par:** 70
  Yds: 6462   **F9 Yds:** 3226   **B9 Yds:** 3236
  Designer: Harry Shapland Colt

DENTON

DENTON GOLF CLUB, Manchester Rd, Denton, Manchester, **MANCHESTER (GREATER)**, M34 3JU, **ENGLAND**.
(T) 0161 3363218

Membership: Members & Public
Size of Complex: 140 Acres

Contact/s:
- **Club Secretary:** Mr William Tewson
- **Professional:** Mr Michael Holingsworth

Course/s:
- **DENTON**
  Description: Parkland, Undulating, Open, Medium Length, Drains Well, Ideal for the Elderly
  Green Speed: Medium
  Built: 1909   **Built On:** Clay
  Number of Holes: 18   **Par:** 71
  Par 3's: 4   **Par 4's:** 11   **Par 5's:** 3
  Yds: 6496   **F9 Yds:** 3211   **B9 Yds:** 3285
  Prevailing Wind: North/West
  Further Information:
  A testing course which is in very good condition.

DERBY

DERBY GOLF CLUB, Shakespeare St, Sinfin, Derby, **DERBYSHIRE**, DE24 9HD, **ENGLAND**.
(T) 01332 766323

Contact/s:
- **Manager:** Mr S Holton

Course/s:
- **DERBY**
  Number of Holes: 18   **Par:** 70
  Yds: 6144

DEREHAM

DEREHAM GOLF CLUB, Quebec Rd, Dereham, **NORFOLK**, NR19 2DS, **ENGLAND**.
(T) 01362 695900

Membership: Members & Public

Contact/s:
- **Club Secretary:** Mr S Kaye
- **Professional:** Mr Robert Curtis
  ☎ 01362 695631

Course/s:
- **DEREHAM**
  Description: Parkland, Undulating, Sheltered, Medium Length, Drains Well
  Green Speed: Medium
  Built: 1934
  Number of Holes: 9   **Par:** 71
  Yds: 6225   **F9 Yds:** 3069   **B9 Yds:** 3156
  Prevailing Wind: South/West
  Further Information:
  9 hole course can be played as an 18 hole course

DERLLYS COURT

DERLLYS COURT GOLF CLUB, Derllys Court, Llysonnen Rd, Carmarthen, **CARMARTHENSHIRE**, SA33 5DT, **WALES**.
(T) 01267 211575
(E) derllys@hotmail.com
(W) www.derllyscourtgolfclub.co.uk

Membership: Public
Size of Complex: 50 Acres

Contact/s:
- **Club Secretary:** Ms Rhian Walters

Course/s:
- **DERLLYS COURT**
  Description: Parkland, Undulating, Open, Medium Length, Drains Well, Ideal for the Elderly
  Green Speed: Fast   **Built On:** Soil
  Number of Holes: 9   **Par:** 35
  Yds: 2800
  Prevailing Wind: South/West
  Designer: Peter Johnson
  Further Information:
  The course is situated within a very scenic area.

DERRY

CITY OF DERRY GOLF CLUB, 49 Victoria Rd, Londonderry, **COUNTY LONDONDERRY**, BT47 2PU, **NORTHERN IRELAND**.
(T) 028 71346369

Membership: Members & Public

Contact/s:
- **Club Secretary:** Mr Terry Phillip
- **Professional:** Mr Michael Doherty
  ☎ 028 71311496

Course/s:
- **DUNHUGH**
  Description: Parkland, Undulating, Open, Long, Drains Well, Ideal for the Elderly
  Green Speed: Medium/Fast
  Built On: Clay
  Number of Holes: 9   **Par:** 33
  Yds: 2354
  Prevailing Wind: South

- **PREHEN**
  Description: Parkland, Undulating, Open, Long, Drains Well, Ideal for the Elderly
  Green Speed: Medium/Fast
  Built: 1912   **Built On:** Clay
  Number of Holes: 18   **Par:** 71
  Record: 64 (Lesley Walker)
  Yds: 5649   **F9 Yds:** 2949   **B9 Yds:** 2700
  Prevailing Wind: South
  Further Information:
  The course overlooks the River Foyle.

DEWLANDS MANOR

DEWLANDS MANOR GOLF COURSE,
Cottage Hill, Rotherfield, Crowborough,
SUSSEX (EAST), TN6 3JN, **ENGLAND**.
(T) 01892 852266

Membership: Public

Contact/s:
- **Professional:** Mr Nick Godin
- **Pro Shop:** Mr Trevor Robins

Course/s:
- **DEWLANDS**
  Description: Short
  Green Speed: Fast
  Built: 1989 **Built On:** Clay/Soil
  Number of Holes: 9 **Par:** 72
  Par 3's: 2 **Par 4's:** 5 **Par 5's:** 2
  Yds: 3186
  Designer: Godin
  Further Information:
  This 9 hole, meadowland course can be
  played as 18 holes and has water features
  throughout. It also has the second highest
  point in Essex.

DEWSBURY DISTRICT

DEWSBURY DISTRICT GOLF CLUB, The
Pinnacle, Sands Lane, Mirfield, **YORKSHIRE
(WEST)**, WF14 8HJ, **ENGLAND**.
(T) 01924 491928

Contact/s:
- **Professional:** Mr Nigel Hirst

Course/s:
- **DEWSBURY DISTRICT**
  Number of Holes: 18 **Par:** 71
  Yds: 6360 **F9 Yds:** 3124 **B9 Yds:** 3236
  Designer: Peter Alliss, Tom Morris

DEWSTOW

DEWSTOW GOLF CLUB, Caerwent,
Caldicot, **MONMOUTHSHIRE**, NP26 5AH,
WALES.
(T) 01291 430444
(W) www.dewstow.com

Membership: Members & Public
Size of Complex: 280 Acres

Contact/s:
- **Club Secretary:** Ms Barbara Hill
- **Professional:** Mr John Skuse
- **Pro Shop:** Mr Andrew Skimore

Course/s:
- **DEWSTOW**
  Number of Holes: 18
- **DEWSTOW**
  Description: Wooded, Parkland,
  Undulating, Open, Medium Length,
  Drains Well, Ideal for the Elderly
  Green Speed: Medium
  Built: 1988 **Built On:** Sand/Soil
  Number of Holes: 18
  Prevailing Wind: South

DIBDEN GOLF CTRE

DIBDEN GOLF CENTRE, Professional Shop,
Main Rd, Dibden, Southampton,
HAMPSHIRE, SO45 5TB, **ENGLAND**.
(T) 023 80207508
(E) jslade.psmith@excite.co.uk
(W) www.nfdc.gov.uk/golf

Contact/s:
- **Professional:** Mr Paul Smith

Course/s:
- **DIBDEN 18 HOLE**
  Description: Parkland
  Number of Holes: 18 **Par:** 70

Par 3's: 5 **Par 4's:** 10 **Par 5's:** 3
Yds: 5886 **F9 Yds:** 3309 **B9 Yds:** 2577
Designer: J Hamilton-Stutt

- **DIBDEN 9 HOLE**
  Number of Holes: 9 **Par:** 29
  Par 3's: 7 **Par 4's:** 2
  Yds: 1520
  Designer: J Hamilton-Stutt

DIDSBURY

DIDSBURY GOLF CLUB, Ford Lane,
Northenden, Manchester, **MANCHESTER
(GREATER)**, M22 4NQ, **ENGLAND**.
(T) 0161 9982811
(E) golf.didsbury@talk21.com
(W) www.didsburygolfclub.com

Contact/s:
- **Manager:** Mr A L Watson
  ☎ 0161 9989278

Course/s:
- **DIDSBURY**
  Number of Holes: 18 **Par:** 70
  Yds: 5993 **F9 Yds:** 2933 **B9 Yds:** 3060

DINAS POWYS

DINAS POWYS GOLF CLUB, Old High
Walls, Dinas Powys, **GLAMORGAN (VALE
OF)**, CF64 4AJ, **WALES**.
(T) 01222 512727

Course/s:
- **DINAS POWYS**
  Number of Holes: 18

DINNATON

DINNATON GOLF CLUB, Blachford Rd,
Ivybridge, **DEVON**, PL21 9HU, **ENGLAND**.
(T) 01752 892512

Contact/s:
- **Club Secretary:** Mr Brian Rimes
  ☎ 01752 892452
- **Professional:** Mr David Ridyard
  ☎ 01752 691288

Course/s:
- **DINNATON SPORTING & COUNTRY CLUB**
  Description: Moorland
  Built: 1989
  Number of Holes: 9 **Par:** 64
  Further Information:
  Challenging course. 9 hole course can be
  played as an 18 hole course

DINSDALE SPA

DINSDALE SPA GOLF CLUB, Neasham Rd,
Middleton St. George, Darlington, **COUNTY
DURHAM**, DL2 1DW, **ENGLAND**.
(T) 01325 332711

Contact/s:
- **Hon Secretary:** Mr E P Davison

Course/s:
- **DINSDALE SPA**
  Number of Holes: 18 **Par:** 71
  Par 3's: 4 **Par 4's:** 11 **Par 5's:** 3
  Yds: 6099 **F9 Yds:** 2726 **B9 Yds:** 3373

DIP FARM

DIP FARM GOLF CLUB, Corton Rd,
Lowestoft, **SUFFOLK**, NR32 4PH, **ENGLAND**.
(T) 01502 513322

Membership: Public
Size of Complex: 11 Acres

Contact/s:
- **Manager:** Mr S Osman

Course/s:

- **DIP FARM**
  Description: Links, Parkland, Hilltop, Cliff
  Top, Undulating, Open, Medium Length,
  Drains Well, Ideal for the Elderly
  Green Speed: Medium/Fast
  Built: 1893 **Built On:** Clay/Soil
  Number of Holes: 9 **Par:** 36 **Record:** 66
  (Andrew Sherborne)
  Yds: 3101
  Designer: Hawtree, S Taylor
  Further Information:
  Can be played as an 18 hole course.

DISLEY

DISLEY GOLF CLUB LTD, Stanley Hall Lane,
Disley, Stockport, **CHESHIRE**, SK12 2JX,
ENGLAND.
(T) 01663 762884

Course/s:
- **DISLEY**
  Number of Holes: 18

DISS

DISS GOLF CLUB, The Common, Stuston,
Diss, **NORFOLK**, IP21 4AA, **ENGLAND**.
(T) 01379 641025
(E) sec.dissgolf@virgin.net
(W) www.club-noticeboard.co.uk/diss

Contact/s:
- **Club Secretary:** Mr Chris Wellstead
- **Professional:** Mr Nigel Taylor
  ☎ 01379 644399

Course/s:
- **DISS**
  Number of Holes: 18 **Par:** 70
  Par 3's: 5 **Par 4's:** 10 **Par 5's:** 3
  Yds: 6262 **F9 Yds:** 3006 **B9 Yds:** 3256

DISTINGTON GOLF

**DISTINGTON GOLF COURSE & DRIVING
RANGE,** Charity Lane, High Harrington,
Workington, **CUMBRIA**, CA14 5RT,
ENGLAND.
(T) 01946 833688

Membership: Members & Public

Contact/s:
- **Professional:** Mr Keith Wareing

Course/s:
- **DISTINGTON**
  Description: Heath Land, Short, Ideal for
  the Elderly
  Green Speed: Slow
  Built: 1993
  Number of Holes: 9
  Designer: Keith Wareing

DJOUCE MOUNTAIN

DJOUCE MOUNTAIN GOLF CLUB,
Roundwood, **COUNTY WICKLOW**,
IRELAND.
(T) 01 2818585

Course/s:
- **DJOUCE MOUNTAIN**
  Number of Holes: 9 **Par:** 35
  Yds: 2830

DOG

DOG GOLF COURSE, Greys Green Farm,
Greys Green, Rotherfield Greys, Henley-on-
Thames, **OXFORDSHIRE**, RG9 4QG,
ENGLAND.
(T) 01491 628578

Contact/s:
- **Professional:** Mr Daryl Scott

Course/s:

🏌 **DOG - 18 HOLE**
Description: Medium Length
Number of Holes: 18 **Par:** 71
Yds: 6000

🏌 **DOG - 9 HOLE**
Description: Short
Number of Holes: 9 **Par:** 27
Par 3's: 9

DOLGELLAU

DOLGELLAU GOLF CLUB, Pencefn Rd, Dolgellau, **GWYNEDD,** LL40 2ES, **WALES.**
(T) 01341 422603

Course/s:

🏌 **DOLGELLAU**
Description: Parkland
Built: 1912
Number of Holes: 9 **Par:** 66
Further Information:
The course is part of the ancient Hengwrt Estate. 9 hole course can be played as an 18 hole course

DOLLAR

DOLLAR GOLF CLUB, Brewlands House, Back Rd, Dollar, **CLACKMANNANSHIRE,** FK14 7EA, **SCOTLAND.**
(T) 01259 742400
(E) dollar.g.c@brewlandshousefreeserve.co.uk
(W) www.dollargolfclub.co.uk
Membership: Members & Public
Size of Complex: 70 Acres

Contact/s:

● **Club Secretary:** Mr J Brown
  ☎ 01259 743497
● **Book Tee Times:** Mr A Wallace

Course/s:

🏌 **DOLLAR**
Description: Heath Land, Undulating, Open, Short, Tight, Drains Well
Green Speed: Medium
Built: 1907 **Built On:** Soil
Number of Holes: 18 **Par:** 69
Par 3's: 4 **Par 4's:** 13 **Par 5's:** 1
Yds: 5242 **F9 Yds:** 2330 **B9 Yds:** 2912
Prevailing Wind: West
Designer: Ben Sayers

DONABATE

DONABATE GOLF CLUB, Balcarrick Rd, Donabate, **COUNTY DUBLIN, IRELAND.**
(T) 01 8436346
(E) golfclub@indigo.ie

Course/s:

🏌 **DONABATE**
Number of Holes: 18

DONAGHADEE

DONAGHADEE GOLF CLUB, 84 Warren Rd, Donaghadee, **COUNTY DOWN,** BT21 0PQ, **NORTHERN IRELAND.**
(T) 028 91883624
Membership: Members & Public
Size of Complex: 85 Acres

Contact/s:

● **Professional:** Mr Gordon Drew
  ☎ 028 91882392

Course/s:

🏌 **DONAGHADEE**
Description: Links, Parkland, Open, Medium Length, Ideal for the Elderly
Green Speed: Medium
Number of Holes: 18 **Par:** 71

Par 3's: 3 **Par 4's:** 13 **Par 5's:** 2
Yds: 5570 **F9 Yds:** 2818 **B9 Yds:** 2752
Further Information:
The course offers scenic views over Copeland Island.

DONCASTER TOWN MOOR

DONCASTER TOWN MOOR GOLF CLUB, Bawtry Rd, Doncaster, **YORKSHIRE (SOUTH),** DN4 5HU, **ENGLAND.**
(T) 01302 533167

Contact/s:

● **Professional:** Mr Steve Shaw
● **Book Tee Times:**
  ☎ 01302 535286

Course/s:

🏌 **DONCASTER TOWN MOOR**
Description: Parkland, Drains Well
Built: 1895
Number of Holes: 18 **Par:** 69

DONEGAL

DONEGAL GOLF CLUB, Murvagh, Laghey, **COUNTY DONEGAL, IRELAND.**
(T) 073 34054

Course/s:

🏌 **DONEGAL**
Number of Holes: 18
Designer: Edward Hackett

DONERAILE

DONERAILE GOLF CLUB, Doneraile, **COUNTY CORK, IRELAND.**
(T) 022 24137

Course/s:

🏌 **DONERAILE**
Number of Holes: 9

DONNINGTON VALLEY

DONNINGTON VALLEY HOTEL & GOLF COURSE, Snelsmore Hse, Snelsmore Common, Donnington, Newbury, **BERKSHIRE,** RG14 3BG, **ENGLAND.**
(T) 01635 568140

Contact/s:

● **Professional:** Mr Martin Balfour
  ☎ 01635 568142

Course/s:

🏌 **DONNINGTON VALLEY**
Built: 1988
Number of Holes: 18 **Par:** 71
Yds: 6353 **F9 Yds:** 3254 **B9 Yds:** 3099

DOOKS

DOOKS GOLF CLUB, Glenbeigh, **COUNTY KERRY, IRELAND.**
(T) 066 9768205
(W) www.dooks.com
Membership: Members & Public
Size of Complex: 100 Acres

Contact/s:

● **Club Secretary:** Ms Breda Sheahan

Course/s:

🏌 **DOOKS**
Description: Links
Green Speed: Fast
Built: 1889 **Built On:** Sand
Number of Holes: 18 **Par:** 70
Yds: 6071 **F9 Yds:** 2810 **B9 Yds:** 3261
Prevailing Wind: West
Designer: Edward Hackett, Donald Steel
Further Information:
One of Ireland's oldest courses, with panoramic views of Dingle Bay.

DOON VALLEY

DOON VALLEY GOLF CLUB, 1 Hillside, Patna, Ayr, **AYRSHIRE (SOUTH),** KA6 7JT, **SCOTLAND.**
(T) 01292 531607

Contact/s:

● **Manager:** Mr H Johnson

Course/s:

🏌 **DOON VALLEY**
Number of Holes: 9

DOONBEG

DOONBEG GOLF CLUB, Doonbeg, **COUNTY CLARE, IRELAND.**
(T) 065 905 5246
(E) links@doonbeggolfclub.com
(W) www.doonbeggolfclub.com

Contact/s:

● **Club Secretary:** Mr Martin Shorter
● **Professional:** Mr Brian Shaw

Course/s:

🏌 **DOONBEG**
Description: Links
Green Speed: Medium/Fast
Number of Holes: 18 **Par:** 72
Yds: 6800
Designer: Greg Norman
Further Information:
Views of the ocean from the green and the fairway.

DORE & TOTLEY

DORE & TOTLEY GOLF CLUB, The Clubhouse, Bradway Rd, Sheffield, **YORKSHIRE (SOUTH),** S17 4QR, **ENGLAND.**
(T) 0114 2369872

Course/s:

🏌 **DORE & TOTLEY**
Number of Holes: 18

DORKING

DORKING GOLF CLUB (THE), Deepdene Ave, Dorking, **SURREY,** RH5 4BX, **ENGLAND.**
(T) 01306 886917

Contact/s:

● **Manager:** Mr P Napier

Course/s:

🏌 **DORKING**
Number of Holes: 9
Designer: James Braid

DORNOCH (ROYAL)

ROYAL DORNOCH GOLF CLUB, Golf Rd, Dornoch, **HIGHLANDS,** IV25 3LW, **SCOTLAND.**
(T) 01862 810219
(E) rdgc@royaldornoch.com
(W) www.royaldornoch.com
Membership: Members & Public

Contact/s:

● **Club Secretary:** Mr John Duncan
  ☎ 01862 811220
● **Professional:** Mr Andrew Skinner
  ☎ 01862 810902

Course/s:

🏌 **CHAMPIONSHIP**
Number of Holes: 18
Yds: 6514 **F9 Yds:** 3221 **B9 Yds:** 3293
Designer: G Duncan, Tom Morris, J Sutherland 🏆

STRUIE
Number of Holes: 18
Yds: 5196 F9 Yds: 2595 B9 Yds: 2601

DORSET HEIGHTS

DORSET HEIGHTS GOLF CLUB,
Belchalwell, Blandford Forum, **DORSET**,
DT11 0EG, **ENGLAND**.
(T) 01258 861386

Course/s:

DORSET HEIGHTS
Number of Holes: 18
Designer: David Astill

DOUGLAS

DOUGLAS GOLF CLUB, Douglas, **ISLE OF
MAN**, IM2 1AE, **ENGLAND**.
(T) 01624 675952

Course/s:

DOUGLAS
Number of Holes: 18

DOUGLAS

DOUGLAS GOLF CLUB, Clubhouse,
Douglas, **COUNTY CORK**, **IRELAND**.
(T) 021 4891086
(E) admin@douglasgolfclub.ie
(W) www.douglasgolfclub.ie

Contact/s:
● Professional: Mr Garry Nicholson

Course/s:

DOUGLAS
Number of Holes: 18 Par: 72
Yds: 6509 F9 Yds: 3161 B9 Yds: 3348
Designer: Peter McEvoy, Harry Varcion

DOUGLAS PARK

DOUGLAS PARK GOLF CLUB, Hillfoot,
Bearsden, Glasgow, **GLASGOW (CITY OF)**,
G61 2TJ, **SCOTLAND**.
(T) 0141 9422220

Membership: Members & Public

Contact/s:
● Club Secretary: Mr Jim Fergusson
  ☎ 0141 9420985
● Professional: Mr David Scott
  ☎ 0141 9421482

Course/s:

DOUGLAS PARK
Description: Parkland, Undulating, Open,
Medium Length, Drains Well
Green Speed: Medium
Built: 1897 Built On: Clay
Number of Holes: 18 Par: 69
Record: 63
Yds: 5761 F9 Yds: 3040 B9 Yds: 2721
Designer: William Fernie
Further Information:
On the site of Antonine Wall.

DOUGLAS WATER

DOUGLAS WATER GOLF CLUB, Ayr Rd,
Rigside, Lanark, **LANARKSHIRE (SOUTH)**,
ML11 9NP, **SCOTLAND**.
(T) 01555 880361

Contact/s:
● Manager: Mr R Mitchell

Course/s:

DOUGLAS WATER
Number of Holes: 9

DOWN (ROYAL COUNTY)

ROYAL COUNTY DOWN GOLF CLUB, 36

Golf Links Rd, Newcastle, **COUNTY DOWN**,
BT33 0AN, **NORTHERN IRELAND**.
(T) 028 43723314
(E) enquiries@royalcountydown.org
(W) www.royalcountydown.org

Contact/s:
● Club Secretary: Mr P Ralph
● Professional: Mr Kevan Whitson

Course/s:

ANNESLEY LINKS
Description: Links
Number of Holes: 18

CHAMPIONSHIP
Description: Championship, Links,
Undulating, Open, Long, Drains Well,
Ideal for the Elderly
Green Speed: Medium
Built: 1889 Built On: Sand
Number of Holes: 18 Par: 71
Designer: Tom Morris
Further Information:
"The outward half especially is as fine a
nine holes as I have ever played." (Quote
by Tom Watson.) ⚑

DOWN ROYAL PARK

DOWN ROYAL PARK GOLF CLUB, 6
Dunygarton Rd, Lisburn, **COUNTY ANTRIM**,
BT27 5RT, **NORTHERN IRELAND**.
(T) 028 92621339

Membership: Members & Public
Size of Complex: 180 Acres

Contact/s:
● Club Secretary: Mr S Higgins
● Professional: Mr C Calder

Course/s:

DOWN ROYAL PARK
Description: Heath Land, Open, Long,
Tight, Drains Well, Ideal for the Elderly
Green Speed: Medium
Built: 1844 Built On: Sand
Number of Holes: 18
Designer: Fred Daley

VALLEY
Number of Holes: 9

DOWNFIELD

DOWNFIELD GOLF CLUB, Turnberry Ave,
Dundee, **ANGUS**, DD2 3QP, **SCOTLAND**.
(T) 01382 889246
(E) downfieldgc@aol.com
(W) www.downfieldgolf.com

Contact/s:
● Club Secretary: Mrs M Stewart

Course/s:

DOWNFIELD
Number of Holes: 18 Par: 73
Par 3's: 4 Par 4's: 9 Par 5's: 5
Yds: 6803 F9 Yds: 3481 B9 Yds: 3322
Designer: C K Cotton

DOWNPATRICK

DOWNPATRICK GOLF CLUB, 43 Saul Rd,
Downpatrick, **COUNTY DOWN**, BT30 6PA,
NORTHERN IRELAND.
(T) 028 44615947
(W) www.downpatrickgolfclub.com

Membership: Members & Public
Size of Complex: 98 Acres

Contact/s:
● Club Secretary: Mr K Laurence
  ☎ 028 444615947

Course/s:

DOWNPATRICK
Description: Parkland, Medium Length,

Ideal for the Elderly
Built: 1930 Built On: Soil
Number of Holes: 18 Par: 70
Par 3's: 4 Par 4's: 12 Par 5's: 2
Yds: 6120 F9 Yds: 3070 B9 Yds: 3050
Designer: Hawtree
Further Information:
It is possible to see the Isle of Man on a
clear day.

DOWNSHIRE

DOWNSHIRE GOLF COURSE,
Easthampstead Pk, Wokingham,
BERKSHIRE, RG40 3DH, **ENGLAND**.
(T) 01344 302030
(E) downshiregc@bracknell-forest.gov.uk
(W) www.bracknell-forest.gov.uk

Contact/s:
● Golf Manager: Mr Paul Stanwick
  ☎ 01344 422708

Course/s:

DOWNSHIRE
Number of Holes: 18 Par: 72
Yds: 6416 F9 Yds: 3232 B9 Yds: 3184

DRAYTON PARK

DRAYTON PARK GOLF COURSE, Steventon
Rd, Drayton, Abingdon, **OXFORDSHIRE**,
OX14 4LA, **ENGLAND**.
(T) 01235 555799

Course/s:

DRAYTON PARK
Number of Holes: 18
Designer: Hawtree

DRAYTON PARK

DRAYTON PARK GOLF CLUB LTD,
Secretary, Drayton Manor Drive, Tamworth,
STAFFORDSHIRE, B78 3TN, **ENGLAND**.
(T) 01827 251139

Contact/s:
● Sales Manager: Mr Francis William
Horton

Course/s:

DRAYTON PARK
Number of Holes: 18
Designer: James Braid

DRIFFIELD

DRIFFIELD GOLF CLUB, Sunderlandwick,
Beverley Rd, Driffield, **YORKSHIRE (EAST)**,
YO25 9AD, **ENGLAND**.
(T) 01377 253116

Contact/s:
● Club Secretary: Mr Peter J Mounfield

Course/s:

DRIFFIELD
Number of Holes: 18 Par: 70
Yds: 6215 F9 Yds: 3228 B9 Yds: 2987

DRIFT

DRIFT GOLF CLUB, The Drift, East Horsley,
Leatherhead, **SURREY**, KT24 5HD,
ENGLAND.
(T) 01483 284641

Membership: Members & Public

Contact/s:
● Club Secretary: Ms D Backett
● Professional: Mr L Greasley
● Pro Shop:
  ☎ 01483 284772

Course/s:

DRIFT
Description: Wooded, Parkland, Medium

Length, Tight, Drains Well
Built: 1975 **Built On:** Clay
Number of Holes: 18
Designer: Robert Sandow
Further Information:
Rhododendrons throughout the course.

DROITWICH

DROITWICH GOLF & COUNTRY CLUB,
West Ford Hse, Ford Lane, Elmbridge,
Droitwich, **WORCESTERSHIRE**, WR9 0BQ,
ENGLAND.
(T) 01905 770129
Contact/s:
● **Manager:** Mr M Aston
Course/s:
🏌 **DROITWICH**
Number of Holes: 18
Designer: James Braid, G Franks

DROMOLAND CASTLE ESTATE

DROMOLAND CASTLE ESTATE, Newmarket
on Fergus, **COUNTY CLARE, IRELAND**.
(T) 061 368144
(E) sales@dromoland.ie
(W) www.dromoland.ie
Contact/s:
● **Club Secretary:** Mr John O'Halloran
Course/s:
🏌 **DROMOLAND CASTLE**
Number of Holes: 18 **Par:** 71
Yds: 6098 **F9 Yds:** 3280 **B9 Yds:** 2818
Designer: Wiggington

DRUIDS GLEN

DRUID'S GLEN GOLF CLUB,
Newtownmountkennedy, **COUNTY
WICKLOW, IRELAND**.
(T) 01 2873600
(E) info@druidsglen.ie
(W) www.druidsglen.ie
Membership: Members & Public
Contact/s:
● **Professional:** Mr Ciaran Monaghan
● **Pro Shop:** Mr Ivan Rodd
● **Book Tee Times:** Ms Jane Ballse
Course/s:
🏌 **DRUIDS GLEN**
Description: Championship, Parkland,
Medium Length, Ideal for the Elderly
Green Speed: Medium
Built: 1995 **Built On:** Sand
Number of Holes: 18 **Par:** 71
Par 3's: 4 **Par 4's:** 11 **Par 5's:** 3
Yds: 7026
Designer: Pat Ruddy, Tom Craddock
Further Information:
An excellent course for champion and
standard golfers alike. It was European
Golf Course of the Year 2002. 🏆

DRUIDS HEATH

DRUIDS HEATH GOLF CLUB LTD, Stonnall
Rd, Walsall, **MIDLANDS (WEST)**, WS9 8JZ,
ENGLAND.
(T) 01922 455595
Contact/s:
● **Administrator:** Mr Andrew O'Neill
Course/s:
🏌 **DRUIDS HEATH**
Number of Holes: 18

DRUMOIG

DRUMOIG HOTEL & GOLF CLUB,

Leuchars, St. Andrews, **FIFE**, KY16 0BE,
SCOTLAND.
(T) 01382 541800
Size of Complex: 320 Acres
Contact/s:
● **Manager:** Mr Chris Walker
Course/s:
🏌 **DRUMOIG GOLF COURSE**
Description: Parkland, Long
Number of Holes: 18 **Par:** 72
Yds: 7006

DRUMPELLIER

DRUMPELLIER GOLF CLUB, Main
Clubhouse, Drumpellier Ave, Coatbridge,
LANARKSHIRE (NORTH), ML5 1RX,
SCOTLAND.
(T) 01236 424139
Course/s:
🏌 **DRUMPELLIER**
Number of Holes: 18
Designer: William Fernie

DUBLIN (ROYAL)

ROYAL DUBLIN GOLF CLUB, North Bull
Island, Dollymount, Dublin, **COUNTY
DUBLIN, IRELAND**.
(T) 00 353 18336346
(E) royaldublin@club.ie
(W) www.globalgolf.com
Contact/s:
● **Club Secretary:** Mr John Lambe
☎ 01 8336346
Course/s:
🏌 **THE ROYAL DUBLIN**
Number of Holes: 18 **Par:** 72
Yds: 6877 **F9 Yds:** 3163 **B9 Yds:** 3714
Designer: Harry Shapland Colt 🏆

DUBLIN MOUNTAIN

DUBLIN MOUNTAIN GOLF CLUB, Gortlum,
Brittas, Dublin, **COUNTY DUBLIN,
IRELAND**.
(T) 01 4582622
Contact/s:
● **General Manager:** Mrs D Carolan
Course/s:
🏌 **DUBLIN MOUNTAIN**
Number of Holes: 18 **Par:** 71
Yds: 5635

DUDDINGSTON

DUDDINGSTON GOLF CLUB LTD, General
Enquiries, 137-139 Duddingston Rd West,
Edinburgh, **EDINBURGH (CITY OF)**, EH15
3QD, **SCOTLAND**.
(T) 0131 6611005
Contact/s:
● **General Manager:** Mr Michael Corsar
Course/s:
🏌 **DUDDINGSTON**
Number of Holes: 18

DUDLEY

DUDLEY GOLF CLUB, Turner's Hill, Rowley
Regis, Warley, Dudley, **MIDLANDS (WEST)**,
B65 9DP, **ENGLAND**.
(T) 01384 233877
Course/s:
🏌 **DUDLEY**
Number of Holes: 18

DUDMOOR

DUDMOOR GOLF COURSE, Dudmoor Farm
Rd, Christchurch, **DORSET**, BH23 6AQ,
ENGLAND.
(T) 01202 483980
Contact/s:
● **Owner:** Mrs S Hornsby
Course/s:
🏌 **DUDMOOR FARM**
Number of Holes: 9 **Par:** 31
Yds: 1575

DUDSBURY

DUDSBURY GOLF CLUB, 64 Christchurch
Rd, Ferndown, **DORSET**, BH22 8ST,
ENGLAND.
(T) 01202 593499
Membership: Members & Public
Size of Complex: 160 Acres
Contact/s:
● **Club Secretary:** Mr Giles Legg
● **Professional:** Mr Mark Thomas
Course/s:
🏌 **DUDSBURY**
Description: Championship, Parkland,
Open, Long
Green Speed: Fast **Built On:** Sand/Soil
Number of Holes: 18 **Par:** 71
Record: 64 (Sion Bebb)
Par 3's: 4 **Par 4's:** 11 **Par 5's:** 3
Yds: 6606 **F9 Yds:** 3139 **B9 Yds:** 3467
Prevailing Wind: South/West
Designer: Donald Steel

DUFF HOUSE ROYAL

DUFF HOUSE ROYAL GOLF CLUB, Office,
The Barnyards, Banff, **ABERDEENSHIRE**,
AB45 3SX, **SCOTLAND**.
(T) 01261 812062
(E) duff_house_royal@btinternet.com
Membership: Members & Public
Contact/s:
● **Club Secretary:** Mr Hamish Liebnitz
● **Professional:** Mr Bob Strachan
☎ 01261 812075
Course/s:
🏌 **DUFF HOUSE ROYAL**
Description: Parkland
Built: 1910 **Built On:** Soil
Number of Holes: 18 **Par:** 68
Par 3's: 4 **Par 4's:** 12 **Par 5's:** 1
Yds: 6164 **F9 Yds:** 2921 **B9 Yds:** 3243
Designer: Alistair MacKenzie
Further Information:
Two tiered greens are a feature of the
course, reflective of the designer Dr
MacKenzie of Augusta Fame.

DUFFTOWN

DUFFTOWN GOLF CLUB, Tomintoul Rd,
Glenrinnes, Dufftown, **ABERDEENSHIRE**,
AB55 4BX, **SCOTLAND**.
(T) 01340 820325
(W)
www.speyside.moray.org/Dufftown/Golfclub
Membership: Members & Public
Contact/s:
● **Book Tee Times:** Mrs M Swann
Course/s:
🏌 **DUFFTOWN**
Description: Parkland, Heath Land,
Medium Length
Green Speed: Medium
Built: 1896 **Built On:** Soil

Number of Holes: 18 Par: 67
Par 3's: 5 Par 4's: 13
Yds: 5308 F9 Yds: 2445 B9 Yds: 2863
Further Information:
The 9th tee is 1200 feet above sea level.
The 10th hole also has a spectacular 339
foot drop from the tee to the green.

DUKES

DUKES GOLF COURSE (THE), Craigton, St.
Andrews, **FIFE**, KY16 8NS, **SCOTLAND**.
(T) 01334 474371
(E) reservations@oldcoursehotel.co.uk
(W) www.oldcoursehotel.co.uk

Membership: Members & Public
Contact/s:
● Club Secretary: Mr Steve Toon
● Professional: Mr Ron Walker
Course/s:
🏌 THE DUKES
Description: Championship, Wooded,
Parkland, Open, Long
Green Speed: Fast
Built: 1995
Number of Holes: 18
Designer: Peter Thomson

DUKES DENE

DUKES DENE GOLF COURSE LTD., Slines
New Rd, Woldingham, Caterham, **SURREY**,
CR3 7HA, **ENGLAND**.
(T) 01883 653501
Contact/s:
● Manager: Mr Andy Crouch
Course/s:
🏌 DUKES DENE
Number of Holes: 18 Par: 71
Yds: 6393 F9 Yds: 3259 B9 Yds: 3134
Designer: Bradford Benz

DUKES MEADOW

DUKES MEADOW GOLF CLUB, Great
Chertsey Rd, Chiswick, London, **LONDON
(GREATER)**, W4 2SH, **ENGLAND**.
(T) 020 89950537
(E) info@golflessons.co.uk
(W) www.golflessons.co.uk

Membership: Members & Public
Contact/s:
● Professional: Mr Malcolm Henbery
☎ 020 89950539
Course/s:
🏌 DUKES MEADOWS
Description: Parkland, Short, Drains Well,
Ideal for the Elderly
Green Speed: Fast
Built: 1995
Number of Holes: 9
Designer: David Williams

DUKINFIELD

DUKINFIELD GOLF CLUB, Yew Tree Lane,
Dukinfield, **CHESHIRE**, SK16 5DB,
ENGLAND.
(T) 0161 3382340
Course/s:
🏌 DUKINFIELD
Number of Holes: 18

DULLATUR

DULLATUR GOLF CLUB, Glen Douglas
Drive, Cumbernauld, Glasgow, **GLASGOW
(CITY OF)**, G68 0DW, **SCOTLAND**.
(T) 01236 723230

Contact/s:
● Manager: Mrs C Miller
Course/s:
🏌 ANTONINE
Number of Holes: 18
Designer: James Braid
🏌 CARRICKSTONE
Number of Holes: 18
Designer: James Braid

DULWICH & SYDENHAM HILL

**DULWICH & SYDENHAM HILL GOLF
CLUB LTD,** Grange Lane, College Rd, London,
LONDON (GREATER), SE21 7LH,
ENGLAND.
(T) 020 8693 3961
Contact/s:
● Club Secretary: Mrs Susan Alexander
● Professional: Mr David Baillie
Course/s:
🏌 DULWICH & SYDENHAM HILL
Number of Holes: 18

DUMBARTON

DUMBARTON GOLF CLUB, Broadmeadow,
Overburn Ave, Dumbarton, **ARGYLL AND
BUTE**, G82 2BQ, **SCOTLAND**.
(T) 01389 732830
Contact/s:
● Club Secretary: Mr David Mitchell
☎ 01389 765995
Course/s:
🏌 DUMBARTON
Number of Holes: 18 Par: 71
Yds: 6017 F9 Yds: 2765 B9 Yds: 3252

DUMFRIES & COUNTY

**DUMFRIES & COUNTY GOLF CLUB
(THE),** Nunfield, Edinburgh Rd, Dumfries,
DUMFRIES AND GALLOWAY, DG1 1JX,
SCOTLAND.
(T) 01387 253585
(E) dumfriescounty@netscapeonline.co.uk
(W) www.dumfriesandcounty-gc.fsnet.co.uk
Size of Complex: 100 Acres
Contact/s:
● Club Secretary: Mr W. Graham
Johnstone
● Professional: Mr Stuart Syme
☎ 01387 268918
Course/s:
🏌 NUNFIELD
Description: Parkland, Undulating, Short,
Tends to Flood
Built: 1912 Built On: Soil
Number of Holes: 18 Par: 69
Par 3's: 4 Par 4's: 13 Par 5's: 1
Yds: 5928 F9 Yds: 3018 B9 Yds: 2910
Prevailing Wind: South/West
Designer: William Fernie

DUMMER

DUMMER GOLF CLUB, Dummer,
Basingstoke, **HAMPSHIRE**, RG25 2AR,
ENGLAND.
(T) 01256 397888
(E) golf@dummergc.co.uk
(W) www.dummergc.co.uk
Contact/s:
● Club Secretary: Mr R Corckhill
● Professional: Mr Andrew Fannon
Course/s:
🏌 DUMMER
Number of Holes: 18 Par: 72

Yds: 6407 F9 Yds: 3165 B9 Yds: 3242
Designer: Peter Alliss, Clive Clark

DUN LAOGHAIRE

DUN LAOGHAIRE GOLF CLUB, Tivoli Rd,
Dun Laoghaire, **COUNTY DUBLIN**,
IRELAND.
(T) 01 2803916
(E) dlgc@iol.ie
Course/s:
🏌 DUN LAOGHAIRE
Number of Holes: 18
Designer: Harry Shapland Colt

DUNARVERTY

DUNAVERTY GOLF CLUB, Southend,
Campbeltown, **ARGYLL AND BUTE**, PA28
6RX, **SCOTLAND**.
(T) 01586 830677
Membership: Members & Public
Contact/s:
● Club Secretary: Mr David MacBryne
● Professional: Mr Ken Campbell
● Pro Shop: Mr Nick Harne
● Book Tee Times: Mr Nick Hind
Course/s:
🏌 DUNARVERTY
Description: Drains Well, Ideal for the
Elderly
Green Speed: Medium
Built: 1889 Built On: Sand
Number of Holes: 18 Par: 66
Par 3's: 7 Par 4's: 10 Par 5's: 1
Yds: 4799 F9 Yds: 2258 B9 Yds: 2541
Further Information:
The course has very well maintained
greens.

DUNBAR

DUNBAR GOLF CLUB, East Links, Dunbar,
LOTHIAN (EAST), EH42 1LL, **SCOTLAND**.
(T) 01368 862317
(W) www.dunbar-golfclub.co.uk
Membership: Members & Public
Contact/s:
● Club Secretary: Ms Liz Thom
● Professional: Mr Jacky Montgomery
● Pro Shop:
☎ 01368 862086
Course/s:
🏌 DUNBAR
Description: Championship, Links, Open,
Long, Tight, Drains Well
Green Speed: Fast
Built: 1856 Built On: Sand
Number of Holes: 18 Par: 71
Yds: 6404 F9 Yds: 3244 B9 Yds: 3160
Prevailing Wind: West
Designer: Tom Morris
Further Information:
The course is located on the North Sea
Coast.

DUNBLANE NEW

DUNBLANE NEW GOLF CLUB LTD, Pro
Shop, Perth Rd, Dunblane, **PERTH AND
KINROSS**, FK15 0LJ, **SCOTLAND**.
(T) 01786 821523
Contact/s:
● Club Secretary: Mr J Dunsore
Course/s:
🏌 DUNBLANE NEW
Number of Holes: 18

DUNDALK

DUNDALK GOLF CLUB, Blackrock, **COUNTY LOUTH**, **IRELAND**.
(T) 042 9321731
(E) dkgc@iol.ie

Contact/s:
● Club Secretary: Mr Terry Sloane

Course/s:
🏌 **DUNDALK**
Number of Holes: 18 Par: 72
Yds: 6776 F9 Yds: 3410 B9 Yds: 3366

DUNDAS PARKS

DUNDAS PARKS GOLF CLUB, Dundas Est, South Queensferry, **LOTHIAN (MID)**, EH30 9PQ, **SCOTLAND**.
(T) 0131 319 1347

Contact/s:
● Administrator: Mrs Christine Wood

Course/s:
🏌 **DUNDAS PARKS**
Number of Holes: 9 Par: 35
Par 3's: 2 Par 4's: 6 Par 5's: 1
Yds: 3028 F9 Yds: 3028
Further Information:
9 hole course can be played as an 18 hole course

DUNFANAGHY

DUNFANAGHY GOLF CLUB, Dunfanaghy, Letterkenny, **COUNTY DONEGAL**, **IRELAND**.
(T) 074 36335
(E) dunfanaghygolf@eircom.net
(W) www.golfdunfanaghy.com

Course/s:
🏌 **DUNFANAGHY**
Number of Holes: 18 Par: 68
Yds: 5506 F9 Yds: 2604 B9 Yds: 2854
Designer: Harry Vardon

DUNFERMLINE

DUNFERMLINE GOLF CLUB, Pitfirrane, Crossford, Dunfermline, **FIFE**, KY12 8QW, **SCOTLAND**.
(T) 01383 723534
(E) pitfirrane@aol.com

Membership: Members & Public

Contact/s:
● Club Secretary: Mr Bob De Rouse
● Professional: Mr Chris Nugent
● Pro Shop:
  ☎ 01383 729061

Course/s:
🏌 **DUNFERMLINE**
Description: Parkland, Breckland, Sheltered, Medium Length, Drains Well, Ideal for the Elderly
Green Speed: Medium
Built: 1953 Built On: Clay
Number of Holes: 18 Par: 72
Par 3's: 5 Par 4's: 8 Par 5's: 5
Yds: 6121 F9 Yds: 2895 B9 Yds: 3226
Prevailing Wind: West
Designer: Stutt

DUNGANNON

DUNGANNON GOLF CLUB, 34 Springfield Lane, Dungannon, **COUNTY TYRONE**, BT70 1QX, **NORTHERN IRELAND**.
(T) 028 87722098

Contact/s:
● Club Secretary: Mr Sam Walker

Course/s:

🏌 **DUNGANNON**
Description: Parkland
Built: 1890
Number of Holes: 18 Par: 72
Par 3's: 5 Par 4's: 8 Par 5's: 5
Yds: 6046 F9 Yds: 3022 B9 Yds: 3024
Designer: S Bacon
Further Information:
There are various water hazards on course. The 9th hole has been re-designed by Darren Clarke.

DUNGARVAN

DUNGARVAN GOLF CLUB, Knocknagranagh, Dungarvan, **COUNTY WATERFORD**, **IRELAND**.
(T) 058 43310

Membership: Members & Public

Contact/s:
● Club Secretary: Ms Irene Howell
● Professional: Mr David Hayes

Course/s:
🏌 **DUNGARVAN**
Description: Championship, Parkland, Undulating, Sheltered, Open, Medium Length, Tight, Drains Well, Ideal for the Elderly
Green Speed: Medium
Built: 1992 Built On: Clay
Number of Holes: 18
Designer: Moss Fives

DUNHAM

DUNHAM GOLF CLUB, Cannister Hall, Little Dunham, King's Lynn, **NORFOLK**, PE32 2DF, **ENGLAND**.
(T) 01328 701718

Contact/s:
● Professional: Mr Gary Potter

Course/s:
🏌 **DUNHAM**
Number of Holes: 9 Par: 66
Yds: 5150

DUNHAM FOREST

DUNHAM FOREST GOLF & COUNTRY CLUB, Oldfield Lane, Dunham Massey, Altrincham, **CHESHIRE**, WA14 4TY, **ENGLAND**.
(T) 0161 9282605

Membership: Members & Public

Contact/s:
● Club Secretary: Ms Sylvia Klaus
● Professional: Mr Ian Wrigley
● Pro Shop: Mr Paul Dennis

Course/s:
🏌 **DUNHAM FOREST**
Description: Parkland, Heath Land, Undulating, Sheltered, Medium Length, Drains Well, Ideal for the Elderly
Green Speed: Fast
Built: 1961 Built On: Soil
Number of Holes: 18
Designer: Peter Alliss

DUNKELD

DUNKELD & BIRNAM GOLF CLUB, Fungarth, Dunkeld, **PERTH AND KINROSS**, PH8 0HU, **SCOTLAND**.
(T) 01350 727524
(W) www.dunkeldandbirnamgolfclub.co.uk

Membership: Members & Public

Contact/s:
● Club Secretary: Mr R Barrance

Course/s:

🏌 **DUNKELD**
Description: Parkland, Heath Land, Open, Medium Length, Drains Well
Green Speed: Medium
Built: 1922 Built On: Sand/Soil
Number of Holes: 18 Par: 70
Par 3's: 4 Par 4's: 12 Par 5's: 2
Yds: 5509 F9 Yds: 2858 B9 Yds: 2651
Further Information:
The course is quiet and has magnificent views and wildlife.

DUNLOE

DUNLOE GOLF COURSE, Dunloe, Killarney, **COUNTY KERRY**, **IRELAND**.
(T) 064 44578

Course/s:
🏌 **DUNLOE**
Number of Holes: 9
Yds: 2500

DUNMORE

DUNMORE GOLF COURSE, Dunmore, Clonakilty, Muckross, **COUNTY CORK**, **IRELAND**.
(T) 023 33352

Course/s:
🏌 **DUNMORE**
Number of Holes: 9
Designer: Edward Hackett

DUNMORE DEMESNE

DUNMORE DEMESNE GOLF CLUB, Tuam Rd, Dunmore, **COUNTY GALWAY**, **IRELAND**.
(T) 093 38709

Course/s:
🏌 **DUNMORE DEMESNE**
Number of Holes: 9

DUNMORE EAST

DUNMORE EAST GOLF CLUB, Dunmore East, Dunmore, **COUNTY WATERFORD**, **IRELAND**.
(T) 051 383151

Contact/s:
● Professional: Derry Kiely

Course/s:
🏌 **DUNMORE EAST**
Description: Parkland, Cliff Top
Built: 1993
Number of Holes: 18 Par: 72
Designer: W H Jones
Further Information:
Overlooks Dunmore East Bay Estuary.

DUNMURRY

DUNMURRY GOLF CLUB, 91 Dunmurry Lane, Dunmurry, Belfast, **COUNTY ANTRIM**, BT17 9JS, **NORTHERN IRELAND**.
(T) 028 90621402

Contact/s:
● Pro Shop:
  ☎ 028 90621314

Course/s:
🏌 **DUNMURRY**
Number of Holes: 18

DUNNERHOLME

DUNNERHOLME GOLF CLUB, Duddon Rd, Askam-in-Furness, **CUMBRIA**, LA16 7AW, **ENGLAND**.
(T) 01229 462675
(E) meg@dunnerholme.co.uk

Contact/s:
- Head Barlady: Ms Meg Tyson
- ☎ 01229 889326

Course/s:

🏌 **DUNNERHOLME**
Description: Links, Parkland
Built: 1905 Built On: Sand
Number of Holes: 10 Par: 71
Yds: 6075 F9 Yds: 2882 B9 Yds: 3193

DUNNIKIER

DUNNIKIER GOLF CLUB, Dunnikier Pk, Kirkcaldy, **FIFE**, KY1 3LP, **SCOTLAND**.
(T) 01592 642121

Membership: Members & Public

Contact/s:
- Club Secretary: Mr Neil Crooks
- Professional: Mr Gregor Whyte

Course/s:

🏌 **DUNNIKIER**
Description: Championship, Parkland, Undulating, Sheltered, Long, Tends to Flood, Ideal for the Elderly
Green Speed: Medium
Built: 1963 Built On: Clay
Number of Holes: 18 Record: 71 (Gregor Whyte)
Prevailing Wind: East

DUNNING

DUNNING GOLF CLUB, Clubhouse/Rollo Pk, Station Rd, Dunning, Perth, **PERTH AND KINROSS**, PH2 0RH, **SCOTLAND**.
(T) 01764 684747

Course/s:

🏌 **DUNNING**
Description: Parkland
Number of Holes: 9 Par: 66
Yds: 4863

DUNS

DUNS GOLF CLUB, Hardens Quarry, Duns, **SCOTTISH BORDERS**, TD11 3NR, **SCOTLAND**.
(T) 01361 882194

Membership: Members & Public
Size of Complex: 100 Acres

Contact/s:
- Club Secretary: Mr Allan Campbell
  ☎ 01361 8822717
- Book Tee Times: Ms Selina Waugh

Course/s:

🏌 **DUNS**
Description: Parkland, Undulating, Medium Length, Drains Well
Green Speed: Medium
Built: 1894 Built On: Soil
Number of Holes: 18 Par: 70
Par 3's: 5 Par 4's: 10 Par 5's: 3
Yds: 6209
Prevailing Wind: West
Designer: A H Scott
Further Information:
Set in the Berwickshire countryside with views across the Tweed Valley south to the Cheviot Hills. Good golf holiday location.

DUNSCAR

DUNSCAR GOLF CLUB, Longworth Lane, Egerton, Bolton, **LANCASHIRE**, BL7 9QY, **ENGLAND**.
(T) 01204 592992

Membership: Members & Public
Size of Complex: 76 Acres

Contact/s:

- Club Secretary: Mr John Jennings
- Professional: Mr Gary Treadgold

Course/s:

🏌 **DUNSCAR**
Description: Wooded, Parkland, Moorland, Undulating, Open, Medium Length, Drains Well, Ideal for the Elderly
Green Speed: Medium
Built: 1908 Built On: Soil
Number of Holes: 18 Record: 69 (Gary Treadgold)
Prevailing Wind: West
Designer: G Lowe
Further Information:
A testing course.

DUNSTABLE DOWNS

DUNSTABLE DOWNS GOLF CLUB, Whipsnade Rd, Kensworth, Dunstable, **BEDFORDSHIRE**, LU6 2NB, **ENGLAND**.
(T) 01582 604472
(E) ddgc@btconnect.com

Contact/s:
- Professional: Mr Michael Weldon

Course/s:

🏌 **DUNSTABLE DOWNS**
Description: Downland
Number of Holes: 18 Par: 70
Yds: 6251 F9 Yds: 3013 B9 Yds: 3238
Designer: James Braid

DUNSTANBURGH CASTLE

DUNSTANBURGH CASTLE GOLF COURSE, Embleton, Alnwick, **NORTHUMBERLAND**, NE66 3XQ, **ENGLAND**.
(T) 01665 576781
(E) enquiries@dunstanburgh.com
(W) www.dunstanburgh.com

Contact/s:
- Book Tee Times: Mrs I Williams

Course/s:

🏌 **DUNSTANBURGH CASTLE**
Description: Links
Built: 1900 Built On: Sand
Number of Holes: 18 Par: 70
Designer: James Braid

DUNTON HILLS

DUNTON HILLS GOLF COURSE, Tilbury Rd, West Horndon, Brentwood, **ESSEX**, CM13 3LU, **ENGLAND**.
(T) 01277 812340

Membership: Public
Size of Complex: 260 Acres

Contact/s:
- Owner: Mr J Dunne

Course/s:

🏌 **DUNTON HILLS 18 HOLE PAR 3**
Description: Parkland, Undulating, Open, Drains Well, Ideal for the Elderly
Green Speed: Medium
Built: 1995 Built On: Clay
Number of Holes: 18

Yds: 2391 F9 Yds: 1221 B9 Yds: 1170
Prevailing Wind: West
Further Information:
The course offers a challenging game.

🏌 **MAIN**
Description: Parkland, Undulating, Sheltered, Open, Drains Well, Ideal for the Elderly
Green Speed: Medium
Built: 1997 Built On: Clay
Number of Holes: 18 Par: 72

Par 3's: 4 Par 4's: 10 Par 5's: 4
Yds: 6446 F9 Yds: 3221 B9 Yds: 3225
Prevailing Wind: West
Further Information:
The course offers a challenging game.

DUNWOOD MANOR

DUNWOOD MANOR GOLF CLUB, Danes Rd, Awbridge, Romsey, **HAMPSHIRE**, SO51 0GF, **ENGLAND**.
(T) 01794 340549
(E) admin@dunwwod-golf.co.uk
(W) www.dunwood-golf.co.uk

Membership: Members & Public

Contact/s:
- Club Secretary: Mr R Basford
- Professional: Mr Heath Teschner
  ☎ 01794 340663

Course/s:

🏌 **DUNWOOD MANOR**
Description: Wooded, Parkland, Undulating
Green Speed: Medium Built: 1970
Number of Holes: 18

DURHAM CITY

DURHAM CITY GOLF CLUB, Littleburn, Langley Moor, Durham, **COUNTY DURHAM**, DH7 8HL, **ENGLAND**.
(T) 0191 3780069

Membership: Members & Public

Contact/s:
- Club Secretary: Mr Ian Wilson
- Professional: Mr Steve Corbally
- Pro Shop:
  ☎ 0191 3780029

Course/s:

🏌 **DURHAM CITY**
Description: Wooded, Parkland, Medium Length, Drains Well, Ideal for the Elderly
Green Speed: Slow/Medium
Built: 1973
Number of Holes: 18 Par: 71
Yds: 6326 F9 Yds: 2996 B9 Yds: 3330
Designer: Chris Stanton
Further Information:
There are various water features throughout the course.

DURNESS

DURNESS GOLF CLUB, Durine, Durness, Lairg, **HIGHLANDS**, IV27 4PG, **SCOTLAND**.
(T) 01971 511364

Membership: Members & Public

Contact/s:
- Club Secretary: Ms Lucy Mackay

Course/s:

🏌 **DURNESS**
Description: Links, Moorland, Undulating, Open, Short, Tight, Drains Well, Ideal for the Elderly
Green Speed: Medium
Built: 1988 Built On: Sand
Number of Holes: 9 Par: 70
Designer: F Keith, Jan Morrison
Further Information:
Can be played as a 18 hole on different coloured markers. Idyllic surroundings overlooking Balnakeil Bay. Fabulous final hole played over a deep gully which the Atlantic Ocean flows into at high tide.

DUXBURY JUBILEE PARK

DUXBURY JUBILEE PARK GOLF CLUB, Duxbury Hall Rd, Chorley, **LANCASHIRE**, PR7 4AS, **ENGLAND**.

(T) 01257 265380&241634

Course/s:

- **DUXBURY JUBILEE PARK**
  Number of Holes: 18
  Designer: Hawtree

DYKE

DYKE GOLF CLUB LTD, Devil's Dyke Rd, Brighton, **SUSSEX (EAST)**, BN1 8YJ, **ENGLAND**.
(T) 01273 857230

Course/s:

- **Club Secretary:** Mr M D Harrity

Course/s:

- **DYKE**
  Number of Holes: 18
  Designer: Hawtree

DYMOCK GRANGE

DYMOCK GRANGE GOLF CLUB,
Leominster Rd, Dymock,
GLOUCESTERSHIRE, GL18 2AN,
ENGLAND.
(T) 01531 890840

Membership: Members & Public
Size of Complex: 80 Acres

Contact/s:

- **Pro Shop:** Mr B Crossman

Course/s:

- **DYMOCK GRANGE**
  Description: Parkland, Sheltered, Medium Length, Drains Well, Ideal for the Elderly
  Green Speed: Medium
  Built: 1995 **Built On:** Clay/Soil
  Number of Holes: 9
  Further Information:
  A flat course.

DYRHAM PARK

DYRHAM PARK COUNTRY CLUB, Galley Lane, Barnet, **HERTFORDSHIRE**, EN5 4RA, **ENGLAND**.
(T) 020 84403904

Contact/s:

- **Manager:** Mr K Sutton

Course/s:

- **DYRHAM PARK**
  Number of Holes: 18

EAGLES

EAGLES GOLF CLUB, 39 School Rd, Tilney All Saints, King's Lynn, **NORFOLK**, PE34 4RS, **ENGLAND**.
(T) 01553 827147

Membership: Members & Public
Size of Complex: 50 Acres

Contact/s:

- **Club Secretary:** Mr David Horn
- **Professional:** Mr N Pickerell
- **Book Tee Times:** Mr R Shipman

Course/s:

- **EAGLES**
  Description: Wooded, Parkland, Medium Length, Drains Well
  Green Speed: Medium **Built On:** Soil
  Number of Holes: 9 **Par:** 32
  Par 3's: 4 **Par 4's:** 5
  Yds: 2142
  Prevailing Wind: West
  Designer: David W Horn

EAGLESCLIFFE

EAGLESCLIFFE AND DISTRICT GOLF CLUB, Clubhouse, Yarm Rd, Eaglescliffe, Stockton-on-Tees, **CLEVELAND**, TS16 0DQ, **ENGLAND**.
(T) 01642 780238
(E) egcsec@lineone.net
(W) www.eaglescliffegolfclub.co.uk

Contact/s:

- **Club Secretary:** Mr M R Sample

Course/s:

- **EAGLESCLIFFE**
  Number of Holes: 18 **Par:** 72
  Yds: 6275 **F9 Yds:** 2973 **B9 Yds:** 3302
  Designer: James Braid, Henry Cotton

EALING

EALING GOLF CLUB, Ealing Golf Course, Perivale Lane, Greenford, **LONDON (GREATER)**, UB6 8SS, **ENGLAND**.
(T) 020 89970937

Contact/s:

- **Club Secretary:** Ms June A Mackison

Course/s:

- **EALING**
  Number of Holes: 18 **Par:** 70
  Yds: 6216 **F9 Yds:** 3068 **B9 Yds:** 3148
  Designer: Harry Shapland Colt

EARLSWOOD

EARLSWOOD GOLF COURSE, Jersey Marine, Neath, **NEATH PORT TALBOT**, SA10 6JP, **WALES**.
(T) 01792 321578

Membership: Public

Contact/s:

- **Club Secretary:** Mr S Gorvett

Course/s:

- **EARLSWOOD**
  Description: Wooded, Hilltop, Undulating, Medium Length, Drains Well
  Green Speed: Fast
  Number of Holes: 18
  Designer: Alistair Gorvett

EASINGWOLD

EASINGWOLD GOLF CLUB, Stillington Rd, Easingwold, York, **YORKSHIRE (NORTH)**, YO61 3ET, **ENGLAND**.
(T) 01347 822474

Contact/s:

- **Owner:** Mr John Hughes

Course/s:

- **EASINGWOLD**
  Number of Holes: 18 **Par:** 73
  Yds: 6705 **F9 Yds:** 3401 **B9 Yds:** 3304
  Designer: Hawtree

EAST ABERDEENSHIRE

EAST ABERDEENSHIRE GOLF CENTRE LTD, Millden Farm, Balmedie, Aberdeen, **ABERDEEN (CITY OF)**, AB23 8YY, **SCOTLAND**.
(T) 01358 742111
(E) info@eagolf.com
(W) www.eagolf.com

Membership: Members & Public

Contact/s:

- **Club Secretary:** Mr Kevin Forrest
- **Professional:** Mr Ian Bratton

Course/s:

- **EAST ABERDEENSHIRE GOLF CENTRE**
  Description: Parkland, Undulating, Open,

Long, Drains Well
  Green Speed: Fast
  Built: 1999
  Number of Holes: 18
  Designer: Ian Creswell

EAST BARNET

EAST BARNET GOLF CLUB, Clifford Rd, Barnet, **HERTFORDSHIRE**, EN5 5NY, **ENGLAND**.
(T) 020 84492366

Course/s:

- **EAST BARNET GOLF COURSE**
  Description: Short
  Number of Holes: 9 **Par:** 29
  Yds: 1836
  Further Information:
  This 9 hole course can be played as an 18 hole.

EAST BERKSHIRE

EAST BERKSHIRE GOLF CLUB, Ravenswood Ave, Crowthorne, **BERKSHIRE**, RG45 6BD, **ENGLAND**.
(T) 01344 772041

Membership: Members & Public

Contact/s:

- **Club Secretary:** Mr John Stocker
- **Professional:** Mr Arthur Roe
  ☎ 01344 774112

Course/s:

- **EAST BERKSHIRE**
  Description: Wooded, Heath Land
  Green Speed: Fast
  Number of Holes: 18 **Par:** 69
  Par 3's: 4 **Par 4's:** 13 **Par 5's:** 1
  Yds: 6344
  Designer: P Paxton

EAST BIERLEY

EAST BIERLEY GOLF CLUB, South View Rd, Bradford, **YORKSHIRE (WEST)**, BD4 6PP, **ENGLAND**.
(T) 01274 680450

Membership: Members & Public
Size of Complex: 35 Acres

Contact/s:

- **Club Secretary:** Mr R J Welsh

Course/s:

- **EAST BIERLEY**
  Description: Moorland, Undulating, Open, Medium Length, Tends to Flood
  Built: 1927 **Built On:** Clay
  Number of Holes: 9
  Prevailing Wind: North

EAST BRIGHTON

EAST BRIGHTON GOLF CLUB, Roedean Rd, Brighton, **SUSSEX (EAST)**, BN2 5RA, **ENGLAND**.
(T) 01273 603989

Contact/s:

- **Professional:** Mr Mark Stuart - William

Course/s:

- **EAST BRIGHTON**
  Description: Downland, Drains Well
  Built: 1893
  Number of Holes: 18 **Par:** 72
  Designer: James Braid

EAST CLARE

EAST CLARE GOLF CLUB, Bodyke, Scariff, **COUNTY CLARE**, **IRELAND**.
(T) 061 921322

Course/s:

⛳ **EAST CLARE**
Number of Holes: 18 Par: 71
Yds: 6476

EAST CORK

EAST CORK GOLF CLUB, Gurtacrue,
Midleton, **COUNTY CORK**, **IRELAND**.
(T) 021 4631687

Course/s:

⛳ **EAST CORK**
Number of Holes: 18
Designer: Edward Hackett

EAST DEVON

EAST DEVON GOLF CLUB, North View Rd,
Budleigh Salterton, **DEVON**, EX9 6BY,
ENGLAND.
(T) 01395 442018

Contact/s:
● Club Secretary: Mr Robert Burley
● Professional: Mr Trevor Underwood

Course/s:

⛳ **EAST DEVON**
Number of Holes: 18

EAST DORSET

EAST DORSET GOLF CLUB, Hyde,
Wareham, **DORSET**, BH20 7NT, **ENGLAND**.
(T) 01929 472244
(W) www.golf.co.uk/edgc

Membership: Members & Public

Contact/s:
● Club Secretary: Mr Brian Lee
● Professional: Mr Derwin Honan

Course/s:

⛳ **LAKELAND**
Description: Heath Land, Undulating,
Open, Long, Drains Well
Green Speed: Medium/Fast
Built: 1981 Built On: Chalk
Number of Holes: 18
Yds: 6580
Designer: Hawtree

⛳ **WOODLAND**
Description: Wooded, Sheltered,
Medium Length, Tight, Drains Well
Green Speed: Medium/Fast
Built: 1981 Built On: Chalk
Number of Holes: 9
Yds: 5032
Designer: Hawtree

EAST HERTS

EAST HERTS GOLF CLUB, Hamels Pk,
Buntingford, **HERTFORDSHIRE**, SG9 9NA,
ENGLAND.
(T) 01920 821978

Membership: Members & Public

Contact/s:
● Club Secretary: Mr C Wilkinson
● Professional: Mr Glen Culmer
  ☎ 01920 821922

Course/s:

⛳ **EAST HERTS**
Description: Parkland, Undulating, Open,
Drains Well
Green Speed: Medium
Built: 1974 Built On: Clay/Soil
Number of Holes: 18 Par: 71
Record: 63 (Billy McColl)
Yds: 6456 F9 Yds: 3282 B9 Yds: 3174
Prevailing Wind: North/West
Further Information:

The course was originally built in 1899 and
reconstructed in 1974.

EAST HORTON GOLF CTRE

EAST HORTON GOLF CENTRE, Mortimers
Lane, Fair Oak, Eastleigh, **HAMPSHIRE**,
SO50 7EA, **ENGLAND**.
(T) 023 80602111

Membership: Members & Public

Contact/s:
● Club Secretary: Mr Trevor Pearce

Course/s:

⛳ **EAST HORTON 9 HOLE**
Number of Holes: 9

⛳ **GREENWOOD**
Description: Parkland, Undulating,
Medium Length
Green Speed: Medium
Built: 1991
Number of Holes: 18
Designer: T Pearce, M Scott

⛳ **PARKLAND**
Description: Parkland, Ideal for the
Elderly
Green Speed: Medium
Built: 1991
Number of Holes: 18
Designer: T Pearce, M Scott

EAST KILBRIDE

EAST KILBRIDE GOLF CLUB, Chapelside
Rd, East Kilbride, Glasgow, **GLASGOW
(CITY OF)**, G74 4PH, **SCOTLAND**.
(T) 01355 247728

Contact/s:
● Club Secretary: Mr W G Gray

Course/s:

⛳ **EAST KILBRIDE**
Number of Holes: 18 Par: 71
Par 3's: 4 Par 4's: 11 Par 5's: 3
Yds: 6402 F9 Yds: 3145 B9 Yds: 3257

EAST RENFREWSHIRE

EAST RENFREWSHIRE GOLF CLUB, Ayr
Rd, Newton Mearns, Glasgow, **GLASGOW
(CITY OF)**, G77 6RT, **SCOTLAND**.
(T) 0135 500256
(E) david@eastrengolfclub.demon.co.uk

Membership: Members & Public

Contact/s:
● Club Secretary: Mr David McKenzie
● Professional: Mr Stuart Russell

Course/s:

⛳ **EAST RENFREWSHIRE**
Description: Parkland, Undulating,
Sheltered, Medium Length, Drains Well,
Ideal for the Elderly
Green Speed: Medium
Built: 1922 Built On: Soil
Number of Holes: 18 Par: 70
Yds: 6097 F9 Yds: 3074 B9 Yds: 3022
Designer: James Braid
Further Information:
The course offers good views of Glasgow.

EAST SUSSEX NATIONAL

EAST SUSSEX NATIONAL GOLF CLUB,
Little Horsted, Uckfield, **SUSSEX (EAST)**,
TN22 5ES, **ENGLAND**.
(T) 01825 880088
(E) golf@eastsussexnational.co.uk
(W) www.eastsussexnational.co.uk

Membership: Members & Public

Contact/s:

● Pro Shop: Mr Dan Agombar
  ☎ 01825 880256
● Book Tee Times:
  ☎ 01825 880232

Course/s:

⛳ **EAST**
Description: Championship, Parkland,
Undulating, Long
Green Speed: Fast
Built: 1990
Number of Holes: 18 Par: 72
Yds: 7138 F9 Yds: 3526 B9 Yds: 3612
Designer: Robert Cupp
Further Information:
Practice facilities consist of a three hole
Academy course, a large range (grass
and mats), undercover bays, quality
practice balls and indoor teaching facility
equipped with state-of-the art A-Star
computer analysis systems.

🏆

⛳ **WEST**
Description: Championship, Parkland,
Undulating, Long
Green Speed: Fast
Built: 1990
Number of Holes: 18 Par: 72
Yds: 7154 F9 Yds: 3580 B9 Yds: 3574
Designer: Robert Cupp

EASTBOURNE DOWNS

EASTBOURNE DOWNS GOLF CLUB, East
Dean Rd, Eastbourne, **SUSSEX (EAST)**,
BN20 8ES, **ENGLAND**.
(T) 01323 720827

Contact/s:
● Professional: Mr Terry Marshall

Course/s:

⛳ **EASTBOURNE DOWNS**
Description: Downland
Built: 1908
Number of Holes: 18 Par: 72
Yds: 6601 F9 Yds: 3464 B9 Yds: 3137
Designer: Taylor
Further Information:
The course offers views over the South
Downs and English Channel.

EASTBOURNE GOLFING PARK

EASTBOURNE GOLFING PARK LTD,
Lottbridge Drove, Eastbourne, **SUSSEX
(EAST)**, BN23 6QJ, **ENGLAND**.
(T) 01323 520400

Membership: Members & Public
Size of Complex: 66 Acres

Contact/s:
● Club Secretary: Mrs Jenny Plumley
● Professional: Mr Barrie Finch
● Book Lessons: Mr Ben Porter

Course/s:

⛳ **EASTBOURNE GOLFING PARK**
Description: Parkland, Open, Short,
Tight, Ideal for the Elderly
Green Speed: Fast
Built: 1991 Built On: Soil
Number of Holes: 9 Par: 66
Par 3's: 3 Par 4's: 6
Yds: 2523 Designer: David Ashton
Further Information:
An easy walking course with pleasant
surroundings.

EASTER MOFFAT

EASTER MOFFAT GOLF CLUB, Mansion
House, Plains, Airdrie, **LANARKSHIRE
(NORTH)**, ML6 8NP, **SCOTLAND**.

(T) 01236 843015
(W) www.emgc.fsnet.co.uk

Contact/s:
- **Club Secretary:** Mr Gordon Miller
- **Professional:** Mr Graham King

Course/s:
EASTER MOFFAT
Description: Wooded, Moorland
Built: 1922
Number of Holes: 18   Par: 72

EASTHAM LODGE

EASTHAM LODGE GOLF CLUB, 117 Ferry Rd, Eastham, Wirral, **MERSEYSIDE**, CH62 0AP, **ENGLAND**.
(T) 0151 3273003

Contact/s:
- **Club Secretary:** Mr C. S Camden
- **Professional:** Mr Nick Sargent
  ☎ 0151 327 3008

Course/s:
EASTHAM LODGE
Description: Wooded, Parkland
Built: 1973
Number of Holes: 18   Par: 68
Yds: 5706   F9 Yds: 2842   B9 Yds: 2864
Designer: Hawtree, D Hemstock

EASTWOOD

EASTWOOD GOLF CLUB, Muirshield, Loganswell, Newton Mearns, Glasgow, **GLASGOW (CITY OF)**, G77 6RX, **SCOTLAND**.
(T) 01355 500280

Membership: Members & Public

Contact/s:
- **Club Secretary:** Mr Vernon Jones
- **Professional:** Mr Iain Darroch
  ☎ 01355 500285

Course/s:
EASTWOOD
Description: Moorland, Undulating, Open, Drains Well
Green Speed: Slow
Built: 1893
Number of Holes: 18   Par: 5374
Par 3's: 5   Par 4's: 12
Yds: 5864   F9 Yds: 2949   B9 Yds: 2717
Designer: Theodore Moone

EATON

EATON GOLF CLUB, Newmarket Rd, Norwich, **NORFOLK**, NR4 6SF, **ENGLAND**.
(T) 01603 451686
(E) administrator@eatongc.co.uk
(W) www.eatongc.co.uk

Membership: Members & Public

Contact/s:
- **Club Secretary:** Mrs L Bovill
- **Professional:** Mr Mark Allen

Course/s:
EATON
Description: Parkland, Undulating, Sheltered, Short, Drains Well
Built: 1910
Number of Holes: 18   Par: 70
Yds: 6114   F9 Yds: 3112   B9 Yds: 3002
Designer: Taylor

EATON

EATON GOLF CLUB, Guy Lane, Waverton, Chester, **CHESHIRE**, CH3 7PH, **ENGLAND**.
(T) 01244 335885
(W) www.eatongolfclub.co.uk

Membership: Members & Public

Contact/s:
- **Club Secretary:** Mrs Kerry Brown
- **Professional:** Mr Neil Dunroe
  ☎ 01244 335826

Course/s:
EATON
Description: Wooded, Parkland, Open
Green Speed: Fast
Built: 1991   Built On: Soil
Number of Holes: 18
Designer: Donald Steel

EDEN

EDEN GOLF CLUB & DRIVING RANGE (THE), Crosby-on-Eden, Carlisle, **CUMBRIA**, CA6 4RA, **ENGLAND**.
(T) 01228 573003
(E) info@edengolf.co.uk
(W) www.edengolf.co.uk

Membership: Members & Public

Contact/s:
- **Professional:** Mr Steve Harrison

Course/s:
EDEN
Description: Championship, Wooded, Parkland
Built: 1992
Number of Holes: 18   Par: 72
Further Information:
The course has well guarded greens with a nice balance of challenging long holes, and slightly easier, though deceptive, shorter holes.

EDENBRIDGE

EDENBRIDGE GOLF & COUNTRY CLUB, Crouch House Rd, Edenbridge, **KENT**, TN8 5LQ, **ENGLAND**.
(T) 01732 867381
(E) david@golf-course-management.com

Contact/s:
- **Professional:** Mr Paul Moger

Course/s:
NEW
Description: Parkland
Built: 1991
Number of Holes: 18   Par: 68
Par 3's: 4   Par 4's: 14
Yds: 5611   F9 Yds: 2680   B9 Yds: 2931
Further Information:
A peaceful course.

OLD
Number of Holes: 18   Par: 72
Par 3's: 4   Par 4's: 10   Par 5's: 4
Yds: 6577   F9 Yds: 3336   B9 Yds: 3241

EDENDERRY

EDENDERRY GOLF CLUB, Edenderry, Edenderry, **COUNTY OFFALY**, **IRELAND**.
(T) 040 531072

Course/s:
EDENDERRY
Number of Holes: 18
Designer: Edward Hackett, Havers

EDENMORE

EDENMORE GOLF COURSE, 70 Drumnabreeze Rd, Magheralin, Craigavon, **COUNTY ARMAGH**, BT67 0RH, **NORTHERN IRELAND**.
(T) 028 92611310

Contact/s:
- **Course Manager:** Mr Kenneth Logan

Course/s:
EDENMORE
Number of Holes: 18   Par: 71
Par 3's: 4   Par 4's: 11   Par 5's: 3
Yds: 6244   F9 Yds: 3135   B9 Yds: 3109
Designer: F Ainsworth

EDGBASTON

EDGBASTON GOLF CLUB LTD, Church Rd, Edgbaston, Birmingham, **MIDLANDS (WEST)**, B15 3TB, **ENGLAND**.
(T) 0121 4541736
(W) www.edgbastongc.co.uk

Membership: Members & Public
Size of Complex: 144 Acres

Contact/s:
- **Club Secretary:** Mr Peter Heath
- **Professional:** Mr Jamie Cundy
  ☎ 0121 4343226
- **Pro Shop:**
  ☎ 0121 4543226

Course/s:
EDGBASTON
Description: Wooded, Parkland, Undulating, Short, Tight, Drains Well
Green Speed: Medium
Built: 1935   Built On: Clay/Soil
Number of Holes: 18   Par: 69
Record: 64 (Peter J Butler)
Par 3's: 4   Par 4's: 13   Par 5's: 1
Yds: 6106   Prevailing Wind: South
Designer: Harry Shapland Colt

EDGWAREBURY

EDGWAREBURY GOLF CLUB, Head Office, Edgware Way, Edgware, **LONDON (GREATER)**, HA8 8DD, **ENGLAND**.
(T) 020 89053393

Contact/s:
- **Greenkeeper:** Mr Terry Allford

Course/s:
EDGWAREBURY
Number of Holes: 9   Par: 27
Par 3's: 9

EDINBURGH WESTERN

EDINBURGH WESTERN GOLF CLUB, 22 Braid Hills Approach, Edinburgh, **EDINBURGH (CITY OF)**, EH10 6JY, **SCOTLAND**.
(T) 0131 4473327

Contact/s:
- **Club Secretary:** Mr Rankin Taylor

Course/s:
EDINBURGH WESTERN
Number of Holes: 18

EDMONDSTOWN

EDMONDSTOWN GOLF CLUB, Edmondstown Rd, Rathfarnham, **COUNTY DUBLIN**, **IRELAND**.
(T) 01 4931082
(E) info@edmondstowngolfclub.ie
(W) www.edmondstowngolfclub.ie

Contact/s:
- **Club Secretary:** Mr Selwyn Davies
  ☎ 49310 82
- **Professional:** Mr Andrew Crofton
  ☎ 01 4941019
- **Book Tee Times:** Ms Angela Sterling

Course/s:
EDMONDSTOWN
Number of Holes: 18
Yds: 6685   F9 Yds: 3490   B9 Yds: 3195
Designer: McAllister

EDWALTON MUNICIPAL

EDWALTON MUNICIPAL GOLF COURSE, Wellin Lane, Edwalton, Nottingham, **NOTTINGHAMSHIRE**, NG12 4AH, **ENGLAND**.
(T) 0115 9231987

Membership: Public

Contact/s:
- **Club Secretary:** Mrs D Parkes
  ☎ 0115 9234775
- **Professional:** Mr John Staples

Course/s:
⛳ **EDWALTON**
  Description: Parkland, Undulating, Open, Medium Length, Tight, Drains Well
  Green Speed: Medium
  Built: 1981 **Built On:** Soil
  Number of Holes: 9
  Further Information:
  Water feature on the 5th hole.

EDZELL

EDZELL GOLF CLUB, The Clubhouse. High St, Edzell, **ANGUS**, DD9 7TF, **SCOTLAND**.
(T) 01356 647283

Membership: Members & Public
Size of Complex: 150 Acres

Contact/s:
- **Club Secretary:** Mr Ian Farquhar
- **Professional:** Mr Alastair Webster
  ☎ 01356 648462

Course/s:
⛳ **EDZELL**
  Description: Wooded, Parkland, Sheltered, Medium Length, Drains Well, Ideal for the Elderly
  Green Speed: Medium
  Built: 1895 **Built On:** Soil
  Number of Holes: 18 **Par:** 71
  Par 3's: 3 **Par 4's:** 13 **Par 5's:** 2
  Yds: 6348 **F9 Yds:** 3262 **B9 Yds:** 3086
  Prevailing Wind: West
  Designer: Simpson

⛳ **WEST WATER**
  Description: Wooded, Parkland, Sheltered, Short, Drains Well, Ideal for the Elderly
  Green Speed: Slow
  Built: 2000 **Built On:** Soil
  Number of Holes: 9
  Designer: Graeme Webster

EFFINGHAM

EFFINGHAM GOLF CLUB, Guildford Rd, Effingham, Leatherhead, **SURREY**, KT24 5PZ, **ENGLAND**.
(T) 01372 452203

Membership: Members & Public

Contact/s:
- **Club Secretary:** Mr J Davies
- **Professional:** Mr S Hoatson
- **Pro Shop:**
  ☎ 01372 452606

Course/s:
⛳ **EFFINGHAM**
  Description: Parkland, Hilltop, Undulating, Open, Medium Length, Tends to Flood
  Green Speed: Medium
  Built: 1926 **Built On:** Chalk
  Number of Holes: 18 **Record:** 64 (Mr Barnes)
  Prevailing Wind: West
  Designer: Harry Shapland Colt

EFFINGHAM PARK

COPFORD MILLENNIUM HOTEL, West Park Rd, Copthorne, Crawley, **SUSSEX (WEST)**, RH10 3EU, **ENGLAND**.
(T) 01342 716528

Membership: Members & Public

Contact/s:
- **Club Secretary:** Mr Ian McRobbie

Course/s:
⛳ **EFFINGHAM PARK**
  Description: Wooded, Parkland, Sheltered, Medium Length, Tight, Drains Well, Ideal for the Elderly
  Green Speed: Medium
  Built: 1980 **Built On:** Clay
  Number of Holes: 9
  Prevailing Wind: South/East

ELDERSLIE

ELDERSLIE GOLF CLUB, 63 Main Rd, Elderslie, Johnstone, **RENFREWSHIRE**, PA5 9AZ, **SCOTLAND**.
(T) 01505 323956

Membership: Members & Public

Contact/s:
- **Club Secretary:** Mrs A Anderson
- **Professional:** Mr R Bowman
- **Pro Shop:**
  ☎ 01505 320032

Course/s:
⛳ **ELDERSLIE**
  Description: Parkland, Hilltop, Sheltered, Medium Length
  Green Speed: Medium
  Built: 1908 **Built On:** Soil
  Number of Holes: 18 **Record:** 61 (Dean Robertson)
  Designer: James Braid
  Further Information:
  The course overlooks Ben Lomond.

ELEMORE

ELEMORE GOLF CLUB, Elemore Lane, Hetton-le-Hole, Houghton Le Spring, **TYNE AND WEAR**, DH5 0QB, **ENGLAND**.
(T) 0191 5173061

Contact/s:
- **Employee:** Mrs B Blenkinsopp

Course/s:
⛳ **ELEMORE**
  Number of Holes: 18 **Par:** 69
  Yds: 5947
  Designer: J Gaunt

ELFORDLEIGH

ELFORDLEIGH HOTEL GOLF & LEISURE, Plympton, Plymouth, **DEVON**, PL7 5EB, **ENGLAND**.
(T) 01752 336428
(W) www.elfordleigh.co.uk

Membership: Members & Public

Contact/s:
- **Professional:** Mr Russ Troake

Course/s:
⛳ **ELFORDLEIGH**
  Description: Championship, Wooded, Parkland, Sheltered, Short, Tight, Drains Well
  Green Speed: Medium **Built On:** Soil
  Number of Holes: 9
  Prevailing Wind: North
  Designer: Taylor

ELIE GOLF

ELIE GOLF HOUSE CLUB, Elie, Leven, **FIFE**, KY9 1AS, **SCOTLAND**.
(T) 01333 330301
(E) sandy@golfhouseclub.freeserve.co.uk

Contact/s:
- **Club Secretary:** Alexander Sneddon
- **Pro Shop:** Robin Wilson
  ☎ 01333 330935

Course/s:
⛳ **ELIE**
  Description: Links, Medium Length, Drains Well
  Green Speed: Fast
  Number of Holes: 18

ELLAND

ELLAND GOLF CLUB, Hammerstones Leach Lane, Elland, **YORKSHIRE (WEST)**, HX5 0TA, **ENGLAND**.
(T) 01422 372505

Membership: Members & Public

Contact/s:
- **Professional:** Mr Nick Kryzwicki
  ☎ 01422 374886

Course/s:
⛳ **ELLAND**
  Description: Wooded, Parkland, Open, Medium Length, Drains Well
  Green Speed: Fast
  Built: 1910 **Built On:** Soil
  Number of Holes: 9 **Par:** 66 **Record:** 66 (James Major)
  Yds: 5498 **F9 Yds:** 2740 **B9 Yds:** 2758
  Prevailing Wind: South/East
  Further Information:
  A good course for beginners.

ELLESBOROUGH

ELLESBOROUGH GOLF CLUB, Secretary, Wendover Rd, Butlers Cross, Aylesbury, **BUCKINGHAMSHIRE**, HP17 0TZ, **ENGLAND**.
(T) 01296 622114

Contact/s:
- **General Manager:** Mr Bob Weeds

Course/s:
⛳ **ELLESBOROUGH**
  Number of Holes: 18 **Par:** 71
  Par 3's: 5 **Par 4's:** 9 **Par 5's:** 4
  Yds: 6360 **F9 Yds:** 3207 **B9 Yds:** 3153
  Designer: James Braid

ELLESMERE

ELLESMERE GOLF CLUB, Old Clough Lane, Worsley, Manchester, **MANCHESTER (GREATER)**, M28 7HZ, **ENGLAND**.
(T) 0161 7902122
(W) www.ellesmeregolf.co.uk

Membership: Members & Public
Size of Complex: 80 Acres

Contact/s:
- **Club Secretary:** Mr Alan Chapman
  ☎ 0161 7990554
- **Professional:** Mr Terry Morley
  ☎ 0161 7908591

Course/s:
⛳ **ELLESMERE**
  Description: Wooded, Parkland, Undulating, Sheltered, Medium Length, Tight, Tends to Flood, Ideal for the Elderly
  Green Speed: Medium
  Built: 1913 **Built On:** Clay
  Number of Holes: 18 **Par:** 70
  Yds: 6265 **F9 Yds:** 3087 **B9 Yds:** 3178

Prevailing Wind: West
Further Information:
The course has excellent greens.

ELLESMERE PORT

ELLESMERE PORT GOLF CLUB, Chester Rd, Childer Thornton, Ellesmere Port, **MERSEYSIDE**, CH66 1QF, **ENGLAND**.
(T) 0151 3397689

Contact/s:
● Owner: Mrs Linda MacDonald

Course/s:
🏌 ELLESMERE PORT
Number of Holes: 18
Designer: Cotton Pennick Lawrie & Partners

ELM PARK GOLF & SPORTS CLUB

ELM PARK GOLF & SPORTS CLUB LTD., Nutley House, Nutley Lane, Dennybrook, Dublin, **COUNTY DUBLIN**, **IRELAND**.
(T) 01 2693438
(E) office@elmparkgolfclub.ie

Contact/s:
● Club Secretary: Mr Adrian McCormack

Course/s:
🏌 ELM PARK GOLF & SPORTS CLUB
Number of Holes: 18 Par: 69
Yds: 5837

ELMGREEN

ELMGREEN GOLF CENTRE, Off Navan Rd, Castleknock, **COUNTY DUBLIN**, **IRELAND**.
(T) 01 8200797

Contact/s:
● Manager: Mr Gerry Carr

Course/s:
🏌 ELMGREEN
Number of Holes: 18 Par: 71
Yds: 5796 F9 Yds: 2871 B9 Yds: 2925

ELMWOOD

ELMWOOD GOLF COURSE & RESTAURANT, Stratheden, Cupar, **FIFE**, KY15 5RS, **SCOTLAND**.
(T) 01334 658780
(W) www.elmwoodgc.co.uk

Contact/s:
● Golf Co-Ordinator: Mrs Irene Jones

Course/s:
🏌 ELMWOOD
Description: Parkland, Undulating, Open, Medium Length, Drains Well, Ideal for the Elderly
Green Speed: Medium
Built: 1997 Built On: Sand
Number of Holes: 18 Par: 70
Par 3's: 4 Par 4's: 12 Par 5's: 2
Yds: 5951 F9 Yds: 2917 B9 Yds: 3034
Prevailing Wind: West
Further Information:
Elmwood is a gently undulating natural golf course. The course is set amongst some of the most scenic countryside in Fife and offers challenging golf to golfers of all ability. Elmwood holds several presitgous awards for environmental excellence. These awards are in recognition of the outstanding work carried out on the course to enhance and improve the course environment.

ELSHAM

ELSHAM GOLF CLUB, Barton Rd, Elsham, Brigg, **LINCOLNSHIRE (NORTH)**, DN20

0LS, **ENGLAND**.
(T) 01652 680291
(E) elshamgolfclub@lineone.net

Contact/s:
● Professional: Mr Stewart Brewer
● Book Tee Times: Mr T Hartley
☎ 01652 680432

Course/s:
🏌 ELSHAM
Description: Parkland
Built: 1900
Number of Holes: 18 Par: 71
Yds: 6402 F9 Yds: 3144 B9 Yds: 3258
Further Information:
Excellent rural course.

ELTHAM WARREN

ELTHAM WARREN GOLF CLUB, Bexley Rd, Eltham, London, **LONDON (GREATER)**, SE9 2PE, **ENGLAND**.
(T) 020 8850 1166 / 4477
(E) secretary@elthamwarren.idps.co.uk

Contact/s:
● Club Secretary: Mr Doug Clare
☎ 020 8850 4477
● Professional: Mr Gary Brett
☎ 020 8859 7909

Course/s:
🏌 ELTHAM WARREN
Description: Parkland
Number of Holes: 9 Par: 69
Yds: 5840 F9 Yds: 2902 B9 Yds: 2938

ELTON FURZE

ELTON FURZE GOLF CLUB, Bullock Rd, Haddon, Peterborough, **CAMBRIDGESHIRE**, PE7 3TT, **ENGLAND**.
(T) 01832 280189
(E) secretary@eltonfurzegolfclub.co.uk
(W) www.eltonfurzegolfclub.co.uk
Size of Complex: 135 Acres

Contact/s:
● Club Secretary: Mrs Helen Barron
● Professional: Mr Frank Kiddie
● Pro Shop: Mr B Stephens
☎ 01832 280614

Course/s:
🏌 ELTON FURZE
Description: Wooded, Parkland, Undulating, Sheltered, Medium Length, Drains Well
Green Speed: Medium
Built: 1992 Built On: Clay
Number of Holes: 18 Par: 70
Yds: 6279 F9 Yds: 3111 B9 Yds: 3168
Designer: Fitton
Further Information:
A challenging course with mature woodland.

ELY CITY

ELY CITY GOLF CLUB, Cambridge Rd, Ely, **CAMBRIDGESHIRE**, CB7 4HX, **ENGLAND**.
(T) 01353 662751

Membership: Members & Public
Size of Complex: 100 Acres

Contact/s:
● Professional: Mr Andrew George
☎ 01353 663317

Course/s:
🏌 ELY
Description: Championship, Parkland, Undulating, Open, Long, Tight, Drains Well, Ideal for the Elderly
Green Speed: Medium
Built: 1962 Built On: Clay

Number of Holes: 18 Par: 72
Record: 65 (Andrew George)
Yds: 6627 F9 Yds: 3325 B9 Yds: 3302
Designer: Henry Cotton
Further Information:
The course offers views of Ely Cathedral.

ENDERBY GOLF CLUB

ENDERBY GOLF CLUB, Mill Lane, Enderby, Leicester, **LEICESTERSHIRE**, LE9 5LH, **ENGLAND**.
(T) 0116 2849388

Course/s:
🏌 ENDERBY
Number of Holes: 9 Par: 31
Yds: 2133
Designer: David Lowe

ENFIELD

ENFIELD GOLF CLUB LTD, Old Park Rd, Enfield, **LONDON (GREATER)**, EN2 7DA, **ENGLAND**.
(T) 020 8363 3970/8366 4492
(E) enfieldgolfclub@dial.pipex.com
(W) www.enfieldgolfclub.co.uk

Contact/s:
● Club Secretary: Mr Nigel Challis
● Professional: Mr Lee Fickling
● Pro Shop:
☎ 020 8366 4492

Course/s:
🏌 ENFIELD
Description: Parkland
Number of Holes: 18 Par: 72
Yds: 6154 F9 Yds: 3301 B9 Yds: 2776
Designer: James Braid

ENMORE PARK

ENMORE PARK GOLF CLUB, Enmore, Bridgwater, **SOMERSET**, TA5 2AN, **ENGLAND**.
(T) 01278 671481
(E) golfclub@enmore.fsnet.co.uk
(W) www.golfdirector.com/enmore
Size of Complex: 110 Acres

Contact/s:
● Club Secretary: Mrs D Weston
● Professional: Mr Nigel Wixon
☎ 01278 671519
● Book Lessons:
☎ 01278 675519

Course/s:
🏌 ENMORE
Description: Parkland, Undulating, Medium Length
Green Speed: Medium
Built: 1932 Built On: Clay/Soil
Number of Holes: 18 Par: 71
Record: 64 (R Davis)
Yds: 6411 F9 Yds: 3088 B9 Yds: 3323
Prevailing Wind: West
Designer: Hawtree
Further Information:
The course was extended to 18 holes in 1971.

ENNIS

ENNIS GOLF CLUB, Drumbiggle, Ennis, **COUNTY CLARE**, **IRELAND**.
(T) 065 6829211
(E) egc@eircom.net
(W) www.golfclub.ennis.ie

Contact/s:
● Manager: Mr Niall O'Donnell
☎ 065 6824074

Course/s:

ENNIS
Number of Holes: 18   Par: 71
Par 3's: 4   Par 4's: 11   Par 5's: 3
Yds: 6095   F9 Yds: 2970   B9 Yds: 3125

ENNISCORTHY

ENNISCORTHY GOLF CLUB,
Knockmarshall, Enniscorthy, **COUNTY WEXFORD**, **IRELAND**.
(T) 054 33191
(E) engc@eircom.net
Course/s:
ENNISCORTHY
Number of Holes: 18
Designer: Edward Hackett

ENNISCRONE

ENNISCRONE GOLF CLUB, Enniscrone, **COUNTY MAYO**, **IRELAND**.
(T) 096 36297
(E) enniscrone@eircom.net
(W) homepage.tinet.ie/~enniscronegolf/
Course/s:
ENNISCRONE
Number of Holes: 18
Designer: Edward Hackett

ENNISKERRY PAR 3

ENNISKERRY PAR 3 GOLF COURSE,
Kilmolin, Enniskerry, **COUNTY WICKLOW**, **IRELAND**.
(T) 01 2867521
Course/s:
ENNISKERRY PAR 3
Number of Holes: 18   Par: 72
Yds: 7050

ENNISKILLEN

ENNISKILLEN GOLF CLUB, Castlecoole Rd, Enniskillen, **COUNTY FERMANAGH**, BT74 6HZ, **NORTHERN IRELAND**.
(T) 028 66325250
(E) enniskillen.golf@btclick.com
(W) home.btclick.com/enniskillen.golf
Membership: Members & Public
Contact/s:
● Club Secretary: Mr William McBrien
Course/s:
ENNISKILLEN
Description: Championship, Wooded, Parkland, Hilltop, Valley, Cliff Top, Undulating, Medium Length, Tight, Drains Well, Ideal for the Elderly
Green Speed: Medium/Fast
Built: 1989   Built On: Sand/Soil
Number of Holes: 18   Par: 71
Par 3's: 4   Par 4's: 11   Par 5's: 3
Yds: 5939   F9 Yds: 3029   B9 Yds: 2910
Further Information:
This beautiful, challenging course offers views of Castle Coole. Darren Clarke has also played here.

ENTRY HILL

ENTRY HILL GOLF COURSE, Entry Hill, Bath, **BATH & SOMERSET (NORTH EAST)**, BA2 5NA, **ENGLAND**.
(T) 01225 834248
Membership: Members & Public/Public
Size of Complex: 33 Acres
Contact/s:
● Club Secretary: Mr John Sercombe
● Professional: Mr Nigel Henderson
Course/s:

ENTRY HILL
Description: Wooded, Parkland, Hilltop, Short
Green Speed: Medium
Built: 1984
Number of Holes: 9   Record: 63 (Ian Hulley)
Prevailing Wind: North
Further Information:
The course offers views of Bath City.

ENVILLE

ENVILLE GOLF CLUB LTD, Highgate Common, Enville, Stourbridge, **MIDLANDS (WEST)**, DY7 5BN, **ENGLAND**.
(T) 01384 872551
Contact/s:
● Manager: Mr R J Bannister
Course/s:
HIGHGATE
Number of Holes: 18
LODGE
Number of Holes: 18

EPPING

EPPING GOLF COURSE (THE), Flux's Lane, Epping, **ESSEX**, CM16 7PE, **ENGLAND**.
(T) 01992 572282
(E) neilsjoberg@hotmail.com
Membership: Members & Public
Size of Complex: 94 Acres
Contact/s:
● Professional: Mr Danny Glenn
Course/s:
EPPING
Description: Wooded, Parkland, Undulating, Open, Medium Length, Tight
Green Speed: Medium
Built: 1996   Built On: Clay
Number of Holes: 18   Par: 68
Par 3's: 5   Par 4's: 12   Par 5's: 1
Yds: 4538   F9 Yds: 2301   B9 Yds: 2237
Prevailing Wind: West
Designer: N & P Sjoberg
Further Information:
10 minute starting, with no starting on the 10th, therefore there are no hold ups.

EPPING FOREST

EPPING FOREST GOLF CLUB, Woolston Manor, Abridge Rd, Chigwell, **ESSEX**, IG7 6BX, **ENGLAND**.
(T) 020 85002549
Membership: Members & Public
Contact/s:
● Club Secretary: Mr Peter Spargo
● Professional: Mr P Eady
  ☎ 020 85598272
Course/s:
MANOR
Description: Championship, Parkland, Valley, Open, Medium Length, Drains Well, Ideal for the Elderly
Green Speed: Fast
Built: 1994   Built On: Sand
Number of Holes: 18   Par: 72
Yds: 6165   F9 Yds: 3149   B9 Yds: 3016
Designer: Neil Coles
Further Information:
The course can be played all year round, offering a challenging, American style of game.

EPPING FOREST (ROYAL)

ROYAL EPPING FOREST GOLF CLUB,

Forest Approach, Chingford, Chingford, **LONDON (GREATER)**, E4 7AZ, **ENGLAND**.
(T) 020 8529 2195
Contact/s:
● Club Secretary: Mr PR Bright-Thomas
● Professional: Mr Andy Traynor
  ☎ 020 8529 5708
Course/s:
ROYAL EPPING FOREST
Description: Wooded
Number of Holes: 18
Yds: 6342

EPSOM

EPSOM GOLF CLUB, Longdown Lane South, Epsom, **SURREY**, KT17 4JR, **ENGLAND**.
(T) 01372 721666
(E) info@epsomgolfclub.co.uk
(W) www.epsomgolfclub.co.uk
Membership: Members & Public
Contact/s:
● Professional: Mr R Goudie
● Pro Shop:
  ☎ 01372 741867
Course/s:
EPSOM
Description: Downland, Valley, Short, Tight, Drains Well
Green Speed: Fast
Built: 1889   Built On: Chalk
Number of Holes: 18   Par: 69
Record: 62 (Keith MacDonald)
Yds: 5658   F9 Yds: 2773   B9 Yds: 2885
Prevailing Wind: South/East
Designer: W Dunn

EREWASH VALLEY

EREWASH VALLEY GOLF CLUB LTD, Golf Club Rd, Stanton-By-Dale, Ilkeston, **DERBYSHIRE**, DE7 4QR, **ENGLAND**.
(T) 0115 9322984
Contact/s:
● Manager: Mr J Beckett
Course/s:
EREWASH VALLEY
Number of Holes: 18
Designer: Hawtree

ERLESTOKE SANDS

ERLESTOKE SANDS GOLF CLUB, Erlestoke, Devizes, **WILTSHIRE**, SN10 5UB, **ENGLAND**.
(T) 01380 831027
Membership: Members & Public
Contact/s:
● Club Secretary: Ms Christine Witt
  ☎ 01380 831069
● Professional: Mr Michael Walters
Course/s:
ERLESTOKE SANDS
Description: Parkland, Open, Medium Length
Green Speed: Medium
Built: 1992
Number of Holes: 18
Designer: Adrian Stiff

ERSKINE

ERSKINE GOLF CLUB, Golf Rd, Bishopton, **RENFREWSHIRE**, PA7 5PH, **SCOTLAND**.
(T) 01505 862302
Contact/s:
● Professional: Mr P Thompson
  ☎ 01505 862108

Course/s:

ERSKINE
Number of Holes: 18 Par: 71
Yds: 6241 F9 Yds: 3058 B9 Yds: 3183

ESKER HILLS

ESKER HILLS GOLF & COUNTRY CLUB,
Ballykilmurray, Tullamore, **COUNTY OFFALY,**
IRELAND.
(T) 050 655999

Course/s:

ESKER HILLS
Description: Drains Well Built On: Sand
Number of Holes: 18 Par: 71
Yds: 6612

ESPORTA DOUGALSTON

ESPORTA DOUGALSTON GOLF COURSE,
Strathblane Rd, Milngavie, Milngavie,
GLASGOW (CITY OF), G62 8HJ,
SCOTLAND.
(T) 0141 9552434

Contact/s:
• **Professional:** Mr Craig Everett
• **Book Tee Times:** Mr Jonathan Wallace

Course/s:

ESPORTA DOUGALSTON
Description: Wooded, Parkland
Built: 1977
Number of Holes: 18 Par: 71
Further Information:
The course is designed around the
colourful contours of the 400 acre
Dougalston country estate with all weather
greens.

ESSEX

ESSEX GOLF & COUNTRY CLUB, Airfield,
Earls Colne, Colchester, **ESSEX,** CO6 2NS,
ENGLAND.
(T) 01787 224466

Contact/s:
• **Professional:** Mr Lee Cocker

Course/s:

COUNTY
Number of Holes: 18 Par: 73
Yds: 6916 F9 Yds: 3394 B9 Yds: 3522
Designer: R Plumbridge

GARDEN
Number of Holes: 9 Par: 34
Designer: R Plumbridge

ESSEX

ESSEX GOLF CLUB LTD, Garon Pk, Eastern
Ave, Southend-on-Sea, **ESSEX,** SS2 5YB,
ENGLAND.
(T) 01702 601701

Course/s:

COURSE #1
Number of Holes: 9 Par: 27
Par 3's: 9

ESSEX
Number of Holes: 18 Par: 70
Yds: 6252

ETCHINGHILL

ETCHINGHILL GOLF CLUB, Canterbury Rd,
Etchinghill, Folkestone, **KENT,** CT18 8FA,
ENGLAND.
(T) 01303 863863

Membership: Members & Public

Contact/s:
• **Professional:** Mr Chris Hodgson

Course/s:

ETCHINGHILL
Description: Hilltop, Valley, Undulating,
Medium Length, Drains Well
Green Speed: Medium/Fast
Built: 1995
Number of Holes: 27
Prevailing Wind: South/West
Designer: P Tory
Further Information:
These three 9 hole courses can be played
in a variety of different ways.

EUROPEAN CLUB

EUROPEAN CLUB (THE), Brittas Bay,
COUNTY WICKLOW, IRELAND.
(T) 040 447415

(E) info@theeuropeanclub.com
(W) www.theeuropeanclub.com

Membership: Members & Public
Size of Complex: 260 Acres

Contact/s:
• **General Manager:** Miss Sidon Ruddy

Course/s:

THE EUROPEAN CLUB
Description: Links, Long
Green Speed: Fast
Built: 1989 Built On: Sand
Number of Holes: 18 Par: 71
Par 3's: 3 Par 4's: 13 Par 5's: 2
Yds: 6690 F9 Yds: 3236 B9 Yds: 3454
Prevailing Wind: South/West
Designer: Pat Ruddy
Further Information:
Ranked 5th golf course in Ireland by the
Irish Golf Institute. There are 2 extra holes
that are in play most days ⛳

EUXTON PARK GOLF CTRE

EUXTON PARK GOLF CENTRE, Euxton
Lane, Euxton, Chorley, **LANCASHIRE,** PR7
6DL, **ENGLAND.**
(T) 01257 261601

Contact/s:
• **Owner:** Mr T Evans

Course/s:

EUXTON
Number of Holes: 9 Par: 27
Par 3's: 9
Yds: 1245

EVESHAM

EVESHAM GOLF CLUB, The Old Worcester
Rd, Fladbury, Pershore,
WORCESTERSHIRE, WR10 2QS,
ENGLAND.
(T) 01386 860395

Contact/s:
• **Club Secretary:** Mrs L Tattersall

Course/s:

EVESHAM
Number of Holes: 9 Par: 72
Yds: 6408

EXETER

EXETER GOLF & COUNTRY CLUB LTD,
Topsham Rd, Exeter, **DEVON,** EX2 7AE,
ENGLAND.
(T) 01392 874139

Contact/s:
• **Professional:** Mr Mike Rowett

Course/s:

EXETER GOLF & COUNTRY CLUB
Description: Parkland
Built: 1895

Number of Holes: 18 Par: 69
Designer: James Braid
Further Information:
Course situated close to City.

EYEMOUTH

EYEMOUTH GOLF CLUB, Gunsgreenhill,
Eyemouth, **SCOTTISH BORDERS,** TD14
5SF, **SCOTLAND.**
(T) 01890 750004

Membership: Members & Public

Contact/s:
• **Professional:** Mr Paul Terras
• **Pro Shop:** Mr Tony McLeman
  ☎ 01890 75004

Course/s:

EYEMOUTH
Description: Championship, Links,
Parkland, Cliff Top, Open, Long
Green Speed: Fast
Built: 1997 Built On: Soil
Number of Holes: 18 Par: 72
Par 3's: 4 Par 4's: 10 Par 5's: 4
Yds: 6283 F9 Yds: 2903 B9 Yds: 3380
Prevailing Wind: West
Designer: J R Bain
Further Information: The course boasts
some of the most scenic and interesting
clifftop holes in Scottish golf. For instance,
the intimidating 6th is a formidable par 3
across a vast gully with the North Sea
crashing below. Magnificent views along
this rugged coastline.

FAIRBOURNE

FAIRBOURNE GOLF CLUB LTD, Penrhyn
Drive North, Fairbourne, **GWYNEDD,** LL38
2DJ, **WALES.**
(T) 01341 250979

Membership: Members & Public

Contact/s:
• **Club Secretary:** Mrs J Waterhouse
  ☎ 01341 250841

Course/s:

FAIRBOURNE 9 HOLE
Description: Links, Short, Tends to Flood,
Ideal for the Elderly
Green Speed: Slow/Medium
Built: 1995
Number of Holes: 9
Yds: 945

FAIRFIELD GOLF & SAILING CLUB

FAIRFIELD GOLF & SAILING CLUB,
Boothdale, Booth Rd, Audenshaw,
Manchester, **MANCHESTER (GREATER),**
M34 5QA, **ENGLAND.**
(T) 0161 301 4528

Contact/s:
• **Manager:** Mr I Jarnes

Course/s:

FAIRFIELD GOLF AND SAILING CLUB
Number of Holes: 18 Par: 68
Yds: 4956

FAIRHAVEN

FAIRHAVEN GOLF CLUB LTD, Lytham Hall
Pk, Blackpool Rd, Lytham St. Annes,
LANCASHIRE, FY8 4JU, **ENGLAND.**
(T) 01253 736741

Course/s:

FAIRHAVEN
Number of Holes: 18 Par: 74
Yds: 6883
Designer: J A Steer

FAIRTHORNE MANOR

FAIRTHORNE MANOR GOLF CLUB,
Fairthorne Manor, Curbridge, Botley,
Southampton, **HAMPSHIRE**, SO30 2GH,
ENGLAND.
(T) 01489 784231

Course/s:

🏌 **FAIRTHORNE**
Built: 1972
Number of Holes: 18 Par: 62
Further Information:
The course was extended to a 18 hole
course in 1994

FAIRWOOD PARK

FAIRWOOD PARK GOLF CLUB, Blackhills
Lane, Fairwood, Upper Killay, Swansea,
SWANSEA, SA2 7JN, **WALES**.
(T) 01792 297849

Membership: Members & Public

Contact/s:
● Club Secretary: Mrs C Beer
● Professional: Mr Gary Hughes
☎ 01792 299194

Course/s:

🏌 **FAIRWOOD PARK**
Description: Championship, Parkland,
Long, Tight
Green Speed: Fast
Built: 1969 Built On: Soil
Number of Holes: 18 Par: 73
Yds: 6754 F9 Yds: 3354 B9 Yds: 3400
Designer: Hawtree
Further Information:
A flat course.

FAITHLEGG

FAITHLEGG GOLF CLUB, Faithlegg,
COUNTY WATERFORD, IRELAND.
(T) 051 382241 / 382688
(E) golf@faithlegg.com
(W) www.faithlegg.com

Membership: Members & Public

Contact/s:
● Club Secretary: Mr John Santry
● Professional: Mr John Dooley
● Book Tee Times: Ms Rose Heely
● Book Lessons:
☎ 087 6683427

Course/s:

🏌 **FAITHLEGG**
Description: Championship, Parkland,
Medium Length
Green Speed: Medium
Built: 1993 Built On: Clay/Sand/Soil
Number of Holes: 18 Par: 72
Record: 66 (Damien McGrane)
Par 3's: 4 Par 4's: 10 Par 5's: 4
Yds: 6284 F9 Yds: 2716 B9 Yds: 3568
Prevailing Wind: North/West
Designer: P Merrigan

FAKENHAM

FAKENHAM GOLF CLUB, Hempton Rd,
Fakenham, **NORFOLK**, NR21 7LA,
ENGLAND.
(T) 01328 862867

Membership: Members & Public

Contact/s:
● Club Secretary: Mr G Cocker
☎ 01328 855665
● Professional: Mr Martyn Clarke
● Pro Shop:
☎ 01328 863534

Course/s:

🏌 **FAKENHAM**
Description: Parkland, Sheltered, Tight,
Tends to Flood
Green Speed: Fast
Built: 1970 Built On: Soil
Number of Holes: 9 Par: 36
Yds: 3160
Prevailing Wind: South/West
Further Information:
Situated within Fakenham Race Course. A
flat course which can be played as an 18
hole course; 9 holes and 15 tees. Three of
the tees are repeated.

FALKIRK

FALKIRK GOLF CLUB, 136 Stirling Rd,
Camelon, **FALKIRK**, FK2 7YP, **SCOTLAND**.
(T) 01324 611061
(E) carmuirs.fgc@virgin.net

Membership: Members & Public
Size of Complex: 116 Acres

Contact/s:
● Club Secretary: Mr John Elliott
● Pro Shop: Mr J Macallum
☎ 01324 612219

Course/s:

🏌 **CARMUIRS**
Description: Parkland, Undulating, Open,
Drains Well
Green Speed: Medium
Built: 1922
Number of Holes: 18 Par: 71
Record: 66 (John McTear)
Par 3's: 5 Par 4's: 9 Par 5's: 4
Yds: 6230 F9 Yds: 3115 B9 Yds: 3115
Prevailing Wind: West
Designer: James Braid
Further Information:
A testing course built on an old mine with
ponds at the 4th and 5th hole.

FALKIRK TRYST

FALKIRK TRYST GOLF CLUB, Burnhead Rd,
Larbert, **FALKIRK**, FK5 4BD, **SCOTLAND**.
(T) 01324 562054

Contact/s:
● Company Secretary: Mr C Chalmers

Course/s:

🏌 **FALKIRK TRYST**
Description: Parkland Built On: Soil
Number of Holes: 18 Par: 70
Yds: 5593 F9 Yds: 2829 B9 Yds: 2764

FALKLAND

FALKLAND GOLF CLUB, Myreside, Falkland,
Cupar, **FIFE**, KY15 7AA, **SCOTLAND**.
(T) 01337 857404

Membership: Members & Public

Contact/s:
● Book Lessons: Mr Stuart Brown

Course/s:

🏌 **FALKLAND**
Description: Wooded, Parkland, Open,
Tight
Green Speed: Fast
Built: 1974 Built On: Soil
Number of Holes: 9
Prevailing Wind: South/West
Further Information:
A tight little course with beautiful views
looking towards Lomond Hill.

FALMOUTH

FALMOUTH GOLF CLUB, Goldenbank,
Falmouth, **CORNWALL**, TR11 5BQ,
ENGLAND.

(T) 01326 314296

Contact/s:
● Club Secretary: Mr R Wooldridge

Course/s:

🏌 **FALMOUTH**
Number of Holes: 18 Par: 71
F9 Yds: 2780 B9 Yds: 2963

FARDEW

FARDEW GOLF CLUB, Nursery Farm, Carr
Lane, East Morton, Keighley, **YORKSHIRE
(WEST)**, BD20 5RY, **ENGLAND**.
(T) 01274 561229
(E) fardew@dial.pipex.com

Membership: Members & Public
Size of Complex: 66 Acres

Contact/s:
● Professional: Mr Ian Bottomley

Course/s:

🏌 **FARDEW**
Description: Wooded, Parkland,
Undulating, Sheltered, Open, Medium
Length, Drains Well, Tends to Flood, Ideal
for the Elderly
Green Speed: Medium
Built: 1992 Built On: Clay/Soil
Number of Holes: 9 Par: 70 Record: 68
(Laurie Turner)
Yds: 5810 F9 Yds: 2999 B9 Yds: 2811
Prevailing Wind: West
Designer: W Adamson
Further Information:
The green is to USGA Specification.

FAREHAM WOODS

FAREHAM WOODS GOLF CLUB, Office/Lee
Ground, West Drive, Fareham, **HAMPSHIRE**,
PO15 6RS, **ENGLAND**.
(T) 01329 844441

Contact/s:
● Professional: Mr Laurance Ross

Course/s:

🏌 **FAREHAM WOODS**
Number of Holes: 18 Par: 69
Yds: 5533

FARINGDON

FARINGDON GOLF COURSE, Great Coxwell
Rd, Great Coxwell, Faringdon,
OXFORDSHIRE, SN7 7LU, **ENGLAND**.
(T) 01367 243944
(W) www.faringdongolfcourse.co.uk

Membership: Public

Contact/s:
● Club Secretary: Mr Geoff Robbins

Course/s:

🏌 **FARINGDON**
Description: Parkland, Undulating,
Sheltered, Open, Short, Tight, Drains Well,
Ideal for the Elderly
Green Speed: Medium
Built: 1989 Built On: Soil
Number of Holes: 9 Par: 27
Par 3's: 9
Yds: 1004 F9 Yds: 1044
Prevailing Wind: South/West
Further Information:
The course is ideal for young families and
can be played as an 18 hole course.

FARLEIGH COURT

FARLEIGH COURT GOLF CLUB, Old
Farleigh Rd, Farleigh, Warlingham, **SURREY**,
CR6 9PX, **ENGLAND**.
(T) 01883 627733

Membership: Members & Public

<u>Contact/s:</u>
- **Professional:** Mr Scott Graham

<u>Course/s:</u>
- **MEMBERS COURSE**
  Description: Valley, Medium Length, Drains Well
  Green Speed: Fast
  Built: 1997 **Built On:** Chalk/Clay
  Number of Holes: 18 **Par:** 72
  Yds: 6409 **F9 Yds:** 3156 **B9 Yds:** 3253
  Designer: John Jacobs

- **VISITORS COURSE**
  Description: Valley, Long, Drains Well
  Green Speed: Fast
  Built: 1997 **Built On:** Chalk/Clay
  Number of Holes: 9 **Par:** 36
  Yds: 3281
  Designer: John Jacobs

FARNHAM

FARNHAM GOLF CLUB LTD, The Sands, Farnham, **SURREY**, GU10 1PX, **ENGLAND**.
(T) 01252 782109
(E) info@farnhamgolfclub.com

Membership: Members & Public

<u>Contact/s:</u>
- **Professional:** Mr Grahame Cowlishaw
  ☎ 01252 782198

<u>Course/s:</u>
- **FARNHAM**
  Description: Parkland, Heath Land, Sheltered, Medium Length, Tight, Drains Well
  Green Speed: Medium
  Built: 1896 **Built On:** Sand
  Number of Holes: 18 **Par:** 72
  Record: 64 (A Lovelace)
  Par 3's: 4 **Par 4's:** 10 **Par 5's:** 4
  Yds: 6447
  Prevailing Wind: West
  Designer: Donald Steel
  Further Information:
  Described by Ronan Rafferty as a hidden gem (Golf Extra, Sky Sports). Tight, small greens with demanding approach shots.

FARNHAM PARK

FARNHAM PARK GOLF COURSE, Park Rd, Stoke Poges, Slough, **BERKSHIRE**, SL2 4PJ, **ENGLAND**.
(T) 01753 643332
(E) farnhamparkgolfclub@btinternet.co.uk

<u>Contact/s:</u>
- **Club Secretary:** Mr M Brooker
  ☎ 01753 647065

<u>Course/s:</u>
- **FARNHAM PARK**
  Number of Holes: 18 **Par:** 71
  Yds: 6172 **F9 Yds:** 2955 **B9 Yds:** 3217
  Designer: Hawtree

FARNHAM PARK PAR 3

FARNHAM PARK PAR 3 GOLF COURSE, Folly Hill, Farnham, **SURREY**, GU9 0AU, **ENGLAND**.
(T) 01252 715216

<u>Contact/s:</u>
- **Owner:** Mr P Chapman

<u>Course/s:</u>
- **FARNHAM PARK**
  Number of Holes: 9
  Yds: 1163
  Designer: Henry Cotton

FARRINGTON

FARRINGTON GOLF CLUB, Marsh Lane, Farrington Gurney, Bristol, **BRISTOL**, BS39 6TS, **ENGLAND**.
(T) 01761 241787
(E) info@farringtongolfclub.net
(W) www.farringtongolfclub.net

Membership: Members & Public

<u>Contact/s:</u>
- **Club Secretary:** Ms Debbie Cole
- **Professional:** Mr Jon Cowgill
- **Pro Shop:** Mr Steve Ritchie

<u>Course/s:</u>
- **EXECUTIVE**
  Description: Championship, Parkland, Undulating, Long, Ideal for the Elderly
  Green Speed: Medium
  Built: 1900 **Built On:** Soil
  Number of Holes: 9 **Par:** 27
  Par 3's: 9
  Yds: 1402
  Prevailing Wind: South/West
  Designer: Peter Thomson
  Further Information:
  9 hole course can be played as an 18 hole course

- **MAIN**
  Built: 1900
  Number of Holes: 18 **Par:** 72
  Par 3's: 4 **Par 4's:** 10 **Par 5's:** 4
  Yds: 6316
  Designer: Peter Thomson

FARTHINGSTONE

FARTHINGSTONE HOTEL GOLF & LEISURE CENTRE, Everdon Rd, Farthingstone, Towcester, **NORTHAMPTONSHIRE**, NN12 8HA, **ENGLAND**.
(T) 01327 361291
(E) interest@farthingstone.co.uk
(W) www.farthingstone.co.uk

<u>Contact/s:</u>
- **Book Tee Times:** Ms Anita Lawson
  ☎ 01327 361533

<u>Course/s:</u>
- **FARTHINGSTONE HOTEL**
  Description: Wooded
  Built: 1973
  Number of Holes: 18 **Par:** 70
  Yds: 6299
  Designer: D Donaldson
  Further Information:
  A course that abounds in challenging features including water hazards.

FAUGHAN VALLEY

FAUGHAN VALLEY GOLF CLUB, 8 Carmoney Rd, Campsie, Londonderry, **COUNTY LONDONDERRY**, BT47 3JH, **NORTHERN IRELAND**.
(T) 028 7186 0707

Membership: Members & Public

<u>Contact/s:</u>
- **Owner:** Mr David Forbes

<u>Course/s:</u>
- **FAUGHAN VALLEY**
  Description: Parkland, Valley, Open, Medium Length, Drains Well, Ideal for the Elderly
  Green Speed: Medium
  Built: 2000
  Number of Holes: 18
  Designer: David Forbes

FAVERSHAM

FAVERSHAM GOLF CLUB LTD, Belmont Pk, Throwley, Faversharn, **KENT**, ME13 0HB, **ENGLAND**.
(T) 01795 890561

<u>Contact/s:</u>
- **Manager:** Mr J Edgington

<u>Course/s:</u>
- **FAVERSHAM**
  Number of Holes: 18 **Par:** 70
  Yds: 6030

FAWKHAM VALLEY GOLF CLUB

FAWKHAM VALLEY GOLF CLUB, Gay Dawn Offices, Fawkham Valley Rd, Fawkham, Longfield, **KENT**, DA3 8LY, **ENGLAND**.
(T) 01474 707144

<u>Contact/s:</u>
- **Club Secretary:** Mr Tony Dart
- **Professional:** Mr Cameron McKillop

<u>Course/s:</u>
- **FAWKHAM VALLEY**
  Description: Wooded
  Number of Holes: 9 **Par:** 36
  Further Information: This 9 hole course can be played as 18 holes.

FELIXSTOWE FERRY

FELIXSTOWE FERRY GOLF CLUB, Ferry Rd, Felixstowe, **SUFFOLK**, IP11 9RY, **ENGLAND**.
(T) 01394 286834

Membership: Mernbers & Public

<u>Contact/s:</u>
- **Professional:** Mr Ian Macpherson

<u>Course/s:</u>
- **MARTELLO**
  Description: Links, Open, Medium Length, Drains Well, Ideal for the Elderly
  Green Speed: Medium
  Built: 1948 **Built On:** Soil
  Number of Holes: 18 **Par:** 72
  Par 3's: 4 **Par 4's:** 10 **Par 5's:** 4
  Yds: 6285 **F9 Yds:** 3268 **B9 Yds:** 3017
  Prevailing Wind: East
  Designer: Henry Cotton
  Further Information:
  Testing course. Course was founded in 1880, but was re-designed after World War II by Henry Colton.

FELTWELL

FELTWELL GOLF CLUB, Witton Rd, Feltwell, Thetford, **NORFOLK**, IP26 4AY, **ENGLAND**.
(T) 01842 827644

Membership: Members & Public
Size of Complex: 57 Acres

<u>Contact/s:</u>
- **Club Secretary:** Mr Steve Waller
- **Professional:** Mr Neil Mitchell
  ☎ 01842 827666

<u>Course/s:</u>
- **FELTWELL**
  Description: Links, Drains Well
  Built: 1972 **Built On:** Chalk
  Number of Holes: 9
  Yds: 6488 **F9 Yds:** 3274 **B9 Yds:** 3214
  Further Information:
  This course is an inland flat links course.

FERENEZE

FERENEZE GOLF CLUB, Fereneze Ave, Barrhead, Glasgow, **GLASGOW (CITY OF)**, G78 1HJ, **SCOTLAND**.

(T) 0141 8811519

Course/s:

🍂 **FERENEZE**
Description: Moorland
Green Speed: Fast
Number of Holes: 18   Par: 70
Yds: 5821

FERMOY

FERMOY GOLF CLUB, Corrin, Fermoy,
COUNTY CORK, **IRELAND**.
(T) 025 32694
(E) fermoygolfclub@eircom.net

Contact/s:
● Club Secretary: Ms Kathleen Murphy

Course/s:

🍂 **FERMOY**
Description: Heath Land
Number of Holes: 18   Par: 72
Yds: 6356

FERNDOWN

FERNDOWN GOLF CLUB, 119 Golf Links
Rd, Ferndown, **DORSET**, BH22 8BU,
ENGLAND.
(T) 01202 874602
(E) ferndowngc@lineone.net
(W) www.ferndowngolfclub.co.uk

Contact/s:
● Club Secretary: Mr Terry Pond
● Professional: Mr Iain Parker
  ☎ 01202 873825

Course/s:

🍂 **PRESIDENTS**
Description: Heath Land, Drains Well
Green Speed: Fast
Built: 1969
Number of Holes: 9   F9 Yds: 2802
Designer: J Hamilton-Stutt
Further Information:
9 hole course can be played as an 18 hole
course

🍂 **THE OLD COURSE**
Description: Championship, Heath Land,
Medium Length, Drains Well
Green Speed: Fast
Built: 1923
Number of Holes: 18   Par: 71
Yds: 6452   F9 Yds: 3190   B9 Yds: 3262
Designer: Harold Hilton 🏆

FERNDOWN FOREST

FERNDOWN FOREST GOLF CENTRE,
Forest Links Rd, Ferndown, **DORSET**, BH22
9QE, **ENGLAND**.
(T) 01202 876096
(E) golfingpleasure@supanet.com
(W) www.ferndown-forest-leisure.co.uk

Contact/s:
● Club Secretary: Ms Christine Lawford
  ☎ 01202 894095
● Professional: Mr Mike Dodd
● Pro Shop: Mr Norman Flindall
  ☎ 01202 892588
● Book Lessons:
  ☎ 01202 894990

Course/s:

🍂 **FERNDOWN FOREST**
Description: Wooded, Parkland, Open,
Short, Drains Well, Ideal for the Elderly
Green Speed: Medium
Built: 1993   Built On: Clay/Soil
Number of Holes: 18   Par: 68
Yds: 5094   F9 Yds: 2264   B9 Yds: 2830
Designer: Guy Hunt

FERNHILL

FERNHILL GOLF & COUNTRY CLUB,
Carrigaline, Carrigaline, **COUNTY CORK**,
IRELAND.
(T) 021 4372226
(E) fernhill@iol.ie
(W) www.fernhillgolfhotel.com

Course/s:

🍂 **FERNHILL HOTEL &**
Description: Parkland
Number of Holes: 18   Par: 69
Yds: 6241

FFESTINIOG

FFESTINIOG GOLF CLUB, Y Cefn,
Ffestiniog, Blaenau Ffestiniog, **GWYNEDD**,
LL41 4LS, **WALES**.
(T) 01766 762637

Course/s:

🍂 **FFESTINIOG**
Number of Holes: 9
Yds: 5505

FILEY

FILEY GOLF CLUB, South Cliff, Filey,
YORKSHIRE (NORTH), YO14 9BQ,
ENGLAND.
(T) 01723 513293

Course/s:

🍂 **FILEY**
Number of Holes: 18   Par: 70
Yds: 6112
Designer: James Braid

FILTON

FILTON GOLF CLUB, Golf Course Lane,
Bristol, **BRISTOL**, BS34 7QS, **ENGLAND**.
(T) 01179 694169
Size of Complex: 150 Acres

Contact/s:
● Club Secretary: Ms Esme Mannering
● Professional: Mr Darren Robinson
  ☎ 01179 696968

Course/s:

🍂 **FILTON**
Description: Parkland, Undulating,
Medium Length, Ideal for the Elderly
Green Speed: Medium/Fast
Built: 1909   Built On: Clay
Number of Holes: 18   Par: 70
Par 3's: 4   Par 4's: 12   Par 5's: 2
Yds: 6318   F9 Yds: 3054   B9 Yds: 3264
Further Information:
Testing course.

FINCHLEY

FINCHLEY GOLF CLUB, Nether Court, Frith
Lane, Mill Hill, London, **LONDON
(GREATER)**, NW7 1PU, **ENGLAND**.
(T) 020 83462436
(E) secretary@finchleygolfclub.co.uk
(W) www.finchleygolfclub.co.uk

Membership: Members & Public

Contact/s:
● Pro Shop: Mr David Brown
  ☎ 020 83465086

Course/s:

🍂 **FINCHLEY**
Description: Parkland Built On: Clay
Number of Holes: 18   Par: 72
Yds: 6356   F9 Yds: 3301   B9 Yds: 3055
Designer: James Braid

FINGLE GLEN

FINGLE GLEN GOLF & COUNTRY CLUB,
Tedburn St Mary, Exeter, **DEVON**, EX6 6AF,
ENGLAND.
(T) 01647 61817

Membership: Members & Public

Contact/s:
● Club Secretary: Mr Peter Miliffe
● Professional: Mr Mervyn Kemp

Course/s:

🍂 **FINGLE GLEN**
Description: Undulating, Medium Length,
Drains Well
Built: 1989
Number of Holes: 9   Par: 66
Par 3's: 3   Par 4's: 6
Yds: 4878
Designer: Bill Pile
Further Information:
9 hole course can be played as an 18 hole
course.

FINNSTOWN FAIRWAYS

FINNSTOWN FAIRWAYS GOLF COURSE,
Finnstwon Country House Hotel, Newcastle
Rd, Lucan, Dublin, **COUNTY DUBLIN**,
IRELAND.
(T) 01628 0644

Course/s:

🍂 **FINNSTOWN FAIRWAYS**
Number of Holes: 9
Designer: R Browne

FINTONA

FINTONA GOLF CLUB, 1 Kiln St, Fintona,
Omagh, **COUNTY TYRONE**, BT78 2BJ,
NORTHERN IRELAND.
(T) 028 82841480

Course/s:

🍂 **FINTONA**
Number of Holes: 9

FISHWICK HALL

FISHWICK HALL GOLF CLUB LTD,
Glenluce Drive, Farringdon Pk, Preston,
LANCASHIRE, PR1 5TD, **ENGLAND**.
(T) 01772 795870

Contact/s:
● Professional: Mr Nick Paranomos
● Book Tee Times: Mr Martin Watson

Course/s:

🍂 **FISHWICK HALL**
Description: Parkland
Built: 1912
Number of Holes: 18   Par: 70

FITZPATRICK FITNESS CTRE

**FITZPATRICK FITNESS CENTRE & GOLF
CLUB**, Tivoli, **COUNTY CORK**, **IRELAND**.
(T) 021 4505128

Course/s:

🍂 **FITZPATRICK SILVER SPRINGS**
Number of Holes: 9
Designer: Edward Hackett

FIVE LAKES HOTEL

**FIVE LAKES HOTEL GOLF & COUNTRY
CLUB**, Tolleshunt Knights, Tolleshunt Knights,
Maldon, **ESSEX**, CM9 8HX, **ENGLAND**.
(T) 01621 862327

Contact/s:
● General Manager: Mr N Byrne

Course/s:

LAKES
Number of Holes: 18
Designer: Hawtree, Taylor

LINKS
Number of Holes: 18
Designer: Hawtree, Taylor

FLACKWELL HEATH

FLACKWELL HEATH GOLF CLUB,
Treadaway Rd, Flackwell Heath, High
Wycombe, **BUCKINGHAMSHIRE**, HP10
9PE, **ENGLAND**.
(T) 01628 530040
(W) www.flackwellheathgolfclub.co.uk

Contact/s:
● **Club Secretary:** Mr Stan Chandler
☎ 01628 520929
● **Professional:** Mr Paul Watson

Course/s:

FLACKWELL HEATH
Number of Holes: 18 Par: 71
Yds: 6211 F9 Yds: 2796 B9 Yds: 3415

FLAMBOROUGH HEAD

FLAMBOROUGH HEAD GOLF CLUB, The
Lighthouse, Lighthouse Rd, Flamborough,
Bridlington, **YORKSHIRE (EAST)**, YO15
1AR, **ENGLAND**.
(T) 01262 850417

Contact/s:
● **Chairman:** Mr J R Crowder

Course/s:

FLAMBOROUGH HEAD
Number of Holes: 18

FLEETWOOD

FLEETWOOD GOLF CLUB LTD, Princes
Way, Fleetwood, **LANCASHIRE**, FY7 8AF,
ENGLAND.
(T) 01253 773573
(E) fleetwoodgc@aol.com
(W) www.fleetwoodgolfclub.org.uk

Membership: Members & Public
Size of Complex: 100 Acres

Contact/s:
● **Club Secretary:** Mr Neil Robinson
● **Professional:** Mr Steve McLaughlin
☎ 01253 873661

Course/s:

FLEETWOOD
Description: Championship, Links, Open,
Long, Drains Well, Ideal for the Elderly
Green Speed: Medium
Built: 1932 Built On: Sand
Number of Holes: 18 Par: 72
Yds: 6557 F9 Yds: 3000 B9 Yds: 3557
Prevailing Wind: South/West
Designer: J A Steer

FLEMING PARK

FLEMING PARK GOLF COURSE, Kingfisher
Rd, Eastleigh, **HAMPSHIRE**, SO50 9LH,
ENGLAND.
(T) 023 80612797

Membership: Members & Public
Size of Complex: 1975 Acres

Contact/s:
● **Club Secretary:** Mr Chris Stricket

Course/s:

FLEMING PARK
Description: Wooded, Undulating, Short,
Tight, Tends to Flood, Ideal for the Elderly
Green Speed: Fast

Built: 1975
Number of Holes: 18 Par: 65
Yds: 4380 F9 Yds: 2448 B9 Yds: 1932
Designer: David Miller
Further Information:
Wildlife throughout the course.

FLEMPTON

FLEMPTON GOLF CLUB, Flempton, Bury St.
Edmunds, **SUFFOLK**, IP28 6EQ, **ENGLAND**.
(T) 01284 728291

Membership: Members & Public
Size of Complex: 56 Acres

Contact/s:
● **Club Secretary:** Mr John Taylor
● **Professional:** Mr Chris Aldred
● **Book Tee Times:** Mr R Brown

Course/s:

FLEMPTON
Description: Parkland, Heath Land,
Medium Length, Drains Well
Green Speed: Medium
Built: 1895 Built On: Soil
Number of Holes: 9 Par: 70
Par 3's: 2 Par 4's: 6 Par 5's: 1
Yds: 6240 F9 Yds: 3120 B9 Yds: 3120
Prevailing Wind: South/West
Designer: James Braid
Further Information:
9 hole course can be played as an 18 hole
course

FLINT

FLINT GOLF CLUB, Cornist Lane, Flint,
FLINTSHIRE, CH6 5HJ, **WALES**.
(T) 01352 732327

Contact/s:
● **Club Secretary:** Mr E Owens

Course/s:

FLINT
Number of Holes: 9
Designer: H G Griffith

FLIXTON

FLIXTON GOLF CLUB (THE), 269 Church
Rd, Urmston, Manchester, **MANCHESTER
(GREATER)**, M41 6EP, **ENGLAND**.
(T) 0161 7482116

Contact/s:
● **Club Secretary:** E G Gill
● **Professional:** Mr David Ware

Course/s:

FLIXTON
Number of Holes: 9 Par: 71
Par 3's: 2 Par 4's: 6 Par 5's: 1
Yds: 6410 F9 Yds: 3195 B9 Yds: 3215
Further Information:
9 hole course can be played as an 18 hole
course

FOLKE GOLF CTRE

FOLKE GOLF CENTRE, Alweston,
Sherborne, **DORSET**, DT9 5HR, **ENGLAND**.
(T) 01963 23330

Membership: Public

Contact/s:
● **Manager:** Mr Steve Harris

Course/s:

FOLKE GOLF COURSE
Description: Parkland, Medium Length
Built On: Clay
Number of Holes: 9 Par: 35
Yds: 2821
Further Information:
The course is gently undulating. This 9

hole course can be played as an 18 hole

FOREST HILL

FOREST HILL GOLF CLUB, Markfield Lane,
Botcheston, Leicester, **LEICESTERSHIRE**,
LE9 9FH, **ENGLAND**.
(T) 01455 824800

Contact/s:
● **Manager:** Mr Samuel Sherwin

Course/s:

FOREST HILL
Number of Holes: 18

FOREST HILLS

FOREST HILLS GOLF CLUB, Mile End Rd,
Coleford, **GLOUCESTERSHIRE**, GL16 7BY,
ENGLAND.
(T) 01594 810620

Membership: Members & Public

Contact/s:
● **Professional:** Mr R Ballard
● **Book Lessons:** Mrs R Ballard

Course/s:

FOREST HILLS
Description: Parkland, Medium Length,
Drains Well
Green Speed: Fast
Built: 1992
Number of Holes: 18 Par: 72
Par 3's: 3 Par 4's: 12 Par 5's: 3
Yds: 6368 F9 Yds: 3352 B9 Yds: 3016
Designer: Adrian Stiff

FOREST OF ARDEN

**MARRIOTT FOREST OF ARDEN HOTEL &
COUNTRY CLUB,** Maxstoke Lane, Meriden,
Coventry, **MIDLANDS (WEST)**, CV7 7HR,
ENGLAND.
(T) 01676 526113
Size of Complex: 10000 Acres

Contact/s:
● **Professional:** Mr Damian Tudor

Course/s:

AYLESFORD
Description: Parkland, Short
Built: 1978
Number of Holes: 18 Par: 72
Designer: Donald Steel
Further Information:
Good for all standards of golfers.

CHAMPIONSHIP - ARDEN
Description: Parkland
Built: 1978
Number of Holes: 18 Par: 72
Par 3's: 4 Par 4's: 10 Par 5's: 4
Yds: 6690
Designer: Donald Steel
Further Information:
A challenging course.

FOREST OF DEAN

FOREST OF DEAN GOLF CLUB (THE),
Lords Hill, Coleford, **GLOUCESTERSHIRE**,
GL16 8BD, **ENGLAND**.
(T) 01594 833689

Membership: Members & Public

Contact/s:
● **Professional:** Mr Andy Grey

Course/s:

FOREST OF DEAN
Description: Parkland, Sheltered, Open,
Medium Length, Tight, Tends to Flood,
Ideal for the Elderly
Green Speed: Fast

Built: 1971 **Built On:** Clay
Number of Holes: 18 **Par:** 70
Record: 62 (Sion Bebb)
Par 3's: 5 **Par 4's:** 10 **Par 5's:** 3
Yds: 6033
Designer: John Day
Further Information:
This flat course has small greens and
water features throughout.

FOREST OF GALTRES

FOREST OF GALTRES GOLF COURSE,
Moorlands Rd, Skelton, York, **YORKSHIRE
(NORTH)**, YO32 2RF, **ENGLAND**.
(T) 01904 766198

Contact/s:
● Club Secretary: Mrs S J Procter
  ☎ 01904 769400
● Professional: Mr Phil Bradley

Course/s:
⛳ **FOREST OF GALTRES**
Number of Holes: 18 **Par:** 72
Par 3's: 4 **Par 4's:** 10 **Par 5's:** 4
Yds: 6386 **F9 Yds:** 3186 **B9 Yds:** 3200
Designer: Simon Gidman

FOREST PARK

FOREST PARK GOLF CLUB, Stockton on the
Forest, York, **YORKSHIRE (NORTH)**, YO32
9UW, **ENGLAND**.
(T) 01904 400425

Membership: Members & Public

Contact/s:
● Club Secretary: Mrs Fiona Crossley

Course/s:
⛳ **FOREST PARK**
Description: Parkland, Long, Drains Well
Green Speed: Medium
Built: 1990 **Built On:** Soil
Number of Holes: 18 **Par:** 71
Par 3's: 4 **Par 4's:** 11 **Par 5's:** 3
Yds: 6660
Further Information:
The course is designed around many
established trees. The Foss Beck winds
its way through the course and comes
into play with many holes.

FOREST PINES

**FOREST PINES GOLF CLUB & DRIVING
RANGE,** Ermine St, Broughton, Brigg,
LINCOLNSHIRE (NORTH), DN20 0AQ,
ENGLAND.
(T) 01652 650756
(E) enquiries@forestpines.co.uk
(W) www.forestpines.co.uk

Contact/s:
● Professional: Mr David Edwards

Course/s:
⛳ **BEECHES**
Description: Heath Land, Undulating,
Open
Number of Holes: 9 **Par:** 35
Par 3's: 3 **Par 4's:** 4 **Par 5's:** 2
Yds: 3102
Designer: John Morgan
Further Information:
There are 27 holes made up of 3 different
9 hole courses.

⛳ **FOREST**
Description: Heath Land, Undulating,
Open
Number of Holes: 9 **Par:** 36
Par 3's: 2 **Par 4's:** 5 **Par 5's:** 2
Yds: 3291
Designer: John Morgan

⛳ **PINES**
Description: Heath Land, Undulating,
Open
Number of Holes: 9 **Par:** 37
Par 3's: 2 **Par 4's:** 4 **Par 5's:** 3
Yds: 3568
Designer: John Morgan

FORFAR

FORFAR GOLF CLUB, Cunninghill, Forfar,
ANGUS, DD8 2RL, **SCOTLAND**.
(T) 01307 462120

Membership: Members & Public

Contact/s:
● Club Secretary: Mr William Baird
● Professional: Mr Peter McNiven

Course/s:
⛳ **FORFAR**
Description: Wooded, Heath Land,
Moorland, Drains Well, Ideal for the Elderly
Green Speed: Fast
Built: 1871 **Built On:** Soil
Number of Holes: 18 **Par:** 69
Yds: 6066 **F9 Yds:** 3008 **B9 Yds:** 3058
Prevailing Wind: South
Designer: Tom Morris
Further Information:
Scottish Pro tournament - 1969. Ideal
place for player. Greens are excellent and
the views are beautiful.

FORMBY

FORMBY GOLF CLUB LTD, Golf Rd,
Liverpool, **MERSEYSIDE**, L37 1LQ,
ENGLAND.
(T) 01704 872164
(E) info@formbygolfclub.co.uk
(W) www.formbygolfclub.co.uk

Membership: Members & Public

Contact/s:
● Club Secretary: Mr K R Wilcox

Course/s:
⛳ **FORMBY**
Description: Links, Wooded, Heath Land
Green Speed: Fast
Built: 1884
Number of Holes: 18 **Par:** 72
Yds: 6701 **F9 Yds:** 3510 **B9 Yds:** 3191
Designer: Harry Shapland Colt, William
Park, Frank Pennink 🏆

FORMBY HALL

FORMBY HALL GOLF CLUB, Southport Old
Rd, Formby, Liverpool, **MERSEYSIDE**, L37
0AB, **ENGLAND**.
(T) 01704 875699

Membership: Members & Public

Contact/s:
● Professional: Mr David Lloyd

Course/s:
⛳ **FORMBY HALL**
Description: Parkland, Open, Long,
Drains Well, Ideal for the Elderly
Green Speed: Slow
Built: 1995 **Built On:** Sand/Soil
Number of Holes: 18 **Par:** 72
Par 3's: 4 **Par 4's:** 10 **Par 5's:** 4
Yds: 6731
Designer: Harry Shapland Colt, William
Park

FORMBY LADIES

FORMBY LADIES GOLF CLUB, Golf Rd,
Liverpool, **MERSEYSIDE**, L37 1YH,
ENGLAND.
(T) 01704 873493

Course/s:
⛳ **FORMBY LADIES**
Number of Holes: 18

FORRES

FORRES GOLF CLUB, Forres Golf Course,
Forres, **MORAY**, IV36 2RD, **SCOTLAND**.
(T) 01309 672250
(W) www.forresgolf.fsnet.co.uk

Membership: Members & Public
Size of Complex: 120 Acres

Contact/s:
● Professional: Mr Sandy Aird

Course/s:
⛳ **FORRES**
Description: Parkland, Medium Length,
Drains Well
Green Speed: Medium
Built: 1889 **Built On:** Sand
Number of Holes: 18 **Par:** 70
Record: 60 (Jim Payne)
Par 3's: 5 **Par 4's:** 11 **Par 5's:** 2
Yds: 6236 **F9 Yds:** 3044 **B9 Yds:** 3192
Prevailing Wind: North
Designer: James Braid, William Park

FORREST LITTLE

FORREST LITTLE GOLF CLUB, Cloghran,
Dublin, **COUNTY DUBLIN**, **IRELAND**.
(T) 01 8401763

Course/s:
⛳ **FORREST LITTLE**
Number of Holes: 18

FORRESTER PARK

**FORRESTER PARK GOLF & TENNIS
CLUB,** Beckingham Rd, Great Totham,
Maldon, **ESSEX**, CM9 8EA, **ENGLAND**.
(T) 01621 891406

Contact/s:
● Professional: Mr Gary Pike

Course/s:
⛳ **FORRESTER PARK**
Description: Parkland, Tight
Built: 1968
Number of Holes: 18 **Par:** 71
Designer: T R Forrester, Muir

FORT AUGUSTUS

FORT AUGUSTUS GOLF CLUB, Market Hill,
Fort Augustus, **HIGHLANDS**, PH32 4DS,
SCOTLAND.
(T) 01320 366660

Course/s:
⛳ **FORT AUGUSTUS**
Number of Holes: 9

FORT WILLIAM

FORT WILLIAM GOLF CLUB, Downview
Avenue, Belfast, **COUNTY ANTRIM**, BT15
4EZ, **NORTHERN IRELAND**.
(T) 028 90370770

Contact/s:
● Club Secretary: Mr M Purdy

Course/s:
⛳ **FORTWILLIAM**
Number of Holes: 18

FORTROSE & ROSEMARKIE

FORTROSE & ROSEMARKIE GOLF CLUB,
Ness Rd East, Fortrose, **HIGHLANDS**, IV10
8SE, **SCOTLAND**.
(T) 01381 620529

(E) secretary@fortrosegolfclub.co.uk
(W) www.fortrosegolfclub.co.uk
Contact/s:
- Club Secretary: Mrs M Collier
Course/s:
- **FORTROSE & ROSEMARKIE**
  Description: Heath Land, Open, Short
  Built: 1888 **Built On:** Sand
  Number of Holes: 18 **Par:** 71
  Par 3's: 3 **Par 4's:** 13 **Par 5's:** 2
  Yds: 5858 **F9 Yds:** 2990 **B9 Yds:** 2724
  Designer: James Braid

FOSSEWAY

FOSSEWAY GOLF CLUB, Charlton Lane,
Midsomer Norton, Bath, **BATH &
SOMERSET (NORTH EAST)**, BA3 4BD,
ENGLAND.
(T) 01761 412214
Course/s:
- **FOSSEWAY COUNTRY CLUB**
  Description: Parkland
  Built: 1970
  Number of Holes: 9 **Par:** 68
  Designer: Cotton, Pennink
  Further Information:
  Views of Mendip Hills. Can be played as
  an 18 hole.

FOTA ISLAND

FOTA ISLAND GOLF CLUB, Fota Island,
Carrigtwohill, **COUNTY CORK**, **IRELAND**.
(T) 021 4883700
(E) fotagolf@iol.ie
(W) www.zenith.ie/fota/golf
Contact/s:
- General Manager: Mr Kevin Mulcahy
  ☎ 021 4885700
Course/s:
- **FOTA ISLAND**
  Number of Holes: 18 **Par:** 71
  Yds: 6927 **F9 Yds:** 3584 **B9 Yds:** 3343
  Designer: Jeff Howes

FOUR MARKS

FOUR MARKS GOLF COURSE, Headmoor
Lane, Off Telegraph Lane, Four Marks, Alton,
HAMPSHIRE, GU34 3ES, **ENGLAND**.
(T) 01420 587214
Membership: Members & Public
Size of Complex: 26 Acres
Contact/s:
- Club Secretary: Mrs Flora Ward
  ☎ 01420 587313
- Professional: Mr Peter Chapman
Course/s:
- **FOUR MARKS**
  Description: Parkland, Hilltop, Short,
  Tight, Drains Well
  Green Speed: Fast
  Built: 1983 **Built On:** Chalk/Clay
  Number of Holes: 9 **Par:** 31
  Par 3's: 5 **Par 4's:** 4
  Yds: 1960
  Prevailing Wind: North
  Designer: D Wright
  Further Information:
  9 hole course can be played as an 18 hole
  course. The course is situated on the
  highest point in Hampshire. A second set
  of tees is being added to each hole.

FOXBRIDGE

FOXBRIDGE GOLF CLUB, Plaistow Rd,
Kirdford, Billingshurst, **SUSSEX (WEST)**,
RH14 0LB, **ENGLAND**.

(T) 01403 753303
Membership: Members & Public
Contact/s:
- Manager: Mr P Clarke
Course/s:
- **FOXBRIDGE**
  Description: Parkland, Sheltered, Long,
  Drains Well, Ideal for the Elderly
  Green Speed: Medium
  Built: 1991
  Number of Holes: 9
  Designer: P A Clark

FOXHILLS GOLF

FOXHILLS GOLF COUNTRY CLUB,
Stonehill Rd, Ottershaw, Chertsey, **SURREY**,
KT16 0EL, **ENGLAND**.
(T) 01932 872050/07000 3694455
(E) golf@foxhills.co.uk
(W) www.foxhills.co.uk
Membership: Members & Public
Contact/s:
- Professional: Mr A Good
- Pro Shop:
  ☎ 01932 704465
- Book Tee Times: Mr Events Office
  ☎ 01932 704445
Course/s:
- **BERNARD HUNT**
  Description: Parkland, Open, Medium
  Length, Tight, Tends to Flood
  Built: 1975 **Built On:** Clay
  Number of Holes: 18 **Par:** 73
  Par 3's: 4 **Par 4's:** 9 **Par 5's:** 5
  Yds: 6770 **F9 Yds:** 3418 **B9 Yds:** 3352
  Designer: Hawtree
- **LONGCROSS**
  Number of Holes: 18 **Par:** 72
  Par 3's: 4 **Par 4's:** 10 **Par 5's:** 4
  Yds: 6453 **F9 Yds:** 3265 **B9 Yds:** 3188
  Designer: Hawtree
- **MANOR**
  Number of Holes: 9 **Par:** 27
  Par 3's: 9
  Yds: 1143 **F9 Yds:** 1143 **B9 Yds:** 1143
  Designer: Hawtree

FOXROCK

FOXROCK GOLF CLUB, Torquay Rd, Fox
Rock, **COUNTY DUBLIN**, **IRELAND**.
(T) 01 2893992
Course/s:
- **FOXROCK**
  Number of Holes: 9

FOYLE

FOYLE INTERNATIONAL GOLF CENTRE,
12 Alder Rd, Londonderry, **COUNTY
LONDONDERRY**, BT48 8DB, **NORTHERN
IRELAND**.
(T) 028 71352222
(W) www.foylegolfcentre.co.uk
Membership: Members & Public
Size of Complex: 150 Acres
Contact/s:
- Club Secretary: Mr George Fitzpatrick
- Professional: Mr Kieran McLaughlin
- Pro Shop: Mrs Margaret Lapsley
Course/s:
- **PARKLAND**
  Description: Championship, Parkland,
  Long, Drains Well
  Green Speed: Medium
  Built: 1994 **Built On:** Sand/Soil
  Number of Holes: 18 **Par:** 72

Par 3's: 3 **Par 4's:** 12 **Par 5's:** 3
Yds: 6368 **F9 Yds:** 3014 **B9 Yds:** 3354
Designer: Frank Ainsworth
- **WOODLANDS PAR 3**
  Description: Parkland, Sheltered, Short,
  Drains Well, Ideal for the Elderly
  Green Speed: Medium
  Built: 1993 **Built On:** Sand/Soil
  Number of Holes: 9 **Par:** 27
  Par 3's: 9
  Yds: 1349
  Designer: Frank Ainsworth
  Further Information:
  The course is ideal for beginners and
  families .

FOYNES

FOYNES GOLF COURSE, Leahies Hse,
Foynes, **COUNTY LIMERICK**, **IRELAND**.
(T) 069 65429
Course/s:
- **FOYNES GOLF COURSE**
  Number of Holes: 9 **Par:** 35
  Yds: 2942

FRANKFIELD

FRANKFIELD GOLF CLUB, Airport Rd,
Frankfield, Douglas, **COUNTY CORK**,
IRELAND.
(T) 021 4363124
Contact/s:
- Professional: Mr Michael Ryan
Course/s:
- **FRANKFIELD COURSE**
  Description: Parkland, Hilltop, Undulating
  Number of Holes: 9 **Par:** 68
  Yds: 5400
  Further Information:
  The whole course overlooks the city of
  Cork

FRASERBURGH

FRASERBURGH GOLF CLUB, Philorth,
Fraserburgh, **ABERDEENSHIRE**, AB43 8TL,
SCOTLAND.
(T) 01346 516616
(E) fburghgolf@aol.com
Membership: Members & Public
Contact/s:
- Pro Shop: Mrs M Gardiner
  ☎ 01346 517898
- Book Tee Times: Mr J Mollison
Course/s:
- **CORBIE HILL**
  Description: Links, Undulating, Sheltered
  Built: 1891 **Built On:** Sand
  Number of Holes: 18 **Par:** 70
  Yds: 6278 **F9 Yds:** 3187 **B9 Yds:** 3091
  Designer: James Braid
- **ROSEHILL**
  Description: Links
  Built: 1881 **Built On:** Sand
  Number of Holes: 9 **Par:** 32

FRESHWATER BAY

FRESHWATER BAY GOLF CLUB, Afton
Down, Freshwater, **ISLE OF WIGHT**, PO40
9TZ, **ENGLAND**.
(T) 01983 752955
(E) fbgc_iow@yahoo.co.uk
(W) www.isle-of-wight.uk.com
Contact/s:
- Club Secretary: Mr Terry Riddett
Course/s:
- **FRESHWATER BAY**

Description: Downland, Open
Built: 1893
Number of Holes: 18 **Par:** 68
Par 3's: 6 **Par 4's:** 10 **Par 5's:** 2
Yds: 5725 **F9 Yds:** 2873 **B9 Yds:** 2852
Designer: Taylor
Further Information:
Views of The Solent and the English Channel.

FRILFORD HEATH

FRILFORD HEATH GOLF CLUB, Frilford Heath, Abingdon, **OXFORDSHIRE**, OX13 5NW, **ENGLAND**.
(T) 01865 390864

Membership: Members & Public

Contact/s:
- **Club Secretary:** Mr Steve Styles
- **Professional:** Mr Derek Craik
  ☎ 01865 390887

Course/s:

🌑 BLUE
Description: Championship, Long
Built: 1994
Number of Holes: 18 **Par:** 72
Record: 68 (Steve Mitchell)
Par 3's: 4 **Par 4's:** 10 **Par 5's:** 4
Yds: 6728 **F9 Yds:** 3291 **B9 Yds:** 3437
Designer: S Gidman

🌑 GREEN
Description: Parkland, Heath Land, Sheltered, Open, Short, Tight, Drains Well, Ideal for the Elderly
Green Speed: Medium
Built: 1908 **Built On:** Sand
Number of Holes: 18 **Par:** 69
Record: 64 (Derek Craik)
Par 3's: 4 **Par 4's:** 13 **Par 5's:** 1
Yds: 6006 **F9 Yds:** 2949 **B9 Yds:** 3057
Designer: D Cotton, J Taylor

🌑 RED
Description: Championship, Long
Number of Holes: 18 **Par:** 73
Record: 68 (Paul Simpson)
Par 3's: 3 **Par 4's:** 11 **Par 5's:** 4
Yds: 6884 **F9 Yds:** 3527 **B9 Yds:** 3357
Designer: D Cotton, J Taylor

FRINTON

FRINTON GOLF CLUB, 1 The Esplanade, Frinton-on-Sea, **ESSEX**, CO13 9EP, **ENGLAND**.
(T) 01255 674618

Contact/s:
- **Company Secretary:** Mr A Cattrill

Course/s:

🌑 LONG
Number of Holes: 18
Designer: William Park

🌑 SHORT
Number of Holes: 9
Designer: William Park

FRODSHAM

FRODSHAM GOLF CLUB, Simons Lane, Frodsham, **CHESHIRE**, WA6 6HE, **ENGLAND**.
(T) 01928 732159

Contact/s:
- **Professional:** Mr Graham Tonge
- **Book Tee Times:** Mr Eric Roylence
  ☎ 01928 739442

Course/s:

🌑 FRODSHAM
Description: Parkland, Undulating
Built: 1990

Number of Holes: 18 **Par:** 70
Designer: John Day

FROME GOLF CLUB

FROME GOLF CLUB, Critchill Manor, Critchill, Frome, **BATH & SOMERSET (NORTH EAST)**, BA11 4LJ, **ENGLAND**.
(T) 01373 453410
(E) frome.golfclub@excite.co.uk

Membership: Members & Public

Contact/s:
- **Club Secretary:** Ms Sue Austin
- **Professional:** Mr Murdoch McEwan

Course/s:

🌑 FROME
Description: Parkland, Valley, Tight, Drains Well, Ideal for the Elderly
Green Speed: Medium
Built: 1992
Number of Holes: 18

FULFORD

FULFORD (YORK) GOLF CLUB LTD, Heslington Lane, Heslington, York, **YORKSHIRE (NORTH)**, YO10 5DY, **ENGLAND**.
(T) 01904 413579

Contact/s:
- **Manager:** Mr R Bramley

Course/s:

🌑 FULFORD
Number of Holes: 18
Designer: Alistair MacKenzie

FULFORD HEATH

FULFORD HEATH GOLF CLUB LTD, Tanners Green Lane, Wythall, Birmingham, **MIDLANDS (WEST)**, B47 6BH, **ENGLAND**.
(T) 01564 824758

Contact/s:
- **Club Secretary:** Mrs M Tuckett
- **Professional:** Mr Mike Herbett
  ☎ 01564 822930

Course/s:

🌑 FULFORD HEATH
Number of Holes: 18 **Par:** 70
Yds: 6179 **F9 Yds:** 2877 **B9 Yds:** 3302
Designer: James Braid, Hawtree

FULNECK

FULNECK GOLF CLUB LTD, Fulneck, Pudsey, **YORKSHIRE (WEST)**, LS28 8NT, **ENGLAND**.
(T) 0113 2565191

Contact/s:
- **Manager:** Mr J A Brogden

Course/s:

🌑 FULNECK
Number of Holes: 9

FULWELL

FULWELL GOLF CLUB, Wellington Rd, Hampton, **LONDON (GREATER)**, TW12 1JY, **ENGLAND**.
(T) 020 89772733

Contact/s:
- **Club Secretary:** Mr P Butcher

Course/s:

🌑 FULWELL
Number of Holes: 18

FURNESS

FURNESS GOLF CLUB, Central Drive, Walney, Barrow-In-Furness, **CUMBRIA**, LA14 3LN, **ENGLAND**.
(T) 01229 471232

Course/s:

🌑 FURNESS
Number of Holes: 18

FURZELEY

FURZELEY GOLF COURSE, Furzeley Rd, Denmead, **HAMPSHIRE**, PO7 6TX, **ENGLAND**.
(T) 023 92231180

Membership: Members & Public

Contact/s:
- **Professional:** Mr Derek Brown

Course/s:

🌑 FURZLEY
Description: Championship, Parkland, Open, Drains Well, Ideal for the Elderly
Green Speed: Medium **Built On:** Clay
Number of Holes: 18
Prevailing Wind: East

FYNN VALLEY

FYNN VALLEY GOLF CLUB, Witnesham, Ipswich, **SUFFOLK**, IP6 9JA, **ENGLAND**.
(T) 01473 785267
(E) enquiries@fynn-valley.co.uk
(W) www.fynn-valley.co.uk

Membership: Members & Public
Size of Complex: 143 Acres

Contact/s:
- **Club Secretary:** Mr A R Tyrrell
  ☎ 01473 785467
- **Professional:** Mr Alex Lucas
  ☎ 01473 785463
- **Pro Shop:** Mrs J Holmes
- **Book Lessons:** Mr Kelvin Vince

Course/s:

🌑 FYNN VALLEY 18 HOLE
Description: Parkland, Undulating, Medium Length, Drains Well
Green Speed: Medium
Built: 1991 **Built On:** Clay
Number of Holes: 18 **Par:** 70
Record: 65 (Paul Wilby, Jon Bevan)
Par 3's: 5 **Par 4's:** 10 **Par 5's:** 3
Yds: 6373 **F9 Yds:** 2984 **B9 Yds:** 3389
Designer: A Tyrrell
Further Information:
Over 100 bunkers on the course.

🌑 FYNN VALLEY 9 HOLE
Description: Parkland, Short, Tight, Drains Well, Ideal for the Elderly
Green Speed: Slow
Built: 1989 **Built On:** Clay
Number of Holes: 9 **Par:** 27
Par 3's: 9
Yds: 1010 **F9 Yds:** 1010
Designer: A Tyrrell
Further Information:
This course is an ideal practice course for beginners, juniors and those wishing to hone their short game.

GAINSBOROUGH

GAINSBOROUGH GOLF CLUB, The Belt Rd, Gainsborough, **LINCOLNSHIRE**, DN21 1PZ, **ENGLAND**.
(T) 01427 810173

Contact/s:
- **Manager:** Mr D Garrison

Course/s:

🔋 **KARSTEN LAKES**
Number of Holes: 18

🔋 **THONOCK PARK**
Number of Holes: 18

GAIRLOCH

GAIRLOCH GOLF CLUB, Gairloch,
HIGHLANDS, IV21 2BE, **SCOTLAND**.
(T) 01445 712407

Contact/s:
● Club Secretary: Mr A Shinkins

Course/s:

🔋 **GARILOCH**
Description: Links
Built: 1898 Built On: Sand
Number of Holes: 9 Par: 63
Designer: Captain Burgess

GALASHIELS

GALASHIELS GOLF CLUB, Ladhope
Recreation Area, Galashiels, **SCOTTISH
BORDERS**, TD1 2NG, **SCOTLAND**.
(T) 01896 753724

Contact/s:
● Club Secretary: Mr Raymond Gass

Course/s:

🔋 **GALASHIELS**
Description: Parkland, Heath Land,
Undulating
Built: 1884
Number of Holes: 18 Par: 67
Designer: James Braid

GALGORM CASTLE

GALGORM CASTLE GOLF CENTRE,
Galgorm Castle, Galgorm Rd, Ballymena,
COUNTY ANTRIM, BT42 1HL, **NORTHERN
IRELAND**.
(T) 028 25646161
(W) www.galgormcastle.com

Membership: Members & Public
Size of Complex: 220 Acres

Contact/s:
● Club Secretary: Mr W A Hawthorne
● Professional: Mr Phil Collins

Course/s:

🔋 **GALGORM CASTLE GOLF & COUNTRY CLUB**
Description: Championship, Wooded,
Parkland, Undulating, Sheltered, Medium
Length, Tight, Drains Well, Ideal for the
Elderly
Green Speed: Fast
Built: 1997 Built On: Sand/Soil
Number of Holes: 18 Par: 72
Par 3's: 4 Par 4's: 10 Par 5's: 4
Yds: 6230 F9 Yds: 3025 B9 Yds: 3205
Prevailing Wind: West
Designer: Simon Gidman
Further Information:
The course is set within the grounds of an
Elizabethan Castle and provides a
challenging game to championship
standards.

GALLOWAY

DUMFRIES & GALLOWAY GOLF CLUB, 2
Laurieston Ave, Dumfries, **DUMFRIES AND
GALLOWAY**, DG2 7NY, **SCOTLAND**.
(T) 01387 263848

Membership: Members & Public

Contact/s:
● Club Secretary: Mr Tom Ross
● Professional: Mr Joe Fergusson
☎ 01387 256902

Course/s:

🔋 **DUMFRIES & GALLOWAY**
Description: Wooded, Parkland, Ideal for
the Elderly
Number of Holes: 18 Par: 70
Record: 65 (Ross Drummond)
Par 3's: 4 Par 4's: 12 Par 5's: 2
Yds: 6306 F9 Yds: 3349 B9 Yds: 2957
Designer: William Fernie

GALWAY

GALWAY GOLF CLUB, Blackrock, Salthill,
COUNTY GALWAY, **IRELAND**.
(T) 091 522033

Course/s:

🔋 **GALWAY**
Number of Holes: 18

GALWAY BAY

**GALWAY BAY GOLF & COUNTRY CLUB
HOTEL,** Renville, Oranmore, **COUNTY
GALWAY**, **IRELAND**.
(T) 091 790500
(E) gbaygolf@iol.ie
(W) www.galwaybaygolf.com

Course/s:

🔋 **GALWAY BAY GOLF & COUNTRY CLUB**
Number of Holes: 18
Designer: Christy O'Connor

GANSTEAD PARK

GANSTEAD PARK GOLF CLUB, Longdales
Lane, Coniston, Hull, **YORKSHIRE (EAST)**,
HU11 4LB, **ENGLAND**.
(T) 01482 817754
(W) www.gansteadpark.co.uk

Contact/s:
● Club Secretary: Mr G Drewery

Course/s:

🔋 **GANSTEAD PARK**
Built: 1976
Number of Holes: 18 Par: 72
Par 3's: 4 Par 4's: 10 Par 5's: 4
Yds: 6444 F9 Yds: 3211 B9 Yds: 3233
Designer: P Green

GANTON

GANTON GOLF CLUB LTD, Station Rd,
Ganton, Scarborough, **YORKSHIRE
(NORTH)**, YO12 4PA, **ENGLAND**.
(T) 01944 710329
(E) secretary@gantongolfclub.fsnet.co.uk

Membership: Members & Public

Contact/s:
● Club Secretary: Maj R G Woolsey
● Professional: Mr G Brown

Course/s:

🔋 **GANTON GOLF CLUB**
Description: Championship, Links, Heath
Land, Open, Drains Well, Ideal for the
Elderly
Green Speed: Fast
Built: 1891 Built On: Sand
Number of Holes: 18 Par: 72
Par 3's: 3 Par 4's: 12 Par 5's: 3
Yds: 6734 F9 Yds: 3468 B9 Yds: 3266
Designer: James Braid, Harry Shapland
Colt, Tom Dunn, Harry Vardon 🏆

GARESFIELD

GARESFIELD GOLF CLUB, Chopwell,
Newcastle Upon Tyne, **TYNE AND WEAR**,
NE17 7AP, **ENGLAND**.
(T) 01207 561278

Course/s:

🔋 **GARESFIELD**
Number of Holes: 18
Designer: Harry Fernie

GARFORTH

GARFORTH GOLF CLUB, Clubhouse, Long
Lane, Garforth, Leeds, **YORKSHIRE (WEST)**,
LS25 2DS, **ENGLAND**.
(T) 0113 2863308
(W) www.garforthgolfclub.co.uk

Contact/s:
● Professional: Mr Ken Findlater

Course/s:

🔋 **GARFORTH**
Number of Holes: 18 Par: 70
Yds: 6304 F9 Yds: 3040 B9 Yds: 3264

GARMOUTH & KINGSTON

GARMOUTH & KINGSTON GOLF CLUB,
Spey St, Garmouth, Fochabers, **MORAY**, IV32
7NJ, **SCOTLAND**.
(T) 01343 870388

Course/s:

🔋 **GARMOUTH & KINGSTON**
Built: 1932 Built On: Sand
Number of Holes: 18 Par: 69
Designer: George Smith
Further Information:
The course has consistently small greens
and numerous hazards that have to be
encountered.

It is situated on the west bank of the River
Spey where you can watch ospreys dive
for fish.

GARNANT PARK

GARNANT PARK GOLF CLUB, Dinefwr Rd,
Garnant, Ammanford,
CARMARTHENSHIRE, SA18 1NP, **WALES**.
(T) 01269 823365

Membership: Members & Public

Contact/s:
● Course Manager: Mr Kerry Jones

Course/s:

🔋 **GARNANT PARK**
Description: Open, Medium Length,
Drains Well
Built: 1996
Number of Holes: 18
Designer: Roger Jones

GARRYLOUGH

GARRYLOUGH GOLF COURSE, Garrylough,
Enniscorthy, **COUNTY WEXFORD**,
IRELAND.
(T) 053 37246

Membership: Members & Public

Contact/s:
● Owner: Mr Desmond Roche

Course/s:

🔋 **GARRYLOUGH GOLF COURSE**
Number of Holes: 18 Par: 54
Yds: 2764

GARSTANG

GARSTANG GOLF CLUB (THE), Bowgreave,
Preston, **LANCASHIRE**, PR3 1YE,
ENGLAND.
(T) 01995 600100

Course/s:

🔋 **GARSTANG COUNTRY HOTEL &**
Number of Holes: 18
Designer: Richard Bradbeer

GATEHOUSE

GATEHOUSE GOLF CLUB, Laurieston Rd, Gatehouse of Fleet, Castle Douglas, **DUMFRIES AND GALLOWAY**, DG7 2BE, **SCOTLAND**.
(T) 01644 450260

Membership: Members & Public

Contact/s:
- **Club Secretary:** Mr Keith Cooper

Course/s:
- **GATEHOUSE**
  Description: Undulating, Sheltered, Open, Short, Drains Well, Ideal for the Elderly
  Green Speed: Fast
  Built: 1921 **Built On:** Sand
  Number of Holes: 9 **Par:** 66
  Par 3's: 4 **Par 4's:** 4 **Par 5's:** 1
  Yds: 5042 **F9 Yds:** 2521 **B9 Yds:** 2521
  Prevailing Wind: West
  Further Information:
  Open all year - no winter greens. 9 hole course can be played as an 18 hole course.

GATHURST

GATHURST GOLF CLUB LTD, Miles Lane, Shevington, Wigan, **LANCASHIRE**, WN6 8EW, **ENGLAND**.
(T) 01257 252861

Contact/s:
- **Manageress:** Ms Isabel Fyffe

Course/s:
- **GATHURST**
  Number of Holes: 18
  Designer: Pearson

GATLEY

GATLEY GOLF CLUB, Waterfall Farm, Styal Rd, Heald Green, Cheadle, **CHESHIRE**, SK8 3TW, **ENGLAND**.
(T) 0161 4372091

Membership: Members & Public

Contact/s:
- **Club Secretary:** Mr C R Hamnett
- **Professional:** Mr J Hopley

Course/s:
- **GATLEY**
  Description: Parkland
  Green Speed: Medium
  Number of Holes: 9

GATTON MANOR

GATTON MANOR HOTEL GOLF & COUNTRY CLUB, Standon Lane, Ockley, Dorking, **SURREY**, RH5 5PQ, **ENGLAND**.
(T) 01306 627557

Contact/s:
- **Professional:** Mr Rae Sargeant

Course/s:
- **GATTON MANOR**
  Description: Championship, Wooded, Parkland
  Built: 1969
  Number of Holes: 18 **Par:** 72
  Designer: Henry Cotton

GAY HILL

GAY HILL GOLF CLUB, Hollywood Lane, Hollywood, Birmingham, **MIDLANDS (WEST)**, B47 5PP, **ENGLAND**.
(T) 0121 4308544

Contact/s:

- **Club Secretary:** Ms Michelle Adderley

Course/s:
- **GAY HILL**
  Number of Holes: 18 **Par:** 72
  Yds: 6406 **F9 Yds:** 3279 **B9 Yds:** 3127

GEDNEY HILL

GEDNEY HILL GOLF CLUB, West Drove, Gedney Hill, Spalding, **LINCOLNSHIRE**, PE12 0NT, **ENGLAND**.
(T) 01406 330922

Contact/s:
- **Professional:** Mr David Hutton

Course/s:
- **GEDNEY HILL**
  Description: Links, Parkland
  Built: 1988
  Number of Holes: 18 **Par:** 70
  Further Information:
  Course is tougher than it looks. Hole no 2 is 671 yards long and holds the title of being the longest hole in Great Britain.

GEORGE WASHINGTON

GEORGE WASHINGTON HOTEL GOLF & COUNTRY CLUB, Stone Cellar Rd, High Usworth, Washington, **TYNE AND WEAR**, NE37 1PH, **ENGLAND**.
(T) 0191 4029988

Contact/s:
- **Professional:** Mr David Patterson

Course/s:
- **GEORGE WASHINGTON**
  Number of Holes: 18 **Par:** 73
  Yds: 6604 **F9 Yds:** 3413 **B9 Yds:** 3191

GERRARDS CROSS

GERRARDS CROSS GOLF CLUB, Chalfont Pk, Chalfont St. Peter, Gerrards Cross, **BUCKINGHAMSHIRE**, SL9 0QA, **ENGLAND**.
(T) 01753 883263

Contact/s:
- **Club Secretary:** Miss I Perkins
- **Professional:** Mr Matthew Barr

Course/s:
- **GERRARDS CROSS**
  Number of Holes: 18 **Par:** 69
  Yds: 5954 **F9 Yds:** 3017 **B9 Yds:** 2937
  Designer: Bill Pedlar

GHYLL

GHYLL GOLF CLUB, Skipton Rd, Barnoldswick, **LANCASHIRE**, BB18 6JH, **ENGLAND**.
(T) 01282 842466

Contact/s:
- **Chairman:** Mr J Ghyll

Course/s:
- **GHYLL**
  Number of Holes: 9

GIFFORD

GIFFORD GOLF CLUB, Edinburgh Rd, Gifford, Haddington, **LOTHIAN (EAST)**, EH41 4QN, **SCOTLAND**.
(T) 01620 810267

Course/s:
- **GIFFORD**
  Number of Holes: 9

GIGHA

GIGHA GOLF COURSE, Isle Of Gigha, Isle of Gigha, **ARGYLL AND BUTE**, PA41 7AA, **SCOTLAND**.
(T) 01583 505287/505254

Course/s:
- **GIGHA**
  Number of Holes: 9

GILLINGHAM

GILLINGHAM GOLF CLUB LTD, Woodlands Rd, Gillingham, **KENT**, ME7 2AP, **ENGLAND**.
(T) 01634 853017

Contact/s:
- **Club Secretary:** Mr L Ogrady

Course/s:
- **GILLINGHAM**
  Number of Holes: 18
  Designer: James Braid

GILNAHIRK

GILNAHIRK GOLF CLUB, Upper Braniel Rd, Belfast, **COUNTY ANTRIM**, BT5 7TX, **NORTHERN IRELAND**.
(T) 028 90448477

Contact/s:
- **Professional:** Mr K Gray

Course/s:
- **GILNAHIRK COURSE**
  Number of Holes: 9 **Par:** 34
  Yds: 2942

GIRTON

GIRTON GOLF CLUB, Dodford Lane, Girton, Cambridge, **CAMBRIDGESHIRE**, CB3 0QE, **ENGLAND**.
(T) 01223 276169

Contact/s:
- **Professional:** Mr Scott Thomson

Course/s:
- **GIRTON**
  Number of Holes: 18 **Par:** 69
  Yds: 6012 **F9 Yds:** 2821 **B9 Yds:** 3191
  Designer: Allan Gow

GIRVAN

GIRVAN GOLF COURSE, Golf Course Rd, Girvan, **AYRSHIRE (SOUTH)**, KA26 9HW, **SCOTLAND**.
(T) 01465 714346
(W) www.golfsouthayrshire.com/girvan.html

Membership: Public

Contact/s:
- **Starter:** Mr Don Malcolm

Course/s:
- **SEMI-LYNX**
  Description: Links, Short, Drains Well
  Green Speed: Medium
  Built: 1800 **Built On:** Sand
  Number of Holes: 18 **Par:** 64
  Par 3's: 8 **Par 4's:** 10
  Yds: 5074
  Designer: James Braid
  Further Information:
  Flat ground along coast.

GLAMORGANSHIRE

GLAMORGANSHIRE GOLF CLUB, Lavernock Rd, Penarth, **GLAMORGAN (VALE OF)**, CF64 5UP, **WALES**.
(T) 029 20701185

Contact/s:
- **Club Secretary:** Mr B Williams

Course/s:

● **GLAMORGANSHIRE**
  Number of Holes: 18

GLASGOW

GLASGOW GOLF CLUB, Killermont,
Bearsden, Glasgow, **GLASGOW (CITY OF)**,
G61 2TW, **SCOTLAND**.
(T) 0141 9421713

Contact/s:
● Club Secretary: Mr David Deas
● Professional: Mr Jack Steven

Course/s:
● **GLASGOW GOLF COURSE**
  Description: Parkland Built On: Clay
  Number of Holes: 18 Par: 70
  Yds: 5982

GLASGOW GAILES

GLASGOW GOLF CLUB, Gailes, Irvine,
AYRSHIRE (NORTH), KA11 5AE,
SCOTLAND.
(T) 01294 311258
(E) manager@glasgowgailes-golf.com
(W) www.glasgowgailes.golf.com

Contact/s:
● Club Secretary: Mr David Deas
  ☎ 01441 9422011
● Professional: Mr Jack Steven
  ☎ 01294 311561

Course/s:
● **GLASGOW GAILES**
  Description: Championship, Links,
  Drains Well
  Green Speed: Fast
  Built: 1892
  Number of Holes: 18 Par: 71
  Yds: 6537
  Designer: William Park ⚑

GLEBE

GLEBE GOLF COURSE, Dunlever, Trim,
COUNTY MEATH, IRELAND.
(T) 046 31926
(E) glebegc@iol.ie
Membership: Public

Contact/s:
● Club Secretary: Breda Bligh

Course/s:
● **GLEBE**
  Description: Parkland, Hilltop,
  Undulating, Long, Drains Well
  Green Speed: Fast
  Built: 1993
  Number of Holes: 18 Par: 73
  Par 3's: 3 Par 4's: 11 Par 5's: 4
  Yds: 6466 F9 Yds: 3308 B9 Yds: 3158
  Designer: Edward Hackett

GLEDDOCH

GLEDDOCH GOLF & COUNTRY CLUB, Old
Greenock Rd, Langbank, Port Glasgow,
RENFREWSHIRE, PA14 6YE, **SCOTLAND**.
(T) 01475 540711
Membership: Members & Public

Contact/s:
● Professional: Mr K Campbell
● Pro Shop: Mrs K Campbell
  ☎ 01475 540704

Course/s:
● **GLEDDOCH GOLF AND COUNTRY CLUB**
  Description: Parkland, Heath Land,
  Hilltop, Undulating, Medium Length,
  Drains Well
  Green Speed: Medium
  Built: 1974

Number of Holes: 18
Designer: J Hamilton-Stutt
Further Information:
Views over Firth of Clyde.

GLEN

GLEN GOLF CLUB NORTH BERWICK,
Tantallon Trce, North Berwick, **LOTHIAN
(EAST)**, EH39 4LE, **SCOTLAND**.
(T) 01620 892221
(W) www.glengolfclub.co.uk
Membership: Members & Public

Contact/s:
● Club Secretary: Mr Kevin Fish
  ☎ 01620 892726
● Book Tee Times: Mr D Brown

Course/s:
● **GLEN**
  Description: Links, Parkland, Open,
  Medium Length, Drains Well
  Green Speed: Fast
  Built: 1906 Built On: Sand
  Number of Holes: 18 Par: 69
  Par 3's: 4 Par 4's: 13 Par 5's: 1
  Yds: 6143 F9 Yds: 3127 B9 Yds: 3016
  Prevailing Wind: West
  Designer: James Braid, Ben Sayers
  Further Information:
  Coastal views. As quoted by Mark
  Mostyn, Location Manager of 'The Little
  Vampire', 'North Berwick has unique,
  dramatic scenic beauty'. Laid out in a
  combination of inland turf and traditional
  Links settings. Views are dominated by
  the Bass Rock, one of the world's largest
  bird sanctuaries, together with a series of
  spectacular islands in the River Forth,
  including Robert Louis Stevenson's own
  'Treasure Island'. The par 3, 13th, 'The
  Sea Hole' is commonly featured in
  television advertisment on both ITV and
  SKY television.

GLEN GORSE

GLEN GORSE GOLF CLUB, Glen Rd, Oadby,
Leicester, **LEICESTERSHIRE**, LE2 4RF,
ENGLAND.
(T) 0116 2714159
(W)
www.ukcourses.co.uk/glengorse/index.htm

Contact/s:
● Professional: Mr Dominic Fitzpatrick
  ☎ 0116 2713748

Course/s:
● **GLEN GORSE**
  Description: Wooded, Parkland
  Built: 1933
  Number of Holes: 18 Par: 72
  Yds: 6648 F9 Yds: 3194 B9 Yds: 3454
  Further Information:
  Tough finish.

GLEN MILL

GLEN MILL GOLF CLUB, Timore, Newcastle,
COUNTY WICKLOW, IRELAND.
(T) 012 810977
(E) glenmill@eircom.net
Membership: Members & Public
Size of Complex: 40 Acres

Contact/s:
● Owner: Mr Michael Byrne
  ☎ 012 810636

Course/s:
● **GLEN MILL**
  Description: Valley, Undulating,
  Sheltered, Short, Drains Well, Ideal for the
  Elderly

Green Speed: Medium/Fast
Built: 1993 Built On: Soil
Number of Holes: 18 Par: 54
Par 3's: 18
Yds: 2521 F9 Yds: 1373 B9 Yds: 1148
Prevailing Wind: West
Designer: Andrew Byrne
Further Information:
The course is built to a full length
standard. A full set of clubs is required.

GLEN OF THE DOWNS

GLEN OF THE DOWNS GOLF CLUB,
Coolnaskeagh, Delgany, **COUNTY
WICKLOW, IRELAND**.
(T) 012 876240
(E) glenofthedowns@eircom.net

Contact/s:
● Club Secretary: Mr Richard O' Hanrahan

Course/s:
● **GLEN OF THE DOWNS**
  Description: Parkland
  Green Speed: Fast
  Built: 1998
  Number of Holes: 18
  Designer: P McEvoy

GLENBERVIE

GLENBERVIE GOLF CLUB LTD, Stirling Rd,
Larbert, **FALKIRK**, FK5 4SJ, **SCOTLAND**.
(T) 01324 562725

Contact/s:
● Professional: Mr J Chillas

Course/s:
● **GLENBERVIE CLUBHOUSE**
  Number of Holes: 18 Par: 71
  Yds: 6423 F9 Yds: 3148 B9 Yds: 3275
  Designer: James Braid

GLENCORSE

GLENCORSE GOLF CLUB, Milton Bridge,
Penicuik, **LOTHIAN (MID)**, EH26 0RD,
SCOTLAND.
(T) 01968 677177

Contact/s:
● Club Secretary: Mr W Oliver
  ☎ 01968 677189
● Professional: Mr Cliff Jones

Course/s:
● **GLENCORSE**
  Number of Holes: 18 Par: 64
  Yds: 5217 F9 Yds: 2552 B9 Yds: 2665
  Designer: William Park

GLENCRUITTEN

GLENCRUITTEN GOLF CLUB, Glencruitten
Rd, Oban, **ARGYLL AND BUTE**, PA34 4PU,
SCOTLAND.
(T) 01631 562868

Contact/s:
● Manager: Mr R Taylor

Course/s:
● **GLENCRUITTEN**
  Description: Parkland, Undulating, Short
  Built: 1908
  Number of Holes: 18 Par: 61
  Designer: James Braid

GLENEAGLES

GLENEAGLES, The Gleneagles Htl,
Auchterarder, **PERTH AND KINROSS**, PH3
1NZ, **SCOTLAND**.
(T) 01764 662231
(E) resort.sales@gleneagles.com
(W) www.gleneagles.com

Membership: Members & Public
<u>Contact/s:</u>
- **Professional:** Mr Sandy Smith
  ☎ 01764 694343
- **Book Tee Times:** Miss Fiona Hay
<u>Course/s:</u>
- **GLENEAGLES 9 HOLE**
  Number of Holes: 9
  Par 3's: 9
  Yds: 1481 **F9 Yds:** 1481
- **KINGS**
  Description: Championship
  Built: 1920
  Number of Holes: 18 **Par:** 71
  Par 3's: 4 **Par 4's:** 11 **Par 5's:** 3
  Yds: 6471 **F9 Yds:** 3195 **B9 Yds:** 3276
  Designer: James Braid
- **PGA CENTENARY**
  Description: Championship
  Built: 1993
  Number of Holes: 18 **Par:** 72
  Par 3's: 5 **Par 4's:** 8 **Par 5's:** 5
  Yds: 6559 **F9 Yds:** 3328 **B9 Yds:** 3231
  Designer: Jack Nicklaus
- **QUEENS**
  Description: Championship, Moorland
  Built: 1924
  Number of Holes: 18 **Par:** 68
  Par 3's: 5 **Par 4's:** 12 **Par 5's:** 1
  Yds: 1481 **F9 Yds:** 3192 **B9 Yds:** 2773
  Designer: James Braid

GLENGARRIFF

GLENGARRIFF GOLF CLUB, Glengarriff,
COUNTY CORK, **IRELAND**.
(T) 027 63150
<u>Course/s:</u>
- **GLENGARRIFF**
  Number of Holes: 9

GLENISLA

GLENISLA GOLF CENTRE, Pitcrocknie,
Alyth, Blairgowrie, **PERTH AND KINROSS**,
PH11 8JJ, **SCOTLAND**.
(T) 01828 632445
(E) info@golf-glenisla.co.uk
(W) www.golf-glenisla.co.uk
Membership: Members & Public
Size of Complex: 180 Acres
<u>Contact/s:</u>
- **Club Secretary:** Mr Graham Jack
<u>Course/s:</u>
- **GLENISLA**
  Description: Parkland, Medium Length,
  Ideal for the Elderly
  Green Speed: Medium
  Built: 1998 **Built On:** Soil
  Number of Holes: 18 **Par:** 71
  Record: 65 (Andrew Crerar)
  Par 3's: 3 **Par 4's:** 13 **Par 5's:** 2
  Yds: 6650
  Designer: Tony Wardle
  Further Information:
  All holes are very different but compliment
  each other to make a fantastic layout.
  Natural water hazards are also
  incorporated into the course.

GLENLO ABBEY

GLENLO ABBEY GOLF COURSE,
Bushypark, Galway, **COUNTY GALWAY**,
IRELAND.
(T) 091 526666
<u>Course/s:</u>
- **GLENLO ABBEY**

Number of Holes: 9
Designer: Jeff Howes

GLENMALURE

GLENMALURE GOLF CLUB, Greenane,
Rathdrum, **COUNTY WICKLOW**, **IRELAND**.
(T) 040 446679
<u>Course/s:</u>
- **GLENMALURE**
  Number of Holes: 18
  Designer: P Suttle

GLENROTHES

GLENROTHES GOLF CLUB, Golf Course Rd,
Glenrothes, **FIFE**, KY6 2LA, **SCOTLAND**.
(T) 01592 754561
<u>Contact/s:</u>
- **Club Secretary:** Mrs P Landells
<u>Course/s:</u>
- **GLENROTHES**
  Number of Holes: 18
  Designer: Stutt

GLOSSOP & DISTRICT

GLOSSOP & DISTRICT GOLF CLUB,
Sheffield Rd, Glossop, **DERBYSHIRE**, SK13
7PU, **ENGLAND**.
(T) 01457 865247
<u>Contact/s:</u>
- **Manager:** Mr D Pernon
<u>Course/s:</u>
- **GLOSSOP AND DISTRICT**
  Number of Holes: 11 **Par:** 68
  Yds: 5759 **F9 Yds:** 2830 **B9 Yds:** 2929
  Further Information:
  9 hole course can be played as an 18 hole
  course

GLOUCESTER

GLOUCESTER GOLF CLUB, Matson Lane,
Robinswood Hill, Gloucester,
GLOUCESTERSHIRE, GL4 6EA, **ENGLAND**.
(T) 01452 411331
<u>Contact/s:</u>
- **Professional:** Mr Chris Gillick
<u>Course/s:</u>
- **GLOUCESTER**
  Built: 1976
  Number of Holes: 18 **Par:** 70
  Further Information:
  The course is built around Robinswood
  Hill and is a challenging course.

GLYN ABBEY

GLYN ABBEY GOLF CLUB, Trimsaran,
Kidwelly, **CARMARTHENSHIRE**, SA17 4LB,
WALES.
(T) 01554 810278
(E) course-enquiries@glynabbey.co.uk
(W) www.glynabbey.co.uk
Membership: Members & Public
Size of Complex: 208 Acres
<u>Contact/s:</u>
- **Professional:** Mr Neil Evans
<u>Course/s:</u>
- **GLYN ABBEY**
  Description: Wooded, Parkland,
  Undulating, Medium Length
  Green Speed: Medium
  Built: 1992 **Built On:** Clay
  Number of Holes: 18 **Par:** 70
  Par 3's: 4 **Par 4's:** 12 **Par 5's:** 2
  Yds: 6173 **F9 Yds:** 3065 **B9 Yds:** 3108
  Designer: Hawtree

Further Information:
Views of the Gwendraeth Valley from all
aspects and there is an abundance of bird
life. The greens are constructed to full
USPGA standards.

GLYNHIR

GLYNHIR GOLF CLUB, Glynhir Rd,
Llandybie, Ammanford,
CARMARTHENSHIRE, SA18 2TF, **WALES**.
(T) 01269 850472
<u>Course/s:</u>
- **GLYNHIR**
  Number of Holes: 18
  Designer: Hawtree

GLYNNEATH

GLYNNEATH GOLF CLUB, Penygraig,
Pontneathvaughan, Nr Glynneath, Neath,
NEATH PORT TALBOT, SA11 5UH, **WALES**.
(T) 01639 720452 or 720452
(W) www.glynneathgolfclub.co.uk
<u>Contact/s:</u>
- **Club Secretary:** Mr David Fellowes
- **Professional:** Mr Neil Evans
<u>Course/s:</u>
- **GLYNNEATH**
  Number of Holes: 18 **Par:** 69
  Yds: 5658 **F9 Yds:** 2733 **B9 Yds:** 2923
  Designer: Cotton Pennick Lawrie &
  Partners

GOAL FARM

GOAL FARM GOLF COURSE, Goal Rd,
Pirbright, Woking, **SURREY**, GU24 0PZ,
ENGLAND.
(T) 01483 473183
Membership: Members & Public
<u>Contact/s:</u>
- **Pro Shop:** Mr R Church
<u>Course/s:</u>
- **GOAL FARM**
  Description: Parkland, Sheltered, Short,
  Tight, Drains Well, Ideal for the Elderly
  Green Speed: Medium
  Built: 1978 **Built On:** Clay
  Number of Holes: 9 **Par:** 27
  Par 3's: 9
  Yds: 1146 **F9 Yds:** 1146
  Prevailing Wind: East
  Designer: B Cox
  Further Information:
  Flat course. One large pond on the 6th
  hole. Also ponds on the 1st and 2nd
  holes.

GOG MAGOG

GOG MAGOG GOLF CLUB, Shelford Bottom,
Cambridge, **CAMBRIDGESHIRE**, CB2 4AB,
ENGLAND.
(T) 01223 247626
(E) secretary@gogmagog.co.uk
(W) www.gogmagog.co.uk
Membership: Members & Public
<u>Contact/s:</u>
- **Club Secretary:** Mr Ian Simpson
- **Professional:** Mr Ian Bamborough
  ☎ 01223 246058
<u>Course/s:</u>
- **THE OLD**
  Description: Championship, Downland,
  Undulating, Open, Long, Drains Well
  Green Speed: Medium
  Built: 1901 **Built On:** Chalk
  Number of Holes: 18 **Par:** 70

Record: 60 (Jason Boast)
Par 3's: 5   Par 4's: 10   Par 5's: 3
Yds: 6181   F9 Yds: 2922   B9 Yds: 3259
Designer: Hawtree
Further Information:
Set in rolling countryside amongst the legendary Gog and Magog hills. It is a downland course with views across Cambridge.

WANDLEBURY
Description: Championship, Parkland, Undulating, Open, Long, Drains Well
Green Speed: Medium
Built: 1901   Built On: Chalk
Number of Holes: 18   Par: 72
Par 3's: 4   Par 4's: 10   Par 5's: 4
Yds: 6366   F9 Yds: 3220   B9 Yds: 3146
Designer: Hawtree
Further Information:
Set in rolling countryside amongst the legendary Gog and Magog hills. It is a downland course with views across Cambridge.

GOGARBURN

GOGARBURN GOLF CLUB, Hanley Lodge, Newbridge, **EDINBURGH (CITY OF)**, EH28 8NN, **SCOTLAND**.
(T) 0131 3334110
Contact/s:
• Club Secretary: Mr Tom Kelly
Course/s:
GOGARBURN 12 HOLE
Description: Parkland, Short
Number of Holes: 12   Par: 64
Yds: 4896

GOLD COAST

GOLD COAST GOLF & LEISURE LTD, Ballinacourty, Dungarvan, **COUNTY WATERFORD, IRELAND**.
(T) 058 44055
(E) info@clonea.com
(W) www.clonea.com
Membership: Members & Public
Size of Complex: 120 Acres
Contact/s:
• Treasurer: Mr Mark Lenihan
  ☎ 05842 416
Course/s:
GOLDCOAST
Description: Championship, Parkland, Cliff Top, Undulating, Open, Short, Drains Well, Ideal for the Elderly
Green Speed: Medium
Built: 1939   Built On: Clay/Soil
Number of Holes: 18   Par: 72
Par 3's: 4   Par 4's: 10   Par 5's: 4
Yds: 6057   F9 Yds: 2803   B9 Yds: 3254
Prevailing Wind: South/West
Designer: Howard Swan

GOLDENHILL

GOLDENHILL GOLF COURSE, Mobberley Rd, Goldenhill, Stoke-on-Trent, **STAFFORDSHIRE**, ST6 5SS, **ENGLAND**.
(T) 01782 234200
Membership: Public
Contact/s:
• Pro Shop: Mr Richard Hulme
Course/s:
GOLDEN HILL
Description: Championship, Parkland, Undulating, Open, Medium Length, Tends to Flood
Green Speed: Fast

Built: 1983
Number of Holes: 18

GOLSPIE

GOLSPIE GOLF CLUB, Ferry Rd, Golspie, **HIGHLANDS**, KW10 6SY, **SCOTLAND**.
(T) 01408 633266
(E) info@golspie-golf-club.co.uk
(W) www.golspie-golf-club.co.uk
Course/s:
GOLSPIE
Description: Wooded, Parkland, Heath Land, Open
Built: 1889   Built On: Sand
Number of Holes: 18   Par: 68
Par 3's: 5   Par 4's: 12   Par 5's: 1
Yds: 5890   F9 Yds: 3046   B9 Yds: 2844
Designer: James Braid

GOODWOOD

GOODWOOD GOLF CLUB LTD (THE), Goodwood, Chichester, **SUSSEX (WEST)**, PO18 0PN, **ENGLAND**.
(T) 01243 774994
Membership: Members & Public
Contact/s:
• Club Secretary: Ms Carol Davidson
• Professional: Mr Keith MacDonald
• Pro Shop: Mr Ross MacDonald
Course/s:
GOODWOOD
Description: Moorland, Hilltop, Undulating, Open, Medium Length, Drains Well
Green Speed: Medium
Built: 1892   Built On: Chalk
Number of Holes: 18   Record: 64 (Gery Orr)
Prevailing Wind: North
Designer: James Braid

GORING AND STREATLEY

GORING AND STREATLEY GOLF CLUB, Rectory Rd, Streatley On Thames, Reading, **BERKSHIRE**, RG8 9QA, **ENGLAND**.
(T) 01491 873229
(E) secretary@goringgc.org
(W) www.goringgc.org
Contact/s:
• Professional: Mr Jason Hadland
  ☎ 01491 873715
• Pro Shop: Mr Danny Gaffney
Course/s:
GORING & STREATLEY
Built: 1928
Number of Holes: 18   Par: 71
Par 3's: 4   Par 4's: 11   Par 5's: 3
Yds: 6320   F9 Yds: 3149   B9 Yds: 3171

GORLESTON

GORLESTON GOLF CLUB LTD, Warren Rd, Gorleston, Great Yarmouth, **NORFOLK**, NR31 6JT, **ENGLAND**.
(T) 01493 662103
Contact/s:
• Manager: Mr P Longbottom
Course/s:
GORLESTON
Number of Holes: 18
Designer: Taylor

GORT

GORT GOLF CLUB, Castle Quarter, Gort, **COUNTY GALWAY, IRELAND**.
(T) 091 632244

Course/s:
GORT
Number of Holes: 18
Designer: Christy O'Connor

GOSFIELD LAKE

GOSFIELD LAKE GOLF CLUB LTD, Secretaries Office, Hall Drive, Gosfield, Halstead, **ESSEX**, CO9 1SE, **ENGLAND**.
(T) 01787 474488
(E) gosfieldlakegc@btconnect.com
(W) www.gosfield-lake-golf-club.co.uk
Contact/s:
• Sole Director: Mr Ralph Younger Rowe
  ☎ 01787 474747
Course/s:
LAKES
Number of Holes: 18   Par: 72
Par 3's: 5   Par 4's: 8   Par 5's: 5
Yds: 6615   F9 Yds: 3271   B9 Yds: 3344
Designer: Henry Cotton, Howard Swan
MEADOWS
Number of Holes: 9   Par: 66
Par 3's: 4   Par 4's: 5
Yds: 4180   F9 Yds: 2088   B9 Yds: 2092
Designer: Henry Cotton, Howard Swan
Further Information: 9 hole course can be played as an 18 hole course

GOSFORTH

GOSFORTH GOLF CLUB, The Bridle Path, Broadway East, Newcastle Upon Tyne, **TYNE AND WEAR**, NE3 5ER, **ENGLAND**.
(T) 0191 2850553
Contact/s:
• Owner: Mr G Garland
Course/s:
GOSFORTH
Number of Holes: 18

GOSPORT & STOKES BAY

GOSPORT & STOKES BAY GOLF CLUB, Alverstoke, Gosport, **HAMPSHIRE**, PO12 2AT, **ENGLAND**.
(T) 02392 581625
Contact/s:
• Manager: Mr P Lucas
Course/s:
GOSPORT & STOKES BAY
Number of Holes: 9   Par: 70
Yds: 5995   F9 Yds: 2944   B9 Yds: 3051
Further Information: 9 hole course can be played as an 18 hole course

GOUROCK

GOUROCK GOLF CLUB, Cowal View, Gourock, **INVERCLYDE**, PA19 1HD, **SCOTLAND**.
(T) 01475 631001
Membership: Members & Public
Contact/s:
• Club Secretary: Mr A Taylor
• Professional: Mr G Clark
• Pro Shop:
  ☎ 01475 636834
Course/s:
GOUROCK
Description: Moorland, Undulating, Long, Tends to Flood
Green Speed: Medium
Built: 1896   Built On: Clay
Number of Holes: 18   Record: 64 (Steve McAllistar)
Designer: James Braid

GOWER

GOWER GOLF COURSE (THE), Cefn Goleu Farm, Gowerton, Swansea, **SWANSEA**, SA4 3HS, **WALES**.
(T) 01792 872480
(W) www.gowergolf.com
Membership: Members & Public
Contact/s:
● Club Secretary: Mr J Morgan
● Professional: Mr A Williamson
● Pro Shop:
☎ 01792 879905
Course/s:
🏌 **GOWER**
Description: Parkland, Undulating, Long, Drains Well
Green Speed: Medium
Built: 1995 Built On: Sand/Soil
Number of Holes: 18 Par: 71
Yds: 6441 F9 Yds: 3072 B9 Yds: 3369
Prevailing Wind: South/West
Designer: Donald Steel
Further Information:
There are ponds on the 8th, 10th and 12th holes.

GOWRAN PARK GOLF & LEISURE

GOWRAN PARK GOLF & LEISURE LTD, Parkgowran, Gowran, **COUNTY KILKENNY**, **IRELAND**.
(T) 056 26699
Membership: Members & Public
Contact/s:
● Club Secretary: Mr Jim Heudith
Course/s:
🏌 **GOWRAN PARK GOLF & LEISURE**
Description: Wooded, Parkland, Tight
Green Speed: Fast
Built: 2001
Number of Holes: 18
Designer: D Howes

GRACEHILL

GRACEHILL GOLF CLUB, 141 Ballinlea Rd, Stranocum, Ballymoney, **COUNTY ANTRIM**, BT53 8PX, **NORTHERN IRELAND**.
(T) 028 20751209
(W) www.gracehillgolfclub.co.uk
Membership: Members & Public
Size of Complex: 250 Acres
Contact/s:
● Owner: Mr James Gillen
Course/s:
🏌 **GRACEHILL**
Description: Championship, Parkland, Undulating, Sheltered, Open, Medium Length, Drains Well, Ideal for the Elderly
Green Speed: Medium
Built: 1995 Built On: Soil
Number of Holes: 18 Par: 72
Par 3's: 4 Par 4's: 10 Par 5's: 4
Yds: 6199 F9 Yds: 3283 B9 Yds: 2916
Prevailing Wind: North/West
Designer: Frank Ainsworth

GRANGE

GRANGE GOLF CLUB, Rathfarnham, Dublin, **COUNTY DUBLIN**, **IRELAND**.
(T) 01 4932889
Course/s:
🏌 **GRANGE**
Number of Holes: 18

GRANGE CASTLE

GRANGE CASTLE GOLF CLUB, Golf Course, Clondalkin, **COUNTY DUBLIN**, **IRELAND**.
(T) 01 4641043
(E) grangecastle@golfdublin.com
Contact/s:
● Professional: Mr Gary Duncan
Course/s:
🏌 **GRANGE CASTLE GOLF COURSE**
Description: Parkland
Number of Holes: 18 Par: 71
Yds: 5966

GRANGE FELL

GRANGE FELL GOLF CLUB, Grange Fell Rd, Grange-over-Sands, **CUMBRIA**, LA11 6HB, **ENGLAND**.
(T) 01539 532536
Contact/s:
● Club Secretary: Mr M Higginson
Course/s:
🏌 **GRANGE FELL**
Number of Holes: 9 Par: 70
Yds: 5278 F9 Yds: 2639 B9 Yds: 2639
Further Information:
9 hole course can be played as an 18 hole course

GRANGE PARK

GRANGE PARK GOLF COURSE, Upper Wortley Rd, Rotherham, **YORKSHIRE (SOUTH)**, S61 2SJ, **ENGLAND**.
(T) 01709 559497
Contact/s:
● Manager: Mr Eric Clark
Course/s:
🏌 **GRANGE PARK**
Number of Holes: 18
Designer: Hawtree

GRANGE PARK

GRANGE PARK GOLF CLUB LTD, Prescot Rd, St. Helens, **MERSEYSIDE**, WA10 3AD, **ENGLAND**.
(T) 01744 22980
Contact/s:
● Accountant: Mr Alan Robert Byron
Course/s:
🏌 **GRANGE PARK**
Number of Holes: 18
Designer: James Braid

GRANGE PARK

GRANGE PARK GOLF COURSE, The Grange, Butterwick Rd, Messingham, Scunthorpe, **LINCOLNSHIRE (NORTH)**, DN17 3PP **ENGLAND**.
(T) 01724 762851
Membership: Public
Contact/s:
● General Manager: Mr Ian Cannon
☎ 01724 762945
Course/s:
🏌 **GRANGE PARK**
Description: Parkland, Open, Medium Length, Drains Well, Ideal for the Elderly
Green Speed: Medium
Built: 1991 Built On: Sand
Number of Holes: 13 Par: 49
Par 3's: 4 Par 4's: 8 Par 5's: 1
Yds: 4141
Prevailing Wind: West

Designer: Raymond Price

GRANGEMOUTH

GRANGEMOUTH GOLF CLUB, Polmonthill, Polmont, **FALKIRK**, FK2 0YE, **SCOTLAND**.
(T) 01324 711500
Course/s:
🏌 **GRANGEMOUTH**
Number of Holes: 18

GRANGE-OVER-SANDS

GRANGE-OVER-SANDS GOLF CLUB, Meathop Rd, Grange-Over-Sands, **CUMBRIA**, LA11 6QX, **ENGLAND**.
(T) 01539 535937
Contact/s:
● Professional: Mr A J Pickering
☎ 01539 533180
Course/s:
🏌 **GRANGE-OVER-SANDS**
Description: Parkland
Built: 1920
Number of Holes: 18 Par: 70
Yds: 5958 F9 Yds: 2858 B9 Yds: 3100

GRANTOWN-ON-SPEY

GRANTOWN-ON-SPEY GOLF CLUB, Golf Course Rd, Grantown On Spey, **MORAY**, PH26 3HY, **SCOTLAND**.
(T) 01479 872079
(E) secretary@grantownspeygolfclub.co.uk
(W) www.grantownonspeygolfclub.co.uk
Membership: Members & Public
Size of Complex: 81 Acres
Contact/s:
● Club Secretary: Mr James S MacPherson
● Pro Shop: Mr John Wilkie
Course/s:
🏌 **GRANTOWN ON SPEY**
Description: Wooded, Parkland, Undulating, Medium Length, Drains Well, Ideal for the Elderly
Green Speed: Medium
Built: 1890 Built On: Soil
Number of Holes: 18 Par: 70
Record: 62 (David Webster)
Par 3's: 3 Par 4's: 14 Par 5's: 1
Yds: 5710 F9 Yds: 3087 B9 Yds: 2623
Prevailing Wind: West
Designer: A C Brown
Further Information:
Course has been re-designed by James Braid and Willie Park. Lots of wildlife on the course.

GRASSMOOR GOLF CTRE

GRASSMOOR GOLF CENTRE, North Wingfield Rd, Grassmoor, Chesterfield, **DERBYSHIRE**, S42 5EA, **ENGLAND**.
(T) 01246 856044
Contact/s:
● Company Secretary: Mrs H Hagues
Course/s:
🏌 **GRASSMOOR GOLF CTRE**
Number of Holes: 18 Par: 69
Yds: 5723 F9 Yds: 3106 B9 Yds: 2617
Designer: Hawtree

GREAT BARR

GREAT BARR GOLF CLUB LTD, Clubhouse, Chapel Lane, Great Barr, Birmingham, **MIDLANDS (WEST)**, B43 7BA, **ENGLAND**.
(T) 0121 3571232

Contact/s:
- **Managing Director:** Mr William Leonard Peach

Course/s:
🏌 **GREAT BARR**
Number of Holes: 18

GREAT HADHAM

GREAT HADHAM GOLF & COUNTRY CLUB, Great Hadham Rd, Much Hadham, **HERTFORDSHIRE**, SG10 6JE, **ENGLAND**.
(T) 01279 843558

Contact/s:
- **Manager:** Mr Tom Streeter

Course/s:
🏌 **GREAT HADHAM**
Number of Holes: 18
Designer: Iain Roberts

GREAT HARWOOD

GREAT HARWOOD GOLF CLUB, Whalley Rd, Great Harwood, Blackburn, **LANCASHIRE**, BB6 7TE, **ENGLAND**.
(T) 01254 884391

Contact/s:
- **Club Secretary:** Mr Jack Spibey

Course/s:
🏌 **GREAT HARWOOD**
Number of Holes: 9 Par: 73
Yds: 6456 F9 Yds: 3187 B9 Yds: 3269
Further Information:
9 hole course can be played as an 18 hole course

GREAT LEVER & FARNWORTH

GREAT LEVER & FARNWORTH GOLF CLUB, Plodder Lane, Farnworth, Bolton, **LANCASHIRE**, BL4 0LQ, **ENGLAND**.
(T) 01204 656137

Contact/s:
- **Club Secretary:** Mrs J Ivill
- **Professional:** Mr Tony Howarth

Course/s:
🏌 **GREAT LEVER & FARNWORTH**
Description: Parkland, Moorland
Built: 1917
Number of Holes: 18 Par: 70

GREAT SALTERNS

GREAT SALTERNS GOLF COURSE, Burrfields Rd, Portsmouth, **HAMPSHIRE**, PO3 5HH, **ENGLAND**.
(T) 023 92664549

Contact/s:
- **Professional:** Mr Terry Healy

Course/s:
🏌 **GREAT SALTERNS PUBLIC**
Description: Parkland
Built: 1920
Number of Holes: 18 Par: 70
Further Information:
Testing course.

GREAT YARMOUTH & CAISTER

GREAT YARMOUTH & CAISTER GOLF CLUB, Beach House, Caister-on-Sea, Great Yarmouth, **NORFOLK**, NR30 5TD, **ENGLAND**.
(T) 01493 728699
(E) office@caistergolf.co.uk
(W) www.caistergolf.co.uk

Contact/s:
- **Club Secretary:** Mr Harry Harvey

- **Professional:** Mr James Hill
- **Pro Shop:**
  ☎ 01493 720421

Course/s:
🏌 **TRADITIONAL LINKS**
Built: 1882
Number of Holes: 18 Par: 70
Yds: 6330 F9 Yds: 3090 B9 Yds: 3240

GREEN HAWORTH

GREEN HAWORTH GOLF CLUB, Green Haworth, Accrington, **LANCASHIRE**, BB5 3SL, **ENGLAND**.
(T) 01254 237580

Contact/s:
- **Club Secretary:** Mr Bill Holstead

Course/s:
🏌 **GREEN HAWORTH**
Number of Holes: 9

GREEN HOTEL

GREEN HOTEL GOLF COURSES, 2 The Muirs, Kinross, **PERTH AND KINROSS**, KY13 7AS, **SCOTLAND**.
(T) 01577 863407

Contact/s:
- **General Manager:** Mr D McCulloch

Course/s:
🏌 **BLUE**
Number of Holes: 18 Par: 71
Yds: 6438 F9 Yds: 3109 B9 Yds: 3329
Designer: David Montgomery

🏌 **RED**
Number of Holes: 18 Par: 73
Yds: 6256 F9 Yds: 6256 B9 Yds: 2852
Designer: David Montgomery

GREEN MEADOW

GREEN MEADOW GOLF & COUNTRY CLUB, Treherbert Rd, Croesyceiliog, Cwmbran, **TORFAEN**, NP44 2BZ, **WALES**.
(T) 01633 869321

Membership: Members & Public

Contact/s:
- **Club Secretary:** Mr Geoff Jenkins
- **Professional:** Mr Peter Stebbings

Course/s:
🏌 **GREEN MEADOW**
Description: Parkland, Hilltop, Undulating, Open, Drains Well
Green Speed: Fast
Built: 1979 **Built On:** Soil
Number of Holes: 18
Designer: P Richardson

GREENACRES

GREENACRES SHORT GOLF, Chenhalls Rd, St. Erth, Hayle, **CORNWALL**, TR27 6HJ, **ENGLAND**.
(T) 01736 757600

Contact/s:
- **Owner:** Mr P Corrigan

Course/s:
🏌 **GREENACRES PAR 3**
Number of Holes: 9 Par: 27
Par 3's: 9
Yds: 1102

GREENACRES GOLF CTRE

GREENACRES GOLF CENTRE, 153 Ballyrobert Rd, Ballyclare, **COUNTY ANTRIM**, BT39 9RT, **NORTHERN IRELAND**.
(T) 028 93352007

Membership: Members & Public
Size of Complex: 138 Acres

Contact/s:
- **Club Secretary:** Ms Marilan Crawford
- **Professional:** Mr Ray Skiellen

Course/s:
🏌 **GREENACRES**
Description: Parkland, Undulating, Sheltered, Open, Medium Length, Tight, Drains Well, Ideal for the Elderly
Green Speed: Medium
Built: 1995 Built On: Soil
Number of Holes: 18 Par: 70
Par 3's: 5 Par 4's: 10 Par 5's: 3
Yds: 5839 F9 Yds: 3109 B9 Yds: 2730
Prevailing Wind: West
Designer: Stephen Crawford
Further Information:
Challenging course built into natural landscape and countryside.

GREENBURN

GREENBURN GOLF CLUB, 6 Greenburn Rd, Fauldhouse, Bathgate, **LOTHIAN (WEST)**, EH47 9HG, **SCOTLAND**.
(T) 01501 771187

Membership: Members & Public

Contact/s:
- **Professional:** Mr Malcolm Leighton

Course/s:
🏌 **GREENBURN**
Description: Moorland, Medium Length, Tight, Ideal for the Elderly
Green Speed: Medium
Built: 1953
Number of Holes: 18

GREENCASTLE

GREENCASTLE GOLF CLUB, Greencastle, **COUNTY DONEGAL**, **IRELAND**.
(T) 077 81013

Course/s:
🏌 **GREENCASTLE**
Number of Holes: 18

GREENISLAND

GREENISLAND GOLF CLUB, 156 Upper Rd, Greenisland, Carrickfergus, **COUNTY ANTRIM**, BT38 8RW, **NORTHERN IRELAND**.
(T) 028 90862236

Course/s:
🏌 **GREENISLAND**
Number of Holes: 9 Par: 71
Yds: 6045 F9 Yds: 2972 B9 Yds: 3073
Further Information:
9 hole course can be played as an 18 hole course

GREENMOUNT

GREENMOUNT GOLF CLUB LTD, Greenhalgh Fold Farm, Greenmount, Bury, **LANCASHIRE**, BL8 4LH, **ENGLAND**.
(T) 01204 883712

Contact/s:
- **Club Secretary:** Mr Martin Barron
  ☎ 01204 888629
- **Professional:** Mr Jason Seed
- **Pro Shop:**
  ☎ 01204 888616

Course/s:
🏌 **OLD**
Description: Parkland, Undulating, Tight
Green Speed: Medium
Built: 1920

Number of Holes: 9 Par: 67
Yds: 5230
Further Information:
9 hole course can be played as an 18 hole course.

🌳 **WHITE**
Description: Parkland, Undulating, Tight
Green Speed: Medium
Built: 1999
Number of Holes: 9 Par: 69
Yds: 5990
Further Information:
9 hole course can be played as an 18 hole course

GREENORE

GREENORE GOLF CLUB, Greenore,
COUNTY LOUTH, IRELAND.
(T) 042 9373212
Course/s:
🌳 **GREENORE**
Number of Holes: 18

GREENWAY HALL

GREENWAY HALL GOLF CLUB, Stanley Rd,
Stockton Brook, Stoke-on-Trent,
STAFFORDSHIRE, ST9 9LJ, **ENGLAND**.
(T) 01782 503158
Contact/s:
● **General Manager:** Mr Stephen Harlock
Course/s:
🌳 **GREENWAY HALL**
Description: Parkland, Heath Land
Built: 1909
Number of Holes: 18 Par: 68
Further Information:
Views of Staffordshire Moorlands.

GREETHAM VALLEY

GREETHAM VALLEY GOLF CLUB,
Clubhouse, Wood Lane, Thistleton, Oakham,
RUTLAND, LE15 7NL, **ENGLAND**.
(T) 01780 460004
Membership: Members & Public
Size of Complex: 267 Acres
Contact/s:
● **Club Secretary:** Mr Ted Hudson
● **Professional:** Mr John Pengelly
Course/s:
🌳 **LAKES**
Description: Parkland, Valley, Undulating,
Open, Drains Well
Green Speed: Fast
Built: 1990 **Built On:** Soil
Number of Holes: 18 Par: 72
Record: 67 (Neil Evans)
Par 3's: 4 Par 4's: 10 Par 5's: 4
Yds: 6736 F9 Yds: 3412 B9 Yds: 3324
Prevailing Wind: West

🌳 **PAR 3**
Number of Holes: 9 Par: 27
Par 3's: 9
Yds: 1263

🌳 **VALLEY**
Description: Parkland, Valley, Undulating,
Open, Drains Well
Green Speed: Fast
Built: 1990 **Built On:** Soil
Number of Holes: 18 Par: 68
Par 3's: 6 Par 4's: 10 Par 5's: 2
Yds: 5595 F9 Yds: 2789 B9 Yds: 2806
Prevailing Wind: West

GRETNA

GRETNA GOLF CLUB, Kirtleview, Gretna,

DUMFRIES AND GALLOWAY, DG16 5HD,
SCOTLAND.
(T) 01461 338464
Contact/s:
● **Owner:** Mr George Bernie
Course/s:
🌳 **GRETNA**
Number of Holes: 9
Designer: N Williams

GREYS GREEN

GREYS GREEN GOLF COURSE, Dog Lane,
Rotherfield Peppard, Henley-on-Thames,
OXFORDSHIRE, RG9 5JU, **ENGLAND**.
(T) 01491 629967
(W) www.greysgreengolf.co.uk
Contact/s:
● **Manager:** Mr D Scott
Course/s:
🌳 **BLUE**
Number of Holes: 9 Par: 27
Yds: 1537

🌳 **RED**
Number of Holes: 18 Par: 70
Yds: 5682 F9 Yds: 2895 B9 Yds: 2787

GREYSTONES

GREYSTONES GOLF CLUB, Greystones,
COUNTY WICKLOW, IRELAND.
(T) 01 2874136
Course/s:
🌳 **GREYSTONES**
Number of Holes: 18

GRIFFIN

GRIFFIN GOLF CLUB, Chaul End Rd,
Caddington, Luton, **BEDFORDSHIRE**, LU1
4AX, **ENGLAND**.
(T) 01582 415573
Contact/s:
● **Club Secretary:** Mr M Smith
Course/s:
🌳 **GRIFFIN**
Number of Holes: 18 Par: 71
Par 3's: 5 Par 4's: 9 Par 5's: 4
Yds: 6240 F9 Yds: 3087 B9 Yds: 3153

GRIMSBY

GRIMSBY GOLF CLUB LTD, Little Coates
Rd, Grimsby, **LINCOLNSHIRE (NORTH
EAST)**, DN34 4LU, **ENGLAND**.
(T) 01472 267727
Course/s:
🌳 **GRIMSBY**
Number of Holes: 18
Designer: Harry Shapland Colt

GRIMSDYKE

GRIMSDYKE GOLF CLUB, Oxhey Lane,
Pinner, **LONDON (GREATER)**, HA5 4AL,
ENGLAND.
(T) 020 84284093
Contact/s:
● **Chief Executive:** Mr D Monk
Course/s:
🌳 **GRIMS DYKE**
Number of Holes: 18
Designer: James Braid

GROVE

GROVE GOLF CLUB, South Cornelly,
Bridgend, **BRIDGEND**, CF33 4RP, **WALES**.

(T) 01656 788771
(W) www.grovegolf.com
Membership: Members & Public
Contact/s:
● **Club Secretary:** Mr Mike Thomas
● **Professional:** Mr Leon Warne
● **Book Tee Times:**
☎ 01656 788300
Course/s:
🌳 **GROVE**
Description: Parkland, Undulating,
Medium Length, Drains Well, Ideal for the
Elderly
Built: 1996
Number of Holes: 18
Designer: J C Williams

GROVE

GROVE GOLF CENTRE, Ford Bridge,
Leominster, **HEREFORDSHIRE**, HR6 0LE,
ENGLAND.
(T) 01568 610602
(E) grove@helme.fslife.co.uk
(W) www.grovegolf.co.uk
Membership: Public
Size of Complex: 40 Acres
Contact/s:
● **Professional:** Mr Phil Brookes
☎ 01568 615333
Course/s:
🌳 **THE GROVE**
Description: Parkland, Undulating, Short,
Tight, Drains Well
Green Speed: Medium
Number of Holes: 9 Par: 30
Par 3's: 6 Par 4's: 3
Yds: 1780 F9 Yds: 1780
Further Information:
USGA spec greens.

GUERNSEY (ROYAL)

ROYAL GUERNSEY GOLF CLUB, L'ancresse
Vale, **GUERNSEY**, GY3 5BY, **ENGLAND**.
(T) 01481 46523
Course/s:
🌳 **ROYAL GUERNSEY**
Number of Holes: 18 Par: 70
Yds: 6206
Designer: A MacKenzie, L Ross

GUILDFORD

GUILDFORD GOLF CLUB, High Path Rd,
Guildford, **SURREY**, GU1 2HL, **ENGLAND**.
(T) 01483 563941
Contact/s:
● **Club Secretary:** Mr B Green
● **Pro Shop:** Mr P Hollington
☎ 01483 566765
Course/s:
🌳 **GUILDFORD**
Number of Holes: 18 Par: 69
Yds: 6090 F9 Yds: 3257 B9 Yds: 2833
Designer: Hawtree, Taylor

GULLANE

GULLANE GOLF CLUB, West Links Rd,
Gullane, **LOTHIAN (EAST)**, EH31 2BB,
SCOTLAND.
(T) 01620 842255
(E) bookings@gullanegolfclub.com
(W) www.gullanegolfclub.com
Membership: Members & Public
Contact/s:
● **Professional:** Mr Jimmy Hume

☎ 01620 843111

Course/s:

⛳ **GULLANE NO. 1**
Description: Championship, Links, Long, Drains Well
Green Speed: Fast
Built: 1882 **Built On:** Sand
Number of Holes: 18 **Par:** 72
Par 3's: 4 **Par 4's:** 10 **Par 5's:** 4
Yds: 6466 **F9 Yds:** 2976 **B9 Yds:** 3490
Prevailing Wind: West
Further Information:
There are magnificent views across Firth of Forth towards Edinburgh and Fife. ⛳

⛳ **GULLANE NO. 2**
Built: 1898
Number of Holes: 18 **Par:** 71
Par 3's: 3 **Par 4's:** 13 **Par 5's:** 2
Yds: 6244 **F9 Yds:** 3136 **B9 Yds:** 3108

⛳ **GULLANE NO. 3**
Built: 1910
Number of Holes: 18 **Par:** 68
Par 3's: 5 **Par 4's:** 12 **Par 5's:** 1
Yds: 5225 **F9 Yds:** 2460 **B9 Yds:** 2765

GWEEDORE

GWEEDORE GOLF CLUB, Magheragallen, Letterkenny, **COUNTY DONEGAL**, **IRELAND**.
(T) 075 31140

Course/s:

⛳ **GWEEDORE**
Number of Holes: 9

HABBERLEY

HABBERLEY GOLF CLUB, Low Habberley, Kidderminster, **WORCESTERSHIRE**, DY11 5RE, **ENGLAND**.
(T) 01562 745756

Course/s:

⛳ **HABBERLEY**
Number of Holes: 9 **Par:** 68
Yds: 5401 **F9 Yds:** 2634 **B9 Yds:** 2727
Further Information:
9 hole course can be played as an 18 hole course

HADDEN HILL

HADDEN HILL GOLF CLUB, Wallingford Rd, North Moreton, Didcot, **OXFORDSHIRE**, OX11 9BJ, **ENGLAND**.
(T) 01235 510410
(E) info@haddenhillgolf.co.uk
(W) www.haddenhillgolf.co.uk

Membership: Members & Public

Contact/s:
● **Club Secretary:** Mr M Morley
● **Professional:** Mr A Walters
● **Pro Shop:** Mr J Mitchell
● **Book Tee Times:** Mr Adrian Walters

Course/s:

⛳ **HADDEN HILL**
Description: Parkland, Hilltop, Undulating, Open, Medium Length, Drains Well, Ideal for the Elderly
Green Speed: Medium
Built: 1990 **Built On:** Clay/Sand
Number of Holes: 18 **Par:** 71
Record: 67 (Paul Simpson)
Par 3's: 4 **Par 4's:** 11 **Par 5's:** 3
Yds: 6563
Prevailing Wind: South/West
Designer: M Morley

HADDINGTON

HADDINGTON GOLF CLUB, Amisfield Pk, Haddington, **LOTHIAN (EAST)**, EH41 4PT, **SCOTLAND**.
(T) 01620 822727

Membership: Members & Public

Contact/s:
● **Professional:** Mr John Sandilands

Course/s:

⛳ **HADDINGTON**
Description: Parkland, Sheltered, Medium Length, Tends to Flood, Ideal for the Elderly
Green Speed: Medium
Built: 1931
Number of Holes: 18 **Par:** 71
Yds: 6317 **F9 Yds:** 3027 **B9 Yds:** 3290
Prevailing Wind: West
Further Information:
The River Tyne comes into play on three holes.

HADLEY WOOD

HADLEY WOOD GOLF CLUB, Beech Hill, Barnet, **HERTFORDSHIRE**, EN4 0JJ, **ENGLAND**.
(T) 020 84494328
(W) www.hadleywoodgc.com

Contact/s:
● **Professional:** Mr Peter Jones

Course/s:

⛳ **HADLEY WOOD**
Description: Undulating
Built: 1922
Number of Holes: 18 **Par:** 72
Yds: 6506 **F9 Yds:** 3236 **B9 Yds:** 3270
Designer: Alistair MacKenzie

HAGGERSTON CASTLE

HAGGERSTON CASTLE GOLF COURSE, Haggerston Castle Holiday Pk, Haggerston, Berwick-upon-Tweed, **NORTHUMBERLAND**, TD15 2NZ, **ENGLAND**.
(T) 01289 381400
(E) brockmillfarmhouse@barclays.net

Membership: Members & Public

Contact/s:
● **Owner:** Mrs A C Rogerson

Course/s:

⛳ **HAGGERSTON**
Description: Wooded, Parkland, Undulating, Sheltered, Short, Tight, Drains Well, Ideal for the Elderly
Green Speed: Fast
Number of Holes: 9
Designer: OCM Associates

HAGGS CASTLE

HAGGS CASTLE GOLF CLUB, 70 Dumbreck Rd, Glasgow, **GLASGOW (CITY OF)**, G41 4SN, **SCOTLAND**.
(T) 0141 4270480

Contact/s:
● **Club Secretary:** Mr I Harvey
● **Professional:** Mr J McAlister

Course/s:

⛳ **HAGGS CASTLE**
Number of Holes: 18

HAGLEY

HAGLEY GOLF & COUNTRY CLUB, Wassell Gr, Hagley, Stourbridge, **MIDLANDS (WEST)**, DY9 9JW, **ENGLAND**.
(T) 01562 883701

Course/s:
⛳ **HAGLEY**
Number of Holes: 18
Designer: Garratt

HAIGH HALL

HAIGH HALL GOLF CLUB, Haigh Country Pk, Haigh, Wigan, **LANCASHIRE**, WN2 1PE, **ENGLAND**.
(T) 01942 833337

Course/s:

⛳ **HAIGH HALL**
Description: Undulating, Ideal for the Elderly
Number of Holes: 9

⛳ **HIMALAYAN PUTTING GREEN**
Description: Undulating, Ideal for the Elderly
Number of Holes: 18

HAINAULT FOREST

HAINAULT FOREST GOLF COMPLEX, P O Box 2204, Romford Rd, Chigwell, **ESSEX**, IG7 4GT, **ENGLAND**.
(T) 020 85002131
(W) www.essexgolfcentre.com

Membership: Public
Size of Complex: 250 Acres

Contact/s:
● **Marketing Manager:** Ms Karen Jeffery
☎ 020 85002470

Course/s:

⛳ **BOTTOM**
Number of Holes: 18 **Par:** 72
Par 3's: 2 **Par 4's:** 14 **Par 5's:** 2
Yds: 6545

⛳ **TOP**
Description: Wooded, Parkland, Undulating, Sheltered, Medium Length
Green Speed: Medium
Built: 1909 **Built On:** Clay
Number of Holes: 18 **Par:** 70
Par 3's: 4 **Par 4's:** 12 **Par 5's:** 2
Yds: 5886
Designer: Taylor
Further Information:
Views over Essex and Home Counties.

HAINSWORTH PARK

HAINSWORTH PARK GOLF CLUB, Burton Holme, Leven Rd, Brandesburton, Driffield, **YORKSHIRE (EAST)**, YO25 8RT, **ENGLAND**.
(T) 01964 542362

Membership: Members & Public
Size of Complex: 100 Acres

Contact/s:
● **Club Secretary:** Mr G S Redshaw
● **Professional:** Mr Paul Binington

Course/s:

⛳ **HAINSWORTH PARK**
Description: Wooded, Parkland, Undulating, Open, Medium Length, Drains Well, Ideal for the Elderly
Green Speed: Medium
Built: 1982 **Built On:** Clay
Number of Holes: 18 **Par:** 71
Prevailing Wind: South/West

HALE

HALE GOLF CLUB, Rappax Rd, Hale, Altrincham, **CHESHIRE**, WA15 0NU, **ENGLAND**.
(T) 0161 9804225

Course/s:

🏌 **HALE**
Number of Holes: 9

HALESOWEN

HALESOWEN GOLF CLUB, The Leasowes,
Leasowes Lane, Halesowen, **MIDLANDS
(WEST)**, B62 8QF, **ENGLAND**.
(T) 0121 5013606
(E) halesowen.gc@virgin.net
(W) www.halesowengolfclub.co.uk

Contact/s:
● **Club Secretary:** Mr P Crumpton
● **Professional:** Mr Jon Nicholas

Course/s:
🏌 **HALESOWEN**
Number of Holes: 18 Par: 69
Yds: 5746 F9 Yds: 2961 B9 Yds: 2785

HALESWORTH

HALESWORTH GOLF CLUB, Bramfield Rd,
Halesworth, **SUFFOLK**, IP19 9XA,
ENGLAND.
(T) 01986 875567

Membership: Members & Public

Contact/s:
● **Professional:** Mr Simon Harrison
☎ 01986 875697

Course/s:
🏌 **HALESWORTH**
Description: Parkland, Open, Long,
Drains Well, Ideal for the Elderly
Built: 1991 Built On: Clay
Number of Holes: 18 Par: 72
Par 3's: 4 Par 4's: 10 Par 5's: 4
Yds: 6363 F9 Yds: 3152 B9 Yds: 3211
Designer: J W Johnson
Further Information:
This is a very quiet course but it is a
temporary course. The full course is
currently under construction and is due for
completion in 2005.

HALIFAX

HALIFAX GOLF CLUB LTD, Union Lane,
Ogden, Halifax, **YORKSHIRE (WEST)**, HX3
6XW, **ENGLAND**.
(T) 01422 244171
Size of Complex: 200 Acres

Contact/s:
● **Club Secretary:** Mr G H Taylor
● **Professional:** Mr Michael Alison
☎ 01422 240047

Course/s:
🏌 **OGDEN**
Description: Moorland, Undulating,
Open, Medium Length, Drains Well
Green Speed: Medium
Built: 1902 Built On: Soil
Number of Holes: 18 Par: 70
Par 3's: 4 Par 4's: 12 Par 5's: 2
Yds: 6037 F9 Yds: 3009 B9 Yds: 3028
Prevailing Wind: West
Designer: James Braid, S Herd
Further Information:
The 17th hole has a drop of 150ft to the
green and could be played with anything
from a wedge to a driver.

HALLAMSHIRE

HALLAMSHIRE GOLF CLUB, Redmires Rd,
Sheffield, **YORKSHIRE (SOUTH)**, S10 4LA,
ENGLAND.
(T) 0114 2305222

Contact/s:
● **Manager:** Mr G Tickell

Course/s:

🏌 **HALLAMSHIRE**
Number of Holes: 18

HALLGARTH

HALLGARTH GOLF & COUNTRY CLUB,
Coatham Mundeville, Darlington, **COUNTY
DURHAM**, DL1 3LU, **ENGLAND**.
(T) 01325 300400

Contact/s:
● **General Manager:** Mr V Johnson

Course/s:
🏌 **HALLGARTH**
Number of Holes: 9
Designer: Brian Moore

HALLOWES

HALLOWES GOLF CLUB, Hallowes Lane,
Dronfield, **DERBYSHIRE**, S18 1UR,
ENGLAND.
(T) 01246 413734

Membership: Members & Public

Contact/s:
● **Club Secretary:** Mr T W Stuart
● **Professional:** Mr Philip Dunn

Course/s:
🏌 **HALLOWES**
Description: Parkland, Hilltop, Open,
Medium Length
Green Speed: Fast
Built: 1892 Built On: Clay
Number of Holes: 18 Par: 71
Record: 64 (Peter Cowan)
Par 3's: 4 Par 4's: 11 Par 5's: 3
Yds: 6342
Designer: G Lowe

HALSTOCK

HALSTOCK GOLF CLUB, Common Lane,
Halstock, Yeovil, **SOMERSET**, BA22 9SF,
ENGLAND.
(T) 01935 891689

Contact/s:
● **Owner:** Mr L Church

Course/s:
🏌 **HALSTOCK GOLF ENTERPRISES**
Description: Parkland, Short
Built: 1988
Number of Holes: 18 Par: 66
Further Information:
This is a testing course.

HALTWHISTLE

HALTWHISTLE GOLF CLUB, Wallend Farm,
Greenhead, Brampton, **CUMBRIA**, CA8 7HN,
ENGLAND.
(T) 01697 747367

Course/s:
🏌 **HALTWHISTLE**
Built: 1967
Number of Holes: 18 Par: 69
Further Information:
Every hole is individual. Demands
accurate approach shots to small, well
kept greens.

HAM MANOR

HAM MANOR GOLF CLUB, West Drive,
Angmering, Littlehampton, **SUSSEX
(WEST)**, BN16 4JE, **ENGLAND**.
(T) 01903 787130
(E) secretary.ham.manor@tinyonline.co.uk

Membership: Members & Public

Contact/s:
● **Professional:** Mr Simon Buckley

☎ 01903 783732

Course/s:
🏌 **HAM MANOR**
Description: Parkland, Sheltered, Open,
Medium Length, Ideal for the Elderly
Green Speed: Medium
Built: 1930 Built On: Clay
Number of Holes: 18 Par: 70
Yds: 6267 F9 Yds: 2992 B9 Yds: 3275
Designer: Harry Shapland Colt

HAMPSHIRE

HAMPSHIRE GOLF CLUB, Winchester Rd,
Goodworth Clatford, Andover, **HAMPSHIRE**,
SP11 7TB, **ENGLAND**.
(T) 01264 356462
(E) enquiries@thehampshiregolfclub.co.uk
(W) www.thehampshiregolfclub.co.uk

Membership: Members & Public

Contact/s:
● **Club Secretary:** Mr Tim Fiducia
● **Professional:** Mr Stewart Cronin
● **Pro Shop:** Mr Brian Gleeson

Course/s:
🏌 **HAMPSHIRE 9 HOLE**
Description: Parkland, Open, Drains Well
Green Speed: Medium
Number of Holes: 9
🏌 **THE HAMPSHIRE**
Number of Holes: 18

HAMPSTEAD

HAMPSTEAD GOLF CLUB, Winnington Rd,
London, **LONDON (GREATER)**, N2 0TU,
ENGLAND.
(T) 020 84557089

Membership: Members & Public

Contact/s:
● **Club Secretary:** Mr Alan Harris
● **Professional:** Mr Peter Brown

Course/s:
🏌 **HAMPSTEAD**
Description: Wooded, Parkland,
Undulating, Sheltered, Medium Length,
Tight, Drains Well
Green Speed: Medium
Built: 1893 Built On: Clay
Number of Holes: 9 Par: 68 Record: 64
(Tony Sheaff)
Yds: 5822 F9 Yds: 2911 B9 Yds: 2911
Prevailing Wind: North/West
Designer: Tom Dunn
Further Information:
Very challenging, tight course and good
greens. 9 hole course can be played as
an 18 hole course

HAMPTON COURT PALACE GOLF CLUB

AMERICAN GOLF CORPORATION,
Hampton Court, Home Pk, Kingston Upon
Thames, **LONDON (GREATER)**, KT1 4AD,
ENGLAND.
(T) 020 8977 2423
(E)
hamptoncourtpalace@americangolf.uk.com

Membership: Members & Public

Contact/s:
● **Professional:** Mr Len Roberts
● **Pro Shop:**
☎ 020 8977 2658

Course/s:
🏌 **HAMPTON COURT PALACE**
Description: Links, Parkland, Open,
Medium Length, Drains Well
Green Speed: Medium

Built: 1895 Built On: Sand
Number of Holes: 18 Par: 71
Yds: 6584 F9 Yds: 3427 B9 Yds: 3157
Designer: William Park Jnr
Further Information:
The club will be starting construction work on a brand new £1 million clubhouse in 2002.

HAMPTWORTH

HAMPTWORTH GOLF & COUNTRY CLUB, Hamptworth Rd, Nr.Landford, Salisbury, **WILTSHIRE**, SP5 2DU, **ENGLAND**.
(T) 01794 390155
(E) info@hamptworthgolf.co.uk
(W) www.hamptworthgolf.co.uk
Membership: Members & Public
Contact/s:
● Club Secretary: Ms Janet Facer
● Professional: Mr Mark White
Course/s:
🌑 HAMPTWORTH
   Description: Championship, Wooded, Undulating, Tight
   Green Speed: Fast
   Built: 1992
   Number of Holes: 18
   Designer: P Saunders

HANBURY MANOR

MARRIOTT HANBURY MANOR GOLF & COUNTRY CLUB, Ware, **HERTFORDSHIRE**, SG12 0SD, **ENGLAND**.
(T) 01920 487722
Membership: Members & Public
Course/s:
🌑 HANBURY MANOR
   Description: Championship
   Number of Holes: 18 Par: 72
   Yds: 7052 F9 Yds: 3566 B9 Yds: 3486
   Designer: Jack Nicklaus

HANDSWORTH

HANDSWORTH GOLF CLUB, Sunningdale Cl, Birmingham, **MIDLANDS (WEST)**, B20 1NP, **ENGLAND**.
(T) 0121 5233594
Contact/s:
● Manager: Mr K A Qualters
Course/s:
🌑 HANDSWORTH
   Number of Holes: 18

HANGING HEATON

HANGING HEATON GOLF CLUB, White Cross Rd, Dewsbury, **YORKSHIRE (WEST)**, WF12 7DT, **ENGLAND**.
(T) 01924 461606
Contact/s:
● Club Secretary: Mr Ken Wood
Course/s:
🌑 HANGING HEATON
   Number of Holes: 9 Par: 69
   Yds: 5836 F9 Yds: 2913 B9 Yds: 2923
   Further Information:
   9 hole course can be played as an 18 hole course

HANKLEY COMMON

HANKLEY COMMON GOLF CLUB & PROFESSIONALS SHOP, The Clubhouse, Tilford, Farnham, **SURREY**, GU10 2DD, **ENGLAND**.
(T) 01252 792493

Contact/s:
● Club Secretary: Mr J S W Scott (ESQ)
● Professional: Mr Peter Stow
   ☎ 01252 793761
Course/s:
🌑 HANKLEY COMMON
   Description: Heath Land
   Number of Holes: 18 Par: 71
   Par 3's: 4 Par 4's: 11 Par 5's: 3
   Yds: 6538 F9 Yds: 3232 B9 Yds: 3306
   Designer: James Braid ⛳

HANOVER

HANOVER GOLF & COUNTRY CLUB, Hullbridge Rd, Rayleigh, **ESSEX**, SS6 9QS, **ENGLAND**.
(T) 01702 232377
Contact/s:
● Professional: Mr A Blackburn
Course/s:
🌑 GEORGIAN
   Number of Holes: 18
   Yds: 6669
🌑 REGENCY
   Number of Holes: 18
   Yds: 3700

HAPPY VALLEY

HAPPY VALLEY GOLF CLUB, Rook Lane, Chaldon, Caterham, **SURREY**, CR3 5AA, **ENGLAND**.
(T) 01883 344555
(E) cgm.wells@virgin.net
(W) www.happyvalley.co.uk
Course/s:
🌑 HAPPY VALLEY
   Description: Valley
   Number of Holes: 18 Par: 72
   Yds: 6333 F9 Yds: 2948 B9 Yds: 3385
   Designer: David Williams

HARBORNE

HARBORNE GOLF CLUB (PRIVATE) LTD, 40 Tennal Rd, Birmingham, **MIDLANDS (WEST)**, B32 2JE, **ENGLAND**.
(T) 0121 4273058
Contact/s:
● Professional: Mr A Quarterman
Course/s:
🌑 HARBORNE
   Description: Parkland
   Number of Holes: 18
   Designer: Harry Shapland Colt

HARBORNE CHURCH FARM

HARBORNE CHURCH FARM GOLF COURSE, Vicarage Rd, Harborne, Birmingham, **MIDLANDS (WEST)**, B17 0SN, **ENGLAND**.
(T) 0121 4271204
Contact/s:
● Manager: Mr Paul Johnson
Course/s:
🌑 HARBORNE CHURCH FARM
   Number of Holes: 9 Par: 66
   Yds: 4538 F9 Yds: 2269 B9 Yds: 2269
   Further Information:
   9 hole course can be played as an 18 hole course

HARBOUR POINT

HARBOUR POINT GOLF CLUB, Clash Rd, Little Island, **COUNTY CORK**, **IRELAND**.
(T) 021 4353719

Contact/s:
● Professional: Mr Morgan D Donovan
Course/s:
🌑 HARBOUR POINT
   Number of Holes: 18 Par: 72
   Yds: 6718 F9 Yds: 3428 B9 Yds: 3290
   Designer: P Merrigan

HARBURN

HARBURN GOLF CLUB, West Calder, **LOTHIAN (WEST)**, EH55 8RS, **SCOTLAND**.
(T) 01506 871131
Course/s:
🌑 HARBURN
   Number of Holes: 18

HAREWOOD DOWNS

HAREWOOD DOWNS GOLF CLUB, Cokes Lane, Chalfont St. Giles, **BUCKINGHAMSHIRE**, HP8 4TA, **ENGLAND**.
(T) 01494 762184
Contact/s:
● Professional: Mr G C Morris
Course/s:
🌑 HAREWOOD DOWNS
   Number of Holes: 18 Par: 69
   Yds: 5958 F9 Yds: 3065 B9 Yds: 2893

HARLECH

ROYAL ST DAVIDS GOLF CLUB (THE), Harlech, **GWYNEDD**, LL46 2UB, **WALES**.
(T) 01766 780361
(W) www.royalstdavids.co.uk
Membership: Members & Public
Size of Complex: 150 Acres
Contact/s:
● Club Secretary: Mr D L Morkill
● Professional: Mr John Barnett
   ☎ 01766 780857
Course/s:
🌑 ROYAL ST DAVIDS
   Description: Links, Open, Long, Tight, Drains Well
   Green Speed: Medium
   Built: 1894 Built On: Sand
   Number of Holes: 18 Par: 69
   Record: 64 (Kevin Stables)
   Par 3's: 5 Par 4's: 11 Par 5's: 2
   Yds: 6428 F9 Yds: 3329 B9 Yds: 3099
   Prevailing Wind: South/West
   Further Information:
   The course has magnificent par 4 holes and 5 varied short holes. A wonderful situation below Harlech Castle with views of Snowdon. ⛳

HARLEYFORD

HARLEYFORD GOLF CLUB, Henley Rd, Marlow, **BUCKINGHAMSHIRE**, SL7 2SP, **ENGLAND**.
(T) 01628 402333
Contact/s:
● Club Secretary: Mr Gloria Elliot
● Professional: Mr Lee Jackson
Course/s:
🌑 HARLEYFORD
   Description: Parkland
   Built: 1996 Number of Holes: 18
   Par: 72 Yds: 6653

HARPENDEN

HARPENDEN GOLF CLUB, Hammonds End, Redbourn Lane, Harpenden, **HERTFORDSHIRE**, AL5 2AX, **ENGLAND**.

(T) 01582 712580

Contact/s:
● General Manager: Mr Frank Clapp

Course/s:
● **HARPENDEN**
Number of Holes: 18 Par: 70
Yds: 6381 F9 Yds: 3203 B9 Yds: 3178
Designer: Hawtree, Taylor

HARPENDEN COMMON

HARPENDEN COMMON GOLF CLUB, East
Common, Harpenden, **HERTFORDSHIRE**,
AL5 1BL, **ENGLAND**.
(T) 01582 715959

Contact/s:
● Professional: Mr Daniel Fitzsimmons
● Book Lessons:
☎ 01582 460655

Course/s:
● **HARPENDEN COMMON**
Description: Parkland
Built: 1931
Number of Holes: 18 Par: 70
Further Information:
Easy walking course.

HARRISON

HARRISON GOLF CLUB, 15 Braid Hills
Approach, Edinburgh, **EDINBURGH (CITY
OF)**, EH10 6JZ, **SCOTLAND**.
(T) 0131 4479929

Contact/s:
● Treasurer: Mr J Tiffiney

HARROGATE

HARROGATE GOLF CLUB LTD, Forest Lane
Head, Harrogate, **YORKSHIRE (NORTH)**,
HG2 7TF, **ENGLAND**.
(T) 01423 860079
(W) www.harrogate-gc.co.uk

Contact/s:
● Club Secretary: Mr Peter Banks
☎ 01423 862999

Course/s:
● **HARROGATE**
Number of Holes: 18 Par: 69
Yds: 6241 F9 Yds: 2904 B9 Yds: 3337
Designer: S Herd

HARROW HILL

HARROW HILL GOLF COURSE, Kenton Rd,
Harrow, **LONDON (GREATER)**, HA1 2BL,
ENGLAND.
(T) 020 88643754

Contact/s:
● General Manager: Mr Simon Bishop

HARTLAND FOREST

HARTLAND FOREST GOLF CLUB,
Woolsery, Bideford, **DEVON**, EX39 5RA,
ENGLAND.
(T) 01237 431442

Contact/s:
● Manager: Mr M Boothroyd

Course/s:
● **HARTLAND FOREST**
Description: Parkland, Long
Number of Holes: 18

HARTLEPOOL

HARTLEPOOL GOLF CLUB LTD, Hart
Warren, Hartlepool, **CLEVELAND**, TS24 9QF,
ENGLAND.

(T) 01429 274398
(W) www.hartlepoolgolfclub.co.uk

Contact/s:
● Club Secretary: Mr G Gordon
● Pro Shop: Mr Malcolm Cole
☎ 01429 267473
● Book Tee Times: Mr Joe Cairns

Course/s:
● **HARTLEPOOL**
Description: Championship, Heath Land,
Sheltered, Ideal for the Elderly
Green Speed: Fast Built On: Sand
Number of Holes: 18

HARTLEY WINTNEY

HARTLEY WINTNEY GOLF CLUB, London
Rd, Hartley Wintney, Hook, **HAMPSHIRE**,
RG27 8RY, **ENGLAND**.
(T) 01252 842214

Course/s:
● **HARTLEY WINTNEY**
Number of Holes: 9

HARTSBOURNE COUNTRY CLUB

**HARTSBOURNE COUNTRY CLUB
(MEMBERS) LTD,** Hartsbourne Ave, Bushey,
Watford, **HERTFORDSHIRE**, WD2 1JW,
ENGLAND.
(T) 020 89501133

Contact/s:
● Project Director: Mr Stephen Fisher

Course/s:
● **HARTSBOURNE**
Number of Holes: 18

HARTSWOOD

HARTSWOOD GOLF COURSE, King
Georges Playing Fields, Ingrave Rd,
Brentwood, **ESSEX**, CM14 5AE, **ENGLAND**.
(T) 01277 218850
(E) info@discountgolfstore.co.uk

Contact/s:
● Manager: Mr S Cole
☎ 01277 218714

Course/s:
● **HARTSWOOD**
Number of Holes: 18 Par: 70
Yds: 6192 F9 Yds: 2952 B9 Yds: 3240

HARWICH & DOVERCOURT

HARWICH & DOVERCOURT GOLF CLUB,
Station Rd, Harwich, **ESSEX**, CO12 4NZ,
ENGLAND.
(T) 01255 503616

Contact/s:
● Club Secretary: Mr John Eldridge

Course/s:
● **HARWICH & DOVERCOURT**
Number of Holes: 9 Par: 35
F9 Yds: 2953

HARWOOD

HARWOOD GOLF CLUB, Roading Brook Rd,
Bolton, **LANCASHIRE**, BL2 4JD, **ENGLAND**.
(T) 01204 362834

Course/s:
● **HARWOOD (BOLTON)**
Number of Holes: 18

HASSOCKS

HASSOCKS GOLF CLUB, London Rd,
Hassocks, **SUSSEX (WEST)**, BN6 9NA,

ENGLAND.
(T) 01273 846630
(W) www.hassocksgolfclub.co.uk
Membership: Members & Public

Contact/s:
● Club Secretary: Ms Jaki Brown

Course/s:
● **HASSOCKS**
Description: Links, Wooded, Parkland,
Undulating, Sheltered, Open, Medium
Length, Tight, Drains Well, Ideal for the
Elderly
Green Speed: Medium
Built: 1995 Built On: Clay/Soil
Number of Holes: 18 Record: 66
(Stewart Crookes)
Designer: Howard Swan
Further Information:
The course has never has temporary greens. It
is tricky but suitable for all golfers.

HASTE HILL

HASTE HILL GOLF COURSE, The Drive,
Northwood, Hillingdon, **LONDON
(GREATER)**, HA6 1HN, **ENGLAND**.
(T) 01923 825224
Membership: Members & Public

Contact/s:
● Professional: Mr Cameron Smillie

Course/s:
● **HASTE HILL**
Description: Wooded, Parkland,
Undulating, Sheltered, Medium Length,
Ideal for the Elderly
Green Speed: Medium
Built: 1927 Built On: Clay
Number of Holes: 18

HASTINGS

HASTINGS GOLF & COUNTRY CLUB,
Beauport Pk, Bootle Rd, St. Leonards-on-Sea,
SUSSEX (EAST), TN37 7BP, **ENGLAND**.
(T) 01424 854243
(E) enquiries@hastingsgolfclub.com
(W) www.hastingsgolfclub.com

Contact/s:
● Manager: Mr Mark Strevett

Course/s:
● **HASTINGS**
Number of Holes: 18 Par: 71
Yds: 6180 F9 Yds: 3098 B9 Yds: 3082

HATCHFORD BROOK

HATCHFORD BROOK GOLF CLUB,
Coventry Rd, Sheldon, Birmingham,
MIDLANDS (WEST), B26 3PY, **ENGLAND**.
(T) 0121 7439821

Contact/s:
● Manager: Mr Mark Hampton

Course/s:
● **HATCHFORD BROOK**
Number of Holes: 18

HATFIELD LONDON

HATFIELD LONDON COUNTRY CLUB,
Bedwell Pk, Essendon, Hatfield,
HERTFORDSHIRE, AL9 6JA, **ENGLAND**.
(T) 01707 642624

Course/s:
● **HATFIELD LONDON**
Number of Holes: 18
Designer: Hawtree

HAVEN PASTURES

HAVEN PASTURES GOLF & COUNTRY CLUB, Haven Pastures, Liveridge Hill, Henley-In-Arden, Solihull, **MIDLANDS (WEST)**, B95 5QS, **ENGLAND**.
(T) 01564 795967

Contact/s:
• General Manager: Mr D Broadhurst

Course/s:
🏌 **HAVEN PASTURES**
Description: Parkland
Number of Holes: 18 Par: 73
Yds: 6507

HAVERFORDWEST

HAVERFORDWEST GOLF CLUB, Narberth Rd, Haverfordwest, **PEMBROKESHIRE**, SA61 2XQ, **WALES**.
(T) 01437 764523

Membership: Members & Public
Size of Complex: 180 Acres

Contact/s:
• Professional: Mr Alex Pile

Course/s:
🏌 **HAVERFORDWEST**
Description: Wooded, Parkland, Undulating, Medium Length, Drains Well, Ideal for the Elderly
Green Speed: Medium/Fast
Built: 1904 Built On: Clay
Number of Holes: 18
Prevailing Wind: South/West
Further Information:
The course is challenging for all types of golfers.

HAVERHILL

HAVERHILL GOLF CLUB LTD, Coupals Rd, Sturmer, Haverhill, **SUFFOLK**, CB9 7UW, **ENGLAND**.
(T) 01440 761951
(E) haverhillgolf@coupalsroad.fsnet.co.uk
(W) www.club-noticeboard.co.uk

Membership: Members & Public
Size of Complex: 130 Acres

Contact/s:
• Club Secretary: Mrs Jill Edwards

Course/s:
🏌 **HAVERHILL**
Description: Wooded, Parkland, Undulating, Open, Tight, Drains Well
Green Speed: Fast
Built: 1973 Built On: Clay/Soil
Number of Holes: 18 Par: 70
Yds: 5929 F9 Yds: 2934 B9 Yds: 2995
Designer: Philip Pilgrim

HAWARDEN

HAWARDEN GOLF CLUB LTD, Groomsdale Lane, Hawarden, Deeside, **FLINTSHIRE**, CH5 3EH, **WALES**.
(T) 01244 520809

Contact/s:
• Club Secretary: Mr T McHue

Course/s:
🏌 **HAWARDEN**
Number of Holes: 18

HAWICK

HAWICK GOLF CLUB, Vertish Hill, Hawick, **SCOTTISH BORDERS**, TD9 0NY, **SCOTLAND**.
(T) 01450 372293

Contact/s:
• Book Tee Times: Mr D Miller

Course/s:
🏌 **HAWICK**
Description: Hilltop
Built: 1877
Number of Holes: 18 Par: 68

HAWKESBURY GOLF CENTRE

HAWKESBURY GOLF CENTRE, Blackhorse Rd, Longford, Coventry, **MIDLANDS (WEST)**, CV6 6HG, **ENGLAND**.
(T) 02476 360580
(E) theresa@hawkesbury.altodigital.co.uk

Membership: Members & Public

Contact/s:
• Club Secretary: Mrs Theresa McGrath
• Professional: Mr Neil Selwyn-Smith

Course/s:
🏌 **HAWKESBURY**
Description: Parkland, Valley, Undulating, Sheltered, Open, Short, Tight, Drains Well, Ideal for the Elderly
Green Speed: Medium/Fast
Built: 1996 Built On: Clay/Soil
Number of Holes: 18 Par: 62
Yds: 3789 F9 Yds: 1910 B9 Yds: 1879
Prevailing Wind: West
Further Information:
Hawkesbury is a fairly flat but interesting course ideally suited to ladies, juniors, seniors and beginners.

HAWKHURST

HAWKHURST GOLF & SQUASH CLUB, The Clubhouse, High St, Hawkhurst, Cranbrook, **KENT**, TN18 4JS, **ENGLAND**.
(T) 01580 754074 or 752396
(E) hawkhead@tesco.net
(W) www.hawkhurstgolfclub.org.uk

Membership: Members & Public

Contact/s:
• Professional: Mr Tony Collins
☎ 01580 753600

Course/s:
🏌 **HAWKHURST**
Description: Parkland, Undulating, Open, Long, Drains Well
Green Speed: Medium
Built: 1968 Built On: Clay
Number of Holes: 9 Par: 70
Par 3's: 2 Par 4's: 7
Yds: 5791 F9 Yds: 2793 B9 Yds: 2998
Prevailing Wind: West
Designer: R Baldock
Further Information:
9 hole course can be played as an 18 hole course

HAWKSTONE PARK

HAWKSTONE PARK HOTEL & GOLF CENTRE, Weston-under-Redcastle, Shrewsbury, **SHROPSHIRE**, SY4 5UY, **ENGLAND**.
(T) 01939 200611
(W) www.hawkstone.co.uk/golf.htm

Course/s:
🏌 **ACADEMY**
Number of Holes: 6
Designer: Brian Huggett

🏌 **HAWKSTONE**
Number of Holes: 18
Designer: Brian Huggett

🏌 **WINDMILL**
Number of Holes: 18

Designer: Brian Huggett

HAYDOCK PARK

HAYDOCK PARK GOLF CLUB, Golborne Pk, Newton Lane, Newton-Le-Willows, **MERSEYSIDE**, WA12 0HX, **ENGLAND**.
(T) 01925 226944
Size of Complex: 84 Acres

Contact/s:
• Club Secretary: Mr J V Smith
☎ 01925 228525
• Professional: Mr Peter Kenwright

Course/s:
🏌 **HAYDOCK PARK**
Description: Parkland, Sheltered, Medium Length, Drains Well, Ideal for the Elderly
Green Speed: Medium
Built: 1877 Built On: Soil
Number of Holes: 18 Par: 70
Par 3's: 5 Par 4's: 10 Par 5's: 3
Yds: 6058 F9 Yds: 3034 B9 Yds: 3024
Prevailing Wind: South/West
Designer: James Braid

HAYLING

HAYLING GOLF CLUB, Links Lane, Hayling Island, **HAMPSHIRE**, PO11 0BX, **ENGLAND**.
(T) 02392 464446
(W) www.haylinggolf.co.uk

Membership: Members & Public
Size of Complex: 190 Acres

Contact/s:
• Club Secretary: Mr Chris Cavill
• Professional: Mr Ray Gadd
☎ 02392 464491

Course/s:
🏌 **HAYLING**
Description: Championship, Links, Open, Long, Drains Well, Ideal for the Elderly
Green Speed: Fast
Built: 1833 Built On: Sand
Number of Holes: 18 Par: 71
Par 3's: 4 Par 4's: 11 Par 5's: 3
Yds: 6531 F9 Yds: 3355 B9 Yds: 3176

HAYSTON

HAYSTON GOLF CLUB, Campsie Rd, Kirkintilloch, Glasgow, **GLASGOW (CITY OF)**, G66 1RN, **SCOTLAND**.
(T) 0141 7761244

Contact/s:
• Club Secretary: Mr J V Carmichael
☎ 0141 7750723
• Professional: Mr Steve Barnett
☎ 0141 7750882

Course/s:
🏌 **HAYSTON**
Number of Holes: 18 Par: 70
Yds: 6042 F9 Yds: 3243 B9 Yds: 2799
Designer: James Braid

HAYWARDS HEATH

HAYWARDS HEATH GOLF CLUB, High Beech Lane, Haywards Heath, **SUSSEX (WEST)**, RH16 1SL, **ENGLAND**.
(T) 01444 414457
(E) haywardsheath.golfclub@virgin.net

Contact/s:
• Club Secretary: Mr G Kullmer

Course/s:
🏌 **HAYWARDS HEATH**
Number of Holes: 18 Par: 71
Yds: 6002 F9 Yds: 2777 B9 Yds: 3225

HAZEL GROVE

HAZEL GROVE GOLF CLUB, Mt Seskin Rd, Tallaght, Jobstown, **COUNTY DUBLIN, IRELAND.**
(T) 01 4520911

Contact/s:
● Secretary/Manager: Mr Pat Foley

Course/s:
● HAZEL GROVE PAR 45
Description: Parkland
Number of Holes: 9 Par: 45
Yds: 2587
Further Information:
This 9 hole course can be played as an 18 hole

HAZEL GROVE

HAZEL GROVE GOLF CLUB, Occupiers Lane, Buxton Rd, Hazel Gr, Stockport, **CHESHIRE,** SK7 6LU, **ENGLAND.**
(T) 0161 4837272

Course/s:
● HAZEL GROVE
Number of Holes: 18

HAZELWOOD GOLF CTRE

HAZELWOOD GOLF CENTRE, Croysdale Ave, Sunbury-on-Thames, **SURREY,** TW16 6QU, **ENGLAND.**
(T) 01932 783496

Contact/s:
● Club Secretary: Mr A Kelly
● Professional: Mr F Sheridan

Course/s:
● HAZELWOOD
Description: Parkland
Number of Holes: 18 Par: 70
Yds: 5660

HAZLEHEAD

HAZLEHEAD GOLF CLUB, Hazlehead, Aberdeen, **ABERDEEN (CITY OF),** AB15 8BD, **SCOTLAND.**
(T) 01224 315747

Contact/s:
● Chairman: Mr B McGry

Course/s:
● HAZLEHEAD PUBLIC
Number of Holes: 18

HAZLEMERE

HAZLEMERE GOLF & COUNTRY CLUB, Penn Rd, Hazlemere, High Wycombe, **BUCKINGHAMSHIRE,** HP15 7LR, **ENGLAND.**
(T) 01494 714722

Course/s:
● HAZLEMERE
Number of Holes: 18
Designer: T Murray

HEADFORT

HEADFORT GOLF CLUB, Kells, **COUNTY MEATH, IRELAND.**
(T) 046 40146

Course/s:
● HEADFORT
Number of Holes: 18

HEADINGLEY

HEADINGLEY GOLF CLUB LTD, Back Church Lane, Leeds, **YORKSHIRE (WEST),** LS16 8DW, **ENGLAND.**
(T) 0113 2679573
(E) headingley-golf@talk21.com

Contact/s:
● Manager: Mr John D Buns

Course/s:
● HEADINGLEY
Number of Holes: 18 Par: 69
Yds: 6298
Designer: Alistair MacKenzie

HEADLEY

HEADLEY GOLF CLUB, Headley Lane, Thornton, Bradford, **YORKSHIRE (WEST),** BD13 3LX, **ENGLAND.**
(T) 01274 833481

Membership: Members & Public
Size of Complex: 40 Acres

Contact/s:
● Club Secretary: Mr Alan Goodman

Course/s:
● HEADLEY
Description: Parkland, Heath Land, Moorland, Hilltop, Undulating, Medium Length, Tight, Drains Well
Green Speed: Medium
Built: 1907 Built On: Clay
Number of Holes: 9 Par: 32
Par 3's: 2 Par 4's: 7
Yds: 4756
Prevailing Wind: North/East
Further Information:
9 hole course can be played as an 18 hole course

HEARSALL

COVENTRY HEARSALL GOLF CLUB (1924) LTD, 33 Beechwood Ave, Coventry, **MIDLANDS (WEST),** CV5 6DF, **ENGLAND.**
(T) 024 76713156

Course/s:
● COVENTRY HEARSALL
Number of Holes: 18 Par: 70
Yds: 5608 F9 Yds: 2893 B9 Yds: 2715

HEATH

HEATH GOLF CLUB, The Heath, Portlaoise, **COUNTY LAOIS, IRELAND.**
(T) 050 246533

Course/s:
● THE HEATH
Number of Holes: 18

HEATHPARK

HEATHPARK GOLF CLUB, Stockley Rd, West Drayton, **LONDON (GREATER),** UB7 9NA, **ENGLAND.**
(T) 01895 444232

Contact/s:
● Owner: Mr B Sharma

Course/s:
● HEATHPARK
Number of Holes: 9
Designer: Neil Coles

HEATON MOOR

HEATON MOOR GOLF CLUB, Mauldeth Rd, Stockport, **CHESHIRE,** SK4 3NX, **ENGLAND.**
(T) 0161 4322134
(E) hmgc@ukgateway.net

Contact/s:
● Professional: Mr Simon Marsh

☎ 0161 4320846

Course/s:
● HEATON MOOR
Number of Holes: 18 Par: 70
Par 3's: 4 Par 4's: 12 Par 5's: 2
Yds: 5968 F9 Yds: 2748 B9 Yds: 3220

HEATON PARK

HEATON PARK GOLF CENTRE (PLAY GOLF LTD), Heaton Pk, Middleton Rd, Prestwich, Manchester, **MANCHESTER (GREATER),** M25 2SW, **ENGLAND.**
(T) 0161 6549899

Membership: Public

Contact/s:
● Club Secretary: Mr Vinny Marcroft
● Professional: Mr Carl Morris

Course/s:
● HEATON PARK GOLF CENTRE
Description: Wooded, Parkland, Hilltop, Undulating, Open, Short, Drains Well
Green Speed: Medium
Built: 1900 Built On: Soil
Number of Holes: 18 Par: 70
Par 3's: 4 Par 4's: 12 Par 5's: 2
Yds: 5815 F9 Yds: 3112 B9 Yds: 2703
Prevailing Wind: North/West
Designer: Taylor
Further Information:
Very testing course.

HEBDEN BRIDGE

HEBDEN BRIDGE GOLF CLUB, The Mount, Wadsworth, Hebden Bridge, **YORKSHIRE (WEST),** HX7 8PH, **ENGLAND.**
(T) 01422 842896

Membership: Members & Public

Contact/s:
● Greenkeeper: Mr Graham Boulton

Course/s:
● HEBDEN BRIDGE
Description: Moorland, Hilltop, Valley, Undulating, Open, Short, Drains Well, Ideal for the Elderly
Green Speed: Medium
Built: 1930 Built On: Soil
Number of Holes: 9 Par: 68 Record: 61
Par 3's: 2 Par 4's:
Yds: 5242 F9 Yds: 2605 B9 Yds: 2637
Prevailing Wind: South/West
Further Information:
9 hole course can be played as an 18 hole course, men play second 9 off yellow tees and ladies play red tees again.

HEDSOR

HEDSOR GOLF COURSE, Broad Lane, Wooburn Green, **BUCKINGHAMSHIRE,** HP10 0JW, **ENGLAND.**
(T) 01628 851285

Membership: Members & Public

Contact/s:
● Club Secretary: Mrs M Brooker
● Professional: Mr S Cannon

Course/s:
● HEDSOR
Description: Wooded, Parkland, Hilltop, Sheltered, Medium Length, Tight, Ideal for the Elderly
Green Speed: Fast
Built: 1999
Number of Holes: 9
Designer: Morris

HELE PARK GOLF CTRE

HELE PARK GOLF CENTRE, Ashburton Rd, Newton Abbot, **DEVON**, TQ12 6JN, **ENGLAND**.
(T) 01626 336060
(W) www.heleparkgolf.co.uk
Membership: Members & Public
Contact/s:
● **Club Secretary:** Mr Alan Taylor
● **Professional:** Mr James Langmead
Course/s:
⛳ **HELE PARK**
   Description: Parkland
   Green Speed: Medium
   Built: 1993
   Number of Holes: 9
   Further Information:
   9 hole course can be played as an 18 hole course

HELENS BAY

HELENS BAY GOLF CLUB, Golf Rd, Helens Bay, Bangor, **COUNTY DOWN**, BT19 1TL, **NORTHERN IRELAND**.
(T) 028 91852815
Membership: Members & Public
Contact/s:
● **Hon Secretary:** Mr Leslie W Mann
Course/s:
⛳ **HELEN'S BAY**
   Description: Parkland, Medium Length, Tight
   Green Speed: Medium
   Built: 1896 **Built On:** Clay/Sand/Soil
   Number of Holes: 9 **Par:** 34 **Record:** 67 (L Esdale)
   Yds: 2574 **F9 Yds:** 2448
   Prevailing Wind: West

HELENSBURGH

HELENSBURGH GOLF CLUB, 25 East Abercromby St, Helensburgh, **ARGYLL AND BUTE**, G84 9HZ, **SCOTLAND**.
(T) 01436 674173
Membership: Members & Public
Contact/s:
● **Professional:** Mr David Fotheringham
Course/s:
⛳ **HELENSBURGH**
   Description: Moorland, Undulating, Short
   Built: 1893 **Built On:** Clay/Soil
   Number of Holes: 18 **Par:** 69
   Yds: 6104
   Designer: James Braid, Tom Morris

HELMSDALE

HELMSDALE GOLF CLUB, Golf Rd, Helmsdale, **HIGHLANDS**, KW8 6JA, **SCOTLAND**.
(T) 01431 821650
Contact/s:
● **Club Secretary:** Mr D Bishop
Course/s:
⛳ **HELMSDALE**
   Number of Holes: 9

HELSBY

HELSBY GOLF CLUB, Towers Lane, Helsby, Frodsham, **CHESHIRE**, WA6 0JB, **ENGLAND**.
(T) 01928 722021
Contact/s:
● **Club Secretary:** Mr L J Norbury

HELSBY

⛳ **HELSBY**
   Number of Holes: 18 **Par:** 70
   Yds: 6265 **F9 Yds:** 3217 **B9 Yds:** 3048
   Designer: James Braid

HELSTON

HELSTON GOLF & LEISURE PARK, Redruth Rd, Wendron, Helston, **CORNWALL**, TR13 0LR, **ENGLAND**.
(T) 01326 565103
Membership: Members & Public
Contact/s:
● **Owner:** Mr A Burns
Course/s:
⛳ **HELSTON**
   Description: Parkland, Undulating, Open, Short
   Green Speed: Fast
   Built: 1987 **Built On:** Soil
   Number of Holes: 18 **Par:** 54
   Par 3's: 18
   Yds: 2000
   Further Information:
   Playable all year round.

HEMINGFORD ABBOT

HEMINGFORD ABBOT GOLF CLUB, Cambridge Rd, Hemingford Abbots, Huntingdon, **CAMBRIDGESHIRE**, PE18 9HQ, **ENGLAND**.
(T) 01480 495000
Course/s:
⛳ **HEMINGFORD ABBOTS**
   Number of Holes: 9
   Designer: Ray Paton

HEMSTED FOREST GOLF CLUB

CRANBROOK GOLF EXECUTIVE, Golf Rd, Benenden, Cranbrook, **KENT**, TN17 4AL, **ENGLAND**.
(T) 01580 712833
(E) golf@hemstedforest.co.uk
Contact/s:
● **Administrator:** Mr K Stevenson
Course/s:
⛳ **EXECUTIVE**
   Number of Holes: 18 **Par:** 70
   Yds: 6056 **F9 Yds:** 3137 **B9 Yds:** 2919
   Designer: Commander J Harris

HENBURY

HENBURY GOLF CLUB, Henbury Hill, Westbury on Trym, Bristol, **BRISTOL**, BS10 7QB, **ENGLAND**.
(T) 01179 500044
(E) thesecretary@henburygolfclub.co.uk
(W) www.henburygolfclub.co.uk
Membership: Members & Public
Size of Complex: 100 Acres
Contact/s:
● **Club Secretary:** Mr Robin White
● **Professional:** Mr Nick Riley
   ☎ 01179 502121
Course/s:
⛳ **HENBURY**
   Description: Parkland, Medium Length
   Number of Holes: 18 **Par:** 69
   Yds: 6007 **F9 Yds:** 3110 **B9 Yds:** 2897

HENDON

HENDON GOLF CLUB, Ashley Walk, London, **LONDON (GREATER)**, NW7 1DU, **ENGLAND**.

(T) 020 83466023
Membership: Members & Public
Size of Complex: 100 Acres
Contact/s:
● **Club Secretary:** Mr David Cooper
● **Professional:** Mr Matt Deal
Course/s:
⛳ **HENDON**
   Description: Wooded, Parkland, Undulating, Sheltered, Short, Tends to Flood, Ideal for the Elderly
   Green Speed: Medium
   Built: 1903 **Built On:** Clay
   Number of Holes: 18 **Record:** 66 (Stuart Murray)
   Prevailing Wind: West
   Designer: Harry Shapland Colt
   Further Information:
   Testing course.

HENLEY

HENLEY GOLF CLUB, Harpsden, Henley-on-Thames, **OXFORDSHIRE**, RG9 4HG, **ENGLAND**.
(T) 01491 575742
Contact/s:
● **Club Secretary:** Mr Andrew Chaundy
● **Professional:** Mr Mark Howell
Course/s:
⛳ **HENLEY**
   Number of Holes: 18 **Par:** 70
   Yds: 6265 **F9 Yds:** 3076 **B9 Yds:** 3189
   Designer: James Braid

HENLEY

HENLEY GOLF & COUNTRY CLUB, Birmingham Rd, Henley-in-Arden, Solihull, **MIDLANDS (WEST)**, B95 5QA, **ENGLAND**.
(T) 01564 793715
Contact/s:
● **Chief Executive:** Mr G Wright
Course/s:
⛳ **HENLEY**
   Number of Holes: 18 **Par:** 73
   Yds: 6933

HENNERTON

HENNERTON GOLF CLUB, Crazies Hill Rd, Wargrave, **BERKSHIRE**, RG10 8LT, **ENGLAND**.
(T) 0118 9401000
(W) www.hennertongolfclub.co.uk
Membership: Members & Public
Size of Complex: 70 Acres
Contact/s:
● **Professional:** Mr William Farrow
Course/s:
⛳ **HENNERTON**
   Description: Parkland, Short
   Green Speed: Slow
   Built: 1992 **Built On:** Chalk/Clay
   Number of Holes: 9 **Par:** 68
   Par 3's: 3 **Par 4's:** 5 **Par 5's:** 1
   Yds: 5460 **F9 Yds:** 2730 **B9 Yds:** 2730
   Prevailing Wind: West
   Designer: D Beard
   Further Information:
   Views of Thames Valley. 9 hole course can be played as an 18 hole course

HEREFORD MUNICIPAL

HEREFORD MUNICIPAL GOLF COURSE, Holmer Rd, Hereford, **HEREFORDSHIRE**, HR4 9UD, **ENGLAND**.
(T) 01432 344376

Membership: Public
Course/s:
🔵 **HEREFORD MUNICIPAL**
Number of Holes: 9

HEREFORDSHIRE

HEREFORDSHIRE GOLF CLUB, Ravens Causeway, Wormsley, Hereford, **HEREFORDSHIRE**, HR4 8LY, **ENGLAND**.
(T) 01432 830219
Contact/s:
● Honary Secretary: Mr T Horobin
Course/s:
🔵 **HEREFORDSHIRE**
Number of Holes: 18   Par: 70
Par 3's: 4   Par 4's: 12   Par 5's: 2
Yds: 6078   F9 Yds: 3156   B9 Yds: 2922
Further Information:
Course is being restructured and so certain yardages, pars and stroke indexes will change early 2002.

HERMITAGE

HERMITAGE GOLF CLUB, Lucan, **COUNTY DUBLIN**, **IRELAND**.
(T) 01 6264781
Contact/s:
● General Manager: Mr Patrick Maguire
🕾 01 6268491
Course/s:
🔵 **HERMITAGE**
Number of Holes: 18   Par: 71
Yds: 6551   F9 Yds: 3102   B9 Yds: 3449

HERNE BAY

HERNE BAY GOLF CLUB, Thanet Way, Herne Bay, **KENT**, CT6 7PG, **ENGLAND**.
(T) 01227 373964
Contact/s:
● Club Secretary: Mr B Warren
● Professional: Mr S Dordoy
Course/s:
🔵 **HERNE BAY**
Number of Holes: 18
Designer: James Braid

HERONS BROOK

HERONS BROOK LEISURE PARK & GOLF CENTRE, Bridge Hill, Narberth, **PEMBROKESHIRE**, SA67 8BU, **WALES**.
(T) 01834 860723
(E) info@herons-brook.co.uk
(W) www.herons-brook.co.uk
Membership: Members & Public
Contact/s:
● Owner: David John
Course/s:
🔵 **KINGS**
Description: Parkland, Undulating, Short
Green Speed: Medium
Built: 1985
Number of Holes: 18
Designer: Owners

🔵 **QUEENS**
Description: Parkland, Undulating, Short
Built: 1985
Number of Holes: 9
Designer: Owners

HERONS REACH

DE VERE BLACKPOOL (HERONS REACH GOLF COURSE), East Pk Blackpool, Blackpool, **LANCASHIRE**, FY3 8LL,

ENGLAND.
(T) 01253 766156/838866
Contact/s:
● Club Secretary: Mr O Banks
● Professional: Mr R Hudson
Course/s:
🔵 **HERONS REACH**
Number of Holes: 18
Designer: P Alliss, Clive Clark

HERSHAM VILLAGE

HERSHAM VILLAGE GOLF CLUB LTD, Assher Rd, Walton-on-Thames, **SURREY**, KT12 4RA, **ENGLAND**.
(T) 01932 267666
Membership: Members & Public
Contact/s:
● Professional: Mr R Hutton
Course/s:
🔵 **HERSHAM VILLAGE**
Description: Wooded, Parkland, Medium Length, Ideal for the Elderly
Built: 1995   Built On: Soil
Number of Holes: 9   Par: 71
Par 3's: 2   Par 4's: 6   Par 5's: 1
Yds: 6159   F9 Yds: 3097   B9 Yds: 3062
Designer: Rodney Hutton
Further Information:
Currently 9 holes with 18 tees. Holes 10 - 18 are currently under construction, due to open early 2002.

HERTFORDSHIRE

AMERICAN GOLF CORPORATION, Broxbournebury Mansion, White Stubbs Lane, Broxbourne, **HERTFORDSHIRE**, EN10 7PY, **ENGLAND**.
(T) 01992 466666
(W) www.americangolf.com
Membership: Members & Public
Size of Complex: 175 Acres
Contact/s:
● Professional: Mr Adrian Shearn
● Book Tee Times: Mr Russell Hurd
Course/s:
🔵 **THE HERTFORDSHIRE**
Description: Wooded, Parkland, Sheltered, Open, Medium Length, Drains Well, Ideal for the Elderly
Green Speed: Medium/Fast
Built: 1993   Built On: Clay/Sand
Number of Holes: 18   Par: 70
Par 3's: 5   Par 4's: 10   Par 5's: 3
Yds: 5853   F9 Yds: 3112   B9 Yds: 2741
Designer: Jack Nicklaus
Further Information:
The course is very rarely closed in the winter.

HESKETH

HESKETH GOLF CLUB, Cockle Dick's Lane, Southport, **MERSEYSIDE**, PR9 9QQ, **ENGLAND**.
(T) 01704 530050
(E) hesketh@ukgolfer.org
(W) www.ukgolfer.org/clubs
Membership: Members & Public
Size of Complex: 139 Acres
Contact/s:
● Club Secretary: Mr Martyn G Senior
🕾 01704 536897
● Professional: Mr John Donoghue
● Book Tee Times: Ms Lynda Edge
Course/s:
🔵 **HESKETH**

Description: Championship, Links, Parkland, Long, Drains Well
Green Speed: Fast
Built: 1885   Built On: Sand
Number of Holes: 18   Par: 72
Record: 66 (Robert Giles)
Par 3's: 4   Par 4's: 11   Par 5's: 3
Yds: 6595   F9 Yds: 3250   B9 Yds: 3345
Prevailing Wind: West
Designer: J Morris
Further Information:
Open qualifying venue.

HESSLE

HESSLE GOLF CLUB, Westfield Rd, Raywell, Cottingham, **YORKSHIRE (EAST)**, HU16 5YL, **ENGLAND**.
(T) 01482 650171
Contact/s:
● Club Secretary: Mr Derrick Pettit
● Professional: Mr Grahame Fieldsend
🕾 01482 650190
Course/s:
🔵 **HESSLE**
Number of Holes: 18   Par: 72
Yds: 6604   F9 Yds: 3136   B9 Yds: 3155
Designer: Peter Alliss, David Thomas

🔵 **HEXHAM**
Description: Parkland, Medium Length, Drains Well
Green Speed: Fast
Built: 1907   Built On: Soil
Number of Holes: 18   Par: 70
Par 3's: 5   Par 4's: 10   Par 5's: 3
Yds: 6301   F9 Yds: 3279   B9 Yds: 3022
Designer: Harry Vardon, James Caird

HESWALL

HESWALL GOLF CLUB, Cottage Lane, Wirral, **MERSEYSIDE**, CH60 8PB, **ENGLAND**.
(T) 0151 3421237/3422193
Contact/s:
● Club Secretary: Mr A Brooker
🕾 0151 3421237
● Professional: Mr A Thompson
🕾 0151 3427431
Course/s:
🔵 **HESWALL**
Description: Parkland, Open, Medium Length, Drains Well, Ideal for the Elderly
Green Speed: Medium   Built On: Clay
Number of Holes: 18   Par: 72
Record: 66 (Alan Thompson)
Par 3's: 4   Par 4's: 10   Par 5's: 4
Yds: 6554
Prevailing Wind: North/West
Further Information:
The course is adjacent to the River Dee.

HEVER

HEVER GOLF CLUB PLC, Hever Rd, Hever, Edenbridge, **KENT**, TN8 7NP, **ENGLAND**.
(T) 01732 700016
Course/s:
🔵 **HEVER**
Number of Holes: 18
Designer: Nicholson

HEWORTH

HEWORTH GOLF CLUB, Muncaster Hse, Muncastergate, York, **YORKSHIRE (NORTH)**, YO31 9JY, **ENGLAND**.
(T) 01904 424618
(E) golf@heworth-gc.fsnet.co.uk
Membership: Members & Public

Contact/s:
- **Club Secretary:** Mr Richard Hunt
  ☎ 01904 426156
- **Professional:** Mr Steve Burdett
  ☎ 01904 422389

Course/s:

⛳ **HEWORTH**
Description: Parkland, Sheltered, Medium Length, Tight, Tends to Flood, Ideal for the Elderly
Green Speed: Medium
Built: 1911 **Built On:** Clay
Number of Holes: 11 **Par:** 70
Yds: 6141 **F9 Yds:** 3023 **B9 Yds:** 3118
Designer: B Cheal
Further Information:
Excellent greens on a course requiring accurate shot making. Rough is not penal but shots can easily be dropped by missing fairway. This 11 hole course has 18 tees and can therefore be played as an 18 hole course.

HEWORTH

HEWORTH GOLF CLUB, Gingling Gate, Heworth, Gateshead, **TYNE AND WEAR**, NE10 8XY, **ENGLAND**.
(T) 0191 4699832

Contact/s:
- **Club Secretary:** Mr Greg Holbrow

Course/s:

⛳ **HEWORTH**
Number of Holes: 18

HEXHAM

HEXHAM GOLF CLUB LTD, Spital Pk, Hexham, **NORTHUMBERLAND**, NE46 3RZ, **ENGLAND**.
(T) 01434 603072
(E) hexham.golf.club@talk21.com
(W) www.hexhamgolfclub.ntb.org.uk

Membership: Members & Public

Contact/s:
- **Club Secretary:** Ms Dawn Wylie
- **Professional:** Mr Martin Forster
  ☎ 01434 604904
- **Book Tee Times:**
  ☎ 01434 603072/604904

Course/s:

⛳ **HEXHAM**
Description: Parkland, Drains Well
Number of Holes: 18 **Par:** 70
Yds: 6301
Further Information:
The course offers stunning views over the confluence of the North and South Tyne and its surrounding countryside.

HEYDON GRANGE

HEYDON GRANGE GOLF & COUNTRY CLUB, Fowlmere Rd, Heydon, Royston, **HERTFORDSHIRE**, SG8 7NS, **ENGLAND**.
(T) 01763 208988

Contact/s:
- **Professional:** Mr John Saxon-Mills

Course/s:

⛳ **CAMBS**
Description: Heath Land
Number of Holes: 9 **Par:** 36
Yds: 3057

⛳ **ESSEX**
Description: Heath Land
Number of Holes: 9 **Par:** 36
Yds: 2880

⛳ **HERTS**
Description: Heath Land
Number of Holes: 9 **Par:** 36
Yds: 2937

HEYROSE

HEYROSE GOLF CLUB, Budworth Rd, Tabley, Knutsford, **CHESHIRE**, WA16 0HZ, **ENGLAND**.
(T) 01565 733664

Contact/s:
- **Professional:** Mr Colin Iddon
  ☎ 01565 734267

Course/s:

⛳ **HEYROSE**
Number of Holes: 18
Designer: Bridge

HEYSHAM

HEYSHAM GOLF CLUB, Trumacar Pk, Middleton Rd, Middleton, Morecambe, **LANCASHIRE**, LA3 3JH, **ENGLAND**.
(T) 01524 851011

Contact/s:
- **Professional:** Mr Ryan Done
- **Book Tee Times:**
  ☎ 01524 852000

Course/s:

⛳ **HEYSHAM**
Description: Links
Built: 1929 **Built On:** Sand
Number of Holes: 18 **Par:** 68
Yds: 5999 **F9 Yds:** 3042 **B9 Yds:** 2559
Designer: A Herd

HICKLETON

HICKLETON GOLF CLUB, Hickleton, Doncaster, **YORKSHIRE (SOUTH)**, DN5 7BE, **ENGLAND**.
(T) 01709 896081

Contact/s:
- **Professional:** Mr Paul Audsley
  ☎ 01709 888436
- **Book Tee Times:** Mrs P Stafford

Course/s:

⛳ **HICKLETON**
Description: Parkland, Undulating, Open, Medium Length, Drains Well
Green Speed: Medium
Built: 1976 **Built On:** Clay
Number of Holes: 18 **Par:** 71
Yds: 6446 **F9 Yds:** 3174 **B9 Yds:** 3272
Designer: Neil Coles, Brian Huggett

HIGH BEECH

HIGH BEECH GOLF COURSE, Wellington Hill, Loughton, **ESSEX**, IG10 4AH, **ENGLAND**.
(T) 020 85087323

Contact/s:
- **Professional:** Mr C Baker

Course/s:

⛳ **HIGH BEECH**
Number of Holes: 9

HIGH ELMS

HIGH ELMS GOLF COURSE, High Elms Rd, Downe, Orpington, **KENT**, BR6 7SL, **ENGLAND**.
(T) 01689 853232

Contact/s:
- **Professional:** Mr Peter Remy

Course/s:

⛳ **HIGH ELMS**
Built: 1968

Number of Holes: 18 **Par:** 71
Designer: Hawthorn
Further Information:
Well established greens.

HIGH LEGH PARK

HIGH LEGH PARK GOLF CLUB THE, Warrington Rd, High Legh, Knutsford, **CHESHIRE**, WA16 0WA, **ENGLAND**.
(T) 01565 830888

Membership: Members Only

Contact/s:
- **Professional:** Mr Anthony Sproston
- **Pro Shop:** Mr Graham Cummins

Course/s:

⛳ **HIGH LEGH PARK GOLF COURSE**
Built: 1997
Number of Holes: 18 **Par:** 70
Yds: 6100
Designer: Mark James

HIGH LODGE

HIGH LODGE SHOOTING SCHOOL & GOLF COURSE, Haw Wood, Hinton, Saxmundham, **SUFFOLK**, IP17 3QT, **ENGLAND**.
(T) 01986 784347
(W) www.highlodge.co.uk

Membership: Public
Size of Complex: 100 Acres

Contact/s:
- **Club Secretary:** Ms Jane Bidwell

Course/s:

⛳ **HIGH LODGE**
Description: Championship, Wooded, Parkland, Hilltop, Undulating, Sheltered, Open, Short, Drains Well, Ideal for the Elderly
Green Speed: Medium
Built: 1998 **Built On:** Clay
Number of Holes: 9 **Par:** 33 **Record:** 63 (Ian Hulley)
Yds: 2500
Prevailing Wind: North/East
Designer: John Bidwell

HIGH POST

HIGH POST GOLF CLUB, High Post, Great Durnford, Salisbury, **WILTSHIRE**, SP4 6AT, **ENGLAND**.
(T) 01722 782356
(E) highpostgolfclub@lineone.net
(W) www.highpostgolfclub.co.uk

Membership: Members & Public

Contact/s:
- **Professional:** Mr I Welding
- **Pro Shop:**
  ☎ 01722 782219

Course/s:

⛳ **HIGH POST**
Description: Undulating, Medium Length, Drains Well
Green Speed: Fast
Built: 1922 **Built On:** Chalk
Number of Holes: 18 **Par:** 70
Record: 65 (Peter Alliss)
Yds: 6305 **F9 Yds:** 3268 **B9 Yds:** 3037
Prevailing Wind: South/West
Designer: Hawtree
Further Information:
Challenging downland course set amongst blackthorn and hawthorn.

HIGH THROSTON

HIGH THROSTON GOLF CLUB, Hart Lane, Hartlepool, **CLEVELAND**, TS26 0JZ, **ENGLAND**.

(T) 01429 275325

Contact/s:
- Club Secretary: Mrs Joyce Sturrock

Course/s:
- **HIGH THROSTON GOLF COURSE**
  Number of Holes: 18 Par: 71

HIGHBULLEN HOTEL

HIGHBULLEN HOTEL GOLF COURSE,
Chittlehamholt, Umberleigh, **DEVON**, EX37
9HD, **ENGLAND**.
(T) 01769 540561

Course/s:
- **HIGHBULLEN HOTEL**
  Number of Holes: 18
  Designer: M Neil, J Hamilton

HIGHCLIFFE CASTLE

HIGHCLIFFE CASTLE GOLF CLUB, 107
Lymington Rd, Christchurch, **DORSET**, BH23
4LA, **ENGLAND**.
(T) 01425 272210

Contact/s:
- Manager: Mr B Lunn

Course/s:
- **HIGHCLIFFE CASTLE**
  Number of Holes: 18

HIGHFIELD

HIGHFIELD GOLF COURSE, Buckholes
Lane, Wheelton, Chorley, **LANCASHIRE**,
PR6 8JF, **ENGLAND**.
(T) 01254 830389

Membership: Public
Size of Complex: 30 Acres

Contact/s:
- General Manager: Mr R J Whalley

Course/s:
- **HIGHFIELD**
  Description: Wooded, Hilltop,
  Undulating, Open, Medium Length, Ideal
  for the Elderly
  Green Speed: Medium
  Built: 1993 Built On: Soil
  Number of Holes: 9 Par: 30
  Prevailing Wind: West
  Further Information:
  Testing course.

HIGHFIELD

HIGHFIELD GOLF COURSE, Carbury,
COUNTY KILDARE, **IRELAND**.
(T) 040 531021
(E) hgc@indigo.ie
(W) www.highfield-golf.ie

Membership: Members & Public
Size of Complex: 200 Acres

Contact/s:
- Professional: Mr Peter O'Hagan

Course/s:
- **HIGHFIELD**
  Description: Parkland, Medium Length,
  Drains Well, Ideal for the Elderly
  Green Speed: Fast
  Built: 1991 Built On: Soil
  Number of Holes: 18 Par: 72
  Record: 69 (Bobby Brown)
  Par 3's: 4 Par 4's: 10 Par 5's: 4
  Yds: 5665 F9 Yds: 3000 B9 Yds: 2665
  Prevailing Wind: West
  Designer: Alan Duggan
  Further Information:
  An easy walking course, yet challenging.
  An exceptional par 3 14th hole over

bulrushes.

HIGHGATE

HIGHGATE GOLF CLUB, Denewood Rd,
London, **LONDON (GREATER)**, N6 4AH,
ENGLAND.
(T) 020 83401906

Membership: Members & Public

Contact/s:
- Club Secretary: Mr Gordon Wilson
- Professional: Mr Robin Turner
  ☎ 020 83405467

Course/s:
- **HIGHGATE**
  Description: Wooded, Parkland,
  Undulating, Sheltered, Medium Length,
  Drains Well
  Green Speed: Fast
  Built: 1906 Built On: Clay
  Number of Holes: 18 Record: 65
  Prevailing Wind: East

HIGHWOODS

HIGHWOODS GOLF CLUB, 47 Ellerslie
Lane, Bexhill-on-Sea, **SUSSEX (EAST)**,
TN39 4LJ, **ENGLAND**.
(T) 01424 212625
Size of Complex: 108 Acres

Contact/s:
- Club Secretary: Mrs S Meadows
- Professional: Mr M Andrews

Course/s:
- **HIGHWOODS**
  Description: Wooded, Parkland,
  Undulating, Sheltered, Medium Length,
  Ideal for the Elderly
  Green Speed: Medium
  Built: 1925 Built On: Clay
  Number of Holes: 18 Par: 70
  Par 3's: 4 Par 4's: 12 Par 5's: 2
  Yds: 6218
  Prevailing Wind: South/West
  Designer: Taylor
  Further Information:
  A stream comes into play on 6 holes.

HIGHWORTH GOLF CENTRE

HIGHWORTH GOLF CENTRE, Swindon Rd,
Highworth, Swindon, **WILTSHIRE**, SN6 7SJ,
ENGLAND.
(T) 01793 766014

Membership: Members & Public

Contact/s:
- Owner: Mr M Toombs

Course/s:
- **HIGHWORTH**
  Number of Holes: 9
  Designer: D Lang, B Sandry, T Watt

HILDEN EUROPRO

HILDEN EUROPRO GOLF CENTRE, Rings
Hill, Hildenborough, Tonbridge, **KENT**, TN11
8LX, **ENGLAND**.
(T) 01732 833607
(E) hgc@centrenet.co.uk
(W) www.europrogolf.com

Membership: Members & Public

Contact/s:
- Club Secretary: Mr Rowan Logan
  ☎ 01732 834404
- Professional: Ms Nicky Way
- Pro Shop: Mr Ian Slush

Course/s:
- **HILDEN GOLF CENTRE**
  Description: Wooded, Short, Tight,

Drains Well, Ideal for the Elderly
  Green Speed: Medium
  Built: 1993 Built On: Clay/Sand
  Number of Holes: 9

HILL VALLEY

HILL VALLEY GOLF & COUNTRY CLUB,
Terrick Rd, Terrick, Whitchurch,
SHROPSHIRE, SY13 4JZ, **ENGLAND**.
(T) 01948 663584

Contact/s:
- Owner: Mr A J Minshall

Course/s:
- **EAST**
  Number of Holes: 18
  Designer: Peter Alliss, David Thomas
- **WEST**
  Number of Holes: 18
  Designer: Peter Alliss, David Thomas

HILL VALLEY GOLF CTRE

HILL VALLEY GOLF CENTRE, 17 Peacock
Rd, Sion Mills, Strabane, **COUNTY TYRONE**,
BT82 9NN, **NORTHERN IRELAND**.
(T) 028 81659599

Contact/s:
- General Manager: Mr David Forbes

Course/s:
- **HILL VALLEY PAR 3**
  Number of Holes: 18 Par: 54
  Par 3's: 18
  Yds: 2610

HILLBARN

HILLBARN GOLF COURSE, 1 Excess
Cottages, Hill Barn Lane, Worthing, **SUSSEX
(WEST)**, BN14 9QE, **ENGLAND**.
(T) 01903 237301

Membership: Public

Contact/s:
- Club Secretary: Mr Simon Blanshard
- Pro Shop: Mr Frazer Moreley

Course/s:
- **HILL BARN MUNICIPAL**
  Description: Wooded, Hilltop,
  Undulating, Open, Medium Length,
  Drains Well
  Green Speed: Medium
  Built: 1930 Built On: Chalk
  Number of Holes: 18 Record: 64 (Brian
  Barnes) Prevailing Wind: South/East

HILLIES PAVILION

HILLIES PAVILION GOLF CLUB, Wentworth
View, Wombwell, Barnsley, **YORKSHIRE
(SOUTH)**, S73 0LA, **ENGLAND**.
(T) 01226 754433

Contact/s:
- Area Manager: Mr W Evans

Course/s:
- **HILLIES PAVILION**
  Description: Short
  Number of Holes: 9 Par: 31
  Yds: 2095

HILLINGDON

HILLINGDON GOLF CLUB, Dorset Way,
Uxbridge, **LONDON (GREATER)**, UB10 0JR,
ENGLAND.
(T) 01895 460035

Course/s:
- **HILLINGDON**
  Number of Holes: 9

HILLSBOROUGH

HILLSBOROUGH GOLF CLUB, Worrall Rd, Sheffield, **YORKSHIRE (SOUTH)**, S6 4BE, **ENGLAND**.
(T) 0114 2332666
(E) admin@hillsboroughgolfclub.co.uk
(W) www.hillsboroughgolfclub.co.uk

Contact/s:
● **Professional:** Mr Lewis Horsman

Course/s:
⛳ **HILLSBOROUGH**
Description: Parkland, Hilltop, Undulating, Drains Well
Green Speed: Medium
Built: 1920 **Built On:** Clay
Number of Holes: 18 **Par:** 71
Record: 63 (Chris Gray)
Yds: 6216 **F9 Yds:** 2998 **B9 Yds:** 3218

HILLSIDE

HILLSIDE GOLF CLUB LTD, Hastings Rd, Southport, **MERSEYSIDE**, PR8 2LU, **ENGLAND**.
(T) 01704 567169
(E) hillside@ukgolfer.org
(W) www.ukgolfer.org/clubs/hillside_m.html

Contact/s:
● **Club Secretary:** Mr John Graham
● **Pro Shop:** Mr Brian Seddon
  ☎ 01704 568360

Course/s:
⛳ **HILLSIDE**
Number of Holes: 18 **Par:** 72
Yds: 6850
Prevailing Wind: South/West
Designer: Hawtree
Further Information:
Greg Norman wrote that 'the back nine holes were the best in Britain'. Peter Aliss said 'there are plenty of testing and scenic holes.' 🏆

HILLTOP

HILLTOP GOLF COURSE, Park Lane, Handsworth, Birmingham, **MIDLANDS (WEST)**, B21 8LJ, **ENGLAND**.
(T) 0121 5544463

Course/s:
⛳ **HILLTOP PUBLIC**
Number of Holes: 18
Designer: Hawtree

HILTON PARK

HILTON PARK GOLF CLUB, Professional Shop, Stockiemuir Rd, Milngavie, Glasgow, **GLASGOW (CITY OF)**, G62 7HB, **SCOTLAND**.
(T) 0141 9565125

Contact/s:
● **Club Secretary:** Mrs J A Warnock

Course/s:
⛳ **ALLANDER**
Number of Holes: 18
Designer: James Braid

⛳ **HILTON**
Number of Holes: 18
Designer: James Braid

HILTON PUCKRUP HALL

HILTON PUCKRUP HALL HOTEL & GOLF CLUB, Puckrup, Tewkesbury, **GLOUCESTERSHIRE**, GL20 6EL, **ENGLAND**.
(T) 01684 296200

Contact/s:

● **Professional:** Mr Kevin Pickett
  ☎ 01684 271591

Course/s:
⛳ **HILTON PUCKRUP HALL**
Number of Holes: 18 **Par:** 70
Par 3's: 5 **Par 4's:** 10 **Par 5's:** 3
Yds: 6189 **F9 Yds:** 3076 **B9 Yds:** 3113
Designer: Simon Gidman

HIMLEY HALL GOLF CTRE

HIMLEY HALL GOLF CENTRE, Log Cabin, Himley Rd, Himley, Dudley, **MIDLANDS (WEST)**, DY3 4DF, **ENGLAND**.
(T) 01902 895207

Contact/s:
● **Partner:** Mr Alan Baker

Course/s:
⛳ **HIMLEY HALL GOLF CTRE**
Number of Holes: 9
Designer: A Baker

HINCKLEY

HINCKLEY GOLF CLUB LTD, Leicester Rd, Hinckley, **LEICESTERSHIRE**, LE10 3DR, **ENGLAND**.
(T) 01455 615014
(E) proshop@hinckleygolfclub.com
(W) www.hinckleygolfclub.com

Membership: Members & Public
Size of Complex: 150 Acres

Contact/s:
● **Club Secretary:** Mr Roy Coley
● **Professional:** Mr Richard Jones
● **Book Lessons:** Mr Nevil Bland

Course/s:
⛳ **HINCKLEY**
Description: Wooded, Parkland, Undulating, Long, Ideal for the Elderly
Green Speed: Fast **Built On:** Soil
Number of Holes: 18 **Par:** 71
Record: 67 (Kevin Dickens)
Par 3's: 4 **Par 4's:** 11 **Par 5's:** 3
Yds: 6529 **F9 Yds:** 3289 **B9 Yds:** 3240
Designer: Meadow
Further Information:
The course is rarely busy.

HINDHEAD

HINDHEAD GOLF CLUB, Churt Rd, Hindhead, **SURREY**, GU26 6HX, **ENGLAND**.
(T) 01428 604614

Membership: Members & Public

Contact/s:
● **Club Secretary:** Mr P Owen
  ☎ 01428 608508
● **Professional:** Mr N Ogilvy
● **Pro Shop:**
  ☎ 01428 604458

Course/s:
⛳ **HINDHEAD**
Description: Heath Land, Hilltop, Valley, Undulating, Medium Length, Drains Well
Built: 1904 **Built On:** Sand/Soil
Number of Holes: 18 **Par:** 70
Record: 63 (A Tillman)
Par 3's: 5 **Par 4's:** 10 **Par 5's:** 3
Yds: 6358
Designer: Taylor
Further Information:
The first 9 holes are sheltered.

HINDLEY HALL

HINDLEY HALL GOLF CLUB, Hall Lane, Aspull, Wigan, **LANCASHIRE**, WN2 2SQ, **ENGLAND**.

(T) 01942 255131

Membership: Members & Public
Size of Complex: 85 Acres

Contact/s:
● **Club Secretary:** Ms Louise Marrow
● **Professional:** Mr Neil Brazell

Course/s:
⛳ **HINDLEY HALL**
Description: Parkland, Undulating, Sheltered, Open, Short, Drains Well, Ideal for the Elderly
Green Speed: Fast
Built: 1905 **Built On:** Clay
Number of Holes: 18
Prevailing Wind: North/West
Further Information:
A golf course with a historical background.

HINKSEY HEIGHTS

HINKSEY HEIGHTS GOLF COURSE, South Hinksey, Oxford, **OXFORDSHIRE**, OX1 5AB, **ENGLAND**.
(T) 01865 327775
(E) play@oxford-golf.co.uk
(W) www.oxford-golf.co.uk

Membership: Members & Public
Size of Complex: 200 Acres

Contact/s:
● **Professional:** Mr Richard Howett

Course/s:
⛳ **HINKSEY HEIGHTS**
Description: Links, Heath Land, Undulating, Open, Long, Tight, Drains Well, Ideal for the Elderly
Green Speed: Fast
Built: 1995 **Built On:** Clay
Number of Holes: 18 **Par:** 74
Par 3's: 3 **Par 4's:** 10 **Par 5's:** 5
Yds: 6680
Designer: David Heads
Further Information:
A challenging golf course with many feature holes. Designed in such a way that you can play every kind of golf shot on the course.

HINTLESHAM HALL

HINTLESHAM HALL GOLF CLUB, Hintlesham Hall, Hintlesham, Ipswich, **SUFFOLK**, IP8 3NS, **ENGLAND**.
(T) 01473 652006
(W) www.hintleshamhallgolfclub.com

Membership: Members & Public

Contact/s:
● **Professional:** Mr Alistair Spink

Course/s:
⛳ **HINTLESHAM HALL**
Description: Championship, Parkland
Green Speed: Medium
Built: 1989 **Built On:** Sand/Soil
Number of Holes: 18
Prevailing Wind: South/West
Designer: Hawtree

HIRSEL

HIRSEL GOLF CLUB, Kelso Rd, Coldstream, **SCOTTISH BORDERS**, TD12 4NJ, **SCOTLAND**.
(T) 01890 882678

Membership: Members & Public
Size of Complex: 120 Acres

Contact/s:
● **Club Secretary:** Mr Keith Lobban

Course/s:

HIRSEL
Description: Championship, Parkland, Hilltop, Valley, Sheltered, Medium Length, Drains Well, Tends to Flood, Ideal for the Elderly
Green Speed: Slow/Medium
Built: 1949   **Built On:** Clay
Number of Holes: 18   **Par:** 70
Yds: 5876   **F9 Yds:** 2702   **B9 Yds:** 3174
Prevailing Wind: West

HOBBS CROSS

HOBBS CROSS GOLF CENTRE, Hobbs Cross Rd, Theydon Garnon, Epping, **ESSEX**, CM16 7NQ, **ENGLAND**.
(T) 01992 561661

Contact/s:
● **Professional:** Mr Andrew Curry

Course/s:
VALLEY
Number of Holes: 9   **Par:** 27
Par 3's: 9
Yds: 1223

WEALD
Number of Holes: 9   **Par:** 35
Par 3's: 2   **Par 4's:** 6   **Par 5's:** 1
Yds: 3005

HOBSON

HOBSON GOLF COURSE, Hobson, Newcastle Upon Tyne, **TYNE AND WEAR**, NE16 6BZ, **ENGLAND**.
(T) 01207 270790

Contact/s:
● **Manager:** Mr D Reed

Course/s:
HOBSON MUNICIPAL
Number of Holes: 18

HOCKLEY

HOCKLEY GOLF CLUB, Twyford, Winchester, **HAMPSHIRE**, SO21 1PL, **ENGLAND**.
(T) 01962 713165

Course/s:
HOCKLEY
Number of Holes: 18
Designer: James Braid

HOEBRIDGE

HOEBRIDGE GOLF CENTRE LTD, Old Woking Rd, Woking, **SURREY**, GU22 8JH, **ENGLAND**.
(T) 01483 722611
(E) info@hoebridge.co.uk
(W) www.hoebridge.co.uk

Membership: Public

Contact/s:
● **Professional:** Mr Tim Powell

Course/s:
MAIN
Description: Parkland
Built: 1982
Number of Holes: 18   **Par:** 72
Par 3's: 5   **Par 4's:** 8   **Par 5's:** 5
Yds: 6536   **F9 Yds:** 3428   **B9 Yds:** 3108
Designer: John Jacobs

SHEY COPSE
Number of Holes: 9   **Par:** 33
Par 3's: 3   **Par 4's:** 6
Yds: 2294

HOLLANDBUSH

HOLLANDBUSH GOLF COURSE, New

Trows Rd, Lesmahagow, Lanark, **LANARKSHIRE (SOUTH)**, ML11 0JS, **SCOTLAND**.
(T) 01555 893484

Contact/s:
● **Club Secretary:** Mr Robert Lynch
● **Professional:** Mr Ian Rae
  ☎ 01555 893646

Course/s:
HOLLAND BUSH
Number of Holes: 18
Designer: J Lawdon, K Pate

HOLLINGBURY PARK

HOLLINGBURY PARK GOLF CLUB, Ditchling Rd, Brighton, **SUSSEX (EAST)**, BN1 7HS, **ENGLAND**.
(T) 01273 552010
(E) enquiries@hollingburygolfclub.co.uk
(W) www.hollingburygolfclub.co.uk

Course/s:
HOLLINGBURY PARK
Number of Holes: 18   **Par:** 72
Yds: 6482   **F9 Yds:** 3324   **B9 Yds:** 3158

HOLLINS HALL

MARRIOTT HOLLINS HALL HOTEL & COUNTRY CLUB, Hollins Hill, Baildon, Shipley, Bradford, **YORKSHIRE (WEST)**, BD17 7QW, **ENGLAND**.
(T) 01274 534212

Course/s:
HOLLINS HALL
Description: Heath Land, Undulating, Open, Drains Well
Built: 1999
Number of Holes: 18   **Par:** 71
Yds: 6671
Further Information:
'The Best New Course I have seen for a long time' - Mark James.

HOLLYSTOWN GOLF

HOLLYSTOWN GOLF, Hollystown, Hollywood Rath, Dublin, **COUNTY DUBLIN**, **IRELAND**.
(T) 01 8207444
(E) info@hollystown.ie
(W) www.hollystown.com

Contact/s:
● **Professional:** Mr Brian Boshell

Course/s:
BLUE
Number of Holes: 9   **Par:** 35
Yds: 3450

RED
Number of Holes: 9   **Par:** 35
Yds: 3072

YELLOW
Number of Holes: 9   **Par:** 35
Yds: 3057

HOLLYWOOD LAKES

HOLLYWOOD LAKES GOLF CLUB, Ballyboughal, **COUNTY DUBLIN**, **IRELAND**.
(T) 01 8433407

Course/s:
HOLLYWOOD LAKES
Description: Parkland
Built: 1994
Number of Holes: 18   **Par:** 72
Designer: M Flanagan

HOLME HALL

HOLME HALL GOLF CLUB, Holme Lane, Bottesford, Scunthorpe, **LINCOLNSHIRE (NORTH)**, DN16 3RF, **ENGLAND**.
(T) 01724 851816

Contact/s:
● **Professional:** Mr Richard McKiernan

Course/s:
HOLME HALL
Number of Holes: 18   **Par:** 71
Par 3's: 4   **Par 4's:** 11   **Par 5's:** 3
Yds: 6404   **F9 Yds:** 3374   **B9 Yds:** 3030

HOLSWORTHY

HOLSWORTHY GOLF CLUB, Killatree, Holsworthy, **DEVON**, EX22 6LP, **ENGLAND**.
(T) 01409 253177

Size of Complex: 100 Acres

Contact/s:
● **Club Secretary:** Mr Barry Megson
● **Professional:** Mr Graham Webb

Course/s:
HOLSWORTHY
Description: Parkland, Open, Medium Length, Ideal for the Elderly
Green Speed: Medium
Built: 1937   **Built On:** Clay
Number of Holes: 18   **Par:** 70
Par 3's: 4   **Par 4's:** 12   **Par 5's:** 2
Yds: 6100   **F9 Yds:** 3052   **B9 Yds:** 3048
Prevailing Wind: North

HOLTYE

HOLTYE GOLF CLUB, Holtye, Cowden, Edenbridge, **KENT**, TN8 7ED, **ENGLAND**.
(T) 01342 850635

Contact/s:
● **Professional:** Mr Kevin Hinton
  ☎ 01342 850957

Course/s:
HOLTYE
Description: Heath Land, Undulating, Sheltered, Medium Length, Tight
Green Speed: Fast
Built: 1893   **Built On:** Sand
Number of Holes: 9   **Par:** 66 Record: 62 (Kevin Hinton)
Yds: 5325   **F9 Yds:** 2687   **B9 Yds:** 2638
Prevailing Wind: West
Further Information:
9 hole course can be played as an 18 hole course

HOLYHEAD

HOLYHEAD GOLF CLUB, Lon Garreg Fawr, Trearddur Bay, Holyhead, **ISLE OF ANGLESEY**, LL65 2YL, **WALES**.
(T) 01407 763279
(E) mgrsec@aol.com
(W) www.holyheadgolfclub.co.uk

Contact/s:
● **Club Secretary:** Mr J A Williams
● **Professional:** Mr Steve Elliot

Course/s:
HOLYHEAD
Number of Holes: 18   **Par:** 71
Yds: 6060   **F9 Yds:** 3256   **B9 Yds:** 2804
Designer: James Braid

HOLYWELL

HOLYWELL GOLF CLUB, Brynford Rd, Brynford, Holywell, **FLINTSHIRE**, CH8 8LQ, **WALES**.
(T) 01352 713937

Contact/s:
- Professional: Mr Matt Parsley

Course/s:
- HOLYWELL
  - Description: Links, Drains Well
  - Built: 1906
  - Number of Holes: 18 Par: 70
  - Further Information:
  - The course has many natural hazards.

HOLYWELL BAY

HOLYWELL BAY GOLF CLUB, Holywell Bay, Newquay, **CORNWALL**, TR8 5PW, **ENGLAND**.
(T) 01637 830095

Course/s:
- HOLYWELL BAY
  - Number of Holes: 18
  - Designer: Hartley

HOLYWOOD

HOLYWOOD GOLF CLUB, Nuns Walk, Demesne Rd, Holywood, **COUNTY DOWN**, BT18 9LE, **NORTHERN IRELAND**.
(T) 028 90423135
(E) mail@holywoodgolfclub.co.uk
Membership: Members & Public
Size of Complex: 90 Acres

Contact/s:
- Professional: Mr Paul Gray
- ☎ 028 90425503
- Book Tee Times: Mr Jerry Fyfe

Course/s:
- HOLYWOOD
  - Description: Parkland, Hilltop, Open, Medium Length, Drains Well
  - Green Speed: Medium
  - Built: 1904 Built On: Soil
  - Number of Holes: 18 Par: 69
  - Record: 64 (Paul Gray)
  - Par 3's: 4 Par 4's: 13 Par 5's: 1
  - Yds: 5973 F9 Yds: 2818 B9 Yds: 3156

HOMELANDS

HOMELAND BETTER GOLF CENTRE (ASHFORD) LTD, Ashford Rd, Kingsnorth, Ashford, **KENT**, TN26 1NJ, **ENGLAND**.
(T) 01233 661620
(E) information@bettergolf.invictanet.co.uk
(W) www.bettergolf.co.uk
Membership: Public

Contact/s:
- Club Secretary: Mr Ian Johnson
- Professional: Mr Tony Bowen
- ☎ 01233 641334

Course/s:
- BETTERGOLF CENTRE
  - Description: Parkland, Short, Ideal for the Elderly
  - Green Speed: Medium
  - Built: 1974 Built On: Clay
  - Number of Holes: 9 Par: 32
  - Par 3's: 4 Par 4's: 5
  - Yds: 2182
  - Prevailing Wind: South/West
  - Designer: Donald Steel
  - Further Information:
  - USGA greens.

HONITON

HONITON GOLF CLUB, Middlehills, Honiton, **DEVON**, EX14 9TR, **ENGLAND**.
(T) 01404 44422

Contact/s:
- Club Secretary: Mr Brian Young

Course/s:
- HONITON
  - Number of Holes: 18 Par: 69
  - Yds: 5709 F9 Yds: 2656 B9 Yds: 3053

HOPEMAN

HOPEMAN GOLF CLUB, Hopeman, Elgin, **MORAY**, IV30 5YA, **SCOTLAND**.
(T) 01343 830578
(E) hopemangc@aol.com
(W) www.hopeman-golf-club.co.uk
Membership: Members & Public

Contact/s:
- Club Secretary: Mr Jim Fraser

Course/s:
- HOPEMAN
  - Description: Links, Cliff Top, Undulating, Medium Length
  - Green Speed: Medium
  - Built: 1921 Built On: Sand
  - Number of Holes: 18 Par: 68
  - Par 3's: 5 Par 4's: 12 Par 5's: 1
  - Yds: 5590 F9 Yds: 2953 B9 Yds: 2637
  - Prevailing Wind: South
  - Further Information:
  - The 12th hole tee is on a cliff and has a drop to the green below which is adjacent to the beach.

HORAM PARK

HORAM PARK GOLF COURSE, Chiddingly Rd, Horam, Heathfield, **SUSSEX (EAST)**, TN21 0JJ, **ENGLAND**.
(T) 01435 813477
(E) angie@horamgolf.freeserve.co.uk
(W) www.horamparkgolf.co.uk

Contact/s:
- PGA Professional: Mr Giles Velvick

Course/s:
- HORAM PARK
  - Built: 1983
  - Number of Holes: 9 Par: 70
  - Par 3's: 3 Par 4's: 4 Par 5's: 2
  - Yds: 6128 F9 Yds: 3092 B9 Yds: 3036
  - Further Information:
  - 9 hole course can be played as an 18 hole course

HORNCASTLE

HORNCASTLE GOLF CLUB (THE), Shearmans Wath, West Ashby, Horncastle, **LINCOLNSHIRE**, LN9 5PP, **ENGLAND**.
(T) 01507 526800

Contact/s:
- Proprietor: Mrs B Wright

Course/s:
- HORNCASTLE
  - Number of Holes: 18 Par: 68
  - Par 3's: 5 Par 4's: 12 Par 5's: 1
  - Yds: 5717 F9 Yds: 2588 B9 Yds: 3129
  - Designer: E C Wright

HORNE PARK

HORNE PARK GOLF COURSE, Croydon Barn Lane, South Godstone, Godstone, **SURREY**, RH9 8JP, **ENGLAND**.
(T) 01342 844443
(W) www.horneparkgolf.co.uk
Membership: Members & Public

Contact/s:
- Professional: Mr Neal Bedward

Course/s:
- HORNE PARK
  - Description: Parkland, Undulating, Open, Short, Drains Well, Tends to Flood, Ideal

for the Elderly
  - Green Speed: Medium/Fast
  - Built: 1994 Built On: Clay/Sand
  - Number of Holes: 9 Par: 68 Record: 66
  - (Neal Bedward)
  - Yds: 5436 F9 Yds: 2718 B9 Yds: 2718
  - Prevailing Wind: West
  - Designer: Howard Swan
  - Further Information:
  - Flat Course. 9 hole course can be played as an 18 hole course

HORNSEA

HORNSEA GOLF CLUB, Rolston Rd, Hornsea, **YORKSHIRE (EAST)**, HU18 1XG, **ENGLAND**.
(T) 01964 532020
(E) secretary@hornseagolfclub.co.uk
(W) www.hornseagolfclub.co.uk
Membership: Members & Public

Contact/s:
- Club Secretary: Ms Angela Howard
- Professional: Mr Stretton Wright

Course/s:
- HORNSEA
  - Description: Wooded, Parkland, Undulating, Open, Medium Length, Tight, Drains Well
  - Green Speed: Fast
  - Built: 1898 Built On: Soil
  - Number of Holes: 18 Par: 72
  - Par 3's: 3 Par 4's: 12 Par 5's: 3
  - Yds: 6661 F9 Yds: 3403 B9 Yds: 3258
  - Prevailing Wind: East

HORSENDEN HILL

HORSENDEN HILL GOLF COURSE, Woodland Rise, Greenford, **LONDON (GREATER)**, UB6 0RD, **ENGLAND**.
(T) 020 89024555

Contact/s:
- Manager: Mr Simon Hoffman

Course/s:
- HORSENDEN HILL
  - Number of Holes: 9

HORSFORTH

HORSFORTH GOLF CLUB LTD, Layton Rise, Horsforth, Leeds, **YORKSHIRE (WEST)**, LS18 5EX, **ENGLAND**.
(T) 0113 2585200

Contact/s:
- Club Secretary: Mrs J Kenny
- Professional: Mr Simon Booth

Course/s:
- HORSFORTH
  - Description: Parkland
  - Built: 1907
  - Number of Holes: 18 Par: 71
  - Yds: 6219 F9 Yds: 3027 B9 Yds: 3192

HORSHAM GOLF

HORSHAM GOLF & FITNESS, Worthing Rd, Horsham, **SUSSEX (WEST)**, RH13 7AX, **ENGLAND**.
(T) 01403 271525
Membership: Members & Public

Contact/s:
- Club Secretary: Ms Elaine Perton
- Professional: Ms Lorraine Cousins
- Pro Shop: Mr Alastair Fit

Course/s:
- HORSHAM GOLF
  - Description: Wooded, Parkland, Sheltered, Open, Short, Tight, Drains Well,

Ideal for the Elderly
Green Speed: Medium
Built: 1994 **Built On:** Clay/Soil
Number of Holes: 9 **Record:** 60 (Jamie Spence)
Further Information:
This course is fairly short and ideal for beginners.

HORSLEY LODGE

HORSLEY LODGE GOLF CLUB, Smalley Mill Rd, Horsley, Derby, **DERBYSHIRE**, DE21 5BL, **ENGLAND**.
(T) 01332 780838
(E) enquiries@horsleylodge.co.uk
(W) www.horsleylodge.co.uk
Membership: Members & Public
Size of Complex: 178 Acres
Contact/s:
● **Club Secretary:** Mr George Johnson
● **Professional:** Mr Graham Lyle
Course/s:
⛳ **HORSLEY LODGE**
Description: Undulating, Sheltered, Long, Drains Well, Ideal for the Elderly
Green Speed: Fast
Built: 1990 **Built On:** Soil
Number of Holes: 18 **Par:** 71
Par 3's: 4 **Par 4's:** 11 **Par 5's:** 3
Yds: 6336 **F9 Yds:** 3002 **B9 Yds:** 3334
Designer: P McEvoy
Further Information:
USGA Greens.

HORTON PARK GOLF

HORTON PARK GOLF & COUNTRY CLUB, Hook Rd, Epsom, **SURREY**, KT19 8QG, **ENGLAND**.
(T) 020 83938400
(E) hortonpark@aol.com
Membership: Members & Public
Contact/s:
● **Professional:** Mr Stuart Walker
● **Book Tee Times:** Mr Mark Woodward
● **Book Lessons:** Mr Marcus Dennell
Course/s:
⛳ **HORTON PARK COUNTRY CLUB**
Description: Parkland, Open, Medium Length, Tends to Flood
Green Speed: Medium
Built: 1987 **Built On:** Clay
Number of Holes: 18 **Par:** 71
Yds: 6293 **F9 Yds:** 3036 **B9 Yds:** 3257
Designer: P Tallack
Further Information:
10th hole green is situated on a small island.

HORWICH

HORWICH GOLF CLUB, Victoria Rd, Horwich, Bolton, **LANCASHIRE**, BL6 5PH, **ENGLAND**.
(T) 01204 696980
Membership: Members & Public
Contact/s:
● **Club Secretary:** Mr C Sherbourne
☎ 01204 695426
Course/s:
⛳ **HORWICH**
Description: Heath Land, Undulating, Short, Tight, Drains Well
Green Speed: Fast
Built: 1895
Number of Holes: 9

HOUGHTON LE SPRING

HOUGHTON LE SPRING GOLF CLUB, Houghton Le Spring, **TYNE AND WEAR**, DH5 8LU, **ENGLAND**.
(T) 0191 5841198
Course/s:
⛳ **HOUGHTON-LE-SPRING**
Number of Holes: 18

HOUGHWOOD

HOUGHWOOD GOLF, Billinge Hill, Crank Rd, Crank, St. Helens, **MERSEYSIDE**, WA11 8RL, **ENGLAND**.
(T) 01744 894754
(W) www.houghwoodgolfclub.co.uk
Membership: Members & Public
Size of Complex: 132 Acres
Contact/s:
● **Professional:** Mr Paul Dickenson
☎ 01744 894444
Course/s:
⛳ **HOUGHWOOD**
Description: Parkland, Hilltop, Undulating, Open, Medium Length, Drains Well
Green Speed: Medium
Built: 1996 **Built On:** Clay/Soil
Number of Holes: 18 **Par:** 70
Par 3's: 5 **Par 4's:** 10 **Par 5's:** 3
Yds: 6202 **F9 Yds:** 2696 **B9 Yds:** 3506
Prevailing Wind: South/West
Designer: Pearson

HOULDSWORTH

HOULDSWORTH GOLF CLUB, Houldsworth Pk, Houldsworth St, Stockport, **CHESHIRE**, SK5 6BN, **ENGLAND**.
(T) 0161 4421712
Contact/s:
● **Professional:** David Naylor
● **Pro Shop:**
☎ 0161 4421714
Course/s:
⛳ **HOULDSWORTH**
Number of Holes: 18

HOUNSLOW HEATH

HOUNSLOW HEATH GOLF COURSE, Staines Rd, Hounslow, **LONDON (GREATER)**, TW4 5DS, **ENGLAND**.
(T) 020 85705271
Contact/s:
● **Manager:** Mr D Carter
Course/s:
⛳ **HOUNSLOW HEATH**
Number of Holes: 18
Designer: Fraser Middleton

HOWLEY HALL

HOWLEY HALL GOLF CLUB, Scotchman Lane, Morley, Leeds, **YORKSHIRE (WEST)**, LS27 0NX, **ENGLAND**.
(T) 01924 350100
(E) office@howleyhall.co.uk
(W) www.howleyhallgolfclub.co.uk
Membership: Members & Public
Contact/s:
● **Club Secretary:** Mr David Jones
● **Professional:** Mr Gary Watkinson
☎ 01924 350102
Course/s:
⛳ **HOWLEY HALL**
Description: Wooded, Parkland,

Undulating, Sheltered, Medium Length, Tight, Drains Well, Ideal for the Elderly
Green Speed: Fast
Built: 1900 **Built On:** Soil
Number of Holes: 18 **Par:** 71
Record: 68 (Jimmy Roberts)
Yds: 6346 **F9 Yds:** 3008 **B9 Yds:** 3338
Prevailing Wind: West

HOWTH

HOWTH GOLF CLUB, Carrickbrack Rd, Sutton, **COUNTY DUBLIN**, **IRELAND**.
(T) 01 8323055
Contact/s:
● **Club Secretary:** Ms Ann MacNeice
Course/s:
⛳ **HOWTH**
Number of Holes: 18 **Par:** 72
Par 3's: 3 **Par 4's:** 12 **Par 5's:** 3
Yds: 6119 **F9 Yds:** 2943 **B9 Yds:** 3176
Designer: James Braid

HOYLAKE MUNICIPAL

HOYLAKE MUNICIPAL GOLF CLUB, Carr Lane, Hoylake, Wirral, **MERSEYSIDE**, CH47 4BG, **ENGLAND**.
(T) 0151 6322956
Membership: Members & Public
Contact/s:
● **Club Secretary:** Mr Mike Down
● **Professional:** Mr Simon Hooton
Course/s:
⛳ **HOYLAKE**
Number of Holes: 18 **Par:** 70
Yds: 6313

HUDDERSFIELD

HUDDERSFIELD GOLF CLUB, Fixby Hall, Fixby, Huddersfield, **YORKSHIRE (WEST)**, HD2 2EP, **ENGLAND**.
(T) 01484 426203
(E) secretary@huddersfield-golf.co.uk
(W) www.huddersfield-golf.co.uk
Membership: Members & Public
Contact/s:
● **Club Secretary:** Mrs D Lockett
● **Professional:** Mr Paul Carmen
☎ 01484 426463
Course/s:
⛳ **HUDDERSFIELD**
Description: Wooded, Parkland, Hilltop, Undulating, Open, Long, Drains Well
Green Speed: Medium/Fast
Built: 1891
Number of Holes: 18 **Par:** 71
Record: 64
Yds: 6447 **F9 Yds:** 3437 **B9 Yds:** 3010
Prevailing Wind: West

HULL

HULL GOLF CLUB (1921) LTD, The Hall, 27 Packman Lane, Hull, **YORKSHIRE (EAST)**, HU10 7TJ, **ENGLAND**.
(T) 01482 658919
Course/s:
⛳ **HULL**
Number of Holes: 18 **Par:** 70
Yds: 6246 **F9 Yds:** 3177 **B9 Yds:** 3069
Designer: James Braid

HUMAX

HUMAX GOLF COURSE, 83 Clerkenwell Rd, London, **LONDON (GREATER)**, EC1M 5RJ, **ENGLAND**.

(T) 020 72785847

Membership: Members & Public

Contact/s:
● **Professional:** Mr John Coe

Course/s:
🏌 **MELBOURNE**
Description: Championship, Wooded, Parkland, Medium Length, Tight, Drains Well
Green Speed: Medium/Fast
Built: 1996 **Built On:** Clay
Number of Holes: 18 **Par:** 72
Record: 65 (John Cole)
Yds: 6173 **F9 Yds:** 2795 **B9 Yds:** 3378
Prevailing Wind: South
Designer: C Sinclair

HUMBERSTON PARK

HUMBERSTON PARK GOLF CLUB, Humberston Ave, Humberston, Grimsby, **LINCOLNSHIRE (NORTH EAST),** DN36 4SJ, **ENGLAND.**
(T) 01472 210404

Membership: Members & Public

Contact/s:
● **Club Secretary:** Mr Bob Bean

Course/s:
🏌 **HUMBERSTON**
Description: Parkland, Undulating, Short, Tight, Ideal for the Elderly
Green Speed: Medium
Built: 1964
Number of Holes: 9

HUMBERSTONE HEIGHTS

HUMBERSTONE HEIGHTS GOLF CLUB, Gipsy Lane, Leicester, **LEICESTERSHIRE,** LE5 0TB, **ENGLAND.**
(T) 0116 2559971

Contact/s:
● **Manager:** Mr P Harfield

Course/s:
🏌 **HUMBERSTONE HEIGHTS**
Number of Holes: 18
Designer: Hawtree

HUNLEY HALL

HUNLEY HALL GOLF CLUB, Ings Lane, Brotton, Saltburn-By-The-Sea, **CLEVELAND,** TS12 2QQ, **ENGLAND.**
(T) 01287 676216
(E) enquiries@hunleyhall.co.uk
(W) www.hunleyhall.co.uk

Membership: Members & Public
Size of Complex: 265 Acres

Contact/s:
● **Club Secretary:** Mr Gordon Brown
● **Professional:** Mr Andrew S Brook
☎ 01287 677444

Course/s:
🏌 **MILLENIUM**
Description: Championship, Wooded, Parkland, Cliff Top, Undulating, Sheltered, Open, Short, Tight, Drains Well, Ideal for the Elderly
Green Speed: Medium
Built: 1993 **Built On:** Clay/Soil
Number of Holes: 27 **Par:** 73
Par 3's: 4 **Par 4's:** 9 **Par 5's:** 5
Yds: 5948 **F9 Yds:** 3076 **B9 Yds:** 2872
Prevailing Wind: South
Designer: John Morgan
Further Information:
27 holes provide 4 different courses. There is a 9 hole and an 18 hole course in play every day. The total pars range from

68 - 73 depending on which course is played.

HUNSTANTON

HUNSTANTON GOLF CLUB, Golf Course Rd, Old Hunstanton, Hunstanton, **NORFOLK,** PE36 6JQ, **ENGLAND.**
(T) 01485 532811

Membership: Members & Public

Contact/s:
● **Club Secretary:** Mr M T Whybrow
● **Professional:** Mr James Dodds

Course/s:
🏌 **HUNSTANTON**
Number of Holes: 18 **Par:** 72
Par 3's: 4 **Par 4's:** 10 **Par 5's:** 4
Yds: 6759 **F9 Yds:** 3454 **B9 Yds:** 3305
Designer: James Braid 🏆

HUNTERCOMBE

HUNTERCOMBE GOLF CLUB, Huntercombe, Nuffield, Henley-on-Thames, **OXFORDSHIRE,** RG9 5SL, **ENGLAND.**
(T) 01491 641241

Contact/s:
● **Club Secretary:** Lt.Col T J Hutchison
☎ 01491 641207
● **Professional:** Mr David Reffin

Course/s:
🏌 **HUNTERCOMBE**
Description: Championship, Wooded, Sheltered, Short, Tight, Drains Well, Ideal for the Elderly
Green Speed: Medium
Built: 1901 **Built On:** Chalk
Number of Holes: 18
Designer: William Park

HUNTLY

HUNTLY GOLF CLUB, Cooper Pk, Huntly, Aberdeen, **ABERDEEN (CITY OF),** AB54 4SH, **SCOTLAND.**
(T) 01466 792643
(E) huntlygc@tinyworld.co.uk
(W) www.huntlygc.com

Membership: Members & Public

Contact/s:
● **Club Secretary:** Mr E A Stott
☎ 01466 792360
● **Pro Shop:** Mr A Aird
☎ 01466 794181

Course/s:
🏌 **HUNTLY**
Description: Parkland, Medium Length
Green Speed: Medium
Built: 1892 **Built On:** Soil
Number of Holes: 18 **Par:** 67
Par 3's: 5 **Par 4's:** 13
Yds: 5399 **F9 Yds:** 2577 **B9 Yds:** 2822
Further Information:
Situated between the River Deveron and the River Bogie.

HURDWICK

HURDWICK GOLF COURSE & CLUB, Tavistock Hamlets, Tavistock, **DEVON,** PL19 8PZ, **ENGLAND.**
(T) 01822 612746

Contact/s:
● **Owner:** Mr R Cullen

Course/s:
🏌 **HURDWICK**
Number of Holes: 18
Designer: Hawtree

HURLSTON

HURLSTON HALL GOLF CLUB, Hurlston Lane, Scarisbrick, Ormskirk, **LANCASHIRE,** L40 8HB, **ENGLAND.**
(T) 01704 840400
(E) hurlston_hall@btinternet.com
(W) www.hurlstonhall.co.uk

Membership: Members & Public
Size of Complex: 135 Acres

Contact/s:
● **Professional:** Mr Jon Esclapez
☎ 01704 841120

Course/s:
🏌 **HURLSTON**
Description: Parkland, Undulating, Long, Drains Well, Ideal for the Elderly
Green Speed: Medium
Built: 1994 **Built On:** Soil
Number of Holes: 18 **Par:** 72
Yds: 6746 **F9 Yds:** 3328 **B9 Yds:** 3418
Designer: Donald Steel
Further Information:
Fair test of golf for both low and high handicap players.

HURST

HURST GOLF COURSE, The Clubhouse, Sandford Lane, Hurst, Reading, **BERKSHIRE,** RG10 0SU, **ENGLAND.**
(T) 0118 9344355
(E) hurst.golf.course@circaleisure.com
(W) www.wokinghamleisure.co.uk

Membership: Members & Public/Public

Contact/s:
● **Club Secretary:** Ms J Giles
☎ 0118 9321779
● **Professional:** Mr Justin Hennersy

Course/s:
🏌 **HURST**
Description: Parkland, Medium Length, Tight
Green Speed: Medium
Built: 1975
Number of Holes: 9

HURTMORE

HURTMORE GOLF CLUB, Hurtmore Rd, Hurtmore, Godalming, **SURREY,** GU7 2RN, **ENGLAND.**
(T) 01483 426492

Membership: Public

Contact/s:
● **Professional:** Ms Maxine Burton
● **Pro Shop:** Mr Simon Marshall

Course/s:
🏌 **HURTMORE**
Description: Parkland, Undulating, Open, Short, Tight, Drains Well
Green Speed: Medium
Built: 1992 **Built On:** Sand
Number of Holes: 18 **Par:** 70
Yds: 5278 **F9 Yds:** 2511 **B9 Yds:** 2767
Designer: Peter Alliss, Clive Clark
Further Information:
90 bunkers throughout the course. Very challenging.

HUYTON & PRESCOT

HUYTON & PRESCOT GOLF CLUB, Hurst Pk, Huyton Lane, Huyton, Liverpool, **MERSEYSIDE,** L36 1UA, **ENGLAND.**
(T) 0151 4893948

Course/s:
🏌 **HUYTON & PRESCOT**
Number of Holes: 18

HYLANDS GOLF COMPLEX

HYLANDS GOLF COMPLEX, Main Rd, Margaretting, Ingatestone, **ESSEX**, CM4 0ET, **ENGLAND**.
(T) 01277 356016
(W) www.hylands-golf-complex.co.uk
Membership: Public
Size of Complex: 180 Acres
<u>Contact/s:</u>
● **Club Secretary:** Mr Lee Porter
<u>Course/s:</u>
● **HANBURY**
Description: Parkland, Undulating, Open, Medium Length, Drains Well, Ideal for the Elderly
Green Speed: Medium
Built: 1996 **Built On:** Clay
Number of Holes: 18 **Par:** 72
Par 3's: 4 **Par 4's:** 10 **Par 5's:** 4
Yds: 6604 **F9 Yds:** 3416 **B9 Yds:** 3188
Prevailing Wind: West
Designer: R Plumbridge
Further Information:
Challenging course.
● **PRYORS**
Description: Parkland, Undulating, Open, Short, Drains Well, Ideal for the Elderly
Green Speed: Medium
Built: 1996 **Built On:** Soil
Number of Holes: 9 **Par:** 66
Par 3's: 4 **Par 4's:** 4 **Par 5's:** 1
Yds: 4890 **F9 Yds:** 2445 **B9 Yds:** 2445
Prevailing Wind: West
Designer: R Plumbridge

HYTHE IMPERIAL

HYTHE IMPERIAL GOLF CLUB, Princes Prde, Hythe, **KENT**, CT21 6AE, **ENGLAND**.
(T) 01303 267441
<u>Course/s:</u>
● **HYTHE IMPERIAL**
Number of Holes: 9

IFIELD

IFIELD GOLF & COUNTRY CLUB, Rusper Rd, Ifield, Crawley, **SUSSEX (WEST)**, RH11 0LN, **ENGLAND**.
(T) 01293 520222
<u>Contact/s:</u>
● **Professional:** Mr Jonathan Earl
<u>Course/s:</u>
● **IFIELD**
Description: Parkland, Undulating
Built: 1927
Number of Holes: 18 **Par:** 70
Yds: 5966 **F9 Yds:** 3028 **B9 Yds:** 2938
Designer: Bernard Darwin

IFORD BRIDGE

IFORD BRIDGE GOLF COURSE, Iford Bridge Golf Course, Barrack Rd, Christchurch, **DORSET**, BH23 2BA, **ENGLAND**.
(T) 01202 473817
<u>Course/s:</u>
● **IFORD BRIDGE**
Number of Holes: 9

ILFORD

ILFORD GOLF CLUB LTD, 291 Wanstead Pk Rd, Ilford, **ESSEX**, IG1 3TR, **ENGLAND**.
(T) 020 85542930
<u>Contact/s:</u>
● **Manager:** Mr John Pascoe
<u>Course/s:</u>

● **ILFORD**
Number of Holes: 18

ILFRACOMBE

ILFRACOMBE GOLF CLUB, Ilfracombe, **DEVON**, EX34 9RT, **ENGLAND**.
(T) 01271 862176
(E) ilfracombe.golfclub@virgin.net
(W) www.ilfracombegolfclub.com
Membership: Members & Public
Size of Complex: 151 Acres
<u>Contact/s:</u>
● **Club Secretary:** Mr Brian Wright
● **Professional:** Mr Mark Davies
<u>Course/s:</u>
● **ILFRACOMBE**
Description: Parkland, Breckland, Cliff Top, Medium Length, Drains Well, Ideal for the Elderly
Built: 1892
Number of Holes: 18 **Par:** 69
Yds: 5795 **F9 Yds:** 2995 **B9 Yds:** 2800
Prevailing Wind: South/West
Designer: K Weir

ILKLEY

ILKLEY GOLF CLUB, Nesfield Rd, Ilkley, **YORKSHIRE (WEST)**, LS29 0BE, **ENGLAND**.
(T) 01943 600214
<u>Contact/s:</u>
● **Manager:** Mr A K Hatfield
<u>Course/s:</u>
● **ILKLEY**
Number of Holes: 18

IMMINGHAM

IMMINGHAM GOLF CLUB, St. Andrews Lane, Church Lane, Immingham, **LINCOLNSHIRE (NORTH EAST)**, DN40 2EU, **ENGLAND**.
(T) 01469 575298
(E) admin@immgc.com
(W) www.immgc.com
Membership: Members & Public
<u>Contact/s:</u>
● **Club Secretary:** Mr Doug McCully
● **Professional:** Mr Nick Harding
☎ 01469 575493
<u>Course/s:</u>
● **IMMINGHAM**
Description: Parkland, Medium Length, Tight, Ideal for the Elderly
Built: 1974 **Built On:** Clay
Number of Holes: 18 **Par:** 71
Par 3's: 4 **Par 4's:** 11 **Par 5's:** 3
Yds: 6215 **F9 Yds:** 3138 **B9 Yds:** 3077
Prevailing Wind: South/West
Designer: Hawtree

INCHMARLO GOLF CTRE

INCHMARLO GOLF CENTRE, Inchmarlo, Banchory, **ABERDEENSHIRE**, AB31 4BQ, **SCOTLAND**.
(T) 01330 822557
(W) www.inchmarlo.com
Membership: Members & Public
Size of Complex: 170 Acres
<u>Contact/s:</u>
● **Professional:** Mr Patrick Lovie
<u>Course/s:</u>
● **INCHMARLO 18 HOLE**
Description: Championship, Wooded, Parkland, Undulating, Sheltered, Long,

Tight, Drains Well
Green Speed: Medium
Built: 2001 **Built On:** Soil
Number of Holes: 18
Designer: Graeme Webster
Further Information:
Opening June 2001.

● **INCHMARLO 9 HOLE**
Built: 1997
Number of Holes: 9

INCO

INCO GOLF CLUB, Clydach, Swansea, **SWANSEA**, SA6 5PQ, .
(T) 01792 844216
<u>Course/s:</u>
● **INCO**
Number of Holes: 18

INGESTRE PARK

INGESTRE PARK GOLF CLUB, Ingestre, Stafford, **STAFFORDSHIRE**, ST18 0RE, **ENGLAND**.
(T) 01889 270845
<u>Course/s:</u>
● **INGESTRE PARK**
Number of Holes: 18 **Par:** 70
Par 3's: 4 **Par 4's:** 12 **Par 5's:** 2
Yds: 6268 **F9 Yds:** 3124 **B9 Yds:** 3144
Designer: Hawtree

INGOL

INGOL GOLF & SQUASH CLUB, Tanterton Hall Rd, Ingol, Preston, **LANCASHIRE**, PR2 7BY, **ENGLAND**.
(T) 01772 734556
(W) www.ingolgolfclub.co.uk
Membership: Members & Public
Size of Complex: 250 Acres
<u>Contact/s:</u>
● **Professional:** Mr Mark Bradley
☎ 01772 769646
<u>Course/s:</u>
● **INGOL**
Description: Parkland, Sheltered, Medium Length, Tight
Green Speed: Medium
Built: 1981 **Built On:** Clay
Number of Holes: 18 **Par:** 72
Record: 67 (M Bradley)
Par 3's: 4 **Par 4's:** 10 **Par 5's:** 4
Yds: 6294 **F9 Yds:** 3459 **B9 Yds:** 2835
Prevailing Wind: South/West
Designer: Henry Cotton
Further Information:
Ingol Golf Course is a good challenge for any calibre of golfer. A tree lined course set in 250 acres, with natural water hazards.

INNELLAN

INNELLAN GOLF CLUB, Knockamillie Rd, Innellan, Dunoon, **ARGYLL AND BUTE**, PA23 7SG, **SCOTLAND**.
(T) 01369 830242
<u>Course/s:</u>
● **INNELLAN**
Description: Moorland, Hilltop, Undulating
Built: 1891 **Number of Holes:** 9 **Par:** 32

INNERLEITHEN

INNERLEITHEN GOLF CLUB, Leithen Rd, Innerleithen, **SCOTTISH BORDERS**, EH44 6HZ, **SCOTLAND**.

(T) 01896 830951

Membership: Members & Public

Contact/s:
- Club Secretary: Mr N Smith
  ☎ 01896 830050

Course/s:

🏌 **INNERLEITHEN**
Description: Parkland, Valley, Sheltered, Medium Length, Drains Well, Ideal for the Elderly
Green Speed: Medium
Built: 1886
Number of Holes: 9   Par: 70
Par 3's: 3   Par 4's: 4   Par 5's: 2
Yds: 6066   F9 Yds: 3033   B9 Yds: 3033
Designer: William Park
Further Information:
9 hole course can be played as an 18 hole course

INSCH

INSCH GOLF CLUB, Golf Trce, Insch, **ABERDEENSHIRE**, AB52 6JY, **SCOTLAND**.
(T) 01464 820363
(E) insch@euphony.net
(W) www.insch4golf.com

Membership: Members & Public

Contact/s:
- Club Secretary: Mr Douglas Cumming
  ☎ 01464 820814

Course/s:

🏌 **INSCH**
Description: Parkland, Medium Length, Drains Well, Ideal for the Elderly
Green Speed: Medium
Built: 1980   Built On: Soil
Number of Holes: 18   Par: 69
Par 3's: 5   Par 4's: 11   Par 5's: 2
Yds: 5414   F9 Yds: 3013   B9 Yds: 2401
Prevailing Wind: West
Designer: Glen Andrews
Further Information:
The course was built in 1980 but was then extended between 1995 - 97.

INVERALLOCHY

INVERALLOCHY GOLF CLUB, Golf Clubhouse, Fraserburgh, **ABERDEENSHIRE**, AB43 8TL, **SCOTLAND**.
(T) 01346 582000

Course/s:

🏌 **INVERALLOCHY**
Number of Holes: 18

INVERGORDON

INVERGORDON GOLF CLUB, King George St, Invergordon, **HIGHLANDS**, IV18 0BB, **SCOTLAND**.
(T) 01349 852715

Contact/s:
- Book Tee Times: Ms Judith Ross

Course/s:

🏌 **INVERGORDON**
Description: Wooded, Parkland
Built: 1893
Number of Holes: 18   Par: 69
Designer: A Rae
Further Information:
Wide, lush fairways with some woodland. Very good greens. Views over Cromarty Firth.

INVERNESS

CULCABOCK, Culcabock Rd, Inverness, **HIGHLANDS**, IV2 3XQ, **SCOTLAND**.

(T) 01463 239882
(E) igc@freeuk.com
(W) www.invernessgolfclub.co.uk

Membership: Members & Public
Size of Complex: 150 Acres

Contact/s:
- Professional: Mr A P Thompson
  ☎ 01463 231989
- Book Tee Times: Mr J S Thompson

Course/s:

🏌 **INVERNESS**
Description: Championship, Wooded, Parkland, Sheltered, Medium Length, Tight, Ideal for the Elderly
Green Speed: Fast
Built: 1883   Built On: Soil
Number of Holes: 18   Par: 69
Record: 62 (N Scott - Smith)
Par 3's: 5   Par 4's: 11   Par 5's: 2
Yds: 6226   F9 Yds: 2988   B9 Yds: 3250
Prevailing Wind: West
Designer: James Braid
Further Information:
Ideally located, situated one mile from the town centre. It is a challenging 18 hole course which is relatively flat and always is in good condition.

INVERURIE

INVERURIE GOLF CLUB, Blackhall Rd, Inverurie, **ABERDEENSHIRE**, AB51 5JB, **SCOTLAND**.
(T) 01467 624080
(W) www.inveruriegc.co.uk

Membership: Members & Public

Contact/s:
- Club Secretary: Ms Barbara Rogerson
- Professional: Mr Mark Lees
  ☎ 01467 620193

Course/s:

🏌 **INVERURIE**
Description: Wooded, Parkland, Sheltered, Short, Tight, Ideal for the Elderly
Green Speed: Medium
Built: 1923   Built On: Clay/Sand/Soil
Number of Holes: 18   Par: 69
Record: 63 (C Gilles)
Par 3's: 4   Par 4's: 13   Par 5's: 1
Yds: 5711   F9 Yds: 2947   B9 Yds: 2764
Prevailing Wind: West

IPSWICH

IPSWICH GOLF CLUB, Purdis Heath, Bucklesham Rd, Ipswich, **SUFFOLK**, IP3 8UQ, **ENGLAND**.
(T) 01473 728941

Membership: Members & Public

Contact/s:
- Club Secretary: Mr Neill Ellice
- Professional: Mr Stephen Whymark
  ☎ 01473 724017

Course/s:

🏌 **IPSWICH 9 HOLE**
Description: Heath Land, Medium Length, Drains Well
Green Speed: Medium
Number of Holes: 9

IRVINE

IRVINE GOLF CLUB THE, Sandy Rd, Bogside, Irvine, **AYRSHIRE (NORTH)**, KA12 8SN, **SCOTLAND**.
(T) 01294 275626

Membership: Members & Public

Contact/s:

- Club Secretary: Mr Bill McMahon
  ☎ 01294 275979
- Pro Shop: Mr Keith Erskine

Course/s:

🏌 **LYNX**
Description: Championship, Links, Open, Medium Length, Drains Well
Green Speed: Fast
Built: 1887   Built On: Sand
Number of Holes: 18   Par: 71
Par 3's: 2   Par 4's: 15   Par 5's: 1
Yds: 6408
Designer: James Braid
Further Information:
Flat course close to sea.

ISLAND

ISLAND GOLF CLUB, Corballis, Donabate, **COUNTY DUBLIN**, **IRELAND**.
(T) 01 8436205
(E) islandgc@iol.ie

Course/s:

🏌 **THE ISLAND**
Description: Links
Number of Holes: 18   Par: 71
Yds: 6053
Designer: Edward Hackett, Hawtree 🏆

ISLE OF PURBECK

ISLE OF PURBECK GOLF CLUB (THE), Corfe Rd, Studland, Swanage, **DORSET**, BH19 3AB, **ENGLAND**.
(T) 01929 450361
(E) enquiries@purbeckgolf.co.uk
(W) www.purbeckgolf.co.uk

Membership: Members & Public

Contact/s:
- Pro Shop: Mr Ian Brake
  ☎ 01929 450354

Course/s:

🏌 **DENE**
Description: Heath Land
Number of Holes: 9
Designer: Harry Shapland Colt

🏌 **PURBECK**
Description: Heath Land
Number of Holes: 18   Par: 70
Yds: 6295
Designer: Harry Shapland Colt 🏆

ISLE OF SKYE

ISLE OF SKYE GOLF CLUB, Sconser, Isle of Skye, **HIGHLANDS**, IV48 8TD, **SCOTLAND**.
(T) 01478 650414
(E) isleofskye.golfclub@btinternet.com
(W) www.uk-golf.com/clubs/isleofskye

Membership: Members & Public

Contact/s:
- Club Secretary: Mr Ian MacMillen
- Book Tee Times: Mr Calum Macaskill

Course/s:

🏌 **ISLE OF SKYE**
Description: Sheltered, Drains Well, Ideal for the Elderly
Green Speed: Medium
Built: 1964   Built On: Soil
Number of Holes: 18   Par: 66
Par 3's: 6   Par 4's: 12
Yds: 4677   F9 Yds: 2387   B9 Yds: 2290
Prevailing Wind: West
Further Information:
Seaside course. All the holes have Gaelic names refering to different land marks.

ISLE OF WEDMORE

ISLE OF WEDMORE GOLF CLUB, Lineage, Lascot Hill, Wedmore, **SOMERSET**, BS28 4QT, **ENGLAND**.
(T) 01934 712452

Contact/s:
- **Professional:** Mr Graham Coombe

Course/s:
ISLE OF WEDMORE
  Description: Parkland
  Built: 1992
  Number of Holes: 18   **Par:** 70
  Designer: T Murray
  Further Information:
  Views of Cheddar Valley from the back 9.
  Good greens all year round.

ISLES OF SCILLY

ISLES OF SCILLY GOLF CLUB, Carn Morvel Downs, St. Marys, **ISLES OF SCILLY**, TR21 0NF, **ENGLAND**.
(T) 01720 422692

Course/s:
ISLES OF SCILLY
  Number of Holes: 9

IVER

IVER GOLF CLUB, Hollow Hill Lane, Iver, **BUCKINGHAMSHIRE**, SL0 0JJ, **ENGLAND**.
(T) 01753 655615

Membership: Members & Public

Contact/s:
- **Professional:** Mr Karl Teschnel
  ☎ 01753 654225

Course/s:
IVER
  Description: Parkland, Open, Ideal for the Elderly
  Green Speed: Medium
  Built: 1983   **Built On:** Soil
  Number of Holes: 18   **Par:** 72
  Par 3's: 4   **Par 4's:** 10   **Par 5's:** 4
  Yds: 6104
  Further Information:
  Raised greens. Testing Par 5's.

IVINGHOE

IVINGHOE GOLF CLUB, Wellcroft, Ivinghoe, Leighton Buzzard, **BEDFORDSHIRE**, LU7 9EF, **ENGLAND**.
(T) 01296 668696

Contact/s:
- **Owner:** Mr P W Garrad

Course/s:
IVINGHOE
  Number of Holes: 9

IVYLEAF

IVYLEAF GOLF COURSE & DRIVING RANGE, Ivyleaf Hill, Bude, **CORNWALL**, EX23 9LD, **ENGLAND**.
(T) 01288 321592
(W) www.bude.co.uk/ivyleaf-golf

Membership: Public

Contact/s:
- **Partner:** Mrs N Stanbury

Course/s:
IVYLEAF
  Description: Hilltop
  Number of Holes: 9   **Par:** 30
  Yds: 1900

IZAAK WALTON

IZAAK WALTON GOLF CLUB LTD, Eccleshall Rd, Cold Norton, Stone, **STAFFORDSHIRE**, ST15 0BZ, **ENGLAND**.
(T) 01785 760900

Contact/s:
- **Club Secretary:** Mr Terry T Tyler

Course/s:
IZAAK WALTON
  Number of Holes: 18

JEDBURGH

JEDBURGH GOLF CLUB, Dunion Rd, Jedburgh, **SCOTTISH BORDERS**, TD8 6TA, **SCOTLAND**.
(T) 01835 863587

Course/s:
JEDBURGH
  Number of Holes: 9

JERSEY (ROYAL)

ROYAL JERSEY GOLF CLUB, Le Chemin au Gredes, Grouville, Jersey, Grouville, **JERSEY**, JE3 9BD, **ENGLAND**.
(T) 01534 854416
(W) www.royaljersey.com

Contact/s:
- **Club Secretary:** Mr D J Atwood

Course/s:
ROYAL JERSEY
  Number of Holes: 18   **Par:** 70
  Yds: 6059
  Further Information:
  Views of Mont Orgueil Castle, Gorey Harbour, and Royal Bay of Grouville.

JOHN O'GAUNT

JOHN O'GAUNT GOLF CLUB, Sutton Pk, Sutton, Sandy, **BEDFORDSHIRE**, SG19 2LY, **ENGLAND**.
(T) 01767 260360

Membership: Members & Public

Contact/s:
- **Pro Shop:** Mr Peter Round

Course/s:
CARTHAGENA
  Description: Championship, Links, Wooded, Parkland, Sheltered, Short, Tight, Drains Well, Ideal for the Elderly
  Built: 1980   **Built On:** Sand
  Number of Holes: 18   **Par:** 69
  Par 3's: 5   **Par 4's:** 11   **Par 5's:** 2
  Yds: 5590   **F9 Yds:** 2577   **B9 Yds:** 3013
  Designer: John O'Gaunt
  Further Information:
  A short, tight course with 3000 trees and views to remember.

JOHN O'GAUNT
  Description: Parkland
  Number of Holes: 18   **Par:** 71
  Par 3's: 3   **Par 4's:** 13   **Par 5's:** 2
  Yds: 6513   **F9 Yds:** 3379   **B9 Yds:** 3134
  Designer: John O'Gaunt

K CLUB

K CLUB (THE), Straffan, **COUNTY KILDARE**, **IRELAND**.
(T) 01 6017300
(E) golf@kclub.ie
(W) www.kclub.ie

Membership: Members & Public

Contact/s:
- **Club Secretary:** Mr Paul Crowe

- **Professional:** Mr Ernie Jones
- **Book Tee Times:** Ms Sandra Walsh
  ☎ 01 6017276

Course/s:
THE K CLUB
  Description: Championship
  Number of Holes: 18   **Par:** 72
  Par 3's: 5   **Par 4's:** 9   **Par 5's:** 4
  Yds: 6829   **F9 Yds:** 3360   **B9 Yds:** 3469
  Designer: Arnold Palmer 🏆

KAMES GOLF

KAMES GOLF & COUNTRY CLUB, Eastend, Cleghorn, Lanark, **LANARKSHIRE (SOUTH)**, ML11 8NR, **SCOTLAND**.
(T) 01555 870015

Membership: Members & Public
Size of Complex: 200 Acres

Contact/s:
- **Joint Owner:** Mr J Forrest

Course/s:
KAMES
  Description: Sheltered, Short, Tight
  Green Speed: Medium
  Built: 1998   **Built On:** Sand
  Number of Holes: 9   **Par:** 33
  Par 3's: 3   **Par 4's:** 6
  Yds: 2538
  Designer: Graham Taylor
  Further Information:
  A delightful but testing short course.

MOUSE VALLEY
  Description: Links, Parkland, Undulating, Medium Length
  Green Speed: Fast
  Built: 1993   **Built On:** Sand
  Number of Holes: 18   **Par:** 70
  Par 3's: 5   **Par 4's:** 10   **Par 5's:** 3
  Yds: 6226
  Designer: Graham Taylor

KANTURK

KANTURK GOLF CLUB, Fairy Hill Kanturk, Kanturk, **COUNTY CORK**, **IRELAND**.
(T) 029 50534

Contact/s:
- **Club Secretary:** Mr Tony McAuliffe
  ☎ 087 2217510

Course/s:
KANTURK GOLF COURSE
  Built: 1973
  Number of Holes: 18
  Yds: 6026
  Designer: Richard Barry

KEDLESTON PARK

KEDLESTON PARK GOLF CLUB, Kedleston, Quarndon, Derby, **DERBYSHIRE**, DE22 5JD, **ENGLAND**.
(T) 01332 840035

Contact/s:
- **Club Secretary:** Mr G Duckmanton
- **Professional:** Mr Paul Wesselingh
- **Book Tee Times:**
  ☎ 01332 841685

Course/s:
KEDLESTON PARK
  Built: 1947
  Number of Holes: 18   **Par:** 72
  Yds: 6675   **F9 Yds:** 3172   **B9 Yds:** 3258
  Designer: James Braid
  Further Information:
  The course is on the grounds of Kedleston Hall stately homes and has USPGA sand based greens.

KEIGHLEY

KEIGHLEY GOLF CLUB, Howden Pk, Utley, Keighley, **YORKSHIRE (WEST)**, BD20 6DH, **ENGLAND**.
(T) 01535 604778
Contact/s:
● **Professional:** Mr Mike Bradley
 ☎ 01535 665370
● **Book Tee Times:**
 ☎ 01535 604778/665370
Course/s:
🏌 **KEIGHLEY**
 Description: Wooded, Parkland
 Built: 1904
 Number of Holes: 18 **Par:**
 Yds: 6141 **F9 Yds:** 3246 **B9 Yds:** 2895
 Further Information:
 The 17th has a reputation as one of the most difficult and dangerous finishing holes in Yorkshire.

KEITH

KEITH GOLF CLUB, Mar Court, Fife Keith, Keith, **MORAY**, AB55 5GF, **SCOTLAND**.
(T) 01542 882469
Contact/s:
● **Club Secretary:** Mr Barry Brown
Course/s:
🏌 **KEITH**
 Number of Holes: 18 **Par:** 69
 Par 3's: 4 **Par 4's:** 13 **Par 5's:** 1
 Yds: 5802 **F9 Yds:** 2839 **B9 Yds:** 2963

KELSO

KELSO GOLF CLUB, Abbotseat Rd, Kelso, **SCOTTISH BORDERS**, TD5 7SL, **SCOTLAND**.
(T) 01573 223009
Course/s:
🏌 **KELSO**
 Description: Parkland
 Built: 1887
 Number of Holes: 18 **Par:** 70
 Designer: James Braid

KEMNAY

KEMNAY GOLF CLUB, Monymusk Rd, Kemnay, **ABERDEENSHIRE**, AB51 5RA, **SCOTLAND**.
(T) 01467 643746
Membership: Members & Public
Contact/s:
● **Club Secretary:** Mr Brian Robertsons
● **Pro Shop:** Mr Ronnie McDonald
 ☎ 01467 642225
Course/s:
🏌 **KEMNAY**
 Description: Parkland, Medium Length
 Green Speed: Medium
 Built: 1908 **Built On:** Soil
 Number of Holes: 18 **Par:** 71
 Par 3's: 5 **Par 4's:** 9 **Par 5's:** 4
 Yds: 6342
 Designer: Greens of Scotland

KENDAL

KENDAL GOLF CLUB, The Heights, Kendal, **CUMBRIA**, LA9 4PQ, **ENGLAND**.
(T) 01539 723499
(W) www.cumbria.com/kendalgc/
Membership: Members & Public
Contact/s:
● **Club Secretary:** Mr Ian Grant
● **Professional:** Mr Peter Scott

Course/s:
🏌 **KENDAL**
 Description: Heath Land, Hilltop, Undulating, Open, Medium Length, Drains Well, Ideal for the Elderly
 Green Speed: Medium
 Built: 1891
 Number of Holes: 18 **Par:** 70
 Record: 63 (J Matthews)
 Par 3's: 5 **Par 4's:** 10 **Par 5's:** 3
 Yds: 5769 **F9 Yds:** 2487 **B9 Yds:** 3282
 Prevailing Wind: West
 Further Information:
 The course is built on limestone and is renowned for its fine greens all year round. It has been quoted in the Guardian as having 'the most magnificent and extensive views of any club in England'.

KENDLESHIRE

KENDLESHIRE GOLF CLUB LTD (THE), Henfield Rd, Coalpit Heath, Bristol, **BRISTOL**, BS36 2TG, **ENGLAND**.
(T) 01179 567007
(W) www.kendleshire.co.uk
Membership: Members & Public
Size of Complex: 120 Acres
Contact/s:
● **Professional:** Mr Paul Barrington
Course/s:
🏌 **THE KENDLESHIRE**
 Description: Parkland, Medium Length
 Green Speed: Fast
 Built: 1997 **Built On:** Clay
 Number of Holes: 18 **Par:** 70
 Record: 63 (Sam Little)
 Par 3's: 5 **Par 4's:** 10 **Par 5's:** 3
 Yds: 6550 **F9 Yds:** 3232 **B9 Yds:** 3318
 Prevailing Wind: South
 Designer: Adrian Stiff

KENILWORTH

KENILWORTH GOLF CLUB LTD, Crew Lane, Kenilworth, **WARWICKSHIRE**, CV8 2EA, **ENGLAND**.
(T) 01926 858517
(E) info@kenilworthgolfclub.fsnet.co.uk
Contact/s:
● **Club Secretary:** Mr John McTavish
● **Professional:** Mr Steve Yates
Course/s:
🏌 **KENILWORTH**
 Number of Holes: 18 **Par:** 73
 Yds: 6400 **F9 Yds:** 3273 **B9 Yds:** 3127
 Designer: Hawtree

KENMARE

KENMARE GOLF CLUB, Kenmare, **COUNTY KERRY**, **IRELAND**.
(T) 064 41291
Course/s:
🏌 **KENMARE**
 Number of Holes: 18
 Designer: Edward Hackett

KENMORE

KENMORE GOLF COURSE, Taymouth Holiday Ctre, Mains Of Taymore, Kenmore, Aberfeldy, **PERTH AND KINROSS**, PH15 2HN, **SCOTLAND**.
(T) 01887 830226
(E) info@taymouth.co.uk
(W) www.taymouth.co.uk
Membership: Members & Public
Course/s:

KENMORE

🏌 **KENMORE**
 Description: Undulating
 Built: 1992
 Number of Holes: 9 **Par:** 70
 Yds: 6052
 Designer: Robin Menzies
 Further Information:
 Easy walking course with good greens all year round, can be played as an 18 hole course using different coloured markers. Beautiful scenery in magnificent Highland countryside.

KENWICK PARK

KENWICK PARK GOLF CLUB PLC, Kenwick Hall, Kenwick, Louth, **LINCOLNSHIRE**, LN11 8NY, **ENGLAND**.
(T) 01507 605134
(E) golfatkenwick@nascr.net
(W) www.louthnet.co.uk
Membership: Members & Public
Contact/s:
● **Club Secretary:** Mr Paddy Shillington
● **Professional:** Mr Eric Sharp
 ☎ 01507 607161
Course/s:
🏌 **KENWICK**
 Description: Wooded, Parkland, Undulating, Medium Length, Drains Well
 Green Speed: Medium
 Built: 1992
 Number of Holes: 18
 Designer: P Tallack

KERRIES

KERRIES GOLF COURSE THE, The Kerries, Tralee, **COUNTY KERRY**, **IRELAND**.
(T) 066 7122112
Membership: Members & Public
Size of Complex: 60 Acres
Contact/s:
● **Club Secretary:** Ms Helen Barrett
Course/s:
🏌 **KERRIES**
 Description: Parkland, Medium Length, Drains Well, Ideal for the Elderly
 Green Speed: Medium
 Number of Holes: 9 **Par:** 67
 Par 3's: 2 **Par 4's:** 6 **Par 5's:** 1
 Yds: 2972
 Designer: A Spring
 Further Information:
 9 hole course can be played as an 18 hole course

KESWICK

KESWICK GOLF CLUB, Threlkeld Hall, Threlkeld, Keswick, **CUMBRIA**, CA12 4SX, **ENGLAND**.
(T) 01768 779013
Course/s:
🏌 **KESWICK**
 Description: Undulating
 Built: 1979
 Number of Holes: 18 **Par:** 71
 Designer: Eric Brown

KETTERING

KETTERING GOLF CLUB, The Headlands, Kettering, **NORTHAMPTONSHIRE**, NN15 6XA, **ENGLAND**.
(T) 01536 512074
Course/s:
🏌 **KETTERING**
 Number of Holes: 18
 Designer: Tom Morris

KIBWORTH

KIBWORTH GOLF CLUB LTD, Weir Rd,
Kibworth, Leicester, **LEICESTERSHIRE**, LE8
0LP, **ENGLAND**.
(T) 0116 2792283

Contact/s:
- **Club Secretary:** Mr J Noble
- **Professional:** Mr Bob Larratt

Course/s:
- **KIBWORTH**
  Description: Parkland
  Built: 1904
  Number of Holes: 18   **Par:** 71
  Further Information:
  A stream crosses through the course.

KIDDERMINSTER

KIDDERMINSTER GOLF CLUB, Russell Rd,
Kidderminster, **WORCESTERSHIRE**, DY10
3HT, **ENGLAND**.
(T) 01562 822303
(E) kidderminstergolfclub@hotmail.com

Contact/s:
- **Club Secretary:** Mr Michael Buchand

Course/s:
- **KIDDERMINSTER**
  Number of Holes: 18   **Par:** 72
  Yds: 6405   **F9 Yds:** 3166   **B9 Yds:** 3239

KILBIRNIE PLACE

KILBIRNIE PLACE GOLF CLUB, Largs Rd,
Kilbirnie, **AYRSHIRE (NORTH)**, KA25 7AT,
SCOTLAND.
(T) 01505 683398

Contact/s:
- **Club Secretary:** Mrs C McGurk
- **Book Tee Times:** Mrs C Marina
  ☎ 01505 684444

Course/s:
- **KILBIRNIE PLACE**
  Description: Parkland, Valley, Medium
  Length, Tends to Flood, Ideal for the
  Elderly
  Green Speed: Medium
  Built: 1800   **Built On:** Soil
  Number of Holes: 18   **Par:** 69
  Par 3's: 5   **Par 4's:** 11   **Par 5's:** 2
  Yds: 5543   **F9 Yds:** 2641   **B9 Yds:** 2902

KILCOCK

KILCOCK GOLF CLUB, Gallow, Kilcock,
COUNTY KILDARE, **IRELAND**.
(T) 01 6284074

Contact/s:
- **Club Secretary:** Mr Seamus Kelly

Course/s:
- **KILCOCK**
  Number of Holes: 18   **Par:** 72
  Yds: 6400   **F9 Yds:** 2970   **B9 Yds:** 3430
  Designer: Edward Hackett

KILCOOLE

KILCOOLE GOLF CLUB, Kilcoole, **COUNTY
DUBLIN**, **IRELAND**.
(T) 01 2872066

Course/s:
- **KILCOOLE**
  Number of Holes: 9

KILKEA CASTLE

KILKEA CASTLE GOLF CLUB, Kilkea,
Castledermot, **COUNTY KILDARE**,
IRELAND.

(T) 050 345555
(E) kilkeagolfclub@eircom.net

Course/s:
- **KILKEA CASTLE**
  Description: Championship, Parkland
  Built: 1995
  Number of Holes: 18   **Par:** 70
  Further Information:
  Course encircles Kilkea Castle.

KILKEE

KILKEE GOLF & COUNTRY CLUB, East
End, Kilkee, **COUNTY CLARE**, **IRELAND**.
(T) 065 9056048
(E) kilkeegolfclub@eircom.net

Membership: Members & Public
Size of Complex: 300 Acres

Contact/s:
- **Club Secretary:** Mr Patrick McInerney
- **Pro Shop:** Mr Ronan Grady

Course/s:
- **KILKEE**
  Description: Links, Cliff Top, Open,
  Medium Length, Drains Well
  Green Speed: Medium
  Built: 1896   **Built On:** Clay
  Number of Holes: 18   **Par:** 69
  Par 3's: 5   **Par 4's:** 11   **Par 5's:** 2
  Yds: 5862
  Prevailing Wind: West
  Designer: Edward Hackett
  Further Information:
  Magnificent scenery with exhilarating
  Atlantic breezes.

KILKEEL

KILKEEL GOLF CLUB, Mourne Pk,
Ballyardle, Kilkeel, Newry, **COUNTY DOWN**,
BT34 4LB, **NORTHERN IRELAND**.
(T) 028 41765095

Contact/s:
- **Book Tee Times:** Mr George Graham

Course/s:
- **KILKEEL**
  Description: Championship, Parkland,
  Sheltered, Medium Length, Drains Well,
  Ideal for the Elderly
  Green Speed: Fast
  Built: 1949   **Built On:** Soil
  Number of Holes: 18   **Par:** 72
  Par 3's: 3   **Par 4's:** 12   **Par 5's:** 3
  Yds: 6579   **F9 Yds:** 3388   **B9 Yds:** 3191
  Designer: Edward Hackett
  Further Information:
  The course offers picturesque views of
  natural beauty.

KILKENNY

KILKENNY GOLF CLUB, Glendine, Kilkenny,
COUNTY KILKENNY, **IRELAND**.
(T) 056 22125

Course/s:
- **KILKENNY**
  Number of Holes: 18

KILLARNEY

KILLARNEY GOLF & FISHING CLUB,
Mahonys Point, Killarney, **COUNTY KERRY**,
IRELAND.
(T) 064 31034
(E) reservations@killarney-golf.com
(W) www.killarney-golf.com

Membership: Members & Public

Contact/s:
- **Club Secretary:** Mr Tom Prendergast

- **Professional:** Mr Tom Coveney
  ☎ 064 31615

Course/s:
- **KILLEEN**
  Number of Holes: 18   **Par:** 72
  Par 3's: 3   **Par 4's:** 12   **Par 5's:** 3
  Yds: 6541   **F9 Yds:** 3054   **B9 Yds:** 3487
  Designer: Edward Hackett, Billy
  O'Sullivan ♟

- **LACKABANE**
  Number of Holes: 18   **Par:** 72
  Yds: 7616   **F9 Yds:** 3802   **B9 Yds:** 3814
  Designer: Donald Steel

- **MAHONY'S POINT**
  Number of Holes: 18   **Par:** 73
  Yds: 7324   **F9 Yds:** 3709   **B9 Yds:** 3614
  Designer: Guy Campbell, Henry
  Longhurst ♟

KILLEEN

KILLEEN GOLF CLUB, Killeenmore, Kill,
COUNTY KILDARE, **IRELAND**.
(T) 045 866003

Course/s:
- **KILLEEN**
  Number of Holes: 18
  Designer: Pat Ruddy

KILLELINE GOLF

KILLELINE GOLF & LEISURE CLUB LTD,
Newcastlewest, **COUNTY LIMERICK**,
IRELAND.
(T) 069 61600

Course/s:
- **KILLELINE**
  Number of Holes: 18

KILLIN

KILLIN GOLF CLUB, Aberfeldy Rd, Killin,
PERTH AND KINROSS, FK21 8TX,
SCOTLAND.
(T) 01567 820312
(E) info@killingolfclub.co.uk
(W) www.killingolfclub.co.uk

Contact/s:
- **Club Secretary:** Mr M Taylor

Course/s:
- **KILLIN**
  Description: Parkland
  Built: 1911
  Number of Holes: 9   **Par:** 33
  Par 3's: 4   **Par 4's:** 4   **Par 5's:** 1
  Yds: 2533   **F9 Yds:** 2533
  Designer: John Duncan
  Further Information:
  The course is set in the breathtaking
  Breadalbane Hills.

KILLIN PARK

KILLIN PARK GOLF & COUNTRY CLUB,
Killin, Dundalk, **COUNTY LOUTH**,
IRELAND.
(T) 042 9339303

Membership: Members & Public

Contact/s:

Course/s:
- **KILLIN PARK**
  Description: Parkland, Short, Drains Well
  Green Speed: Medium
  Number of Holes: 18

KILLINBEG

KILLINBEG GOLF CLUB, Killin Pk, Dundalk, **COUNTY LOUTH**, **IRELAND**.
(T) 042 9339303

Course/s:
🏌 **KILLINBEG**
Number of Holes: 18
Designer: Edward Hackett

KILLINEY

KILLINEY GOLF CLUB, Ballinclea Rd, Killiney, **COUNTY DUBLIN**, **IRELAND**.
(T) 01 2851983

Course/s:
🏌 **KILLINEY**
Number of Holes: 9

KILLIOW PARK

KILLIOW PARK GOLF, Killiow, Truro, **CORNWALL**, TR3 6AG, **ENGLAND**.
(T) 01872 270246
(E) office@killiow.fsnet.co.uk

Contact/s:
● Club Secretary: Mr John Crowson
☎ 01872 240915

Course/s:
🏌 **KILLIOW PARK**
Number of Holes: 18 Par: 69
Yds: 5274 F9 Yds: 2615 B9 Yds: 2659
Designer: R Oliver

KILLORGLIN

KILLORGLIN GOLF CLUB, Stealroe, Killorglin, **COUNTY KERRY**, **IRELAND**.
(T) 066 9761979
(E) kilgolf@iol.ie

Contact/s:
● Manager: Mr Billy Dodd

Course/s:
🏌 **KILLORGLIN**
Number of Holes: 18 Par: 72
Yds: 6467 F9 Yds: 3318 B9 Yds: 3149
Designer: Edward Hackett

KILLYMOON

KILLYMOON GOLF CLUB, 200 Killymoon Rd, Cookstown, **COUNTY TYRONE**, BT80 8TW, **NORTHERN IRELAND**.
(T) 028 86763762

Contact/s:
● Club Secretary: Mrs V Wilson
● Professional: Mr Gary Chambers
☎ 020 86763460

Course/s:
🏌 **KILLYMOON**
Number of Holes: 18 Par: 70
Par 3's: 6 Par 4's: 8 Par 5's: 4
Yds: 5496 F9 Yds: 2652 B9 Yds: 2844

KILMACOLM

KILMACOLM GOLF CLUB, Porterfield Rd, Kilmacolm, **INVERCLYDE**, PA13 4PD, **SCOTLAND**.
(T) 01505 872139

Course/s:
🏌 **KILMACOLM**
Number of Holes: 18
Designer: W Campbell

KILMARNOCK

KILMARNOCK (BARASSIE) GOLF CLUB, 29 Hillhouse Rd, Troon, **AYRSHIRE**

(SOUTH), KA10 6SY, **SCOTLAND**.
(T) 01292 313920

Contact/s:
● Club Secretary: Mr Donald Wilson
● Professional: Mr G Howie

Course/s:
🏌 **KILMARNOCK**
Number of Holes: 18 Par: 72
Yds: 6817 F9 Yds: 3360 B9 Yds: 3457
Designer: Theodore Moone

🏌 **NEW 9 HOLE**
Number of Holes: 9
Designer: Theodore Moone

KILNWICK PERCY

KILNWICK PERCY GOLF CLUB, Home Farm, Kilnwick Percy, Pocklington, York, **YORKSHIRE (NORTH)**, YO42 1UF, **ENGLAND**.
(T) 01759 303090

Membership: Members & Public

Contact/s:
● Club Secretary: Mrs E A Clayton
● Professional: Mr Joe Townhill

Course/s:
🏌 **KILNWICK PERCY**
Description: Parkland, Hilltop, Undulating, Medium Length
Green Speed: Medium
Built: 1994
Number of Holes: 18
Designer: John Day

KILREA

KILREA GOLF COURSE, Drumagarner Rd, Kilrea, **COUNTY LONDONDERRY**, BT51 5TB, **NORTHERN IRELAND**.
(T) 01266 821048

Contact/s:
● Club Secretary: Mr D Clark

Course/s:
🏌 **KILREA**
Description: Undulating, Tight
Number of Holes: 9
Yds: 4326

KILRUSH

KILRUSH GOLF CLUB, Ballykett, Kilrush, **COUNTY CLARE**, **IRELAND**.
(T) 065 9051138
(E) kelgolf@iol.ie
(W) www.westclare.com

Contact/s:
● Professional: Mr Sean O'Connor

Course/s:
🏌 **KILRUSH**
Description: Undulating
Built: 1934
Number of Holes: 18 Par: 70
Further Information:
There are water hazards and bunkers throughout the course.

KILSPINDIE

KILSPINDIE GOLF CLUB, Aberlady, Longniddry, **LOTHIAN (EAST)**, EH32 0QD, **SCOTLAND**.
(T) 01875 870358

Course/s:
🏌 **KILSPINDIE**
Description: Links
Number of Holes: 18 Par: 69
Yds: 5422

KILSYTH LENNOX

KILSYTH LENNOX GOLF CLUB, Tak-Ma-Doon Rd, Kilsyth, Glasgow, **GLASGOW (CITY OF)**, G65 0RS, **SCOTLAND**.
(T) 01236 824115

Contact/s:
● Club Secretary: Mr A Stephenson

Course/s:
🏌 **KILSYTH LENNOX**
Description: Parkland, Moorland, Undulating
Number of Holes: 18 Par: 70
Par 3's: 5 Par 4's: 10 Par 5's: 3
Yds: 5931 F9 Yds: 3177 B9 Yds: 2754

KILTERNAN

KILTERNAN GOLF & COUNTRY CLUB, Kilternan, **COUNTY DUBLIN**, **IRELAND**.
(T) 01 2955559
(E) kgc@kilternan-hotel.ie

Contact/s:
● Club Secretary: Mr Jimmy Kinsella
● Professional: Mr Tom Murphy

Course/s:
🏌 **KILTERNAN**
Number of Holes: 18 Par: 68
Yds: 5413
Designer: Edward Hackett

KILTON FOREST

KILTON FOREST GOLF CLUB, Blyth Rd, Worksop, **NOTTINGHAMSHIRE**, S81 0TL, **ENGLAND**.
(T) 01909 479199

Membership: Public

Contact/s:
● Club Secretary: Mr A Mansbridge
☎ 01909 486269
● Professional: Mr Stuart Betteridge
☎ 01909 486563

Course/s:
🏌 **KILTON**
Description: Parkland, Heath Land, Undulating, Open, Medium Length, Drains Well
Green Speed: Medium Built On: Sand
Number of Holes: 18 Par: 72
Yds: 6424 F9 Yds: 3124 B9 Yds: 3300

KILWORTH SPRINGS

KILWORTH SPRINGS GOLF CLUB, South Kilworth Rd, North Kilworth, Lutterworth, **LEICESTERSHIRE**, LE17 6HJ, **ENGLAND**.
(T) 01858 575082

Contact/s:
● Club Secretary: Mr K Mattock
● Professional: Mr N Melvin

Course/s:
🏌 **KILWORTH SPRINGS**
Number of Holes: 18 Par: 72
Yds: 6718

KING EDWARD BAY

KING EDWARD BAY GOLF CLUB, Howstrake, Groudle Rd, Onchan, **ISLE OF MAN**, IM3 2JR, **ENGLAND**.
(T) 01624 672709

Contact/s:
● Club Secretary: Mr B Holt
☎ 01624 670977
● Professional: Mr D Jones

Course/s:
🏌 **KING EDWARD BAY**

Number of Holes: 18 Par: 67
Yds: 5457
Designer: Tom Morris

KING JAMES VI

KING JAMES VI GOLF CLUB, Moncreiffe Island, Perth, **PERTH AND KINROSS**, PH2 8NR, **SCOTLAND**.
(T) 01738 445132

Contact/s:
● Club Secretary: Mrs H Blair
Course/s:
🟢 KING JAMES VI
Number of Holes: 18 Par: 70
Par 3's: 4 Par 4's: 12 Par 5's: 2
Yds: 6038 F9 Yds: 3158 B9 Yds: 2880
Designer: Tom Morris

KINGFISHER

KINGFISHER GOLF & COUNTRY CLUB,
Buckingham Rd, Wicken, Milton Keynes, **BUCKINGHAMSHIRE**, MK19 6DG, **ENGLAND**.
(T) 01908 560354

Contact/s:
● Manager: Mr M Bott
Course/s:
🟢 COURSE #1
Number of Holes: 9
Further Information:
Ideal for beginners and improvers.

KINGHORN

KINGHORN GOLF CLUB, Macduff Cres, Kinghorn, **FIFE**, KY9 3RF, **SCOTLAND**.
(T) 01592 890345

Membership: Members & Public

Contact/s:
● Club Secretary: Mr Ian Gow
  ☎ 01592 265445
Course/s:
🟢 KINGHORN
Description: Links
Green Speed: Medium
Built: 1890 Built On: Chalk/Sand
Number of Holes: 18 Par: 65
Par 3's: 7 Par 4's: 11
Yds: 5166 F9 Yds: 2788 B9 Yds: 2378
Further Information:
Challenging course with good greens and wonderful views across the Firth of Forth.

KINGS ACRE

KINGS ACRE GOLF COURSE, Lasswade, **LOTHIAN (MID)**, EH18 1AU, **SCOTLAND**.
(T) 0131 6633456
(E) info@kings-acregolf.com
(W) www.kings-acregolf.com

Membership: Members & Public

Contact/s:
● Club Secretary: Ms Lizzie King
● Professional: Mr Alan Murdoch
Course/s:
🟢 KINGS ACRE
Description: Wooded, Parkland, Undulating, Medium Length, Drains Well
Green Speed: Fast
Built: 1997
Number of Holes: 18 Par: 70
Yds: 5935
Designer: Graeme Webster

KINGS HILL

KINGS HILL GOLF CLUB LTD, Discovery Drive, Kings Hill, West Malling, **KENT**, ME19 4AF, **ENGLAND**.
(T) 01732 875040

Membership: Kings Hill
● Pro Shop:
  ☎ 01732 842121

KINGS LINKS GOLF CTRE

KINGS LINKS GOLF CENTRE, Golf Rd, Aberdeen, **ABERDEEN (CITY OF)**, AB24 1RZ, **SCOTLAND**.
(T) 01224 641644

Membership: Public

Contact/s:
● Professional: Mr B Davidson
  ☎ 01224 641577
Course/s:
🟢 KINGS LINKS
Description: Links
Number of Holes: 18
Yds: 6386

KING'S LYNN

KING'S LYNN GOLF CLUB, Castle Rising, King's Lynn, **NORFOLK**, PE31 6BD, **ENGLAND**.
(T) 01553 631654

Membership: Members & Public

Contact/s:
● Professional: Mr John Reynolds
  ☎ 01553 631655
Course/s:
🟢 KING'S LYNN
Description: Wooded, Sheltered, Tight, Drains Well
Green Speed: Medium
Built: 1972 Built On: Sand
Number of Holes: 18 Par: 72
Par 3's: 3 Par 4's: 12 Par 5's: 3
Yds: 6609 F9 Yds: 3609 B9 Yds: 3000
Designer: Peter Alliss, David Thomas

KINGS NORTON

KINGS NORTON GOLF CLUB LTD, Office, Brockhill Lane, Alvechurch, Birmingham, **MIDLANDS (WEST)**, B48 7ED, **ENGLAND**.
(T) 01564 826706
(E) info@kingsnortongolfclub.co.uk
(W) www.kingsnortongolfclub.co.uk

Course/s:
🟢 BLUE
Number of Holes: 9 Par: 36
Par 3's: 2 Par 4's: 5 Par 5's: 2
Yds: 3392
Designer: Hawtree

🟢 RED
Number of Holes: 9 Par: 36
Par 3's: 2 Par 4's: 5 Par 5's: 2
Yds: 3356
Designer: Hawtree

🟢 YELLOW
Number of Holes: 9 Par: 36
Par 3's: 2 Par 4's: 5 Par 5's: 2
Yds: 3256
Designer: Hawtree

KINGSBARNS GOLF LINKS

KINGSBARNS GOLF LINKS, Kingsbarns, St. Andrews, **FIFE**, KY16 8QD, **SCOTLAND**.
(T) 01334 460860
(E) info@kingsbarns.com

Membership: Public

Contact/s:
● Pro Shop: Mr Alan Purdie
  ☎ 01334 460865
Course/s:
🟢 KINGSBARN
Description: Championship, Links
Green Speed: Fast
Built: 2000
Number of Holes: 18 Par: 72
Yds: 6652 F9 Yds: 3283 B9 Yds: 3369
Designer: Kyle Phillips

KINGSDOWN

KINGSDOWN GOLF CLUB, Kingsdown, Corsham, **WILTSHIRE**, SN13 8BS, **ENGLAND**.
(T) 01225 743472
(E) kingsdowngc@genie.co.uk

Membership: Members & Public

Contact/s:
● Club Secretary: Mr J Elliott
● Professional: Mr A Butler
● Pro Shop:
  ☎ 01225 742634
Course/s:
🟢 KINGSDOWN
Description: Downland, Open, Medium Length, Drains Well, Ideal for the Elderly
Green Speed: Medium
Built: 1881 Built On: Soil
Number of Holes: 18 Par: 72
Yds: 6445 F9 Yds: 3251 B9 Yds: 3194

KINGSTHORPE

KINGSTHORPE GOLF CLUB, Kingsley Rd, Northampton, **NORTHAMPTONSHIRE**, NN2 7BU, **ENGLAND**.
(T) 01604 719602
(E) kingsthorpe.gc@lineone.net
(W) www.kingsthorpe-golf.co.uk

Membership: Members & Public
Size of Complex: 75 Acres

Contact/s:
● Professional: Mr P Armstrong
Course/s:
🟢 KINGSTHORPE
Description: Parkland, Undulating, Short, Tight, Drains Well
Green Speed: Medium Built: 1914
Built On: Sand Number of Holes: 18
Par: 69 Record: 64 (Bob Larratt)
Yds: 5918 F9 Yds: 2648 B9 Yds: 3270
Prevailing Wind: West
Designer: Charles Hugh Alison

KINGSWAY

KINGSWAY GOLF COURSE, Scunthorpe, **LINCOLNSHIRE (NORTH)**, DN15 7ER, **ENGLAND**.
(T) 01724 840945

Course/s:
🟢 KINGSWAY
Number of Holes: 9 Par: 29

KINGSWAY

KINGSWAY GOLF CENTRE, Cambridge Rd, Melbourn, Royston, **HERTFORDSHIRE**, SG8 6EY, **ENGLAND**.
(T) 01763 262727

Contact/s:
● Club Secretary: Mrs J Trim
● Professional: Mr D Hastings
Course/s:
🟢 KINGSWAY
Number of Holes: 9
Yds: 2500

KINGSWOOD

KINGSWOOD GOLF & COUNTRY CLUB,
Sandy Lane, Kingswood, Tadworth, **SURREY**,
KT20 6NE, **ENGLAND**.
(T) 01737 832334

Membership: Members & Public

Contact/s:
• **Professional:** Mr T Sims

Course/s:
⛳ **KINGSWOOD**
  Description: Parkland, Hilltop, Open,
  Long
  Green Speed: Medium
  Built: 1925 **Built On:** Clay/Soil
  Number of Holes: 18 **Par:** 73
  Yds: 6904
  Designer: James Braid
  Further Information:
  Flat course lined with mature trees.

KINGSWOOD

KINGSWOOD GOLF COURSE, Thorne Rd,
Hatfield, Doncaster, **YORKSHIRE (SOUTH)**,
DN7 6EP, **ENGLAND**.
(T) 01405 741343

Membership: Public
Size of Complex: 102 Acres

Contact/s:
• **Club Secretary:** Mr J B Wright
• **Professional:** Mr J Drury

Course/s:
⛳ **KINGSWOOD**
  Description: Parkland, Open, Medium
  Length, Tight, Tends to Flood, Ideal for the
  Elderly
  Green Speed: Medium
  Built: 1994 **Built On:** Clay
  Number of Holes: 18 **Par:** 70
  Record: 68 (Jonathan Drury)
  Par 3's: 4 **Par 4's:** 12 **Par 5's:** 2
  Yds: 6002 **F9 Yds:** 2921 **B9 Yds:** 3081
  Prevailing Wind: East
  Designer: John Hunt

KINGTON

KINGTON GOLF CLUB, Pro Shop,
Clubhouse, Bradnor, Kington,
HEREFORDSHIRE, HR5 3RE, **ENGLAND**.
(T) 01544 231320

Contact/s:
• **Professional:** Mr Andy Gealy

Course/s:
⛳ **KINGTON**
  Number of Holes: 18
  Yds: 5766
  Designer: Hutchinson

KINGUSSIE

KINGUSSIE GOLF CLUB, Stewards House
Kingussie Golf Club, Kingussie,
HIGHLANDS, PH21 1LR, **SCOTLAND**.
(T) 01540 661600
(E) kinggolf@globalnet.co.uk
(W) www.kingussie-golf.co.uk

Contact/s:
• **Club Secretary:** Mr Norman MacWilliam

Course/s:
⛳ **KINGUSSIE**
  Number of Holes: 18 **Par:** 67
  Yds: 5411 **F9 Yds:** 2749 **B9 Yds:** 2662
  Designer: Harry Vardon

KINLOSS

KINLOSS COUNTRY GOLF COURSE,

Clubhouse, Kinloss, Forres, **MORAY**, IV36
2UB, **SCOTLAND**.
(T) 01343 850585

Membership: Members & Public
Size of Complex: 100 Acres

Contact/s:
• **Owner:** Mr Gerald Verner
  ☎ 01343 850242

Course/s:
⛳ **KINLOSS 1**
  Description: Parkland, Undulating,
  Medium Length, Drains Well
  Green Speed: Medium
  Built: 1996 **Built On:** Soil
  Number of Holes: 9 **Par:** 34
  Par 3's: 3 **Par 4's:** 5 **Par 5's:** 1
  Yds: 2535
  Prevailing Wind: West
  Designer: Greens of Scotland
  Further Information:
  Caters for golfers of all standards. Can be
  played as an 18 hole course by
  combining Kinross 1 with Kinross 2.

⛳ **KINLOSS 2**
  Description: Medium Length, Drains Well
  Green Speed: Medium
  Built: 2001
  Number of Holes: 9 **Par:** 35
  Yds: 2931
  Further Information:
  Can be played as an 18 hole course by
  combining Kinross 2 with Kinross 1.

KINMEL PARK GOLF

KINMEL PARK GOLF LTD, Abergele Rd,
Bodelwyddan, Rhyl, **DENBIGHSHIRE**, LL18
5SR, **WALES**.
(T) 01745 833548

Membership: Public

Contact/s:
• **Sole Director:** Mrs Louise
  Fetherstonhaugh

Course/s:
⛳ **KINMEL PARK**
  Description: Parkland
  Built: 1988
  Number of Holes: 9
  Designer: Peter Stebbings

KINROSS

KINROSS GOLF CLUB, The Beeches,
Kinross, **PERTH AND KINROSS**, KY13 8EU,
SCOTLAND.
(T) 01577 862237

Course/s:
⛳ **BLUE**
  Number of Holes: 18 **Par:** 71
  Yds: 6438

⛳ **RED**
  Number of Holes: 18 **Par:** 73
  Yds: 6256

KINSALE

KINSALE GOLF CLUB FARRANGALWAY,
Farrangalway, Kinsale, **COUNTY CORK**,
IRELAND.
(T) 021 4774722
(E) kinsaleg@indigo.ie
(W) www.kinsalegolf.com

Membership: Members & Public
Size of Complex: 130 Acres

Contact/s:
• **Club Secretary:** Mr Tom Crowley
  ☎ 08763 23992
• **Professional:** Mr Gee Broderick

☎ 021 4773258
• **Book Tee Times:** Ms Delia Higgins

Course/s:
⛳ **FARRANGALWAY**
  Description: Championship, Wooded,
  Parkland, Long, Drains Well, Ideal for the
  Elderly
  Green Speed: Fast
  Built: 1994 **Built On:** Soil
  Number of Holes: 18 **Par:** 71
  Yds: 6440 **F9 Yds:** 3202 **B9 Yds:** 3238
  Designer: Jack Kenneally

⛳ **RINGENANE**
  Description: Wooded, Parkland,
  Undulating, Short, Tight, Drains Well
  Number of Holes: 9
  Yds: 2700 **F9 Yds:** 2700
  Designer: Jack Kenneally

KINSALE

KINSALE GOLF COURSE, Llanerch-Y-Mor,
Holywell, **FLINTSHIRE**, CH8 9DX, **WALES**.
(T) 01745 561080

Membership: Public

Contact/s:
• **Club Secretary:** Mr Alan Norwood

Course/s:
⛳ **KINSALE**
  Description: Parkland, Undulating,
  Medium Length
  Green Speed: Medium
  Built: 1992
  Number of Holes: 9

KINTORE

KINTORE GOLF CLUB, Balbithan, Kintore,
Inverurie, **ABERDEENSHIRE**, AB51 0UR,
SCOTLAND.
(T) 01467 632631
(E) kintoregolfclub@lineone.net

Membership: Public

Contact/s:
• **Club Secretary:** Mr James Black
• **Book Tee Times:** Mr Charlie Lindsay

Course/s:
⛳ **KINTORE**
  Description: Wooded, Parkland,
  Undulating, Drains Well
  Built: 1911 **Built On:** Sand
  Number of Holes: 18 **Par:** 70
  Yds: 6019 **F9 Yds:** 3377 **B9 Yds:** 2642
  Further Information:
  Contrasting old and new nines. The newer
  holes are lined by trees and criss-crossed
  by burns in a delightful but testing layout.
  The final six holes, part of the old nine, are
  short and relatively hilly and demand
  careful club selection. Great views of the
  River Don.

KIRBY MUXLOE

KIRBY MUXLOE GOLF CLUB, Clubhouse,
Station Rd, Kirby Muxloe, Leicester,
LEICESTERSHIRE, LE9 2EP, **ENGLAND**.
(T) 0116 2393457

Membership: Members & Public
Size of Complex: 130 Acres

Contact/s:
• **Club Secretary:** Mr Robert Wildsmith
• **Professional:** Mr Bruce Whipham

Course/s:
⛳ **KIRBY MUXLOE**
  Description: Parkland, Undulating,
  Sheltered, Medium Length, Drains Well,
  Ideal for the Elderly

Green Speed: Medium
Built: 1893 Built On: Clay
Number of Holes: 18 Par: 70
Record: 62 (Bruce Whipman)
Yds: 6279 F9 Yds: 3182 B9 Yds: 3097
Prevailing Wind: East

KIRKBY LONSDALE

KIRKBY LONSDALE GOLF CLUB, Scaleber
Lane, Barbon, Carnforth, **LANCASHIRE**, LA6
2LJ, **ENGLAND**.
(T) 01524 276365
(E) klgolf@dial.pipex.com
(W) www.klgolf.dial.pipex.com

Membership: Members & Public
Size of Complex: 167 Acres

Contact/s:
● **Club Secretary:** Mr Geoffrey Hall
  ☎ 01524 276366
● **Book Lessons:** Mr Chris Barrett

Course/s:
⛳ **KIRKBY LONSDALE**
  Description: Parkland, Moorland,
  Undulating, Medium Length
  Green Speed: Medium
  Built: 1991 Built On: Clay
  Number of Holes: 18 Par: 72
  Par 3's: 4 Par 4's: 10 Par 5's: 4
  Yds: 6481 F9 Yds: 3189 B9 Yds: 3292
  Prevailing Wind: West
  Designer: Bill Squires
  Further Information:
  Surrounded by outstanding natural
  beauty.

KIRKBYMOORSIDE

KIRKBYMOORSIDE GOLF CLUB LTD,
Manor Vale, Kirkbymoorside, York,
YORKSHIRE (NORTH), YO62 6EG,
ENGLAND.
(T) 01751 431525
(E) enqs@kmsgolf.fsnet.co.uk
(W) www.kirkbymoorsidegolf.co.uk

Contact/s:
● **Professional:** Mr Chris Tyson
  ☎ 01751 430402

Course/s:
⛳ **KIRKBYMOORSIDE**
  Description: Wooded, Parkland,
  Moorland
  Built: 1952
  Number of Holes: 18 Par: 69
  Yds: 6112 F9 Yds: 2841 B9 Yds: 3271

KIRKCALDY

KIRKCALDY GOLF CLUB, Balwearie Rd,
Kirkcaldy, **FIFE**, KY2 5LT, **SCOTLAND**.
(T) 01592 205240

Contact/s:
● **Professional:** Mr Anthony Caira

Course/s:
⛳ **KIRKCALDY**
  Description: Parkland
  Built: 1904
  Number of Holes: 18 Par: 71
  Par 3's: 4 Par 4's: 11 Par 5's: 3
  Yds: 6038 F9 Yds: 2923 B9 Yds: 3115

KIRKCUDBRIGHT

KIRKCUDBRIGHT GOLF CLUB, Stirling
Cres, Kirkcudbright, **DUMFRIES AND
GALLOWAY**, DG6 4EZ, **SCOTLAND**.
(T) 01557 330314

Membership: Members & Public

Contact/s:
● **Club Secretary:** Mr David Mackenzie

● **Pro Shop:** Mrs Flora McGown

Course/s:
⛳ **KIRKCUDBRIGHT**
  Description: Parkland, Breckland,
  Undulating, Open, Medium Length,
  Drains Well, Ideal for the Elderly
  Green Speed: Medium
  Built: 1893 Built On: Sand
  Number of Holes: 18 Par: 69
  Par 3's: 5 Par 4's: 11 Par 5's: 2
  Yds: 5717 F9 Yds: 2900 B9 Yds: 2817
  Prevailing Wind: South/West

KIRKHILL

KIRKHILL GOLF CLUB, Greenlees Rd,
Cambuslang, Glasgow, **GLASGOW (CITY
OF)**, G72 8YN, **SCOTLAND**.
(T) 0141 6413083

Membership: Members & Public

Contact/s:
● **Club Secretary:** Mr Jack Young
● **Professional:** Mr Duncan Williamson
  ☎ 0141 6417972

Course/s:
⛳ **KIRKHILL GOLF COURSE**
  Description: Parkland, Undulating, Open,
  Drains Well
  Built: 1910 Built On: Soil
  Number of Holes: 18 Par: 70
  Record: 65 (Stuart Abernethy)
  Par 3's: 5 Par 4's: 10 Par 5's: 3
  Yds: 6030 F9 Yds: 3004 B9 Yds: 3026
  Prevailing Wind: West
  Designer: James Braid
  Further Information:
  A river runs into play on 4 holes.

KIRKINTILLOCH

KIRKINTILLOCH GOLF CLUB, Kirkintilloch,
Glasgow, **GLASGOW (CITY OF)**, G66 1RN,
SCOTLAND.
(T) 0141 7752387

Contact/s:
● **Club Secretary:** Mr I M Gray

Course/s:
⛳ **KIRKINTILLOCH**
  Number of Holes: 18
  Yds: 5269
  Designer: James Braid

KIRKISTOWN CASTLE

KIRKISTOWN CASTLE GOLF CLUB, 142
Main Rd, Cloughey, Newtownards, **COUNTY
DOWN**, BT22 1JA, **NORTHERN IRELAND**.
(T) 028 42771233
(E) kirkistown@aol.com
(W) www.kcgc.org

Membership: Members & Public

Contact/s:
● **Professional:** Mr Jonathan Peden
● **Book Tee Times:** Ms Rosemary Coulter

Course/s:
⛳ **KIRKISTOWN CASTLE**
  Description: Links, Drains Well
  Built: 1902
  Number of Holes: 18 Par: 69
  Yds: 5616 F9 Yds: 2776 B9 Yds: 2840
  Designer: James Braid

KIRRIEMUIR

KIRRIEMUIR GOLF CLUB, Shielhill Rd,
Northmuir, Kirriemuir, **ANGUS**, DD8 4LN,
SCOTLAND.
(T) 01575 573317
(E) info@kirriemuirgolfclub.co.uk

(W) www.kirriemuirgolfclub.co.uk

Membership: Members & Public
Size of Complex: 65 Acres

Contact/s:
● **Professional:** Mrs Karyn Dallas

Course/s:
⛳ **KIRRIEMUIR**
  Description: Parkland, Heath Land,
  Sheltered, Short, Drains Well, Ideal for the
  Elderly
  Green Speed: Medium
  Built: 1908 Built On: Soil
  Number of Holes: 18 Par: 68
  Record: 63 (D Huish)
  Par 3's: 4 Par 4's: 14
  Yds: 5510
  Designer: James Braid
  Further Information:
  The course is ideal if you want to play 36
  holes in a day. Panoramic views and a
  good test of golf for all levels of golfers.

KIRTLINGTON

KIRTLINGTON GOLF CLUB, Vicarage Farm,
Kirtlington, Kidlington, **OXFORDSHIRE**, OX5
3JY, **ENGLAND**.
(T) 01869 351133

Course/s:
⛳ **COURSE #1**
  Number of Holes: 18 Par: 70
  Yds: 6107 F9 Yds: 3149 B9 Yds: 2958

KIRTON HOLME

KIRTON HOLME GOLF COURSE, The Croft,
Kirton Holme, Boston, **LINCOLNSHIRE**,
PE20 1SY, **ENGLAND**.
(T) 01205 290669

Membership: Members & Public
Size of Complex: 40 Acres

Contact/s:
● **Club Secretary:** Mrs T Welberry
  ☎ 01205 290560
● **Book Tee Times:** Mr T Welberry

Course/s:
⛳ **KIRTON HOLME**
  Description: Parkland, Open, Medium
  Length, Drains Well, Ideal for the Elderly
  Green Speed: Medium
  Built: 1992
  Number of Holes: 9
  Yds: 2884
  Prevailing Wind: South/West
  Designer: D Welberry

KNARESBOROUGH

KNARESBOROUGH GOLF CLUB, Butter
Hills, Boroughbridge Rd, Knaresborough,
YORKSHIRE (NORTH), HG5 0QQ,
ENGLAND.
(T) 01423 862690

Contact/s:
● **Manager:** Mr J Hall

Course/s:
⛳ **KNARESBOROUGH**
  Number of Holes: 18 Par: 70
  Yds: 6413 F9 Yds: 2952 B9 Yds: 3461
  Designer: Hawtree

KNEBWORTH

KNEBWORTH GOLF CLUB, Deards End
Lane, Knebworth, **HERTFORDSHIRE**, SG3
6NL, **ENGLAND**.
(T) 01438 812488

Contact/s:
● **Club Secretary:** Mr M Parsons (MBE)

- **Professional:** Mr G Parker
  ☎ 01428 812757
Course/s:
- **KNEBWORTH**
  Number of Holes: 18 **Par:** 71
  Par 3's: 4 **Par 4's:** 11 **Par 5's:** 3
  Yds: 6492 **F9 Yds:** 3180 **B9 Yds:** 3312
  Designer: William Park

KNIGHTON

KNIGHTON GOLF CLUB, Ffrydd Wood,
Knighton, **POWYS**, LD7 1DG, **WALES**.
(T) 01547 528646
Contact/s:
- **Club Secretary:** Mr Wayne Aspley
  ☎ 01547 520297
Course/s:
- **KNIGHTON**
  Description: Moorland
  Built: 1913
  Number of Holes: 9 **Par:** 68
  Yds: 5362 **F9 Yds:** 2681 **B9 Yds:** 2681
  Designer: Harry Vardon
  Further Information:
  Views of English and Welsh border and
  Offas Dykes. A 9 hole course that can be
  played as an 18 hole course

KNIGHTON HEATH

KNIGHTON HEATH GOLF CLUB, Francis
Ave, Bournemouth, **DORSET**, BH11 8NX,
ENGLAND.
(T) 01202 572633
Contact/s:
- **Club Manager:** Mr Richard Bestwick
Course/s:
- **KNIGHTON HEATH**
  Number of Holes: 18 **Par:** 68
  Yds: 5655 **F9 Yds:** 2942 **B9 Yds:** 2713

KNIGHTS GRANGE

**KNIGHTS GRANGE SPORTS COMPLEX &
GOLF COURSE,** Grange Lane, Winsford,
CHESHIRE, CW7 2PT, **ENGLAND**.
(T) 01606 552780
Course/s:
- **KNIGHTS GRANGE**
  Number of Holes: 18 **Par:** 71
  Yds: 6010 **F9 Yds:** 3215 **B9 Yds:** 2795

KNIGHTSWOOD

KNIGHTSWOOD GOLF CLUB, Lincoln
Avenue, Knightswood, Glasgow, **GLASGOW
(CITY OF)**, G13 3DN, **SCOTLAND**.
(T) 0141 954 6495
Membership: Members & Public
Contact/s:
- **Club Secretary:** Mr James Dean
- **Book Tee Times:** Mr Frank McAvoy
Course/s:
- **KNIGHTSWOOD**
  Description: Parkland, Open, Medium
  Length, Tends to Flood, Ideal for the
  Elderly
  Green Speed: Medium
  Built: 1930
  Number of Holes: 9
  Yds: 2792

KNOCK

KNOCK GOLF CLUB LTD, Upper
Newtownards Rd, Dundonald, Belfast,
COUNTY ANTRIM, BT16 2QX, **NORTHERN
IRELAND**.

(T) 028 90483825
Membership: Members & Public
Size of Complex: 90 Acres
Contact/s:
- **Club Secretary:** Mr George Managh
- **Professional:** Mr Gordon Fareweather
Course/s:
- **KNOCK**
  Description: Parkland, Undulating, Open,
  Medium Length, Drains Well, Ideal for the
  Elderly
  Green Speed: Fast
  Built: 1921 **Built On:** Soil
  Number of Holes: 18 **Par:** 70
  Par 3's: 3 **Par 4's:** 14 **Par 5's:** 1
  Yds: 6402 **F9 Yds:** 3267 **B9 Yds:** 3135
  Prevailing Wind: West
  Designer: Charles Hugh Alison, Harry
  Shapland Colt, Alistair MacKenzie
  Further Information:
  Tree lined parkland with stream running
  into play on several holes.

KNOCKANALLY

KNOCKANALLY GOLF CLUB, Knockanally,
Donadea, **COUNTY KILDARE**, **IRELAND**.
(T) 045 869322
Contact/s:
- **Club Secretary:** Mr Noel Lyons
Course/s:
- **KNOCKANALLY**
  Number of Holes: 18
  Yds: 6424

KNOLE PARK

KNOLE PARK GOLF CLUB, Seal Hollow Rd,
Sevenoaks, **KENT**, TN15 0HJ, **ENGLAND**.
(T) 01732 451740
Contact/s:
- **Club Secretary:** Mr A P Mitchell
  ☎ 01732 452150
- **Professional:** Mr Phil Sykes
Course/s:
- **KNOLE PARK**
  Description: Breckland, Valley,
  Undulating, Open, Medium Length,
  Drains Well
  Green Speed: Fast
  Built: 1924
  Number of Holes: 18 **Par:** 70
  Yds: 6266 **F9 Yds:** 3136 **B9 Yds:** 3130
  Prevailing Wind: South/West
  Designer: J F Abercromby
  Further Information:
  Set in Knole Park with deer running free.

KNOTT END

KNOTT END GOLF CLUB LTD., Wyre Side,
Knott End-on-Sea, Poulton-Le-Fylde,
LANCASHIRE, FY6 0AA, **ENGLAND**.
(T) 01253 811365
Membership: Members & Public
Contact/s:
- **Club Secretary:** Mr Tony Crossly
- **Professional:** Mr Paul Walker
- **Book Tee Times:** Miss Louise Freeman
Course/s:
- **KNOTT END**
  Description: Links, Moorland,
  Undulating, Open, Medium Length,
  Drains Well, Ideal for the Elderly
  Green Speed: Medium
  Built: 1911 **Built On:** Clay
  Number of Holes: 18 **Par:** 69
  Record: 68 (Paul Walker)
  Yds: 5843 **F9 Yds:** 3133 **B9 Yds:** 2710

  Prevailing Wind: North/West
  Designer: James Braid
  Further Information:
  Course in excellent condition.

KNOTTY HILL GOLF CTRE

KNOTTY HILL GOLF CENTRE, Sedgefield,
Stockton-on-Tees, **CLEVELAND**, TS21 2BB,
ENGLAND.
(T) 01740 620320
(E) khgc21@btopenworld.com
Membership: Members & Public
Contact/s:
- **Club Secretary:** Ms Judy Reynolds
Course/s:
- **BISHOPS**
  Description: Wooded, Parkland, Valley,
  Undulating, Open, Long, Drains Well,
  Ideal for the Elderly
  Green Speed: Medium
  Built: 1998 **Built On:** Sand/Soil
  Number of Holes: 18 **Par:** 70
  Yds: 5886 **F9 Yds:** 2984 **B9 Yds:** 2902
  Prevailing Wind: West
  Designer: C Stanton
- **PRINCES**
  Description: Wooded, Parkland, Valley,
  Undulating, Ideal for the Elderly
  Green Speed: Medium
  Built: 1991 **Built On:** Soil
  Number of Holes: 18 **Par:** 72
  Yds: 6577 **F9 Yds:** 3502 **B9 Yds:** 3075
  Prevailing Wind: West
  Designer: C Stanton

KNOWLE

KNOWLE GOLF CLUB, West Town Lane,
Brislington, Bristol, **BRISTOL**, BS4 5DF,
ENGLAND.
(T) 01179 770660
Membership: Members & Public
Size of Complex: 95 Acres
Contact/s:
- **Professional:** Mr G M Brand
Course/s:
- **KNOWLE**
  Description: Parkland, Undulating,
  Medium Length, Drains Well, Ideal for the
  Elderly
  Green Speed: Medium
  Built: 1905
  Number of Holes: 18 **Par:** 69
  Par 3's: 5 **Par 4's:** 11 **Par 5's:** 2
  Yds: 6016 **F9 Yds:** 2864 **B9 Yds:** 3152
  Prevailing Wind: South/West
  Designer: Taylor
  Further Information:
  Beautifully designed course with many
  interesting holes.

KNUTSFORD

KNUTSFORD GOLF CLUB, Mereheath Lane,
Knutsford, **CHESHIRE**, WA16 6HS,
ENGLAND.
(T) 01565 633355
Course/s:
- **KNUTSFORD**
  Number of Holes: 9

KYLES OF BUTE

KYLES OF BUTE GOLF CLUB,
Tighnabruaich, **ARGYLL AND BUTE**, PA21
2EE, **SCOTLAND**.
(T) 01700 811603
Course/s:

KYLES OF BUTE
Number of Holes: 9　Par: 66
Yds: 4380
Further Information:
9 hole course can be played as an 18 hole course.

LA GRANDE MARE
LA GRANDE MARE GOLF CLUB, Vazon Bay, Castel, Guernsey, **CHANNEL ISLANDS**, **ENGLAND**.
(T) 01481 255313
Membership: Members & Public
Size of Complex: 110 Acres
Contact/s:
● Club Secretary: Mr J Vermeulen
☎ 01481 253544
Course/s:
🏌 LA GRANDE MARE
Description: Parkland, Short
Built On: Clay
Number of Holes: 18　Par: 64
Par 3's: 9　Par 4's: 8　Par 5's: 1
Yds: 4517　F9 Yds: 2169　B9 Yds: 2348
Designer: Fred Hawtree
Further Information:
Mallards, Moorhens, Hooper Swans, Brent Geese and other migratory birds can be seen from the fairways, feeding in the lakes.

LA MOYE
LA MOYE GOLF CLUB, La Route Orange, La Moye, St Brelade, **JERSEY**, JE3 8GQ, **ENGLAND**.
(T) 01534 743401
Course/s:
🏌 LA MOYE
Number of Holes: 18　Par: 72
Yds: 6664　F9 Yds: 3413　B9 Yds: 3251
Designer: James Braid

LADBROOK PARK
LADBROOK PARK GOLF CLUB LTD, Poolhead Lane, Tanworth-In-Arden, Solihull, **MIDLANDS (WEST)**, B94 5ED, **ENGLAND**.
(T) 01564 742264
(E) secretary@ladbrookparkgolfclub.fsnet.co.uk
Contact/s:
● Professional: Mr Richard Mountford
☎ 01564 742581
Course/s:
🏌 LADBROOK PARK
Number of Holes: 18　Par: 71
Yds: 6427　F9 Yds: 3384　B9 Yds: 3043
Designer: Harry Shapland Colt

LADIES PANMURE
LADIES PANMURE GOLF CLUB, 7 Princes St, Monifieth, Dundee, **ANGUS**, DD5 4AW, **SCOTLAND**.
(T) 01382 535206
Course/s:
🏌 MEDAL

LADYBANK
LADYBANK GOLF CLUB, Annsmuir, Ladybank, Cupar, **FIFE**, KY15 7RA, **SCOTLAND**.
(T) 01337 830320
(E) ladybankgc@aol.com
Membership: Members & Public
Contact/s:

● Club Secretary: Mr David Allan
● Professional: Mr Martin Gray
☎ 01337 830725
Course/s:
🏌 LADYBANK
Description: Championship, Wooded, Moorland, Sheltered, Long, Drains Well, Ideal for the Elderly
Green Speed: Medium
Built: 1879　Built On: Soil
Number of Holes: 18　Par: 71
Yds: 6299　F9 Yds: 3139　B9 Yds: 3160
Prevailing Wind: South/West
Designer: James Braid, Tom Morris
Further Information:
An easy walking, very scenic course. 🏌

LAGGANMORE
LAGGANMORE GOLF CLUB, Lagganmore, Portpatrick, Stranraer, **DUMFRIES AND GALLOWAY**, DG9 9AB, **SCOTLAND**.
(T) 01776 810262
(W) www.lagganmoregolf.co.uk
Membership: Public
Contact/s:
● Club Secretary: Mr N McIntyre
● Book Tee Times: Reception
Course/s:
🏌 LAGGANMORE
Description: Parkland, Sheltered, Medium Length, Tight, Drains Well
Green Speed: Medium
Built: 1990　Built On: Soil
Number of Holes: 18
Prevailing Wind: West
Designer: N Williams
Further Information:
A flat course.

LAHINCH
LAHINCH GOLF CLUB, Lahinch, **COUNTY CLARE**, **IRELAND**.
(T) 065 7081003
(E) lgc@iol.ie
(W) www.lahinchgolf.com
Membership: Members & Public
Course/s:
🏌 CASTLE
Number of Holes: 18　Par: 70
Par 3's: 5　Par 4's: 10　Par 5's: 3
Yds: 5594　F9 Yds: 2609　B9 Yds: 2985
Designer: Alistair MacKenzie
🏌 OLD
Number of Holes: 18　Par: 72
Par 3's: 4　Par 4's: 10　Par 5's: 4
Yds: 6453　F9 Yds: 3156　B9 Yds: 3297
Designer: Gibson, Alistair MacKenzie 🏌

LAKESIDE
LAKESIDE GOLF CLUB, Water St, Margam, Port Talbot, **NEATH PORT TALBOT**, SA13 2PA, **WALES**.
(T) 01639 899959
Membership: Members & Public
Contact/s:
● Professional: Mr M Wootton
Course/s:
🏌 LAKESIDE
Description: Links, Parkland, Open, Short, Drains Well, Ideal for the Elderly
Green Speed: Fast
Built: 1992　Built On: Sand/Soil
Number of Holes: 18
Prevailing Wind: West
Designer: Matthew Wootton
Further Information:

A flat course.

LAKESIDE LODGE
LAKESIDE LODGE GOLF CLUB, Fen Rd, Pidley, Huntingdon, **CAMBRIDGESHIRE**, PE28 3DD, **ENGLAND**.
(T) 01487 740540
Membership: Members & Public
Size of Complex: 240 Acres
Contact/s:
● Club Secretary: Ms Jane Hopkins
● Professional: Mr Scott Waterman
☎ 01487 741541
Course/s:
🏌 CHURCH
Number of Holes: 6
🏌 LODGE
Description: Parkland, Undulating, Open, Long, Drains Well, Ideal for the Elderly
Green Speed: Fast
Built: 1992　Built On: Clay
Number of Holes: 18
Designer: Alistair Headley
🏌 MANOR
Number of Holes: 9

LALEHAM
LALEHAM GOLF CLUB, Laleham Reach, Chertsey, **SURREY**, KT16 8RP, **ENGLAND**.
(T) 01932 564211
(W) www.laleham-golf.co.uk
Contact/s:
● Club Secretary: Mrs P Kennett
● Professional: Mr H Stott
● Pro Shop:
☎ 01932 562877
Course/s:
🏌 LALEHAM
Number of Holes: 18　Par: 70
Yds: 6241　F9 Yds: 2963　B9 Yds: 3278

LAMBERHURST
LAMBERHURST GOLF CLUB, Church Rd, Lamberhurst, Tunbridge Wells, **KENT**, TN3 8DT, **ENGLAND**.
(T) 01892 890552
Membership: Members & Public
Contact/s:
● Club Secretary: Mr Bob Walden
☎ 01892 890591
● Professional: Mr Brian Impett
● Book Tee Times:
☎ 01892 890882
Course/s:
🏌 LAMBERHURST
Description: Parkland, Undulating, Sheltered, Medium Length, Tends to Flood
Green Speed: Fast
Built: 1891　Built On: Clay
Number of Holes: 18　Par: 72
Yds: 6275　F9 Yds: 3086　B9 Yds: 3189
Prevailing Wind: West
Further Information:
A River runs through the course.

LAMBOURNE CLUB
LAMBOURNE CLUB (THE), Dropmore Rd, Burnham, Slough, **BERKSHIRE**, SL1 8NF, **ENGLAND**.
(T) 01628 666755
Membership: Members & Public
Contact/s:
● Professional: Mr David Hart

☎ 01628 662936

Course/s:

LAMBOURNE.
Description: Parkland, Open, Long, Drains Well
Green Speed: Medium
Built: 1992 **Built On:** Clay
Number of Holes: 18 **Record:** 67 (Paul Robshaw)
Designer: Donald Steel
Further Information:
Lambourne is a flat course.

LAMLASH

LAMLASH GOLF CLUB, Lamlash, **ISLE OF ARRAN**, KA27 8JU, **SCOTLAND**.
(T) 01770 600196
(W) www.arrangolf.co.uk

Contact/s:
● Club Secretary: Mr J Henderson
  ☎ 01770 600296

Course/s:

LAMLASH
Number of Holes: 18 **Par:** 64
Par 3's: 8 **Par 4's:** 10
Yds: 4640 **F9 Yds:** 2555 **B9 Yds:** 2085
Designer: William Auchterlonie

LANARK

LANARK GOLF CLUB, The Moor, Whitelees Rd, Lanark, **LANARKSHIRE (SOUTH)**, ML11 7RX, **SCOTLAND**.
(T) 01555 663219
(E) lanarkgolfclub@talk21.com

Contact/s:
● Club Secretary: Mr George Cuthill
● Professional: Mr Alan White
  ☎ 01555 661456

Course/s:

OLD
Description: Championship, Moorland, Undulating, Open, Medium Length, Drains Well
Green Speed: Fast
Built: 1851 **Built On:** Sand
Number of Holes: 18 **Par:** 70
Yds: 6306 **F9 Yds:** 3356 **B9 Yds:** 2950
Prevailing Wind: West
Designer: Tom Morris

WEE
Built: 1851
Number of Holes: 9 **Par:** 28
Yds: 1489

LANCASTER

LANCASTER GOLF CLUB, Ashton Rd, Lancaster, **LANCASHIRE**, LA2 0AA, **ENGLAND**.
(T) 01524 751105

Contact/s:
● Club Secretary: Phil Irvine
● Professional: David Sutcliffe

Course/s:

LANCASTER GOLF CLUB
Number of Holes: 18 **Par:** 71
Yds: 6288

LANCASTER

LANCASTER GOLF CLUB LTD, Ashton Hall, Aston-With-Stodday, Lancaster, **LANCASHIRE**, LA2 0AJ, **ENGLAND**.
(T) 01524 751247

Contact/s:
● Book Tee Times: Mr David Sutcliffe

Course/s:

LANCASTER
Description: Parkland, Undulating
Built: 1932
Number of Holes: 18 **Par:** 71
Designer: James Braid

LANES

LANES GOLF COURSE, Muddy Lane, Stoke Rd, Slough, **BERKSHIRE**, SL2 5AQ, **ENGLAND**.
(T) 01753 554840

Contact/s:
● Manager: Mr P Warner

Course/s:

LANES
Number of Holes: 9 **Par:** 32
Yds: 2074

LANGDON HILLS GOLF CTRE

LANGDON HILLS GOLF CENTRE, Lower Dunton Rd, Bulphan, Upminster, **ESSEX**, RM14 3TY, **ENGLAND**.
(T) 01268 544300

Contact/s:
● Professional: Mr Terry Moncur

Course/s:

BULPHAN
Description: Parkland, Undulating
Built: 1991
Number of Holes: 9 **Par:** 37

HORNDON
Description: Parkland, Undulating
Built: 1991
Number of Holes: 9 **Par:** 36

LANGDON
Description: Parkland, Undulating
Built: 1991
Number of Holes: 9 **Par:** 35
Further Information:
Dramatic views across London.

LANGHOLM

LANGHOLM GOLF CLUB, Whitaside, Langholm, **DUMFRIES AND GALLOWAY**, DG13 0JR, **SCOTLAND**.
(T) 01387 380673/81247

Course/s:

LANGHOLM
Number of Holes: 9

LANGLAND BAY

LANGLAND BAY GOLF CLUB, Langland Bay Rd, Langland, Swansea, **SWANSEA**, SA3 4QR, **WALES**.
(T) 01792 366023

Contact/s:
● Club Secretary: Mrs L Coleman
  ☎ 01792 361721
● Professional: Mr Mark Evans
● Pro Shop:
  ☎ 01792 366186

Course/s:

LANGLAND BAY
Description: Links, Parkland, Cliff Top, Undulating, Open, Short, Tight, Drains Well
Green Speed: Fast
Built: 1904 **Built On:** Sand/Soil
Number of Holes: 18
Prevailing Wind: South/West
Designer: Henry Cotton
Further Information:
Challenging course with panoramic views.

LANGLANDS

LANGLANDS GOLF CLUB, Langlands Rd, East Kilbride, Glasgow, **GLASGOW (CITY OF)**, G75 9DW, **SCOTLAND**.
(T) 01355 224685

Course/s:

COURSE #1
Number of Holes: 18
Yds: 6202

LANGLEY PARK

LANGLEY PARK GOLF CLUB, Barnfield Wood Rd, Beckenham, **KENT**, BR3 6SZ, **ENGLAND**.
(T) 020 86501663
(E) cslpgc@aol.com

Contact/s:
● Professional: Mr Colin Staff
● Pro Shop: Mr Gary Wallis
● Book Tee Times:
  ☎ 020 86586849

Course/s:

LANGLEY PARK
Description: Championship, Parkland, Sheltered, Long, Tight, Tends to Flood, Ideal for the Elderly
Green Speed: Fast **Built On:** Clay
Number of Holes: 18
Designer: Taylor

LANHYDROCK

LANHYDROCK GOLF CLUB, Lostwithiel Rd, Lanhydrock, Bodmin, **CORNWALL**, PL30 5AQ, **ENGLAND**.
(T) 01208 73600
(W) www.lanhydrock-golf.co.uk

Contact/s:
● Joint Director: Mr G Bond

Course/s:

LANHYDROCK
Number of Holes: 18 **Par:** 70
Par 3's: 4 **Par 4's:** 12 **Par 5's:** 2
Yds: 6100 **F9 Yds:** 3151 **B9 Yds:** 2949
Designer: J Hamilton-Stutt

LANSDOWN

LANSDOWN GOLF CLUB, Lansdown, Bath, **BATH & SOMERSET (NORTH EAST)**, BA1 9BT, **ENGLAND**.
(T) 01225 425007

Contact/s:
● Golf Manager: Mr Terry Mercer
  ☎ 01225 420242

Course/s:

LANSDOWN
Number of Holes: 18 **Par:** 71
Par 3's: 5 **Par 4's:** 9 **Par 5's:** 4
Yds: 6316 **F9 Yds:** 3136 **B9 Yds:** 3180
Designer: C A Whitcombe

LANSIL

LANSIL GOLF CLUB, Caton Rd, Lancaster, **LANCASHIRE**, LA1 3PE, **ENGLAND**.
(T) 01524 61233

Course/s:

LANSIL
Description: Parkland
Built: 1947
Number of Holes: 9 **Par:** 70
Further Information:
This 9 hole course can be played as an 18 hole

LARGS

LARGS GOLF CLUB, Irvine Rd, Largs, **AYRSHIRE (NORTH)**, KA30 8EU, **SCOTLAND**.
(T) 01475 673594
Membership: Members & Public
Contact/s:
- **Club Secretary:** Mr Donald H MacGillivhay
- **Professional:** Mr Kenneth Docherty
  ☎ 01475 686192
Course/s:
- ⛳ **LARGS**
  Description: Wooded, Parkland, Undulating, Medium Length
  Built: 1891
  Number of Holes: 18 **Par:** 70
  Par 3's: 4 **Par 4's:** 12 **Par 5's:** 2
  Yds: 6115 **F9 Yds:** 2822 **B9 Yds:** 3293
  Further Information:
  Superb views over River Clyde towards Arran and Cumbrae.

LARKHALL

LARKHALL GOLF COURSE, Bookings, Burnhead Rd, Ashgill, Larkhall, **LANARKSHIRE (SOUTH)**, ML9 3AB, **SCOTLAND**.
(T) 01698 881113
Course/s:
- ⛳ **LARKHALL**
  Number of Holes: 9

LARNE

LARNE GOLF CLUB, 54 Ferris Bay Rd, Islandmagee, Larne, **COUNTY ANTRIM**, BT40 3RT, **NORTHERN IRELAND**.
(T) 028 93382228
Membership: Members & Public
Contact/s:
- **Club Secretary:** Mr R I Johnstone
Course/s:
- ⛳ **LARNE**
  Description: Links, Undulating, Open, Long, Drains Well, Ideal for the Elderly
  Green Speed: Fast
  Built: 1894 **Built On:** Sand
  Number of Holes: 9 **Par:** 35
  Par 3's: 2 **Par 4's:** 6 **Par 5's:** 1
  Yds: 3144 **F9 Yds:** 3144
  Designer: G L Bailie
  Further Information:
  Beautiful views over the coast of Scotland.

LAUDER

LAUDER GOLF COURSE, Galashiels Rd, Lauder, **SCOTTISH BORDERS**, TD2 6RS, **SCOTLAND**.
(T) 01578 722526
(W) www.laudergolfclub.org.uk
Contact/s:
- **Assistant Manager:** Mr Robert Towers
  ☎ 01578 722240
Course/s:
- ⛳ **ROYAL BURGH OF LAUDER**
  Description: Downland
  Built: 1896
  Number of Holes: 9 **Par:** 72
  Par 3's: 1 **Par 4's:** 7 **Par 5's:** 1
  Yds: 6050 **F9 Yds:** 3001 **B9 Yds:** 3049
  Further Information:
  On gently sloping Lauder Hill, offering fine views of Lauderdale. 9 hole course can be played as an 18 hole course

LAUNCESTON

LAUNCESTON GOLF CLUB, North St, Launceston, **CORNWALL**, PL15 8HF, **ENGLAND**.
(T) 01566 773442
Membership: Members & Public
Contact/s:
- **Club Secretary:** Mr C S Hicks
- **Professional:** Mr J Tozer
Course/s:
- ⛳ **LAUNCESTON**
  Description: Parkland
  Number of Holes: 18 **Par:** 70
  Par 3's: 5 **Par 4's:** 10 **Par 5's:** 3
  Yds: 6055 **F9 Yds:** 3116 **B9 Yds:** 2939

LAVENDER PARK

LAVENDER PARK GOLF CENTRE, Swinley Rd, Ascot, **BERKSHIRE**, SL5 8BD, **ENGLAND**.
(T) 01344 893344
(E) lavenderpark@yahoo.co.uk
Membership: Public
Size of Complex: 23 Acres
Contact/s:
- **Pro Shop:** Mr David Johnson
Course/s:
- ⛳ **LAVENDER PARK**
  Description: Wooded, Parkland, Short
  Green Speed: Medium
  Built: 1975 **Built On:** Soil
  Number of Holes: 9 **Par:** 28

LAYTOWN & BETTYSTOWN

LAYTOWN & BETTYSTOWN GOLF CLUB, Bettystown, **COUNTY MEATH**, **IRELAND**.
(T) 041 9827534
Course/s:
- ⛳ **LAYTOWN & BETTYSTOWN**
  Number of Holes: 18

LEA MARSTON

LEA MARSTON HOTEL & LEISURE COMPLEX, Lea Marston Hotel & Leisure Complex, Haunch Lane, Lea Marston, Sutton Coldfield, **MIDLANDS (WEST)**, B76 0BY, **ENGLAND**.
(T) 01675 470707
Contact/s:
- **Manager:** Mr Darren Lewis
Course/s:
- ⛳ **LEA MARSTON**
  Number of Holes: 9
  Designer: J R Blake

LEADHILLS

LEADHILLS GOLF CLUB, Leadhills, Biggar, **LANARKSHIRE (SOUTH)**, ML12 6XR, **SCOTLAND**.
(T) 01659 74456
Course/s:
- ⛳ **LEADHILLS**
  Number of Holes: 9

LEAMINGTON & COUNTY

LEAMINGTON & COUNTY GOLF CLUB, Golf Lane, Whitnash, Leamington Spa, **WARWICKSHIRE**, CV31 2QA, **ENGLAND**.
(T) 01926 425961
(W) www.leamingtongolf.co.uk
Membership: Members & Public
Contact/s:

- **Club Secretary:** Mrs Sally Cooknell
- **Professional:** Mr Julian Mellor
  ☎ 01926 428014
Course/s:
- ⛳ **LEAMINGTON & COUNTY**
  Description: Parkland, Undulating, Open, Medium Length, Drains Well
  Green Speed: Medium
  Built: 1908 **Built On:** Clay
  Number of Holes: 18 **Par:** 71
  Record: 65 (James Court)
  Par 3's: 4 **Par 4's:** 11 **Par 5's:** 3
  Yds: 6439 **F9 Yds:** 3411 **B9 Yds:** 3028
  Prevailing Wind: West
  Designer: Harry Shapland Colt

LEASOWE

LEASOWE GOLF CLUB, Leasowe Rd, Wirral, **MERSEYSIDE**, CH46 3RD, **ENGLAND**.
(T) 0151 6775852
Contact/s:
- **Professional:** Mr Andrew Ayre
  ☎ 0151 6785460
Course/s:
- ⛳ **LEASOWE**
  Description: Links, Open, Medium Length, Drains Well, Ideal for the Elderly
  Green Speed: Medium
  Built: 1812 **Built On:** Sand
  Number of Holes: 18 **Par:** 71
  Par 3's: 3 **Par 4's:** 13 **Par 5's:** 2
  Yds: 6263
  Prevailing Wind: West
  Designer: John Ball

LEATHERHEAD

LEATHERHEAD GOLF CLUB, Kingston Rd, Leatherhead, **SURREY**, KT22 0EE, **ENGLAND**.
(T) 01372 843966
Contact/s:
- **Joint Director:** Mr Michael William Latham
Course/s:
- ⛳ **LEATHERHEAD**
  Number of Holes: 18

LECKFORD

LECKFORD GOLF COURSE, Leckford, Stockbridge, **HAMPSHIRE**, SO20 6JF, **ENGLAND**.
(T) 01264 810320
Contact/s:
- **Manager:** Mr J Wood
Course/s:
- ⛳ **LECKFORD**
  Number of Holes: 9

LEE ON THE SOLENT

LEE ON THE SOLENT GOLF CLUB, Brune Lane, Lee-on-The-Solent, **HAMPSHIRE**, PO13 9PB, **ENGLAND**.
(T) 023 92551170
Membership: Members & Public
Contact/s:
- **Professional:** Mr John Richardson
  ☎ 023 92551181
- **Pro Shop:** Mr Warren Skelton
Course/s:
- ⛳ **LEE-ON-SOLENT**
  Description: Wooded, Parkland, Heath Land, Undulating, Open, Short, Tight, Drains Well, Ideal for the Elderly
  Green Speed: Medium
  Built: 1905 **Built On:** Clay/Sand

Number of Holes: 18 Par: 69
Par 3's: 5 Par 4's: 11 Par 5's: 2
Yds: 5933 F9 Yds: 3053 B9 Yds: 2880

LEE PARK

LEE PARK GOLF CLUB, Childwall Valley Rd,
Liverpool, **MERSEYSIDE**, L27 3YA,
ENGLAND.
(T) 0151 4873882
Size of Complex: 84 Acres

Contact/s:
● General Manager: Mrs Angela Fagan
Course/s:
 LEE PARK
  Description: Parkland, Undulating,
  Sheltered, Medium Length, Drains Well,
  Ideal for the Elderly
  Green Speed: Medium
  Built: 1954 Built On: Clay
  Number of Holes: 18 Par: 72
  Par 3's: 4 Par 4's: 10 Par 5's: 4
  Yds: 6108
  Designer: Cotton

LEE VALLEY

LEE VALLEY (PAR 3) GOLF COURSE, Lea
Bridge Rd, London, **LONDON (GREATER)**,
E10 7NU, **ENGLAND**.
(T) 020 88033611

Membership: Members & Public

Contact/s:
● General Manager: Mr Peter Saunder
Course/s:
 LEE VALLEY
  Description: Moorland, Drains Well
  Built: 1950 Built On: Soil
  Number of Holes: 18
  Yds: 4974 F9 Yds: 2417 B9 Yds: 2557
  Prevailing Wind: South

LEE VALLEY

LEE VALLEY LEISURE GOLF COURSE, Lee
Valley Leisure Ctre, Picketts Lock Lane,
Edmonton, London, **LONDON (GREATER)**,
N9 0AS, **ENGLAND**.
(T) 020 8803 3611

Membership: Public

Contact/s:
● Professional: Mr Richard Gerken
Course/s:
 LEE VALLEY
  Description: Parkland, Short
  Number of Holes: 18
  Yds: 4902
  Further Information:
  A flat but challenging course with a lake
  and the River Lea as water hazards.

LEE VALLEY

LEE VALLEY GOLF CLUB, Clashmore,
Ovens, **COUNTY CORK**, **IRELAND**.
(T) 021 7331721
(E) leevalleygolfclub@eircom.net
(W) www.leevalleygcc.ie
Contact/s:
 LEE VALLEY
  Number of Holes: 18
  Designer: Christy O'Connor

LEE VALLEY GOLF CTRE

LEE VALLEY GOLF CENTRE, Wigwam Lane,
Hucknall, Nottingham,
NOTTINGHAMSHIRE, NG15 7TA,
ENGLAND.

(T) 0115 9642037
Contact/s:
● General Manager: Mr B R Goodman
Course/s:
 LEE VALLEY 18 HOLE
  Number of Holes: 18 Par: 72
  Yds: 6233

 LEE VALLEY 9 HOLE
  Number of Holes: 9 Par: 27
  Yds: 1230

LEEDS

LEEDS GOLF CLUB, Cobble Hill Links,
Elmete Lane, Leeds, **YORKSHIRE (WEST)**,
LS8 2LJ, **ENGLAND**.
(T) 0113 2658775
Contact/s:
● Professional: Mr Simon Longster
● Book Tee Times:
  ☎ 0113 2658786
Course/s:
 LEEDS
  Description: Parkland
  Built: 1896
  Number of Holes: 18 Par: 69

LEEDS CASTLE

LEEDS CASTLE GOLF COURSE, Ashford
Rd, Maidstone, **KENT**, ME17 1PL,
ENGLAND.
(T) 01622 880467
(W) www.leeds-castle.co.uk
Membership: Public
Size of Complex: 564 Acres
Contact/s:
● Professional: Mr Steve Purves
Course/s:
 LEEDS CASTLE
  Description: Parkland
  Built: 1924
  Number of Holes: 9 Par: 33
  Yds: 2681
  Designer: Neil Coles
  Further Information:
  Course surrounds a medieval castle and
  moat.

LEEDS GOLF CTRE

LEEDS GOLF CENTRE, Wike Ridge Lane,
Wike, Leeds, **YORKSHIRE (WEST)**, LS17
9JW, **ENGLAND**.
(T) 0113 2886000
(E) info@leedsgolfcentre.co.uk
(W) www.leedsgolfcentre.co.uk
Membership: Members & Public
Contact/s:
● Professional: Mr Neil Harvey
● Pro Shop: Mr Adam Gay
Course/s:
 THE OAKS
  Description: Parkland
  Green Speed: Medium
  Built: 1994 Built On: Sand
  Number of Holes: 12 Par: 36
  Prevailing Wind: West
  Designer: Donald Steel
  Further Information:
  Course was originally a 9 hole course, and
  has been extended to 12 holes.

 WIKE RIDGE
  Description: Parkland, Heath Land,
  Undulating, Open, Medium Length,
  Drains Well, Ideal for the Elderly
  Green Speed: Medium
  Built: 1993 Built On: Sand

Number of Holes: 18 Par: 72
Record: 66 (S Oxley, Adam Gay)
Prevailing Wind: West
Designer: Donald Steel

LEEK

LEEK GOLF CLUB LTD, Cheddleton Rd,
Leek, **STAFFORDSHIRE**, ST13 5RE,
ENGLAND.
(T) 01538 384779
Contact/s:
● Professional: Mr Ian Benson
  ☎ 01538 384767
Course/s:
 LEEK
  Number of Holes: 18 Par: 70
  Yds: 6218 F9 Yds: 2896 B9 Yds: 3322

LEES HALL

LEES HALL GOLF CLUB LTD, Hemsworth
Rd, Sheffield, **YORKSHIRE (SOUTH)**, S8
8LL, **ENGLAND**.
(T) 0114 2507868
Contact/s:
● Director: Mr Clive Taylor
Course/s:
 LEES HALL
  Number of Holes: 18

LEICESTER

LEICESTERSHIRE GOLF CLUB, Evington
Lane, Leicester, **LEICESTERSHIRE**, LE5
6DJ, **ENGLAND**.
(T) 0116 2738825

Membership: Members & Public

Contact/s:
● Club Secretary: Mr Colin Chapman
● Professional: Mr Andrew Jones
● Book Lessons: Mr Darren Jones
Course/s:
 THE LEICESTERSHIRE
  Description: Wooded, Parkland,
  Undulating, Sheltered, Long, Drains Well
  Built: 1890 Built On: Soil
  Number of Holes: 18 Record: 68
  (Darren Jones)
  Designer: Hawtree

LEIGH

LEIGH GOLF CLUB, Kenyon Hall, Broseley
Lane, Culcheth, Warrington, **CHESHIRE**,
WA3 4BG, **ENGLAND**.
(T) 01925 762013

Membership: Members & Public

Contact/s:
● Club Secretary: Mr P Saunders
  ☎ 01925 762943
● Professional: Mr Andrew Baguley
Course/s:
 LEIGH
  Description: Wooded, Parkland, Medium
  Length, Tight Green Speed: Medium
  Built: 1906 Built On: Clay/Soil
  Number of Holes: 18 Par: 69
  Par 3's: 4 Par 4's: 13 Par 5's: 1
  Yds: 5884
  Designer: James Braid

LEIGHTON BUZZARD

LEIGHTON BUZZARD GOLF CLUB,
Plantation Rd, Leighton Buzzard,
BEDFORDSHIRE, LU7 3JF, **ENGLAND**.
(T) 01525 244800
Contact/s:

- **Club Secretary:** Mr John Burchell
- **Professional:** Mr Maurice Campbell
- ☎ 01525 244815

Course/s:

🟢 **LEIGHTON BUZZARD**
Description: Wooded, Parkland, Medium Length, Tight, Ideal for the Elderly
Green Speed: Medium
Built: 1925
Number of Holes: 18 **Par:** 71
Record: 65 (Mark Litton)
Yds: 6101 **F9 Yds:** 3141 **B9 Yds:** 2960
Prevailing Wind: West

LENZIE

LENZIE GOLF CLUB, 19 Crosshill Rd, Lenzie, Glasgow, **GLASGOW (CITY OF),** G66 5DA, **SCOTLAND.**
(T) 0141 7761535
(E) scottdavidson@lenziegolfclub.demon.co.uk
(W) www.lenziegolfclub.com

Contact/s:

- **Club Secretary:** Mr Scott Davidson
- **Professional:** Mr Jim McCallum
  ☎ 0141 7777748
- **Book Tee Times:**
  ☎ 0141 7761535/8123018

Course/s:

🟢 **LENZIE**
Description: Parkland, Moorland
Built: 1889
Number of Holes: 18 **Par:** 69
Yds: 5984 **F9 Yds:** 2713 **B9 Yds:** 3271

LEOMINSTER

LEOMINSTER GOLF CLUB, Ford Bridge, Leominster, **HEREFORDSHIRE,** HR6 0LE, **ENGLAND.**
(T) 01568 610055

Membership: Members & Public

Contact/s:

- **Club Secretary:** Mr Les Green
- **Professional:** Mr Andrew Ferriday
- **Book Tee Times:** Mr J Kingsword
- **Book Lessons:**
  ☎ 01568 611402

Course/s:

🟢 **LEOMINSTER**
Description: Parkland, Undulating, Open, Medium Length
Green Speed: Slow
Built: 1967
Number of Holes: 18 **Par:** 70
Yds: 6026 **F9 Yds:** 3162 **B9 Yds:** 2864
Prevailing Wind: West
Designer: Robert Sandow

LEOPARDSTOWN

LEOPARDSTOWN GOLF CENTRE, Fox Rock, **COUNTY DUBLIN, IRELAND.**
(T) 01 2895341

Membership: Members & Public

Contact/s:

- **Professional:** Mr Michael Allan

Course/s:

🟢 **LEOPARDSTOWN**
Description: Parkland, Short, Drains Well, Ideal for the Elderly
Green Speed: Medium
Built: 1963
Number of Holes: 18
Yds: 4384

LES MIELLES

LES MIELLES GOLF & COUNTRY CLUB, St. Ouen's Bay, Jersey, Channel Islands, JE3 7PQ, .
(T) 01534 482787

Course/s:

🟢 **LES MIELLES**
Number of Holes: 18 **Par:** 70
Yds: 5633
Designer: J Le Brun, R Whitehead

LESLIE

LESLIE GOLF CLUB, Leslie, Glenrothes, **FIFE,** KY6 3EZ, **SCOTLAND.**
(T) 01592 620040

Membership: Members & Public

Contact/s:

- **Club Secretary:** Mr Jack Ganson

Course/s:

🟢 **LESLIE**
Description: Wooded, Parkland, Open, Short, Tight
Green Speed: Medium
Built: 1898 **Built On:** Soil
Number of Holes: 9
Prevailing Wind: West
Designer: Tom Morris

LETCHWORTH

LETCHWORTH GOLF CLUB, Letchworth Lane, Letchworth, **HERTFORDSHIRE,** SG6 3NH, **ENGLAND.**
(T) 01462 480637

Course/s:

🟢 **LETCHWORTH**
Number of Holes: 18
Designer: Harry Vardon

LETHAM GRANGE RESORT

LETHAM GRANGE RESORT, Colliston, Arbroath, **ANGUS,** DD11 4RL, **SCOTLAND.**
(T) 01241 890377
(E) lethamgrange@sol.co.uk
(W) www.lethamgrange.co.uk

Contact/s:

- **Manager:** Mr S Moir

Course/s:

🟢 **GLENS**
Built: 1987
Number of Holes: 18 **Par:** 68
Designer: G K Smith, Donald Steel

🟢 **OLD**
Built: 1987
Number of Holes: 18 **Par:** 73
Designer: G K Smith, Donald Steel
Further Information:
Championship layout, combines tree filled fairways and water in play on 13 holes.

LETHAMHILL

LETHAMHILL GOLF COURSE, Cumbernauld Rd, Glasgow, **GLASGOW (CITY OF),** G33 1AH, **SCOTLAND.**
(T) 0141 7706220

Contact/s:

- **Professional:** Mr Gary Taggart
  ☎ 0141 770 7135

Course/s:

🟢 **LETHAMHILL**
Number of Holes: 18 **Par:** 70
Yds: 5836 **F9 Yds:** 3001 **B9 Yds:** 2835

LETTERKENNY

LETTERKENNY GOLF CLUB, Barnhill, Letterkenny, **COUNTY DONEGAL, IRELAND.**
(T) 074 21150

Course/s:

🟢 **LETTERKENNY**
Number of Holes: 18
Yds: 6299
Designer: Edward Hackett

LEVEN LINKS

LEVEN LINKS GOLF COURSE, The Promenade, Leven, **FIFE,** KY8 4HS, **SCOTLAND.**
(T) 01333 428859

Contact/s:

- **Treasurer:** Mr A Herd

Course/s:

🟢 **LEVEN LINKS**
Description: Links, Drains Well
Built On: Sand
Number of Holes: 18
Yds: 6421
Prevailing Wind: West
Designer: Tom Morris

LEVEN THISTLE

LEVEN THISTLE GOLF CLUB, 3 Balfour St, Leven, **FIFE,** KY8 4JF, **SCOTLAND.**
(T) 01333 426333

Membership: Members & Public

Contact/s:

- **Book Tee Times:** Mr A Herd
  ☎ 01333 421390

Course/s:

🟢 **LEVEN LINKS**
Description: Championship, Links, Medium Length, Drains Well, Ideal for the Elderly
Green Speed: Fast
Built: 1867
Number of Holes: 18

LEWES

LEWES GOLF CLUB, Chapel Hill, Lewes, **SUSSEX (EAST),** BN7 2BB, **ENGLAND.**
(T) 01273 473245

Contact/s:

- **Professional:** Mr Paul Dobson

Course/s:

🟢 **LEWES**
Description: Downland, Undulating, Drains Well
Built: 1896
Number of Holes: 18 **Par:** 71
Designer: Jack Rowe
Further Information:
Challenging course.

LEXDEN

LEXDEN WOOD GOLF CLUB, Bakers Lane, Colchester, **ESSEX,** CO3 4AU, **ENGLAND.**
(T) 01206 843333

Membership: Members & Public

Contact/s:

- **Club Secretary:** Miss Jo Rizzato
- **Professional:** Mr Pete McBride
- **Pro Shop:** Mr Jamie Lowe

Course/s:

🟢 **LEXDEN WOOD**
Description: Wooded, Parkland, Sheltered, Short, Drains Well, Ideal for the

Elderly
Green Speed: Medium
Built: 1992 **Built On:** Soil
Number of Holes: 18 **Par:** 67
Record: 63 (Jamie Lowe)

Yds: 5354 **F9 Yds:** 2770 **B9 Yds:** 2584
Prevailing Wind: West
Designer: N Williams
Further Information:
A brook runs through the course.

LEYLAND

LEYLAND GOLF CLUB, Wigan Rd, Leyland,
Preston, **LANCASHIRE**, PR5 2UD,
ENGLAND.
(T) 01772 436457
(E) manager@leylandgolfclub.com
(W) www.leylandgolfclub.com

Membership: Members & Public
Size of Complex: 136 Acres

Contact/s:
● **Club Secretary:** Mr John Ross
● **Professional:** Mr Colin Burgess

Course/s:
⛳ **LEYLAND**
Description: Parkland, Open, Medium
Length, Drains Well, Ideal for the Elderly
Green Speed: Medium/Fast
Built: 1923 **Built On:** Soil
Number of Holes: 18 **Par:** 70
Record: 64 (Colin Burgess)
Yds: 6124 **F9 Yds:** 3000 **B9 Yds:** 3124
Prevailing Wind: West

LIBBATON

LIBBATON GOLF CLUB LTD, Libbaton Golf
Course, High Bickington, Umberleigh,
DEVON, EX37 9BS, **ENGLAND**.
(T) 01769 560167

Contact/s:
● **Owner:** Mr Gerald Herniman

Course/s:
⛳ **LIBBATON**
Number of Holes: 18
Designer: Badham

LIBERTON

LIBERTON GOLF CLUB, 297 Gilmerton Rd,
Edinburgh, **EDINBURGH (CITY OF)**, EH16
5UJ, **SCOTLAND**.
(T) 0131 6643009

Membership: Members & Public

Contact/s:
● **Club Secretary:** Mr T Watson
● **Pro Shop:** Mr Ian Seath
  ☎ 0131 6641056

Course/s:
⛳ **LIBERTON**
Description: Parkland, Short
Green Speed: Medium
Number of Holes: 18 **Par:** 67
Yds: 5306

LICKEY HILLS

LICKEY HILLS GOLF COURSE, Rosehill,
Rednal, Birmingham, **MIDLANDS (WEST)**,
B45 8RR, **ENGLAND**.
(T) 0121 4533159

Course/s:
⛳ **LICKEY HILLS**
Number of Holes: 18

LIGHTCLIFFE

LIGHTCLIFFE GOLF CLUB (THE), Knowle
Top Rd, Lightcliffe, Halifax, **YORKSHIRE
(WEST)**, HX3 8SW, **ENGLAND**.
(T) 01422 202459

Contact/s:
● **Professional:** Mr Robert Kershaw
● **Book Tee Times:**
  ☎ 01422 204081

Course/s:
⛳ **LIGHTCLIFFE**
Description: Wooded, Parkland
Built: 1907
Number of Holes: 9 **Par:** 68
Further Information:
9 hole course can be played as an 18
course.

LILLESHALL HALL

LILLESHALL HALL GOLF CLUB, Lilleshall,
Newport, **SHROPSHIRE**, TF10 9AS,
ENGLAND.
(T) 01952 604104

Contact/s:
● **Club Secretary:** Mr F R Price

Course/s:
⛳ **LILLESHALL HALL**
Number of Holes: 18
Designer: Harry Shapland Colt

LILLEY BROOK

LILLEY BROOK GOLF CLUB, Cirencester
Rd, Charlton Kings, Cheltenham,
GLOUCESTERSHIRE, GL53 8EG,
ENGLAND.
(T) 01242 526785

Membership: Members & Public

Contact/s:
● **Professional:** Mr F Haddon

Course/s:
⛳ **LILLEY BROOK**
Description: Parkland, Undulating,
Sheltered, Medium Length, Tight, Tends to
Flood
Green Speed: Medium
Built: 1922 **Built On:** Clay
Number of Holes: 18 **Par:** 69
Record: 61 (Stewart Little)
Yds: 6212 **F9 Yds:** 3326 **B9 Yds:** 2886
Designer: Alistair MacKenzie

LIME TREES PARK

LIME TREES PARK GOLF CLUB, Ruislip
Rd, Northolt, **LONDON (GREATER)**, UB5
6QZ, **ENGLAND**.
(T) 020 88420442

Contact/s:
● **Manager:** Mr Mark Corbin

Course/s:
⛳ **LIME TREES PARK**
Number of Holes: 9

LIMERICK

LIMERICK GOLF CLUB, Ballyclough,
Limerick, **COUNTY LIMERICK**, **IRELAND**.
(T) 061 415146
(E) lgc@eircom.net
(W) www.limerickgc.com
Size of Complex: 122 Acres

Contact/s:
● **Club Secretary:** Mr Stephen Keogh
● **Professional:** Mr Lee Harrington
  ☎ 06141 2492
● **Book Tee Times:** Ms Sheila Roche

Fitzgerald
Course/s:
⛳ **LIMERICK**
Description: Parkland, Undulating,
Sheltered, Medium Length, Tight, Ideal for
the Elderly
Green Speed: Medium
Built: 1919 **Built On:** Clay
Number of Holes: 18 **Par:** 72
Record: 63 (Stuart Appleby)
Par 3's: 3 **Par 4's:** 12 **Par 5's:** 3
Yds: 6473 **F9 Yds:** 3382 **B9 Yds:** 3091
Designer: Alistair MacKenzie

LIMERICK (COUNTY)

**LIMERICK COUNTY GOLF & COUNTRY
CLUB,** Ballyneety, Limerick, **COUNTY
LIMERICK**, **IRELAND**.
(T) 061 351881
(E) lcgolf@iol.ie
(W) www.limerickcounty.com

Contact/s:
● **General Manager:** Mr G McKeon

Course/s:
⛳ **LIMERICK COUNTY**
Description: Championship, Undulating
Built: 1994
Number of Holes: 18 **Par:** 72
Designer: D Smyth

LIMPSFIELD CHART

LIMPSFIELD CHART GOLF CLUB,
Limpsfield, Oxted, **SURREY**, RH8 0SL,
ENGLAND.
(T) 01883 722106

Membership: Members & Public

Contact/s:
● **Club Secretary:** Mr Mike Baker
  ☎ 01883 723405

Course/s:
⛳ **LIMPSFIELD CHART**
Description: Heath Land, Sheltered,
Medium Length, Tight, Drains Well, Ideal
for the Elderly
Green Speed: Medium
Built: 1889 **Built On:** Soil
Number of Holes: 9 **Par:** 70 **Record:** 64
(Brian Huggett)
Par 3's: 2 **Par 4's:** 6 **Par 5's:** 1
Yds: 5718 **F9 Yds:** 2860 **B9 Yds:** 2858
Further Information:
Flat course tree lined with heather and
gorse. 9 hole course can be played as an
18 hole course

LINCOLN

LINCOLN GOLF CLUB, Torksey, Lincoln,
LINCOLNSHIRE, LN1 2EG, **ENGLAND**.
(T) 01427 718721
(E) info@lincolngc.co.uk
(W) www.lincolngc.co.uk

Contact/s:
● **Professional:** Mr Ashley Carter
  ☎ 01427 718273
● **Book Tee Times:** Mr Derek Linton

Course/s:
⛳ **LINCOLN**
Description: Championship, Links,
Undulating, Open, Medium Length, Tight,
Drains Well, Ideal for the Elderly
Green Speed: Fast
Built: 1891 **Built On:** Sand
Number of Holes: 18 **Par:** 71
Par 3's: 3 **Par 4's:** 13 **Par 5's:** 2
Yds: 6438 **F9 Yds:** 3254 **B9 Yds:** 3184
Prevailing Wind: West

LINDEN HALL

LINDEN HALL GOLF CLUB, Longhorsley, Morpeth, **NORTHUMBERLAND**, NE65 8XF, **ENGLAND**.
(T) 01670 788050
(E) stay@lindenhall.co.uk
(W) www.lindenhall.co.uk

Membership: Members & Public
Size of Complex: 240 Acres

Contact/s:
• Professional: Mr David Curry

Course/s:
🏌 LINDEN HALL
   Description: Parkland, Undulating, Sheltered, Drains Well, Ideal for the Elderly
   Green Speed: Medium
   Built: 1997
   Number of Holes: 18 **Par:** 72
   Record: 68 (Michael Ure)
   Prevailing Wind: West
   Designer: Jonathan Gaunt

LINDRICK

LINDRICK GOLF CLUB (SHEFFIELD & DISTRICT), Lindrick Common, Worksop, **NOTTINGHAMSHIRE**, S81 8BH, **ENGLAND**.
(T) 01909 475282
(W) www.lindrickgolf.com

Membership: Members & Public
Size of Complex: 205 Acres

Contact/s:
• Club Secretary: Lt Cdr R J M Jack
• Professional: Mr John R King
   ☎ 01909 475820
• Book Lessons: Mr J R King

Course/s:
🏌 LINDRICK
   Description: Heath Land, Drains Well
   Green Speed: Fast
   Built: 1891
   Number of Holes: 18 **Par:** 71
   Record: 67 (C Smellie)
   Par 3's: 4 **Par 4's:** 11 **Par 5's:** 3
   Yds: 6606
   Further Information:
   The course is built on magnesium sandstone and as a result drains very well. The course remains in excellent condition throughout the year. 🏌

LINGDALE

LINGDALE GOLF CLUB, Clubhouse, Joe Moores Lane, Woodhouse Eaves, Loughborough, **LEICESTERSHIRE**, LE12 8TF, **ENGLAND**.
(T) 01509 890684

Membership: Members & Public
Size of Complex: 120 Acres

Contact/s:
• Club Secretary: Mr Maurice Green
• Professional: Mr Peter Sellears

Course/s:
🏌 LINGDALE
   Description: Parkland, Medium Length, Tight, Ideal for the Elderly
   Green Speed: Fast
   Built: 1967 **Built On:** Soil
   Number of Holes: 18 **Par:** 71
   Yds: 6545 **F9 Yds:** 3332 **B9 Yds:** 3213
   Prevailing Wind: West
   Designer: David Tucker

LINGFIELD PARK

LINGFIELD PARK GOLF CLUB, Racecourse Rd, Lingfield, **SURREY**, RH7 6PQ, **ENGLAND**.
(T) 01342 832659

Contact/s:
• Professional: Mr Chris Morley

Course/s:
🏌 LINGFIELD PARK
   Description: Parkland
   Built: 1987
   Number of Holes: 18 **Par:** 72
   Further Information:
   Water hazards on course.

LINKS

LINKS GOLF CLUB, Cambridge Rd, Newmarket, **SUFFOLK**, CB8 0TG, **ENGLAND**.
(T) 01638 663000

Course/s:
🏌 LINKS
   Number of Holes: 18
   Designer: Colonel Hotchkin

LINLITHGOW

LINLITHGOW GOLF CLUB, Braehead, Linlithgow, **LOTHIAN (WEST)**, EH49 6QF, **SCOTLAND**.
(T) 01506 842585
(E) info@linlithgowgolf.co.uk
(W) www.linlithgowgolf.co.uk

Membership: Members & Public
Size of Complex: 80 Acres

Contact/s:
• Club Secretary: Mr W S Christie
• Professional: Mr Steven Rosie
   ☎ 01506 844365
• Book Tee Times:
   ☎ 01506 844356

Course/s:
🏌 LINLITHGOW
   Description: Parkland, Hilltop, Undulating, Short, Drains Well
   Green Speed: Medium
   Built: 1913 **Built On:** Soil
   Number of Holes: 18 **Par:** 70
   Par 3's: 4 **Par 4's:** 12 **Par 5's:** 2
   Yds: 5729 **F9 Yds:** 2637 **B9 Yds:** 3092
   Designer: R Simpson
   Further Information:
   Panoramic views of historic Linlithgow and Forth Valley.

LINN PARK

LINN PARK GOLF COURSE, Simshill Rd, Glasgow, **GLASGOW (CITY OF)**, G44 5TA, **SCOTLAND**.
(T) 0141 6375871

Course/s:
🏌 LINN PARK
   Number of Holes: 18 **Par:** 65
   Yds: 4592

LIPHOOK

LIPHOOK GOLF CLUB, Wheatsheaf Enclosure, Liphook, **HAMPSHIRE**, GU30 7EH, **ENGLAND**.
(T) 01428 723785/ 723271
(E) liphookgolfclub@btconnect.com

Contact/s:
• Club Secretary: Mr Barry Morgan
• Professional: Mr Geoffrey Lee

Course/s:
🏌 LIPHOOK
   Number of Holes: 18 **Par:** 70
   Yds: 6167 **F9 Yds:** 3057 **B9 Yds:** 3110
   Designer: A C Groome 🏌

LISBURN

LISBURN GOLF CLUB, 68 Eglantine Rd, Lisburn, **COUNTY ANTRIM**, BT27 5RQ, **NORTHERN IRELAND**.
(T) 028 92662186
(E) lisburngolfclub@aol.com

Membership: Members & Public
Size of Complex: 124 Acres

Contact/s:
• Club Secretary: Miss K Fletcher
• Professional: Mr S Hanill
   ☎ 028 92677217

Course/s:
🏌 LISBURN
   Description: Championship, Parkland, Undulating, Long, Tight, Drains Well, Ideal for the Elderly
   Green Speed: Fast
   Built: 1971 **Built On:** Clay/Sand
   Number of Holes: 18 **Par:** 72
   Record: 62 (Dave Fagherty)
   Yds: 6647 **F9 Yds:** 3219 **B9 Yds:** 3428
   Prevailing Wind: West
   Designer: Hawtree
   Further Information:
   Cascading water feature. Challenging game.

LISMORE

LISMORE GOLF CLUB, Lismore, **COUNTY WATERFORD**, **IRELAND**.
(T) 058 54026

Course/s:
🏌 LISMORE
   Number of Holes: 9 **Par:** 67
   Yds: 5788

LISSELAN

LISSELAN GOLF COURSE, Clonakilty, Lisselan, **COUNTY CORK**, **IRELAND**.
(T) 023 33552

Membership: Public

Contact/s:
• Book Tee Times: Mr Mark Coombes

Course/s:
🏌 LISSELAN ESTATE
   Description: Parkland, Medium Length, Ideal for the Elderly
   Green Speed: Medium
   Built: 1994
   Number of Holes: 6
   Designer: Jack Kenneally
   Further Information:
   Each hole has 3 tees, so the course can be played as a 9 or an 18 hole course.

LISTOWEL

LISTOWEL GOLF CLUB, Feale View, Listowel, **COUNTY KERRY**, **IRELAND**.
(T) 068 21592

Course/s:
🏌 COURSE #1
   Number of Holes: 9 **Par:** 35

LITTLE ASTON

LITTLE ASTON GOLF CLUB, Roman Rd, Streetly, Sutton Coldfield, **MIDLANDS (WEST)**, B74 3AN, **ENGLAND**.
(T) 0121 3532942
(W) www.littleastongolf.co.uk

Contact/s:
• Professional: Mr John Anderson
   ☎ 0121 3530330

Course/s:

LITTLE ASTON
Description: Championship
Number of Holes: 18   Par: 72
Yds: 6397
Designer: Harry Vardon
Further Information:
'This course must have the best fairways in the world ... Gatton, Gleneagles and Hoylake are in the running for top place, but even they must be runners up alongside Little Aston.' (Henry Cotton).

LITTLE CHALFONT

LITTLE CHALFONT GOLF CLUB, Lodge Lane, Chalfont St. Giles, **BUCKINGHAMSHIRE**, HP8 4AJ, **ENGLAND**.
(T) 01494 764877

Contact/s:
- Owner: Mr Mike Dunne

Course/s:

LITTLE CHALFONT
Number of Holes: 9

LITTLE HAY

LITTLE HAY GOLF COURSE, Box Lane, Bovingdon, Hemel Hempstead, **HERTFORDSHIRE**, HP3 0DQ, **ENGLAND**.
(T) 01442 833798

Membership: Public

Contact/s:
- Professional: Mr Nick Allen
- Pro Shop: Mr Chris Gordon

Course/s:

LITTLE HAY
Description: Parkland, Open, Medium Length, Tends to Flood
Green Speed: Medium
Built: 1978   Built On: Clay
Number of Holes: 18   Par: 71
Par 3's: 4   Par 4's: 11   Par 5's: 3
Yds: 6300
Prevailing Wind: North/West
Designer: Hawtree
Further Information:
Flat course with views of the valley.

LITTLE LAKES

LITTLE LAKES GOLF AND COUNTRY CLUB, Lye Head, Bewdley, Worcester, **WORCESTERSHIRE**, DY12 2UZ, **ENGLAND**.
(T) 01299 266385

Contact/s:
- Professional: M A Laing

Course/s:

LITTLE LAKES
Description: Parkland, Undulating
Built: 1975
Number of Holes: 18   Par: 69
Designer: M Laing

LITTLE LAKES

LITTLE LAKES LTD, Middle Lane, Hadzor, Droitwich, **WORCESTERSHIRE**, WR9 7DP, **ENGLAND**.
(T) 01905 796375
(E) info@littlelakes.co.uk
(W) www.gaudet-luce.co.uk

Membership: Members & Public

Contact/s:
- Professional: Mr Phil Cundy
- Book Tee Times: Mr Adam Whiting

Course/s:

GAUDET - LUCE
Description: Parkland, Medium Length

Green Speed: Medium
Built: 1994   Built On: Clay
Number of Holes: 18   Par: 70
Par 3's: 5   Par 4's: 10   Par 5's: 3
Yds: 5827
Prevailing Wind: South/West
Designer: M Laing

LITTLEHAMPTON GOLF

LITTLEHAMPTON GOLF CLUB, Rope Walk, Littlehampton, **SUSSEX (WEST)**, BN17 5DL, **ENGLAND**.
(T) 01903 717170

Contact/s:
- Club Secretary: Mr S Graham
- Professional: Mr Guy McQuitty
  ☎ 01903 716369

Course/s:

LITTLEHAMPTON GOLF
Number of Holes: 18   Par: 70
Yds: 6226   F9 Yds: 3131   B9 Yds: 3095

LITTLEHILL

LITTLEHILL GOLF COURSE, Littlehill Golf Club, Auchinairn Rd, Bishopbriggs, Glasgow, **GLASGOW (CITY OF)**, G64 1UT, **SCOTLAND**.
(T) 0141 7721916

Contact/s:
- Manager: Mr John Hepburn

Course/s:

LITTLEHILLS
Number of Holes: 18

LITTLESTONE

LITTLESTONE GOLF CLUB, St. Andrews Rd, Littlestone, New Romney, **KENT**, TN28 8RB, **ENGLAND**.
(T) 01797 363355
(E) secretary@littlestonegolfclub.org.uk
(W) www.littlestonegolfclub.org.uk

Contact/s:
- Professional: Mr Andrew Jones
  ☎ 01797 362231
- Book Tee Times: Mr Brian Nute

Course/s:

LITTLESTONE
Description: Championship, Links, Undulating, Open, Drains Well, Ideal for the Elderly
Green Speed: Fast
Built: 1888   Built On: Sand
Number of Holes: 18   Par: 71
Yds: 6486   F9 Yds: 3190   B9 Yds: 3296
Designer: L Purves

LIVERPOOL (ROYAL)

ROYAL LIVERPOOL GOLF CLUB, Meols Drive, Hoylake, Wirral, **MERSEYSIDE**, CH47 4AL, **ENGLAND**.
(T) 0151 6323101
(E) sec@royal-liverpool-golf.com
(W) www.royal-liverpool-golf.com

Membership: Members & Public

Contact/s:
- Club Secretary: Mr C T Moore
- Professional: Mr John Heggarty
  ☎ 0151 6325868
- Book Tee Times: Mrs Carol Kaye

Course/s:

ROYAL LIVERPOOL
Description: Championship, Links
Built: 1869
Number of Holes: 18   Par: 72
Yds: 7165   F9 Yds: 3517   B9 Yds: 3648

Designer: Robert Chambers, Jim Morris
Further Information:
Flat course.

LIVERPOOL MUNICIPAL

LIVERPOOL MUNICIPAL GOLF COURSE, Ingoe Lane, Liverpool, **MERSEYSIDE**, L32 4SS, **ENGLAND**.
(T) 0151 5465435

Membership: Members & Public/Public

Contact/s:
- Club Secretary: Mr P Brown
- Professional: Mr Dave Weston
  ☎ 0151 5467031

Course/s:

LIVERPOOL MUNICIPAL
Description: Parkland, Open, Long, Tends to Flood, Ideal for the Elderly
Green Speed: Medium
Built: 1946   Built On: Clay/Soil
Number of Holes: 18
Prevailing Wind: North/West

LLANDRINDOD WELLS

LLANDRINDOD WELLS GOLF CLUB, Llandrindod Wells, **POWYS**, LD1 5NY, **WALES**.
(T) 01597 823873
(E) secretary@lwgc.co.uk
(W) www.lwgc.co.uk

Contact/s:
- Club Secretary: Mr Robert Southcott

Course/s:

LLANDRINDOD WELLS
Description: Links
Built: 1905
Number of Holes: 18   Par: 69
Par 3's: 6   Par 4's: 9   Par 5's: 3
Yds: 5759   F9 Yds: 2852   B9 Yds: 2907
Further Information:
Natural hazards.

LLANFAIRFECHAN

LLANFAIRFECHAN GOLF CLUB, Clubhouse, Ffordd Llanerch, Llanfairfechan, **GWYNEDD**, LL33 0EB, **WALES**.
(T) 01248 680144

Contact/s:
- Club Secretary: Mr Charles Worth

Course/s:

LLANFAIRFECHAN
Number of Holes: 9

LLANGEFNI PUBLIC

LLANGEFNI PUBLIC GOLF COURSE, Rhosmeirch, Llangefni, **ISLE OF ANGLESEY**, LL77 7TQ, **WALES**.
(T) 01248 722193

Course/s:

LLANGEFNI (PUBLIC)
Number of Holes: 9
Yds: 1467
Designer: Hawtree

LLANISHEN

LLANISHEN GOLF CLUB, Heol Hir, Cardiff, **GLAMORGAN (VALE OF)**, CF14 9UD, **WALES**.
(T) 029 20755078

Contact/s:
- Club Secretary: Mr E W Page
- Professional: Mr A Jones

Course/s:

LLANISHEN

Number of Holes: 18 Par: 68
Yds: 5327 F9 Yds: 2401 B9 Yds: 2926

LLANSTEFFAN

LLANSTEFFAN GOLF COURSE, Llansteffan, Carmarthen, **CARMARTHENSHIRE**, SA33 5LU, **WALES**.
(T) 01267 241526

Course/s:
- **LLANSTEFFAN**
  Number of Holes: 9 Par: 30
  Yds: 2165

LLANTRISANT & PONTYCLUN

LLANTRISANT & PONTYCLUN GOLF CLUB, Ely Valley Rd, Talbot Green, Pontyclun, **RHONDDA CYNON TAFF**, CF72 8AL, **WALES**.
(T) 01443 228169
(E) lpgc@barbox.net

Contact/s:
- **Club Secretary:** Mr J D Jones
  ☎ 01443 224601
- **Professional:** Mr M D Phillips

Course/s:
- **LLANTRISANT & PONTYCLUN**
  Number of Holes: 18 Par: 68
  Par 3's: 5 Par 4's: 12 Par 5's: 1
  Yds: 5328 F9 Yds: 2654 B9 Yds: 2674

LLANWERN

LLANWERN GOLF CLUB LTD, Tennyson Ave, Llanwern Village, Newport, **NEWPORT**, NP18 2DW, **WALES**.
(T) 01633 412029

Membership: Members & Public

Contact/s:
- **Club Secretary:** Mr Mike Penny
- **Professional:** Mr Stephen Price

Course/s:
- **LLANWERN**
  Description: Parkland, Medium Length, Tight, Ideal for the Elderly
  Green Speed: Fast
  Built: 1927 Built On: Clay
  Number of Holes: 18 Par: 70
  Par 3's: 5 Par 4's: 10 Par 5's: 3
  Yds: 6177

LLANYMYNECH

LLANYMYNECH GOLF CLUB, Pant, Oswestry, **SHROPSHIRE**, SY10 8LB, **ENGLAND**.
(T) 01691 830983

Contact/s:
- **Club Secretary:** Mr D Thomas
- **Pro Shop:** Mr A Griffiths
  ☎ 01691 830879

Course/s:
- **LLANYMYNECH**
  Number of Holes: 18 Par: 70
  Yds: 6047 F9 Yds: 3036 B9 Yds: 3011

LLANYRAFON

LLANYRAFON GOLF COURSE, Llanfrechfa Way, Llanyravon, Cwmbran, **TORFAEN**, NP44 8HT, **WALES**.
(T) 01633 874636

Course/s:
- **LLANYRAFON GOLF COURSE**
  Number of Holes: 9 Par: 27
  Par 3's: 9
  Yds: 1283

LOBDEN

LOBDEN GOLF CLUB, The Rake, Whitworth, Rochdale, **LANCASHIRE**, OL12 8XJ, **ENGLAND**.
(T) 01706 343228

Contact/s:
- **Club Secretary:** Mr N Danby

Course/s:
- **LOBDEN**
  Number of Holes: 9 Par: 68
  Yds: 5697

LOCH LOMOND

LOCH LOMOND GOLF CLUB, Rossdhu House, Luss, Alexandria, **ARGYLL AND BUTE**, G83 8NT, **SCOTLAND**.
(T) 01436 655555
(E) info@lochlomond.com
(W) www.lochlomond.com

Membership: Members Only

Contact/s:
- **Marketing Manager:** Ms Joanne McGhee

Course/s:
- **LOCH LOMOND**
  Description: Championship, Wooded, Drains Well, Ideal for the Elderly
  Number of Holes: 18 Par: 71
  Yds: 7060 F9 Yds: 3520 B9 Yds: 3540
  Designer: J Morris, T Weiskopf 🏆

LOCH NESS

LOCH NESS GOLF COURSE, Castle Heather, Inverness, **HIGHLANDS**, IV2 6AA, **SCOTLAND**.
(T) 01463 713335
(E) info@golflochness.com
(W) www.golflochness.com

Contact/s:
- **Professional:** Mr Martin Piggot
  ☎ 01463 713334

Course/s:
- **LOCH NESS**
  Description: Parkland
  Built: 1996
  Number of Holes: 18 Par: 73
  Par 3's: 3 Par 4's: 11 Par 5's: 4
  Yds: 6772 F9 Yds: 3388 B9 Yds: 3384
  Further Information:
  Outstanding views over Inverness, Maray Firth and surrounding hills. Signature hole is the 14th, a par 3 with a 76 yard carry over a cavernous gully to the green.

LOCHCARRON

LOCHCARRON GOLF CLUB, East End, Lochcarron, **HIGHLANDS**, 1V54 8YU, **SCOTLAND**.
(T) 01520 722257

Contact/s:
- **Honorary Secretary:** Mr A Beattie
  ☎ 01520 766211

Course/s:
- **LOCHCARRON**
  Number of Holes: 9 Par: 62
  Yds: 3578 F9 Yds: 1789 B9 Yds: 1789

LOCHEND

LOCHEND GOLF CLUB, 147 Craigentinny Rd, Edinburgh, **EDINBURGH (CITY OF)**, EH7 6QN, **SCOTLAND**.
(T) 0131 5547960

Course/s:

- **COURSE #1**
  Number of Holes: 18 Par: 66
  Yds: 5418

LOCHGELLY

LOCHGELLY GOLF CLUB, Cartmore Rd, Lochgelly, **FIFE**, KY5 9PB, **SCOTLAND**.
(T) 01592 782589

Membership: Members & Public

Contact/s:
- **Professional:** Mr Martin Goldie

Course/s:
- **LOCHGELLY**
  Description: Wooded, Parkland, Breckland, Valley, Open, Medium Length, Drains Well, Ideal for the Elderly
  Green Speed: Medium
  Built: 1885 Built On: Soil
  Number of Holes: 18 Record: 68 (Martin Goldie)
  Prevailing Wind: East
  Further Information:
  Challenging course with good conditions.

LOCHGILPHEAD

LOCHGILPHEAD GOLF CLUB, Blarbuie Rd, Lochgilphead, **ARGYLL AND BUTE**, PA31 8LE, **SCOTLAND**.
(T) 01546 602340

Course/s:
- **LOCHGILPHEAD**
  Number of Holes: 9
  Designer: I McCamond

LOCHMABEN

LOCHMABEN GOLF CLUB, Castlehill Gate, Lockmaben, **DUMFRIES AND GALLOWAY**, DG11 1NT, **SCOTLAND**.
(T) 01387 810552

Membership: Members & Public
Size of Complex: 85 Acres

Contact/s:
- **Club Secretary:** Mr J M Dickie
  ☎ 01387 810713

Course/s:
- **LOCHMABEN**
  Description: Parkland, Undulating, Medium Length, Drains Well
  Green Speed: Medium
  Built: 1927 Built On: Soil
  Number of Holes: 18 Par: 67
  Par 3's: 6 Par 4's: 11 Par 5's: 1
  Yds: 5357 F9 Yds: 2452 B9 Yds: 2905
  Prevailing Wind: South/West
  Designer: James Braid, Committee
  Further Information:
  This attractive course is surrounding the Kirk Loch.

LOCHORE MEADOWS

LOCHORE MEADOWS COUNTRY PARK GOLF COURSE, Lochore Meadows Country Pk, Crosshill, Lochore, Lochgelly, **FIFE**, KY5 8BA, **SCOTLAND**.
(T) 01592 414300

Course/s:
- **LOCHORE MEADOWS**
  Number of Holes: 9 Par: 72
  Yds: 6070
  Further Information:
  9 hole course can be played as an 18 hole course.

LOCHRANZA GOLF

LOCHRANZA GOLF COURSE, Lochranza, **ISLE OF ARRAN,** KA27 8HL, **SCOTLAND.**
(T) 01770 830273
(W) www.arran.net/lochranza/golfcourse
Course/s:
🏌 **LOCHRANZA GOLF**
Built: 1899
Number of Holes: 9 **Par:** 70
Designer: I Robertson
Further Information:
Testing, fun and defined. Wonderful seaside setting with mature trees with a river through the course. Wild red deer graze the course and golden eagles soar overhead.

LOCHWINNOCH

LOCHWINNOCH GOLF CLUB, Burnfoot Rd, Lochwinnoch, **RENFREWSHIRE,** PA12 4AN, **SCOTLAND.**
(T) 01505 842153
(E) admin@lochwinnochgolf.co.uk
(W) www.lochwinnochgolf.co.uk
Contact/s:
● **Professional:** Mr Gerry Reilly
● **Book Tee Times:**
☎ 01505 843029/842153
Course/s:
🏌 **LOCHWINNOCH**
Description: Parkland
Built: 1897
Number of Holes: 18 **Par:** 71
Yds: 6025 **F9 Yds:** 3193 **B9 Yds:** 2832
Further Information:
Extensive views over Renfrewshire countryside.

LOCKERBIE

LOCKERBIE GOLF CLUB, Corrie Rd, Lockerbie, **DUMFRIES AND GALLOWAY,** DG11 2NP, **SCOTLAND.**
(T) 01576 203363
Membership: Members & Public
Size of Complex: 70 Acres
Contact/s:
● **Club Secretary:** Mr J Thomson
Course/s:
🏌 **LOCKERBIE**
Description: Wooded, Parkland, Short, Tight, Drains Well
Built: 1889
Number of Holes: 18 **Par:** 67
Yds: 5693 **F9 Yds:** 2845 **B9 Yds:** 2848
Designer: James Braid

LOFTHOUSE HILL

LOFTHOUSE HILL GOLF CLUB, Leeds Rd, Wakefield, **YORKSHIRE (WEST),** WF3 3LR, **ENGLAND.**
(T) 01924 823703
Membership: Members & Public
Contact/s:
● **Club Secretary:** Mr D Edwards
● **Pro Shop:** Mr S Middleton
Course/s:
🏌 **LOFTHOUSE HILL**
Description: Wooded, Parkland, Valley, Undulating, Sheltered, Medium Length, Tight
Green Speed: Medium
Built: 1995 **Built On:** Clay/Soil
Number of Holes: 18 **Par:** 70
Par 3's: 5 **Par 4's:** 10 **Par 5's:** 3
Yds: 5933 **F9 Yds:** 2950 **B9 Yds:** 2983

Prevailing Wind: East
Designer: Taylor
Further Information:
Inland dune type banks.

LONDON

LONDON GOLF CLUB (THE), South Ash Manor Est, Ash, Sevenoaks, **KENT,** TN15 7EN, **ENGLAND.**
(T) 01474 879899
Contact/s:
● **Professional:** Mr Bill Longmuir
Course/s:
🏌 **HERITAGE**
Number of Holes: 18 **Par:** 72
Par 3's: 4 **Par 4's:** 10 **Par 5's:** 4
Yds: 6771 **F9 Yds:** 3354 **B9 Yds:** 3417
Designer: Jack Nicklaus

🏌 **INTERNATIONAL**
Number of Holes: 18 **Par:** 72
Par 3's: 5 **Par 4's:** 8 **Par 5's:** 5
Yds: 6574 **F9 Yds:** 3167 **B9 Yds:** 3407
Designer: Ron Kirby

LONDON BEACH

LONDON BEACH GOLF CLUB, Ashford Rd, St. Michaels, Tenterden, **KENT,** TN30 6SP, **ENGLAND.**
(T) 01580 766279
(W) www.londonbeach.com
Membership: Members & Public
Size of Complex: 106 Acres
Contact/s:
● **Professional:** Mr Mark Chilcott
Course/s:
🏌 **LONDON BEACH**
Description: Championship, Parkland, Undulating, Sheltered, Long, Drains Well, Ideal for the Elderly
Green Speed: Fast
Built: 1997 **Built On:** Clay
Number of Holes: 9 **Par:** 36
Par 3's: 2 **Par 4's:** 5 **Par 5's:** 2
Yds: 2989
Prevailing Wind: South/West
Further Information:
Situated in Weald of Kent. 9 hole course can be played as an 18 hole course

LONDON SCOTTISH

LONDON SCOTTISH GOLF CLUB, Clubhouse, Windmill Rd, London, **LONDON (GREATER),** SW19 5NQ, **ENGLAND.**
(T) 0208 7891207
Membership: Members & Public
Contact/s:
● **Club Secretary:** Mr Steve Barr
Course/s:
🏌 **LONDON SCOTTISH**
Description: Parkland, Open, Short, Drains Well
Green Speed: Medium/Fast
Built: 1865 **Built On:** Clay/Sand/Soil
Number of Holes: 18
Yds: 5458
Designer: William Dunn
Further Information:
Flat course.

LONG ASHTON

LONG ASHTON GOLF CLUB, Clevedon Rd, Long Ashton, Bristol, **BRISTOL,** BS41 9DW, **ENGLAND.**
(T) 01275 392229
(E) secretary@longashtongc.co.uk

(W) www.longashtongolfclub.co.uk
Membership: Members & Public
Size of Complex: 160 Acres
Contact/s:
● **Professional:** Mr Mike Hart
Course/s:
🏌 **LONG ASHTON**
Description: Parkland, Hilltop, Medium Length, Drains Well, Ideal for the Elderly
Green Speed: Medium/Fast
Built: 1893
Number of Holes: 18 **Par:** 71
Record: 65 (Andrew Oldcorn)
Par 3's: 3 **Par 4's:** 13 **Par 5's:** 2
Yds: 6381 **F9 Yds:** 3101 **B9 Yds:** 3280
Prevailing Wind: South/West
Designer: Hawtree, S Taylor

LONG SUTTON

LONG SUTTON GOLF CLUB, Long Sutton, Langport, **SOMERSET,** TA10 9JU, **ENGLAND.**
(T) 01458 241017
Membership: Members & Public
Size of Complex: 118 Acres
Contact/s:
● **Club Secretary:** Mrs Marlene Cox
● **Professional:** Mr Andrew Hayes
Course/s:
🏌 **LONG SUTTON**
Description: Parkland, Undulating, Tends to Flood, Ideal for the Elderly
Green Speed: Medium
Built: 1990 **Built On:** Clay/Soil
Number of Holes: 18 **Par:** 71
Record: 70 (Andrew Hayes)
Par 3's: 5 **Par 4's:** 9 **Par 5's:** 4
Yds: 6329
Designer: P Dawson
Further Information:
You will make full use of a full set of clubs. The course record is only 1 under par after nine years of play.

LONGCLIFFE

LONGCLIFFE GOLF CLUB, Snells Nook Lane, Nanpantan, Loughborough, **LEICESTERSHIRE,** LE11 3YA, **ENGLAND.**
(T) 01509 239129
(E) longcliffegolf@btconnect.com
Membership: Members & Public
Size of Complex: 150 Acres
Contact/s:
● **Club Secretary:** Mr Paul Keeling
● **Professional:** Mr David Mee
☎ 01509 231450
Course/s:
🏌 **LONGCLIFFE**
Description: Championship, Wooded, Heath Land, Undulating, Sheltered, Medium Length, Drains Well
Green Speed: Fast
Built: 1905 **Built On:** Soil
Number of Holes: 18 **Par:** 72
Yds: 6625 **F9 Yds:** 3342 **B9 Yds:** 3283
Prevailing Wind: East/West
Designer: W Williamson
Further Information:
English golf union championship course.

LONGFORD (COUNTY)

COUNTY LONGFORD GOLF CLUB, Glack, Longford, **COUNTY LONGFORD, IRELAND.**
(T) 043 46310
Contact/s:
● **Club Secretary:** Mr Enda Dooley

Course/s:

● **LONGFORD**
   Description: Parkland, Undulating, Medium Length, Drains Well
   Built: 1900 **Built On:** Soil
   Number of Holes: 18 **Par:** 70
   Yds: 5765 **F9 Yds:** 2673 **B9 Yds:** 3092

LONGHIRST HALL

LONGHIRST HALL GOLF COURSE, Longhirst, Morpeth, **NORTHUMBERLAND**, NE61 3LL, **ENGLAND**.
(T) 01670 858519
(E) enquiries@longhirstgolf.co.uk
(W) www.longhirstgolf.co.uk
Membership: Members & Public

Contact/s:

● **Book Tee Times:** Mr Ian Brodie
   ☎ 01670 791505

Course/s:

● **THE NEW**
   Description: Parkland
   Built: 2001
   Number of Holes: 18 **Par:** 70
   Par 3's: 5 **Par 4's:** 10 **Par 5's:** 3
   Yds: 6109 **F9 Yds:** 3017 **B9 Yds:** 3092
   Further Information:
   Open Tuesday, Thursday and Saturday from the 01/05/02. Mixes with the back 9 holes of the Old Course.

● **THE OLD**
   Description: Parkland
   Built: 1997
   Number of Holes: 18 **Par:** 73
   Par 3's: 3 **Par 4's:** 11 **Par 5's:** 4
   Yds: 6568 **F9 Yds:** 3189 **B9 Yds:** 3379
   Further Information:
   Used as a 9 hole course until the 01/05/02 as the New Course uses the back 9 holes.

LONGLEY PARK

LONGLEY PARK GOLF CLUB, Maple St, Huddersfield, **YORKSHIRE (WEST)**, HD5 9AX, **ENGLAND**.
(T) 01484 426932

Contact/s:

● **Professional:** Mr Nick Leeming
● **Book Tee Times:**
   ☎ 01484 422304

Course/s:

● **LONGLEY PARK**
   Description: Wooded
   Built: 1911
   Number of Holes: 9 **Par:** 66

LONGNIDDRY

LONGNIDDRY GOLF CLUB LTD, Links Rd, Longniddry, **LOTHIAN (EAST)**, EH32 0NL, **SCOTLAND**.
(T) 01875 852228
(W) www.longniddrygolfclub.co.uk

Course/s:

● **LONGNIDDRY**
   Number of Holes: 18 **Par:** 68
   Par 3's: 4 **Par 4's:** 14
   Yds: 6186 **F9 Yds:** 3115 **B9 Yds:** 3071
   Designer: Harry Shapland Colt

LONGRIDGE

LONGRIDGE GOLF CLUB, Fell Barn, Jeffrey Hill, Longridge, Preston, **LANCASHIRE**, PR3 2TU, **ENGLAND**.
(T) 01772 783291

Course/s:

● **LONGRIDGE**

Number of Holes: 18

LOOE

LOOE GOLF CLUB, Bin Down, Looe, **CORNWALL**, PL13 1PX, **ENGLAND**.
(T) 01503 240239

Contact/s:

● **Professional:** Mr Alastair MacDonald

Course/s:

● **LOOE**
   Description: Parkland
   Built: 1930
   Number of Holes: 18
   Designer: Harry Vardon

LOSTWITHIEL

LOSTWITHIEL GOLF & COUNTRY CLUB, Lower Polscoe, Lostwithiel, **CORNWALL**, PL22 0HQ, **ENGLAND**.
(T) 01208 873822
(E) reception@golfhotel.co.uk
(W) www.golf-hotel.co.uk
Membership: Members & Public
Size of Complex: 150 Acres

Contact/s:

● **Club Secretary:** Mr David Higman
● **Professional:** Mr Tony Nash

Course/s:

● **LOSTWITHIEL**
   Description: Wooded, Parkland, Hilltop, Valley, Undulating, Sheltered, Medium Length, Tight, Drains Well, Ideal for the Elderly
   Green Speed: Medium
   Built: 1991 **Built On:** Soil
   Number of Holes: 18 **Par:** 72
   Record: 64 (Tony Nash)
   Par 3's: 5 **Par 4's:** 8 **Par 5's:** 5
   Yds: 5984 **F9 Yds:** 3422 **B9 Yds:** 2562
   Prevailing Wind: West
   Designer: Stuart Wood
   Further Information:
   The challenging front 9 offers magnificent views of the surrounding countryside, while the back 9 is situated in leaf parkland, flanked by the River Fowey.

LOTHIANBURN

LOTHIANBURN GOLF CLUB, 106A Biggar Rd, Edinburgh, **EDINBURGH (CITY OF)**, EH10 7DU, **SCOTLAND**.
(T) 0131 4452206

Contact/s:

● **Professional:** Mr Kurt Mungall
● **Book Tee Times:**
   ☎ 0131 4452288

Course/s:

● **LOTHIANBURN**
   Description: Heath Land, Hilltop, Open, Medium Length, Tight
   Built: 1893
   Number of Holes: 18 **Par:** 71
   Designer: James Braid

LOUDOUN

LOUDOUN GOLF CLUB, Newmiln Rd, Galston, **AYRSHIRE (EAST)**, KA4 8PA, **SCOTLAND**.
(T) 01563 821993

Contact/s:

● **Club Secretary:** Mr W F Dougan
● **Book Tee Times:** Ms L Gilliland

Course/s:

● **LOUDOUN GOWF CLUB**
   Description: Wooded, Parkland, Valley

Built: 1909
Number of Holes: 18 **Par:** 68

LOUGHREA

LOUGHREA GOLF CLUB, Graigue, Loughrea, **COUNTY GALWAY**, **IRELAND**.
(T) 091 841049

Course/s:

● **LOUGHREA**
   Number of Holes: 9
   Designer: Edward Hackett

LOUGHTON

LOUGHTON GOLF CLUB LTD, Clays Lane, Loughton, **ESSEX**, IG10 2RZ, **ENGLAND**.
(T) 020 85022923

Contact/s:

● **Professional:** Mr Richard Clayton

Course/s:

● **LOUGHTON**
   Number of Holes: 9 **Par:** 33
   Yds: 2326 **F9 Yds:** 2326

LOUTH

LOUTH GOLF CLUB, Crowtree Lane, Louth, **LINCOLNSHIRE**, LN11 9LJ, **ENGLAND**.
(T) 01507 603681
(E) louthgolfclub1992@btinternet.com
(W) www.louthgolfclub.com

Contact/s:

● **Professional:** Mr Allan Blundell
   ☎ 01507 604648

Course/s:

● **LOUTH**
   Description: Wooded, Parkland
   Built: 1965
   Number of Holes: 18 **Par:** 72
   Yds: 6430 **F9 Yds:** 2981 **B9 Yds:** 3449
   Further Information:
   Views across the Wolds.

LOUTH (COUNTY)

COUNTY LOUTH GOLF CLUB, Baltray, Drogheda, **COUNTY LOUTH**, **IRELAND**.
(T) 041 9822323
(E) baltray@indigo.ie
Membership: Members & Public
Size of Complex: 200 Acres

Contact/s:

● **Club Secretary:** Mr Peter Stewart
● **Professional:** Mr Paddy McGuirk
   ☎ 041 9822444

Course/s:

● **LOUTH**
   Description: Championship, Links, Undulating, Medium Length
   Green Speed: Fast
   Built: 1892 **Built On:** Sand
   Number of Holes: 18 **Par:** 73
   Record: 64 (Eamon Darey)
   Par 3's: 4 **Par 4's:** 9 **Par 5's:** 5
   Yds: 6783
   Designer: Simpson
   Further Information:
   A course to suit all handicaps. ♟

LOW LAITHES

LOW LAITHES GOLF CLUB LTD, Lowlaithes Golf House, Park Mill Lane, Ossett, **YORKSHIRE (WEST)**, WF5 9AP, **ENGLAND**.
(T) 01924 274667

Contact/s:

● **Manager:** Mr P Browning

Course/s:

LOW LAITHES
Number of Holes: 18
Designer: Alistair MacKenzie

LOWES PARK

LOWES PARK GOLF CLUB LTD, Hilltop, Lowes Rd, Bury, **LANCASHIRE**, BL9 6SU, **ENGLAND**.
(T) 0161 7639503

Contact/s:
● **Club Secretary:** Mr John Entwistle

Course/s:
🍂 **LOWES PARK**
Number of Holes: 9 **Par:** 70
Yds: 6006 **F9 Yds:** 2964 **B9 Yds:** 3042

LUCAN

LUCAN GOLF CLUB, Celbridge Rd, Lucan, **COUNTY DUBLIN**, **IRELAND**.
(T) 01 6280246

Course/s:
🍂 **LUCAN**
Number of Holes: 18
Designer: Edward Hackett

LUDLOW

LUDLOW GOLF CLUB, Bromfield, Ludlow, **SHROPSHIRE**, SY8 2BT, **ENGLAND**.
(T) 01584 856366

Contact/s:
● **Professional:** Mr Russell Price

Course/s:
🍂 **LUDLOW**
Description: Heath Land, Drains Well
Built: 1889
Number of Holes: 18 **Par:** 70
Yds: 6277 **F9 Yds:** 3444 **B9 Yds:** 2833
Further Information:
Easy walking with hazards such as gorse and two quarries.

LUFFENHAM HEATH

LUFFENHAM HEATH, South Luffenham Rd, Ketton, Stamford, **LINCOLNSHIRE**, PE9 3UU, **ENGLAND**.
(T) 01780 720205
(E) jringleby@theluffenhamheathgc.co.uk

Membership: Members & Public
Size of Complex: 160 Acres

Contact/s:
● **Club Secretary:** Mr John Ingleby
● **Professional:** Mr Ian Burnett
☎ 01780 720298

Course/s:
🍂 **LUFFENHAM HEATH**
Description: Heath Land, Undulating, Sheltered, Medium Length, Tight, Drains Well, Ideal for the Elderly
Green Speed: Fast
Built: 1911 **Built On:** Clay
Number of Holes: 18 **Par:** 70
Record: 65 (Robert Stevens)
Yds: 6315 **F9 Yds:** 2980 **B9 Yds:** 3335
Prevailing Wind: South/West
Designer: James Braid

LUFFNESS

LUFFNESS NEW GOLF CLUB, Aberlady, Longniddry, **LOTHIAN (EAST)**, EH32 0QA, **SCOTLAND**.
(T) 01620 843336

Membership: Members & Public

Contact/s:
● **Club Secretary:** Mr Donald Leckie

Course/s:
🍂 **LUFFNESS**
Description: Links, Sheltered, Drains Well, Ideal for the Elderly
Number of Holes: 18 **Record:** 62
Prevailing Wind: East
Designer: Tom Morris

LULLINGSTONE PARK

LULLINGSTONE PARK & GOLF COURSES, Parkgate Rd, Chelsfield, Orpington, **KENT**, BR6 7PX, **ENGLAND**.
(T) 01959 533793

Membership: Members & Public
Size of Complex: 650 Acres

Contact/s:
● **Professional:** Mr Mark Watt

Course/s:
🍂 **LULLINGSTONE PARK 18 HOLE**
Description: Parkland, Undulating, Open, Long, Drains Well, Ideal for the Elderly
Green Speed: Medium **Built On:** Chalk
Number of Holes: 18
Prevailing Wind: North/West

🍂 **LULLINGSTONE PARK 9 HOLE**
Description: Parkland, Undulating, Open, Medium Length, Ideal for the Elderly
Green Speed: Medium **Built On:** Chalk
Number of Holes: 9
Prevailing Wind: North/West

LUNDIN

LUNDIN GOLF CLUB, Golf Rd, Lundin Links, Leven, **FIFE**, KY8 6BA, **SCOTLAND**.
(T) 01333 320051
(W) www.lundingolfclub.co.uk

Membership: Members & Public
Size of Complex: 138 Acres

Contact/s:
● **Club Secretary:** Mr David Thomson
☎ 01333 320202
● **Professional:** Mr David Webster

Course/s:
🍂 **LUNDIN**
Description: Championship, Links, Undulating, Open, Medium Length, Drains Well, Ideal for the Elderly
Green Speed: Fast
Built: 1868 **Built On:** Sand
Number of Holes: 18 **Par:** 71
Record: 63 (Andrew Hare)
Par 3's: 3 **Par 4's:** 13 **Par 5's:** 2
Yds: 6394 **F9 Yds:** 3219 **B9 Yds:** 3175
Prevailing Wind: West
Designer: James Braid
Further Information:
This course was voted 75th in the UK by Golf Monthly. The course is very challenging with the potential for disaster on every hole. The old railway line bisects the course and presents a visible out of bounds for several drives. Greens are of good size quality with subtle undulations. A good test of golf - but not for the very high handicapper.

LUNDIN LADIES

LUNDIN LADIES GOLF CLUB, Woodielea Rd, Lundin Links, Leven, **FIFE**, KY8 6AR, **SCOTLAND**.
(T) 01333 320832
(E) lundinladies@madasafish.com

Contact/s:
● **Club Secretary:** Ms Marion Mitchell

Course/s:
🍂 **LUNDIN LADIES**

Number of Holes: 9 **Par:** 68
Yds: 4730

LURGAN

LURGAN GOLF CLUB, Golf Clubhouse, Windsor Ave, Lurgan, Craigavon, **COUNTY ARMAGH**, BT67 9BN, **NORTHERN IRELAND**.
(T) 028 38322087

Course/s:
🍂 **LURGAN**
Number of Holes: 18
Designer: A Pennink

LUTON GOLF CTRE

LUTON GOLF CENTRE, Wandon End, Luton, **BEDFORDSHIRE**, LU2 8NX, **ENGLAND**.
(T) 01582 731135

Contact/s:
● **Owner:** Mr R Allen

Course/s:
🍂 **LUTON GOLF CTRE**
Number of Holes: 9 **Par:** 28
Par 3's: 8 **Par 4's:** 1
Yds: 1163

LUTTERWORTH

LUTTERWORTH GOLF CLUB, Rugby Rd, Lutterworth, **LEICESTERSHIRE**, LE17 4HN, **ENGLAND**.
(T) 01455 552532

Contact/s:
● **Club Secretary:** Mr John Faulks

Course/s:
🍂 **LUTTERWORTH**
Number of Holes: 18 **Par:** 70
Yds: 6226 **F9 Yds:** 3107 **B9 Yds:** 3119

LUTTRELLSTOWN CASTLE

LUTTRELLSTOWN CASTLE GOLF & COUNTRY CLUB, Castleknock, Luttrellstown, Dublin, **COUNTY DUBLIN**, **IRELAND**.
(T) 01 8089900
(E) enquiries@luttrellstown.ie
(W) www.luttrellstown.ie

Course/s:
🍂 **LUTTRELLSTOWN CASTLE**
Number of Holes: 18
Designer: N Bielenberg

LYBSTER

LYBSTER GOLF CLUB, Main St, Caithness, Lybster, **HIGHLANDS**, KW3 6AE, **SCOTLAND**.

Course/s:
🍂 **LYBSTER**
Number of Holes: 9

LYDD

LYDD GOLF CLUB & DRIVING RANGE, Romney Rd, Lydd, Romney Marsh, **KENT**, TN29 9LS, **ENGLAND**.
(T) 01797 321201
(E) info@lyddgolfclub.co.uk
(W) www.lyddgolfclub.co.uk

Contact/s:
● **Professional:** Mr Stuart Smith

Course/s:
🍂 **LYDD**
Description: Links
Built: 1994
Number of Holes: 18 **Par:** 71
Yds: 6517 **F9 Yds:** 3234 **B9 Yds:** 3283

Designer: Mike Smith
Further Information:
Wide fairways and many water features.

LYDNEY

LYDNEY GOLF CLUB, The Links, Lakeside
Ave, Lydney, **GLOUCESTERSHIRE,** GL15
5QG, **ENGLAND.**
(T) 01594 842614

Contact/s:
● **Manager:** Mr R H Watkins

Course/s:
● **LYDNEY**
Number of Holes: 9

LYME REGIS

LYME REGIS GOLF CLUB, Timber Hill,
Lyme Regis, **DORSET,** DT7 3HQ, **ENGLAND.**
(T) 01297 442963

Contact/s:
● **Professional:** Mr Andrew Black
☎ 01297 443822
● **Book Tee Times:** Mr Brian Wheeler

Course/s:
● **LYME REGIS**
Description: Cliff Top
Built: 1893
Number of Holes: 18 **Par:** 71
Par 3's: 4 **Par 4's:** 11 **Par 5's:** 3
Yds: 6264 **F9 Yds:** 3082 **B9 Yds:** 3182
Designer: Donald Steel
Further Information:
Coastal views.

LYMM

LYMM GOLF CLUB, Whitbarrow Rd, Lymm,
CHESHIRE, WA13 9AN, **ENGLAND.**
(T) 01925 752177

Membership: Members & Public

Contact/s:
● **Club Secretary:** Miss Stephanie Nash
☎ 01925 755020
● **Professional:** Mr Stephen McCarthy
☎ 01925 755054

Course/s:
● **LYMM**
Description: Wooded, Parkland,
Undulating, Medium Length, Tight
Green Speed: Medium/Fast
Built On: Clay/Sand/Soil
Number of Holes: 18

LYNEDOCH & MURRAYSHALL

**MURRAYSHALL COUNTRY HOUSE HOTEL
& GOLF COURSE,** Murrayshall, Perth,
PERTH AND KINROSS, PH2 7PH,
SCOTLAND.
(T) 01738 552784

Size of Complex: 300 Acres

Contact/s:
● **Professional:** Mr Alan Reid

Course/s:
● **LYNEDOCH**
Description: Wooded
Built: 1999
Number of Holes: 18 **Par:** 69
Further Information:
This course's maturity is impressive. 18
holes carved through a beautiful natural
landscape of Scots Pines, bracken filled
glens, open ditches and burns.

● **MURRAYSHALL**
Description: Wooded, Parkland,
Undulating
Built: 1981

Number of Holes: 18 **Par:** 73
Designer: J Hamilton-Stutt
Further Information:
There are water hazards, white sand
bunkers and stone bridges throughout
course.

LYNEHAM

LYNEHAM GOLF CLUB, Lyneham, Chipping
Norton, **OXFORDSHIRE,** OX7 6QQ,
ENGLAND.
(T) 01993 831841
(E) golf@lynehamgc.freeserve.co.uk

Membership: Members & Public

Contact/s:
● **Club Secretary:** Mr C Howkins
● **Professional:** Mr J Fincher
● **Pro Shop:** Mr P Bennett

Course/s:
● **LYNEHAM**
Description: Parkland, Open, Drains Well,
Ideal for the Elderly
Green Speed: Medium
Built: 1990 **Built On:** Clay
Number of Holes: 18 **Par:** 72
Record: 66 (Jonathan Dunn)
Par 3's: 3 **Par 4's:** 12 **Par 5's:** 3
Yds: 6707 **F9 Yds:** 3251 **B9 Yds:** 3456
Designer: D G Carpenter
Further Information:
Area of outstanding beauty.

LYONS GATE

LYONS GATE GOLF COURSE, Lyons Gate,
Dorchester, **DORSET,** DT2 7AZ, **ENGLAND.**
(T) 01300 345239

Contact/s:
● **Owner:** Mrs P Pires

Course/s:
● **LYONS GATE GOLF COURSE**
Number of Holes: 9 **Par:** 60
Yds: 3834 **F9 Yds:** 1868 **B9 Yds:** 1966
Further Information:
Course has 9 holes but 18 tees

LYSHOTT HEATH

LYSHOTT HEATH GOLF CLUB, Millbrook,
Bedford, **BEDFORDSHIRE,** MK45 2JB,
ENGLAND.
(T) 01525 840252
(E) enquiries@lyshott-heath.com
(W) www.lyshott-heath.com

Contact/s:
● **Professional:** Mr Geraint Dixon

Course/s:
● **LYSHOTT HEATH**
Description: Parkland, Long, Drains Well
Number of Holes: 18 **Par:** 74
Yds: 7021 **F9 Yds:** 3282 **B9 Yds:** 3739
Designer: W Sutherland

LYTHAM & ST ANNES (ROYAL)

ROYAL LYTHAM & ST ANNES, Links Gate,
Lytham St. Annes, **LANCASHIRE,** FY8 3LQ,
ENGLAND.
(T) 01253 724206
(E) info@royallytham.co.uk
(W) www.royallythamgolf.co.uk

Membership: Members & Public

Contact/s:
● **Club Secretary:** Mr Lytton Goodwyn
● **Professional:** Mr Eddie Birchdnough
● **Book Tee Times:** Ms Hilary Harrison
☎ ext. 229

Course/s:

● **LYTHAM ST ANNES**
Description: Championship, Links, Open,
Drains Well
Number of Holes: 18 **Par:** 71
Yds: 6334 **F9 Yds:** 3088 **B9 Yds:** 3246
♣

LYTHAM GREEN

LYTHAM GREEN DRIVE GOLF CLUB,
Ballam Rd, Lytham St. Annes, **LANCASHIRE,**
FY8 4LE, **ENGLAND.**
(T) 01253 737390
(E) green@greendrive.fsnet.co.uk

Membership: Members & Public

Contact/s:
● **Club Secretary:** Mr Stephen Higham
● **Professional:** Mr Andrew Lancaster

Course/s:
● **LYTHAM GREEN**
Description: Wooded, Sheltered,
Medium Length
Green Speed: Fast
Built: 1913 **Built On:** Clay/Soil
Number of Holes: 18 **Par:** 70
Yds: 6163 **F9 Yds:** 3108 **B9 Yds:** 3055
Prevailing Wind: South

MACCLESFIELD

MACCLESFIELD GOLF CLUB, The Hollins,
Macclesfield, **CHESHIRE,** SK11 7EA,
ENGLAND.
(T) 01625 615845
(E) secretary@maccgolflclub.co.uk
(W) www.maccgolflub.co.uk

Membership: Members & Public

Contact/s:
● **Professional:** Mr Tony Taylor
☎ 01625 616952

Course/s:
● **MACCLESFIELD**
Description: Heath Land
Built: 1889
Number of Holes: 18 **Par:** 70
Yds: 5700 **F9 Yds:** 3084 **B9 Yds:** 2616
Designer: Hawtree

MACHRIE

MACHRIE HOTEL & GOLF LINKS, Port
Ellen, Isle Of Islay, **ARGYLL AND BUTE,**
PA42 7AN, **SCOTLAND.**
(T) 01496 302310
(E) machrie@machrie.com
(W) www.machrie.com

Membership: Members & Public

Contact/s:
● **Club Secretary:** Mr Tom Dunn

Course/s:
● **MACHRIE**
Built: 1891 **Built On:** Sand
Number of Holes: 18 **Par:** 71
Par 3's: 3 **Par 4's:** 13 **Par 5's:** 2
Yds: 6292 **F9 Yds:** 3194 **B9 Yds:** 3098
Designer: Willie Campbell ♣

MACHRIE BAY

MACHRIE BAY GOLF CLUB, Machrie, **ISLE
OF ARRAN,** KA27 8DZ, **SCOTLAND.**
(T) 01770 850232

Course/s:
● **MACHRIE BAY**
Number of Holes: 9
Designer: William Fernie

MACHRIHANISH

MACHRIHANISH GOLF CLUB,
Machrihanish, Campbeltown, **ARGYLL AND BUTE**, PA28 6PT, **SCOTLAND**.
(T) 01586 810277
(E) captain@machgolf.com
(W) www.machgolf.com

Membership: Members & Public

Contact/s:
- **Club Secretary:** Mrs Anna Anderson
- **Professional:** Mr Ken Campbell

Course/s:
🏌 **MACHRIHANISH 18 HOLE**
  Description: Links, Open, Short, Tight, Drains Well
  Green Speed: Slow/Medium
  Built: 1876 **Built On:** Sand/Soil
  Number of Holes: 18 **Par:** 70
  Yds: 6225
  Prevailing Wind: South/West
  Further Information:
  Beautiful greens. 🏆

🏌 **MACHRIHANISH 9 HOLE**
  Number of Holes: 9
  Yds: 2395

MACHYNLLETH

MACHYNLLETH GOLF CLUB, Newtown Rd, Felingerrig, Machynlleth, **POWYS**, SY20 8UH, **WALES**.
(T) 01654 702000

Course/s:
🏌 **MACHYNLLETH**
  Number of Holes: 9

MAESDU

MAESDU GOLF CLUB, Professional, Hospital Rd, Llandudno, **CONWY**, LL30 1HU, **WALES**.
(T) 01492 875195

Contact/s:
- **Club Secretary:** Mr G Dean

Course/s:
🏌 **LLANDUDNO (MAESDU)**
  Number of Holes: 18

MAESTEG

MAESTEG GOLF CLUB, Mount Pleasant, Neath Rd, Maesteg, **BRIDGEND**, CF34 9PR, **WALES**.
(T) 01656 734106

Contact/s:
- **Club Secretary:** Mr Keith Lewis

Course/s:
🏌 **MAESTEG**
  Number of Holes: 18
  Designer: James Braid

MAGDALENE FIELDS

MAGDALENE FIELDS GOLF CLUB,
Magdalene Fields, Berwick-upon-Tweed, **NORTHUMBERLAND**, TD15 1NE, **ENGLAND**.
(T) 01289 306384
(W) www.magdalene-fields.co.uk

Membership: Members & Public

Contact/s:
- **Club Secretary:** Mr M J Lynch

Course/s:
🏌 **MAGDALENE FIELDS**
  Description: Parkland, Cliff Top, Ideal for the Elderly
  Green Speed: Medium
  Built: 1903 **Built On:** Clay/Soil
  Number of Holes: 18 **Par:** 72
  Par 3's: 3 **Par 4's:** 12 **Par 5's:** 3
  Yds: 6407 **F9 Yds:** 3290 **B9 Yds:** 3117
  Designer: William Park
  Further Information:
  Stunning views Southward to Holy Island and Westward to the Elizabethan Town Walls.

MAGNOLIA PARK

MAGNOLIA PARK GOLF & COUNTRY CLUB, Arncott Rd, Boarstall, Boardstall, **BUCKINGHAMSHIRE**, HP18 9XX, **ENGLAND**.
(T) 01844 239700
(E) info@magnoliapark.co.uk
(W) www.magnoliapark.co.uk

Membership: Members & Public
Size of Complex: 200 Acres

Contact/s:
- **Director Of Golf:** Mr A Taylor

Course/s:
🏌 **MAGNOLIA PARK**
  Description: Championship, Undulating, Open, Medium Length, Drains Well
  Green Speed: Fast
  Built: 1998 **Built On:** Clay
  Number of Holes: 18 **Par:** 73
  Record: 65 (Andrew McKenna)
  Yds: 6902 **F9 Yds:** 3507 **B9 Yds:** 3395
  Designer: Jonathan Gaunt

MAHEE ISLAND

MAHEE ISLAND GOLF CLUB, Mahee Island, Comber, Newtownards, **COUNTY DOWN**, BT23 6EP, **NORTHERN IRELAND**.
(T) 028 97541234

Course/s:
🏌 **MAHEE ISLAND**
  Description: Parkland, Undulating
  Built: 1929
  Number of Holes: 9 **Par:** 68

MAHON MUNICIPAL

MAHON MUNICIPAL GOLF CLUB,
Blackrock, Cork, **COUNTY CORK**, **IRELAND**.
(T) 021 294280

Membership: Public

Course/s:
🏌 **MAHON MUNICIPAL**
  Number of Holes: 18
  Designer: Edward Hackett

MAHON MUNICIPAL

MAHON MUNICIPAL GOLF CLUB,
Lackduv, Macroom, **COUNTY CORK**, **IRELAND**.
(T) 026 41072
(E) mcroomgc@iol.ie

Membership: Public

Course/s:
🏌 **MAHON MUNICIPAL**
  Number of Holes: 18
  Designer: Edward Hackett

MAIDENHEAD

MAIDENHEAD GOLF CLUB,
Shoppenhangers Rd, Maidenhead, **BERKSHIRE**, SL6 2PZ, **ENGLAND**.
(T) 01628 624693

Membership: Members & Public

Contact/s:
- **Club Secretary:** Mr T P Jackson
- **Professional:** Mr Steve Geary
  ☎ 01628 624067

Course/s:
🏌 **MAIDENHEAD**
  Description: Parkland, Sheltered, Medium Length, Tight, Drains Well, Ideal for the Elderly
  Green Speed: Medium/Fast
  Built: 1896 **Built On:** Gravel
  Number of Holes: 18 **Record:** 65 (S Maynard)
  Designer: Simpson

MALAHIDE

MALAHIDE GOLF CLUB, Beechwood, The Grange, Malahide, **COUNTY DUBLIN**, **IRELAND**.
(T) 01 8461611
(E) malgc@clubi.ie
(W) www.malahidegolfclub.ie

Membership: Members & Public
Size of Complex: 200 Acres

Contact/s:
- **Club Secretary:** Mr Sean Maguire
- **Professional:** Mr John Murray
- **Book Tee Times:** Mr John McCormack
- **Book Lessons:**
  ☎ 01 846 0002

Course/s:
🏌 **MAIN**
  Description: Parkland, Medium Length
  Green Speed: Medium
  Built: 1990 **Built On:** Sand
  Number of Holes: 27 **Par:** 70
  Yds: 5752 **F9 Yds:** 2888 **B9 Yds:** 2864
  Designer: Edward Hackett
  Further Information: Course can be played as a 9 hole or an 18 hole course.

MALDEN

MALDEN GOLF CLUB, Traps Lane, New Malden, **SURREY**, KT3 4RS, **ENGLAND**.
(T) 020 89420654

Course/s:
🏌 **MALDEN**
  Number of Holes: 18

MALDON

MALDON GOLF CLUB, Beeleigh, Maldon, **ESSEX**, CM9 6LL, **ENGLAND**.
(T) 01621 853212
(E) maldon.golf@virgin.net

Contact/s:
- **Club Secretary:** Mr G R Bezant

Course/s:
🏌 **MALDON**
  Number of Holes: 9 **Par:** 71
  Yds: 6253 **F9 Yds:** 3028 **B9 Yds:** 3225
  Designer: Thompson

MALKINS BANK

MALKINS BANK GOLF COURSE,
Professional, Betchton Rd, Malkins Bank, Sandbach, **CHESHIRE**, CW11 4XN, **ENGLAND**.
(T) 01270 765931

Contact/s:
- **Professional:** Mr David Wheeler

Course/s:
🏌 **MALKINS BANK**
  Number of Holes: 18 **Par:** 70
  Yds: 5972 **F9 Yds:** 3077 **B9 Yds:** 2895
  Designer: Hawtree

MALLOW

MALLOW GOLF CLUB, Ballyellis, Mallow, **COUNTY CORK**, **IRELAND**.
(T) 022 21145
(W) www.golfeurope.com/clubs/mallow/
Contact/s:
● Club Secretary: Mr Michael O'Sullivan
　☎ 022 22591
● Professional: Mr Sean Conway
● Pro Shop:
　☎ 022 43424
Course/s:
⛳ **MALLOW**
Description: Parkland
Number of Holes: 18　Par: 72
Yds: 5960

MALONE

MALONE GOLF CLUB, Drumbeg, Dunmurry, Belfast, **COUNTY ANTRIM**, BT17 9LB, **NORTHERN IRELAND**.
(T) 028 90612758
(W) www.malonegolfclub.co.uk
Contact/s:
● Manager: Mr N Agate
Course/s:
⛳ **EDENDERRY**
Number of Holes: 9
⛳ **MAIN**
Number of Holes: 18　Par: 71
Yds: 6599　F9 Yds: 3401　B9 Yds: 3198

MALTON

MALTON GOLF COURSE, Malton Lane, Meldreth, Royston, **HERTFORDSHIRE**, SG8 6PE, **ENGLAND**.
(T) 01763 262200
(W) www.maltongolf.co.uk
Membership: Members & Public
Size of Complex: 235 Acres
Contact/s:
● Book Tee Times: Mrs Julia Wright
Course/s:
⛳ **MALTON**
Description: Parkland, Undulating, Medium Length, Drains Well, Ideal for the Elderly
Green Speed: Medium
Built: 1993　Built On: Clay
Number of Holes: 18　Par: 72
Par 3's: 4　Par 4's: 10　Par 5's: 4
Yds: 6708　F9 Yds: 3398　B9 Yds: 3310
Designer: Bruce Critchley, Peter Bancroft
Further Information:
Very peaceful, with plenty of wildlife.

MALTON & NORTON

MALTON & NORTON GOLF CLUB, Welham Rd, Norton, Malton, **YORKSHIRE (NORTH)**, YO17 9QE, **ENGLAND**.
(T) 01653 693882
(E) maltonandnorton@golcl.fsnet.co.uk
(W) www.maltongolfclub.co.uk
Contact/s:
● Club Secretary: Mr Eddie Harrison
Course/s:
⛳ **DERWENT**
Number of Holes: 18　Par: 72
Par 3's: 4　Par 4's: 10　Par 5's: 4
Yds: 6295　F9 Yds: 3045　B9 Yds: 3250
⛳ **PARK**
Number of Holes: 18　Par: 72
Par 3's: 4　Par 4's: 10　Par 5's: 4
Yds: 6251　F9 Yds: 3206　B9 Yds: 3045

⛳ **WELHAM**
Number of Holes: 18　Par: 72
Par 3's: 4　Par 4's: 10　Par 5's: 4
Yds: 6456　F9 Yds: 3250　B9 Yds: 3206

MANCHESTER

MANCHESTER GOLF CLUB, Rochdale Rd, Middleton, Manchester, **MANCHESTER (GREATER)**, M24 6QP, **ENGLAND**.
(T) 0161 6432718/ 6433202
(E) mgc@zen.co.uk
(W) www.manchestergc.co.uk
Membership: Members & Public
Size of Complex: 247 Acres
Contact/s:
● Club Secretary: Mr Ken Flett
● Professional: Mr Brian Connor
● Pro Shop: Mr Stanley Whitehead
Course/s:
⛳ **MANCHESTER**
Description: Championship, Moorland, Undulating, Open, Drains Well
Green Speed: Fast
Built: 1882　Built On: Sand
Number of Holes: 18　Par: 72
Yds: 6519　F9 Yds: 3267　B9 Yds: 3252
Designer: Harry Shapland Colt

MANGOTSFIELD

MANGOTSFIELD GOLF CLUB, Carsons Rd, Mangotsfield, Bristol, **BRISTOL**, BS16 9LW, **ENGLAND**.
(T) 01179 565501
Contact/s:
● Sole Director: Mr Stephen Payne
Course/s:
⛳ **MANGOTSFIELD**
Number of Holes: 18
Designer: John Day

MANNAN CASTLE

MANNAN CASTLE GOLF CLUB, Donaghmoyne, Carrickmacross, Mannan, **COUNTY MONAGHAN**, **IRELAND**.
(T) 042 9663308
Course/s:
⛳ **MANNAN CASTLE**
Number of Holes: 9
Designer: F Ainsworth

MANNINGS HEATH

EXCLUSIVE HOTELS AND CROFT CLUB, Hammerpond Rd, Mannings Heath, Horsham, **SUSSEX (WEST)**, RH13 6PG, **ENGLAND**.
(T) 01403 210228
(W) www.exclusivehotel.co.uk
Membership: Members & Public
Size of Complex: 500 Acres
Contact/s:
● Professional: Mr Clive Tucker
Course/s:
⛳ **KINGFISHER**
Description: Undulating, Sheltered, Open, Drains Well
Green Speed: Fast
Built: 1905　Built On: Clay
Number of Holes: 18　Par: 70
Par 3's: 4　Par 4's: 12　Par 5's: 2
Yds: 6217　F9 Yds: 3082　B9 Yds: 3135
Prevailing Wind: South/East
Designer: David Williams
Further Information:
The Kingfisher course is extremely testing, therefore it may be advisable to have lessons before playing on the course.

⛳ **WATERFALL**
Description: Wooded
Number of Holes: 18　Par: 73
Par 3's: 3　Par 4's: 11　Par 5's: 4
Yds: 6412　F9 Yds: 3252　B9 Yds: 3160

MANOR

MANOR GOLF CLUB & DRIVING RANGE (THE), Bradford Rd, Drighlington, Bradford, **YORKSHIRE (WEST)**, BD11 1AB, **ENGLAND**.
(T) 0113 2852644
Membership: Members & Public
Size of Complex: 160 Acres
Contact/s:
● Club Secretary: Mr Nigel Potts
● Professional: Mr Gary Day
Course/s:
⛳ **MANOR**
Description: Championship, Wooded, Parkland, Hilltop, Undulating, Sheltered, Open, Medium Length, Drains Well, Ideal for the Elderly
Green Speed: Medium/Fast
Built: 1995　Built On: Sand/Soil
Number of Holes: 18　Par: 72
Par 3's: 3　Par 4's: 12　Par 5's: 3
Yds: 6073　F9 Yds: 3043　B9 Yds: 3030
Prevailing Wind: South/West
Designer: D Hemstock
Further Information:
A very challenging course.

MANOR

MANOR GOLF CLUB LTD (THE), Leese Hill, Kingstone, Uttoxeter, **STAFFORDSHIRE**, ST14 8QT, **ENGLAND**.
(T) 01889 563234
Contact/s:
● Manager: Mrs Ruby Miles
Course/s:
⛳ **MANOR GOLF COURSE**
Number of Holes: 18　Par: 71
Yds: 6008

MANOR

MANOR GOLF COURSE (THE), Laceby, Barton St, Grimsby, **LINCOLNSHIRE (NORTH EAST)**, DN37 7EA, **ENGLAND**.
(T) 01472 873468
Contact/s:
● Club Secretary: Mrs J MacKay
Course/s:
⛳ **MANOR**
Number of Holes: 18　Par: 72
Yds: 6343　F9 Yds: 3140　B9 Yds: 3203

MANOR

MANOR GOLF CLUB, Kearsley Golf Ctre, Moss Lane, Kearsley, Bolton, **LANCASHIRE**, BL4 8SF, **ENGLAND**.
(T) 01204 705651
(W) www.manorsports.com
Membership: Members & Public
Contact/s:
● General Manager: Mr Geoff Yates
Course/s:
⛳ **MANOR**
Number of Holes: 18　Par: 66
Par 3's: 8　Par 4's: 8　Par 5's: 2
Yds: 4828

MANOR HOUSE

MANOR HOUSE GOLF CLUB, Castle Combe, Chippenham, **WILTSHIRE,** SN14 7JW, **ENGLAND.**
(T) 01249 783101
(E) enquiries@manorhousegolfclub.com
(W) www.exclusivehotels.co.uk

Contact/s:
- **Professional:** Mr Peter Green

Course/s:
- **THE MANOR HOUSE AT CASTLE COMBE**
  Description: Championship
  Built: 1992
  Number of Holes: 18 **Par:** 71
  Par 3's: 5 **Par 4's:** 9 **Par 5's:** 4
  Yds: 6286 **F9 Yds:** 3121 **B9 Yds:** 3165
  Designer: Peter Alliss, Clive Clark

MANOR HOUSE

MANOR HOUSE HOTEL & GOLF COURSE, Moretonhampstead, North Bovey, Newton Abbot, **DEVON,** TQ13 8RE, **ENGLAND.**
(T) 01647 445012/440998
(E) manortee@aol.com
(W) www.principalhotels.co.uk

Contact/s:
- **Club Secretary:** Mr R Lewis

Course/s:
- **MANOR HOUSE HOTEL**
  Number of Holes: 18 **Par:** 69
  Par 3's: 4 **Par 4's:** 13 **Par 5's:** 1
  Yds: 6016 **F9 Yds:** 3078 **B9 Yds:** 2938
  Designer: J F Abercromby

MANOR OF GROVES

MANOR OF GROVES GOLF & COUNTRY CLUB (THE), High Wych, Sawbridgeworth, **HERTFORDSHIRE,** CM21 0LA, **ENGLAND.**
(T) 01279 722333

Membership: Members & Public
Size of Complex: 150 Acres

Contact/s:
- **Club Secretary:** Mrs A Devera-Lee
- **Professional:** Mr Craig Laurence
- **Pro Shop:**
  ☎ 01279 721486

Course/s:
- **MANOR OF GROVES**
  Description: Championship, Parkland, Undulating, Medium Length, Drains Well
  Green Speed: Fast
  Built: 1990 **Built On:** Clay/Soil
  Number of Holes: 18 **Par:** 71
  Record: 64 (Jon Bevan)
  Par 3's: 4 **Par 4's:** 11 **Par 5's:** 3
  Yds: 6228 **F9 Yds:** 3092 **B9 Yds:** 3136
  Designer: Stewart Sharer
  Further Information:
  There are water features throughout the course.

MANSFIELD WOODHOUSE

MANSFIELD WOODHOUSE GOLF CLUB, Leeming Lane North, Mansfield Woodhouse, Mansfield, **NOTTINGHAMSHIRE,** NG19 9EU, **ENGLAND.**
(T) 01623 623521

Membership: Members & Public

Contact/s:
- **Club Secretary:** Mr J Bentley
- **Pro Shop:** Mr S Highfield

Course/s:
- **MANSFIELD WOODHOUSE**
  Description: Parkland, Open, Medium Length, Drains Well

Green Speed: Slow
Built: 1973 **Built On:** Sand
Number of Holes: 9
Designer: Horsman
Further Information:
Flat course.

MAPLEDURHAM

MAPLEDURHAM PUBLIC GOLF & HEALTH CLUB, Chazey Heath, Mapledurham, Reading, **BERKSHIRE,** RG4 7UD, **ENGLAND.**
(T) 0118 9463353

Membership: Members & Public
Size of Complex: 158 Acres

Contact/s:
- **Professional:** Mr Douglas Burton

Course/s:
- **MAPLEDURHAM**
  Description: Wooded, Parkland, Undulating, Sheltered, Open, Short, Drains Well, Ideal for the Elderly
  Green Speed: Medium
  Built: 1992 **Built On:** Soil
  Number of Holes: 18 **Par:** 69
  Yds: 5635 **F9 Yds:** 2927 **B9 Yds:** 2708
  Designer: Robert Sandow

MAPPERLEY

MAPPERLEY GOLF CLUB, Central Ave, Plains Rd, Nottingham, **NOTTINGHAMSHIRE,** NG3 5RH, **ENGLAND.**
(T) 0115 9556672

Contact/s:
- **Professional:** Mr Jasen Barker

Course/s:
- **MAPPERLEY**
  Number of Holes: 18 **Par:** 71
  Yds: 6307 **F9 Yds:** 3016 **B9 Yds:** 3291
  Designer: John Mason

MARCH

MARCH GOLF CLUB, Frogs Abbey, Grange Rd, March, **CAMBRIDGESHIRE,** PE15 0YH, **ENGLAND.**
(T) 01354 652364

Membership: Members & Public
Size of Complex: 69 Acres

Contact/s:
- **Club Secretary:** Mr A P Cranstoun
- **Professional:** Mr Stewart Brown
  ☎ 01354 657255

Course/s:
- **MARCH**
  Description: Parkland, Open, Long, Drains Well, Ideal for the Elderly
  Green Speed: Medium
  Built: 1923 **Built On:** Clay
  Number of Holes: 9 **Par:** 70
  Par 3's: 3 **Par 4's:** 4 **Par 5's:** 2
  Yds: 6204 **F9 Yds:** 3135 **B9 Yds:** 3069
  Further Information:
  This 9 hole course has 18 tees, therefore it can be played as an 18 hole course. The course has 2 ponds and a challenging 9th hole.

MARDYKE VALLEY GOLF CTRE

MARDYKE VALLEY GOLF CENTRE LTD, South Rd, South Ockendon, **ESSEX,** RM15 6RR, **ENGLAND.**
(T) 01708 855011

Membership: Members & Public

Contact/s:

- **Club Secretary:** Mr Mike Reid
- **Professional:** Mr Matt Reid

Course/s:
- **MARDYKE VALLEY 9 HOLE**
  Number of Holes: 9 **Par:** 37
  Par 3's: 1 **Par 4's:** 6 **Par 5's:** 2
  Yds: 3347
  Further Information:
  New 9 hole course opened August 2001. 9 more holes to follow.

- **THE VALLEY**
  Description: Parkland, Valley, Undulating, Medium Length
  Green Speed: Medium
  Number of Holes: 9 **Par:** 35
  Par 3's: 3 **Par 4's:** 4 **Par 5's:** 2
  Yds: 2750 **Designer:** Mike Reid

MARKET DRAYTON

MARKET DRAYTON GOLF CLUB, Sutton Lane, Sutton, Market Drayton, **SHROPSHIRE,** TF9 2HX, **ENGLAND.**
(T) 01630 652266

Course/s:
- **MARKET DRAYTON**
  Number of Holes: 18

MARKET HARBOROUGH

MARKET HARBOROUGH GOLF CLUB, Harborough Rd, Great Oxendon, Market Harborough, **LEICESTERSHIRE,** LE16 8NB, **ENGLAND.**
(T) 01858 463684

Course/s:
- **MARKET HARBOROUGH**
  Number of Holes: 18
  Designer: Howard Swan

MARKET RASEN & DISTRICT

MARKET RASEN & DISTRICT GOLF CLUB, Legsby Rd, Market Rasen, **LINCOLNSHIRE,** LN8 3DZ, **ENGLAND.**
(T) 01673 842319

Contact/s:
- **Club Secretary:** Mr J Brown
- **Professional:** Mr A M Chester
  ☎ 01673 842416

Course/s:
- **MARKET RASEN**
  Number of Holes: 18 **Par:** 71
  Par 3's: 4 **Par 4's:** 11 **Par 5's:** 3
  Yds: 6209 **F9 Yds:** 3125 **B9 Yds:** 3084

MARLAND

MARLAND GOLF COURSE, Springfield Pk, Rochdale, **LANCASHIRE,** OL11 4RE, **ENGLAND.**
(T) 01706 649801

Course/s:
- **SPRINGFIELD PARK**
  Number of Holes: 18

MARLBOROUGH

MARLBOROUGH GOLF CLUB, The Common, Marlborough, **WILTSHIRE,** SN8 1DU, **ENGLAND.**
(T) 01672 512493

Contact/s:
- **Professional:** Mr Simon Amor

Course/s:
- **MARLBOROUGH**
  Number of Holes: 18 **Par:** 72
  Yds: 6491 **F9 Yds:** 3202 **B9 Yds:** 3289

MARPLE

MARPLE GOLF CLUB LTD, Barnsfold Rd, Marple, Stockport, **CHESHIRE**, SK6 7EL, **ENGLAND**.
(T) 0161 4272311
Membership: Members & Public
Contact/s:
• **Professional:** Mr D Myers
  ☎ 0161 4271195
Course/s:
🏌 **MARPLE**
  Number of Holes: 18 **Par:** 67
  Yds: 5565

MARSDEN

MARSDEN GOLF CLUB, Mount Rd, Marsden, Huddersfield, **YORKSHIRE (WEST)**, HD7 6NN, **ENGLAND**.
(T) 01484 844253
Membership: Members & Public
Contact/s:
• **Club Secretary:** Mr G M Sykes
• **Professional:** Mr Nick Kryzwicki
Course/s:
🏌 **MARSDEN**
  Description: Moorland, Hilltop, Undulating, Open, Medium Length, Drains Well, Ideal for the Elderly
  Green Speed: Fast
  Built: 1921 **Built On:** Soil
  Number of Holes: 9 **Par:** 68 **Record:** 68 (C Whitely)
  Yds: 5702
  Prevailing Wind: West
  Designer: Alistair MacKenzie

MARSDEN PARK PUBLIC

MARSDEN PARK PUBLIC GOLF COURSE, Townhouse Rd, Nelson, **LANCASHIRE**, BB9 8DG, **ENGLAND**.
(T) 01282 661912
Contact/s:
• **Club Secretary:** Mr Brian Goodwin
  ☎ 01282 450398
• **Professional:** Mr Martin Ross
Course/s:
🏌 **MARSDEN PARK PUBLIC**
  Number of Holes: 18

MARTIN

MARTIN GOLF CLUB (THE), Overburn Ave, Dumbarton, **ARGYLL AND BUTE**, G82 2BQ, **SCOTLAND**.
(T) 01389 732830
Course/s:
🏌 **THE MARTIN GOLF COURSE**
  Number of Holes: 18 **Par:** 71
  Yds: 5969

MARTIN MOOR

MARTIN MOOR GOLF CLUB, Martin Rd, Blankney, Lincoln, **LINCOLNSHIRE**, LN4 3BE, **ENGLAND**.
(T) 01526 378243
Membership: Members & Public
Size of Complex: 62 Acres
Contact/s:
• **Pro Shop:** Mr M Lovett
Course/s:
🏌 **MARTIN MOOR**
  Description: Parkland, Open, Long, Drains Well, Ideal for the Elderly
  Green Speed: Medium

Built: 1992 **Built On:** Clay
Number of Holes: 9 **Par:** 72
Yds: 6325 **F9 Yds:** 3178 **B9 Yds:** 3147
Designer: Harrison
Further Information:
There are ponds throughout the course.

MARTON MEADOWS

MARTON MEADOWS GOLF COURSE, New House Farm, Marton, Macclesfield, **CHESHIRE**, SK11 9HF, **ENGLAND**.
(T) 01260 224708
Membership: Public
Contact/s:
• **Owner:** Mr T Darbyshire
Course/s:
🏌 **MARTON MEADOWS**
  Description: Wooded, Undulating, Short, Drains Well, Ideal for the Elderly
  Green Speed: Medium
  Built: 1998
  Number of Holes: 9
  Designer: Pearson

MARYPORT

MARYPORT GOLF CLUB, Bankend, Maryport, **CUMBRIA**, CA15 6PA, **ENGLAND**.
(T) 01900 812605
Contact/s:
• **Club Secretary:** Mr J M Potter
Course/s:
🏌 **MARYPORT**
  Description: Links, Parkland, Undulating, Open
  Built: 1905 **Built On:** Sand
  Number of Holes: 18 **Par:** 70
  Yds: 5982 **F9 Yds:** 3088 **B9 Yds:** 2894
  Further Information:
  Views over Solway Firth.

MASHAM

MASHAM GOLF CLUB, Burnholn, Swinton Rd, Masham, Ripon, **YORKSHIRE (NORTH)**, HG4 4HT, **ENGLAND**.
(T) 01765 689379
Course/s:
🏌 **MASHAM**
  Number of Holes: 9

MASSEREENE

MASSEREENE GOLF CLUB, 51 Lough Rd, Antrim, **COUNTY ANTRIM**, BT41 4DQ, **NORTHERN IRELAND**.
(T) 028 94428096
(E) massereenegc@utuinternet.com
Contact/s:
• **Manager:** Mrs Stephanie Greene
Course/s:
🏌 **MASSEREENE**
  Number of Holes: 18 **Par:** 72
  Yds: 6309
  Designer: Hawtree

MATTISHALL

MATTISHALL GOLF CLUB, South Green, Mattishall, Dereham, **NORFOLK**, NR20 3JZ, **ENGLAND**.
(T) 01362 850111
Contact/s:
• **Owner:** Mr B C Todd
Course/s:
🏌 **MATTISHALL**
  Number of Holes: 9 **Par:** 70

Par 3's: 2 **Par 4's:** 6 **Par 5's:** 1
Yds: 6170 **F9 Yds:** 3099 **B9 Yds:** 3071
Designer: B Todd
Further Information:
9 hole course can be played as an 18 hole course

MAXSTOKE PARK

MAXSTOKE PARK GOLF CLUB LTD, Castle Lane, Maxstoke, Coleshill, Birmingham, **MIDLANDS (WEST)**, B46 2RD, **ENGLAND**.
(T) 01675 462158
Contact/s:
• **Manageress:** Mrs S Cardwell
Course/s:
🏌 **MAXSTOKE PARK**
  Number of Holes: 18

MAYBOLE MUNICIPAL

MAYBOLE MUNICIPAL GOLF CLUB, Memorial Pk, Maybole, **AYRSHIRE (SOUTH)**, KA19 7DX, **SCOTLAND**.
(T) 01655 889770
Membership: Public
Contact/s:
• **Book Tee Times:** Mr Richard Shields
Course/s:
🏌 **MAYBOLE MUNICIPAL**
  Description: Undulating
  Green Speed: Fast
  Built: 1924
  Number of Holes: 9

MAYLANDS

MAYLANDS GOLF CLUB, Colchester Rd, Romford, **ESSEX**, RM3 0AZ, **ENGLAND**.
(T) 01708 373080
Contact/s:
• **Professional:** Mr John Hopkin
Course/s:
🏌 **MAYLANDS**
  Description: Wooded, Parkland
  Built: 1936
  Number of Holes: 18
  Designer: Harry Shapland Colt
  Further Information:
  Deer are often seen in the woodland.

MAYWOOD

MAYWOOD GOLF CLUB, Rushy Lane, Risley, Derby, **DERBYSHIRE**, DE72 3ST, **ENGLAND**.
(T) 0115 9392306
Membership: Members & Public
Size of Complex: 100 Acres
Contact/s:
• **Club Secretary:** Mrs Tory Moon
• **Professional:** Mr Simon Sherratt
  ☎ 0115 9490043
Course/s:
🏌 **MAYWOOD**
  Description: Parkland, Undulating, Sheltered, Ideal for the Elderly
  Green Speed: Medium
  Built: 1990 **Built On:** Clay/Sand
  Number of Holes: 18 **Par:** 72
  Record: 70 (Simon Sherratt)
  Yds: 6424 **F9 Yds:** 3159 **B9 Yds:** 3265
  Designer: P Moon
  Further Information:
  There are moats around the greens.

MEATH (COUNTY)

COUNTY MEATH GOLF CLUB, Newtownmoynagh, Trim, **COUNTY MEATH, IRELAND**.
(T) 046 31463

Course/s:

● **MEATH**
Number of Holes: 18
Designer: T Craddock, Edward Hackett

MELDRUM HOUSE

MELDRUM HOUSE GOLF CLUB, Meldrum House Estate, Oldmeldrum, Aberdeen, **ABERDEEN (CITY OF)**, AB51 0AE, **SCOTLAND**.
(T) 01651 873553
(W) www.meldrumhouse.co.uk

Membership: Members & Public
Size of Complex: 175 Acres

Contact/s:
● **Club Secretary:** Mr David Andrews
● **Pro Shop:** Mr Neil Marr
● **Book Tee Times:** Mr Morgan Fisher

Course/s:

● **THE KNIGHTS**
Description: Championship, Parkland, Medium Length
Green Speed: Fast **Built On:** Soil
Number of Holes: 18   **Par:** 70
Record: 70 (Neil Marr)
Designer: Graeme Webster
Further Information:
The course has attractive water features and abundant wildlife.

MELLOR & TOWNSCLIFFE

MELLOR & TOWNSCLIFFE GOLF CLUB LTD, Gibb Lane, Mellor, Stockport, **CHESHIRE**, SK6 5NA, **ENGLAND**.
(T) 0161 4275759

Contact/s:
● **Professional:** Mr Gary Broadley

Course/s:

● **OLD**
Description: Parkland, Moorland, Undulating
Built: 1894
Number of Holes: 18   **Par:** 70

● **VALLEY**
Description: Parkland, Moorland, Undulating
Built: 1894
Number of Holes: 18   **Par:** 72

MELROSE

MELROSE GOLF CLUB, Dingleton Rd, Melrose, **SCOTTISH BORDERS**, TD6 9QY, **SCOTLAND**.
(T) 01896 822855

Contact/s:
● **Book Tee Times:** Mr D Campbell

Course/s:

● **MELROSE**
Description: Wooded
Built: 1880
Number of Holes: 9   **Par:** 70
Yds: 5562   **F9 Yds:** 2753   **B9 Yds:** 2809

MELTHAM

MELTHAM GOLF CLUB, Thick Hollins, Meltham, Huddersfield, **YORKSHIRE (WEST)**, HD7 3DQ, **ENGLAND**.
(T) 01484 850227
(W) www.meltham-golf.co.uk

Membership: Members & Public
Size of Complex: 120 Acres

Contact/s:
● **Club Secretary:** Mr Christopher Naylor
● **Professional:** Mr Paul Davies

Course/s:

● **MELTHAM**
Description: Wooded, Parkland, Undulating, Open, Medium Length, Drains Well, Ideal for the Elderly
Green Speed: Medium
Built: 1908   **Built On:** Soil
Number of Holes: 18   **Par:** 71
Record: 68 (Anthony Sheard)
Yds: 6396   **F9 Yds:** 3335   **B9 Yds:** 3061
Prevailing Wind: West
Designer: A Herd
Further Information:
A very popular course.

MELTON MOWBRAY

MELTON MOWBRAY GOLF CLUB, Waltham Rd, Thorpe Arnold, Melton Mowbray, **LEICESTERSHIRE**, LE14 4SD, **ENGLAND**.
(T) 01664 562118
(E) mmgc@lei44sd.fsbusiness.co.uk
(W) www.mmgc.org

Contact/s:
● **Club Secretary:** Ms Angela Sallis
● **Professional:** Mr James Hetherington
● **Book Tee Times:**
  ☎ 01664 569629

Course/s:

● **MELTON MOWBRAY**
Built: 1925
Number of Holes: 18   **Par:** 70
Par 3's: 4   **Par 4's:** 12   **Par 5's:** 2
Yds: 6222   **F9 Yds:** 2952   **B9 Yds:** 3270
Further Information:
An easy walking course.

MELTON MOWBRAY TOWN EST

MELTON MOWBRAY TOWN ESTATE GOLF COURSE, 2 Park Lane, Melton Mowbray, **LEICESTERSHIRE**, LE13 0PT, **ENGLAND**.
(T) 01664 567846

Course/s:

● **TOWN ESTATE**
Number of Holes: 12

MENDIP

MENDIP GOLF CLUB LTD (THE), Gurney Slade, Radstock, Bath, **BATH & SOMERSET (NORTH EAST)**, BA3 4UT, **ENGLAND**.
(T) 01749 840793
(W) www.mendipgolfclub.co.uk
Size of Complex: 200 Acres

Contact/s:
● **Club Secretary:** Mr Jim Scott
  ☎ 01749 840570
● **Professional:** Mr Adrian Marsh

Course/s:

● **MENDIP**
Description: Parkland, Heath Land, Hilltop, Undulating, Medium Length, Drains Well
Green Speed: Medium/Fast
Built: 1908   **Built On:** Soil
Number of Holes: 18   **Par:** 71
Yds: 6383   **F9 Yds:** 3405   **B9 Yds:** 2978
Prevailing Wind: South/West
Designer: Harry Shapland Colt

MENDIP SPRING

MENDIP SPRING GOLF & COUNTRY CLUB, Honeyhall Lane, Congresbury, Bristol, **BRISTOL**, BS49 5JT, **ENGLAND**.
(T) 01934 852322
(W) www.mendipspring.co.uk

Membership: Members & Public

Contact/s:
● **Club Secretary:** Mr A Melbuish
● **Professional:** Mr R Moss

Course/s:

● **BRINSEA**
Description: Championship, Parkland, Open, Long, Ideal for the Elderly
Built: 1990
Number of Holes: 18   **Par:** 71
Par 3's: 5   **Par 4's:** 9   **Par 5's:** 4
Yds: 6241   **F9 Yds:** 2841   **B9 Yds:** 3400

● **LAKESIDE**
Description: Championship, Parkland, Open, Long, Ideal for the Elderly
Built: 1990
Number of Holes: 9   **Par:** 68
Par 3's: 2   **Par 4's:** 7
Yds: 4658   **F9 Yds:** 2329   **B9 Yds:** 2329
Further Information:
9 hole course can be played as an 18 hole course.

MENTMORE

MENTMORE GOLF & COUNTRY CLUB, Mentmore, Leighton Buzzard, **BEDFORDSHIRE**, LU7 0UA, **ENGLAND**.
(T) 01296 662020

Contact/s:
● **Professional:** Mr Rob Davies

Course/s:

● **ROSEBERY**
Description: Championship, Wooded, Parkland
Built: 1992
Number of Holes: 18   **Par:** 72
Designer: Robert Sandow

● **ROTHSCHILD**
Description: Championship, Wooded, Parkland
Built: 1992
Number of Holes: 18   **Par:** 72
Designer: Robert Sandow

MEOLE BRACE

MEOLE BRACE GOLF COURSE, Oteley Rd, Shrewsbury, **SHROPSHIRE**, SY2 6QQ, **ENGLAND**.
(T) 01743 364050

Contact/s:
● **Professional:** Mr I Doran

Course/s:

● **MEOLE BRACE**
Number of Holes: 9

MEON VALLEY

MARRIOTT MEON VALLEY HOTEL COUNTRY CLUB, Sandy Lane, Shedfield, Southampton, **HAMPSHIRE**, SO32 2HQ, **ENGLAND**.
(T) 01329 833455
(W) www.marriott.com/marriott/sougs

Membership: Members & Public

Contact/s:
● **Professional:** Mr Rod Cameron
  ☎ 01329 832184

Course/s:

● **MEON**
Description: Championship, Wooded, Undulating, Sheltered, Medium Length, Tight, Ideal for the Elderly
Green Speed: Medium **Built On:** Clay

Number of Holes: 18   **Par:** 71
Par 3's: 4   **Par 4's:** 11   **Par 5's:** 3
Yds: 6520   **F9 Yds:** 3434   **B9 Yds:** 3086
Prevailing Wind: South/West
Designer: J Hamilton-Stutt

🏌 **VALLEY**
Number of Holes: 9
Designer: J Hamilton-Stutt

MERCHANTS OF EDINBURGH

**MERCHANTS OF EDINBURGH GOLF
CLUB,** 10 Craighill Gardens, Edinburgh,
EDINBURGH (CITY OF), EH10 5PY,
SCOTLAND.
(T) 0131 4471219

Contact/s:
● **Club Secretary:** Mr John Elvin
● **Professional:** Mr Neil Colguhoun

Course/s:
🏌 **MERCHANTS OF EDINBURGH**
Number of Holes: 18   **Par:** 65
Yds: 4898   **F9 Yds:** 2661   **B9 Yds:** 2237
Designer: Ross

MERE

MERE GOLF & COUNTRY CLUB, Chester
Rd, Mere, Knutsford, **CHESHIRE**, WA16 6LJ,
ENGLAND.
(T) 01565 830155
(W) www.meregolf.co.uk

Membership: Members & Public

Contact/s:
● **Club Secretary:** Mr Stuart Janvier
● **Professional:** Mr Peter Eyre
● **Pro Shop:**
☎ 01565 830219

Course/s:
🏌 **MERE**
Description: Championship, Parkland,
Open, Medium Length, Drains Well, Ideal
for the Elderly
Green Speed: Medium
Built: 1934   **Built On:** Soil
Number of Holes: 18   **Par:** 71
Record: 64 (Paul McGinley)
Par 3's: 4   **Par 4's:** 11   **Par 5's:** 3
Yds: 6566   **F9 Yds:** 3290   **B9 Yds:** 3276
Prevailing Wind: East
Designer: James Braid
Further Information:
Hosts for the European PGA Seniors
Tournament of Champions - 2001.

MERLIN

MERLIN GOLF CLUB, Mawgan Porth,
Newquay, **CORNWALL**, TR8 4DN,
ENGLAND.
(T) 01841 540222
(W) www.merlingolfcourse.co.uk

Membership: Members & Public

Contact/s:
● **Club Secretary:** Mrs M Oliver

Course/s:
🏌 **MERLIN**
Description: Heath Land, Hilltop
Built: 1991
Number of Holes: 18   **Par:** 71
Par 3's: 5   **Par 4's:** 9   **Par 5's:** 4
Yds: 6210   **F9 Yds:** 2949   **B9 Yds:** 3261
Designer: R Oliver

MERRIST WOOD

MERRIST WOOD, Coombe Lane,
Worplesdon, Guildford, **SURREY**, GU3 3PE,
ENGLAND.

(T) 01483 884050

Contact/s:
● **Manager:** Mr Richard Penley-Martin

Course/s:
🏌 **MERRIST WOOD**
Number of Holes: 18   **Par:** 72
Yds: 6574
Designer: David Williams

MERSEY VALLEY

MERSEY VALLEY GOLF CLUB LTD,
Warrington Rd, Bold Heath, Widnes,
CHESHIRE, WA8 3XL, **ENGLAND**.
(T) 0151 4246060

Membership: Members & Public

Contact/s:
● **Club Secretary:** Mr B Woolrich
● **Professional:** Mr Andy Stevenson

Course/s:
🏌 **MERSEY VALLEY**
Description: Parkland, Medium Length,
Drains Well, Ideal for the Elderly
Green Speed: Medium
Built: 1995
Number of Holes: 18
Designer: Roger Bush

MERTHYR CILSANWS

MERTHYR CILSANWS GOLF CLUB,
Clubhouse, Cefn Coed, Merthyr Tydfil,
GLAMORGAN (VALE OF), CF48 2NU,
WALES.
(T) 01685 723308

Contact/s:
● **Club Secretary:** Mr Viv Price

Course/s:
🏌 **MERTHYR CILSANWS**
Number of Holes: 18
Designer: R Mathias, V Price

MERTHYR TYDFIL

MERTHYR TYDFIL GOLF CLUB, Cilsanws
Mountain, Cefn Coed, Merthyr Tydfil,
GLAMORGAN (VALE OF), CF48 2NU,
WALES.
(T) 01685 388141

Contact/s:
● **Club Secretary:** Mr Viv Price
☎ 01685 723308

Course/s:
🏌 **MERTHYR TYDFIL**
Description: Short
Built: 1909
Number of Holes: 18   **Par:** 69
Par 3's: 5   **Par 4's:** 11   **Par 5's:** 2
Yds: 5647   **F9 Yds:** 2844   **B9 Yds:** 2803
Further Information:
Mountain top course.

MICKLEOVER

MICKLEOVER GOLF CLUB LTD, Uttoxeter
Rd, Mickleover, Derby, **DERBYSHIRE**, DE3
5AD, **ENGLAND**.
(T) 01332 518662/513339

Contact/s:
● **Club Secretary:** Mr Doug Rodgeils
☎ 01332 512092

Course/s:
🏌 **MICKLEOVER**
Number of Holes: 18   **Par:** 68
Par 3's: 4   **Par 4's:** 14
Yds: 5708   **F9 Yds:** 2853   **B9 Yds:** 2855
Designer: Frank Pennink

MID KENT

MID KENT GOLF CLUB, Singlewell Rd,
Gravesend, **KENT**, DA11 7RB, **ENGLAND**.
(T) 01474 568035

Course/s:
🏌 **MID KENT**
Number of Holes: 18
Designer: Frank Pennink

MID SUSSEX

MID SUSSEX GOLF CLUB, Spatham Lane,
Ditchling, **SUSSEX (EAST)**, BN6 8XJ,
ENGLAND.
(T) 01273 846567
(E) admin@midsussexgolfclub.co.uk
(W) www.midsussexgolfclub.co.uk

Membership: Members & Public
Size of Complex: 187 Acres

Contact/s:
● **Professional:** Mr Chris Connell

Course/s:
🏌 **MID SUSSEX**
Description: Parkland, Open, Medium
Length, Drains Well, Ideal for the Elderly
Green Speed: Medium/Fast
Built: 1995
Number of Holes: 18   **Par:** 71
Yds: 6462   **F9 Yds:** 3097   **B9 Yds:** 3365
Prevailing Wind: South/West
Designer: David Williams
Further Information:
This is a challenging course in a beautiful
location, near to the South Downs.

MID WALES GOLF CTRE

MID WALES GOLF CENTRE, Maesmawr,
Caersws, **POWYS**, SY17 5SB, **WALES**.
(T) 01686 688303

Contact/s:
● **Manager:** Mr C Evans

Course/s:
🏌 **MID-WALES GOLF CENTRE**
Number of Holes: 9
Designer: Jim Walters

MID YORKSHIRE

MID YORKSHIRE GOLF CLUB LTD,
Havercroft Lane, Darrington, Pontefract,
YORKSHIRE (WEST), WF8 3BP, **ENGLAND**.
(T) 01977 704522

Membership: Members & Public
Size of Complex: 180 Acres

Contact/s:
● **Club Secretary:** Mrs Linda Darwood
● **Professional:** Mr Alastair Cobbett
☎ 01977 600844
● **Book Lessons:** Mr James Major

Course/s:
🏌 **MID YORKSHIRE**
Description: Parkland, Undulating,
Medium Length, Drains Well
Green Speed: Medium
Built: 1990   **Built On:** Chalk
Number of Holes: 18   **Par:** 72
Record: 69 (Grant Jackson)
Par 3's: 3   **Par 4's:** 12   **Par 5's:** 3
Yds: 6466
Prevailing Wind: West
Designer: Steve Marnoch
Further Information:
Due to the excellent drainage, full greens
are open all year round on this
challenging course.

MIDDLESBROUGH

MIDDLESBROUGH GOLF CLUB, Brass
Castle Lane, Marton-In-Cleveland,
Middlesbrough, **CLEVELAND**, TS8 9EE,
ENGLAND.
(T) 01642 311515

Contact/s:
* Club Secretary: Mr P M Jackson

Course/s:
* MIDDLESBROUGH
    Number of Holes: 18   Par: 70
    Yds: 6278   F9 Yds: 3129   B9 Yds: 3149

MIDDLESBROUGH MUNICIPAL

**MIDDLESBROUGH MUNICIPAL GOLF
CENTRE,** Ladgate Lane, Middlesbrough,
CLEVELAND, TS5 7YZ, **ENGLAND**.
(T) 01642 300720
(E) hope@munigolfshopfsbusiness.co.uk
(W) www.mmgolf.co.uk

Membership: Members & Public/Public

Contact/s:
* Professional: Mr Alan Hope

Course/s:
* MIDDLESBROUGH MUNICIPAL
    Description: Parkland
    Green Speed: Slow
    Built: 1977
    Number of Holes: 18
    Designer: Shuttleworth

MIDDLETON HALL

MIDDLETON HALL GOLF CLUB, Hall
Orchards, Middleton, King's Lynn,
NORFOLK, PE32 1RH, **ENGLAND**.
(T) 01553 841800
(E) middleton-hall@btclick.com
(W) www.middletonhall.co.uk

Contact/s:
* Club Secretary: Mr J Holland
* Professional: Mr Steve White
    ☎ 01553 841801

Course/s:
* MIDDLETON HALL
    Description: Parkland, Undulating,
    Sheltered, Medium Length, Tight
    Built: 1989
    Number of Holes: 18   Par: 71
    Par 3's: 5   Par 4's: 9   Par 5's: 4
    Yds: 6004   F9 Yds: 3028   B9 Yds: 2976
    Designer: P Scott
    Further Information:
    Many water features throughout course.

MIDDLETON PARK MUNICIPAL

**MIDDLETON PARK MUNICIPAL GOLF
CLUB,** Off Beeston Ring Rd, Leeds,
YORKSHIRE (WEST), LS10 3TN,
ENGLAND.
(T) 0113 2709506

Membership: Public

Contact/s:
* Manager: Mr A Newboult

Course/s:
* MIDDLETON PARK MUNICIPAL
    Number of Holes: 18

MID-HERTS

MID-HERTS GOLF CLUB, Lower Gustard
Wood, Wheathampstead, St. Albans,
HERTFORDSHIRE, AL4 8RS, **ENGLAND**.
(T) 01582 832242
(E) secretary@mid-hertsgolfclub.co.uk
(W) www.mid-hertsgolfclub.co.uk

Contact/s:
* Club Secretary: Mr R Gourdon
* Professional: Mr Barney Puttick
    ☎ 01582 832788

Course/s:
* MID HERTS
    Number of Holes: 18   Par: 69
    Yds: 6060   F9 Yds: 2929   B9 Yds: 3131

MID-SURREY (ROYAL)

ROYAL MID-SURREY GOLF CLUB, Old
Deer Pk, Twickenham Rd, Richmond,
SURREY, TW9 2SB, **ENGLAND**.
(T) 020 89401894
(E) secretary@rmsgc.co.uk
(W) www.rmsgc.co.uk

Membership: Members & Public

Contact/s:
* Club Secretary: Mr A Marsden
* Professional: Mr P Talbot

Course/s:
* INNER
    Number of Holes: 18   Par: 71
    Yds: 5446   F9 Yds: 2738   B9 Yds: 2708
    Designer: Taylor
* OUTER
    Description: Parkland, Sheltered,
    Medium Length, Tight, Drains Well, Ideal
    for the Elderly
    Green Speed: Medium
    Built: 1894
    Number of Holes: 18   Par: 69
    Yds: 6385   F9 Yds: 3006   B9 Yds: 3379
    Designer: Taylor
    Further Information:
    This is a flat course.

MILE END

MILE END GOLF CLUB, Shrewsbury Rd,
Oswestry, **SHROPSHIRE**, SY11 4JF,
ENGLAND.
(T) 01691 671246

Contact/s:
* Professional: Mr Scott Carpenter

Course/s:
* MILE END
    Description: Undulating, Tight
    Built: 1992
    Number of Holes: 18   Par: 71
    Yds: 6194   F9 Yds: 3031   B9 Yds: 3163
    Designer: Gough, Price
    Further Information:
    Gently undulating course with water
    features.

MILFORD GOLF CLUB

AMERICAN GOLF CORPORATION, Station
Lane, Milford, Godalming, **SURREY**, GU8
5HS, **ENGLAND**.
(T) 01483 419200
(E) milford@americangolf.uk.com

Membership: Members & Public

Contact/s:
* Professional: Mr Paul Creanter
* Pro Shop:
    ☎ 01483 416291

Course/s:
* MILFORD
    Description: Wooded, Parkland,
    Undulating, Open, Short, Drains Well
    Green Speed: Medium
    Built: 1993   Built On: Soil
    Number of Holes: 18   Par: 69
    Yds: 5960   F9 Yds: 2896   B9 Yds: 3064
    Designer: Peter Alliss, Clive Clark
    Further Information:

A challenging course with distinct areas of
meadow.

MILFORD HAVEN

MILFORD HAVEN GOLF CLUB, Woodbine
House, Hubberston, Milford Haven,
PEMBROKESHIRE, SA73 3RX, **WALES**.
(T) 01646 697762
(E) enquiries@mhgc.co.uk
(W) www.mhgc.co.uk

Contact/s:
* Club Secretary: Mr Steven Brown

Course/s:
* MILFORD HAVEN
    Number of Holes: 18   Par: 71
    Yds: 6035   F9 Yds: 3118   B9 Yds: 2917

MILL GREEN GOLF CLUB

AMERICAN GOLF CORPORATION, Gypsy
Lane, Welwyn Garden City,
HERTFORDSHIRE, AL7 4TY, **ENGLAND**.
(T) 01707 276900
(E) millgreen@americangolf.uk.com
(W) www.americangolf.com

Membership: Members & Public
Size of Complex: 200 Acres

Contact/s:
* Professional: Mr Ian Parker
* Pro Shop:
    ☎ 01707 270542

Course/s:
* MILL GREEN
    Description: Wooded, Undulating, Open,
    Long, Drains Well
    Green Speed: Fast
    Built: 1993
    Number of Holes: 18   Par: 72
    Yds: 6615   F9 Yds: 3380   B9 Yds: 3235
    Prevailing Wind: South/West
    Designer: Peter Alliss, Clive Clark
    Further Information:
    This challenging course is built on
    aggregate soil.

MILL HILL

MILL HILL GOLF CLUB LTD, 100 Barnet
Way, Mill Hill, London, **LONDON
(GREATER)**, NW7 3AL, **ENGLAND**.
(T) 020 89597261

Contact/s:
* Professional: Mr David Beal

Course/s:
* MILL HILL
    Description: Parkland, Drains Well
    Built: 1925
    Number of Holes: 18   Par: 69
    Par 3's: 4   Par 4's: 13   Par 5's: 1
    Yds: 6247   F9 Yds: 3133   B9 Yds: 3114
    Prevailing Wind: North
    Designer: J F Abercromby, Harry
    Shapland Colt

MILL RIDE

MILL RIDE GOLF CLUB, Mill Ride, Ascot,
BERKSHIRE, SL5 8LT, **ENGLAND**.
(T) 01344 886777
(W) www.mill-ride.com

Membership: Members & Public
Size of Complex: 150 Acres

Contact/s:
* Professional: Mr Terry Wild
* Pro Shop: Mr Russell Neil
* Book Tee Times: Mr Jamie Hillman
    ☎ 01344 891025
* Book Lessons: Mr Greg Devane

Course/s:

● **MILL RIDE**
Description: Championship, Links, Wooded, Parkland, Medium Length, Drains Well
Green Speed: Medium
Built: 1991 Built On: Clay
Number of Holes: 18 Par: 72
Par 3's: 4 Par 4's: 10 Par 5's: 4
Yds: 6413
Designer: Donald Steel
Further Information:
The course is always in excellent condition, maintained by Mill Greens' Master Greenkeeper, Gordon Irvine.

MILLERS BARN GOLF PARK

MILLERS BARN GOLF PARK, Jaywick Lane, Jaywick, Clacton-on-Sea, **ESSEX**, CO15 2GF, **ENGLAND**.
(T) 01255 424826

Membership: Members & Public
Contact/s:
● Professional: Mr P Berry

Course/s:
● **MILLERS BARN**
Description: Parkland, Ideal for the Elderly
Green Speed: Medium
Built:
Number of Holes: 9

MILLFIELD GOLF

MILLFIELD GOLF RANGE & COURSE, Broom Hills, Laughterton, Lincoln, **LINCOLNSHIRE**, LN1 2LB, **ENGLAND**.
(T) 01427 718255

Contact/s:
● Professional: Mr John Murray

Course/s:
● **FAMILY 18**
Number of Holes: 18 Par: 61
Yds: 4485

● **FAMILY 9**
Number of Holes: 9
Yds: 1355

● **MILLFIELD**
Number of Holes: 18 Par: 72
Yds: 6004 F9 Yds: 2875 B9 Yds: 3129

MILLPORT

MILLPORT GOLF CLUB, Golf Rd, Millport, **AYRSHIRE (NORTH)**, KA28 0HB, **SCOTLAND**.
(T) 01475 530306

Membership: Members & Public
Size of Complex: 150 Acres
Contact/s:
● Club Secretary: Mr Desmond Donnelly
● Professional: Mr Hal Lee
☎ 01475 530305

Course/s:
● **MILLPORT**
Description: Links, Undulating, Open, Medium Length, Drains Well
Green Speed: Medium
Built: 1888 Built On: Clay/Soil
Number of Holes: 18 Par: 68
Par 3's: 4 Par 4's: 14
Yds: 5828
Designer: James Braid

MILLTOWN

MILLTOWN GOLF CLUB, Lr Churchtown Rd,

Milltown, **COUNTY DUBLIN**, **IRELAND**.
(T) 01 4976090

Course/s:
● **MILLTOWN**
Number of Holes: 18
Designer: F Davis

MILNATHORT

MILNATHORT GOLF CLUB, South St, Milnathort, Kinross, **PERTH AND KINROSS**, KY13 9XA, **SCOTLAND**.
(T) 01577 864069
(E) milnathortgolf@ukgateway.net

Membership: Members & Public
Size of Complex: 45 Acres
Contact/s:
● Greenkeeper: Mr Jason Kirk

Course/s:
● **MILNATHORT**
Description: Parkland, Undulating, Drains Well
Green Speed: Medium
Built: 1910 Built On: Soil
Number of Holes: 9 Par: 71
Par 3's: 2 Par 4's: 6 Par 5's: 1
Yds: 5985 F9 Yds: 2962 B9 Yds: 3023
Further Information:
9 hole course can be played as an 18 hole course, using the different coloured markers. Gently undulating, with a reputation for excellent greens.

MILNGAVIE

MILNGAVIE GOLF CLUB, Milngavie, Glasgow, **GLASGOW (CITY OF)**, G62 8EP, **SCOTLAND**.
(T) 0141 9561619

Contact/s:
● Company Secretary: Miss S McGuiness

Course/s:
● **MILNGAVIE**
Number of Holes: 18
Designer: William Auchterlonie

MINCHINHAMPTON

MINCHINHAMPTON GOLF CLUB, New Courses, Minchinhampton, Stroud, **GLOUCESTERSHIRE**, GL6 9BE, **ENGLAND**.
(T) 01453 833866

Membership: Members & Public
Contact/s:
● Club Secretary: Mr D Calvert
● Professional: Mr C Steele
● Pro Shop:
☎ 01453 837351

Course/s:
● **AVENING**
Description: Parkland, Sheltered, Medium Length, Drains Well
Green Speed: Medium
Built: 1975 Built On: Chalk
Number of Holes: 18
Yds: 6263
Prevailing Wind: South/West
Designer: Hawtree

● **CHERINGTON**
Description: Links, Undulating, Open, Medium Length, Drains Well
Green Speed: Medium
Built: 1995 Built On: Chalk
Number of Holes: 18
Yds: 6387
Prevailing Wind: South/West
Designer: Hawtree

MINEHEAD & WEST SOMERSET

MINEHEAD & WEST SOMERSET GOLF CLUB, Clubhouse, Warren Rd, Minehead, **SOMERSET**, TA24 5SJ, **ENGLAND**.
(T) 01643 702057
(E) secretary@mineheadgolf.co.uk
(W) www.mineheadgolfclub.co.uk

Membership: Members & Public
Size of Complex: 75 Acres
Contact/s:
● Club Secretary: Mr Bob Rayner
● Professional: Mr Ian Read
☎ 01643 704378

Course/s:
● **MINEHEAD & WEST SOMERSET**
Description: Links, Parkland, Open, Medium Length, Drains Well
Green Speed: Medium
Built: 1882 Built On: Sand/Soil
Number of Holes: 18 Par: 71
Record: 68 (Bernard Hunt)
Par 3's: 4 Par 4's: 11 Par 5's: 3
Yds: 6228 F9 Yds: 3393 B9 Yds: 2835

MINTO

MINTO GOLF CLUB, Minto, Hawick, **SCOTTISH BORDERS**, TD9 8SH, **SCOTLAND**.
(T) 01450 870220

Contact/s:
● Club Secretary: Mr Peter Brown
☎ 01450 375841

Course/s:
● **MINTO**
Description: Parkland
Built: 1928
Number of Holes: 18 Par: 69
Par 3's: 4 Par 4's: 13 Par 5's: 1
Yds: 5542 F9 Yds: 2785 B9 Yds: 2757

MITCHAM

MITCHAM GOLF CLUB, Carshalton Rd, Mitcham, **SURREY**, CR4 4HN, **ENGLAND**.
(T) 020 86484197

Course/s:
● **MITCHAM**
Number of Holes: 18 Par: 68
Yds: 5535 F9 Yds: 2649 B9 Yds: 2886
Designer: Tom Morris, T Scott

MITCHELSTOWN

MITCHELSTOWN GOLF CLUB, Mitchelstown, **COUNTY CORK**, **IRELAND**.
(T) 025 24072

Course/s:
● **MITCHELSTOWN**
Number of Holes: 18
Designer: David Jones

MOATE

MOATE GOLF CLUB, Aghanargit, Moate, **COUNTY WESTMEATH**, **IRELAND**.
(T) 090 281271

Course/s:
● **MOATE**
Description: Ideal for the Elderly
Built: 1993
Number of Holes: 18 Par: 72
Designer: R Browne
Further Information:
Easy walking course.

MOATLANDS

MOATLANDS GOLF CLUB, Watermans Lane, Paddock Wood, Tonbridge, **KENT**, TN12 6ND, **ENGLAND**.
(T) 01892 724400
(E) moatlandsgolf@btconnect.com
(W) www.moatlands.com
Size of Complex: 260 Acres

Contact/s:
● **Professional:** Mr Simon Wood
● **Book Lessons:**
  ☎ 01892 724252

Course/s:
🏌 **MOATLANDS**
  Description: Parkland, Drains Well
  Built: 1993 **Built On:** Sand
  Number of Holes: 18 **Par:** 72
  Par 3's: 4 **Par 4's:** 10 **Par 5's:** 4
  Yds: 6693 **F9 Yds:** 3338 **B9 Yds:** 3355
  Further Information:
  Views of Kentish Wealds.

MOBBERLEY

MOBBERLEY GOLF CLUB, Burleyhurst Lane, Mobberley, Knutsford, **CHESHIRE**, WA16 7JZ, **ENGLAND**.
(T) 01565 880188

Membership: Members & Public

Contact/s:
● **Professional:** Mr Stephen Dewhurst

Course/s:
🏌 **MOBBERLEY**
  Description: Parkland, Undulating
  Green Speed: Medium
  Built: 1995
  Number of Holes: 9

MOFFAT

MOFFAT GOLF CLUB, Coatshill, Moffat, **DUMFRIES AND GALLOWAY**, DG10 9SB, **SCOTLAND**.
(T) 01683 220020
(W) www.moffatgolfclub.co.uk

Contact/s:
● **Clubmaster:** Mr Toby Downer

Course/s:
🏌 **THE MOFFAT**
  Description: Moorland
  Built: 1905
  Number of Holes: 18 **Par:** 69
  Yds: 5259 **F9 Yds:** 2575 **B9 Yds:** 2684
  Designer: Ben Sayers

MOLD

MOLD GOLF CLUB, Coron, Cilcain Rd, Pantymwyn, Mold, **FLINTSHIRE**, CH7 5EH, **WALES**.
(T) 01352 741513
(E) info@moldgolfclub.co.uk
(W) www.moldgolfclub.co.uk

Membership: Members & Public

Contact/s:
● **Club Secretary:** Mr P Mather
● **Professional:** Mr Mark Jordan
  ☎ 01352 740318

Course/s:
🏌 **MOLD**
  Description: Parkland, Moorland, Breckland, Hilltop, Open, Short, Tight, Drains Well
  Number of Holes: 18
  Designer: Members
  Further Information:
  This testing course is in a very quiet and picturesque location.

MOLLINGTON GRANGE

MOLLINGTON GRANGE GOLF CLUB, Townfield Lane, Mollington, Chester, **CHESHIRE**, CH1 6NJ, **ENGLAND**.
(T) 01244 851185
(W) www.mollingtongolfclub.co.uk

Membership: Members & Public

Contact/s:
● **Club Secretary:** Ms M Whitehead
● **Professional:** Mr Lee Corcoran
  ☎ 01244 851141

Course/s:
🏌 **MOLLINGTON GRANGE**
  Description: Championship, Undulating, Open, Long, Ideal for the Elderly
  Green Speed: Medium
  Built: 1999
  Number of Holes: 18
  Designer: Garry Chubb

MONIFIETH GOLF LINKS

MONIFIETH GOLF LINKS, Princes St, Monifieth, Dundee, **ANGUS**, DD5 4AW, **SCOTLAND**.
(T) 01382 532767
(E) monifiethgolf@freeuk.com
(W) www.monifiethgolf.co.uk

Membership: Members & Public

Contact/s:
● **Club Secretary:** Mr Sandy Fife
  ☎ 01382 535553
● **Professional:** Mr Ian McLeod
  ☎ 01382 532945

Course/s:
🏌 **ASHLUDIE**
  Description: Links, Wooded, Parkland, Open, Short, Drains Well, Ideal for the Elderly
  Green Speed: Medium
  Built: 1905 **Built On:** Clay
  Number of Holes: 18 **Par:** 68
  Par 3's: 4 **Par 4's:** 14
  Yds: 5123 **F9 Yds:** 2370 **B9 Yds:** 2753
  Prevailing Wind: South/West
  Further Information:
  This is a compact but challenging course.

🏌 **MEDAL**
  Description: Links, Wooded, Parkland, Sheltered, Long, Tight, Ideal for the Elderly
  Green Speed: Medium
  Built: 1858 **Built On:** Chalk
  Number of Holes: 18 **Par:** 71
  Par 3's: 3 **Par 4's:** 13 **Par 5's:** 2
  Yds: 6655 **F9 Yds:** 3458 **B9 Yds:** 3197
  Prevailing Wind: West
  Designer: A Robertson

MONKSTOWN

MONKSTOWN GOLF CLUB, Parkgarriffe, Monkstown, **COUNTY CORK**, **IRELAND**.
(T) 021 4841376

Contact/s:
● **Club Secretary:** G A Finn
● **Professional:** Mr Batt Murphy
  ☎ 021 841686

Course/s:
🏌 **MONKSTOWN**
  Description: Parkland
  Number of Holes: 18
  Yds: 6202
  Further Information:
  Various interesting water features along the course.

MONKTON PARK PAR 3

MONKTON PARK PAR 3, Monkton Pk, Chippenham, **WILTSHIRE**, SN15 3PE, **ENGLAND**.
(T) 01249 653928
(W) www.pitchandputtgolf.com

Contact/s:
● **Owner:** Mrs B Dawson

Course/s:
🏌 **PITCH AND PUTT**
  Number of Holes: 9 **Par:** 27
  Par 3's: 9
  Yds: 979

MONMOUTH

MONMOUTH GOLF CLUB, Leasbrook Lane, Monmouth, **MONMOUTHSHIRE**, NP25 3SN, **WALES**.
(T) 01600 712212

Membership: Members & Public
Size of Complex: 150 Acres

Contact/s:
● **Club Secretary:** Mrs Elizabeth Edwards
  ☎ 01600 772399
● **Professional:** Mr Brian Girling

Course/s:
🏌 **MONMOUTH**
  Description: Wooded, Parkland, Hilltop, Valley, Undulating. Open, Medium Length, Tends to Flood
  Green Speed: Fast
  Built: 1923 **Built On:** Clay
  Number of Holes: 18 **Par:** 69
  Yds: 5698
  Further Information:
  Beautiful scenery with abundant wildlife. There is a pond on the 14th hole.

MONMOUTHSHIRE

MONMOUTHSHIRE GOLF CLUB, Llanfoist, Abergavenny, **MONMOUTHSHIRE**, NP7 9HE, **WALES**.
(T) 01873 852606
(E) secretary@macabergavenny.fsnet.co.uk

Membership: Members & Public
Size of Complex: 98 Acres

Contact/s:
● **Professional:** Mr Brian Edwards
  ☎ 01873 852532

Course/s:
🏌 **MONMOUTHSHIRE**
  Description: Parkland, Undulating, Sheltered, Medium Length, Drains Well, Tends to Flood
  Green Speed: Medium
  Built: 1892 **Built On:** Soil
  Number of Holes: 18
  Prevailing Wind: East
  Designer: James Braid
  Further Information:
  Well established course set in beautiful surroundings.

MONTROSE (ROYAL)

ROYAL MONTROSE GOLF CLUB, Dorward Rd, Montrose, **ANGUS**, DD10 8SB, **SCOTLAND**.
(T) 01674 672376

Contact/s:
● **Treasurer:** Mr A G Ramsey

Course/s:
🏌 **ROYAL MONTROSE**
  Number of Holes: 18 **Par:** 72
  Yds: 6506

MONTROSE LINKS TRUST

MONTROSE LINKS TRUST, Traill Drive, Montrose, **ANGUS**, DD10 8SW, **SCOTLAND**.
(T) 01674 672932
(E) secretary@montroselinks.co.uk
(W) www.montroselinks.co.uk

Membership: Members & Public

Contact/s:
- **Club Secretary:** Mrs Margaret Stewart
- **Professional:** Mr Jason J Boyd
  ☎ 01674 672634

Course/s:
- **BROOMFIELD**
  Built: 1915
  Number of Holes: 18   **Par:** 66
  Yds: 4830   **F9 Yds:** 2384   **B9 Yds:** 2446
  Designer: Tom Morris, William Park
- **MEDAL**
  Description: Championship
  Built: 1915
  Number of Holes: 18   **Par:** 71
  Yds: 6544   **F9 Yds:** 3224   **B9 Yds:** 3320
  Designer: Tom Morris, William Park

MOOR ALLERTON

MOOR ALLERTON GOLF CLUB LTD, Clubhouse, Coal Rd, Wike, Leeds, **YORKSHIRE (WEST)**, LS17 9NH, **ENGLAND**.
(T) 0113 2665209

Contact/s:
- **Chief Executive:** Mr Nick Lomas

Course/s:
- **BLACKMOOR**
  Number of Holes: 18   **Par:** 71
  Yds: 6450
  Designer: Robert Trent Jones
- **HIGH**
  Number of Holes: 18   **Par:** 72
  Yds: 6609
  Designer: Robert Trent Jones
- **LAKES**
  Number of Holes: 18   **Par:** 71
  Yds: 6221
  Designer: Robert Trent Jones

MOOR HALL

MOOR HALL GOLF CLUB LTD, Moor Hall Drive, Sutton Coldfield, **MIDLANDS (WEST)**, B75 6LN, **ENGLAND**.
(T) 0121 3086130
(E) manager@moorhallgolfclub.fsnet.co.uk
(W) www.18global.com

Contact/s:
- **Professional:** Mr Alan Partridge

Course/s:
- **MOOR HALL**
  Description: Parkland
  Built: 1932
  Number of Holes: 18   **Par:** 70
  Par 3's: 4   **Par 4's:** 12   **Par 5's:** 2
  Yds: 6249   **F9 Yds:** 3264   **B9 Yds:** 2985
  Designer: Frederick George Hawtree, J H Taylor

MOOR PARK

MOOR PARK GOLF CLUB, Moor Pk, Rickmansworth, **HERTFORDSHIRE**, WD3 1QN, **ENGLAND**.
(T) 01923 774113

Membership: Members & Public

Contact/s:
- **Professional:** Mr Lawrence Farmer

Course/s:
- **HIGH**
  Number of Holes: 18
  Designer: Harry Shapland Colt
- **WEST**
  Number of Holes: 18
  Designer: Harry Shapland Colt

MOORE PLACE

MOORE PLACE GOLF COURSE, Portsmouth Rd, Esher, **SURREY**, KT10 9LN, **ENGLAND**.
(T) 01372 463533
(E) mooreplacegc@tinyworld.co.uk
(W) www.moore-place.co.uk

Membership: Public

Contact/s:
- **Professional:** Mr N Gadd

Course/s:
- **MOORE PLACE**
  Description: Wooded, Parkland, Undulating, Sheltered, Medium Length, Tight, Drains Well
  Green Speed: Medium
  Built: 1926   **Built On:** Sand/Soil
  Number of Holes: 9   **Par:** 66
  Par 3's: 3   **Par 4's:** 6
  Yds: 4156   **F9 Yds:** 2078   **B9 Yds:** 2078
  Designer: Harry Vardon, David Allen, Nick Gadd
  Further Information:
  9 hole course can be played as an 18 hole course

MOOR-PARK

MOOR-PARK GOLF COURSE, The Manor, Follistown Navan, Moortown, **COUNTY MEATH**, **IRELAND**.
(T) 046 27661

Contact/s:
- **Manager:** Mr Martin Fagan

Course/s:
- **MOOR-PARK GOLF COURSE**
  Description: Parkland
  Number of Holes: 18   **Par:** 72
  Yds: 6400

MOORS VALLEY GOLF CTRE

MOORS VALLEY GOLF CENTRE, Horton Rd, Ashley Heath, Ringwood, **HAMPSHIRE**, BH24 2ET, **ENGLAND**.
(T) 01425 479776
(E) mvalley@eastdorset.golf.uk

Contact/s:
- **Manager:** Mr Desmond Meharg

Course/s:
- **MOORS VALLEY**
  Description: Parkland, Heath Land, Short
  Number of Holes: 18   **Par:** 72
  Par 3's: 4   **Par 4's:** 10   **Par 5's:** 4
  Yds: 6337   **F9 Yds:** 3230   **B9 Yds:** 3107
  Designer: Hawtree

MOORTOWN

MOORTOWN GOLF CLUB LTD, Harrogate Rd, Leeds, **YORKSHIRE (WEST)**, LS17 7DB, **ENGLAND**.
(T) 0113 2686521
(E) secretary@moortown-gc.co.uk
(W) www.moortown-gc.co.uk

Membership: Members & Public

Contact/s:
- **Club Secretary:** Mr Kenneth Coutts Bradley

Course/s:
- **MOORTOWN**
  Description: Moorland
  Number of Holes: 18   **Par:** 72
  Yds: 6995   **F9 Yds:** 3603   **B9 Yds:** 3392
  Designer: Alistair MacKenzie ♟

MORAY

MORAY GOLF CLUB, Stotfield Rd, Lossiemouth, **MORAY**, IV31 6QS, **SCOTLAND**.
(T) 01343 812018
(E) sectretary@moraygolf.co.uk
(W) www.moraygolf.co.uk

Contact/s:
- **Professional:** Mr Alistair Thomson

Course/s:
- **NEW**
  Description: Championship
  Built: 1976
  Number of Holes: 18   **Par:** 69
  Yds: 6004   **F9 Yds:** 2912   **B9 Yds:** 3092
- **OLD**
  Description: Championship
  Built: 1889
  Number of Holes: 18   **Par:** 71
  Yds: 6578   **F9 Yds:** 3177   **B9 Yds:** 3401

MORECAMBE

MORECAMBE GOLF CLUB LTD, Marine Rd East, Morecambe, **LANCASHIRE**, LA4 6AJ, **ENGLAND**.
(T) 01524 400088
(E) morecambegolf@btconnect.com

Contact/s:
- **Club Secretary:** Mrs Helen Ball
- **Professional:** Mr Simon Fletcher
  ☎ 01524 415596

Course/s:
- **MORECAMBE**
  Number of Holes: 18   **Par:** 67
  Par 3's: 5   **Par 4's:** 13
  Yds: 5750   **F9 Yds:** 3061   **B9 Yds:** 2689
  Designer: Alistair MacKenzie

MORLAIS CASTLE

MORLAIS CASTLE GOLF CLUB, Pant, Merthyr Tydfil, **GLAMORGAN (VALE OF)**, CF48 2UY, **WALES**.
(T) 01685 722822

Contact/s:
- **Club Secretary:** Mr Meurig Price

Course/s:
- **MORLAIS CASTLE**
  Description: Moorland, Long, Drains Well
  Number of Holes: 18   **Par:** 71
  Yds: 6320
  Further Information:
  A mountain course with fantastic views overlooking the Brecon Beacons National Park.

MORLEY HAYES

MORLEY HAYES GOLF COURSE, Main Rd, Morley, Ilkeston, **DERBYSHIRE**, DE7 6DG, **ENGLAND**.
(T) 01332 780480
(E) enquiries@morleyhayes.com
(W) www.morleyhayes.com

Membership: Public

Contact/s:
- **Book Tee Times:** Ms Patricia Straw
  ☎ 01332 782000

Course/s:

MANOR
Description: Championship, Wooded, Parkland, Long
Built: 1992
Number of Holes: 18 **Par:** 72
Par 3's: 3 **Par 4's:** 12 **Par 5's:** 3
Yds: 6482 **F9 Yds:** 3146 **B9 Yds:** 3336
Further Information:
Water features and Deer Park.

TOWER
Description: Championship, Parkland
Built: 1992
Number of Holes: 9 **Par:** 32
Par 3's: 5 **Par 4's:** 3 **Par 5's:** 1
Yds: 1614

MORPETH

MORPETH GOLF CLUB LTD, Loansdean, Morpeth, **NORTHUMBERLAND**, NE61 2BT, **ENGLAND**.
(T) 01670 515675 or 504942
(E) morpethgolf@aol.com
(W) www.morpethgolf.co.uk
Contact/s:
* **Professional:** Mr Martin Jackson
  ☎ 01670 515675
Course/s:
MORPETH
Description: Parkland
Built: 1906
Number of Holes: 18 **Par:** 71
Yds: 6104 **F9 Yds:** 3227 **B9 Yds:** 2877
Designer: Harry Vardon

MORRISTON

MORRISTON GOLF CLUB, 160 Clasemont Rd, Morriston, Swansea, **SWANSEA**, SA6 6AJ, **WALES**.
(T) 01792 796528
Membership: Members & Public
Contact/s:
* **Club Secretary:** Mr V Thomas
* **Professional:** Mr Deryl Rees
* **Pro Shop:**
  ☎ 01792 772335
Course/s:
MORRISTON
Description: Parkland, Undulating, Sheltered, Medium Length, Tight
Green Speed: Medium
Built: 1919 **Built On:** Clay
Number of Holes: 18 **Par:** 68
Yds: 5755 **F9 Yds:** 2720 **B9 Yds:** 3035
Further Information:
The course has 2 ponds and a quarry alongside the 15th hole.

MORTEHOE & WOOLACOMBE

MORTEHOE & WOOLACOMBE GOLF COURSE, 1 Easewell Farm, Mortehoe, Woolacombe, **DEVON**, EX34 7EH, **ENGLAND**.
(T) 01271 870225
Membership: Members & Public
Contact/s:
* **Club Secretary:** Mr M Wilkinson
* **Pro Shop:** Mr P Adams
Course/s:
MORTEHOE & WOOLACOMBE
Description: Parkland, Hilltop, Short, Tight, Drains Well
Built: 1989
Number of Holes: 18 **Par:** 66
Par 3's: 6 **Par 4's:** 12
Yds: 4729 **F9 Yds:** 2300 **B9 Yds:** 2429
Designer: H T Ellis

MORTONHALL

MORTONHALL GOLF CLUB, Braid Rd, Edinburgh, **EDINBURGH (CITY OF)**, EH10 6PB, **SCOTLAND**.
(T) 0131 4472411
Contact/s:
* **Manageress:** Mrs C Morrison
Course/s:
MORTONHALL
Number of Holes: 18
Designer: James Braid, Hawtree

MOSELEY

MOSELEY GOLF CLUB LTD, Springfield Rd, Kings Heath, Birmingham, **MIDLANDS (WEST)**, B14 7DX, **ENGLAND**.
(T) 0121 4444957
(E) admin@mosgolf.freeserve.co.uk
(W) www.wugc.co.uk/moseley
Contact/s:
* **Club Secretary:** Mr Tony Jowle
* **Professional:** Mr Martin Griffin
  ☎ 0121 444 2063
Course/s:
MOSELEY
Number of Holes: 18 **Par:** 70
Par 3's: 4 **Par 4's:** 12 **Par 5's:** 2
Yds: 6315 **F9 Yds:** 3216 **B9 Yds:** 3099

MOSS VALLEY

MOSS VALLEY GOLF COURSE, Moss Rd, Moss, Wrexham, **WREXHAM**, LL11 6HA, **WALES**.
(T) 01978 720518
(E) info@mossvalleygolf.com
(W) www.mossvalleygolf.com
Membership: Members & Public
Contact/s:
* **Club Secretary:** Mr John Parry
Course/s:
MOSS VALLEY
Description: Wooded, Valley, Short, Ideal for the Elderly
Green Speed: Medium/Fast
Built: 1973 **Built On:** Soil
Number of Holes: 9 **Par:** 34
Par 3's: 3 **Par 4's:** 5 **Par 5's:** 1
Yds: 2641
Prevailing Wind: West
Further Information:
Beautiful views and very challenging course.

MOSSOCK HALL

MOSSOCK HALL GOLF CLUB, Liverpool Rd, Bickerstaffe, Ormskirk, **LANCASHIRE**, L39 0EE, **ENGLAND**.
(T) 01695 424962
Membership: Members & Public
Size of Complex: 180 Acres
Contact/s:
* **Professional:** Mr Phil Atkiss
* **Book Tee Times:**
  ☎ 01695 424969
Course/s:
MOSSOCK HALL
Description: Wooded, Parkland, Tight, Ideal for the Elderly
Green Speed: Medium/Fast
Built: 1996 **Built On:** Clay/Soil
Number of Holes: 18 **Par:** 71
Par 3's: 4 **Par 4's:** 11 **Par 5's:** 3
Yds: 6375 **F9 Yds:** 3317 **B9 Yds:** 3058
Prevailing Wind: West
Designer: Steve Marnoch

MOTE PARK GOLF HUT

MOTE PARK GOLF HUT, Mote Pk, Mote Ave, Maidstone, **KENT**, ME15 8NQ, **ENGLAND**.
(T) 01622 754770
Membership: Public
Contact/s:
* **Professional:** Mr David Bugg
* **Book Tee Times:** Mr Colin Magee
* **Book Lessons:**
  ☎ 01245 257682
Course/s:
MOTE PARK 18 HOLE PUTTING GREEN
Description: Parkland, Medium Length, Ideal for the Elderly
Green Speed: Medium
Built: 1950
Number of Holes: 18
MOTE PARK PITCH AND PUTT PAR 3
Description: Parkland, Short, Ideal for the Elderly
Green Speed: Medium
Built: 1950
Number of Holes: 18

MOTTRAM HALL

DE VERE MOTTRAM HALL HOTEL, Wilmslow Rd, Mottram St Andrew, Prestbury, Macclesfield, **CHESHIRE**, SK10 4QT, **ENGLAND**.
(T) 01625 828135
(E) dmh.sales@devere-hotels.com
(W) www.devere-hotels.com
Contact/s:
* **Professional:** Mr Tim Rastall
  ☎ 01625 820064
* **Book Tee Times:** Golf Shop
Course/s:
MOTTRAM HALL
Description: Wooded, Undulating
Built: 1991
Number of Holes: 18 **Par:** 72
Yds: 7006 **F9 Yds:** 3357 **B9 Yds:** 3649
Designer: Peter Alliss

MOUNT ELLEN

MOUNT ELLEN GOLF CLUB, Johnston House, Johnston Rd, Gartcosh, Glasgow, **GLASGOW (CITY OF)**, G69 8EY, **SCOTLAND**.
(T) 01236 872277
Contact/s:
* **Manager:** Mrs M Doyal
Course/s:
MOUNT ELLEN
Number of Holes: 18

MOUNT JULIET

MOUNT JULIET ESTATE, Thomastown, **COUNTY KILKENNY**, **IRELAND**.
(T) 056 73000
(E) info@mountjuliet.com
(W) www.mountjuliet.com
Membership: Members & Public
Size of Complex: 1500 Acres
Contact/s:
* **Professional:** Mr Brendan McDermot
* **Book Tee Times:** Ms Deirdre Brennan
Course/s:
JACK NICKLAUS SIGNATURE
Description: Championship, Wooded, Parkland, Sheltered **Built On:** Soil
Number of Holes: 18 **Par:** 72
Yds: 6683 **Designer:** Jack Nicklaus ♟

MOUNT MURRAY

MOUNT MURRAY HOTEL & COUNTRY CLUB, Ballacutchel Rd, Mount Murray, Douglas, **ISLE OF MAN**, IM4 2HT, **ENGLAND**.
(T) 01624 661111

Contact/s:
● **Professional:** Mr Andrew Dyson
● **Book Tee Times:**
  ☎ 01624 661111 ext 3023

Course/s:
⛳ **MOUNT MURRAY**
  Description: Championship
  Built: 1994
  Number of Holes: 18   **Par:** 72
  Further Information:
  Superb greens.

MOUNT OBER

MOUNT OBER GOLF & COUNTRY CLUB, 24 Ballymaconaghy Rd, Knockbracken, Belfast, **COUNTY ANTRIM**, BT8 6SB, **NORTHERN IRELAND**.
(T) 028 90792108
(E) mt.ober@ukonline.co.uk

Contact/s:
● **Professional:** Mr Geoff Loughrey
  ☎ 028 90701648

Course/s:
⛳ **MOUNT OBER**
  Description: Parkland, Undulating
  Built: 1985
  Number of Holes: 18   **Par:** 67
  Par 3's: 7   **Par 4's:** 9   **Par 5's:** 2
  Yds: 5448   **F9 Yds:** 2758   **B9 Yds:** 2690
  Further Information:
  Testing course.

MOUNT OSWALD MANOR

MOUNT OSWALD MANOR & GOLF COURSE, South Rd, Durham, **COUNTY DURHAM**, DH1 3TQ, **ENGLAND**.
(T) 0191 3867527
(E) information@mountoswald.co.uk

Contact/s:
● **Owner:** Mr S Reeve

Course/s:
⛳ **MOUNT OSWALD MANOR**
  Number of Holes: 18   **Par:** 71
  Yds: 5984   **F9 Yds:** 3020   **B9 Yds:** 2964

MOUNT PLEASANT

MOUNT PLEASANT GOLF CLUB, Station Rd, Lower Stondon, Henlow, **BEDFORDSHIRE**, SG16 6JL, **ENGLAND**.
(T) 01462 850999
(W) www.mountpleasantgolfclub.co.uk

Membership: Members & Public
Size of Complex: 70 Acres

Contact/s:
● **Professional:** Mr Paul Williams
● **Book Lessons:** Mr Mike Roberts

Course/s:
⛳ **MOUNT PLEASANT 18 TEES**
  Description: Parkland, Undulating, Medium Length, Drains Well, Ideal for the Elderly
  Green Speed: Fast
  Built: 1991   **Built On:** Chalk/Sand/Soil
  Number of Holes: 9   **Par:** 70
  Par 3's: 1   **Par 4's:** 7   **Par 5's:** 1
  Yds: 6003   **F9 Yds:** 3163   **B9 Yds:** 2840
  Designer: D Young
  Further Information:
  9 hole course can be played as an 18 hole course

MOUNT TEMPLE

MOUNT TEMPLE CHAMPIONSHIP COURSE, Mount Temple Village, Moate, **COUNTY WESTMEATH**, **IRELAND**.
(T) 090 281841
(E) mttemple@iol.ie
(W) www.revelations.co.uk/golf/index.html

Contact/s:
● **Proprietor:** Mr Michael Dolan

Course/s:
⛳ **MOUNT TEMPLE**
  Number of Holes: 18   **Par:** 71
  Yds: 6421
  Designer: O'Dolan

MOUNT WOLSELEY HOTEL

MOUNT WOLSELEY HOTEL GOLF & COUNTRY CLUB, Mount Wolseley, Tullow, **COUNTY CARLOW**, **IRELAND**.
(T) 050 351674
(E) info@mountwolseleyhotel.com
(W) www.mountwolseley.ie

Contact/s:
● **Club Secretary:** Ms Brenda Morrisey
● **Professional:** Mr Jimmy Bulger

Course/s:
⛳ **MOUNT WOLSELEY GOLF COURSE**
  Description: Parkland
  Number of Holes: 18   **Par:** 72
  Yds: 7200

MOUNTAIN ASH

MOUNTAIN ASH GOLF CLUB, The Clubhouse, Cefnpennar, Mountain Ash, **RHONDDA CYNON TAFF**, CF45 4DT, **WALES**.
(T) 01443 479459

Membership: Members & Public
Size of Complex: 100 Acres

Contact/s:
● **Professional:** Mr Marcus Wills
  ☎ 01443 478770

Course/s:
⛳ **MOUNTAIN ASH**
  Description: Moorland, Hilltop, Valley, Undulating, Open, Short, Drains Well
  Green Speed: Slow
  Built: 1908   **Built On:** Clay/Soil
  Number of Holes: 18   **Par:** 69
  Par 3's: 5   **Par 4's:** 11   **Par 5's:** 2
  Yds: 5553   **F9 Yds:** 2811   **B9 Yds:** 2742

MOUNTAIN VIEW

MOUNTAIN VIEW, Kiltorcan, Ballyhale, **COUNTY KILKENNY**, **IRELAND**.
(T) 056 68122

Membership: Members & Public

Contact/s:
● **Club Secretary:** Ms Margaret Fennelly

Course/s:
⛳ **MOUNTAIN VIEW**
  Description: Parkland, Hilltop, Drains Well
  Green Speed: Fast
  Number of Holes: 18
  Designer: John O' Sullivan

MOUNTBELLEW

MOUNTBELLEW GOLF CLUB, Mountbellew, Ballinasloe, **COUNTY GALWAY**, **IRELAND**.
(T) 090 579259

Course/s:
⛳ **MOUNTBELLEW**
  Description: Parkland
  Number of Holes: 9
  Yds: 5564

MOUNTRATH

MOUNTRATH GOLF CLUB, Knockanina, Mountrath, **COUNTY LAOIS**, **IRELAND**.
(T) 050 232558

Contact/s:
● **Club Secretary:** J Mulhare
  ☎ 050 32421

Course/s:
⛳ **MOUNTRATH**
  Number of Holes: 18
  Yds: 6020

MOWSBURY

MOWSBURY GOLF & SQUASH COMPLEX, Cleat Hill, Kimbolton Rd, Bedford, **BEDFORDSHIRE**, MK41 8DQ, **ENGLAND**.
(T) 01234 771041

Membership: Members & Public
Size of Complex: 150 Acres

Contact/s:
● **Club Secretary:** Mr Malcolm Summers
● **Professional:** Mr Gerry Richardson

Course/s:
⛳ **MOWSBURY**
  Description: Parkland, Undulating, Medium Length, Drains Well, Ideal for the Elderly
  Green Speed: Medium
  Built: 1974   **Built On:** Clay
  Number of Holes: 18   **Par:** 72
  Par 3's: 4   **Par 4's:** 10   **Par 5's:** 4
  Yds: 6472   **F9 Yds:** 3192   **B9 Yds:** 3280
  Prevailing Wind: South/West
  Designer: Hawtree
  Further Information:
  Excellent conditions with panoramic views from the course.

MOY BALLEY PAR 3

MOY BALLEY PAR 3 GOLF COURSE & DRIVING RANGE, Quignalegan, Ballina, **COUNTY MAYO**, **IRELAND**.
(T) 096 72939

Contact/s:
● **Director:** Mr John O'Boyle

Course/s:
⛳ **BLIND BROOK**
  Number of Holes: 9

MOYOLA PARK

MOYOLA PARK GOLF CLUB, 15 Curran Rd, Castledawson, Magherafelt, **COUNTY LONDONDERRY**, BT45 8DG, **NORTHERN IRELAND**.
(T) 028 79468468

Contact/s:
● **Club Secretary:** Mr L Hastings
● **Professional:** Mr V Teague
  ☎ 028 7946 8830

Course/s:
⛳ **MOYOLA PARK**
  Number of Holes: 18
  Designer: D Patterson

MUCKHART

MUCKHART GOLF CLUB, Drumburn Rd, Muckhart, Dollar, **CLACKMANNANSHIRE**, FK14 7JH, **SCOTLAND**.
(T) 01259 781423

Membership: Members & Public

Contact/s:
● **Club Secretary:** Mr Alexander Robertson
● **Professional:** Mr Keith Salmoni
☎ 01259 781419

Course/s:
● MUCKHART
Description: Wooded, Parkland, Undulating, Long, Drains Well
Built: 1971 **Built On:** Sand/Soil
Number of Holes: 18

● NAEMOOR
Description: Wooded, Parkland, Undulating, Long, Drains Well
Built: 1906 **Built On:** Sand/Soil
Number of Holes: 9

● NEW 9 HOLE
Description: Wooded, Parkland, Undulating, Long, Drains Well, Ideal for the Elderly
Built: 1997 **Built On:** Sand/Soil
Number of Holes: 9

MUIR OF ORD

MUIR OF ORD GOLF CLUB, Great North Rd, Muir Of Ord, **HIGHLANDS**, IV6 7SX, **SCOTLAND**.
(T) 01463 870825
(E) muirgolf@supanet.com
(W) www.golfhighland.co.uk

Contact/s:
● **Club Secretary:** Mrs J Gibson
● **Book Tee Times:**
☎ 01483 870825

Course/s:
● MUIR OF ORD
Description: Heath Land, Moorland, Tight
Built: 1875
Number of Holes: 18 **Par:** 68
Par 3's: 5 **Par 4's:** 12 **Par 5's:** 1
Yds: 5596 **F9 Yds:** 2885 **B9 Yds:** 2711
Designer: James Braid

MUIRFIELD

MUIRFIELD GOLF COURSE, Gullane, **LOTHIAN (EAST)**, EH31 2EG, **SCOTLAND**.
(T) 01620 842123

Membership: Members Only

Contact/s:
● **Club Secretary:** Mr J A Prideaux

Course/s:
● MUIRFIELD, HON. COMPANY OF EDINBURGH GOLFERS
Description: Championship, Links, Drains Well
Built: 1891
Number of Holes: 18 **Par:** 70
Par 3's: 4 **Par 4's:** 12 **Par 5's:** 2
Yds: 6601 **F9 Yds:** 3329 **B9 Yds:** 3272
Designer: Tom Morris ♟

MULLINGAR

MULLINGAR GOLF CLUB, Belvedere, Mullingar, **COUNTY WESTMEATH**, **IRELAND**.
(T) 044 48366

Course/s:
● MULLINGAR
Number of Holes: 18

Designer: James Braid

MULLION

MULLION GOLF CLUB, Cury, Helston, **CORNWALL**, TR12 7BP, **ENGLAND**.
(T) 01326 241176
(E) secretary@mulliongolfclub.plus.net

Contact/s:
● **Professional:** Mr Phil Blundell

Course/s:
● MULLION
Description: Links, Cliff Top
Built: 1895
Number of Holes: 18 **Par:** 70
Yds: 6037 **F9 Yds:** 3185 **B9 Yds:** 2852
Designer: W Sich

MULRANNY

MULRANNY GOLF CLUB, Mulranny, Westport, **COUNTY MAYO**, **IRELAND**.
(T) 098 36262

Membership: Members & Public

Contact/s:
● **Club Secretary:** Ciaran Moran
☎ 098 36116

Course/s:
● MULRANNY
Description: Links
Built: 1894
Number of Holes: 9

MUNDESLEY

MUNDESLEY GOLF CLUB, Links Rd, Mundesley, Norwich, **NORFOLK**, NR11 8ES, **ENGLAND**.
(T) 01263 720279

Membership: Members & Public

Contact/s:
● **Club Secretary:** Mr J Woodhouse
● **Professional:** Mr T Symmons

Course/s:
● MUNDESLEY
Description: Parkland, Undulating, Short, Tight
Green Speed: Medium
Built: 1901 **Built On:** Soil
Number of Holes: 9 **Par:** 68
Further Information:
This challenging course is 1 mile from the sea.

MURCAR

MURCAR GOLF CLUB, Murcar, Bridge Of Don, Aberdeen, **ABERDEEN (CITY OF)**, AB23 8BD, **SCOTLAND**.
(T) 01224 704354/704345
(E) murcar-golf-club@lineone.net
(W) www.murcar.co.uk

Membership: Members & Public

Contact/s:
● **Club Secretary:** Mr David Corstorphine
● **Professional:** Mr Gary Forbes
☎ 01224 704370

Course/s:
● MURCAR
Description: Links, Cliff Top
Built: 1909 **Built On:** Sand
Number of Holes: 18 **Par:** 71
Par 3's: 3 **Par 4's:** 13 **Par 5's:** 2
Yds: 6241
Designer: Simpson
Further Information:
There are large sand dunes on the course. ♟

● STRABATHIE
Built: 1966 **Built On:** Sand
Number of Holes: 9 **Par:** 35

MURRAYFIELD

MURRAYFIELD GOLF CLUB LTD, 43 Murrayfield Rd, Edinburgh, **EDINBURGH (CITY OF)**, EH12 6EU, **SCOTLAND**.
(T) 0131 3371009

Contact/s:
● **Club Secretary:** Mrs M K Hermiston
☎ 0131 3373478

Course/s:
● MURRAYFIELD
Number of Holes: 18
Yds: 5727

MUSKERRY

MUSKERRY GOLF CLUB, Carrigrohane, **COUNTY CORK**, **IRELAND**.
(T) 021 4385297

Membership: Members & Public

Contact/s:
● **Professional:** Mr Martin Lehane

Course/s:
● MUSKERRY
Number of Holes: 18 **Par:** 71
Par 3's: 4 **Par 4's:** 11 **Par 5's:** 3
Yds: 6026 **F9 Yds:** 2996 **B9 Yds:** 3029
Designer: Alistair MacKenzie

MUSSELBURGH

MUSSELBURGH GOLF CLUB, Monktonhall, Musselburgh, **LOTHIAN (MID)**, EH21 6SA, **SCOTLAND**.
(T) 0131 6652005

Membership: Members & Public
Size of Complex: 150 Acres

Contact/s:
● **Club Secretary:** Mr David McLeod
● **Professional:** Mr Frazer Mann
● **Pro Shop:**
☎ 0131 6657055

Course/s:
● MUSSELBURGH
Description: Parkland, Undulating, Sheltered, Long, Tends to Flood
Green Speed: Medium
Built: 1938
Number of Holes: 18 **Par:** 71
Yds: 6241 **F9 Yds:** 3350 **B9 Yds:** 3375
Prevailing Wind: East
Designer: James Braid

MUSSELBURGH (ROYAL)

ROYAL MUSSELBURGH GOLF CLUB, Prestongrange House, Prestonpans, **LOTHIAN (EAST)**, EH32 9RT, **SCOTLAND**.
(T) 01875 813671

Membership: Members & Public

Course/s:
● ROYAL MUSSELBURGH
Description: Championship
Number of Holes: 18
Designer: James Braid

MUSSELBURGH LINKS

MUSSELBURGH LINKS GOLF COURSE, The Old Golf Course, The Stanters Hut, Balcarres Rd, Musselburgh, **LOTHIAN (EAST)**, EH21 7SD, **SCOTLAND**.
(T) 0131 6655438
(W) www.musselburgholdlinks.co.uk

Membership: Members & Public

Musselburgh — Nefyn & District

A-Z GOLF CLUBS/COURSES

Contact/s:
- Club Secretary: Mr L D Freedman
- ☎ 0131 6654861

Course/s:
● **THE OLD**
Description: Championship, Links, Open, Drains Well, Ideal for the Elderly
Green Speed: Medium
Built: 1567 Built On: Sand
Number of Holes: 9 Par: 68
Par 3's: 3 Par 4's: 5 Par 5's: 1
Yds: 5616 F9 Yds: 2808 B9 Yds: 2808
Further Information:
The Old Golf Course is the oldest playing golf course in the world.

MUSWELL HILL

MUSWELL HILL GOLF CLUB, Clubhouse, Rhodes Ave, London, **LONDON (GREATER)**, N22 7UT, **ENGLAND**.
(T) 020 88881764

Membership: Members & Public
Size of Complex: 84 Acres

Contact/s:
- Club Secretary: Mrs Janet Underhill
- Professional: Mr David Wilton

Course/s:
● **MUSWELL HILL**
Description: Wooded, Parkland, Drains Well
Green Speed: Fast
Built: 1893 Built On: Clay
Number of Holes: 18 Par: 71
Yds: 6438 F9 Yds: 3301 B9 Yds: 3137

MUTHILL

MUTHILL GOLF CLUB, Peat Rd, Muthill, **PERTH AND KINROSS**, PH5 2DA, **SCOTLAND**.
(T) 01764 681523
(E) muthillgolfclub@lineone.net

Contact/s:
- Club Secretary: Mr Jim Elder

Course/s:
● **MUTHILL**
Description: Parkland, Undulating, Short, Drains Well, Ideal for the Elderly
Green Speed: Medium
Built: 1935 Built On: Soil
Number of Holes: 9 Par: 66
Par 3's: 3 Par 4's: 6
Yds: 4700 F9 Yds: 2350 B9 Yds: 2350
Prevailing Wind: West
Further Information:
Tight fairways and small greens. This 9 hole course can also be played as an 18 hole course.

MYTTON FOLD

MYTTON FOLD HOTEL & GOLF COMPLEX, Whalley Rd, Langho, Blackburn, **LANCASHIRE**, BB6 8AB, **ENGLAND**.
(T) 01254 240662
(E) golf_info@myttonfold.co.uk
(W) www.myttonfold.co.uk

Membership: Members & Public

Contact/s:
- Professional: Mr Gary Coope
- Book Tee Times:
  ☎ 01254 245392 or 240662

Course/s:
● **MYTTON FOLD**
Description: Parkland, Undulating
Built: 1994 Built On: Soil
Number of Holes: 18 Par: 70
Designer: Frank Hargreaves

NAAS

NAAS GOLF CLUB, Kerdiffstown, Naas, **COUNTY KILDARE**, **IRELAND**.
(T) 045 874644

Contact/s:
- Club Secretary: Mr Michael Conway

Course/s:
● **NAAS**
Number of Holes: 18
Yds: 6230

NAIRN

NAIRN GOLF CLUB (THE), Seabank Rd, Nairn, **HIGHLANDS**, IV12 4HB, **SCOTLAND**.
(T) 01667 453208
(E) bookings@nairngolfclub.co.uk
(W) www.nairngolfclub.co.uk

Membership: Members & Public

Contact/s:
- Club Secretary: Mr J G Somerville

Course/s:
● **NAIRN**
Description: Championship, Links, Open
Built: 1887
Number of Holes: 18 Par: 72
Par 3's: 4 Par 4's: 10 Par 5's: 4
Yds: 6430 F9 Yds: 3080 B9 Yds: 3350
Designer: Archie Simpson, Old Tom Morris, James Braid
Further Information:
Traditional Scottish links course. ♟

● **NEWTON**
Description: Links, Open
Built: 1887
Number of Holes: 9 Par: 58
Par 3's: 7 Par 4's: 2
Yds: 3542 F9 Yds: 1771 B9 Yds: 1771
Designer: Archie Simpson, Old Tom Morris, James Braid
Further Information:
Traditional Scottish links course. Can be played as an 18 hole course.

NAIRN DUNBAR

NAIRN DUNBAR GOLF CLUB, Lochloy Rd, Nairn, **HIGHLANDS**, IV12 5AE, **SCOTLAND**.
(T) 01667 452741
(E) secretary@nairndunbar.com

Contact/s:
- Club Secretary: Mrs S Falconer

Course/s:
● **NAIRN DUNBAR**
Number of Holes: 18 Par: 72
Yds: 6720 F9 Yds: 3319 B9 Yds: 3401

NARIN/PORTNOO

NARIN/PORTNOO GOLF CLUB, Narin, **COUNTY DONEGAL**, **IRELAND**.
(T) 075 45107

Membership: Members & Public
Size of Complex: 135 Acres

Contact/s:
- Club Secretary: Mr Enda Bonner
- Pro Shop: Mr Dom Gallagher
- Book Tee Times: Mr Sean Murphy

Course/s:
● **NARIN & PORTNOO**
Description: Links
Green Speed: Medium
Built: 1931 Built On: Sand
Number of Holes: 18 Record: 63 (Bobby Browne)
Further Information:
Excellent coastal scenery.

NAUNTON DOWNS

NAUNTON DOWNS GOLF CLUB LTD, Naunton, Cheltenham, **GLOUCESTERSHIRE**, GL54 3AE, **ENGLAND**.
(T) 01451 850092

Contact/s:
- Professional: Mr Nick Ellis

Course/s:
● **NAUNTON DOWNS**
Built: 1993
Number of Holes: 18 Par: 71
Yds: 6135 F9 Yds: 3026 B9 Yds: 3109
Designer: J Pott
Further Information:
A course for all golfing abilities.

NAZEING

NAZEING GOLF CLUB, Middle St, Nazeing, Waltham Abbey, **ESSEX**, EN9 2LW, **ENGLAND**.
(T) 01992 893798

Contact/s:
- Professional: Mr Robert Green

Course/s:
● **NAZEING**
Description: Parkland
Built: 1992 Built On: Sand
Number of Holes: 18 Par: 72
Designer: M Gillete

NEATH

NEATH GOLF CLUB, Cadoxton, Neath, **NEATH PORT TALBOT**, SA10 8AH, **WALES**.
(T) 01639 632759

Contact/s:
- Club Secretary: Mr D Hughes
- Professional: Mr E M Bennett
- Pro Shop:
  ☎ 01639 633693

Course/s:
● **NEATH**
Description: Heath Land, Hilltop, Undulating, Sheltered, Medium Length, Drains Well
Green Speed: Fast
Built: 1935 Built On: Soil
Number of Holes: 18
Designer: James Braid
Further Information:
There are 50 bunkers on the course.

NEFYN & DISTRICT

NEFYN & DISTRICT GOLF CLUB, Lon Golf, Morfa Nefyn, Pwllheli, **GWYNEDD**, LL53 6DA, **WALES**.
(T) 01758 720966
(E) nefyngolf@tesco.net
(W) www.nefyn-golf-club.com

Contact/s:
- Club Secretary: Mr J.B Owens
- Professional: Mr J Froom
  ☎ 01758 720102

Course/s:
● **NEW**
Number of Holes: 18 Par: 71
Yds: 6548 F9 Yds: 3198 B9 Yds: 3350
Designer: James Braid

● **OLD**
Number of Holes: 18 Par: 70
Yds: 6108 F9 Yds: 3069 B9 Yds: 3039
Designer: James Braid

NELSON

NELSON GOLF CLUB, Kings Causeway, Brierfield, Nelson, **LANCASHIRE**, BB9 0EU, **ENGLAND**.
(T) 01282 614583

Contact/s:
- **Professional:** Mr Nigel Sumner
- **Book Tee Times:**
  ☎ 01282 611834 or 617000

Course/s:
🏌 **NELSON**
Description: Moorland
Built: 1902
Number of Holes: 18 Par: 70
Yds: 6007 F9 Yds: 2994 B9 Yds: 3013
Designer: Alistair MacKenzie

NENAGH

NENAGH GOLF CLUB, Beechwood, Nenagh, **COUNTY TIPPERARY**, **IRELAND**.
(T) 067 31476

Course/s:
🏌 **NENAGH**
Number of Holes: 18
Designer: Edward Hackett

NEVILL

NEVILL GOLF CLUB, Benhall Mill Rd, Tunbridge Wells, **KENT**, TN2 5JW, **ENGLAND**.
(T) 01892 525818
(W) www.nevillgolfclub.co.uk

Contact/s:
- **Club Secretary:** Mr Tony Fensom

Course/s:
🏌 **NEVILL**
Number of Holes: 18 Par: 70
Par 3's: 5 Par 4's: 9 Par 5's: 4
Yds: 6349 F9 Yds: 3022 B9 Yds: 3327

NEW

NEW GOLF CLUB (THE), 3-5 Gibson Pl, St. Andrews, **FIFE**, KY16 9JE, **SCOTLAND**.
(T) 01334 472262
(E) golf@standrewgolfclub.soc.co.uk

Membership: Members & Public

Contact/s:
- **Club Secretary:** Mr Campbell Graham

Course/s:
🏌 **NEW**
Description: Links, Open, Short, Drains Well, Ideal for the Elderly
Green Speed: Fast
Built: 1902 Built On: Sand
Number of Holes: 18
Prevailing Wind: West

NEW CUMNOCK

NEW CUMNOCK GOLF CLUB, Cumnock Rd, New Cumnock, Lochhill, **AYRSHIRE (EAST)**, KA18 4PN, **SCOTLAND**.
(T) 01290 338848

Course/s:
🏌 **NEW CUMNOCK**
Number of Holes: 9
Designer: William Fernie

NEW FOREST

NEW FOREST GOLF CLUB, Southampton Rd, Lyndhurst, **HAMPSHIRE**, SO43 7BU, **ENGLAND**.
(T) 023 80282752

Contact/s:
- **Club Secretary:** Mrs L Dyer
- **Professional:** Mr Danny Harris

Course/s:
🏌 **NEW FOREST**
Description: Heath Land
Built: 1848
Number of Holes: 18 Par: 69
Par 3's: 7 Par 4's: 7 Par 5's: 4
Yds: 5772 F9 Yds: 3202 B9 Yds: 2570
Further Information:
The course is situated in the centre of New Forest.

NEW GALLOWAY

NEW GALLOWAY GOLF CLUB, High St, New Galloway, Castle Douglas, **DUMFRIES AND GALLOWAY**, DG7 3RN, **SCOTLAND**.
(T) 01644 420737
(W) www.nggc.co.uk

Membership: Members & Public
Size of Complex: 65 Acres

Contact/s:
- **Club Secretary:** Mr Neville White

Course/s:
🏌 **NEW GALLOWAY**
Description: Wooded, Heath Land, Moorland, Hilltop, Undulating, Sheltered, Open, Short, Tight, Drains Well
Green Speed: Fast
Built: 1902 Built On: Soil
Number of Holes: 9 Par: 66
Yds: 4540 F9 Yds: 2270 B9 Yds: 2270
Prevailing Wind: South/West
Designer: James Braid
Further Information:
9 hole course can be played as an 18 hole course

NEW MILLS

NEW MILLS GOLF CLUB, Shaw Marsh, Newmills, Stockport, **CHESHIRE**, SK12 4QE, **ENGLAND**.
(T) 01663 743485
(E) professional@newmillsgolfclub.co.uk

Contact/s:
- **Club Secretary:** P Jenkinson
  ☎ 01663 744305
- **Professional:** Mr Carl P Cross
  ☎ 01663 746161

Course/s:
🏌 **NEW MILLS**
Number of Holes: 9
Yds: 5633

NEW NORTH MANCHESTER

NEW NORTH MANCHESTER GOLF CLUB LTD (THE), Rhodes Hse, Manchester Old Rd, Middleton, Manchester, **MANCHESTER (GREATER)**, M24 4PE, **ENGLAND**.
(T) 0161 6439033

Contact/s:
- **Club Secretary:** Mr D Parkinson
- **Professional:** Mr Jason Pell

Course/s:
🏌 **NORTH MANCHESTER**
Number of Holes: 18 Par: 72
Yds: 6542 F9 Yds: 3372 B9 Yds: 3170
Designer: James Braid

NEW ROSS

NEW ROSS GOLF CLUB, Tinneranny, New Ross, **COUNTY WEXFORD**, **IRELAND**.
(T) 051 421433

Course/s:

🏌 **NEW ROSS**
Number of Holes: 18
Designer: D Smyth

NEW ZEALAND

NEW ZEALAND GOLF CLUB LTD, Woodham Lane, Woodham, Addlestone, **SURREY**, KT15 3QD, **ENGLAND**.
(T) 01932 349619

Membership: Members & Public

Contact/s:
- **Club Secretary:** Mr RA Marret Esq.
  ☎ 01932 345049
- **Professional:** Mr VR Elvidge

Course/s:
🏌 **NEW ZEALAND**
Description: Heath Land, Sheltered
Number of Holes: 18 Par: 68
Yds: 6012
Designer: Fergurson, Muir, Simpson 🏆

NEWARK

NEWARK GOLF CLUB CO LTD, Coddington, Coddington, Newark, **NOTTINGHAMSHIRE**, NG24 2QX, **ENGLAND**.
(T) 01636 626282

Contact/s:
- **Club Secretary:** Mr P Snow
- **Professional:** Mr P Lockley

Course/s:
🏌 **NEWARK**
Number of Holes: 18 Par: 71
Yds: 6458 F9 Yds: 3444 B9 Yds: 3014

NEWBATTLE

NEWBATTLE GOLF CLUB LTD, Abbey Rd, Dalkeith, **LOTHIAN (MID)**, EH22 3AD, **SCOTLAND**.
(T) 0131 6631819

Contact/s:
- **Club Secretary:** Mr H Stanners
- **Pro Shop:** Mr Scott McDonald
  ☎ 0131 6601631

Course/s:
🏌 **NEWBATTLE**
Number of Holes: 18
Designer: Harry Shapland Colt

NEWBIGGIN

NEWBIGGIN GOLF CLUB, Newbiggin-By-The-Sea, **NORTHUMBERLAND**, NE64 6DW, **ENGLAND**.
(T) 01670 817344

Contact/s:
- **Accountant:** Mr Alan McBride

Course/s:
🏌 **NEWBIGGIN**
Number of Holes: 18

NEWBOLD COMYN

NEWBOLD COMYN GOLF COURSE, Newbold Trce East, Leamington Spa, **WARWICKSHIRE**, CV32 4EW, **ENGLAND**.
(T) 01926 421157

Membership: Members & Public/Public

Contact/s:
- **Club Secretary:** Mr Colin Baker
- **Pro Shop:** Mr Ricky Carvell

Course/s:
🏌 **NEWBOLD COMYN**
Description: Wooded, Undulating, Sheltered, Open, Medium Length, Drains Well

Green Speed: Fast
Built: 1974 **Built On:** Clay
Number of Holes: 18
Further Information:
With views of Warwick Castle, this challenging course has an extremely long par 4 on the 9th hole.

NEWBRIDGE

NEWBRIDGE GOLF CLUB LTD,
Barrettstown, Newbridge, **COUNTY KILDARE**, **IRELAND**.
(T) 045 486110
(E) newbridgegolf@esatclear.ie
(W) www.newbridgegolf.ie

Course/s:
🌑 **NEWBRIDGE**
Number of Holes: 18

NEWBURGH-ON-YTHAN

NEWBURGH-ON-YTHAN GOLF CLUB,
Beach Rd, Newburgh, Ellon, **ABERDEENSHIRE**, AB41 6BY, **SCOTLAND**.
(T) 01358 789058
(E) secretary@newbury-on-ythan.co.uk
(W) www.newburgh-on-ythan.co.uk

Membership: Members & Public

Contact/s:
● **Club Secretary:** Mr John Geoghagan
☎ 01358 789084

Course/s:
🌑 **NEWBURGH-ON-YTHAN**
Description: Links, Undulating
Built: 1888 **Built On:** Sand
Number of Holes: 18 **Par:** 72
Par 3's: 3 **Par 4's:** 12 **Par 5's:** 3
Yds: 6162
Designer: Greens of Scotland

NEWBURY & CROOKHAM

NEWBURY & CROOKHAM GOLF CLUB, 34 Burys Bank Rd, Greenham, Newbury, **BERKSHIRE**, RG19 8BZ, **ENGLAND**.
(T) 01635 40035

Membership: Members & Public

Contact/s:
● **Club Secretary:** Mrs J R Hearsey
● **Professional:** Mr David Harris
☎ 01635 31201

Course/s:
🌑 **NEWBURY & CROOKHAM**
Description: Wooded, Parkland, Undulating, Short, Drains Well
Green Speed: Medium
Built: 1873 **Built On:** Clay/Soil
Number of Holes: 18 **Par:** 69
Par 3's: 5 **Par 4's:** 11 **Par 5's:** 2
Yds: 5940 **F9 Yds:** 2773 **B9 Yds:** 3167
Further Information:
A challenging course with interesting bunkers.

NEWBURY RACECOURSE

NEWBURY RACECOURSE GOLF CENTRE (THE), Newbury Racecourse, Newbury, **BERKSHIRE**, RG14 7NZ, **ENGLAND**.
(T) 01635 551464

Contact/s:
● **Club Secretary:** Mr P Henderson
☎ 01635 580784
● **Professional:** Mr Nick Mitchell

Course/s:
🌑 **NEWBURY**
Number of Holes: 18 **Par:** 71

NEWCASTLE

CITY OF NEWCASTLE GOLF CLUB, Three Mile Bridge, Great North Rd, Gosforth, Newcastle Upon Tyne, **TYNE AND WEAR**, NE3 2DR, **ENGLAND**.
(T) 0191 2851775

Contact/s:
● **Professional:** Mr Steve Mckenna

Course/s:
🌑 **CITY OF NEWCASTLE**
Number of Holes: 18 **Par:** 72
Yds: 6528 **F9 Yds:** 3189 **B9 Yds:** 3339
Designer: Harry Vardon

NEWCASTLE UNITED

NEWCASTLE UNITED GOLF CLUB, 60 Ponteland Rd, Cowgate, Newcastle Upon Tyne, **TYNE AND WEAR**, NE5 3JW, **ENGLAND**.
(T) 0191 2864323

Contact/s:
● **Club Secretary:** Mr John Simpson

Course/s:
🌑 **NEWCASTLE UNITED**
Number of Holes: 18

NEWCASTLE WEST

NEWCASTLE WEST (ARDAGH) GOLF CLUB, Ardagh, **COUNTY LIMERICK**, **IRELAND**.
(T) 069 76500

Course/s:
🌑 **NEWCASTLE WEST**
Built: 1938
Number of Holes: 18 **Par:** 71
Designer: A Spring

NEWCASTLETON

NEWCASTLETON GOLF CLUB, Holm Hill, Newcastleton, **SCOTTISH BORDERS**, TD9 0QD, **SCOTLAND**.
(T) 01387 375257

Contact/s:
● **Book Tee Times:** Mr F Ewart

Course/s:
🌑 **NEWCASTLETON**
Description: Hilltop
Built: 1894
Number of Holes: 9 **Par:** 70
Designer: J Shade
Further Information:
9 hole course can be played as an 18 hole course

NEWCASTLE-UNDER-LYME

NEWCASTLE-UNDER-LYME GOLF CLUB,
Whitmore Rd, Newcastle, **STAFFORDSHIRE**, ST5 2QB, **ENGLAND**.
(T) 01782 617006

Contact/s:
● **Professional:** Mr Paul Symonds

Course/s:
🌑 **NEWCASTLE-UNDER-LYME**
Description: Wooded, Parkland
Built: 1908
Number of Holes: 18 **Par:** 72
Yds: 6450
Further Information:
There are many demanding shots to greens.

NEWENT

NEWENT GOLF COURSE, Cold Harbour Lane, Newent, **GLOUCESTERSHIRE**, GL18 1DJ, **ENGLAND**.
(T) 01531 820478
(E) newentgc@aol.com
(W) www.short-golf-break.com

Membership: Public
Size of Complex: 40 Acres

Contact/s:
● **Professional:** Mr Ian Brown
● **Book Tee Times:** Mr Tom Brown

Course/s:
🌑 **NEWENT**
Description: Short, Drains Well, Ideal for the Elderly
Green Speed: Fast
Built: 1994 **Built On:** Sand
Number of Holes: 9 **Par:** 33
Par 3's: 3 **Par 4's:** 6
Yds: 2003
Prevailing Wind: West
Designer: Tom Brown
Further Information:
This easy walking course is open all year round and trolleys are never restricted, as the course drains so well.

NEWLANDS

NEWLANDS GOLF CLUB, Clondalkin, Dublin, **COUNTY DUBLIN**, **IRELAND**.
(T) 01 4592903

Contact/s:
● **Professional:** Mr Karl O'Donnell

Course/s:
🌑 **NEWLANDS**
Number of Holes: 18

NEWMACHAR

NEWMACHAR GOLF CLUB, Swailend, Newmachar, Aberdeen, **ABERDEEN (CITY OF)**, AB21 7UU, **SCOTLAND**.
(T) 01651 863002
(E) info@newmachargolfclub.co.uk
(W) www.newmachargolfclub.co.uk

Membership: Members & Public

Contact/s:
● **Pro Shop:** Mr Gordon Simpson
☎ 01651 863222
● **Book Tee Times:**
☎ 01651 862127

Course/s:
🌑 **HAWKSHILL**
Description: Wooded, Parkland
Built: 1990 **Built On:** Soil
Number of Holes: 18 **Par:** 72
Yds: 6623 **F9 Yds:** 3211 **B9 Yds:** 3412
Designer: Peter Alliss, David Thomas

🌑 **SWAILEND**
Built: 1990
Number of Holes: 18 **Par:** 72
Yds: 6388 **F9 Yds:** 3051 **B9 Yds:** 3337
Designer: Peter Alliss, David Thomas

NEWPORT

NEWPORT (PEMBS) GOLF CLUB, Golf Course Rd, Newport, **PEMBROKESHIRE**, SA42 0NR, **WALES**.
(T) 01239 820244
(E) newportgc@lineone.net
(W) www.newportgc.sagenet.co.uk

Membership: Members & Public
Size of Complex: 45 Acres

Contact/s:
● **Club Secretary:** Mr David Owen
● **Professional:** Mr Julian Noott

Course/s:
🌑 **NEWPORT (PEMB)**

Description: Links, Heath Land, Cliff Top, Undulating, Open, Medium Length, Drains Well, Ideal for the Elderly
Green Speed: Medium
Built: 1925 **Built On:** Sand
Number of Holes: 9 **Par:** 70
Yds: 6003 **F9 Yds:** 3030 **B9 Yds:** 2973
Prevailing Wind: South/West
Designer: James Braid
Further Information:
9 hole course can be played as an 18 hole course

NEWPORT

NEWPORT GOLF CLUB, St. Georges Lane, Newport, **ISLE OF WIGHT**, PO30 3BA, **ENGLAND**.
(T) 01983 525076
Contact/s:
• Chairman: Mr D Boon
Course/s:
🏌 **NEWPORT**
Number of Holes: 9

NEWPORT GOLF

NEWPORT GOLF CLUB, Great Oak, Rogerstone, Newport, **NEWPORT**, NP10 9FX, **WALES**.
(T) 01633 894496
Contact/s:
• Manager: Mr P Mayo
Course/s:
🏌 **NEWPORT**
Number of Holes: 18

NEWQUAY

NEWQUAY GOLF CLUB, Tower Rd, Newquay, **CORNWALL**, TR7 1LT, **ENGLAND**.
(T) 01637 872091
Contact/s:
• Club Secretary: Mr G Binney
  ☎ 01637 874354
• Professional: Mr A J Cullen
  ☎ 01637 874830
Course/s:
🏌 **NEWQUAY**
Number of Holes: 18 **Par:** 69
Par 3's: 5 **Par 4's:** 11 **Par 5's:** 2
Yds: 6136 **F9 Yds:** 2973 **B9 Yds:** 3163
Designer: Harry Shapland Colt

NEWRY

NEWRY GOLF COURSE, 11 Forkhill Rd, Newry, **COUNTY DOWN**, BT35 8LZ, **NORTHERN IRELAND**.
(T) 028 30 263871
Course/s:
🏌 **NEWRY**
Number of Holes: 18 **Par:** 72
Par 3's: 18
Yds: 6625
Designer: Michael Heaney

NEWTON ABBOT

NEWTON ABBOT (STOVER) GOLF CLUB, Bovey Rd, Liverton, Newton Abbot, **DEVON**, TQ12 6QQ, **ENGLAND**.
(T) 01626 352460
(W) www.stovergolfclub.com
Membership: Members & Public
Size of Complex: 90 Acres
Contact/s:
• Club Secretary: Mr Geoff Rees
• Professional: Mr Malcolm Craig

☎ 01626 362078
Course/s:
🏌 **NEWTON ABOT (STOVER)**
Description: Wooded, Parkland, Valley, Sheltered, Medium Length, Tight, Drains Well
Green Speed: Medium
Built: 1930 **Built On:** Clay
Number of Holes: 18 **Par:** 69
Par 3's: 5 **Par 4's:** 11 **Par 5's:** 2
Yds: 5764 **F9 Yds:** 2745 **B9 Yds:** 3019
Prevailing Wind: South

NEWTON GREEN

NEWTON GREEN GOLF CLUB, The Green, Newton, Sudbury, **SUFFOLK**, CO10 0QN, **ENGLAND**.
(T) 01787 377217
(E) thesecretary@newtongreengolfclub.fsnet.co.uk
(W) www.newtongreengolfclub.fsnet.co.uk
Membership: Members & Public
Size of Complex: 100 Acres
Contact/s:
• Club Secretary: Mr Ken Mazdon
• Professional: Mr Tim Cooper
  ☎ 01787 313215
Course/s:
🏌 **NEWTON GREEN**
Description: Parkland, Open, Medium Length, Tends to Flood, Ideal for the Elderly
Green Speed: Medium
Built: 1907 **Built On:** Soil
Number of Holes: 18 **Par:** 69
Record: 63 (Steve Wordley)
Prevailing Wind: South/West
Further Information:
The course has two distinct halves. The front nine is very open, and in contrast, the back nine is tight.

NEWTON STEWART

NEWTON STEWART GOLF CLUB, Kirroughtree Ave, Minnigaff, Newton Stewart, **DUMFRIES AND GALLOWAY**, DG8 6PF, **SCOTLAND**.
(T) 01671 402172
(E) enquiries@newtonstewartgolfclub.co.uk
(W) www.newtonstewartgolfclub.co.uk
Membership: Members & Public
Contact/s:
• Club Secretary: Mr Michael Large
• Book Tee Times: Mr J Cloy
Course/s:
🏌 **NEWTON STEWART**
Description: Parkland, Undulating, Sheltered, Medium Length, Tight, Drains Well
Green Speed: Medium
Built: 1896 **Built On:** Clay
Number of Holes: 18 **Par:** 69
Par 3's: 5 **Par 4's:** 11 **Par 5's:** 2
Yds: 5903 **F9 Yds:** 2928 **B9 Yds:** 2975
Prevailing Wind: South
Further Information:
This is a scenic parkland course between Galloway Hills and the sea, with a pond at the 10th hole.

NEWTONMORE

NEWTONMORE GOLF CLUB, Golf Course Rd, Newtonmore, **HIGHLANDS**, PH20 1AT, **SCOTLAND**.
(T) 01540 673328
Contact/s:

• Club Secretary: Mr G Spinks
• Professional: Mr R Henderson
  ☎ 01540 673611
Course/s:
🏌 **NEWTONMORE**
Description: Parkland, Open
Green Speed: Fast
Built: 1893
Number of Holes: 18

NEWTOWNSTEWART

NEWTOWNSTEWART GOLF CLUB, 38 Golf Course Rd, Newtownstewart, Omagh, **COUNTY TYRONE**, BT78 4HU, **NORTHERN IRELAND**.
(T) 028 81661466
(W) www.globalgolf.com
Membership: Members & Public
Contact/s:
• Club Secretary: Mr James Mackie
• Pro Shop: Mr Adrian Fletcher
Course/s:
🏌 **NEWTOWNSTEWART**
Description: Parkland **Built On:** Soil
Number of Holes: 18 **Par:** 70
Par 3's: 5 **Par 4's:** 10 **Par 5's:** 3
Yds: 5341 **F9 Yds:** 2612 **B9 Yds:** 2729
Designer: Frank Pennink

NIDDRY CASTLE

NIDDRY CASTLE GOLF CLUB, Castle Rd, Winchburgh, Broxburn, **LOTHIAN (WEST)**, EH52 6RQ, **SCOTLAND**.
(T) 01506 891097
Course/s:
🏌 **NIDDRY CASTLE**
Description: Parkland
Number of Holes: 9 **Par:** 70
Yds: 5202
Designer: Derek Smith

NIGG BAY

NIGG BAY GOLF CLUB, St. Fitticks Rd, Aberdeen, **ABERDEEN (CITY OF)**, AB11 9QT, **SCOTLAND**.
(T) 01224 871286
Contact/s:
• Company Secretary: Mr G Riley
Course/s:
🏌 **BALNAGASK**
Number of Holes: 18 **Par:** 70
Yds: 6065 **F9 Yds:** 2948 **B9 Yds:** 3117

NIZELS

NIZELS GOLF CLUB, Nizels Lane, Hildenborough, Tonbridge, **KENT**, TN11 8NU, **ENGLAND**.
(T) 01732 833138
(W) www.clubhaus.com
Contact/s:
• Professional: Mr Ally Mellor
Course/s:
🏌 **NIZELS**
Number of Holes: 18 **Par:** 72
Yds: 6297 **F9 Yds:** 3285 **B9 Yds:** 3012
Designer: D Donaldson, Edwards

NORFOLK

NORFOLK GOLF & COUNTRY CLUB, Hingham Rd, Reymerston, Norwich, **NORFOLK**, NR9 4CQ, **ENGLAND**.
(T) 01362 850297
Contact/s:
• Owner: Mr E Shah

Course/s:
- 🏌 REYMERSTON
  Number of Holes: 18

NORMANBY HALL

NORMANBY HALL GOLF CLUB, Pro Shop, Normanby Pk, Normanby, Scunthorpe, **LINCOLNSHIRE (NORTH),** DN15 9HU, **ENGLAND.**
(T) 01724 720226

Contact/s:
- **Employee:** Mr C Mann

Course/s:
- 🏌 NORMANBY HALL
  Number of Holes: 18
  Designer: Hawtree

NORMANTON

NORMANTON GOLF CLUB, Hatfield Hall, Aberford Rd, Stanley, Wakefield, **YORKSHIRE (WEST),** WF3 4JP, **ENGLAND.**
(T) 01924 200900

Contact/s:
- **Professional:** Mr F Houlgate

Course/s:
- 🏌 NORMANTON
  Number of Holes: 18 Par: 70
  Yds: 6191

NORTH BERWICK

NORTH BERWICK GOLF CLUB, Beach Rd, North Berwick, **LOTHIAN (EAST),** EH39 4BB, **SCOTLAND.**
(T) 01620 894766
(E) bookingoffice@nbgc.golfagent.co.uk

Membership: Members & Public

Contact/s:
- **Club Secretary:** Mr Norman Wilson
  ☎ 01620 895040
- **Professional:** Mr David Huish
  ☎ 01620 893233
- **Book Tee Times:** Ms Norma Ogg
  ☎ 01620 892135
- **Book Lessons:** Mr Martin Huish

Course/s:
- 🏌 WEST LINKS
  Description: Championship, Links, Undulating, Open, Drains Well
  Green Speed: Fast
  Built: 1832 Built On: Sand
  Number of Holes: 18
  Par 3's: 4 Par 4's: 11 Par 5's: 3
  Yds: 6420 F9 Yds: 3128 B9 Yds: 3292
  Prevailing Wind: West
  Further Information:
  A river runs through the course. 🏌

NORTH CLIFF

NORTH CLIFF GOLF CLUB LTD, Northcliff Ave, Scarborough, **YORKSHIRE (NORTH),** YO12 6PP, **ENGLAND.**
(T) 01723 360786
(W) www.ncgc.co.uk

Contact/s:
- **Professional:** Mr S N Deller

Course/s:
- 🏌 SCARBOROUGH NORTH CLIFF
  Number of Holes: 18 Par: 71
  Yds: 6425 F9 Yds: 3454 B9 Yds: 2971
  Designer: James Braid

NORTH DEVON (ROYAL)

ROYAL NORTH DEVON GOLF CLUB, Golf Links Rd, Westward Ho!, Bideford, **DEVON,**

EX39 1HD, **ENGLAND.**
(T) 01237 473817
(E) info@royalnorthdevongolfclub.co.uk
(W) www.royalnorthdevongolfclub.co.uk

Membership: Members & Public

Contact/s:
- **Club Secretary:** Mr Robert Fowler
- **Professional:** Mr Richard Herring
  ☎ 01237 477598
- **Pro Shop:** Mr John Wenham

Course/s:
- 🏌 ROYAL NORTH
  Description: Links, Open, Long, Drains Well
  Built: 1864 Built On: Sand
  Number of Holes: 18 Par: 72
  Par 3's: 4 Par 4's: 10 Par 5's: 4
  Yds: 6653 F9 Yds: 3292 B9 Yds: 3361
  Prevailing Wind: South/West
  Designer: Tom Morris
  Further Information:
  Please avoid slow play at all times. 🏌

NORTH DOWNS

NORTH DOWNS GOLF CLUB, Northdown Rd, Woldingham, Caterham, **SURREY,** CR3 7AA, **ENGLAND.**
(T) 01883 652057
(E) info@northdownsgolfclub.co.uk
(W) www.northdownsgolfclub.co.uk

Contact/s:
- **Club Secretary:** Mr David M Sinden

Course/s:
- 🏌 NORTH DOWNS
  Description: Hilltop, Short, Drains Well
  Number of Holes: 18 Par: 69
  Par 3's: 4 Par 4's: 13 Par 5's: 1
  Yds: 5843 F9 Yds: 2943 B9 Yds: 2900
  Designer: J J Frank Pennink

NORTH FORELAND

NORTH FORELAND GOLF CLUB, Convent Rd, Broadstairs, **KENT,** CT10 3PU, **ENGLAND.**
(T) 01843 861069

Membership: Members & Public

Contact/s:
- **General Manager:** Mr Brian Preston
  ☎ 01843 862140

Course/s:
- 🏌 MAIN
  Description: Championship, Links, Cliff Top, Open, Medium Length, Drains Well, Ideal for the Elderly
  Green Speed: Medium Built On: Chalk
  Number of Holes: 18 Record: 65 (Philip Walton)
  Prevailing Wind: East
  Designer: Fowler, Simpson
  Further Information:
  The North Foreland lighthouse can be seen from the course.
- 🏌 PAR 3
  Number of Holes: 18

NORTH HANTS FLEET

NORTH HANTS FLEET GOLF CLUB, The Clubhouse, Minley Rd, Fleet, **HAMPSHIRE,** GU51 1RF, **ENGLAND.**
(T) 01252 616443

Membership: Members & Public

Contact/s:
- **Club Secretary:** Mr Gordon Hogg
- **Professional:** Mr George Porter
- **Book Lessons:**

☎ 01252 616655

Course/s:
- 🏌 NORTH HANTS FLEET
  Description: Heath Land, Undulating, Sheltered, Ideal for the Elderly
  Green Speed: Medium
  Built: 1904 Built On: Sand
  Number of Holes: 18 Par: 71
  Yds: 6519 F9 Yds: 3293 B9 Yds: 3226
  Designer: James Braid

NORTH INCH MUNICIPAL

NORTH INCH GOLF (MUNICIPAL) COURSE, Perth, **PERTH AND KINROSS,** PH1 5HT, **SCOTLAND.**
(T) 01738 636481

Membership: Public

Course/s:
- 🏌 NORTH INCH
  Number of Holes: 18 Par: 68
  Yds: 5401 F9 Yds: 2960 B9 Yds: 2441
  Designer: Tom Morris

NORTH MIDDLESEX

NORTH MIDDLESEX GOLF CLUB, Manor Hse, Friern Barnet Lane, London, **LONDON (GREATER),** N20 0NL, **ENGLAND.**
(T) 020 8445 1604
(E) office@northmiddlesexgc.co.uk

Contact/s:
- **Professional:** Mr Freddy George
  ☎ 020 8445 3060

Course/s:
- 🏌 NORTH MIDDLESEX
  Number of Holes: 18 Par: 69
  Yds: 5594 F9 Yds: 2870 B9 Yds: 2724
  Designer: William Park

NORTH OXFORD

NORTH OXFORD GOLF CLUB, Banbury Rd, Oxford, **OXFORDSHIRE,** OX2 8EZ, **ENGLAND.**
(T) 01865 554415
(W) www.nogc.co.uk

Contact/s:
- **Club Secretary:**
  ☎ 01865 554924

Course/s:
- 🏌 NORTH OXFORD
  Number of Holes: 18

NORTH SHORE

NORTH SHORE GOLF CLUB, North Shore Rd, Skegness, **LINCOLNSHIRE,** PE25 1DN, **ENGLAND.**
(T) 01754 763298
(E) golf@north-shore.co.uk
(W) www.north-shore.co.uk

Contact/s:
- **Professional:** Mr John Cornelius

Course/s:
- 🏌 NORTH SHORE HOTEL &
  Description: Links, Parkland
  Built: 1910
  Number of Holes: 18 Par: 71
  Yds: 6257 F9 Yds: 3368 B9 Yds: 2889
  Designer: James Braid

NORTH WALES

NORTH WALES GOLF CLUB, 72 Bryniau Rd, West Shore, Llandudno, **CONWY,** LL30 2DZ, **WALES.**
(T) 01492 875325
(E) nwgc@northwales.uk.com

(W) www.northwales.uk.com/nwgc

Membership: Members & Public

Contact/s:
- **Club Secretary:** Mr W R Williams
- **Professional:** Mr R A Bradbury
  ☎ 01492 876878

Course/s:

🏌 **NORTH WALES**
Description: Championship, Links, Undulating, Open, Medium Length, Tight, Drains Well, Ideal for the Elderly
Green Speed: Fast
Built: 1894 **Built On:** Sand
Number of Holes: 18 **Par:** 71
Par 3's: 4 **Par 4's:** 11 **Par 5's:** 3
Yds: 6287 **F9 Yds:** 3368 **B9 Yds:** 2874

NORTH WARWICKSHIRE

NORTH WARWICKSHIRE GOLF CLUB,
Hampton Lane, Meriden, Coventry,
MIDLANDS (WEST), CV7 7LL, **ENGLAND**.
(T) 01676 522915

Contact/s:
- **Professional:** Mr Andrew Bownes
  ☎ 01676 522259

Course/s:

🏌 **NORTH WARWICKSHIRE**
Number of Holes: 9 **Par:** 72
Yds: 6274 **F9 Yds:** 3087 **B9 Yds:** 3187
Further Information:
9 hole course can be played as an 18 hole course

NORTH WEALD

NORTH WEALD GOLF CLUB, Rayley Lane, North Weald, Epping, **ESSEX**, CM16 6AR, **ENGLAND**.
(T) 01992 522418

Contact/s:
- **Manager:** Mr P H Newson

Course/s:

🏌 **NORTH WEALD**
Number of Holes: 18 **Par:** 71
Yds: 6311 **F9 Yds:** 3047 **B9 Yds:** 3264

NORTH WEALD PAR 3

NORTH WEALD PAR 3 GOLF COURSE,
Epping Rd, North Weald, Epping, **ESSEX**, CM16 6BJ, **ENGLAND**.
(T) 01992 524142

Contact/s:
- **Owner:** Mr C Baker

Course/s:

🏌 **NORTH WEALD PAR 3 COURSE**
Number of Holes: 9

NORTH WEST

NORTH WEST GOLF CLUB, Lisfannon, Fahan, Buncrana, **COUNTY DONEGAL**, **IRELAND**.
(T) 077 61027

Contact/s:
- **Professional:** Mr S McBriarty
  ☎ 077 61715

Course/s:

🏌 **NORTH WEST**
Number of Holes: 18 **Par:** 70
Yds: 6277 **F9 Yds:** 3095 **B9 Yds:** 3183

NORTH WILTS

NORTH WILTS GOLF CLUB (THE),
Bishop's Cannings, Devizes, **WILTSHIRE**, SN10 2LP, **ENGLAND**.

(T) 01380 860466

Contact/s:
- **Computing Director:** Mr John William Taylor

Course/s:

🏌 **NORTH WILTS**
Number of Holes: 18

NORTH WORCESTERSHIRE

NORTH WORCESTERSHIRE GOLF CLUB,
Frankley Beeches Rd, Northfield, Birmingham, **MIDLANDS (WEST)**, B31 5LP, **ENGLAND**.
(T) 0121 4751047

Membership: Members & Public

Contact/s:
- **Club Secretary:** Mr Dennis Wilson
- **Professional:** Mr Finlay Clark
  ☎ 0121 4755721

Course/s:

🏌 **NORTH WORCESTERSHIRE**
Description: Parkland, Undulating, Short, Tight
Green Speed: Medium
Built: 1907
Number of Holes: 18
Designer: James Braid

NORTHAMPTON

NORTHAMPTON GOLF CLUB, Harlestone, Northampton, **NORTHAMPTONSHIRE**, NN7 4EF, **ENGLAND**.
(T) 01604 845102

Membership: Members & Public
Size of Complex: 280 Acres

Contact/s:
- **Professional:** Mr K Dickens

Course/s:

🏌 **NORTHAMPTON**
Description: Parkland, Undulating, Sheltered, Open, Long, Drains Well
Green Speed: Medium
Built: 1990 **Built On:** Sand
Number of Holes: 18 **Par:** 72
Record: 67 (A Hare, J Higgins, D Eddiford)
Yds: 6615
Prevailing Wind: West
Designer: Donald Steel
Further Information:
The course offers views of Althorp Estate.

NORTHAMPTONSHIRE COUNTY

NORTHAMPTONSHIRE COUNTY GOLF CLUB, Golf Lane, Church Brampton, Northampton, **NORTHAMPTONSHIRE**, NN6 8AZ, **ENGLAND**.
(T) 01604 842170

Contact/s:
- **Club Secretary:** Mr M E Wadley
- **Professional:** Mr Tim Rouse
  ☎ 01604 842226

Course/s:

🏌 **NORTHAMPTONSHIRE COUNTY**
Description: Championship, Heath Land, Undulating, Open, Medium Length, Drains Well
Built: 1909
Number of Holes: 18 **Par:** 70
Par 3's: 4 **Par 4's:** 12 **Par 5's:** 2
Yds: 6221
Prevailing Wind: West
Designer: Harry Shapland Colt

NORTHCLIFFE

NORTHCLIFFE GOLF CLUB, High Bank

Lane, Shipley, **YORKSHIRE (WEST)**, BD18 4LJ, **ENGLAND**.
(T) 01274 596731
(E) northcliffe@bigfoot.com
(W) www.northcliffegolfclubshipley.co.uk

Membership: Members & Public

Contact/s:
- **Club Secretary:** Mr Ian Collins
- **Professional:** Mr Mick Hillas
  ☎ 01274 587193

Course/s:

🏌 **NORTHCLIFFE**
Description: Parkland, Undulating, Open, Medium Length, Drains Well
Green Speed: Medium
Built: 1921 **Built On:** Soil
Number of Holes: 18 **Par:** 71
Par 3's: 4 **Par 4's:** 11 **Par 5's:** 3
Yds: 6113 **F9 Yds:** 3130 **B9 Yds:** 2983
Designer: James Braid, Harry Vardon

NORTHENDEN

NORTHENDEN GOLF CLUB (THE), Palatine Rd, Manchester, **MANCHESTER (GREATER)**, M22 4FR, **ENGLAND**.
(T) 0161 9984738

Course/s:

🏌 **NORTHENDEN**
Number of Holes: 18
Designer: Renouf

NORTHERN

NORTHERN GOLF CLUB, 22 Golf Rd, Aberdeen, **ABERDEEN (CITY OF)**, AB24 5QB, **SCOTLAND**.
(T) 01224 622679

Membership: Members & Public

Contact/s:
- **Club Secretary:** Mr A Garner
- **Professional:** Mr B Davidson
  ☎ 01224 641577

Course/s:

🏌 **NORTHERN GOLF CLUB 18 HOLE**
Number of Holes: 18
Yds: 6304

🏌 **NORTHERN GOLF CLUB 6 HOLE**
Number of Holes: 6
Yds: 1376

NORTHOP

NORTHOP COUNTRY PARK GOLF CLUB,
Northop Country Pk, Northop, Mold, **FLINTSHIRE**, CH7 6WA, **WALES**.
(T) 01352 840440

Membership: Members & Public
Size of Complex: 250 Acres

Contact/s:
- **Professional:** Mr B Lewis
- **Book Tee Times:** Mr M Pritchard

Course/s:

🏌 **NORTHOP**
Description: Championship, Parkland
Green Speed: Fast
Built: 1994 **Built On:** Soil
Number of Holes: 18 **Par:** 72
Par 3's: 4 **Par 4's:** 10 **Par 5's:** 4
Yds: 6333 **F9 Yds:** 3257 **B9 Yds:** 3076
Designer: John Jacobs

NORTHUMBERLAND

NORTHUMBERLAND GOLF CLUB LTD (THE), High Gosforth Pk, Newcastle Upon Tyne, **TYNE AND WEAR**, NE3 5HT, **ENGLAND**.

(T) 0191 2362498

Contact/s:
- Accountant: Mr John Colin Fitzpatrick

Course/s:
- **NORTHUMBERLAND**
  Number of Holes: 18

NORTHWOOD

NORTHWOOD GOLF CLUB, Rickmansworth Rd, Northwood, **LONDON (GREATER)**, HA6 2QW, **ENGLAND**.
(T) 01923 821384
(E) secretary@northwoodgc.co.uk

Contact/s:
- Club Secretary: Mr Kevin Loosemore
- Professional: Mr Chris Holdsworth
  ☎ 01923 820112

Course/s:
- **NORTHWOOD**
  Description: Parkland, Undulating
  Built: 1891
  Number of Holes: 18 Par: 71
  Yds: 6535 F9 Yds: 3472 B9 Yds: 3063

NORTON

HARPERS GOLF AND LEISURE, Norton Golf Course, Junction Rd, Norton, Stockton-on-Tees, **CLEVELAND**, TS20 1SU, **ENGLAND**.
(T) 01642 676385

Membership: Public

Contact/s:
- Club Secretary: Mrs Diane Harper
  ☎ 01642 674636

Course/s:
- **NORTON**
  Description: Parkland, Open, Medium Length, Ideal for the Elderly
  Green Speed: Medium
  Built: 1992
  Number of Holes: 18 Par: 70
  Par 3's: 5 Par 4's: 10 Par 5's: 3
  Yds: 5855 F9 Yds: 2927 B9 Yds: 2928
  Designer: T Harper
  Further Information:
  The course has a dual layout.

NORWICH (ROYAL)

ROYAL NORWICH GOLF CLUB (THE), Drayton High Rd, Hellesdon, Norwich, **NORFOLK**, NR6 5AH, **ENGLAND**.
(T) 01603 442298
(E) mail@royalnorwichgolf.co.uk
(W) www.royalnorwichgolf.co.uk

Membership: Members & Public
Size of Complex: 134 Acres

Contact/s:
- Professional: Mr Dean Futter
  ☎ 01603 408459

Course/s:
- **ROYAL NORWICH**
  Description: Championship, Wooded, Parkland, Undulating, Medium Length, Tight, Drains Well
  Green Speed: Medium
  Built: 1893 Built On: Sand
  Number of Holes: 18 Par: 72
  Record: 65 (D Whittle)
  Par 3's: 3 Par 4's: 12 Par 5's: 3
  Yds: 6314 F9 Yds: 2999 B9 Yds: 3315
  Prevailing Wind: West
  Designer: James Braid

NORWOOD PARK

NORWOOD PARK GOLF COURSE LTD,

Norwood Hall, Southwell, **NOTTINGHAMSHIRE**, NG25 0PF, **ENGLAND**.
(T) 01636 816626
(E) norwoodgolf@mail.com
(W) www.norwoodpark.org.uk

Membership: Members & Public
Size of Complex: 130 Acres

Contact/s:
- Club Secretary: Mr Ron Beckett
- Professional: Mr Paul Thornton
- Pro Shop: Miss Sylvia Martin

Course/s:
- **NORWOOD PARK**
  Description: Wooded, Parkland, Undulating, Sheltered, Long, Drains Well, Ideal for the Elderly
  Green Speed: Medium
  Built: 1996
  Number of Holes: 9 Par: 72
  Par 3's: 2 Par 4's: 5 Par 5's: 2
  Yds: 6666 F9 Yds: 3333 B9 Yds: 3333
  Prevailing Wind: West
  Designer: Clyde B Johnston
  Further Information:
  The course is superbly laid out in the grounds of a country estate. A second 9 holes are due to open in summer 2002.

NOTLEYS

NOTLEYS GOLF CLUB (THE), The Green, White Notley, Witham, **ESSEX**, CM8 1RG, **ENGLAND**.
(T) 01376 329328

Membership: Members & Public

Contact/s:
- Owner: Mr David Bugg

Course/s:
- **NOTLEYS**
  Description: Valley
  Green Speed: Medium Built On: Soil
  Number of Holes: 18 Par: 71
  Par 3's: 5 Par 4's: 9 Par 5's: 4
  Yds: 6022
  Designer: John Day
  Further Information:
  There are views across valley.

NOTTINGHAM CITY

NOTTINGHAM CITY GOLF CLUB, Professional Shop, Lawton Drive, Nottingham, **NOTTINGHAMSHIRE**, NG6 8BL, **ENGLAND**.
(T) 0115 9278021

Contact/s:
- Manager: Mr C Jepson

Course/s:
- **NOTTINGHAM CITY**
  Number of Holes: 18
  Designer: James Braid

NOTTS

NOTTS GOLF CLUB LTD, Derby Rd, Kirkby in Ashfield, Nottingham, **NOTTINGHAMSHIRE**, NG17 7QR, **ENGLAND**.
(T) 01623 753225

Membership: Members & Public
Size of Complex: 550 Acres

Contact/s:
- Club Secretary: Mr Ian Symington
- Professional: Mr Alasdair Thomas
  ☎ 01623 753087

Course/s:
- **NOTTS**
  Description: Heath Land, Long

Green Speed: Fast
Built: 1901 Built On: Sand
Number of Holes: 20 Par: 72
Record: 64 (John Bland)
Par 3's: 3 Par 4's: 12 Par 5's: 3
Yds: 6876 F9 Yds: 3399 B9 Yds: 3477
Prevailing Wind: West
Designer: William Park
Further Information:
This is a challenging and varied course. When playing 9 holes, holes 8a and 9a steer you back towards the clubhouse and you miss out holes 8 and 9. When playing 18 holes, holes 8a and 9a are missed out, leaving 18 holes to be played.
🍸

NUNEATON

NUNEATON GOLF CLUB, Golf Drive, Nuneaton, **WARWICKSHIRE**, CV11 6QF, **ENGLAND**.
(T) 024 76347810

Contact/s:
- Professional: Mr Jonathan Salter
  ☎ 024 76340201
- Book Tee Times: Mr Jonathon Salter

Course/s:
- **NUNEATON**
  Description: Parkland, Tight
  Built: 1905
  Number of Holes: 18 Par: 71
  Further Information:
  A very testing course.

NUREMORE HOTEL

NUREMORE HOTEL & COUNTRY CLUB, Carrickmacross, **COUNTY MONAGHAN**, **IRELAND**.
(T) 042 61438 or 64016

Contact/s:
- PGA Professional: Mr Maurice Cassidy

Course/s:
- **NUREMORE HOTEL**
  Number of Holes: 18 Par: 71
  Yds: 6398 F9 Yds: 3126 B9 Yds: 3272
  Designer: Edward Hackett

OADBY

OADBY GOLF CLUB, Office, Leicester Rd, Oadby, Leicester, **LEICESTERSHIRE**, LE2 4AB, **ENGLAND**.
(T) 0116 2709052

Membership: Members & Public
Size of Complex: 120 Acres

Contact/s:
- Club Secretary: Mr Phil Goodman
- Professional: Mr Andrew Wells

Course/s:
- **OADBY**
  Description: Wooded, Parkland, Undulating, Open, Tight, Drains Well, Ideal for the Elderly
  Green Speed: Medium
  Built: 1974 Built On: Clay
  Number of Holes: 18
  Prevailing Wind: North/South

OAK HILL PARK

OAK HILL PARK GOLF COURSE, Parkside Gardens, East Barnet, Barnet, **HERTFORDSHIRE**, EN4 8JP, **ENGLAND**.
(T) 020 83683949

Course/s:
- **OAK HILL PARK**
  Number of Holes: 9

OAK LEAF

OAK LEAF GOLF COMPLEX, School Aycliffe Lane, School Aycliffe, Newton Aycliffe, **COUNTY DURHAM**, DL5 6QZ, **ENGLAND**.
(T) 01325 310820

Membership: Members & Public

Contact/s:
- **Club Secretary:** Mr Ron Mitchi
- **Professional:** Mr Andrew White

Course/s:
- **OAK LEAF**
  Description: Parkland, Undulating, Open, Medium Length, Tight, Tends to Flood, Ideal for the Elderly
  Green Speed: Medium
  Built: 1976 **Built On:** Clay
  Number of Holes: 18 **Par:** 70
  Par 3's: 3 **Par 4's:** 12 **Par 5's:** 2
  Yds: 5818 **F9 Yds:** 3225 **B9 Yds:** 2593

OAK MEADOW

OAK MEADOW GOLF CLUB, New Rd, Starcross, Exeter, **DEVON**, EX6 8QG, **ENGLAND**.
(T) 01626 891918

Contact/s:
- **Manager:** Mr R Williams

Course/s:
- **STARCROSS**
  Number of Holes: 9

OAK PARK GOLF CLUB

AMERICAN GOLF CORPORATION, Heath Lane, Crondall, Farnham, **SURREY**, GU10 5PB, **ENGLAND**.
(T) 01252 850850
(E) oakpark@americangolf.co.uk
(W) www.americangolf.com

Membership: Members & Public

Contact/s:
- **Professional:** Mr G Murton

Course/s:
- **VILLAGE**
  Description: Wooded, Parkland, Open
  Number of Holes: 9 **Par:** 36
  Par 3's: 1 **Par 4's:** 7 **Par 5's:** 1
  Yds: 3279
  Designer: P Dawson
  Further Information:
  The Village is a flat course.

- **WOODLAND**
  Description: Wooded, Parkland, Undulating, Sheltered, Medium Length, Tight, Drains Well
  Green Speed: Medium
  Built: 1983 **Built On:** Chalk/Sand
  Number of Holes: 18 **Par:** 70
  Par 3's: 4 **Par 4's:** 12 **Par 5's:** 2
  Yds: 6352 **F9 Yds:** 3051 **B9 Yds:** 3301
  Designer: P Dawson
  Further Information:
  There are many mature trees on the fairways.

OAKDALE

OAKDALE GOLF COURSE, Llwynon Lane, Oakdale, Blackwood, **CAERPHILLY**, NP12 0NF, **WALES**.
(T) 01495 220044

Membership: Members & Public
Size of Complex: 32 Acres

Contact/s:
- **Club Secretary:** Mr S Lewis-Jones

- **Pro Shop:** Mr Patrick Lewis-Jones
- **Book Lessons:** Mr Paul Glyn

Course/s:
- **OAKDALE**
  Description: Parkland, Undulating, Sheltered, Medium Length, Drains Well, Ideal for the Elderly
  Green Speed: Fast
  Built: 1990 **Built On:** Sand
  Number of Holes: 9 **Par:** 28
  Yds: 1508
  Prevailing Wind: South/East
  Designer: Ian Goodenough
  Further Information:
  Lovely scenery and excellent greens.

OAKDALE

OAKDALE GOLF CLUB, Oakdale, Harrogate, **YORKSHIRE (NORTH)**, HG1 2LN, **ENGLAND**.
(T) 01423 502806

Contact/s:
- **Manager:** Mr D Rodgers

Course/s:
- **OAKDALE**
  Number of Holes: 18
  Designer: Alistair MacKenzie

OAKE MANOR

OAKE MANOR GOLF CLUB, Oake, Taunton, **SOMERSET**, TA4 1BA, **ENGLAND**.
(T) 01823 461993
(E) golf@oakemanor.com
(W) www.oakemanor.com

Contact/s:
- **Professional:** Mr Russell Gardner

Course/s:
- **OAKE MANOR**
  Built: 1993
  Number of Holes: 18 **Par:** 70
  Yds: 6109 **F9 Yds:** 3128 **B9 Yds:** 2981
  Designer: Adrian Stiff
  Further Information:
  Challenging course for all standards.
  Views of Quantock and Blackdown hills.

OAKLAND PARK

OAKLAND PARK GOLF CLUB, Three Households, Chalfont St. Giles, **BUCKINGHAMSHIRE**, HP8 4LW, **ENGLAND**.
(T) 01494 871277

Membership: Members & Public
Size of Complex: 65 Acres

Contact/s:
- **Professional:** Mr Alistair Thatcher
- **Pro Shop:** Ms Susan Balmforth

Course/s:
- **OAKLAND PARK**
  Description: Parkland, Undulating, Short, Ideal for the Elderly
  Number of Holes: 18 **Par:** 67
  Yds: 5246 **F9 Yds:** 2445 **B9 Yds:** 2501
  Designer: Jonathan Gaunt

OAKMERE PARK

OAKMERE PARK GOLF COURSE, Oaks Lane, Oxton, Southwell, **NOTTINGHAMSHIRE**, NG25 0RH, **ENGLAND**.
(T) 01159 653545
(E) enquiries@oakmerepark.co.uk
(W) www.oakmerepark.co.uk

Membership: Members & Public

Contact/s:

- **Professional:** Mr D St John-Jones
- **Book Tee Times:** Miss B Hurt

Course/s:
- **OAKMERE PARK**
  Description: Parkland, Undulating, Open, Drains Well **Green Speed:** Fast
  Built: 1975 **Built On:** Sand
  Number of Holes: 18 **Par:** 72
  Par 3's: 4 **Par 4's:** 10 **Par 5's:** 4
  Yds: 6612 **F9 Yds:** 3499 **B9 Yds:** 3113
  Designer: Frank Pennink

OAKRIDGE

OAKRIDGE GOLF CLUB, Arley Lane, Ansley, Nuneaton, **WARWICKSHIRE**, CV10 9PH, **ENGLAND**.
(T) 01676 540542

Course/s:
- **OAKRIDGE**
  Number of Holes: 18
  Designer: Algy Jayes

OAKS

OAKS GOLF CLUB (THE), Aughton Common, Aughton, York, **YORKSHIRE (NORTH)**, YO42 4PW, **ENGLAND**.
(T) 01757 288577
(E) oaksgolfclub@hotmail.com
(W) www.theoaksgolfclub.co.uk

Membership: The Oaks

Contact/s:
- **Professional:** Mr Joe Townhill
  ☎ 01757 288007
- **Pro Shop:** Mr Stuart Robson

Course/s:
- **MEDIUM/FAST Built On:** 18
  Number of Holes: 1996 **Par:** Julian Covey

OAKS SPORTS CTRE

OAKS SPORTS CENTRE, Woodmansterne Rd, Carshalton, **SURREY**, SM5 4AN, **ENGLAND**.
(T) 020 86483363
(E) golf@oaks.sagehost.co.uk
(W) www.oakssportscentre.co.uk

Contact/s:
- **Company Secretary:** Mr D J Capper

Course/s:
- **OAKS 18 HOLE**
  Number of Holes: 18 **Par:** 70
  Par 3's: 5 **Par 4's:** 10 **Par 5's:** 3
  Yds: 6033 **F9 Yds:** 2910 **B9 Yds:** 3123

- **OAKS 9 HOLE**
  Number of Holes: 9 **Par:** 28
  Par 3's: 8 **Par 4's:** 1
  Yds: 1443

OAKSEY

OAKSEY PARK GOLF & LEISURE, Lowfield Farm, Oaksey, Malmesbury, **WILTSHIRE**, SN16 9SB, **ENGLAND**.
(T) 01666 577995

Membership: Members & Public

Contact/s:
- **Professional:** Mr D Karroll

Course/s:
- **OAKSEY**
  Description: Parkland
  Number of Holes: 9
  Designer: Chapman, Warren
  Further Information:
  Located on the west side of the Cotswold Water Parks.

OAST GOLF CTRE

OAST GOLF CENTRE LTD (THE), Church Rd, Tonge, Sittingbourne, **KENT**, ME9 9AR, **ENGLAND**.
(T) 01795 473527

Course/s:

🏌 **THE OAST GOLF CENTRE**
Number of Holes: 9
Designer: D Chambers

OAST PARK

OAST PARK GOLF CLUB, Sandy Lane, Snodland, **KENT**, ME6 5LG, **ENGLAND**.
(T) 01634 242661

Contact/s:
● Owner: Mr M Stone

Course/s:

🏌 **OASTPARK**
Number of Holes: 18
Designer: J D Banks

OGBOURNE DOWNS

OGBOURNE DOWNS GOLF CLUB, Ogbourne St. George, Marlborough, **WILTSHIRE**, SN8 1TB, **ENGLAND**.
(T) 01672 841217

Contact/s:
● Administration: Miss M Green
☎ 01672 841327

Course/s:

🏌 **OGBOURNE DOWNS**
Description: Downland, Undulating, Drains Well
Built: 1907 Built On: Chalk
Number of Holes: 18 Par: 71
Yds: 6175 F9 Yds: 2944 B9 Yds: 3231
Designer: Taylor
Further Information:
A challenging course.

OKEHAMPTON

OKEHAMPTON GOLF CLUB, Tors Rd, Okehampton, **DEVON**, EX20 1EF, **ENGLAND**.
(T) 01837 52113
(E) okehamptongc@btconnect.com
(W) www.okehamptongc.co.uk

Membership: Members & Public
Size of Complex: 72 Acres

Contact/s:
● Professional: Mr Simon Jefferies

Course/s:

🏌 **OKEHAMPTON**
Description: Moorland, Valley, Sheltered, Short, Tight, Drains Well
Green Speed: Fast
Built: 1913 Built On: Soil
Number of Holes: 18 Par: 68
Record: 68 (Simon Jefferies)
Par 3's: 5 Par 4's: 12 Par 5's: 1
Yds: 5281 F9 Yds: 2627 B9 Yds: 2654
Prevailing Wind: West
Designer: Taylor

OLD COLWYN

OLD COLWYN GOLF CLUB, Woodland Ave, Old Colwyn, Colwyn Bay, **CONWY**, LL29 9NL, **WALES**.
(T) 01492 515581

Course/s:

🏌 **OLD COLWYN**
Description: Undulating
Built: 1907
Number of Holes: 9 Par: 68
Designer: James Braid

Further Information:
Meadowland course which can be played as an 18 hole course

OLD CONNA

OLD CONNA GOLF CLUB, Ferndale Rd, Bray, **COUNTY WICKLOW**, **IRELAND**.
(T) 01 2826055

Course/s:

🏌 **OLD CONNA**
Number of Holes: 18
Designer: Edward Hackett

OLD FOLD MANOR

OLD FOLD MANOR GOLF CLUB, Old Fold Lane, Barnet, **HERTFORDSHIRE**, EN5 4QN, **ENGLAND**.
(T) 020 8449 1650
(W) www.oldfoldmanor.co.uk

Membership: Members & Public

Contact/s:
● Professional: Mr Peter McEvoy
☎ 020 8440 7488

Course/s:

🏌 **OLD FOLD MANOR**
Description: Heath Land, Medium Length, Drains Well
Green Speed: Fast Built On: Clay
Number of Holes: 18 Par: 71
Yds: 6447 F9 Yds: 3218 B9 Yds: 3229
Prevailing Wind: North

OLD HEAD GOLF LINKS

OLD HEAD GOLF LINKS, Kinsale, **COUNTY CORK**, **IRELAND**.
(T) 021 4778444
(E) info@oldheadgolf.ie
(W) www.oldheadgolflinks.com

Membership: Members Only

Contact/s:
● President: Mr John O'Connor

Course/s:

🏌 **CHAMPIONSHIP**
Number of Holes: 18 Par: 72
Yds: 7300

OLD LINKS

OLD LINKS GOLF CLUB (BOLTON) LTD, Chorley Old Rd, Bolton, **LANCASHIRE**, BL1 5SU, **ENGLAND**.
(T) 01204 843089

Contact/s:
● Pro Shop: Mr P Horridge
☎ 01204 846571

Course/s:

🏌 **OLD LINKS (BOLTON)**
Number of Holes: 18
Designer: Alistair MacKenzie

OLD NENE

OLD NENE GOLF & COUNTRY CLUB, Muchwood Lane, Bodsey, Ramsey, **CAMBRIDGESHIRE**, PE17 1XQ, **ENGLAND**.
(T) 01487 815622

Contact/s:
● Company Secretary: Mrs P B Cade

Course/s:

🏌 **OLD NENE**
Built: 1992
Number of Holes: 9 Par: 70
Designer: R Edrich
Further Information:
The course has won an Eastern Region

Environmental Award. A 9 hole course that can be played as an 18 hole course

OLD PADESWOOD

OLD PADESWOOD GOLF CLUB LTD, Station Lane, Padeswood, Mold, **FLINTSHIRE**, CH7 4JD, **WALES**.
(T) 01244 547701

Membership: Members & Public

Contact/s:
● Club Secretary: Mr Brian Slater
● Professional: Mr Tony Davies

Course/s:

🏌 **OLD PADESWOOD**
Description: Championship, Wooded, Hilltop, Valley, Long, Drains Well, Tends to Flood, Ideal for the Elderly
Green Speed: Medium
Built: 1933 Built On: Clay/Sand
Number of Holes: 18 Par: 72
Par 3's: 4 Par 4's: 10 Par 5's: 4
Yds: 6190 F9 Yds: 3107 B9 Yds: 3083
Prevailing Wind: West

OLD RECTORY

OLD RECTORY GOLF CLUB, Llangattock, Crickhowell, **POWYS**, NP8 1PH, **WALES**.
(T) 01873 810373

Course/s:

🏌 **OLD RECTORY**
Number of Holes: 9

OLD THORNS

OLD THORNS HOTEL, GOLF & COUNTRY CLUB, Griggs Green, Liphook, **HAMPSHIRE**, GU30 7PE, **ENGLAND**.
(T) 01428 724555
(E) info@oldthorns.com
(W) www.oldthorns.com

Membership: Members & Public
Size of Complex: 400 Acres

Contact/s:
● Professional: Mr Kieron Stevenson Henry
☎ 01428 722183
● Book Tee Times: Mr Kieron Stevenson

Course/s:

🏌 **OLD THORNS**
Description: Championship, Parkland, Heath Land, Undulating, Medium Length, Tends to Flood
Green Speed: Medium
Built: 1982 Built On: Sand/Soil
Number of Holes: 18 Par: 72
Record: 69 (Isao Aoki)
Par 3's: 4 Par 4's: 10 Par 5's: 4
Yds: 6130 F9 Yds: 2996
Designer: Commander J Harris, Peter Alliss
Further Information:
A challenge to golfers of all standards.

OLDFIELD

OLDFIELD GOLF COURSE, Kilmashogue Lane, Dublin 16, Dublin, **COUNTY DUBLIN**, **IRELAND**.
(T) 01 4937475

Course/s:

🏌 **OLDFIELD GOLF COURSE**
Number of Holes: 9 Par: 64
Yds: 4958 F9 Yds: 2479 B9 Yds: 2479
Further Information:
Can be played as an 18 hole course

OLDHAM

OLDHAM GOLF CLUB, Lees New Rd, Oldham, **MANCHESTER (GREATER)**, OL4 5PN, **ENGLAND**.
(T) 0161 6244986

Membership: Members & Public

Contact/s:
- **Club Secretary:** Mr John Brookes
- **Professional:** Mr Chris Atkinson
- **Pro Shop:**
  ☎ 0161 6268346

Course/s:
- **OLDHAM**
  Description: Wooded, Moorland, Hilltop, Open, Short, Drains Well
  Green Speed: Medium
  Built: 1892 **Built On:** Clay
  Number of Holes: 18 **Par:** 66
  Prevailing Wind: West

OLDMELDRUM

OLDMELDRUM GOLF CLUB, Kirk Brae, Oldmeldrum, **ABERDEENSHIRE**, AB51 0DJ, **SCOTLAND**.
(T) 01467 873555

Membership: Members & Public

Contact/s:
- **Club Secretary:** Mr John Page
  ☎ 01651 872648
- **Professional:** Mr Hamish Love
  ☎ 01651 873555

Course/s:
- **OLDMELDRUM**
  Description: Parkland, Open, Medium Length, Drains Well, Ideal for the Elderly
  Green Speed: Medium
  Built: 1885 **Built On:** Soil
  Number of Holes: 18 **Par:** 70
  Par 3's: 4 **Par 4's:** 12 **Par 5's:** 2
  Yds: 5988 **F9 Yds:** 3082 **B9 Yds:** 2906
  Further Information:
  The course was extended to 18 holes between 1987 - 1989. The course requires accuracy of the tee and a good short game on the approach to the small and tricky greens.

OLTON

OLTON GOLF CLUB LTD, Mirfield Rd, Solihull, **MIDLANDS (WEST)**, B91 1JH, **ENGLAND**.
(T) 0121 7051083

Contact/s:
- **Manager:** Mr M Firman

Course/s:
- **OLTON**
  Number of Holes: 18
  Designer: Taylor

OMAGH

OMAGH GOLF CLUB, 83 Dublin Rd, Omagh, **COUNTY TYRONE**, BT78 1HQ, **NORTHERN IRELAND**.
(T) 028 82243160

Contact/s:
- **Club Secretary:** Mrs Florence Caldwell

Course/s:
- **OMAGH**
  Description: Parkland, Undulating, Open, Medium Length, Drains Well
  Green Speed: Medium
  Built: 1910 **Built On:** Soil
  Number of Holes: 18 **Par:** 71
  Yds: 5866 **F9 Yds:** 3284 **B9 Yds:** 2582

OMBERSLEY

OMBERSLEY GOLF CLUB, Bishops Wood Rd, Lineholt, Ombersley, Droitwich, **WORCESTERSHIRE**, WR9 0LE, **ENGLAND**.
(T) 01905 620747

Course/s:
- **OMBERSLEY**
  Number of Holes: 18
  Designer: David Morgan

ONNELEY

ONNELEY GOLF CLUB, Bar Hill Rd, Onneley, Crewe, **CHESHIRE**, CW3 9QF, **ENGLAND**.
(T) 01782 750577

Contact/s:
- **Club Secretary:** Mr P Ball
  ☎ 01782 846759

Course/s:
- **ONNELEY**
  Description: Parkland
  Number of Holes: 18 **Par:** 71
  Par 3's: 3 **Par 4's:** 13 **Par 5's:** 2
  Yds: 5781 **F9 Yds:** 2724 **B9 Yds:** 3057

OPEN

OPEN GOLF CENTRE, Newtown House, St Margarets, **COUNTY DUBLIN**, **IRELAND**.
(T) 01 8640324
(E) opengolf@iol.ie

Membership: Members & Public/Public
Size of Complex: 200 Acres

Contact/s:
- **Professional:** Ms Sue Bamford

Course/s:
- **BLUE NINE**
  Description: Parkland, Valley, Open, Medium Length, Tight, Drains Well, Ideal for the Elderly
  Green Speed: Fast
  Built: 1994 **Built On:** Soil
  Number of Holes: 9 **Par:** 31
  Par 3's: 5 **Par 4's:** 4
  Yds: 2579

- **RED NINE**
  Description: Parkland, Medium Length
  Green Speed: Medium/Fast
  Built On: Clay
  Number of Holes: 9 **Par:** 35
  Par 3's: 2 **Par 4's:** 5 **Par 5's:** 2
  Yds: 3612
  Designer: Hawtree
  Further Information:
  Challenging course with well protected greens. Can be played as an 18 hole course, by combining the Red and Yellow courses.

- **YELLOW NINE**
  Number of Holes: 9 **Par:** 36
  Par 3's: 2 **Par 4's:** 5 **Par 5's:** 2
  Yds: 3510
  Designer: R Yates

ORCHARD

ORCHARD GOLF COURSE, Yew Tree Farm, Main Rd, Huntley, Gloucester, **GLOUCESTERSHIRE**, GL19 3EA, **ENGLAND**.
(T) 01452 830005

Membership: Members & Public

Contact/s:
- **Club Secretary:** Mr A Akerman
- **Professional:** Mr A Cameron

Course/s:
- **ORCHARD**
  Description: Wooded, Undulating, Open, Short, Drains Well
  Green Speed: Fast
  Built: 1995 **Built On:** Soil
  Number of Holes: 9
  Further Information:
  The course has been built in an orchard.

ORCHARDLEIGH

ORCHARDLEIGH GOLF CLUB, Orchardleigh, Frome, **BATH & SOMERSET (NORTH EAST)**, BA11 2PH, **ENGLAND**.
(T) 01373 454206

Contact/s:
- **Manager:** Mr T Atkinson

Course/s:
- **ORCHARDLEIGH**
  Description: Parkland
  Built: 1996
  Number of Holes: 18 **Par:** 72
  Designer: Brian Huggett
  Further Information:
  There are water features on seven holes.

ORKNEY

ORKNEY GOLF CLUB, Grainbank, St. Ola, Kirkwall, **ORKNEY ISLES**, KW15 1RD, **SCOTLAND**.
(T) 01856 872457

Course/s:
- **ORKNEY**
  Number of Holes: 18

ORMEAU

ORMEAU GOLF CLUB, 50 Park Rd, Belfast, **COUNTY ANTRIM**, BT7 2FX, **NORTHERN IRELAND**.
(T) 028 90640999
(E) ormeaugolfclub@utvinternet.com
(W) www.ormeaugolfclub.co.uk

Membership: Members & Public
Size of Complex: 2688 Acres

Contact/s:
- **Pro Shop:** Mr Bertie Willson
- **Book Lessons:** Mr Bertie Wilson

Course/s:
- **ORMEAU**
  Description: Parkland, Sheltered, Drains Well, Ideal for the Elderly
  Built: 1893
  Number of Holes: 9 **Par:** 68
  Par 3's: 3 **Par 4's:** 5 **Par 5's:** 1
  Yds: 5376 **F9 Yds:** 2688 **B9 Yds:** 2688
  Prevailing Wind: North
  Further Information:
  9 hole course can be played as an 18 hole course

ORMONDE FIELDS

ORMONDE FIELDS GOLF CLUB, Ormonde Fields House, Nottingham Rd, Codnor, Ripley, **DERBYSHIRE**, DE5 9RG, **ENGLAND**.
(T) 01773 570043

Membership: Members & Public

Contact/s:
- **Club Secretary:** Mr Keith Constable

Course/s:
- **ORMONDE**
  Description: Parkland, Undulating, Sheltered, Medium Length
  Green Speed: Medium
  Built: 1930 **Built On:** Clay
  Number of Holes: 18 **Par:** 72
  Par 3's: 4 **Par 4's:** 10 **Par 5's:** 4
  Yds: 6504 **F9 Yds:** 3358 **B9 Yds:** 3146

Designer: John Fearn
Further Information:
Views of Codnor Castle.

ORMSKIRK

ORMSKIRK GOLF CLUB, Secretary, Cranes Lane, Lathom, Ormskirk, **LANCASHIRE**, L40 5UJ, **ENGLAND**.
(T) 01695 572781

Course/s:
🏌 **ORMSKIRK**
Number of Holes: 18

ORSETT

ORSETT GOLF CLUB LTD, Brentwood Rd, Orsett, Grays, **ESSEX**, RM16 3DS, **ENGLAND**.
(T) 01375 891352

Membership: Members & Public

Contact/s:
● **Professional:** Mr Paul Joiner

Course/s:
🏌 **ORSETT**
Description: Championship, Heath Land, Undulating, Open, Drains Well
Green Speed: Medium
Built: 1899 **Built On:** Sand
Number of Holes: 18 **Par:** 72
Par 3's: 4 **Par 4's:** 10 **Par 5's:** 4
Yds: 6090 **F9 Yds:** 3126 **B9 Yds:** 2964
Designer: James Braid
Further Information:
Challenging game.

ORTON MEADOWS

ORTON MEADOWS GOLF COURSE, Harn Lane, Orton Waterville, Peterborough, **CAMBRIDGESHIRE**, PE2 5UU, **ENGLAND**.
(T) 01733 237478
(W) www.ortonmeadowsgolfcourse.co.uk

Membership: Members & Public

Contact/s:
● **Professional:** Mr Jason Mitchell

Course/s:
🏌 **ORTON MEADOWS**
Description: Parkland, Medium Length, Tight, Drains Well, Ideal for the Elderly
Green Speed: Medium
Built: 1982
Number of Holes: 18 **Par:** 67
Record: 64 (Jason Mitchell)
Par 3's: 7 **Par 4's:** 9 **Par 5's:** 2
Yds: 5613 **F9 Yds:** 3300 **B9 Yds:** 2313
Designer: Fitton
Further Information:
Ther is an abundance of wild fowl on the lakes.

OSBORNE

OSBORNE GOLF CLUB, Osborne House Estate, East Cowes, **ISLE OF WIGHT**, PO32 6JX, **ENGLAND**.
(T) 01983 295421

Contact/s:
● **Club Secretary:** Mr R Jones

Course/s:
🏌 **OSBORNE**
Number of Holes: 9

OSIERS FARM

OSIERS FARM GOLF COURSE, London Rd, Petworth, **SUSSEX (WEST)**, GU28 9LX, **ENGLAND**.
(T) 01798 344097

Contact/s:
● **Owner:** Mr Timothy Duncton

Course/s:
🏌 **OSIERS FARM**
Number of Holes: 18
Yds: 6191

OSWESTRY

OSWESTRY GOLF CLUB, Queens Head, Oswestry, **SHROPSHIRE**, SY11 4ED, **ENGLAND**.
(T) 01691 610221

Membership: Members & Public

Contact/s:
● **Club Secretary:** Mr Arther Jennings
● **Professional:** Mr David Skelton
● **Book Tee Times:**
 ☎ 01691 610448

Course/s:
🏌 **OSWESTRY**
Description: Parkland, Undulating, Open, Drains Well, Ideal for the Elderly
Green Speed: Medium
Built: 1933 **Built On:** Sand
Number of Holes: 18 **Par:** 70
Par 3's: 4 **Par 4's:** 12 **Par 5's:** 2
Yds: 6024 **F9 Yds:** 3113 **B9 Yds:** 2911
Designer: James Braid

OTLEY

OTLEY GOLF CLUB, West Busk Lane, Otley, **YORKSHIRE (WEST)**, LS21 3NG, **ENGLAND**.
(T) 01943 465329
(E) office@otley-golfclub.co.uk
(W) www.otleygc.fsnet.co.uk

Membership: Members & Public
Size of Complex: 130 Acres

Contact/s:
● **Club Secretary:** Mr Peter Clarke
● **Professional:** Mr Andy Ingram
● **Pro Shop:** Mr Steven Tomkinson
● **Book Lessons:**
 ☎ 01943 465329 ext 203

Course/s:
🏌 **OTLEY**
Description: Parkland
Green Speed: Fast
Built: 1906 **Built On:** Soil
Number of Holes: 18 **Par:** 70
Par 3's: 4 **Par 4's:** 12 **Par 5's:** 2
Yds: 6225 **F9 Yds:** 3360 **B9 Yds:** 2865
Prevailing Wind: West
Further Information:
The course is always in superb condition and is a test of golfing skill, not stamina.

OTTER VALLEY GOLF CTRE

OTTER VALLEY GOLF CENTRE, Upottery, Honiton, **DEVON**, EX14 9QP, **ENGLAND**.
(T) 01404 861266
(W) www.otter-golf.co.uk

Membership: Members & Public

Contact/s:
● **Club Secretary:** Mr Michael Arscott
● **Professional:** Mr Andrew Thomson

Course/s:
🏌 **OTTER VALLEY**
Description: Parkland, Valley, Undulating, Short, Drains Well
Green Speed: Medium
Built: 1997
Number of Holes: 9
Designer: Andrew Thompson

OTTERBOURNE

OTTERBOURNE GOLF COURSE, Poles Lane, Otterbourne, Winchester, **HAMPSHIRE**, SO21 2DZ, **ENGLAND**.
(T) 01962 775225

Membership: Public

Contact/s:
● **Book Tee Times:** Mr Gary Buck

Course/s:
🏌 **OTTERBOURNE**
Description: Parkland, Open, Short, Ideal for the Elderly
Green Speed: Medium **Built On:** Soil
Number of Holes: 9

OTWAY

OTWAY GOLF CLUB, Macamisa, Saltpans, Rathmullan, **COUNTY DONEGAL**, **IRELAND**.
(T) 074 58319

Contact/s:
● **Club Secretary:** H Gallagher

Course/s:
🏌 **OTWAY**
Number of Holes: 9
Yds: 4234

OUGHTERARD

OUGHTERARD GOLF CLUB, Gurthreeva, Oughterard, **COUNTY GALWAY**, **IRELAND**.
(T) 091 552131

Course/s:
🏌 **OUGHTERARD**
Number of Holes: 18

OULTON PARK

OULTON PARK GOLF COURSE, Rothwell Lane, Oulton, Leeds, **YORKSHIRE (WEST)**, LS26 8EX, **ENGLAND**.
(T) 0113 2823152

Membership: Members & Public/Public

Contact/s:
● **Club Secretary:** Mr Alan Cooper
● **Professional:** Mr Steven Gromit

Course/s:
🏌 **MAIN**
Description: Wooded, Parkland, Undulating, Sheltered, Open, Long, Tight, Tends to Flood
Green Speed: Medium
Built: 1991 **Built On:** Clay
Number of Holes: 9
Prevailing Wind: South/East
Designer: Peter Alliss

🏌 **SHORT**
Number of Holes: 9
Designer: Peter Alliss

OUNDLE

OUNDLE GOLF CLUB, Benefield Rd, Oundle, Peterborough, **CAMBRIDGESHIRE**, PE8 4EZ, **ENGLAND**.
(T) 01832 272273
(E) office@oundlegolfclub.fsnet.co.uk

Membership: Members & Public
Size of Complex: 98 Acres

Contact/s:
● **Club Secretary:** Mrs Joan Markall
● **Professional:** Mr Richard Keys

Course/s:
🏌 **OUNDLE**
Description: Parkland, Undulating,

Sheltered, Medium Length, Drains Well
Green Speed: Medium
Built: 1893   **Built On:** Clay
Number of Holes: 18   **Par:** 72
Par 3's: 3   **Par 4's:** 12   **Par 5's:** 3
Yds: 6235   **F9 Yds:** 3311   **B9 Yds:** 2924
Further Information:
Views of the village of Oundle.

OUSE VALLEY

OUSE VALLEY GOLF CLUB, Bromham Rd,
Biddenham, Bedford, **BEDFORDSHIRE**,
MK40 4AF, **ENGLAND**.
(T) 01234 261669
(W) www.kolvengolf.com

Membership: Members & Public
Size of Complex: 110 Acres

Contact/s:
●   Club Secretary: Mr M Rizzi

Course/s:
●   **OUSE VALLEY GOLF COURSE**
    Number of Holes: 18   **Par:** 72
    Yds: 6305

OUTLANE

OUTLANE GOLF CLUB LTD, Slack Lane,
New Hey Rd, Huddersfield, **YORKSHIRE
(WEST)**, HD3 3YL, **ENGLAND**.
(T) 01422 374762
(W) www.outlanegolfclub.co.uk

Membership: Members & Public

Contact/s:
●   Club Secretary: Mr Peter Brennan
●   Professional: Mr David Chapman

Course/s:
●   **OUTLANE**
    Description: Moorland, Undulating,
    Open, Medium Length
    Green Speed: Medium **Built On:** Clay
    Number of Holes: 18   **Record:** 66
    (James Barrow)
    Prevailing Wind: East

OVERSTONE PARK

OVERSTONE PARK LTD, Overstone Pk,
Billing Lane, Overstone, Northampton,
NORTHAMPTONSHIRE, NN6 0AP,
ENGLAND.
(T) 01604 643555

Contact/s:
●   Manager: Mr Alan McLundie

Course/s:
●   **OVERSTONE PARK**
    Number of Holes: 18

OWMBY

OWMBY GOLF CLUB, Owmby Cliff Rd,
Owmby-by-Spital, Market Rasen,
LINCOLNSHIRE, LN8 2AB, **ENGLAND**.
(T) 01673 878420

Membership: Members & Public

Contact/s:
●   Club Secretary: Mr J Buttery
    ☎ 01522 754270
●   Professional: Mr Graham Taylor
    ☎ 01673 844233

Course/s:
●   **OWMBY**
    Description: Parkland, Undulating,
    Sheltered, Long, Drains Well, Ideal for the
    Elderly
    Green Speed: Medium
    Built: 1995
    Number of Holes: 9
    Designer: Bud Edmonson

OWSTON PARK

OWSTON PARK GOLF COURSE & SHOP,
Owston Lane, Carcroft, Doncaster,
YORKSHIRE (SOUTH), DN6 8EF,
ENGLAND.
(T) 01302 330821

Contact/s:
●   Owner: Mr Mike Parker

Course/s:
●   **OWSTON PARK**
    Number of Holes: 9   **Par:** 35
    Yds: 2866   **F9 Yds:** 2866
    Designer: M Parker

OXFORDSHIRE

OXFORDSHIRE GOLF CLUB (THE), Rycote
Lane, Thame, **OXFORDSHIRE**, OX9 2PU,
ENGLAND.
(T) 01844 278505

Contact/s:
●   Operations Manager: Mr Richard Moan

Course/s:
●   **THE OXFORDSHIRE**
    Number of Holes: 18   **Par:** 72
    Yds: 7187   **F9 Yds:** 3514   **B9 Yds:** 3673
    Designer: Rees Jones

OXHEY PARK

OXHEY PARK GOLF CLUB, Prestwick Rd,
Watford, **HERTFORDSHIRE**, WD1 6DX,
ENGLAND.
(T) 01923 248213

Membership: Members & Public

Contact/s:
●   Professional: Mr James Wright

Course/s:
●   **OXHEY PARK**
    Description: Wooded, Undulating,
    Sheltered, Short, Drains Well, Ideal for the
    Elderly
    Green Speed: Medium
    Built: 1990   **Built On:** Clay
    Number of Holes: 9
    Designer: K Slight

OXLEY PARK

OXLEY PARK GOLF CLUB LTD, Stafford Rd,
Wolverhampton, **MIDLANDS (WEST)**, WV10
6DE, **ENGLAND**.
(T) 01902 425892

Contact/s:
●   Club Secretary: Mrs K Mann

Course/s:
●   **OXLEY PARK**
    Number of Holes: 18   **Par:** 71
    Yds: 6226   **F9 Yds:** 3185   **B9 Yds:** 3041
    Designer: Harry Shapland Colt

PACHESHAM PARK GOLF CTRE

PACHESHAM PARK GOLF CENTRE,
Oaklawn Rd, Leatherhead, **SURREY**, KT22
0BT, **ENGLAND**.
(T) 01372 843453
(E) pacheshamm2m@fs.net

Contact/s:
●   Owner: Mr P Taylor

Course/s:
●   **PACHESHAM PARK GOLF CTRE**
    Number of Holes: 9   **Par:** 70
    Par 3's: 2   **Par 4's:** 6   **Par 5's:** 1
    Yds: 5608   **F9 Yds:** 2804   **B9 Yds:** 2804
    Designer: Taylor

Further Information:
9 hole course can be played as an 18 hole
course

PADBROOK PARK

**PADBROOK PARK GOLF & COUNTRY
CLUB,** Padbrook Pk, Cullompton, **DEVON**,
EX15 1RU, **ENGLAND**.
(T) 01884 38286

Contact/s:
●   Professional: Mr Stewart Adwick

Course/s:
●   **PADBROOK PARK**
    Description: Wooded, Parkland, Drains
    Well
    Built: 1992
    Number of Holes: 9   **Par:** 70
    Designer: Robert Sandow
    Further Information:
    9 hole course can be played as an 18 hole
    course

PADESWOOD & BUCKLEY

PADESWOOD & BUCKLEY GOLF CLUB,
The Caia, Station Lane, Padeswood, Mold,
FLINTSHIRE, CH7 4JD, **WALES**.
(T) 01244 550537

Membership: Members & Public
Size of Complex: 95 Acres

Contact/s:
●   Club Secretary: Mr Malcom Conway
●   Professional: Mr David Ashton

Course/s:
●   **PADESWOOD & BUCKLEY**
    Description: Championship, Wooded,
    Parkland, Sheltered, Open, Medium
    Length, Drains Well, Ideal for the Elderly
    Green Speed: Fast
    Built: 1976   **Built On:** Soil
    Number of Holes: 18
    Prevailing Wind: South/West
    Designer: Williams

PAINSWICK

PAINSWICK GOLF CLUB, Golf Course Rd,
Painswick, Stroud, **GLOUCESTERSHIRE**,
GL6 6TL, **ENGLAND**.
(T) 01452 812180

Contact/s:
●   Club Secretary: Mr A Layton-Smith
    ☎ 01452 612622
●   Pro Shop: Mr N Wolcott
    ☎ 01452 814004

Course/s:
●   **PAINSWICK**
    Description: Parkland, Hilltop,
    Undulating, Short, Drains Well
    Green Speed: Medium
    Built: 1891
    Number of Holes: 18   **Par:** 67
    Par 3's: 7   **Par 4's:** 9   **Par 5's:** 2
    Yds: 4832
    Prevailing Wind: West

PAINTHORPE HOUSE

**PAINTHORPE HOUSE GOLF & COUNTRY
CLUB,** Painthorpe Lane, Crigglestone,
Wakefield, **YORKSHIRE (WEST)**, WF4 3HF,
ENGLAND.
(T) 01924 255083

Contact/s:
●   Club Secretary: Mr H Kershaw
    ☎ 01924 274527

Course/s:
●   **PAINTHORPE HOUSE**

Number of Holes: 9 **Par**: 31
Par 3's: 5 Par 4's: 4
Yds: 4520
Further Information:
9 hole course can be played as an 18 hole
course

PAISLEY

PAISLEY GOLF CLUB (THE), Braehead Rd,
Paisley, **RENFREWSHIRE**, PA2 8TZ,
SCOTLAND.
(T) 0141 8843903
(E) paisleygc@onetel.net.uk
(W) www.paisleygc.com

Membership: Members & Public

Contact/s:
● **Professional:** Mr Gordon Stewart
● **Pro Shop:**
   ☎ 0141 8844114

Course/s:
● **PAISLEY**
   Description: Moorland, Hilltop,
   Undulating, Open, Long, Drains Well
   Green Speed: Medium
   Built: 1951 **Built On:** Soil
   Number of Holes: 18 **Par:** 71
   Par 3's: 4 **Par 4's:** 11 **Par 5's:** 3
   Yds: 6466 **F9 Yds:** 3332 **B9 Yds:** 3134
   Further Information:
   The course has views over Clyde Valley.
   Burn, heather and gorse can be found
   throughout the course.

PALACERIGG

PALACERIGG GOLF CLUB, Palacerigg
Country Pk, Cumbernauld, **LANARKSHIRE
(NORTH)**, G67 2BY, **SCOTLAND**.
(T) 01236 734969
(E) palacerigg_golfclub@lineone.net
(W) www.palacerigggolfclub.co.uk

Membership: Members & Public

Contact/s:
● **Club Secretary:** Mr David Cooper
● **Book Tee Times:** Mr John Murphy
   ☎ 01236 721461

Course/s:
● **PALACERIGG**
   Description: Wooded, Parkland,
   Undulating, Medium Length
   Green Speed: Medium
   Built: 1974 **Built On:** Clay
   Number of Holes: 18 **Par:** 72
   Record: 66 (Russell Weir)
   Par 3's: 3 **Par 4's:** 12 **Par 5's:** 3
   Yds: 6444
   Designer: Henry Cotton

PALLEG

PALLEG GOLF CLUB, Palleg Rd, Lower
Cwmtwrch, Swansea, **SWANSEA**, SA9 2QQ,
WALES.
(T) 01639 842193

Contact/s:
● **Club Secretary:** D W Moses

Course/s:
● **PALLEG**
   Number of Holes: 9
   Yds: 3209

PANMURE

PANMURE GOLF CLUB, Burnside Rd, Barry,
Carnoustie, **ANGUS**, DD7 7RT, **SCOTLAND**.
(T) 01241 855120

Membership: Members & Public

Contact/s:

● **Club Secretary:** Major G W Paton
● **Professional:** Mr Nim Macintosh
● **Book Lessons:** Mr Nim McIntosh

Course/s:
● **PANMURE**
   Description: Links, Medium Length, Ideal
   for the Elderly
   Green Speed: Medium
   Built: 1900 **Built On:** Clay
   Number of Holes: 18 **Par:** 70
   Yds: 6317 **F9 Yds:** 3009 **B9 Yds:** 3308
   Prevailing Wind: South/West

PANNAL

PANNAL GOLF CLUB, Follifoot Rd, Pannal,
Harrogate, **YORKSHIRE (NORTH)**, HG3
1ES, **ENGLAND**.
(T) 01423 872628
(E) pannalgolfclub@btconnect.com
(W) www.pannalgolfclub.co.uk
Size of Complex: 120 Acres

Contact/s:
● **Club Secretary:** Mr Richard Braddon
● **Professional:** Mr David Padgett
   ☎ 01423 872620
● **Book Tee Times:**
   ☎ 01423 871620

Course/s:
● **PANNAL**
   Description: Championship, Parkland,
   Moorland
   Green Speed: Fast
   Built: 1906 **Built On:** Clay
   Number of Holes: 18 **Par:** 72
   Par 3's: 4 **Par 4's:** 10 **Par 5's:** 4
   Yds: 6464
   Prevailing Wind: South/West
   Designer: S Herd

PANSHANGER GOLF COMPLEX

PANSHANGER GOLF COMPLEX, Old Herns
Lane, Welwyn Garden City,
HERTFORDSHIRE, AL7 2ED, **ENGLAND**.
(T) 01707 333350

Membership: Public

Contact/s:
● **Club Secretary:** Mrs Shiela Ryan
● **Professional:** Mr Bryan Lewis
● **Pro Shop:** Mrs R Preece
   ☎ 01707 399507

Course/s:
● **PANSHANGER GOLF COMPLEX**
   Description: Wooded, Valley, Undulating,
   Sheltered, Medium Length, Drains Well
   Green Speed: Medium/Fast
   Built: 1974 **Built On:** Chalk
   Number of Holes: 18
   Designer: Peter Kirkham
   Further Information:
   View overlooking Mimram Valley.

PANTYDDERWEN

PANTYDDERWEN GOLF COURSE,
Llangain, Carmarthen,
CARMARTHENSHIRE, SA33 5AH, **WALES**.
(T) 01267 241560

Contact/s:
● **Owner:** Ms C D Griffths

Course/s:
● **PANTYDDERWEN**
   Number of Holes: 9

PARASAMPIA

PARASAMPIA GOLF & COUNTRY CLUB,
Grove Rd, Donnington, Newbury,
BERKSHIRE, RG14 2LA, **ENGLAND**.

(T) 01635 581000
(E) enquiries@parasampia.com
(W) www.parasampia.com

Contact/s:
● **Professional:** Mr G Williams
   ☎ 01635 551975

Course/s:
● **PARASAMPIA**
   Description: Championship, Parkland,
   Undulating, Long, Drains Well
   Green Speed: Medium
   Built: 1993
   Number of Holes: 18 **Par:** 72
   Designer: Peter Alliss

PARC

PARC GOLF COURSE, Church Lane,
Newport, **NEWPORT**, NP1 9TU, **WALES**.
(T) 01633 680933

Contact/s:
● **Owner:** Mrs H Hicks

Course/s:
● **PARC**
   Number of Holes: 18
   Designer: T F Hicks, Peter Alliss

PARK

PARK GOLF COURSE (THE), Avington,
Winchester, **HAMPSHIRE**, SO21 1DA,
ENGLAND.
(T) 01962 779955

Membership: Members & Public

Contact/s:
● **Club Secretary:** Mr Robert N Stent

Course/s:
● **PARK**
   Description: Parkland, Undulating, Open,
   Medium Length, Ideal for the Elderly
   Green Speed: Medium **Built On:** Chalk
   Number of Holes: 9 **Par:** 31
   Par 3's: 5 **Par 4's:** 4
   Yds: 3898 **F9 Yds:** 1949 **B9 Yds:** 1949
   Further Information: 9 hole course can
   be played as an 18 hole course

PARK

PARK GOLF CLUB, Pk Rd West, Southport,
MERSEYSIDE, PR9 0JS, **ENGLAND**.
(T) 01704 530133

Contact/s:
● **Club Secretary:** Mr P Devereux

Course/s:
● **PARK**
   Number of Holes: 18

PARK HILL

PARK HILL GOLF CLUB, Pk Hill, Seagrave,
Loughborough, **LEICESTERSHIRE**, LE12
7NG, **ENGLAND**.
(T) 01509 815454
(E) mail@parkhillgolf.co.uk

Membership: Members & Public
Size of Complex: 180 Acres

Contact/s:
● **Professional:** Mr Matthew Ulyett
● **Book Tee Times:** Mr Jonathan Hutson

Course/s:
● **PARK HILL**
   Description: Championship
   Built: 1994
   Number of Holes: 18 **Par:** 73
   Yds: 7219 **F9 Yds:** 3258 **B9 Yds:** 3458
   Further Information:
   This is a challenging course.

PARK TONGLAND

PARK OF TONGLAND LEISURE LTD, Castle Douglas Rd, Tongland, Dumfries & Galloway, Kirkcudbright, **DUMFRIES AND GALLOWAY**, DG6 4NE, **SCOTLAND**.
(T) 01556 680226

Membership: Members & Public
Size of Complex: 38 Acres

Contact/s:
- **Club Secretary:** Mrs Jennifer Dawn Moor
- **Professional:** Mr Gordon Gray

Course/s:
- **PARK OF TONGLAND**
  Description: Parkland, Short, Tight, Drains Well, Ideal for the Elderly
  Green Speed: Medium
  Built: 1996 **Built On:** Soil
  Number of Holes: 9 **Par:** 27
  Par 3's: 9
  Yds: 870
  Prevailing Wind: West
  Designer: Brian Moore
  Further Information:
  The course is a 9 hole, par 3 with 18 different tee positions.

PARK WOOD

PARK WOOD GOLF CLUB, Office, Chestnut Ave, Westerham, **KENT**, TN16 2EG, **ENGLAND**.
(T) 01959 577765

Course/s:
- **PARK WOOD**
  Description: Drains Well
  Number of Holes: 18 **Par:** 72
  Yds: 6835
  Further Information:
  Greens to USPGA standards

PARKHALL

PARKHALL GOLF COURSE, Hulme Road, Hulme Lane, Weston Coyney, Stoke-on-Trent, **STAFFORDSHIRE**, ST3 5BH, **ENGLAND**.
(T) 01782 599584

Contact/s:
- **Manager:** Mr Paul Davis

Course/s:
- **PARKHALL PAR 3**
  Description: Heath Land
  Number of Holes: 18 **Par:** 54
  Yds: 2335

PARKLANDS

PARKLANDS GOLF CLUB, Gosforth Pk Golfing Complex, High Gosforth Pk, Newcastle Upon Tyne, **TYNE AND WEAR**, NE3 5HQ, **ENGLAND**.
(T) 0191 2364867

Course/s:
- **PARKLANDS**
  Number of Holes: 18

PARKNASILLA

PARKNASILLA GOLF CLUB, Parknasilla, Nr Sneem, Parknasilla, **COUNTY KERRY**, **IRELAND**.
(T) 064 45122

Contact/s:
- **Club Secretary:** Mr Maurice Walsh

Course/s:
- **PARKNASILLA**
  Number of Holes: 9
  Yds: 6044
  Designer: Arthur Spring

PARKSTONE

PARKSTONE GOLF CLUB, 49a Links Rd, Parkstone, Poole, **DORSET**, BH14 9QS, **ENGLAND**.
(T) 01202 707138
(W) www.parkstonegolfclub.co.uk

Membership: Members & Public

Contact/s:
- **Club Secretary:** Mr J M Harper
- **Professional:** Mr Martyn Thompson

Course/s:
- **PARKSTONE**
  Description: Links, Undulating, Medium Length, Tends to Flood
  Green Speed: Medium
  Built: 1911 **Built On:** Sand
  Number of Holes: 18 **Par:** 72
  Record: 65
  Yds: 6263 **F9 Yds:** 3168 **B9 Yds:** 3095
  Designer: James Braid, William Park ⚑

PARLEY

PARLEY GOLF CLUB, Parley, Christchurch, **DORSET**, BH23 6BB, **ENGLAND**.
(T) 01202 591600

Membership: Members & Public

Contact/s:
- **Professional:** Mr Peter Thompson
  ☎ 01202 593131

Course/s:
- **PARLEY**
  Description: Parkland, Undulating, Medium Length, Tight, Drains Well, Ideal for the Elderly
  Green Speed: Medium
  Built: 1992 **Built On:** Soil
  Number of Holes: 9
  Designer: P Goodfellow

PATSHULL PARK

PATSHULL PARK HOTEL GOLF & COUNTRY CLUB, Burnhill Green, Wolverhampton, **MIDLANDS (WEST)**, WV6 7HR, **ENGLAND**.
(T) 01902 700342

Membership: Members & Public

Contact/s:
- **Manager:** Mr R Bissell

Course/s:
- **PATSHULL PARK HOTEL**
  Number of Holes: 18
  Designer: John Jacobs

PAULTONS GOLF CENTRE

AMERICAN GOLF CORPORATION, Old Salisbury Rd, Ower, Romsey, **HAMPSHIRE**, SO51 6AN, **ENGLAND**.
(T) 02380 813992
(E) paultonsgolfcentre@americangolf.com
(W) www.americangolf.com

Membership: Public
Size of Complex: 200 Acres

Contact/s:
- **Professional:** Mr Mark Williams

Course/s:
- **PAULTONS 18 HOLE MASTER**
  Description: Wooded, Parkland, Medium Length, Drains Well, Ideal for the Elderly
  Green Speed: Medium
  Built: 1994
  Number of Holes: 18 **Par:** 71
  Par 3's: 5 **Par 4's:** 9 **Par 5's:** 4
  F9 Yds: 3189 **B9 Yds:** 3049
  Designer: J Smith

- **PAULTONS PAR 3**
  Number of Holes: 9 **Par:** 27
  Par 3's: 9
  Designer: J Smith

PAVENHAM

PAVENHAM PARK GOLF CLUB, Pavenham, Bedford, **BEDFORDSHIRE**, MK43 7PE, **ENGLAND**.
(T) 01234 822202
(W) www.kolvengolf.com

Membership: Members & Public
Size of Complex: 178 Acres

Contact/s:
- **Club Secretary:** Mr R Walpole
- **Professional:** Mr Kevin Nicholas

Course/s:
- **PAVENHAM PARK**
  Description: Parkland, Undulating, Open, Medium Length, Drains Well
  Green Speed: Medium
  Built: 1993 **Built On:** Clay
  Number of Holes: 18 **Par:** 72
  Record: 63 (Allun Evans)
  Par 3's: 5 **Par 4's:** 8 **Par 5's:** 5
  Yds: 6467 **F9 Yds:** 3233 **B9 Yds:** 3234
  Designer: Zac Thompson, Derek Young
  Further Information:
  No winter greens.

PAXHILL PARK

PAXHILL PARK GOLF CLUB, East Mascalls Lane, Lindfield, Haywards Heath, **SUSSEX (WEST)**, RH16 2QN, **ENGLAND**.
(T) 01444 484000
(E) johnbowen@paxhillpark.fsnet.co.uk
(W) www.paxhillpark.com

Contact/s:
- **Professional:** Mr M Green

Course/s:
- **PAXHILL PARK**
  Description: Parkland
  Built: 1990
  Number of Holes: 18 **Par:** 70
  Par 3's: 4 **Par 4's:** 12 **Par 5's:** 2
  Yds: 6120 **F9 Yds:** 3185 **B9 Yds:** 2935
  Designer: P Tallack

PEACEHAVEN

PEACEHAVEN GOLF CLUB, Brighton Rd, Newhaven, **SUSSEX (EAST)**, BN9 9UH, **ENGLAND**.
(T) 01273 512602

Membership: Members & Public

Contact/s:
- **Professional:** Mr Ian Pearson

Course/s:
- **PEACEHAVEN**
  Description: Downland
  Number of Holes: 9
  Designer: James Braid
  Further Information:
  9 hole course can be played as an 18 hole course

PEDHAM PLACE GOLF CTRE

PEDHAM PLACE GOLF CENTRE, London Rd, Swanley, **KENT**, BR8 8PP, **ENGLAND**.
(T) 01322 867000
(E) golf@ppgc.co.uk
(W) www.ppgc.co.uk

Membership: Public

Contact/s:
- **Professional:** Mr Ron Mitchell

Course/s:

RED
Description: Links
Green Speed: Medium
Built: 1996
Number of Holes: 9 Par: 34
Yds: 2263

YELLOW
Description: Links, Medium Length, Drains Well
Green Speed: Medium
Number of Holes: 18 Par: 71
Yds: 5864 F9 Yds: 2788 B9 Yds: 3076

PEEBLES

PEEBLES GOLF CLUB LTD, Kirkland St, Peebles, **SCOTTISH BORDERS**, EH45 8EU, **SCOTLAND**.
(T) 01721 720197
(W) www.peeblesgolfclub.co.uk

Membership: Members & Public
Size of Complex: 130 Acres

Contact/s:
● Club Secretary: Mr Hugh Gilmore
  ☎ 01721 720099
● Professional: Mr Craig Imlah

Course/s:

THE KIRLANDS
Description: Championship, Parkland, Undulating, Sheltered, Medium Length, Drains Well
Green Speed: Medium
Built: 1905 Built On: Soil
Number of Holes: 18 Par: 70
Par 3's: 4 Par 4's: 12 Par 5's: 2
Yds: 6160
Designer: Harry Shapland Colt

PEEL

PEEL GOLF CLUB, Rheast Lane, Peel, **ISLE OF MAN**, IM5 1BG, **ENGLAND**.
(T) 01624 842227

Course/s:

PEEL
Number of Holes: 18
Designer: Robert Braide

PENFOLD PARK

PENFOLD PARK GOLF COURSE, St. Albans Rd, Watford, **HERTFORDSHIRE**, WD2 7NB, **ENGLAND**.
(T) 01923 671365
(E) penfoldparkgolf@aol.com

Membership: Public

Contact/s:
● Club Secretary: Mr Lorraine White
● Professional: Mr Mike Lovegrove

Course/s:

PENFOLD PARK
Description: Wooded, Short, Tight, Drains Well, Ideal for the Elderly
Green Speed: Medium
Built: 1980
Number of Holes: 9

PENLANLAS

PENLANLAS GOLF CLUB, Penlanlas, Rhydyfelin, Aberystwyth, **CEREDIGION**, SY23 4QE, **WALES**.
(T) 01970 625319

Contact/s:
● Partner: Mr M Lloyd

Course/s:

PENLANLAS
Built: 1993
Number of Holes: 18 Par: 62

Par 3's: 10 Par 4's: 8
Yds: 4119 F9 Yds: 2089 B9 Yds: 2030
Further Information:
This 9 hole course has 14 separate tees and therefore can be played as an 18 hole course, playing 4 tees twice.

PENMAENMAWR

PENMAENMAWR GOLF CLUB, Conway Old Rd, Penmaenmawr, **CONWY**, LL34 6RD, **WALES**.
(T) 01492 623330

Contact/s:
● Club Secretary: Mrs J E Jones

Course/s:

PENMAENMAWR
Description: Parkland, Drains Well
Built: 1910
Number of Holes: 9 Par: 67
Further Information:
Sea and mountain views. 9 hole course can be played as an 18 hole course

PENN

PENN GOLF CLUB, Penn Common, Wolverhampton, **MIDLANDS (WEST)**, WV4 5JN, **ENGLAND**.
(T) 01902 341142

Course/s:

PENN
Number of Holes: 18

PENNANT PARK

PENNANT PARK GOLF CLUB, Cae Goch Farm, Whitford, Holywell, **FLINTSHIRE**, CH8 9EP, **WALES**.
(T) 01745 563000

Membership: Members & Public

Contact/s:
● Owner: Mr R Jones

Course/s:

PENNANT PARK
Number of Holes: 18 Par: 70

PENNARD

PENNARD GOLF CLUB, 2 Southgate Rd, Southgate, Swansea, **SWANSEA**, SA3 2BT, **WALES**.
(T) 01792 233451
(W) www.pennardgolfclub.co.uk

Membership: Members & Public

Contact/s:
● Club Secretary: Mr E M Howell
  ☎ 01792 233131
● Professional: Mr Andrew Baven
● Pro Shop: Mr Mike Bennett

Course/s:

PENNARD
Description: Championship, Links, Cliff Top, Open, Medium Length, Drains Well
Green Speed: Fast
Built: 1896 Built On: Sand
Number of Holes: 18
Prevailing Wind: South/West
Designer: James Braid
Further Information:
The course offers panoramic views.

PENNINGTON

PENNINGTON GOLF COURSE, St. Helens Rd, Leigh, **LANCASHIRE**, WN7 3PA, **ENGLAND**.
(T) 01942 682852

Contact/s:

● Manager: Mr T Kirshaw

Course/s:

PENNINGTON
Number of Holes: 9

PENNYHILL PARK

PENNYHILL PARK HOTEL & COUNTRY CLUB, London Rd, Bagshot, **SURREY**, GU19 5ET, **ENGLAND**.
(T) 01276 471774

Course/s:

PENNYHILL PARK
Number of Holes: 9

PENRHOS

PENRHOS GOLF & COUNTRY CLUB, Llanrhystud, **CEREDIGION**, SY23 5AY, **WALES**.
(T) 01974 202999
(E) info@penrhosgolf.co.uk
(W) www.penrhosgolf.co.uk

Membership: Members & Public

Contact/s:
● Club Secretary: Mr Rowland Rees-Evans
● Professional: Mr Paul Diamond

Course/s:

ACADEMY
Description: Parkland, Open, Short, Drains Well, Ideal for the Elderly
Green Speed: Slow
Built: 1996 Built On: Clay/Soil
Number of Holes: 9
Designer: John Evans

PENRHOS
Number of Holes: 18 Par: 72
Par 3's: 4 Par 4's: 10 Par 5's: 4
Yds: 6641 F9 Yds: 3241 B9 Yds: 3400
Designer: Jim Walters

PENRITH

PENRITH GOLF CLUB, Salkeld Rd, Maidenhill, Penrith, **CUMBRIA**, CA11 8SG, **ENGLAND**.
(T) 01768 891919

Contact/s:
● Club Secretary: Mr D Noble

Course/s:

PENRITH
Number of Holes: 18 Par: 69
Par 3's: 5 Par 4's: 11 Par 5's: 2
Yds: 6047 F9 Yds: 3132 B9 Yds: 2915

PENWORTHAM

PENWORTHAM GOLF CLUB, Blundell Lane, Penwortham, Preston, **LANCASHIRE**, PR1 0AX, **ENGLAND**.
(T) 01772 743207

Contact/s:
● Accountant: Mr Geoffrey David Brown

Course/s:

PENWORTHAM
Number of Holes: 18

PEOVER

PEOVER GOLF CLUB, Plumley Moor Rd, Lower Peover, Knutsford, **CHESHIRE**, WA16 9SE, **ENGLAND**.
(T) 01565 723337
(W) www.peovergolfclub.co.uk

Membership: Members & Public/Public

Contact/s:
● Club Secretary: Mrs J Baker

- **Professional:** Mr Bobby Young
- **Pro Shop:** Ms Julie Naylor

Course/s:

🏌 **PEOVER**
Description: Parkland
Green Speed: Medium
Built: 1991
Number of Holes: 18 **Par:** 72
Par 3's: 4 **Par 4's:** 10 **Par 5's:** 4
Yds: 6702 **F9 Yds:** 3325 **B9 Yds:** 3377

PERDISWELL PARK GOLF COURSE

PERDISWELL PARK GOLF CENTRE,
Bilford Rd, Worcester, **WORCESTERSHIRE**,
WR3 8DX, **ENGLAND**.
(T) 01905 754668

Membership: Members & Public/Public

Contact/s:
- **Club Secretary:** Mr Richard Gardner
- **Professional:** Mr Mark Woodward

Course/s:

🏌 **PERDISWELL PARK**
Description: Parkland, Short, Drains Well,
Ideal for the Elderly
Green Speed: Medium
Number of Holes: 18

PERIVALE PARK

PERIVALE PARK GOLF COURSE,
Stockdove Way, Greenford, **LONDON
(GREATER)**, UB6 8EN, **ENGLAND**.
(T) 020 85757116

Contact/s:
- **Manager:** Mr P Brayant

Course/s:

🏌 **PERIVALE PARK**
Number of Holes: 9

PERRANPORTH

PERRANPORTH GOLF CLUB, Brudnick Hill,
Perranporth, **CORNWALL**, TR6 0AB,
ENGLAND.
(T) 01872 572701

Membership: Members & Public

Contact/s:
- **Club Secretary:** Mr David Mugford
- **Professional:** Mr D Michell
  ☎ 01872 572317

Course/s:

🏌 **PERRANPORTH**
Description: Links, Drains Well
Built: 1927
Number of Holes: 18 **Par:** 72
Yds: 6286 **F9 Yds:** 3145 **B9 Yds:** 3141
Designer: James Braid

PERTON PARK

PERTON PARK GOLF CLUB, Wrottesley Pk
Rd, Perton, Wolverhampton, **MIDLANDS
(WEST)**, WV6 7HL, **ENGLAND**.
(T) 01902 380103
(W) www.pertongolfclub.co.uk

Contact/s:
- **Manager:** Mr E Greenway

Course/s:

🏌 **PERTON PARK**
Description: Long
Built: 1990
Number of Holes: 18 **Par:** 72
Yds: 6520 **F9 Yds:** 3254 **B9 Yds:** 3266

PETERBOROUGH MILTON

PETERBOROUGH MILTON GOLF CLUB,

Milton Ferry, Milton, Peterborough,
CAMBRIDGESHIRE, PE6 7AG, **ENGLAND**.
(T) 01733 380793
(E) miltongolfclub@aol.com
(W) www.peterboroughmiltongolfclub.co.uk

Membership: Members & Public

Contact/s:
- **Club Secretary:** Mr Andy Izod
  ☎ 01733 380489
- **Professional:** Mr Mike Gallagher

Course/s:

🏌 **PETERBOROUGH MILTON**
Description: Championship, Parkland,
Sheltered, Drains Well, Ideal for the Elderly
Green Speed: Medium/Fast
Built: 1938 **Built On:** Clay
Number of Holes: 18 **Par:** 71
Par 3's: 4 **Par 4's:** 11 **Par 5's:** 3
Yds: 6218 **F9 Yds:** 3182 **B9 Yds:** 3036
Designer: James Braid

PETERCULTER

PETERCULTER GOLF CLUB, Burnside Rd,
Old Town, Peterculter, **ABERDEENSHIRE**,
AB14 0LN, **SCOTLAND**.
(T) 01224 735239
(E) info@peterctergolfclub.co.uk
(W) www.peterctergolfclub.co.uk

Membership: Members & Public

Contact/s:
- **Professional:** Mr Dean G Vannel
  ☎ 01224 734994

Course/s:

🏌 **PETERCULTER**
Description: Parkland, Valley, Undulating,
Sheltered, Tends to Flood, Ideal for the
Elderly
Built: 1989
Number of Holes: 18 **Par:** 71
Yds: 6207 **F9 Yds:** 3135 **B9 Yds:** 3072
Designer: Greens of Scotland
Further Information:
The course offers views of the River Dee.

PETERHEAD

PETERHEAD GOLF CLUB, Craiguwan Links,
Riverside Drive, Peterhead,
ABERDEENSHIRE, AB42 1SY, **SCOTLAND**.
(T) 01779 472149

Membership: Members & Public

Contact/s:
- **Club Secretary:** Mr David Wood
  ☎ 01779 480725

Course/s:

🏌 **NEW**
Description: Links, Parkland
Green Speed: Fast
Built: 1841 **Built On:** Sand
Number of Holes: 9 **Par:** 31

🏌 **OLD**
Description: Links, Parkland
Green Speed: Fast
Built: 1841 **Built On:** Sand
Number of Holes: 18 **Par:** 70

PETERSFIELD

**PETERSFIELD GOLF CLUB (OLD
COURSE),** Sussex Rd, Petersfield,
HAMPSHIRE, GU31 4EJ, **ENGLAND**.
(T) 01730 267732

Course/s:

🏌 **PETERSFIELD**
Number of Holes: 9

PETERSFIELD

PETERSFIELD GOLF CLUB, Tankerdale
Lane, Liss, **HAMPSHIRE**, GU33 7QY,
ENGLAND.
(T) 01730 895216

Contact/s:
- **Owner:** Mr Greg Hughes

Course/s:

🏌 **PETERSFIELD (NEW)**
Number of Holes: 18

PETERSTONE LAKES

PETERSTONE LAKES GOLF CLUB,
Peterstone Wentlooge, Cardiff, **GLAMORGAN
(VALE OF)**, CF3 2TN, **WALES**.
(T) 01633 680009
(W) www.peterstonelakes.com

Membership: Members & Public

Contact/s:
- **Professional:** Mr D Clark

Course/s:

🏌 **PETERSTONE**
Description: Links, Parkland, Open,
Long, Drains Well, Ideal for the Elderly
Green Speed: Fast
Built: 1990 **Built On:** Clay
Number of Holes: 18
Prevailing Wind: West
Designer: Robert Sandow
Further Information:
A flat course.

PETWORTH

PETWORTH GOLF CLUB, London Rd,
Petworth, **SUSSEX (WEST)**, GU28 9LX,
ENGLAND.
(T) 01798 344097

Membership: Public
Size of Complex: 120 Acres

Contact/s:
- **Club Secretary:** Mr Dennis Windows
  ☎ 01730 817707
- **Professional:** Mr John Little
  ☎ 01428 605093
- **Pro Shop:** Mr Andy Long

Course/s:

🏌 **PETWORTH G.C**
Description: Wooded, Undulating, Open,
Medium Length
Green Speed: Medium
Built: 1989 **Built On:** Clay
Number of Holes: 18 **Par:** 71
Record: 71 (John Edwards)
Par 3's: 4 **Par 4's:** 11 **Par 5's:** 3
Yds: 6191 **F9 Yds:** 3402 **B9 Yds:** 2789
Prevailing Wind: East
Designer: Chris Duncton, Tim Duncton

PEWIT

PEWIT GOLF COURSE, 40 West End Drive,
Ilkeston, **DERBYSHIRE**, DE7 5GH,
ENGLAND.
(T) 0115 9307704

Membership: Public

Contact/s:
- **Recreation Manager:** Mr Chris Buxton
  ☎ 0115 9071142

Course/s:

🏌 **PEWIT**
Description: Parkland, Undulating, Open,
Medium Length, Tends to Flood
Green Speed: Fast
Built: 1940 **Built On:** Clay
Number of Holes: 9

PHOENIX

PHOENIX GOLF CLUB, Pavilion Lane, Brinsworth, Rotherham, **YORKSHIRE (SOUTH)**, S60 5PA, **ENGLAND**.
(T) 01709 363788

Contact/s:
● **Manager:** Mr A White

Course/s:
🏌 **PHOENIX**
Number of Holes: 18
Designer: Cotton

PIKEFOLD

PIKEFOLD GOLF CLUB, Hills Lane, Unsworth, Bury, **LANCASHIRE**, BL9 8QP, **ENGLAND**.
(T) 0161 7663561
(W) www.pikefoldgolfclub.co.uk

Membership: Members & Public
Size of Complex: 87 Acres

Contact/s:
● **Club Secretary:** Mr John O'Donald
● **Professional:** Mr Michael Vipond

Course/s:
🏌 **PIKEFOLD**
Description: Parkland, Undulating, Open, Long, Drains Well, Ideal for the Elderly
Green Speed: Fast
Built: 1909 **Built On:** Clay/Soil
Number of Holes: 9
Prevailing Wind: North/West
Designer: Steve Marnoch

PINE RIDGE GOLF CTRE

PINE RIDGE GOLF CENTRE, Old Bisley Rd, Frimley, Camberley, **SURREY**, GU16 5NX, **ENGLAND**.
(T) 01276 675444
(W) www.pineridgegolf.co.uk

Membership: Public

Contact/s:
● **Club Secretary:** Mr P Sefton

Course/s:
🏌 **PINE RIDGE**
Description: Wooded, Sheltered, Medium Length, Drains Well
Green Speed: Medium
Built: 1992
Number of Holes: 18
Designer: Clive Smith
Further Information:
There are two reservoirs on the course.

PINE VALLEY PAR 3

PINE VALLEY PAR 3 GOLF COURSE, Mt Venus Rd, Rockbrook, Dublin, **COUNTY DUBLIN**, **IRELAND**.
(T) 01 4939148

Course/s:
🏌 **PINE VALLEY GOLF COURSE**
Number of Holes: 18 **Par:** 54
Par 3's: 18
Yds: 2779 **F9 Yds:** 1442 **B9 Yds:** 1337

PINES

PINES GOLF CENTRE (THE), Lockerbie Rd, Dumfries, **DUMFRIES AND GALLOWAY**, DG1 3PF, **SCOTLAND**.
(T) 01387 247444
(E) admin@pinesgolf.com
(W) www.pinesgolf.com

Membership: Members & Public
Size of Complex: 100 Acres

Contact/s:
● **Professional:** Mr Jim Davidson

Course/s:
🏌 **PINES**
Description: Wooded, Parkland, Heath Land, Undulating, Medium Length, Tight, Drains Well, Ideal for the Elderly
Green Speed: Medium
Built: 1997 **Built On:** Sand/Soil
Number of Holes: 18 **Par:** 69
Par 3's: 4 **Par 4's:** 13 **Par 5's:** 1
Yds: 5851 **F9 Yds:** 3032 **B9 Yds:** 2819
Prevailing Wind: South/West
Designer: D Gray
Further Information:
The course is generally in excellent condition and temporary greens are never used.

PIPERDAM GOLF

PIPERDAM GOLF & COUNTRY PARK, Fowlis, Invergowrie, Dundee, **ANGUS**, DD2 5LP, **SCOTLAND**.
(T) 01382 581374

Membership: Members & Public

Contact/s:
● **General Manager:** Mr Derek McFarland

Course/s:
🏌 **OSPREY**
Description: Championship, Parkland, Undulating, Medium Length, Drains Well
Green Speed: Medium
Built: 1997 **Built On:** Sand/Soil
Number of Holes: 18 **Par:** 68
Par 3's: 4 **Par 4's:** 9 **Par 5's:** 4
Yds: 6526
Prevailing Wind: West
Further Information:
The course has fantastic scenery, built around the Loch where you can feed osprey.

PITCHEROAK

PITCHEROAK GOLF COURSE, Plymouth Rd, Redditch, **WORCESTERSHIRE**, B97 4PB, **ENGLAND**.
(T) 01527 541054

Membership: Public

Contact/s:
● **Professional:** Mr David Stewart

Course/s:
🏌 **PITCHEROAK**
Description: Parkland, Undulating, Short, Tight, Drains Well
Green Speed: Medium
Built: 1973 **Built On:** Clay
Number of Holes: 9 **Par:** 32 **Record:** 61 (David Stewart)
Further Information:
9 hole course can be played as an 18 hole course

PITLOCHRY

PITLOCHRY GOLF CLUB, Pitlochry, **PERTH AND KINROSS**, PH16 5QY, **SCOTLAND**.
(T) 01796 472334

Contact/s:
● **Chairman:** Mr Dougal Sperin

Course/s:
🏌 **PITLOCHRY**
Number of Holes: 18
Designer: William Fernie

PITREAVIE

PITREAVIE (DUNFERMLINE) GOLF CLUB, Queensferry Rd, Dunfermline, **FIFE**, KY11 8PR, **SCOTLAND**.
(T) 01383 723151

Membership: Members & Public

Contact/s:
● **Club Secretary:** Mr Edward Comerford
● **Professional:** Mr Paul Brookes

Course/s:
🏌 **PITREAVIE**
Description: Wooded, Parkland, Hilltop, Undulating, Sheltered, Open, Medium Length, Drains Well, Ideal for the Elderly
Green Speed: Medium
Built: 1922 **Built On:** Clay/Soil
Number of Holes: 18 **Record:** 69 (Paul Brookes)
Prevailing Wind: East
Designer: Alistair MacKenzie
Further Information:
The greens are very testing with big slopes.

PLASSEY

PLASSEY GOLF COURSE (THE), Plassey Leisure Complex, Eyton, Wrexham, **WREXHAM**, LL13 0SP, **WALES**.
(T) 01978 780020
(W) www.theplassey.co.uk/golfcourse.htm

Membership: Members & Public
Size of Complex: 300 Acres

Contact/s:
● **Club Secretary:** Mr James Taylor

Course/s:
🏌 **THE PLASSEY**
Description: Championship, Parkland, Undulating, Open, Short
Green Speed: Medium
Built: 1992 **Built On:** Soil
Number of Holes: 9 **Par:** 64
Par 3's: 4 **Par 4's:** 5
Yds: 4761 **F9 Yds:** 2327 **B9 Yds:** 2434
Prevailing Wind: West
Further Information:
Set in a quiet rural area, 9 hole course can be played as an 18 hole course

PLEASINGTON

PLEASINGTON GOLF CLUB, Pleasington Lane, Pleasington, Blackburn, **LANCASHIRE**, BB2 5JF, **ENGLAND**.
(T) 01254 202177

Membership: Members & Public

Contact/s:
● **Club Secretary:** Mrs Jean Leyland
● **Professional:** Mr Ged Furey

Course/s:
🏌 **PLEASINGTON**
Description: Championship, Parkland, Undulating, Sheltered, Open, Long, Drains Well
Green Speed: Medium
Built: 1891 **Built On:** Sand
Number of Holes: 18 **Par:** 71
Record: 64
Par 3's: 4 **Par 4's:** 11 **Par 5's:** 3
Yds: 6402 **F9 Yds:** 3376 **B9 Yds:** 3026
Prevailing Wind: North/West

POCOCKE

POCOCKE GOLF COURSE, Johnswell Rd, Kilkenny, **COUNTY KILKENNY**, **IRELAND**.
(T) 056 51666

Membership: Public

Size of Complex: 32 Acres

Contact/s:
- Pro Shop: Mr Robert Falsey

Course/s:
- **POCOCKE**
  Description: Parkland, Open, Short, Drains Well, Ideal for the Elderly
  Green Speed: Medium
  Built: 1992 **Built On:** Sand/Soil
  Number of Holes: 18 **Par:** 55
  Par 3's: 18
  Yds: 2696 **F9 Yds:** 1251 **B9 Yds:** 1444

POLKEMMET

POLKEMMET GOLF COURSE & DRIVING RANGE, Whitburn, Bathgate, **LOTHIAN (WEST)**, EH47 0AD, **SCOTLAND**.
(T) 01501 743905

Membership: Public

Contact/s:
- Manager: Mr John Fleming

Course/s:
- **POLKEMMET COUNTRY PARK**
  Number of Holes: 9 **Par:** 37
  Par 3's: 1 **Par 4's:** 6 **Par 5's:** 2
  Yds: 2969
  Further Information:
  9 hole course can be played as an 18 hole course

POLLOK

POLLOK GOLF CLUB (THE), 90 Barrhead Rd, Glasgow, **GLASGOW (CITY OF)**, G43 1BG, **SCOTLAND**.
(T) 0141 6321080

Course/s:
- **POLLOK**
  Number of Holes: 18
  Designer: James Braid

POLMONT

POLMONT GOLF CLUB LTD, Manurlrigg, Maddiston, **FALKIRK**, FK2 0LS, **SCOTLAND**.
(T) 01324 711277

Membership: Members & Public
Size of Complex: 34 Acres

Contact/s:
- Club Secretary: Mr Peter Lees
  ☎ 01324 713811

Course/s:
- **POLMONT**
  Description: Wooded, Parkland, Undulating
  Built: 1901
  Number of Holes: 9 **Par:** 72
  Par 3's: 2 **Par 4's:** 5 **Par 5's:** 2
  Yds: 6030 **F9 Yds:** 3015 **B9 Yds:** 3015
  Further Information:
  9 hole course can be played as an 18 hole course

PONTARDAWE

PONTARDAWE GOLF CLUB (THE), Cefn Llan Rd, Pontardawe, Swansea, **SWANSEA**, SA8 4SH, **WALES**.
(T) 01792 863118

Course/s:
- **PONTARDAWE**
  Number of Holes: 18 **Par:** 70
  Yds: 6003 **F9 Yds:** 2950 **B9 Yds:** 3053

PONTEFRACT

PONTEFRACT GOLF COURSE, Golf Hse, Pontefract Pk, Pontefract, **YORKSHIRE (WEST)**, WF8 4RB, **ENGLAND**.
(T) 01977 723490

Membership: Members & Public/Public

Contact/s:
- Club Secretary: Mr Pat Ambler
  ☎ 01977 7367242
- Professional: Mr Roger Holland
- Pro Shop: Mr Nick Selvi
  ☎ 01924 360282

Course/s:
- **PONTEFRACT**
  Description: Wooded, Parkland, Undulating, Sheltered, Open, Short, Tight, Drains Well
  Green Speed: Medium
  Built: 1991 **Built On:** Chalk/Clay
  Number of Holes: 18 **Record:** 65 (Bob Wilson)
  Prevailing Wind: West

PONTEFRACT & DISTRICT

PONTEFRACT & DISTRICT GOLF CLUB, Pk Lane, Pontefract, **YORKSHIRE (WEST)**, WF8 4QS, **ENGLAND**.
(T) 01977 798886

Contact/s:
- Manager: Mr Phillip Morris

Course/s:
- **PONTEFRACT**
  Number of Holes: 18

PONTELAND

PONTELAND GOLF CLUB LTD, 53 Bell Villas, Ponteland, Newcastle Upon Tyne, **TYNE AND WEAR**, NE20 9BD, **ENGLAND**.
(T) 01661 822689

Contact/s:
- Club Secretary: Mr J N Dobson
- Professional: Mr Alan Robson-Crosby

Course/s:
- **PONTELAND**
  Number of Holes: 18 **Par:** 72
  Yds: 6523 **F9 Yds:** 3170 **B9 Yds:** 3353

PONTNEWYDD

PONTNEWYDD GOLF CLUB, Maesgwyn Farm, Upper Cwmbran, Cwmbran, **TORFAEN**, NP44 1AB, **WALES**.
(T) 01633 482170

Contact/s:
- Honorary Secretary: Mr C T Phillips
  ☎ 01633 484447

Course/s:
- **PONTNEWYDD**
  Number of Holes: 11 **Par:** 68
  Par 3's: 3 **Par 4's:** 7 **Par 5's:** 1
  Yds: 5278 **F9 Yds:** 2626 **B9 Yds:** 2652
  Further Information:
  10 hole course can be played as an 18 hole course; the 5th and 14th holes are interchangable.

PONTYPOOL

PONTYPOOL GOLF CLUB, Lasgarn Lane, Trevethin, Pontypool, **MONMOUTHSHIRE**, NP4 8TR, **WALES**.
(T) 01495 763655

Membership: Members & Public
Size of Complex: 156 Acres

Contact/s:
- Club Secretary: Mr Les Dodd
- Professional: Mr James Howard
  ☎ 01495 755544

Course/s:
- **PONTYPOOL**
  Description: Hilltop, Cliff Top, Undulating, Open, Tends to Flood
  Green Speed: Medium
  Built: 1903 **Built On:** Clay
  Number of Holes: 18 **Par:** 69
  Yds: 5963 **F9 Yds:** 3216 **B9 Yds:** 2747
  Prevailing Wind: South/West
  Further Information:
  This course has been built on the top of a mountain and has views of the Bristol channel.

PONTYPRIDD

PONTYPRIDD GOLF CLUB, Office, The Common, Pontypridd, **RHONDDA CYNON TAFF**, CF37 4DJ, **WALES**.
(T) 01443 491210

Contact/s:
- Manageress: Miss Victoria Hooley

Course/s:
- **PONTYPRIDD**
  Number of Holes: 18

PORT BANNATYNE

PORT BANNATYNE GOLF CLUB, Bannatyne Mains Rd, Port Bannatyne, Isle Of Bute, **ARGYLL AND BUTE**, PA20 0PH, **SCOTLAND**.
(T) 01700 504544

Membership: Members & Public

Contact/s:
- Book Tee Times: Mr Iain L MacLeod
  ☎ 01700 502009

Course/s:
- **PORT BANNATYNE**
  Description: Moorland, Hilltop, Open, Short, Drains Well
  Green Speed: Medium
  Built: 1912 **Built On:** Clay
  Number of Holes: 18 **Par:** 68
  Par 3's: 4 **Par 4's:** 14
  Yds: 5085 **F9 Yds:** 2629 **B9 Yds:** 2456
  Designer: Morrison
  Further Information:
  Panoramic views over Kames Bay to the Cowal Hills, Kyles of Bute, Loch Fyne and Kintyre.

PORT GLASGOW

PORT GLASGOW GOLF CLUB, Devol Rd, Port Glasgow, **RENFREWSHIRE**, PA14 5XE, **SCOTLAND**.
(T) 01475 704181

Contact/s:
- Honorary Secretary: Mr Alex Hughes

Course/s:
- **PORT GLASGOW**
  Number of Holes: 18 **Par:** 68
  Par 3's: 6 **Par 4's:** 10 **Par 5's:** 2
  Yds: 5712 **F9 Yds:** 3024 **B9 Yds:** 2688

PORT ST MARY

PORT ST MARY GOLF CLUB, Kallow Point Rd, Port St Mary, Port St Mary, **ISLE OF MAN**, **ENGLAND**.
(T) 01624 834932

Course/s:
- **PORT ST MARY**
  Number of Holes: 9
  Designer: George Duncan

PORT TALBOT

BRITISH STEEL PORT TALBOT GOLF CLUB, Matgam, Port Talbot, **NEATH PORT TALBOT**, SA13 2NF, **WALES**.
(T) 01639 814182
Course/s:
🏌 **PORT TALBOT**
  Number of Holes: 9

PORTADOWN

PORTADOWN GOLF CLUB, Secretary, 192 Gilford Rd, Portadown, Craigavon, **COUNTY ARMAGH**, BT63 5LF, **NORTHERN IRELAND**.
(T) 028 38355356
Contact/s:
• Club Secretary: Mrs M E Holloway
• Professional: Mr P Stevenson
Course/s:
🏌 **PORTADOWN**
  Number of Holes: 18 Par: 70
  Par 3's: 4 Par 4's: 12 Par 5's: 2
  Yds: 6130 F9 Yds: 3024 B9 Yds: 3106

PORTAL

PORTAL GOLF & COUNTRY CLUB, Cobblers Cross Lane, Tarporley, **CHESHIRE**, CW6 0DJ, **ENGLAND**.
(T) 01829 733933
(E) portalgolf@aol.com
(W) www.portalgolf.co.uk
Contact/s:
• Chief Executive: Mr D Wills
Course/s:
🏌 **ARDERNE**
  Number of Holes: 9 Par: 30
  Yds: 1724
  Designer: Mike Slater

🏌 **CHAMPIONSHIP**
  Built: 1980
  Number of Holes: 18 Par: 73
  Yds: 7037 F9 Yds: 3592 B9 Yds: 3445
  Designer: Donald Steel

🏌 **PREMIER**
  Built: 1990
  Number of Holes: 18 Par: 71
  Yds: 6538 F9 Yds: 3087 B9 Yds: 3451
  Designer: Tim Rouse

PORTAL PREMIER

PORTAL PREMIER GOLF & COUNTRY CLUB, Forest Rd, Tarporley, **CHESHIRE**, CW6 0JA, **ENGLAND**.
(T) 01829 733884
(E) julie@portal.aol
(W) www.portalpremier.co.uk
Membership: Members & Public
Contact/s:
• Professional: Ms Judy Statham
  ☎ 01829 733703
Course/s:
🏌 **PORTAL PREMIER**
  Description: Parkland, Undulating, Medium Length, Drains Well
  Green Speed: Medium
  Built: 1990
  Number of Holes: 18
  Designer: Tim Rouse

PORTARLINGTON

PORTARLINGTON GOLF CLUB, Garrhinch, Portarlington, **COUNTY LAOIS**, **IRELAND**.
(T) 050 223115

Course/s:
🏌 **PORTARLINGTON**
  Number of Holes: 18
  Designer: Edward Hackett

PORTER'S PARK

PORTER'S PARK GOLF CLUB, Shenley Hill, Radlett, **HERTFORDSHIRE**, WD7 7AZ, **ENGLAND**.
(T) 01923 854127
Membership: Members & Public
Contact/s:
• Club Secretary: Mr P Marshall
• Professional: Mr David Gleeson
  ☎ 01923 854366
Course/s:
🏌 **PORTER'S PARK**
  Built: 1890
  Number of Holes: 18

PORTHCAWL (ROYAL)

ROYAL PORTHCAWL GOLF CLUB, General Enquiries, Royal Porthcawl Golf Club, Porthcawl, **BRIDGEND**, CF36 3UW, **WALES**.
(T) 01656 773702
(W) www.royalporthcawl.com
Membership: Members & Public
Contact/s:
• Club Secretary: Mr S W Prescott
Course/s:
🏌 **ROYAL PORTHCAWL**
  Built: 1892
  Number of Holes: 18 Par: 72
  Par 3's: 4 Par 4's: 10 Par 5's: 4
  Yds: 6432 F9 Yds: 3182 B9 Yds: 3250
  Designer: Hawtree, Hunter, Simpson, Taylor 🏆

PORTHMADOG

PORTHMADOG GOLF CLUB, Secretary, Morfa Bychan, Porthmadog, **GWYNEDD**, LL49 9UU, **WALES**.
(T) 01766 514124
Course/s:
🏌 **PORTHMADOG**
  Number of Holes: 18
  Designer: James Braid

PORTHPEAN

PORTHPEAN GOLF CLUB, Porthpean, St. Austell, **CORNWALL**, PL26 6AY, **ENGLAND**.
(T) 01726 64613
Membership: Public
Contact/s:
• Club Secretary: Mrs K Tucker
Course/s:
🏌 **PORTHPEAN**
  Description: Parkland
  Number of Holes: 18 Par: 67
  Yds: 5210 F9 Yds: 2987 B9 Yds: 2223

PORTLAOISE PAR 3

PORTLAOISE PAR 3 GOLF COURSE, Meelick, Portlaoise, **COUNTY LAOIS**, **IRELAND**.
(T) 050 261557
Course/s:
🏌 **PORTLAOISE GOLF COURSE**
  Number of Holes: 18 Par: 57
  Par 3's: 15 Par 4's: 3
  Yds: 4621 F9 Yds: 1469 B9 Yds: 3152
  Further Information:
  Par 3 course, with the exception of holes

8, 9, and 11, which are all par 4

PORTLETHEN

PORTLETHEN GOLF CLUB, Badentoy Rd, Portlethen, Aberdeen, **ABERDEEN (CITY OF)**, AB12 4YA, **SCOTLAND**.
(T) 01224 781090
Membership: Members & Public
Contact/s:
• Professional: Ms Muriel Thompson
  ☎ 01224 782571
Course/s:
🏌 **PORTLETHEN**
  Description: Parkland, Undulating, Long
  Built: 1989 Built On: Soil
  Number of Holes: 18 Par: 72
  Yds: 6670 F9 Yds: 3327 B9 Yds: 3343
  Prevailing Wind: North
  Designer: C Sinclair

PORTMARNOCK

PORTMARNOCK GOLF CLUB, Portmarnock, **COUNTY DUBLIN**, **IRELAND**.
(T) 01 8462968
(E) info@portmarnockgolfclub.ie
(W) www.portmarnockgolfclub.ie/
Membership: Members & Public
Contact/s:
• Club Secretary: Mr John Quigley
• Book Tee Times: Miss Liz Rooney
Course/s:
🏌 **OLD**
  Description: Links, Long
  Built: 1894 Built On: Sand
  Number of Holes: 27 Par: 72
  Yds: 6900
  Designer: W C Pickeman, George Ross
  🏆

PORTMARNOCK HOTEL

PORTMARNOCK HOTEL & GOLF LINKS, Strand Rd, Portmarnock, **COUNTY DUBLIN**, **IRELAND**.
(T) 01 8460611
(E) reservations@portmarnock.com
(W) www.portmarnock.com
Membership: Public
Contact/s:
• Director Of Golf: Mrs Moira Cassady
Course/s:
🏌 **PORTMARNOCK LINKS**
  Description: Links, Undulating, Medium Length, Drains Well Built On: Sand
  Number of Holes: 18
  Designer: Bernhard Langer
  Further Information:
  There are 97 bunkers throughout the course.

PORTMORE GOLF PARK

PORTMORE GOLF PARK, Landkey Rd, Barnstaple, **DEVON**, EX32 9LB, **ENGLAND**.
(T) 01271 378378
(W) www.portmoregolf.co.uk
Membership: Members & Public
Size of Complex: 180 Acres
Contact/s:
• Club Secretary: Mr Colin Webber
• Professional: Mr Steven Goulds
Course/s:
🏌 **BARUM**
  Description: Wooded, Parkland, Sheltered, Medium Length, Drains Well
  Green Speed: Fast

Built: 1995 **Built On:** Sand
Number of Holes: 9 **Par:** 70
Par 3's: 2 **Par 4's:** 6 **Par 5's:** 1
Yds: 6096 **F9 Yds:** 3048 **B9 Yds:** 3048
Prevailing Wind: South/West
Designer: Hawtree
Further Information:
Barum can be played as an 18 hole course using different coloured markers. Alternatively the Barum course can be combined with the Landkey course to create an 18 hole round. All societies are welcome.

⛳ **LANDKEY**
Description: Wooded, Parkland, Sheltered, Medium Length, Drains Well
Green Speed: Fast **Built On:** Sand
Number of Holes: 9 **Par:** 54
Par 3's: 9
Yds: 3176 **F9 Yds:** 1588 **B9 Yds:** 1588
Further Information:
Landkey can be played as an 18 hole course using different coloured markers. Alternatively the Landkey course can be combined with the Barum course to create an 18 hole round.

PORTOBELLO

PORTOBELLO GOLF COURSE, Pavilion, Stanley St, Edinburgh, **EDINBURGH (CITY OF)**, EH15 1JJ, **SCOTLAND**.
(T) 0131 6694361
Contact/s:
• **Manager:** Mr R Winkler
Course/s:
⛳ **PORTOBELLO**
Number of Holes: 9

PORTPATRICK - DUNSKEY

PORTPATRICK GOLF CLUB, Golf Course Rd, Portpatrick, Stranraer, **DUMFRIES AND GALLOWAY**, DG9 8TB, **SCOTLAND**.
(T) 01776 810273
Membership: Members & Public
Size of Complex: 175 Acres
Contact/s:
• **Club Secretary:** Mr J A Hornbeery
• **Book Tee Times:** Mr J A Horbery
Course/s:
⛳ **DINVIN**
Description: Heath Land, Short, Drains Well
Built: 1910 **Built On:** Soil
Number of Holes: 9 **Par:** 27 **Record:** 23 (W M Lockie)
Par 3's: 9
Yds: 1504
Designer: Dunskey Estates
Further Information:
Excellent course for beginners or players without a handicap.

⛳ **DUNSKEY**
Description: Cliff Top, Undulating, Open, Medium Length, Drains Well
Green Speed: Fast
Built: 1903 **Built On:** Soil
Number of Holes: 18 **Par:** 70
Record: 63 (Gary Weir, Stephen McAllister)
Par 3's: 4 **Par 4's:** 12 **Par 5's:** 2
Yds: 5890
Prevailing Wind: South/West
Designer: W M Hunter
Further Information:
The course is very well maintained and gives exceptional views of the Irish coastline, Hull of Kintyre & Isle of Man.

PORTRUSH (ROYAL)

ROYAL PORTRUSH GOLF CLUB, Dunluce Rd, Portrush, **COUNTY ANTRIM**, BT56 8JQ, **NORTHERN IRELAND**.
(T) 028 70822311
(E) info@royalportrushgolfclub.com
(W) www.royalportrushgolfclub.com
Membership: Members & Public
Contact/s:
• **Club Secretary:** Ms Wilma Erskin
• **Professional:** Mr Gary McNeill
☎ 028 7082 3335
Course/s:
⛳ **DUNLUCE**
Description: Links
Built: 1888 **Built On:** Sand
Number of Holes: 18 **Par:** 72
Yds: 6818
Designer: Harry Shapland Colt 🏆
⛳ **VALLEY**
Number of Holes: 18
Designer: Harry Shapland Colt

PORTSALON

PORTSALON GOLF CLUB, Portsalon, Letterkenny, **COUNTY DONEGAL**, **IRELAND**.
(T) 074 59459
Course/s:
⛳ **PORTSALON**
Number of Holes: 18

PORTSMOUTH

PORTSMOUTH GOLF CLUB, Crookhorn Lane, Waterlooville, **HAMPSHIRE**, PO7 5QL, **ENGLAND**.
(T) 023 92372210
(E) info@portsmouthgc.com
(W) www.portsmouthgc.com
Membership: Members & Public
Contact/s:
• **Club Secretary:** Mr David Houlihan
☎ 02392 201827
• **Professional:** Mr Jason Banting
Course/s:
⛳ **PORTSMOUTH**
Description: Hilltop, Undulating, Medium Length
Green Speed: Medium
Built: 1970
Number of Holes: 18 **Par:** 69
Yds: 6139 **F9 Yds:** 3122 **B9 Yds:** 3017
Designer: Hawtree
Further Information:
Views of Portsmouth Harbour and the South Downs.

PORTSTEWART

PORTSTEWART GOLF CLUB, 117 Strand Rd, Portstewart, **COUNTY LONDONDERRY**, BT55 7PG, **NORTHERN IRELAND**.
(T) 028 70832015
(E) bill@portstewartgc.co.uk
(W) www.portstewartgc.co.uk
Membership: Members & Public
Contact/s:
• **Professional:** Alan Hunter
Course/s:
⛳ **OLD**
Number of Holes: 18 **Par:** 64
Yds: 4730
⛳ **RIVERSIDE**
Number of Holes: 9

⛳ **STRAND**
Description: Championship, Links
Built On: Sand
Number of Holes: 18 **Par:** 72
Yds: 6779
Designer: Griffin, Harris, Park 🏆

PORTUMNA

PORTUMNA GOLF CLUB, Portumna, **COUNTY GALWAY**, **IRELAND**.
(T) 050 941059
Course/s:
⛳ **PORTUMNA**
Number of Holes: 18
Designer: Edward Connaughton

POTTERGATE

POTTERGATE GOLF CLUB, Moor Lane, Branston, Lincoln, **LINCOLNSHIRE**, LN4 1JA, **ENGLAND**.
(T) 01522 794867
Membership: Members & Public
Size of Complex: 55 Acres
Contact/s:
• **Club Secretary:** Mr Nigel Marshalsay
☎ 01522 791935
• **Professional:** Mr Lee Tasker
Course/s:
⛳ **POTTERGATE**
Description: Parkland, Valley, Undulating, Sheltered, Medium Length, Drains Well, Ideal for the Elderly
Green Speed: Fast
Built: 1993 **Built On:** Sand
Number of Holes: 9
Prevailing Wind: West
Designer: Bailey

POTTERS BAR

POTTERS BAR GOLF CLUB, Darkes Lane, Potters Bar, **HERTFORDSHIRE**, EN6 1DE, **ENGLAND**.
(T) 01707 652020
Course/s:
⛳ **POTTERS BAR**
Number of Holes: 18
Designer: James Braid

POULT WOOD GOLF CTRE

POULT WOOD GOLF CENTRE, Higham Lane, Tonbridge, **KENT**, TN11 9QR, **ENGLAND**.
(T) 01732 364039
Contact/s:
• **Manager:** Mr C Miller
Course/s:
⛳ **POULTWOOD PUBLIC**
Number of Holes: 18

POULTON LE FYLDE

POULTON LE FYLDE GOLF CLUB, Breck Rd, Poulton-Le-Fylde, **LANCASHIRE**, FY6 7HJ, **ENGLAND**.
(T) 01253 893150
Course/s:
⛳ **POULTON LE FYLDE**
Number of Holes: 9
Designer: E Astbury

POWERSCOURT

POWERSCOURT GOLF CLUB PLC, Powerscourt, Enniskerry, **COUNTY WICKLOW**, **IRELAND**.

(T) 01 2046033
(E) golfclub@powerscourt.ie
(W) www.powerscourt.ie/golfclub
Membership: Members & Public
Size of Complex: 1000 Acres
Contact/s:
- **Club Secretary:** Mr Anthony Collins
- **Professional:** Mr Paul Thompson
- **Pro Shop:** Ms Helen O'Malley
- **Book Tee Times:** Ms Noeleen Corrigan
Course/s:
- **POWERSCOURT**
  Description: Championship, Parkland, Undulating, Sheltered, Open, Medium Length, Drains Well, Ideal for the Elderly
  Green Speed: Medium/Fast
  Built: 1996 **Built On:** Soil
  Number of Holes: 18 **Par:** 74
  Record: 68 (Paul Thompson)
  Par 3's: 4 **Par 4's:** 10 **Par 5's:** 4
  Yds: 6487 **F9 Yds:** 3226 **B9 Yds:** 3261
  Prevailing Wind: South
  Designer: P McEvoy
  Further Information:
  This free draining course with links characteristics offers stunning views to the sea and the Sugar Loaf Mountain.

POWFOOT

POWFOOT GOLF CLUB, Cummertrees, Powfoot, Annan, **DUMFRIES AND GALLOWAY**, DG12 5QE, **SCOTLAND**.
(T) 01461 700276
(E) bsutherland@powfootgolfclub.fsnet.co.uk
(W) www.powfoot.com
Membership: Members & Public
Contact/s:
- **Professional:** Mr Gareth Dick
Course/s:
- **POWFOOT**
  Description: Links, Breckland, Open, Medium Length, Drains Well, Ideal for the Elderly
  Green Speed: Medium/Fast
  Built: 1903 **Built On:** Sand
  Number of Holes: 18 **Par:** 69
  Record: 71 (Gareth Dick)
  Par 3's: 4 **Par 4's:** 13 **Par 5's:** 1
  Yds: 6255 **F9 Yds:** 3159 **B9 Yds:** 3096
  Prevailing Wind: East
  Designer: James Braid
  Further Information:
  On a clear day it is possible to see the Isle of Man.

PRAA SANDS

PRAA SANDS GOLF CLUB, Germoe Crossroads, Praa Sands, Penzance, **CORNWALL**, TR20 9TQ, **ENGLAND**.
(T) 01736 763445
Membership: Members & Public
Contact/s:
- **Club Secretary:** Mr Simon Edwards
Course/s:
- **PRAA SANDS**
  Description: Parkland
  Number of Holes: 9 **Par:** 62
  Par 3's: 5 **Par 4's:** 4
  Yds: 4122 **F9 Yds:** 2061 **B9 Yds:** 2061
  Designer: R Hamilton
  Further Information:
  9 hole course can be played as an 18 hole course

PRENTON

PRENTON GOLF CLUB, Golf Links Rd, Birkenhead, **MERSEYSIDE**, CH42 8LW,

ENGLAND.
(T) 0151 6081461
Size of Complex: 150 Acres
Contact/s:
- **Professional:** Mr Robin Thompson
  ☎ 0151 6081636
Course/s:
- **PRENTON**
  Description: Parkland, Undulating, Open, Long, Drains Well
  Green Speed: Medium
  Built: 1905 **Built On:** Soil
  Number of Holes: 18
  Designer: James Braid

PRESTATYN

PRESTATYN GOLF CLUB, Marine Rd East, Prestatyn, **DENBIGHSHIRE**, LL19 7HS, **WALES**.
(T) 01745 854320
(E) manager@prestatyngc.co.uk
(W) www.prestatyngc.co.uk
Membership: Members & Public
Size of Complex: 180 Acres
Contact/s:
- **Club Secretary:** Mr Roy Woodruff
  ☎ 01745 888353
- **Professional:** Mr Malcolm Staton
  ☎ 01745 852083
Course/s:
- **PRESTATYN**
  Description: Championship, Links, Long, Drains Well, Ideal for the Elderly
  Green Speed: Fast
  Built: 1905 **Built On:** Sand
  Number of Holes: 18 **Par:** 72
  Yds: 6564 **F9 Yds:** 3466 **B9 Yds:** 3098
  Prevailing Wind: West
  Designer: J Collins

PRESTBURY

PRESTBURY GOLF CLUB, Macclesfield Rd, Prestbury, Macclesfield, **CHESHIRE**, SK10 4BJ, **ENGLAND**.
(T) 01625 828241
(E) office@prestburygolfclub.com
(W) www.prestburygolfclub.com
Contact/s:
- **Manager:** Mr N Wright
Course/s:
- **PRESTBURY**
  Number of Holes: 18 **Par:** 71
  Yds: 6359 **F9 Yds:** 3285 **B9 Yds:** 3074
  Designer: Harry Shapland Colt

PRESTON

PRESTON GOLF CLUB, Fulwood Old Hall, Fulwood Hall Lane, Preston, **LANCASHIRE**, PR2 8DD, **ENGLAND**.
(T) 01772 700022
Membership: Members & Public
Size of Complex: 150 Acres
Contact/s:
- **Club Secretary:** Mr D Sanders
  ☎ 01772 700011
- **Professional:** Mr A Greenbank
Course/s:
- **PRESTON (FULWOOD)**
  Description: Wooded, Parkland, Undulating, Sheltered, Medium Length
  Green Speed: Medium
  Built: 1892 **Built On:** Clay
  Number of Holes: 18 **Par:** 71
  Designer: James Braid
  Further Information:
  The course is traditional of its era, the

bunkers all have Braid rolled over faces. Holes 2 - 4 and 17 are particularly challenging and holes 14 - 18 have extremely demanding finishes.

PRESTONFIELD

PRESTONFIELD GOLF CLUB, 6 Priestfield Rd North, Edinburgh, **EDINBURGH (CITY OF)**, EH16 5HS, **SCOTLAND**.
(T) 0131 6671381
(E) prestonfield@btclick.com
(W) www.prestonfieldgolfclub.co.uk
Membership: Members & Public
Contact/s:
- **Club Secretary:** Mr A Robertson
Course/s:
- **PRESTONFIELD**
  Description: Parkland
  Built: 1920
  Number of Holes: 18 **Par:** 70
  Yds: 6214 **F9 Yds:** 3087 **B9 Yds:** 3127
  Designer: James Braid

PRESTWICH

PRESTWICH GOLF CLUB, Hilton Lane, Prestwich, Manchester, **MANCHESTER (GREATER)**, M25 9XB, **ENGLAND**.
(T) 0161 7732544
Contact/s:
- **Club Secretary:** Mr S Wakefield
- **Professional:**
  ☎ 0161 7731404
Course/s:
- **PRESTWICH**
  Number of Holes: 18 **Par:** 64
  Yds: 4806 **F9 Yds:** 2493 **B9 Yds:** 2313

PRESTWICK

PRESTWICK GOLF CLUB, 2 Links Rd, Prestwick, **AYRSHIRE (SOUTH)**, KA9 1QG, **SCOTLAND**.
(T) 01292 477404
(E) bookings@prestwickgc.co.uk
(W) www.prestwickgc.co.uk
Membership: Members & Public
Contact/s:
- **Club Secretary:** Mr Ian Bunch
- **Professional:** Mr Frank Rennie
  ☎ 01292 479483
Course/s:
- **PRESTWICK**
  Description: Links, Open, Long
  Green Speed: Fast
  Built: 1851 **Built On:** Sand
  Number of Holes: 18 **Par:** 71
  Par 3's: 3 **Par 4's:** 13 **Par 5's:** 2
  Yds: 6544 **F9 Yds:** 3250 **B9 Yds:** 3294
  Designer: Tom Morris ♛

PRESTWICK ST CUTHBERT

PRESTWICK ST CUTHBERT GOLF CLUB, East Rd, Prestwick, **AYRSHIRE (SOUTH)**, KA9 2SX, **SCOTLAND**.
(T) 01292 477101
Membership: Members & Public
Course/s:
- **PRESTWICK ST CUTHBERT**
  Description: Parkland
  Built: 1899
  Number of Holes: 18 **Par:** 71

PRESTWICK ST NICHOLAS

PRESTWICK ST NICHOLAS GOLF CLUB,
31 Grangemuir Rd, Prestwick, **AYRSHIRE (SOUTH)**, KA9 1SN, **SCOTLAND**.
(T) 01292 473903

Course/s:
- **PRESTWICK ST NICHOLAS**
  Number of Holes: 18
  Designer: Charles Hunter

PRINCES

PRINCES GOLF CLUB (SANDWICH),
Princes Drive, Sandwich Bay, Sandwich, **KENT**, CT13 9QB, **ENGLAND**.
(T) 01304 613797
(E) golf@princes-leisure.co.uk
(W) www.princes-leisure.co.uk

Membership: Members & Public

Contact/s:
- **Club Secretary:** Mrs Ali McGuirk
  ☎ 01304 611118
- **Professional:** Mr Derek Barbour

Course/s:
- **DUNES**
  Number of Holes: 9   **Par:** 36
  Par 3's: 2   **Par 4's:** 5   **Par 5's:** 2
  Yds: 3343

- **HIMALAYAS**
  Description: Championship, Links, Open, Long, Drains Well, Ideal for the Elderly
  Green Speed: Medium
  Built: 1951   **Built On:** Sand
  Number of Holes: 9   **Par:** 35 **Record:** 64 (Howard Clark)
  Par 3's: 2   **Par 4's:** 6   **Par 5's:** 1
  Yds: 3017
  Prevailing Wind: South/West
  Designer: Deeley, Lucas, Mallaby
  Further Information:
  Any two 9 holes can be played together as 18 holes.

- **SHORE**
  Number of Holes: 9   **Par:** 36
  Par 3's: 2   **Par 4's:** 5   **Par 5's:** 2
  Yds: 3347

PRINCE'S

PRINCE'S GOLF COURSE, Llanfaes, Beaumaris, **ISLE OF ANGLESEY**, LL58 8HU, **WALES**.
(T) 01248 811717

Membership: Members & Public

Contact/s:
- **Club Secretary:** Mr Peter Maton

Course/s:
- **PRINCES'**
  Description: Wooded, Parkland, Medium Length
  Green Speed: Fast
  Built: 1996
  Number of Holes: 18
  Designer: Rodger Jones

PRINCES GOLF & LEISURE CLUB

PRINCES GOLF & LEISURE CLUB (THE),
Darenth Rd, Dartford, **KENT**, DA1 1LZ, **ENGLAND**.
(T) 01322 276565

Course/s:
- **PRINCES COURSE**
  Number of Holes: 9   **Par:** 54
  Par 3's: 9
  Yds: 2040   **F9 Yds:** 1020   **B9 Yds:** 1020
  Further Information:

Can be played as an 18 hole course

PRINCES RISBOROUGH

PRINCES RISBOROUGH GOLF CLUB, Lee Rd, Saunderton Lee, Princes Risborough, **BUCKINGHAMSHIRE**, HP27 9NX, **ENGLAND**.
(T) 01844 346989
(W) www.prgc.co.uk

Membership: Members & Public

Contact/s:
- **Professional:** Mr Simon Lowry

Course/s:
- **PRINCES RISBOROUGH**
  Description: Parkland, Undulating, Sheltered, Short, Tight, Drains Well
  Green Speed: Medium
  Built: 1990   **Built On:** Chalk
  Number of Holes: 9   **Par:** 68 **Record:** 63 (Mark Booth)
  Par 3's: 2   **Par 4's:** 7
  Yds: 5522   **F9 Yds:** 2785   **B9 Yds:** 2737
  Prevailing Wind: West
  Designer: Guy Hunt
  Further Information:
  9 hole course can be played as an 18 hole course

PRIORS

PRIORS GOLF COURSE, Horseman Side, Navestockside, Brentwood, **ESSEX**, CM14 5ST, **ENGLAND**.
(T) 01277 373344
(E) staplefordabbotts@americangolf.uk.com
(W) www.americangolf.com

Membership: Members & Public

Contact/s:
- **Professional:** Mr Alan Hall
- **Book Tee Times:** Mr Denis Newell

Course/s:
- **PRIORS**
  Description: Parkland, Undulating, Open, Short, Drains Well
  Green Speed: Medium
  Built: 1992   **Built On:** Clay
  Number of Holes: 18
  Prevailing Wind: South/East
  Designer: Howard Swan

PRISKILLY

PRISKILLY FOREST GOLF CLUB, Priskilly Forest, Castle Morris, Haverfordwest, **PEMBROKESHIRE**, SA62 5EH, **WALES**.
(T) 01348 840276
(E) jevans@priskilly-forest.co.uk
(W) www.priskilly-forest.co.uk

Membership: Public
Size of Complex: 45 Acres

Contact/s:
- **Professional:** Mr S Parsons
- **Pro Shop:** Mr Phil Evans

Course/s:
- **PRISIKILLY**
  Description: Parkland, Undulating, Sheltered, Medium Length, Drains Well
  Green Speed: Medium
  Built: 1992   **Built On:** Soil
  Number of Holes: 9   **Par:** 70
  Yds: 5900   **F9 Yds:** 2950   **B9 Yds:** 2950
  Prevailing Wind: West
  Designer: J Walters
  Further Information:
  This challebging course is set in the grounds of an old manor house.

PRUDHOE

PRUDHOE GOLF CLUB, Eastwood Pk, Prudhoe, **NORTHUMBERLAND**, NE42 5DX, **ENGLAND**.
(T) 01661 832466

Contact/s:
- **Professional:** Mr John Crawford
- **Book Tee Times:**
  ☎ 01661 836188

Course/s:
- **PRUDHOE**
  Description: Parkland, Undulating
  Built: 1930
  Number of Holes: 18   **Par:** 69

PRYORS HAYES

PRYORS HAYES GOLF CLUB, Willington Rd, Tarvin, Chester, **CHESHIRE**, CH3 8NL, **ENGLAND**.
(T) 01829 741250 or 740140
(E) info@pryors-hayes.co.uk
(W) www.pryors-hayes.co.uk

Membership: Members & Public

Contact/s:
- **Club Secretary:** Ms Joan Quinn
- **Professional:** Mr Sean O'Conner

Course/s:
- **PRYORS HAYES**
  Description: Parkland, Short, Ideal for the Elderly
  Built: 1993
  Number of Holes: 18
  Designer: John Day

PUCKS CASTLE PAR 3

PUCKS CASTLE PAR 3, Pucks Castle Lane Rathmichael, Wicklow, **COUNTY WICKLOW**, **IRELAND**.
(T) 012 954281

Course/s:
- **COURSE #1**
  Number of Holes: 18   **Par:** 54
  Par 3's: 18

PUMPHERSTON

PUMPHERSTON GOLF CLUB,
Drumshoreland Rd, Pumpherston, Livingston, **LOTHIAN (WEST)**, EH53 0LQ, **SCOTLAND**.
(T) 01506 432869

Contact/s:
- **Golf Co-Ordinator:** Mr J S Lamond

Course/s:
- **PUMPHERSTON**
  Number of Holes: 18   **Par:** 70
  Yds: 6022   **F9 Yds:** 2956   **B9 Yds:** 3066

PURLEY CHASE

PURLEY CHASE GOLF CLUB, Pipers Lane, Ridge Lane, Nuneaton, **WARWICKSHIRE**, CV10 0RB, **ENGLAND**.
(T) 01203 393118

Course/s:
- **PURLEY CHASE**
  Number of Holes: 18   **Par:** 72
  Yds: 6772

PURLEY DOWNS

PURLEY DOWNS GOLF CLUB, 106 Purley Downs Rd, South Croydon, **SURREY**, CR2 0RB, **ENGLAND**.
(T) 020 86578347
(E) info@purleydowns.cc.uk

Contact/s:
- Club Secretary: Mr P Gallienne

Course/s:
- 🏌 **PURLEY DOWNS**
  Number of Holes: 18   Par: 70
  Yds: 6286   F9 Yds: 3086   B9 Yds: 3200
  Designer: Harry Shapland Colt, J Taylor

PUTTENHAM

PUTTENHAM GOLF CLUB LTD, Heath Rd,
Puttenham, Guildford, **SURREY**, GU3 1AL,
ENGLAND.
(T) 01483 810498

Membership: Members & Public
Size of Complex: 140 Acres

Contact/s:
- Professional: Mr Gary Simmons
  ☎ 01483 810277
- Pro Shop: Mr Dean Lintott
- Book Tee Times: Mrs Kate Sturrock

Course/s:
- 🏌 **PUTTENHAM**
  Description: Wooded, Heath Land,
  Undulating, Medium Length, Tight, Drains
  Well
  Green Speed: Medium
  Built: 1894   Built On: Sand/Soil
  Number of Holes: 18   Par: 71
  Par 3's: 3   Par 4's: 13   Par 5's: 2
  Yds: 6211   F9 Yds: 3088   B9 Yds: 3123
  Designer: Donald Steel

PWLLHELI

PWLLHELI GOLF CLUB, Golf Rd, Pwllheli,
GWYNEDD, LL53 5PS, **WALES**.
(T) 01758 701644

Contact/s:
- Professional: Mr J Pilkington

Course/s:
- 🏌 **PWLLHELI**
  Number of Holes: 18   Par: 69
  Par 3's: 3   Par 4's: 15
  Yds: 6108   F9 Yds: 3183   B9 Yds: 2925
  Designer: Tom Morris

PYLE & KENFIG

PYLE & KENFIG GOLF CLUB, Kenfig,
Bridgend, **BRIDGEND**, CF33 4PU, **WALES**.
(T) 01656 783093

Contact/s:
- Company Secretary: Mr S Anthony

Course/s:
- 🏌 **PYLE & KENFIG**
  Number of Holes: 18
  Designer: Harry Shapland Colt

PYPE HAYES

PYPE HAYES GOLF COURSE, Eachelhurst
Rd, Walmley, Sutton Coldfield, **MIDLANDS
(WEST)**, B76 1EP, **ENGLAND**.
(T) 0121 3511014

Membership: Public

Contact/s:
- Manager: Mr J Bayliss

Course/s:
- 🏌 **PYPE HAYES**
  Description: Parkland, Open
  Built: 1933
  Number of Holes: 18
  Designer: Bobby Jones
  Further Information:
  Top public course, awarded by Fore
  Readers in 1997.

PYRFORD GOLF CLUB

AMERICAN GOLF CORPORATION, Warren
Lane, Pyrford, Woking, **SURREY**, GU22 8XR,
ENGLAND.
(T) 01483 723555
(E) pyrford@americangolf.com
(W) www.americangolf.com

Membership: Members & Public
Size of Complex: 100 Acres

Contact/s:
- Professional: Mr D Brewer
  ☎ 01483 751070

Course/s:
- 🏌 **PYRFORD**
  Description: Links, Wooded, Parkland,
  Open, Medium Length, Tight, Drains Well
  Green Speed: Medium
  Built: 1993
  Number of Holes: 18   Par: 70
  Record: 63 (Jeremy Bennett)
  Prevailing Wind: South/West
  Designer: Peter Alliss, Clive Clark
  Further Information:
  A flat, challenging course with water
  coming into play on 13 holes.

PYTCHLEY GOLF LODGE

PYTCHLEY GOLF LODGE (THE), Pytchley
Lane, Kettering, **NORTHAMPTONSHIRE**,
NN14 1EY, **ENGLAND**.
(T) 01536 511527

Membership: Members & Public

Contact/s:
- Club Secretary: David Nash
- Professional: Peter Machin
  ☎ 01536 512000
- Book Lessons: Jim Delves

Course/s:
- 🏌 **PYTCHLEY GOLF LODGE**
  Description: Parkland, Undulating, Short,
  Drains Well, Ideal for the Elderly
  Green Speed: Medium
  Built: 2000
  Number of Holes: 9
  Designer: Roger Griffiths Associates
  Ruby

QUEENS PARK

QUEENS PARK GOLF COURSE, Queens Pk
West Drive, Bournemouth, **DORSET**, BH8
9BY, **ENGLAND**.
(T) 01202 396817

Contact/s:
- Manager: Mr R Hill

Course/s:
- 🏌 **QUEEN'S PARK**
  Number of Holes: 18

QUEENS PARK

QUEENS PARK GOLF COURSE, Queen's Pk
Drive, Crewe, **CHESHIRE**, CW2 7SB,
ENGLAND.
(T) 01270 666724

Course/s:
- 🏌 **QUEEN'S PARK**
  Number of Holes: 9

QUEENSBURY

QUEENSBURY GOLF CLUB, Brighouse Rd,
Queensbury, Bradford, **YORKSHIRE
(WEST)**, BD13 1QF, **ENGLAND**.
(T) 01274 882155

Contact/s:
- Club Secretary: Mr Barry Cox

Course/s:
- 🏌 **QUEENSBURY**
  Number of Holes: 9   Par: 32
  Yds: 2401   F9 Yds: 2401

QUINNAGH HOUSE PAR 3

QUINNAGH HOUSE PAR 3, Quinnagh,
Carlow, **COUNTY CARLOW**, **IRELAND**.
(T) 050 342088

Course/s:
- 🏌 **COURSE #1**
  Number of Holes: 18   Par: 54
  Par 3's: 18
  Yds: 2850

RADCLIFFE-ON-TRENT

RADCLIFFE-ON-TRENT GOLF CLUB,
Dewberry Lane, Cropwell Rd, Radcliffe-on-
Trent, Nottingham, **NOTTINGHAMSHIRE**,
NG12 2JH, **ENGLAND**.
(T) 0115 9333000
(E) les.rotgc@talk21.com
(W) www.radcliffeontrentgc.com
Size of Complex: 110 Acres

Contact/s:
- Club Secretary: Mr L Wake

Course/s:
- 🏌 **RADCLIFFE-ON-TRENT**
  Description: Parkland, Undulating,
  Medium Length, Drains Well
  Green Speed: Medium
  Built: 1909   Built On: Clay
  Number of Holes: 18   Par: 70
  Par 3's: 4   Par 4's: 12   Par 5's: 2
  Yds: 6381   F9 Yds: 3225   B9 Yds: 3156
  Designer: Pennink, Tom Williamson
  Further Information:
  The 16th - 18th holes are particularly
  challenging.

RADISSON ROE PARK

**RADISSON ROE PARK HOTEL & GOLF
RESORT,** Roe Pk, Limavady, **COUNTY
LONDONDERRY**, BT49 9LB, **NORTHERN
IRELAND**.
(T) 028 71722222

Course/s:
- 🏌 **RADISSON ROE PARK**
  Number of Holes: 18
  Designer: Frank Ainsworth

RADNOR GOLF & SKI CTRE

RADNOR GOLF & SKI CENTRE, Radnor Rd,
Treleigh, Redruth, **CORNWALL**, TR16 5EL,
ENGLAND.
(T) 01209 211059
(W) www.radnorgolfski.fsnet.co.uk

Contact/s:
- Owner: Mr Gordon Wallbank

Course/s:
- 🏌 **RADNOR**
  Number of Holes: 9   Par: 27
  Par 3's: 9
  Yds: 1312

RADYR

RADYR GOLF CLUB, Drysgol Rd, Radyr,
Cardiff, **GLAMORGAN (VALE OF)**, CF15
8BS, **WALES**.
(T) 029 2084 2408
(E)
themanager@radyrgolfclub.sagehost.co.uk
(W) www.radyrgolf.co.uk

Contact/s:
- Club Manager: Mr Alan M Edwards

Course/s:

⛳ **RADYR**
Number of Holes: 18   Par: 69
Yds: 6078   F9 Yds: 3124   B9 Yds: 2954

RAF ST ATHAN

RAF ST. ATHAN GOLF CLUB, Clive Rd, St. Athan, Barry, **GLAMORGAN (VALE OF),** CF62 4JD, **WALES**.
(T) 01446 797186

Contact/s:
● Club Manager: Mr P F Woodhouse
    ☎ 01446 751043

Course/s:

⛳ **RAF ST ATHAN**
Number of Holes: 9   Par: 72
Yds: 6480   F9 Yds: 3086   B9 Yds: 3086

RAGLAN PARC

RAGLAN PARC GOLF CLUB, Station Rd, Raglan, Usk, **MONMOUTHSHIRE,** NP15 2ER, **WALES**.
(T) 01291 690077

Membership: Members & Public

Contact/s:
● Club Secretary: Mr Andrew Crump
● Professional: Mr Garath Cace
● Pro Shop: Ms Simone Clay

Course/s:

⛳ **RAGLAN PARC**
Description: Parkland, Undulating, Sheltered, Open, Medium Length, Drains Well, Ideal for the Elderly
Green Speed: Medium
Built: 1994   Built On: Sand/Soil
Number of Holes: 18

RALSTON

RALSTON GOLF CLUB, Strathmore Ave, Paisley, **RENFREWSHIRE,** PA1 3DT, **SCOTLAND**.
(T) 0141 8821349

Contact/s:
● Club Secretary: Mr J Pearson
● Professional: Mr C Munro
● Pro Shop:
    ☎ 0141 8104925

Course/s:

⛳ **RALSTON**
Description: Parkland, Undulating, Open, Long, Tight, Drains Well
Green Speed: Medium
Built: 1904   Built On: Clay
Number of Holes: 18   Par: 71
Yds: 6113   F9 Yds: 2961   B9 Yds: 3152
Designer: James Braid
Further Information:
The course has a pond on the 18th hole.

RAMADA HOTEL

RAMADA HOTEL & RESORT, Matson Lane, Matson, Gloucester, **GLOUCESTERSHIRE,** GL4 6EA, **ENGLAND**.
(T) 01452 525653

Contact/s:
● Assistant Professional: Mr Keith Wood

Course/s:

⛳ **JARVIS GLOUCESTER HOTEL & COUNTRY CLUB**
Number of Holes: 18

RAMSDALE PARK

RAMSDALE PARK GOLF CENTRE, The Clubhouse, Oxton Rd, Calverton, Nottingham, **NOTTINGHAMSHIRE,** NG14 6NU, **ENGLAND**.
(T) 0115 9655600

Membership: Public
Size of Complex: 320 Acres

Contact/s:
● Professional: Mr Robert Macey

Course/s:

⛳ **RAMSDALE PARK MAIN**
Description: Parkland, Undulating, Open, Medium Length
Green Speed: Medium
Built: 1992   Built On: Clay/Sand
Number of Holes: 18   Par: 71
Yds: 6546   F9 Yds: 3091   B9 Yds: 3455
Designer: Hawtree

⛳ **THE PAR 3**
Built: 1992
Number of Holes: 18
Designer: Hawtree

RAMSEY

RAMSEY GOLF CLUB, Brookfield, Ramsey, **ISLE OF MAN,** IM8 2AH, **ENGLAND**.
(T) 01624 812244

Contact/s:
● Club Secretary: Mrs J Hignett

Course/s:

⛳ **RAMSEY**
Number of Holes: 18   Par: 70
Par 3's: 5   Par 4's: 10   Par 5's: 3
Yds: 5982   F9 Yds: 2877   B9 Yds: 3105
Designer: James Braid

RAMSEY CLUB

RAMSEY GOLF CLUB, 4 Abbey Trce, Ramsey, Huntingdon, **CAMBRIDGESHIRE,** PE26 1DD, **ENGLAND**.
(T) 01487 812600

Contact/s:
● Club Secretary: Mr Brian Goddard
● Professional: Mr Stewart Scott
    ☎ 01487 813022

Course/s:

⛳ **RAMSEY CLUB**
Description: Parkland, Sheltered, Medium Length, Tight, Tends to Flood, Ideal for the Elderly
Green Speed: Medium/Fast
Built: 1965   Built On: Clay
Number of Holes: 18   Par: 71
Par 3's: 6   Par 4's: 7   Par 5's: 5
Yds: 6163
Designer: J Hamilton-Stutt
Further Information:
The course has fantastic panoramic views.

RAMSIDE

RAMSIDE GOLF CLUB, Ramside Hall Hotel, Durham, **COUNTY DURHAM,** DH1 1TD, **ENGLAND**.
(T) 0191 3869514

Membership: Members & Public

Contact/s:
● Captain: Mr Neil Dunningham

Course/s:

⛳ **BISHOPS**
Description: Championship, Parkland, Open, Long, Drains Well, Ideal for the Elderly
Green Speed: Medium
Built On: Clay/Sand
Number of Holes: 9
Prevailing Wind: West

Designer: Jonathan Gaunt

⛳ **CATHEDRAL**
Description: Championship, Parkland, Open, Long, Drains Well, Ideal for the Elderly
Green Speed: Medium
Built: 1996   Built On: Clay/Sand
Number of Holes: 9
Prevailing Wind: West
Designer: Jonathan Gaunt

⛳ **PRINCES**
Description: Championship, Parkland, Long, Drains Well, Ideal for the Elderly
Green Speed: Medium
Built: 1996   Built On: Clay/Sand
Number of Holes: 9   Record: 66
Prevailing Wind: West
Designer: Jonathan Gaunt

RANFURLY

OLD COURSE, RANFURLY GOLF CLUB (THE), Ranfurly Pl, Bridge Of Weir, **RENFREWSHIRE,** PA11 3DE, **SCOTLAND**.
(T) 01505 613214
(W) www.oldranfurly.com

Membership: Members & Public

Contact/s:
● Club Secretary: Mr Q McClymont
    ☎ 01505 613514
● Book Tee Times: Mrs E Shearer
    ☎ 01505 613612

Course/s:

⛳ **THE OLD, RANFURLY**
Description: Heath Land, Moorland, Undulating, Open, Medium Length, Tight, Drains Well
Green Speed: Medium
Built: 1905   Built On: Soil
Number of Holes: 18   Par: 70
Record: 65 (Campbell Elliot)
Prevailing Wind: South/West
Designer: William Park

RANFURLY CASTLE

RANFURLY CASTLE GOLF CLUB LTD, Golf Course Rd, Bridge Of Weir, **RENFREWSHIRE,** PA11 3HN, **SCOTLAND**.
(T) 01505 614795

Contact/s:
● Company Secretary: Mr J King

Course/s:

⛳ **RANFURLY CASTLE**
Number of Holes: 18   Par: 70
Yds: 6284   F9 Yds: 3044   B9 Yds: 3240
Designer: W Auchterlomie, A Kirkcaldy

RATHASPECK MANOR

RATHASPECK MANOR GOLF COURSE, Rathaspeck, **COUNTY WEXFORD, IRELAND**.
(T) 053 42661
(W) www.theaa.com/hotels/43155.html

Course/s:

⛳ **RATHASPECK MANOR GOLF COURSE**
Number of Holes: 18   Par: 54
Par 3's: 18
Yds: 2500

RATHBANE

RATHBANE GOLF COURSE, Rathbane, **COUNTY LIMERICK, IRELAND**.
(T) 061 313655

Membership: Members & Public

Contact/s:
● Professional: Mr Noel Cassidy

Course/s:

🏌 **RATHBONE**
Description: Parkland, Medium Length, Drains Well
Green Speed: Medium
Built: 1997
Number of Holes: 18
Designer: James Healy

RATHDOWNEY

RATHDOWNEY GOLF CLUB, Rathdowney, **COUNTY LAOIS**, **IRELAND**.
(T) 050 546170

Contact/s:
● **Honorary Secretary:** Mr Sean Bolger
☎ 050 546233

Course/s:

🏌 **RATHDOWNEY**
Number of Holes: 18   **Par:** 71
Par 3's: 4   **Par 4's:** 11   **Par 5's:** 3
Yds: 5864   **F9 Yds:** 2944   **B9 Yds:** 2920
Designer: Edward Hackett

RATHFARNHAM

RATHFARNHAM GOLF CLUB, Newtown, Rathfarnham, Dublin, **COUNTY DUBLIN**, **IRELAND**.
(T) 01 4931201

Contact/s:
● **Club Secretary:** Mr Colin McInerey
● **Professional:** Mr Brian O'Hara

Course/s:

🏌 **RATHFARNHAM**
Number of Holes: 9   **Par:** 71
Par 3's: 2   **Par 4's:** 5   **Par 5's:** 2
Yds: 5693   **F9 Yds:** 2845   **B9 Yds:** 2848
Designer: John Jacobs
Further Information:
9 hole course can be played as an 18 hole course

RATHMORE

RATHMORE GOLF CLUB, Bushmills Rd, Portrush, **COUNTY ANTRIM**, BT56 8JG, **NORTHERN IRELAND**.
(T) 028 70822996

Contact/s:
● **Owner:** Mr D Williamson

Course/s:

🏌 **RATHMORE**
Number of Holes: 18

RATHO PARK

RATHO PARK GOLF CLUB LTD, Secretary, Newbridge, **EDINBURGH (CITY OF)**, EH28 8NX, **SCOTLAND**.
(T) 0131 3331752

Contact/s:
● **Manager:** Mr J Preston

Course/s:

🏌 **RATHO PARK**
Number of Holes: 18
Designer: James Braid

RATHSALLAGH

RATHSALLAGH GOLF & COUNTRY CLUB, Rathsallagh, Dunlavin, **COUNTY WICKLOW**, **IRELAND**.
(T) 045 403316
(E) info@rathsallagh.com
(W) www.rathsallagh.com

Membership: Members & Public
Size of Complex: 260 Acres

Contact/s:
● **Professional:** Mr Brendan McDaid
● **Pro Shop:** Mr Kevin McGrath
● **Book Tee Times:** Ms Maeve Byrne

Course/s:

🏌 **RATHSALLAGH**
Description: Championship, Wooded, Parkland, Long, Drains Well
Green Speed: Fast
Built: 1994   **Built On:** Sand
Number of Holes: 18   **Par:** 72
Par 3's: 4   **Par 4's:** 10   **Par 5's:** 4
Yds: 6481   **F9 Yds:** 3227   **B9 Yds:** 3254
Designer: P McEvoy, Christy O'Connor

RAVELSTON

RAVELSTON GOLF CLUB LTD, 24 Ravelston Dykes Rd, Edinburgh, **EDINBURGH (CITY OF)**, EH4 3NZ, **SCOTLAND**.
(T) 0131 3432177

Contact/s:
● **Club Secretary:** Mr Jim Lowrie

Course/s:

🏌 **RAVELSTON**
Number of Holes: 9   **Par:** 66
Yds: 5218   **F9 Yds:** 2609   **B9 Yds:** 2609
Designer: James Braid

RAVEN HALL

RAVEN HALL COUNTRY HOUSE HOTEL GOLF COURSE, Ravenscar, Scarborough, **YORKSHIRE (NORTH)**, YO13 0ET, **ENGLAND**.
(T) 01723 870353

Course/s:

🏌 **RAVEN HALL HOTEL**
Number of Holes: 9

RAVENMEADOW

RAVENMEADOW GOLF CLUB LTD, Clubhouse/Professional, Hindlip Lane, Hindlip, Worcester, **WORCESTERSHIRE**, WR3 8SA, **ENGLAND**.
(T) 01905 757525

Membership: Public

Course/s:

🏌 **RAVENMEADOW**
Number of Holes: 18

RAVENSPARK

RAVENSPARK GOLF COURSE, 12-13 Kidsneuk, Irvine, **AYRSHIRE (NORTH)**, KA12 8SR, **SCOTLAND**.
(T) 01294 271293
(W) www.irgc.co.uk

Membership: Public

Contact/s:
● **Club Secretary:** Mr Sandy Howie
● **Professional:** Mr Peter Bond
☎ 01294 276467

Course/s:

🏌 **RAVENSPARK**
Description: Parkland, Medium Length, Ideal for the Elderly
Green Speed: Medium
Built: 1807   **Built On:** Clay
Number of Holes: 18   **Par:** 71
Yds: 6457   **F9 Yds:** 3145   **B9 Yds:** 3312
Further Information:
Ravenspark is a flat course.

RAVENSWORTH

RAVENSWORTH GOLF CLUB, Moss Side, Gateshead, **TYNE AND WEAR**, NE9 7UU,

ENGLAND.
(T) 0191 4876014
(W) www.ravensworthgolfclub.co.uk

Contact/s:
● **Chairman:** Mr Collin A Reay
☎ 0191 4206696

Course/s:

🏌 **RAVENSWORTH**
Number of Holes: 18   **Par:** 69
Yds: 5966   **F9 Yds:** 3005   **B9 Yds:** 2961
Designer: J W Fraser

RAWDON

RAWDON GOLF & LAWN TENNIS CLUB, Buckstone Drive, Rawdon, Leeds, **YORKSHIRE (WEST)**, LS19 6BD, **ENGLAND**.
(T) 0113 2505017

Contact/s:
● **Treasurer:** Mr J Cartwright

Course/s:

🏌 **RAWDON**
Number of Holes: 9

READING

READING GOLF CLUB, 17 Kidmore End Rd, Emmer Green, Reading, **BERKSHIRE**, RG4 8SG, **ENGLAND**.
(T) 0118 9472909

Membership: Members & Public

Contact/s:
● **Club Secretary:** Mr Roy Brown
● **Professional:** Mr Scott Fotheringham
☎ 0118 9476115

Course/s:

🏌 **READING**
Description: Championship, Wooded, Parkland, Medium Length
Number of Holes: 18   **Par:** 70
Record: 64 (Tim Morrison)
Par 3's: 4   **Par 4's:** 12   **Par 5's:** 2
Yds: 6212   **F9 Yds:** 3129   **B9 Yds:** 3083

REASEHEATH

REASEHEATH GOLF CLUB, Reaseheath College, Nantwich, **CHESHIRE**, CW5 6DF, **ENGLAND**.
(T) 01270 625131

Course/s:

🏌 **REASEHEATH**
Number of Holes: 9
Designer: D Mortram

REAY

REAY GOLF CLUB, Reay, Thurso, **HIGHLANDS**, KW14 7RE, **SCOTLAND**.
(T) 01847 811288
(E) info@reaygolfclub.co.uk
(W) www.reaygolfclub.co.uk

Membership: Members & Public

Contact/s:
● **Club Secretary:** Mr W D McIntosh

Course/s:

🏌 **REAY**
Description: Links, Undulating, Open, Medium Length, Drains Well
Green Speed: Fast
Built: 1893   **Built On:** Sand
Number of Holes: 18   **Par:** 69
Par 3's: 6   **Par 4's:** 9   **Par 5's:** 3
Yds: 5831   **F9 Yds:** 3005   **B9 Yds:** 2826
Prevailing Wind: West
Designer: James Braid
Further Information:

The course is the most northerly 18 hole seaside links on the British mainland. Unique in that it opens and closes with a par 3. Donald Steel is quoted as saying 'links as natural as any I have seen. A wonderful example of classic links with typical wiry turf. A fast running character, glorious setting and excellent green positions. It must be preserved'.

RECTORY

RECTORY PARK GOLF CLUB, Huxley Cl, Off Church Road, Northolt, **LONDON (GREATER)**, UB5 5UL, **ENGLAND**.
(T) 020 88415550

Membership: Public

Contact/s:
- **Manager:** Mrs C Gribben

Course/s:
- **RECTORY PARK**
  Number of Holes: 9

REDBOURN

REDBOURN GOLF CLUB, Kingsbourne Green Lane, Redbourn, St. Albans, **HERTFORDSHIRE**, AL3 7QA, **ENGLAND**.
(T) 01582 793493
(E) enquiries@redbourngolfclub.com
(W) www.redbourngolfclub.com

Contact/s:
- **Club Secretary:** Mr Roy Fay

Course/s:
- **KINSBOURNE**
  Number of Holes: 9
- **VER**
  Number of Holes: 18   Par: 70
  Yds: 6506   F9 Yds: 3136   B9 Yds: 3370

REDCASTLE

REDCASTLE GOLF COURSE, Redcastle, Moville, **COUNTY DONEGAL**, **IRELAND**.
(T) 07782 073

Course/s:
- **REDCASTLE**
  Number of Holes: 9

REDDISH VALE

REDDISH VALE GOLF CLUB LTD, The Golf House, Southcliffe Rd, South Reddish, Stockport, **CHESHIRE**, SK5 7EE, **ENGLAND**.
(T) 0161 4802359
(E) mandy@rvgc.fsbusiness.co.uk
(W) www.reddishvalegolfclub.co.uk

Membership: Members & Public

Contact/s:
- **Club Secretary:** Mr Bryan Rendell J.P
- **Professional:** Mr Bob Freeman
  ☎ 0161 4803824

Course/s:
- **REDDISH VALE**
  Description: Parkland, Moorland, Valley, Undulating, Medium Length, Tight, Drains Well
  Green Speed: Fast
  Built: 1912   Built On: Soil
  Number of Holes: 18   Par: 69
  Par 3's: 5   Par 4's: 11   Par 5's: 2
  Yds: 6086   F9 Yds: 2770   B9 Yds: 3316
  Designer: Alistair MacKenzie

REDDITCH

REDDITCH GOLF CLUB, Lower Grinsty, Green Lane, Callow Hill, Redditch, **WORCESTERSHIRE**, B97 5PJ, **ENGLAND**.

(T) 01527 543079

Membership: Members & Public

Contact/s:
- **Club Secretary:** Mr Tom Sheldon
- **Professional:** Mr David Down

Course/s:
- **REDDITCH**
  Description: Wooded, Parkland, Sheltered, Open, Medium Length, Tight, Drains Well
  Green Speed: Medium
  Built: 1971
  Number of Holes: 18   Par: 72
  Record: 68
  Yds: 6494   F9 Yds: 3246   B9 Yds: 3248
  Designer: Frank Pennink
  Further Information:
  The 14th hole is a signature hole.

REDHILL & REIGATE

REDHILL & REIGATE GOLF CLUB, Clarence Lodge, Pendleton Rd, Redhill, **SURREY**, RH1 6LB, **ENGLAND**.
(T) 01737 240777
(E) redhillandreigategolfclub@btopenworld.com

Membership: Members & Public
Size of Complex: 100 Acres

Contact/s:
- **Professional:** Mr Warren Pike
  ☎ 01737 244433
- **Book Tee Times:** Mr W Pike

Course/s:
- **REDHILL & REIGATE**
  Description: Wooded, Parkland, Short, Tight, Tends to Flood, Ideal for the Elderly
  Green Speed: Medium
  Built: 1887   Built On: Clay
  Number of Holes: 18   Par: 68
  Par 3's: 5   Par 4's: 12   Par 5's: 1
  Yds: 5272   F9 Yds: 2465   B9 Yds: 2807
  Designer: James Braid
  Further Information:
  This is a flat course.

REDHILL GOLF CTRE

REDHILL GOLF CENTRE, Canada Ave, Redhill, **SURREY**, RH1 5BF, **ENGLAND**.
(T) 01737 770204

Membership: Public

Contact/s:
- **Professional:** Mr James Edgar
- **Pro Shop:** Mr S Furlonger

Course/s:
- **REDHILL**
  Description: Parkland, Open, Short, Tight, Ideal for the Elderly
  Green Speed: Medium
  Built: 1992   Built On: Clay
  Number of Holes: 9   Par: 29
  Yds: 1632
  Further Information:
  This is a flat course.

REDLIBBETS

REDLIBBETS GOLF CLUB, West Yoke, Ash, Sevenoaks, **KENT**, TN15 7HT, **ENGLAND**.
(T) 01474 879190

Membership: Members & Public

Contact/s:
- **Professional:** Mr Ross Taylor
  ☎ 01474 872278

Course/s:
- **REDLIBBETS**
  Description: Championship, Wooded,

Valley, Undulating, Sheltered, Medium Length, Tight, Drains Well
  Green Speed: Medium
  Built: 1995   Built On: Chalk
  Number of Holes: 18   Par: 72
  Record: 69
  Yds: 6639   F9 Yds: 3218   B9 Yds: 3421
  Designer: Jonathan Gaunt
  Further Information:
  The bunker on the 14th hole is a 2nd World War bomb crater.

REGENT PARK

REGENT PARK GOLF CLUB, Links Rd, Lostock, Bolton, **LANCASHIRE**, BL6 4AF, **ENGLAND**.
(T) 01204 844170

Contact/s:
- **Manager:** Mr K Davies

Course/s:
- **REGENT PARK**
  Number of Holes: 18

REGIMENT

REGIMENT WAY GOLF CENTRE (THE), Pratts Farm, Pratts Farm Lane, Little Waltham, Chelmsford, **ESSEX**, CM3 3PR, **ENGLAND**.
(T) 01245 361100/ 362210

Membership: Members & Public

Contact/s:
- **Club Secretary:** Mr Roger Pamphilon
- **Professional:** Mr Ian Warn
- **Pro Shop:** Mr Dave March

Course/s:
- **REGIMENT WAY**
  Description: Parkland, Open, Medium Length, Drains Well, Ideal for the Elderly
  Green Speed: Medium
  Built: 1994   Built On: Soil
  Number of Holes: 9   Par: 32
  Par 3's: 4   Par 4's: 5
  Prevailing Wind: South/West
  Designer: R Clark, R Stubbings
  Further Information: 9 hole course can be played as an 18 hole course

REIGATE HEATH

REIGATE HEATH GOLF CLUB, Golf Clubhouse, Reigate Heath, Reigate, **SURREY**, RH2 8QR, **ENGLAND**.
(T) 01737 226793

Course/s:
- **REIGATE HEATH**
  Number of Holes: 9

REIGATE HILL

REIGATE HILL GOLF CLUB, Gatton Bottom, Reigate, **SURREY**, RH2 0TU, **ENGLAND**.
(T) 01737 645577
(E) info@reigatehillgolfclub.co.uk

Membership: Members & Public
Size of Complex: 150 Acres

Contact/s:
- **Professional:** Mr C Forsyth

Course/s:
- **REIGATE HILL**
  Description: Parkland, Undulating, Open, Medium Length
  Green Speed: Medium
  Built: 1995   Built On: Clay/Sand
  Number of Holes: 18   Par: 72
  Yds: 6175   F9 Yds: 3038   B9 Yds: 3137
  Designer: David Williams
  Further Information: There are 96 bunkers throughout the course.

RENFREW

RENFREW GOLF CLUB, Inchinnan Rd, Renfrew, **RENFREWSHIRE**, PA4 9EG, **SCOTLAND**.
(T) 0141 8851754

Contact/s:
- Club Secretary: Mr Ian Murchison
- Professional: Mr Stephen Thompson

Course/s:
- 🏌 **RENFREW**
  Number of Holes: 18 Par: 72
  Yds: 6518 F9 Yds: 3508 B9 Yds: 3310
  Designer: Commander J Harris

RENISHAW PARK

RENISHAW PARK GOLF CLUB, Golf Hse, Mill Lane, Renishaw, Sheffield, **YORKSHIRE (SOUTH)**, S21 3UZ, **ENGLAND**.
(T) 01246 432044

Contact/s:
- Club Secretary: Mr T Childs

Course/s:
- 🏌 **RENISHAW PARK**
  Number of Holes: 18 Par: 71
  Yds: 6107 F9 Yds: 2700 B9 Yds: 3407
  Designer: George Sitwell

RENVYLE HOUSE

RENVYLE HOUSE HOTEL GOLF COURSE, Renvyle, Connemara, **COUNTY GALWAY**, **IRELAND**.
(T) 095 43511

Course/s:
- 🏌 **RENVYLE HOUSE**
  Number of Holes: 9

RETFORD

RETFORD GOLF CLUB, Brecks Rd, Retford, **NOTTINGHAMSHIRE**, DN22 7UA, **ENGLAND**.
(T) 01777 703733

Membership: Members & Public

Contact/s:
- Professional: Mr C Morris

Course/s:
- 🏌 **RETFORD**
  Description: Parkland, Undulating, Sheltered, Medium Length, Drains Well
  Green Speed: Fast
  Built: 1920 Built On: Sand
  Number of Holes: 18
  Prevailing Wind: South/West
  Designer: Tom Williamson

RHONDDA

RHONDDA GOLF CLUB, Penrhys, Ferndale, **RHONDDA CYNON TAFF**, CF43 3PW, **WALES**.
(T) 01443 441384

Contact/s:
- Professional: Mr Gareth Bebb
- Pro Shop:
  ☎ 01443 441385

Course/s:
- 🏌 **RHONDDA**
  Description: Moorland, Tight
  Built: 1911
  Number of Holes: 18 Par: 70

RHOSGOCH GOLF

RHOSGOCH GOLF & LEISURE CLUB, Rhosgoch, Builth Wells, **POWYS**, LD2 3JY,

WALES.
(T) 01497 851251

Contact/s:
- Steward: Mr Andrew Davies

Course/s:
- 🏌 **RHOSGOCH**
  Number of Holes: 9 Par: 68
  Yds: 4955 F9 Yds: 2432 B9 Yds: 2523

RHOS-ON-SEA

RHOS-ON-SEA GOLF CLUB, Penrhyn Bay, Llandudno, **CONWY**, LL30 3PU, **WALES**.
(T) 01492 549641

Membership: Members & Public

Contact/s:
- Club Secretary: Mr John Bray
- Professional: Mr Mike Macara
  ☎ 01492 548115
- Pro Shop: Mr Mark Williams

Course/s:
- 🏌 **RHOS-ON-SEA**
  Description: Links, Parkland, Undulating, Open, Medium Length, Drains Well, Ideal for the Elderly
  Green Speed: Medium
  Built: 1899 Built On: Clay
  Number of Holes: 18 Par: 69
  Yds: 6064 F9 Yds: 2979 B9 Yds: 3085
  Designer: Simpson

RHUDDLAN

RHUDDLAN GOLF CLUB, The Professional Shop, Meliden Rd, Rhuddlan, Rhyl, **DENBIGHSHIRE**, LL18 6LB, **WALES**.
(T) 01745 590898

Membership: Members & Public

Contact/s:
- Club Secretary: Mr David Morris
- Professional: Mr Andrew Carr

Course/s:
- 🏌 **RHUDDLAN**
  Description: Championship, Wooded, Parkland, Open, Long, Drains Well, Ideal for the Elderly
  Green Speed: Medium
  Built: 1930 Built On: Clay/Soil
  Number of Holes: 18 Par: 72
  Yds: 6294 F9 Yds: 3129 B9 Yds: 3165
  Prevailing Wind: North/West
  Designer: Hawtree

RHYL

RHYL GOLF CLUB, Rhyl Coast Rd, Rhyl, **DENBIGHSHIRE**, LL18 3RE, **WALES**.
(T) 01745 353171
(W) www.rhylgolfclub.com

Membership: Members & Public
Size of Complex: 59.7 Acres

Contact/s:
- Club Secretary: Mr Ian Doig
- Professional: Mr Tim Leah

Course/s:
- 🏌 **RHYL**
  Description: Links, Open, Long, Drains Well
  Green Speed: Fast
  Built: 1890 Built On: Sand
  Number of Holes: 9 Record: 64
  Prevailing Wind: South/West
  Designer: James Braid
  Further Information:
  Positioned opposite Snowdonia, this is a challenging 9 hole course.

RICCARTON

RICCARTON GOLF CLUB, Carlisle Rd, Fernigar, Hamilton, **LANARKSHIRE (SOUTH)**, ML3 7UE, **SCOTLAND**.
(T) 01698 282872

Course/s:
- 🏌 **HAMILTON**
  Number of Holes: 18
  Designer: James Braid

RICHINGS PARK

RICHINGS PARK GOLF & COUNTRY CLUB, North Pk, Iver, **BUCKINGHAMSHIRE**, SL0 9DL, **ENGLAND**.
(T) 01753 655370
(W) www.richingspark.co.uk

Membership: Members & Public

Contact/s:
- Club Secretary: Mr Sean Kelly
  ☎ 01753 655409

Course/s:
- 🏌 **RICHINGS PARK**
  Description: Parkland, Medium Length, Ideal for the Elderly
  Number of Holes: 18 Par: 70
  Par 3's: 4 Par 4's: 12 Par 5's: 2
  Yds: 6210
  Designer: Alan Higgins

RICHMOND

RICHMOND GOLF CLUB, Sudbrook Pk, Sudbrook Lane, Richmond, **SURREY**, TW10 7AS, **ENGLAND**.
(T) 020 89401463

Contact/s:
- Manager: Mr R L Wilkins

Course/s:
- 🏌 **THE RICHMOND**
  Number of Holes: 18

RICHMOND

RICHMOND GOLF CLUB, Bend Hagg Hse, Bend Hagg, Richmond, **YORKSHIRE (NORTH)**, DL10 5EX, **ENGLAND**.
(T) 01748 823231

Contact/s:
- Club Secretary: Mr B Aston
- Pro Shop: Mr Paul Jackson

Course/s:
- 🏌 **RICHMOND**
  Number of Holes: 18
  Designer: Pennink

RICHMOND PARK

RICHMOND PARK GOLF CLUB, Saham Rd, Watton, Thetford, **NORFOLK**, IP25 6EA, **ENGLAND**.
(T) 01953 881803
Size of Complex: 100 Acres

Contact/s:
- Professional: Mr Alan Hemsley

Course/s:
- 🏌 **RICHMOND PARK**
  Description: Wooded, Parkland, Tight
  Built: 1990
  Number of Holes: 18 Par: 71
  Yds: 6300
  Designer: D Jessup, D Scott
  Further Information:
  The Little Wissey River runs through the course.

RICHMOND PARK

RICHMOND PARK GOLF COURSE,
Roehampton Gate, Priory Lane, London,
LONDON (GREATER), SW15 5JR,
ENGLAND.
(T) 020 88781858
(W) www.gcmgolf.com
Membership: Members & Public
Contact/s:
- **Professional:** Mr Andrew Morgan
Course/s:
- **DUKES**
  Green Speed: Medium
  Built: 1930 **Built On:** Soil
  Number of Holes: 18 **Par:** 69
  Yds: 6036 **F9 Yds:** 3121 **B9 Yds:** 2915
  Prevailing Wind: South
  Designer: Hawtree
- **PRINCES**
  Green Speed: Medium
  Built: 1930 **Built On:** Soil
  Number of Holes: 18 **Par:** 69
  Yds: 5868 **F9 Yds:** 2903 **B9 Yds:** 2965
  Prevailing Wind: South
  Designer: Hawtree

RICKMANSWORTH

RICKMANSWORTH GOLF COURSE, Moor
Lane, Rickmansworth, **HERTFORDSHIRE**,
WD3 1QL, **ENGLAND**.
(T) 01923 775278
Membership: Members & Public
Contact/s:
- **Club Secretary:** Mr Rod Botham
- **Professional:** Mr Alan Dobbins
Course/s:
- **RICKMANSWORTH PUBLIC**
  Description: Parkland, Undulating,
  Sheltered, Short, Tight
  Green Speed: Medium/Fast
  Built On: Chalk
  Number of Holes: 18 **Par:** 65
  Yds: 4557
  Designer: Harry Shapland Colt
  Further Information:
  Challenging course built on the side of a
  hill.

RIDDLESDEN

RIDDLESDEN GOLF CLUB, Howden Rough,
Riddlesden, Keighley, **YORKSHIRE (WEST)**,
BD20 5QN, **ENGLAND**.
(T) 01535 602148
Contact/s:
- **President:** Mr Colin Stead
Course/s:
- **RIDDLESDEN**
  Built: 1927
  Number of Holes: 18 **Par:** 63
  Yds: 4295 **F9 Yds:** 2257 **B9 Yds:** 2038
  Further Information:
  Views over Aire Valley and Howorth
  Moors.

RIDGE GOLF CLUB

AMERICAN GOLF CORPORATION,
Chartway St, East Sutton, Sutton Valence,
Maidstone, **KENT**, ME17 3JB, **ENGLAND**.
(T) 01622 844382
(E) ridge@americangolf.uk.com
(W) www.americangolf.com
Size of Complex: 120 Acres
Contact/s:
- **Professional:** Mr James Cornish
  ☎ 01622 844243

Course/s:
- **RIDGE**
  Description: Parkland, Sheltered,
  Medium Length, Drains Well, Ideal for the
  Elderly
  Green Speed: Fast
  Built: 1993 **Built On:** Soil
  Number of Holes: 18 **Par:** 71
  Record: 67 (Sam Goode)
  Yds: 5942 **Prevailing Wind:** North/East
  Designer: P Dawson
  Further Information:
  With views over the Weald of Kent, each
  hole presents a challenge for even the
  most accomplished golfer.

RING OF KERRY

**RING OF KERRY GOLF & COUNTRY
CLUB,** Templenoe, Kenmare, **COUNTY
KERRY**, **IRELAND**.
(T) 064 42000
(E) reservations@ringofkerrygolf.com
(W) www.ringofkerrygolf.com
Membership: Members & Public
Contact/s:
- **Club Secretary:** Mr Dominic Reid
- **Professional:** Mr Jamie Bowman
- **Book Tee Times:** Ms Fionulla O'Connor
Course/s:
- **RING OF KERRY**
  Description: Parkland, Heath Land
  Green Speed: Medium
  Built: 1998
  Number of Holes: 18
  Designer: Edward Hackett

RINGDUFFERIN

RINGDUFFERIN GOLF COURSE,
Ringdufferin Rd, Toye, Downpatrick, **COUNTY
DOWN**, BT30 9PH, **NORTHERN IRELAND**.
(T) 028 44828812
Size of Complex: 120 Acres
Contact/s:
- **Owner:** Mr J Lindsay
Course/s:
- **RINGDUFFERIN**
  Number of Holes: 9
- **RINGDUFFERIN**
  Description: Parkland, Undulating,
  Sheltered, Medium Length, Drains Well
  Built: 1993
  Number of Holes: 18
  Designer: Frank Ainsworth

RINGWAY

RINGWAY GOLF CLUB LTD (THE), Hale
Mount, Hale Barns, Altrincham, **CHESHIRE**,
WA15 8SW, **ENGLAND**.
(T) 0161 9802630
(E) enquiries@ringwaygolfclub.co.uk
Membership: Members & Public
Contact/s:
- **Club Secretary:** Mr A Scully
- **Professional:** Mr N Ryan
Course/s:
- **RINGWAY**
  Description: Parkland, Medium Length,
  Ideal for the Elderly
  Green Speed: Medium
  Built: 1909 **Built On:** Clay
  Number of Holes: 18 **Par:** 71
  Record: 66 (Mike Holllingworth)
  Par 3's: 4 **Par 4's:** 11 **Par 5's:** 3
  Yds: 6489
  Prevailing Wind: West
  Designer: Harry Shapland Colt

Further Information:
The course has 7 par 4's of 400 yards or
more.

RIPON CITY

RIPON CITY GOLF CLUB, Palace Rd, Ripon,
YORKSHIRE (NORTH), HG4 3HH,
ENGLAND.
(T) 01765 603640
Contact/s:
- **Chairman:** Mr F B Taylor
Course/s:
- **RIPON CITY**
  Number of Holes: 18
  Designer: Harry Vardon

RISEBRIDGE

RISEBRIDGE GOLF CENTRE, Risebridge
Chase, Lower Bedfords Rd, Romford, **ESSEX**,
RM1 4DG, **ENGLAND**.
(T) 01708 741429
Contact/s:
- **Head Professional:** Mr Paul Jennings
Course/s:
- **RISEBRIDGE 18 HOLE**
  Number of Holes: 18 **Par:** 71
  Designer: Hawtree
- **RISEBRIDGE 9 HOLE**
  Number of Holes: 9
  Designer: Hawtree

RISHTON

RISHTON GOLF CLUB, Station Rd, Rishton,
Blackburn, **LANCASHIRE**, BB1 4HG,
ENGLAND.
(T) 01254 884442
Contact/s:
- **Manageress:** Mrs M Mayor
Course/s:
- **RISHTON**
  Number of Holes: 9

RIVENHALL OAKS

RIVENHALL OAKS GOLF COURSE, Forest
Rd, Witham, **ESSEX**, CM8 2PS, **ENGLAND**.
(T) 01376 510222
Contact/s:
- **Owner:** Mr S Brice
Course/s:
- **RIVENHALL OAKS 9 HOLE**
  Number of Holes: 9
  Yds: 3128

RIVERSIDE

RIVERSIDE GOLF COURSE & CENTRE,
Trent Side, Lenton Lane, Nottingham,
NOTTINGHAMSHIRE, NG7 2SA, **ENGLAND**.
(T) 0115 9862179
Membership: Public
Size of Complex: 26 Acres
Contact/s:
- **Club Secretary:** Mr G Meek
  ☎ 0115 9862139
- **Professional:** Ms Kirsty Thomas
Course/s:
- **RIVERSIDE**
  Number of Holes: 9

ROBIN HOOD

ROBIN HOOD GOLF CLUB, Owston Hall, Nr
Asken, Doncaster, **YORKSHIRE (SOUTH)**,
DN6 9JF, **ENGLAND**.

(T) 01302 722231
(E) robinhoodgc@tesco.net
(W) www.robinhoodgolfclub.com

Membership: Members & Public

Contact/s:
● **Club Secretary:** Mr Colin Fanswell
● **Professional:** Mr Jason Laszkowicz

Course/s:
🏌 **ROBIN HOOD**
Description: Championship, Parkland, Open, Long, Tight, Drains Well, Ideal for the Elderly
Green Speed: Medium
Built: 1995 **Built On:** Clay
Number of Holes: 18 **Par:** 72
Record: 68 (Robert Wragg)
Par 3's: 4 **Par 4's:** 10 **Par 5's:** 4
Yds: 6535 **F9 Yds:** 3305 **B9 Yds:** 3230
Designer: W Adamson

ROBIN HOOD

ROBIN HOOD GOLF CLUB, St. Bernards Rd, Solihull, **MIDLANDS (WEST),** B92 7DJ, **ENGLAND.**
(T) 0121 7060061

Membership: Members & Public

Contact/s:
● **Club Secretary:** Mrs P Hollingsworth
● **Professional:** Mr A Harvey
☎ 0121 7060806

Course/s:
🏌 **ROBIN HOOD**
Description: Wooded, Parkland, Sheltered, Medium Length
Green Speed: Medium
Built: 1893 **Built On:** Clay
Number of Holes: 18 **Par:** 72
Yds: 6635 **F9 Yds:** 3246 **B9 Yds:** 3389
Designer: Harry Shapland Colt

ROCHDALE

ROCHDALE GOLF CLUB LTD, Edenfield Rd, Rochdale, **LANCASHIRE,** OL11 5YR, **ENGLAND.**
(T) 01706 643818

Contact/s:
● **Club Secretary:** Mrs P Chappel

Course/s:
🏌 **ROCHDALE**
Number of Holes: 18
Designer: G Lowe

ROCHESTER & COBHAM

ROCHESTER & COBHAM PARK GOLF CLUB LTD, Park Pale by Rochester, Rochester, **KENT,** ME2 3UL, **ENGLAND.**
(T) 01474 823658
(E) info@rochesterandcobhamgc.co.uk
(W) www.rochesterandcobhamgc.co.uk

Membership: Members & Public

Contact/s:
● **Club Secretary:** Mr John Irvine
● **Professional:** Mr Iain Higgins

Course/s:
🏌 **ROCHESTER & COBHAM PARK**
Description: Championship, Parkland, Undulating, Sheltered, Open, Long, Drains Well, Ideal for the Elderly
Green Speed: Medium
Built: 1891 **Built On:** Soil
Number of Holes: 18 **Par:** 71
Yds: 6254 **F9 Yds:** 3112 **B9 Yds:** 3142
Designer: Donald Steel

ROCHFORD HUNDRED

ROCHFORD HUNDRED GOLF CLUB, Hall Rd, Rochford, **ESSEX,** SS4 1NW, **ENGLAND.**
(T) 01702 544302

Contact/s:
● **Manager:** Mr Alan Bobfield

Course/s:
🏌 **ROCHFORD HUNDRED**
Number of Holes: 18
Designer: James Braid

ROCKMOUNT

ROCKMOUNT GOLF CLUB, 28 Drumalig Rd, Carryduff, Belfast, **COUNTY DOWN,** BT8 8EQ, **NORTHERN IRELAND.**
(T) 028 90812279

Contact/s:
● **Manager:** Mrs Shirley Graham

Course/s:
🏌 **ROCKMOUNT**
Number of Holes: 18 **Par:** 72

RODWAY HILL

RODWAY HILL GOLF COURSE, Newent Rd, Highnam, Gloucester, **GLOUCESTERSHIRE,** GL2 8DN, **ENGLAND.**
(T) 01452 384222

Contact/s:
● **Professional:** Mr Tony Grubb

Course/s:
🏌 **RODWAY HILL**
Built: 1991
Number of Holes: 18 **Par:** 70
Designer: John Gabb
Further Information:
Views of the Cotswolds.

ROKER PARK

ROKER PARK GOLF CLUB, Pro Shop/Holly Lane, Aldershot Rd, Worplesdon, Guildford, **SURREY,** GU3 3PB, **ENGLAND.**
(T) 01483 236677

Contact/s:
● **Manager:** Mr Kevin Warne

Course/s:
🏌 **ROKER PARK**
Number of Holes: 9
Designer: W V Roker

ROLLS OF MONMOUTH

ROLLS OF MONMOUTH (THE), Monmouth, **MONMOUTHSHIRE,** NP25 5HG, **WALES.**
(T) 01600 715353
(W) www.therollsgolfclub.co.uk

Membership: Members & Public
Size of Complex: 990 Acres

Contact/s:
● **Club Secretary:** Mrs Sandra Orton

Course/s:
🏌 **THE ROLLS OF MONMOUTH**
Description: Parkland, Undulating, Open, Long, Drains Well
Green Speed: Medium
Built: 1982 **Built On:** Clay
Number of Holes: 18 **Par:** 72
Yds: 6283 **F9 Yds:** 3097 **B9 Yds:** 3186

ROMANBY

ROMANBY GOLF COURSE LTD, Professional Shop, Yafforth Rd, Romanby, Northallerton, **YORKSHIRE (NORTH),** DL7 0PE, **ENGLAND.**

(T) 01609 779988

Contact/s:
● **Manager:** Mr T Jenkins

Course/s:
🏌 **ROMANBY**
Number of Holes: 18
Designer: W Adamson

ROMFORD

ROMFORD GOLF CLUB LTD, Heath Drive, Romford, **ESSEX,** RM2 5QB, **ENGLAND.**
(T) 01708 740986

Membership: Members & Public

Contact/s:
● **Club Secretary:** Mrs Hazel Robinson
● **Professional:** Mr Chris Goddard

Course/s:
🏌 **ROMFORD**
Description: Championship, Parkland, Open, Medium Length, Drains Well, Ideal for the Elderly
Green Speed: Medium
Built: 1894 **Built On:** Soil
Number of Holes: 18
Prevailing Wind: South/West
Designer: Harry Shapland Colt

ROMILEY

ROMILEY GOLF CLUB, Goosehouse Green, Romiley, Stockport, **CHESHIRE,** SK6 4LJ, **ENGLAND.**
(T) 0161 4302392

Contact/s:
● **Club Secretary:** Mr P R Trafford

Course/s:
🏌 **ROMILEY**
Number of Holes: 18 **Par:** 70
Yds: 6412 **F9 Yds:** 3112 **B9 Yds:** 3300

ROMNEY WARREN

ROMNEY WARREN GOLF CLUB, St. Andrews Rd, Littlestone, New Romney, **KENT,** TN28 8RB, **ENGLAND.**
(T) 01797 362231
(W) www.romneywarrengolfclub.org.uk

Contact/s:
● **Professional:** Mr Andrew Jones

Course/s:
🏌 **ROMNEY WARREN**
Description: Championship, Links, Undulating, Open, Short, Ideal for the Elderly
Green Speed: Fast
Built: 1992 **Built On:** Sand
Number of Holes: 18 **Par:** 67
Yds: 5126 **F9 Yds:** 2341 **B9 Yds:** 2785
Prevailing Wind: South

ROMSEY

ROMSEY GOLF CLUB LTD, Romsey Rd, Nursling, Southampton, **HAMPSHIRE,** SO16 0XW, **ENGLAND.**
(T) 023 80734637
(E) secretary@romseygolfclub.com
(W) www.romseygolfclub.com

Contact/s:
● **Club Secretary:** Mr John H Solly
● **Pro Shop:** Mr Mark Desmond

Course/s:
🏌 **ROMSEY**
Description: Wooded, Parkland, Undulating, Sheltered, Medium Length, Tight
Green Speed: Medium

Built: 1900
Number of Holes: 18 Par: 69
Record: 64 (J Slade)
Par 3's: 4 Par 4's: 13 Par 5's: 1
Yds: 5856 F9 Yds: 2732 B9 Yds: 3124
Prevailing Wind: South/West
Further Information:
Built on the Broadland Estate, the course has a very picturesque setting.

RONAN VALLEY

RONAN VALLEY GOLF COURSE, 61 Ballyronan Rd, Magherafelt, **COUNTY LONDONDERRY**, BT45 6EW, **NORTHERN IRELAND**.
(T) 028 79300400

Contact/s:
● Partner: Mr John Tohill

Course/s:
🦅 RONAN VALLEY
Number of Holes: 9

ROODLEA

ROODLEA GOLF COURSE, Coylton, Ayr, **AYRSHIRE (SOUTH)**, KA6 6EP, **SCOTLAND**.
(T) 01292 570727
(W) www.eurogolfing.com

Contact/s:
● Owner: Mr A Howat

Course/s:
🦅 ROODLEA PAR 3
Number of Holes: 18 Par: 54
Yds: 2650
Further Information:
An interesting and challenging course.

ROOKERY PARK

ROOKERY PARK GOLF CLUB, Beccles Rd, Carlton Colville, Lowestoft, **SUFFOLK**, NR33 8HJ, **ENGLAND**.
(T) 01502 574009

Contact/s:
● Manager: Mr David Kelly

Course/s:
🦅 ROOKERY PARK
Number of Holes: 18
Designer: C D Lawrie

ROOKWOOD

ROOKWOOD GOLF COURSE, Robin Hood Lane, Warnham, Horsham, **SUSSEX (WEST)**, RH12 3RR, **ENGLAND**.
(T) 01403 250168

Membership: Members & Public
Size of Complex: 165 Acres

Contact/s:
● Club Secretary: Mr Stewart Judd
● Professional: Mr Tony Clingan
● Pro Shop:
  ☎ 01403 791555

Course/s:
🦅 ROOKWOOD
Description: Wooded, Parkland, Undulating, Open, Medium Length, Tight, Drains Well, Ideal for the Elderly
Green Speed: Medium
Built: 1992 Built On: Clay
Number of Holes: 18 Record: 67 (Stewart McGalin)
Prevailing Wind: West
Designer: John Fortune

ROPSLEY

ROPSLEY GOLF COURSE (THE), Crown Hill, Ropsley, Grantham, **LINCOLNSHIRE**, NG33 4BH, **ENGLAND**.
(T) 01476 585252

ROSAPENNA

ROSAPENNA GOLF CLUB, Downings, Rosapenna, **COUNTY DONEGAL**, **IRELAND**.
(T) 074 55301

Course/s:
🦅 ROSAPENNA
Number of Holes: 18
Designer: Tom Morris

ROSCOMMON

ROSCOMMON GOLF CLUB, Mote Pk, Roscommon, **COUNTY ROSCOMMON**, **IRELAND**.
(T) 090 326382

Membership: Members & Public
Size of Complex: 130 Acres

Contact/s:
● Club Secretary: Ms Cathal McConn
  ☎ 090 326062

Course/s:
🦅 ROSCOMMON
Description: Championship, Parkland, Undulating, Long, Ideal for the Elderly
Green Speed: Medium
Built: 1930 Built On: Sand/Soil
Number of Holes: 18 Par: 72
Par 3's: 4 Par 4's: 10 Par 5's: 4
Yds: 5901 F9 Yds: 2895 B9 Yds: 3006
Designer: Edward Connaughton

ROSCREA

ROSCREA GOLF CLUB, Derryvale, Roscrea, **COUNTY TIPPERARY**, **IRELAND**.
(T) 050 521130

Course/s:
🦅 ROSCREA
Number of Holes: 18 Par: 71
Yds: 5782

ROSEBERRY GRANGE

ROSEBERRY GRANGE GOLF COURSE & CLUB, Grange Villa, Chester Le Street, **COUNTY DURHAM**, DH2 3NF, **ENGLAND**.
(T) 0191 3700660

Membership: Members & Public

Contact/s:
● Club Secretary: Mr Raymond McClermot
● Professional: Mr Alan Hartley

Course/s:
🦅 ROSEBERRY GRANGE
Description: Parkland, Undulating, Open, Long, Drains Well, Ideal for the Elderly
Green Speed: Fast Built On: Clay
Number of Holes: 18 Par: 71
Yds: 6023 F9 Yds: 3142 B9 Yds: 2881

ROSENDALE GOLF CLUB

ROSENDALE GOLF CLUB, Ewood Lane, Haslingden, Rossendale, **LANCASHIRE**, BB4 6LH, **ENGLAND**.
(T) 01706 213616
(W) www.rossendalegolfclub.co.uk

Contact/s:
● PGA Professional: Mr S Nicholls

Course/s:
🦅 ROSENDALE
Number of Holes: 18 Par: 72
Yds: 6293 F9 Yds: 3041 B9 Yds: 3252

ROSERROW

ROSERROW GOLF & COUNTRY CLUB, Blandings, St. Minver, Wadebridge, **CORNWALL**, PL27 6QT, **ENGLAND**.
(T) 01208 863000

Membership: Members & Public
Size of Complex: 400 Acres

Contact/s:
● Professional: Mr Andrew Cullen

Course/s:
🦅 ROSERROW
Description: Parkland, Open, Medium Length, Drains Well
Green Speed: Medium
Built: 1997 Built On: Soil
Number of Holes: 18 Par: 72
Yds: 6551 F9 Yds: 3395 B9 Yds: 3156

ROSS GOLF

ROSS GOLF CLUB, Ross Rd, Killarney, **COUNTY KERRY**, **IRELAND**.
(T) 064 31125
(E) info@rossgolfclub.com
(W) www.rossgolfclub.com

Membership: Members & Public

Contact/s:
● Secretary/Manager: Mr Alan O'Meara

Course/s:
🦅 ROSS GOLF CLUB
Number of Holes: 9 Par: 36
Par 3's: 2 Par 4's: 5 Par 5's: 2
Yds: 3108
Further Information:
Can be played as an 18 hole course.

ROSSHILL PAR 3

ROSSHILL PAR 3 GOLF COURSE, Roscam, Rosshill, **COUNTY GALWAY**, **IRELAND**.
(T) 091 753950
(E) rosshill@ebookireland.com
(W) www.ebookireland.com

Course/s:
🦅 ROSSHILL PAR 3
Built: 1991
Number of Holes: 18 Par: 54
Par 3's: 18
Yds: 2740 F9 Yds: 1373 B9 Yds: 1367
Prevailing Wind: West

ROSSLARE

ROSSLARE GOLF CLUB, Rosslare, **COUNTY WEXFORD**, **IRELAND**.
(T) 053 32203
(E) office@rosslaregolf.com
(W) www.iol.ie/~rgolfclb/

Contact/s:
● Professional: Mr Johnny Young

Course/s:
🦅 NEW
Number of Holes: 9
Designer: Hawtree, Taylor
🦅 OLD
Number of Holes: 18 Par: 72
Yds: 6608 F9 Yds: 3376 B9 Yds: 3232
Designer: Hawtree, Taylor

ROSSMORE

ROSSMORE GOLF CLUB, Rossmore Pk, Cootehill Rd, Rossmore, **COUNTY MONAGHAN**, **IRELAND**.
(T) 047 81316

Contact/s:

A-Z GOLF CLUBS/COURSES

Rossmore — Rowlands Castle

• **Club Secretary:** Jimmy McKenna
Course/s:
🏌 **ROSSMORE**
Number of Holes: 18
Par 3's: 4 Par 4's: 12 Par 5's: 2
Yds: 6082
Designer: D Smyth

ROSS-ON-WYE

ROSS-ON-WYE GOLF CLUB, Professional Shop, Gorsley, Ross-on-Wye, **HEREFORDSHIRE**, HR9 7UT, **ENGLAND**.
(T) 01989 720439
Course/s:
🏌 **ROSS-ON-WYE**
Number of Holes: 18

ROTHBURY

ROTHBURY GOLF CLUB, Old Race Course, Rothbury, Morpeth, **NORTHUMBERLAND**, NE65 7TR, **ENGLAND**.
(T) 01669 620718 or 621271
Course/s:
🏌 **ROTHBURY**
Number of Holes: 9
Designer: J Radcliffe

ROTHER VALLEY GOLF

ROTHER VALLEY GOLF CENTRE, Mansfield Rd, Wales Bar, Sheffield, **YORKSHIRE (SOUTH)**, S26 5PQ, **ENGLAND**.
(T) 0114 2473000
Membership: Members & Public
Contact/s:
• **Professional:** Mr Jason Ripley
Course/s:
🏌 **PAR 3**
Number of Holes: 9
Par 3's: 9

🏌 **ROTHER VALLEY**
Description: Parkland, Hilltop, Valley, Undulating, Long
Green Speed: Medium
Built: 1994
Number of Holes: 18
Designer: Michael Shattock

ROTHERHAM

ROTHERHAM GOLF CLUB LTD, Doncaster Rd, Thrybergh, Rotherham, **YORKSHIRE (SOUTH)**, S65 4NU, **ENGLAND**.
(T) 01709 850466
Contact/s:
• **Accountant:** Mr Martyn George Woodcock
Course/s:
🏌 **ROTHERHAM**
Number of Holes: 18
Designer: James Braid, S Herd

ROTHES

ROTHES GOLF CLUB, Blackhall, Rothes, Aberlour, **MORAY**, AB38 7AN, **SCOTLAND**.
(T) 01340 831443
Course/s:
🏌 **ROTHES**
Description: Wooded, Parkland, Hilltop
Built: 1990
Number of Holes: 9 Par: 68
Designer: John Souter
Further Information:
9 hole course can be played as an 18 hole

course

ROTHESAY

ROTHESAY GOLF CLUB, Glebelands Rd, Rothesay, **ARGYLL AND BUTE**, PA20 9HN, **SCOTLAND**.
(T) 01700 503554
Contact/s:
• **Professional:** Mr Jim Dougal
Course/s:
🏌 **ROTHESAY**
Number of Holes: 18 Par: 69
Yds: 5419 F9 Yds: 2845 B9 Yds: 2574
Designer: James Braid, Ben Sayers

ROTHLEY PARK

ROTHLEY PARK GOLF CLUB, Westfield Lane, Rothley, Leicester, **LEICESTERSHIRE**, LE7 7LH, **ENGLAND**.
(T) 0116 2302809
(W) www.rothleypark.com
Contact/s:
• **Club Secretary:** Mr S G Winterton
Course/s:
🏌 **ROTHLEY PARK**
Number of Holes: 18 Par: 71
Yds: 6477 F9 Yds: 2970 B9 Yds: 3507

ROUNDHAY

ROUNDHAY GOLF CLUB, Pk Lane, Roundhay, Leeds, **YORKSHIRE (WEST)**, LS8 2EJ, **ENGLAND**.
(T) 0113 2662695
Membership: Members & Public
Contact/s:
• **Club Secretary:** Mr Bob McLauchlan
  ☎ 0113 2664225
• **Professional:** Mr James Pape
  ☎ 0113 2661686
Course/s:
🏌 **ROUNDHAY**
Description: Wooded, Parkland, Undulating, Sheltered, Short, Tight, Drains Well, Ideal for the Elderly
Green Speed: Slow
Built: 1922 Built On: Sand
Number of Holes: 9 Par: 70
Par 3's: 2 Par 4's: 6 Par 5's: 1
Yds: 5136 F9 Yds: 2568 B9 Yds: 2568
Prevailing Wind: West
Further Information:
9 hole course can be played as an 18 hole course

ROUNDWOOD

ROUNDWOOD GOLF CLUB, Ballinahinch, Newtownmountkennedy, **COUNTY WICKLOW, IRELAND**.
(T) 01 2818488
(W) www.golfgreenfees.co.uk/repmid/roundwoodgc.shtml
Course/s:
🏌 **ROUNDWOOD COURSE**
Description: Wooded, Parkland, Heath Land, Long, Tight
Number of Holes: 18 Par: 72
Yds: 6685

ROUNDWOOD HALL

ROUNDWOOD HALL GOLF CLUB, Lyminge, Folkestone, **KENT**, CT18 8DJ, **ENGLAND**.
(T) 01303 862260
Membership: Public

Contact/s:
• **Club Secretary:** Mrs Barbara Boot
• **Professional:** Mr Andrew Harris
Course/s:
🏌 **ROUNDWOOD HALL**
Description: Wooded, Parkland, Undulating, Open, Short, Drains Well, Ideal for the Elderly
Green Speed: Medium
Built: 1993 Built On: Chalk/Clay
Number of Holes: 9 Par: 29
Par 3's: 7 Par 4's: 2
Yds: 1183
Prevailing Wind: South/West
Designer: B Boot
Further Information:
This 9 hole course has views over South Downs and can also be played as an 18 hole course.

ROUTENBURN

ROUTENBURN GOLF COURSE, Routenburn Rd, Largs, **AYRSHIRE (NORTH)**, KA30 8SQ, **SCOTLAND**.
(T) 01475 673230
Membership: Members & Public
Size of Complex: 100 Acres
Contact/s:
• **Professional:** Mr Greg McQueen
  ☎ 01475 687240
Course/s:
🏌 **ROUTENBURN**
Description: Heath Land, Hilltop, Sheltered, Open, Short, Tight, Drains Well
Green Speed: Slow
Built: 1897 Built On: Clay
Number of Holes: 18 Par: 68
Record: 65 (Sam Torrance)
Par 3's: 6 Par 4's: 10 Par 5's: 2
Yds: 5604
Designer: James Braid
Further Information:
There are burns & ditches throughout the course, with views over Firth of Clyde.

ROWANY

ROWANY GOLF CLUB, Rowany Drive, Port Erin, **ISLE OF MAN**, IM9 6LN, **ENGLAND**.
(T) 01624 834108or834072
Course/s:
🏌 **ROWANY**
Number of Holes: 18
Designer: G Lowe

ROWLANDS CASTLE

ROWLANDS CASTLE GOLF CLUB, 31 Links Lane, Rowlands Castle, **HAMPSHIRE**, PO9 6AE, **ENGLAND**.
(T) 023 92412784
Size of Complex: 149 Acres
Contact/s:
• **Club Secretary:** Mr K D Fisher
• **Professional:** Mr P Klepacz
  ☎ 023 92412785
Course/s:
🏌 **ROWLANDS CASTLE**
Description: Wooded, Parkland, Long, Ideal for the Elderly
Green Speed: Medium
Built: 1902 Built On: Clay
Number of Holes: 18 Par: 73
Record: 67 (M Gregson)
Par 3's: 2 Par 4's: 13 Par 5's: 3
Yds: 6620
Designer: Harry Shapland Colt

ROXBURGHE

ROXBURGHE GOLF COURSE, The Roxburghe Hotel & Golf Course, Heiton, Kelso, **SCOTTISH BORDERS**, TD5 8JZ, **SCOTLAND**.
(T) 01573 450333
(E) golf@roxburghe.net
(W) www.roxburghe.net

Membership: Members & Public
Size of Complex: 200 Acres

Contact/s:
● **Professional:** Mr Craig Montgomerie

Course/s:
🏌 **ROXBURGHE**
　Description: Championship, Wooded, Parkland
　Number of Holes: 18　**Par:** 72
　Par 3's: 4　**Par 4's:** 10　**Par 5's:** 4
　Yds: 6925　**F9 Yds:** 3401　**B9 Yds:** 3524
　Designer: David Thomas
　Further Information:
　The course is flanked by the River Teviot to the west which comes into play as a water hazard. ⛳

ROYSTON

ROYSTON GOLF CLUB LTD, Baldock Rd, Royston, **HERTFORDSHIRE**, SG8 5BG, **ENGLAND**.
(T) 01763 242696
(E) roystongolf@btconnect.com
Size of Complex: 200 Acres

Contact/s:
● **Club Secretary:** Mr Jim Beech
● **Professional:** Mr Sean Clark
● **Book Tee Times:**
　☎ 01763 243476

Course/s:
🏌 **ROYSTON**
　Description: Heath Land, Hilltop, Open, Medium Length, Tight, Drains Well
　Green Speed: Medium **Built On:** Chalk
　Number of Holes: 18　**Par:** 70
　Record: 63 (Brian Waites)
　Par 3's: 5　**Par 4's:** 10　**Par 5's:** 3
　Yds: 5959　**F9 Yds:** 3071　**B9 Yds:** 2888
　Designer: Harry Vardon

RUDDING PARK

RUDDING PARK GOLF COURSE, Rudding Lane, Follifoot, Harrogate, **YORKSHIRE (NORTH)**, HG3 1DJ, **ENGLAND**.
(T) 01423 872100
(E) golfadmin@ruddingpark.com
(W) www.ruddingpark.com

Membership: Members & Public

Contact/s:
● **Club Secretary:** Mr Mark Mackaness
● **Professional:** Mr Mark Moore
　☎ 01423 873400

Course/s:
🏌 **RUDDING PARK**
　Description: Wooded, Parkland, Undulating, Long
　Green Speed: Medium
　Built: 1995
　Number of Holes: 18
　Designer: Hawtree

RUDDINGTON GRANGE

RUDDINGTON GRANGE GOLF CLUB, Wilford Rd, Ruddington, Nottingham, **NOTTINGHAMSHIRE**, NG11 6NB, **ENGLAND**.
(T) 0115 9846141
(W) www.ruddingtongrange.com

Contact/s:
● **Club Secretary:** Mr Alan Johnson
● **Professional:** Mr Rob Simpson
　☎ 0115 9211951

Course/s:
🏌 **RUDDINGTON GRANGE**
　Description: Parkland
　Built: 1988
　Number of Holes: 18　**Par:** 72
　Further Information:
　There are water hazards on eight holes.

RUFFORD PARK GOLF CTRE

RUFFORD PARK GOLF CENTRE, Rufford Lane, Rufford, Ollerton, **NOTTINGHAMSHIRE**, NG22 9DG, **ENGLAND**.
(T) 01623 825253
(E) enquiries@ruffordgolf.co.uk

Membership: Members & Public

Contact/s:
● **Club Secretary:** Mrs Kay Whitehead
● **Professional:** Mr John Vaughan
　☎ 07971 144040
● **Book Lessons:** Mr W Laughton

Course/s:
🏌 **RUFFORD PARK**
　Description: Wooded, Parkland, Undulating, Medium Length, Drains Well
　Green Speed: Medium
　Built: 1994 **Built On:** Sand
　Number of Holes: 18　**Par:** 70
　Par 3's: 4　**Par 4's:** 12　**Par 5's:** 2
　Yds: 6186　**F9 Yds:** 3084　**B9 Yds:** 3102
　Designer: D Hemstock

RUGBY

RUGBY GOLF CLUB, Clifton Rd, Rugby, **WARWICKSHIRE**, CV21 3RD, **ENGLAND**.
(T) 01788 542306

Contact/s:
● **Club Secretary:** Mr N Towler

Course/s:
🏌 **RUGBY**
　Number of Holes: 18

RUISLIP GOLF CTRE

RUISLIP GOLF CENTRE, Ickenham Rd, Ruislip, **LONDON (GREATER)**, HA4 7DQ, **ENGLAND**.
(T) 01895 638081

Contact/s:
● **Pro Shop:** Mr G Lloyd
　☎ 01895 638833

Course/s:
🏌 **RUISLIP**
　Number of Holes: 18
　Designer: S Herd

RUNCORN

RUNCORN GOLF CLUB, The Heath, Clifton Rd, Runcorn, **CHESHIRE**, WA7 4SU, **ENGLAND**.
(T) 01928 564791

Contact/s:
● **Professional:** Mr A Franklin
● **Book Tee Times:**
　☎ 01928 574214/564791

Course/s:
🏌 **RUNCORN**
　Description: Parkland
　Built: 1909
　Number of Holes: 18　**Par:** 69

RUSH

RUSH GOLF CLUB, Rush, Arbury, Rush, **COUNTY DUBLIN**, **IRELAND**.
(T) 01 8437548

Course/s:
🏌 **RUSH**
　Number of Holes: 9

RUSHCLIFFE

RUSHCLIFFE GOLF CLUB, Stocking Lane, East Leake, Loughborough, **LEICESTERSHIRE**, LE12 5RL, **ENGLAND**.
(T) 01509 852959
(E) rushcliffegc@netscapeonline.co.uk

Contact/s:
● **Club Secretary:** Mr K Hodkinson

Course/s:
🏌 **RUSHCLIFFE**
　Number of Holes: 18　**Par:** 70
　Yds: 6009　**F9 Yds:** 2887　**B9 Yds:** 3122

RUSHDEN

RUSHDEN GOLF CLUB, Secretary, Kimbolton Rd, Chelveston, Wellingborough, **NORTHAMPTONSHIRE**, NN9 6AN, **ENGLAND**.
(T) 01933 418511

Contact/s:
● **Club Secretary:** Mr S P Trayhorn

Course/s:
🏌 **RUSHDEN**
　Number of Holes: 10　**Par:** 71
　Yds: 6249　**F9 Yds:** 3093　**B9 Yds:** 3156
　Further Information:
　9 hole course can be played as an 18 hole course; two of the holes are played once and the other eight are played twice.

RUSHMERE

RUSHMERE GOLF CLUB, Rushmere Heath, Ipswich, **SUFFOLK**, IP4 5QQ, **ENGLAND**.
(T) 01473 725648
(E) rushmeregolfclub@talk21.com
(W) www.club-noticeboard.co.uk/rushmere

Membership: Members & Public
Size of Complex: 150 Acres

Contact/s:
● **Club Secretary:** Mr Tony Harris
● **Professional:** Mr Nick McNeil

Course/s:
🏌 **RUSHMERE**
　Description: Heath Land, Undulating, Open, Medium Length, Drains Well, Ideal for the Elderly
　Green Speed: Fast
　Built: 1900 **Built On:** Sand
　Number of Holes: 18　**Par:** 70
　Record: 64 (Kevin Eagle)
　Par 3's: 5　**Par 4's:** 10　**Par 5's:** 3
　Yds: 6262　**F9 Yds:** 3008　**B9 Yds:** 3254
　Prevailing Wind: East

RUSHMORE PARK

RUSHMORE PARK GOLF CLUB, Rushmore Pk, Tollard Royal, Salisbury, **WILTSHIRE**, SP5 5QB, **ENGLAND**.
(T) 01725 516326
(W) www.rushmore-estate.co.uk

Membership: Members & Public

Contact/s:
● **Pro Shop:** Mr S McDonagh

Course/s:
🏌 **RUSHMORE PARK**

Description: Wooded, Parkland, Undulating, Sheltered, Medium Length, Tight, Drains Well
Green Speed: Medium
Built: 1992 **Built On:** Chalk
Number of Holes: 18 **Par:** 71
Par 3's: 3 **Par 4's:** 13 **Par 5's:** 2
Yds: 5613
Designer: D Pottage

RUSPER

RUSPER GOLF CLUB, Rusper Rd, Newdigate, **SURREY**, RH5 5BX, **ENGLAND**.
(T) 01293 871456

Membership: Members & Public
Contact/s:
● **Club Secretary:** Mrs Jill Thornhill
● **Professional:** Ms Janice Arnold
● **Pro Shop:**
☎ 01293 871871
● **Book Lessons:** Mrs Janice Arnold
Course/s:
🟤 **RUSPER**
Description: Wooded, Parkland, Medium Length, Tight, Tends to Flood, Ideal for the Elderly
Green Speed: Medium
Built: 1992 **Built On:** Clay
Number of Holes: 18 **Par:** 71
Record: 67 (Robert Dickman)
Par 3's: 4 **Par 4's:** 11 **Par 5's:** 3
Yds: 6218
Designer: Tony Blunden, Hawtree
Further Information:
The course is ideal for the experienced golfer as well as the beginner. The course offers tight, tree lined fairways with short carries from the tees, and good natural water hazards. This 9 hole course has 18 tees and therefore it can be played as an 18 hole course.

RUSTINGTON

RUSTINGTON GOLF CENTRE, Golfers Lane, Angmering, Littlehampton, **SUSSEX (WEST)**, BN16 4NB, **ENGLAND**.
(T) 01903 850790
(W) www.rgcgolf.com

Membership: Members & Public
Size of Complex: 350 Acres
Contact/s:
● **Club Secretary:** Ms Pauline Phillips
Course/s:
🟤 **RUSTINGTON**
Description: Open, Medium Length, Drains Well
Green Speed: Medium
Built: 1992 **Built On:** Soil
Number of Holes: 9 **Par:** 70
Par 3's: 3 **Par 4's:** 4 **Par 5's:** 2
Yds: 5735 **F9 Yds:** 2849 **B9 Yds:** 2886
Prevailing Wind: North
Designer: David Williams
Further Information:
9 hole course can be played as an 18 hole course

RUTHERFORD CASTLE

RUTHERFORD CASTLE GOLF CLUB, West Linton, **SCOTTISH BORDERS**, EH46 7AS, **SCOTLAND**.
(T) 01968 661233
(W) www.ruth-castlegc.co.uk

Membership: Members & Public
Contact/s:
● **Book Tee Times:** Ms Wendy Mitchell
Course/s:

🟤 **RUTHERFORD CASTLE**
Description: Championship, Parkland, Open, Long, Drains Well
Green Speed: Fast
Built: 1998
Number of Holes: 18 **Par:** 72
Par 3's: 4 **Par 4's:** 10 **Par 5's:** 4
Yds: 6525 **F9 Yds:** 3280 **B9 Yds:** 3245
Designer: OCM Associates

RUTHIN-PWLLGLAS

RUTHIN-PWLLGLAS GOLF CLUB, Pwllglas, Ruthin, **DENBIGHSHIRE**, LL15 2PE, **WALES**.
(T) 01824 702383 or 702296

Contact/s:
● **Professional:** Mr M Jones
Course/s:

🟤 **RUTHIN-PWLLGLAS**
Description: Parkland, Undulating
Built: 1903
Number of Holes: 10 **Par:** 66
Further Information:
Views of Clwyd Valley.

RUTLAND COUNTY

RUTLAND COUNTY GOLF CLUB, Great North Rd, Great Casterton, Stamford, **LINCOLNSHIRE**, PE9 4AQ, **ENGLAND**.
(T) 01780 460239

Membership: Members & Public
Contact/s:
● **Professional:** Mr James Darroch
Course/s:

🟤 **RUTLAND COUNTY**
Description: Links, Open, Medium Length, Drains Well, Ideal for the Elderly
Green Speed: Medium/Fast
Built: 1991 **Built On:** Chalk/Soil
Number of Holes: 18 **Par:** 71
Yds: 6401 **F9 Yds:** 3361 **B9 Yds:** 3040
Prevailing Wind: West
Designer: C Sinclair

RUTLAND WATER

RUTLAND WATER GOLF FARM, Lodge Farm, Manton Rd, Edith Weston, Oakham, **RUTLAND**, LE15 8HB, **ENGLAND**.
(T) 01572 737525

Membership: Public
Contact/s:
● **Owner:** Mr Steve Makey
☎ 01780 721429
Course/s:

🟤 **RUTLAND WATER**
Description: Wooded, Parkland, Undulating, Short
Green Speed: Medium
Built: 1990
Number of Holes: 12
Designer: Steve Makey

RUXLEY PARK

AMERICAN GOLF CORPORATION, Sandy Lane, St. Pauls Cray, Orpington, **KENT**, BR5 3HY, **ENGLAND**.
(T) 01689 871490
(E) orpington@americangolf.uk.com
(W) www.americangolf.com

Membership: Members & Public
Contact/s:
● **Club Secretary:** Mr P Davis
● **Professional:** Mr Gary Stewart
Course/s:
🟤 **COURSE #1**

🟤 **RUXLEY PARK 18 HOLE**
Description: Parkland, Hilltop, Undulating, Open, Medium Length, Drains Well
Green Speed: Medium **Built On:** Clay
Number of Holes: 18 **Par:** 69
Yds: 6450
Prevailing Wind: North

🟤 **RUXLEY PARK 9 HOLE**
Description: Parkland, Hilltop, Undulating, Open, Short, Drains Well
Green Speed: Medium/Fast
Built: 1970 **Built On:** Clay
Number of Holes: 9 **Par:** 32
Yds: 2140
Prevailing Wind: North

RYBURN

RYBURN GOLF CLUB (THE), The Shaw, Norland, Sowerby Bridge, **YORKSHIRE (WEST)**, HX6 3QP, **ENGLAND**.
(T) 01422 831355

Contact/s:
● **Company Secretary:** Mr J Hoyle
Course/s:
🟤 **RYBURN**
Number of Holes: 9

RYDE

RYDE GOLF CLUB, Binstead Rd, Ryde, **ISLE OF WIGHT**, PO33 3NF, **ENGLAND**.
(T) 01983 614809
(E) secretary@rydegolf.co.uk
(W) www.rydegolf.co.uk

Contact/s:
● **Club Secretary:** Mr Alan Goodhall
● **Pro Shop:** Mr Richard Dean
☎ 01983 562088
Course/s:
🟤 **RYDE**
Description: Parkland, Undulating, Sheltered, Medium Length, Tends to Flood, Ideal for the Elderly
Green Speed: Medium
Built: 1923 **Built On:** Clay
Number of Holes: 9 **Par:** 33
Par 3's: 4 **Par 4's:** 4 **Par 5's:** 1
Yds: 2672 **Prevailing Wind:** West
Designer: J Hamilton-Stutt

RYE

RYE GOLF CLUB, New Lydd Rd, Camber, Rye, **SUSSEX (EAST)**, TN31 7QS, **ENGLAND**.
(T) 01797 225241

Membership: Members & Public
Contact/s:
● **Club Secretary:** Mr J Smith
● **Professional:** Mr Michael Lee
☎ 01797 225218
Course/s:
🟤 **JUBILEE**
Description: Links, Open
Number of Holes: 9
Designer: Harry Shapland Colt

🟤 **OLD**
Description: Links, Open
Number of Holes: 18 **Par:** 68
Yds: 6308 **F9 Yds:** 2992 **B9 Yds:** 3316
Designer: Harry Shapland Colt 🟡

RYE HILL

RYE HILL GOLF COURSE, Barn Farm, Milcombe, Banbury, **OXFORDSHIRE**, OX15 4RU, **ENGLAND**.

Membership: Members & Public

Contact/s:
● **Professional:** Mr Tony Pennock

Course/s:
🔵 **RYE HILL**
Description: Championship, Heath Land, Undulating, Open, Long, Drains Well
Green Speed: Fast
Built: 1993 **Built On:** Sand
Number of Holes: 18 **Par:** 72
Record: 70 (Paul Robshaw)
Par 3's: 3 **Par 4's:** 12 **Par 5's:** 3
Yds: 6919
Prevailing Wind: North/West

RYHOPE

RYHOPE GOLF COURSE, Leechmore Way, Ryhope, Sunderland, **TYNE AND WEAR**, SR2 0DH, **ENGLAND**.
(T) 0191 5237333

Course/s:
🔵 **RYHOPE**
Number of Holes: 18

RYSTON PARK

RYSTON PARK GOLF CLUB, Ely Rd, Denver, Downham Market, **NORFOLK**, PE38 0HH, **ENGLAND**.
(T) 01366 382133
Size of Complex: 63 Acres

Contact/s:
● **Club Secretary:** Mr J Flogdell
● **Professional:** Ms Alison Sheard

Course/s:
🔵 **RYSTON PARK**
Description: Parkland, Sheltered, Medium Length, Tight, Drains Well
Green Speed: Fast
Built: 1933 **Built On:** Soil
Number of Holes: 9
Designer: James Braid
Further Information:
This flat course has 3 ponds.

RYTON

RYTON GOLF CLUB, Clara Vale, Ryton, **TYNE AND WEAR**, NE40 3TD, **ENGLAND**.
(T) 0191 4133253

Course/s:
🔵 **RYTON**
Description: Parkland, Moorland, Short, Tight
Built: 1891
Number of Holes: 18 **Par:** 70

SADDLEWORTH

SADDLEWORTH GOLF CLUB, Club Secretary & Pro, Ladcastle Rd, Uppermill, Oldham, **MANCHESTER (GREATER)**, OL3 6LT, **ENGLAND**.
(T) 01457 873653

Contact/s:
● **Club Secretary:** Mr Alan Gleave
● **Professional:** Mr Robert Johnson
☎ 01457 810412

Course/s:
🔵 **SADDLEWORTH**
Number of Holes: 18
Yds: 5992 **F9 Yds:** 2900 **B9 Yds:** 3092
Designer: G Lowe, Alistair MacKenzie

SAFFRON WALDEN

SAFFRON WALDEN GOLF CLUB, Windmill Hill, Saffron Walden, **ESSEX**, CB10 1BX, **ENGLAND**.
(T) 01799 522786
(E) office@swgc.com

Contact/s:
● **Professional:** Mr Philip Davis

Course/s:
🔵 **SAFFRON WALDEN**
Number of Holes: 18 **Par:** 72
Par 3's: 4 **Par 4's:** 10 **Par 5's:** 4
Yds: 6606 **F9 Yds:** 3411 **B9 Yds:** 3195

SALE

SALE GOLF CLUB, Golf Rd, Sale, **CHESHIRE**, M33 2XU, **ENGLAND**.
(T) 0161 9736138

Contact/s:
● **Professional:** Mr M Stewart

Course/s:
🔵 **SALE**
Number of Holes: 18 **Par:** 70
Yds: 6126 **F9 Yds:** 3173 **B9 Yds:** 2953

SALINE

SALINE GOLF CLUB, Kinneddar Hill, Dunfermline, **FIFE**, KY12 9NS, **SCOTLAND**.
(T) 01383 852591

Membership: Members & Public

Contact/s:
● **Club Secretary:** Mr Tommy Doherty

Course/s:
🔵 **SALINE**
Description: Parkland, Hilltop, Undulating, Open, Medium Length, Drains Well, Ideal for the Elderly
Green Speed: Medium
Built: 1912 **Built On:** Soil
Number of Holes: 9 **Par:** 68
Yds: 5302 **F9 Yds:** 2651 **B9 Yds:** 2651
Prevailing Wind: West
Further Information:
This physically demanding 9 hole course can be played as an 18 hole course.

SALISBURY & SOUTH WILTS

SALISBURY & SOUTH WILTS GOLF CLUB, The Clubhouse, Netherhampton Lane, Netherhampton, Salisbury, **WILTSHIRE**, SP2 8PR, **ENGLAND**.
(T) 01722 742645
(W) www.salisburygolf.co.uk

Membership: Members & Public

Contact/s:
● **Professional:** Mr G Teschner
● **Pro Shop:** Mr J Cave
☎ 01722 742929

Course/s:
🔵 **BIBURY**
Number of Holes: 9
Designer: S Gidman, J H Taylor
🔵 **MAIN**
Description: Downland, Undulating, Open, Medium Length, Drains Well
Green Speed: Medium
Built: 1888 **Built On:** Chalk
Number of Holes: 18 **Par:** 71
Record: 61 (Stuart Smith)
Yds: 6485 **F9 Yds:** 3351 **B9 Yds:** 3134
Designer: S Gidman, J H Taylor

SALTBURN

SALTBURN GOLF CLUB, Golf Clubhouse/Hobhill, Guisborough Rd, Saltburn-By-The-Sea, **CLEVELAND**, TS12 1NJ, **ENGLAND**.
(T) 01287 622812

Course/s:
🔵 **SALTBURN BY THE SEA**
Number of Holes: 18
Designer: James Braid

SALTFORD

SALTFORD GOLF CLUB LTD, Golf Club Lane, Saltford, Bristol, **BRISTOL**, BS31 3AA, **ENGLAND**.
(T) 01225 873513

Contact/s:
● **Chairman:** Mr Brian Saxby Organ

Course/s:
🔵 **SALTFORD**
Number of Holes: 18

SAND MARTINS

SAND MARTINS GOLF CLUB, Finchampstead Rd, Finchampstead, Wokingham, **BERKSHIRE**, RG40 3RQ, **ENGLAND**.
(T) 0118 9770265
(E) info@sandmartins.com
(W) www.sandmartins.com

Membership: Members & Public

Contact/s:
● **Club Secretary:** Ms Elizabeth Roginski
● **Professional:** Mr Andrew Hall

Course/s:
🔵 **SAND MARTINS**
Description: Championship, Links, Parkland, Undulating, Long, Tight, Drains Well
Green Speed: Fast
Built: 1993 **Built On:** Sand
Number of Holes: 18 **Par:** 70
Par 3's: 5 **Par 4's:** 10 **Par 5's:** 3
Yds: 5970 **F9 Yds:** 3010 **B9 Yds:** 2960
Designer: Edward Fox

SAND MOOR

SAND MOOR GOLF CLUB LTD, Alwoodley Lane, Leeds, **YORKSHIRE (WEST)**, LS17 7DJ, **ENGLAND**.
(T) 0113 2681685
(E) sandmoorgolf@btclick.com

Contact/s:
● **Club Secretary:** Mr Ian Kerr
☎ 0113 2685180

Course/s:
🔵 **SAND MOOR**
Number of Holes: 18 **Par:** 71
Yds: 6429 **F9 Yds:** 3304 **B9 Yds:** 3125
Designer: Alistair MacKenzie

SANDBACH

SANDBACH GOLF CLUB, Middlewich Rd, Sandbach, **CHESHIRE**, CW11 3NT, **ENGLAND**.
(T) 01270 762117

Contact/s:
● **Treasurer:** Mr D Braithwaite

Course/s:
🔵 **SANDBACH**
Number of Holes: 9 **Par:** 68
Yds: 5598 **F9 Yds:** 2791 **B9 Yds:** 2807
Further Information:
Can also be played as an 18 hole course. Some holes have two sets of tees.

SANDFORD SPRINGS

SANDFORD SPRINGS GOLF CLUB,
Wolverton, Tadley, **HAMPSHIRE**, RG26 5RT,
ENGLAND.
(T) 01635 296800
Membership: Members & Public
Contact/s:
● **Golf Manager:** Mr Gary Edmunds
☎ 01635 296808
Course/s:
🏌 **LAKES**
Built: 1990
Number of Holes: 9　**Par:** 35
Par 3's: 2　**Par 4's:** 6　**Par 5's:** 1
Yds: 3047
Designer: Nick Faldo, Bernhard
Gallagher, Hawtree
🏌 **PARKS**
Built: 1988
Number of Holes: 9　**Par:** 34
Par 3's: 2　**Par 4's:** 7
Yds: 2944
Designer: Nick Faldo, Bernhard
Gallagher, Hawtree
Further Information:
The course's distinct club logo and
characteristics have been inspired by the
number of roman artefacts which have
been discovered on the grounds of the
course.
🏌 **WOODS**
Built: 1988
Number of Holes: 9　**Par:** 36
Par 3's: 1　**Par 4's:** 7　**Par 5's:** 1
Yds: 3157
Designer: Nick Faldo, Bernhard
Gallagher, Hawtree

SANDHILL

SANDHILL GOLF RANGE, Middlecliffe Lane,
Little Houghton, Barnsley, **YORKSHIRE
(SOUTH)**, S72 0HW, **ENGLAND**.
(T) 01226 751775
Contact/s:
● **Owner:** Mr Ian Foster
Course/s:
🏌 **SANDHILL**
Built: 1993
Number of Holes: 18
Designer: John Royston

SANDILANDS & LEISURE

SANDILANDS GOLF CLUB & LEISURE,
Roman Bank, Sandilands, Mablethorpe,
LINCOLNSHIRE, LN12 2RJ, **ENGLAND**.
(T) 01507 441432
Membership: Members & Public
Contact/s:
● **Professional:** Mr Jim Payne
● **Book Tee Times:** Ms Michelle Parkinson
Course/s:
🏌 **SANDILANDS**
Description: Links, Open, Long, Drains
Well, Ideal for the Elderly
Green Speed: Fast
Built: 1901　**Built On:** Sand
Number of Holes: 18
Prevailing Wind: North

SANDIWAY

SANDIWAY GOLF CLUB LTD, Chester Rd,
Sandiway, Northwich, **CHESHIRE**, CW8 2DJ,
ENGLAND.
(T) 01606 883247
(E) sandiwaygc@cwcom.net
(W) www.sandiwaygolf.co.uk
Contact/s:
● **Club Secretary:** Mr R H Owens
Course/s:
🏌 **SANDIWAY**
Number of Holes: 18　**Par:** 70
Yds: 6404　**F9 Yds:** 3341　**B9 Yds:** 3063
Designer: Ted Ray

SANDOWN GOLF CTRE

SANDOWN GOLF CENTRE, Sandown Pk,
Moore Lane, Esher, **SURREY**, KT10 8AN,
ENGLAND.
(T) 01372 461234
Membership: Members & Public
Contact/s:
● **Professional:** Mr J Skimmer
● **Pro Shop:** Mr David Parr
Course/s:
🏌 **NEW**
Number of Holes: 9
🏌 **PAR 3**
Description: Heath Land, Open, Medium
Length, Drains Well, Ideal for the Elderly
Green Speed: Medium
Built: 1971　**Built On:** Clay
Number of Holes: 9
Designer: John Jacobs
Further Information:
A flat course situated in the centre of
Sandown Race Course.

SANDWELL PARK

SANDWELL PARK GOLF CLUB LTD,
Birmingham Rd, West Bromwich,
MIDLANDS (WEST), B71 4JJ, **ENGLAND**.
(T) 0121 5534637
(E) secretary@sandwellparkgolfclub.co.uk
(W) www.sandwellparkgolfclub.co.uk
Membership: Members & Public
Size of Complex: 200 Acres
Contact/s:
● **Club Secretary:** Mr David Paterson
● **Professional:** Mr Nigel Wylie
☎ 0121 5534384
Course/s:
🏌 **SANDWELL PARK**
Description: Wooded, Heath Land,
Undulating, Sheltered, Medium Length,
Tight, Drains Well
Green Speed: Fast
Built: 1897　**Built On:** Clay/Soil
Number of Holes: 18　**Par:** 71
Record: 64 (Matthew McGuire)
Par 3's: 4　**Par 4's:** 11　**Par 5's:** 3
Yds: 6204　**F9 Yds:** 3204　**B9 Yds:** 3000
Designer: Harry Shapland Colt
Further Information:
This is a testing course and has fast
greens.

SANDY LODGE

SANDY LODGE GOLF CLUB LTD, Sandy
Lodge Lane, Northwood, **LONDON
(GREATER)**, HA6 2JD, **ENGLAND**.
(T) 01923 825429
Contact/s:
● **Manager:** Ms Heather Inman
Course/s:
🏌 **SANDY LODGE**
Number of Holes: 18　**Par:** 71
Yds: 6459　**F9 Yds:** 3173　**B9 Yds:** 3286
Designer: Harry Vardon

SANDYHILLS

SANDYHILLS GOLF CLUB, 223 Sandyhills
Rd, Glasgow, **GLASGOW (CITY OF)**, G32
9NA, **SCOTLAND**.
(T) 0141 7631099
Contact/s:
● **Manager:** Mr B MacGowan
Course/s:
🏌 **SANDYHILLS**
Number of Holes: 18　**Par:** 72
Yds: 6253

SANQUHAR

SANQUHAR GOLF CLUB, Euchan Golf
Course, Sanquhar, **DUMFRIES AND
GALLOWAY**, DG4 6LA, **SCOTLAND**.
(T) 01659 50577
Contact/s:
● **Treasurer:** Mr V Johnson
Course/s:
🏌 **SANQUHAR**
Number of Holes: 9

SAPEY

SAPEY GOLF CLUB, Upper Sapey,
Worcester, **WORCESTERSHIRE**, WR6 6XT,
ENGLAND.
(T) 01886 853288
(W) www.sapeygolf.co.uk
Membership: Members & Public
Contact/s:
● **Club Secretary:** Ms Lyn Stevenson
● **Professional:** Mr Chris Knowles
Course/s:
🏌 **THE OAKS**
Built: 1999
Number of Holes: 9　**Par:** 27
Par 3's: 9
Yds: 1203
🏌 **THE ROWAN**
Description: Parkland, Open, Drains Well,
Ideal for the Elderly
Built: 1999　**Built On:** Sand
Number of Holes: 18　**Par:** 69
Par 3's: 6　**Par 4's:** 9　**Par 5's:** 3
Yds: 5935　**F9 Yds:** 2911　**B9 Yds:** 3024

SARON

SARON GOLF COURSE, Penwern, Saron,
Llandysul, **CARMARTHENSHIRE**, SA44
5EL, **WALES**.
(T) 01559 370705
Contact/s:
● **Owner:** Mrs G Whitton
Course/s:
🏌 **SARON**
Number of Holes: 18　**Par:** 66
Yds: 4446　**F9 Yds:** 2300　**B9 Yds:** 2146

SAUNTON

SAUNTON GOLF CLUB LTD, Saunton,
Braunton, **DEVON**, EX33 1LG, **ENGLAND**.
(T) 01271 812436
(E) info@sauntongolf.co.uk
(W) www.sauntongolf.co.uk
Membership: Members & Public
Size of Complex: 475 Acres
Contact/s:
● **Club Secretary:** Mr Trevor C Reynolds
● **Professional:** Mr Albert Mackenzie
☎ 01271 812013
● **Book Tee Times:** Mr Trevor Reynolds

Course/s:

EAST
Description: Championship, Links, Long,
Drains Well, Ideal for the Elderly
Green Speed: Fast
Built: 1897 **Built On:** Sand
Number of Holes: 18 **Par:** 71
Record: 66 (J Taylor)
Par 3's: 3 **Par 4's:** 13 **Par 5's:** 2
Yds: 6373 **F9 Yds:** 3303 **B9 Yds:** 3070
Prevailing Wind: West
Designer: Herbert Fowler
Further Information:
Rated 25th in Golf World British Isle
Ratings November 2000.

WEST
Description: Championship, Links,
Medium Length, Drains Well, Ideal for the
Elderly
Green Speed: Fast
Built: 1973 **Built On:** Sand
Number of Holes: 18 **Par:** 71
Par 3's: 5 **Par 4's:** 9 **Par 5's:** 4
Yds: 6138 **F9 Yds:** 3033 **B9 Yds:** 3105
Prevailing Wind: West
Designer: Frank Pennink
Further Information:
Rated 83rd in the Golf World British Isles
Ratings November 2000.

SCARBOROUGH SOUTH CLIFF

**SCARBOROUGH SOUTH CLIFF GOLF
CLUB LTD,** Deepdale Ave, Scarborough,
YORKSHIRE (NORTH), YO11 2UE,
ENGLAND.
(T) 01723 360522

Contact/s:
- **Professional:** Mr Tony Skingle

Course/s:

SCARBOROUGH SOUTH CLIFF
Description: Cliff Top, Undulating
Built: 1903
Number of Holes: 18 **Par:** 70
Designer: Alistair MacKenzie

SCARCROFT

SCARCROFT GOLF CLUB, Syke Lane,
Scarcroft, Leeds, **YORKSHIRE (WEST)**,
LS14 3BQ, **ENGLAND**.
(T) 0113 2892263

Contact/s:
- **General Manager:** Mr T B Davey

Course/s:

SCARCROFT
Number of Holes: 18
Designer: Charles MacKenzie

SCARKE

**SCARKE GOLF COURSE & DRIVING
RANGE,** Scarke, **COUNTY WEXFORD**,
IRELAND.
(T) 051 421483

Course/s:

SCARKE PAR 3
Number of Holes: 27
Par 3's: 27

SCARTHINGWELL

SCARTHINGWELL GOLF COUSRE,
Scarthingwell, Tadcaster, **YORKSHIRE
(NORTH)**, LS24 9PF, **ENGLAND**.
(T) 01937 557878

Membership: Members & Public
Size of Complex: 120 Acres

Contact/s:

- **Club Secretary:** Mrs Eileen Moore
- **Professional:** Mr Steve Footman
  ☎ 01937 557864

Course/s:

SCARTHINGWELL
Description: Wooded, Parkland, Medium
Length, Drains Well, Ideal for the Elderly
Green Speed: Medium
Built: 1992 **Built On:** Soil
Number of Holes: 18 **Par:** 72
Par 3's: 3 **Par 4's:** 12 **Par 5's:** 3
Yds: 6276

SCOONIE

SCOONIE GOLF COURSE, North Links,
Leven, **FIFE**, KY8 4SP, **SCOTLAND**.
(T) 01333 423437

Course/s:

SCOONIE
Number of Holes: 18

SCOTSCRAIG

SCOTSCRAIG GOLF CLUB, Golf Rd,
Tayport, **FIFE**, DD6 9DZ, **SCOTLAND**.
(T) 01382 552515
(E) scotscraig@scottishgolf.com

Membership: Members & Public

Contact/s:
- **Club Secretary:** Mr B D Liddle
- **Professional:** Mr Stuart Campbell
  ☎ 01382 552855

Course/s:

SCOTSCRAIG
Description: Championship, Links, Heath
Land, Sheltered, Medium Length, Drains
Well, Ideal for the Elderly
Green Speed: Fast
Built: 1817 **Built On:** Clay
Number of Holes: 18 **Record:** 72
(Stuart Campbell)
Prevailing Wind: West
Designer: Tom Morris

SCRABO

SCRABO GOLF CLUB, 233 Scrabo Rd,
Newtownards, **COUNTY DOWN**, BT23 4SL,
NORTHERN IRELAND.
(T) 028 91812355
(W) www.scrabo-golf-club.org

Membership: Members & Public

Contact/s:
- **Professional:** Mr Paul McCrystal
  ☎ 028 91817848
- **Book Tee Times:** Mrs Christine Hamil

Course/s:

SCRABO
Description: Links, Parkland, Hilltop,
Open, Medium Length, Drains Well
Green Speed: Medium
Built: 1907
Number of Holes: 18 **Par:** 71
Yds: 6227 **F9 Yds:** 3236 **B9 Yds:** 2991
Prevailing Wind: East

SCRAPTOFT

SCRAPTOFT GOLF CLUB, Beeby Rd,
Scraptoft, Leicester, **LEICESTERSHIRE**, LE7
9SJ, **ENGLAND**.
(T) 0116 2419000

Contact/s:
- **Professional:** Mr Simon Wood

Course/s:

SCRAPTOFT
Description: Parkland
Built: 1928

Number of Holes: 18 **Par:** 70

SEACROFT

SEACROFT GOLF LINKS, Drummond Rd,
Skegness, **LINCOLNSHIRE**, PE25 3AU,
ENGLAND.
(T) 01754 763020
(E) enquiries@seacroft-golfclub.co.uk
(W) www.seacroft-golfclub.co.uk

Membership: Members & Public
Size of Complex: 190 Acres

Contact/s:
- **Club Secretary:** Mr Richard England
- **Professional:** Mr Robin Lawie
  ☎ 01754 769624

Course/s:

SEACROFT
Description: Championship, Links,
Undulating, Medium Length, Tight, Drains
Well, Ideal for the Elderly
Green Speed: Fast
Built: 1895 **Built On:** Sand
Number of Holes: 18 **Par:** 71
Record: 66 (Chris Hall)
Par 3's: 4 **Par 4's:** 11 **Par 5's:** 3
Yds: 6479
Prevailing Wind: North/South
Designer: William Fernie
Further Information:
The last links course on the east coast
before Seaton Carew in Northumberland.

SEAFORD

SEAFORD GOLF CLUB, Firle Rd, Seaford,
SUSSEX (EAST), BN25 2JD, **ENGLAND**.
(T) 01323 892442
(W) www.seafordgolfclub.co.uk

Membership: Members & Public

Contact/s:
- **Club Secretary:** Mr P Court
- **Professional:** Mr David Mills
  ☎ 01323 894160
- **Pro Shop:** Mr Clay Morris

Course/s:

BLATCHINGTON
Description: Undulating, Medium Length,
Drains Well
Green Speed: Medium
Built: 1907 **Built On:** Chalk
Number of Holes: 18 **Par:** 69
Yds: 6233 **F9 Yds:** 3070 **B9 Yds:** 3163
Prevailing Wind: West
Designer: Taylor
Further Information:
A fair but true test of golf with only 1 par 5
and several long par 4's. The club
operates a Dormy House with full play and
stay facilities for up to 22 visiting players.

SEAFORD HEAD

SEAFORD HEAD GOLF COURSE,
Southdown Rd, Seaford, **SUSSEX (EAST)**,
BN25 4JS, **ENGLAND**.
(T) 01323 894843

Contact/s:
- **Manager:** Mr A Lowles

Course/s:

SEAFORD HEAD
Number of Holes: 18

SEAHAM HARBOUR

SEAHAM HARBOUR GOLF CLUB LTD,
Clubhouse, Shrewsbury St, Seaham,
COUNTY DURHAM, SR7 7RD, **ENGLAND**.
(T) 0191 5130837
Size of Complex: 90 Acres

Contact/s:
- **Club Secretary:** Mr Vincent Smith
  ☎ 0191 5811268
- **Pro Shop:** Mr Glyn Jones

Course/s:
🏌 **SEAHAM**
  Description: Parkland, Undulating, Open, Medium Length, Tends to Flood, Ideal for the Elderly
  Built: 1911
  Number of Holes: 18
  Prevailing Wind: West

SEAHOUSES

SEAHOUSES GOLF CLUB, Beadnell Rd, Seahouses, **NORTHUMBERLAND**, NE68 7XT, **ENGLAND**.
(T) 01665 720794

Contact/s:
- **Book Tee Times:** Mr John Gray

Course/s:
🏌 **SEAHOUSES**
  Description: Links
  Built: 1913 **Built On:** Sand
  Number of Holes: 18 **Par:** 67

SEAPOINT

SEAPOINT GOLF CLUB, Termonfeckin, **COUNTY LOUTH**, **IRELAND**.
(T) 041 9822333
(E) golflinks@seapoint.ie
(W) www.golfclubireland.com/seapoint/

Contact/s:
- **Professional:** Mr David Carroll

Course/s:
🏌 **SEAPOINT**
  Description: Championship, Links, Drains Well
  Built: 1993
  Number of Holes: 18 **Par:** 72
  Yds: 7000
  Designer: D Smyth

SEASCALE

SEASCALE GOLF CLUB, The Banks, Seascale, **CUMBRIA**, CA20 1QL, **ENGLAND**.
(T) 01946 721366

Contact/s:
- **Professional:** Mr Sean Rudd
  ☎ 01946 721779

Course/s:
🏌 **SEASCALE**
  Description: Links, Undulating
  Built: 1893 **Built On:** Sand
  Number of Holes: 18 **Par:** 71
  Designer: W Campbell

SEATON CAREW

SEATON CAREW GOLF CLUB, Tees Rd, Seaton Carew, Hartlepool, **CLEVELAND**, TS25 1DE, **ENGLAND**.
(T) 01429 266249
(W) www.seatoncarewgolfclub.org.uk

Membership: Members & Public

Contact/s:
- **Professional:** Mr W Hector
  ☎ 01429 890660

Course/s:
🏌 **BRABAZON COURSE**
  Number of Holes: 18 **Par:** 73
  Par 3's: 3 **Par 4's:** 11 **Par 5's:** 4
  Further Information:
  The course shares fourteen of the holes

---

used on the Old Course, and also includes four new holes constructed out of the sand dunes

🏌 **OLD COURSE**
  Built: 1925
  Number of Holes: 18 **Par:** 72
  Par 3's: 3 **Par 4's:** 12 **Par 5's:** 3
  Yds: 6662
  Designer: Alistair MacKenzie 🏆

SECKFORD

SECKFORD GOLF CLUB, Seckford Hall Rd, Great Bealings, Woodbridge, **SUFFOLK**, IP13 6NT, **ENGLAND**.
(T) 01394 388000

Course/s:
🏌 **SECKFORD**
  Number of Holes: 18
  Designer: J Johnson

SEDBURGH

SEDBERGH GOLF CLUB, Abbot Holme Farm, Millthrop, Sedbergh, **CUMBRIA**, LA10 5SS, **ENGLAND**.
(T) 01539 621551

Contact/s:
- **Club Secretary:** Mr David Lord
  ☎ 01539 620993

Course/s:
🏌 **SEDBURGH**
  Description: Wooded, Parkland
  Built: 1896
  Number of Holes: 9 **Par:** 70 **Record:** 66 (Paul Eales)
  Par 3's: 3 **Par 4's:** 4 **Par 5's:** 2
  Yds: 5624 **F9 Yds:** 2716 **B9 Yds:** 2908
  Designer: W G Squires
  Further Information:
  9 hole course can be played as an 18 hole course

SEDGLEY GOLF CTRE

SEDGLEY GOLF CENTRE, Sandyfields Rd, Dudley, **MIDLANDS (WEST)**, DY3 3DL, **ENGLAND**.
(T) 01902 880503

Contact/s:
- **Manager:** Mr W G Cox

Course/s:
🏌 **SEDGLEY GOLF CTRE**
  Number of Holes: 9
  Designer: W Cox

SEDLESCOMBE

SEDLESCOMBE GOLF CLUB, Kent St, Sedlescombe, Battle, **SUSSEX (EAST)**, TN33 0SD, **ENGLAND**.
(T) 01424 871717
(W) www.golfschool.co.uk

Membership: Members & Public
Size of Complex: 97 Acres

Contact/s:
- **Club Secretary:** Mr Duncan Campbell
- **Professional:** Mr James Andrews
- **Pro Shop:** Mr Tim Underhill
  ☎ 01424 871700

Course/s:
🏌 **SEDLESCOMBE**
  Description: Parkland, Undulating, Medium Length, Drains Well
  Green Speed: Medium
  Built: 1980 **Built On:** Clay
  Number of Holes: 18

SEEDY MILL

SEEDY MILL GOLF CLUB, Tennants Lane, Elmhurst, Lichfield, **STAFFORDSHIRE**, WS13 8HE, **ENGLAND**.
(T) 01543 417333
(E) info@clubhaus.com
(W) www.clubhaus.com

Contact/s:
- **General Manager:** Mr S Dixon

Course/s:
🏌 **MILL**
  Description: Parkland
  Built: 1991
  Number of Holes: 18 **Par:** 72
  Yds: 6305 **F9 Yds:** 3121 **B9 Yds:** 3184
  Designer: Hawtree
  Further Information:
  Mature rural parkland course.

🏌 **SPIRES**
  Description: Parkland
  Built: 1991
  Number of Holes: 9 **Par:** 27
  Yds: 1250
  Further Information:
  US style par 3 course.

SELBY

SELBY GOLF CLUB LTD, Brayton, Selby, **YORKSHIRE (NORTH)**, YO8 9LD, **ENGLAND**.
(T) 01757 228785
(E) selbygolfclub@hotmail.com
(W) www.selbygolfclub.co.uk

Contact/s:
- **Manager:** Mr Neil Proctor
  ☎ 01757 228622

Course/s:
🏌 **SELBY**
  Number of Holes: 18 **Par:** 71
  Yds: 6374 **F9 Yds:** 3307 **B9 Yds:** 3067
  Designer: Hawtree, Donald Steel, Taylor

SELKIRK

SELKIRK GOLF CLUB, Selkirk Hill, Selkirk, **SCOTTISH BORDERS**, TD7 4NW, **SCOTLAND**.
(T) 01750 20621

Membership: Members & Public
Size of Complex: 42 Acres

Contact/s:
- **Club Secretary:** Mr A Wilson

Course/s:
🏌 **SELKIRK**
  Description: Heath Land, Undulating, Open, Medium Length, Drains Well
  Green Speed: Medium
  Built: 1883
  Number of Holes: 9 **Par:** 68
  Par 3's: 3 **Par 4's:** 5 **Par 5's:** 1
  Yds: 5575 **F9 Yds:** 2765 **B9 Yds:** 2810
  Prevailing Wind: West
  Further Information:
  This variable course can also be played as 18 hole using different coloured markers.

SELSDON PARK

SELSDON PARK HOTEL & GOLF COURSE, Addington Rd, Sanderstead, Croydon, **SURREY**, CR2 8YA, **ENGLAND**.
(T) 01816 578811

Contact/s:
- **Professional:** Mr Malcolm Churchill

Course/s:
🏌 **SELSDON PARK**
  Description: Championship, Parkland

Built: 1929
Number of Holes: 18   **Par:** 73
Designer: Taylor
Further Information:
Challenging course.

SELSEY

SELSEY GOLF CLUB, Golf Links Lane,
Selsey, Chichester, **SUSSEX (WEST)**, PO20
9DP **ENGLAND**.
(T) 01243 602203

Membership: Members & Public

Contact/s:
- **Club Secretary:** Mr Percy Carter
- **Professional:** Mr Peter Grindley

Course/s:
- **SELSEY**
  Description: Links, Open, Tight, Tends to
  Flood, Ideal for the Elderly
  Green Speed: Slow
  Built: 1908   **Built On:** Clay
  Number of Holes: 9   **Record:** 64
  Prevailing Wind: South/West
  Designer: Taylor

SENE VALLEY

SENE VALLEY GOLF CLUB, Sene,
Blackhouse Hill, Folkestone, **KENT**, CT18
8BL, **ENGLAND**.
(T) 01303 268513

Membership: Members & Public
Size of Complex: 150 Acres

Contact/s:
- **General Manager:** Mr Gordon Sykes

Course/s:
- **SENE VALLEY**
  Description: Parkland, Undulating, Open,
  Medium Length, Drains Well
  Green Speed: Medium
  Built: 1966   **Built On:** Chalk/Clay
  Number of Holes: 18
  Prevailing Wind: South/West
  Designer: Henry Cotton
  Further Information:
  Magnificent views across the English
  Channel.

SERLBY PARK

SERLBY PARK GOLF CLUB, Serlby,
Doncaster, **YORKSHIRE (SOUTH)**, DN10
6BA, **ENGLAND**.
(T) 01777 818268

Contact/s:
- **Club Secretary:** Mr Ken Crook

Course/s:
- **SERLBY PARK**
  Number of Holes: 11
  Designer: Galway

SETTLE

SETTLE GOLF CLUB, Buckhaw Brow,
Giggleswick, Settle, **YORKSHIRE (NORTH)**,
BD24 0DH, **ENGLAND**.
(T) 01729 825288

Course/s:
- **SETTLE**
  Number of Holes: 9
  Designer: Harry Vardon

SEVEN MEADOWS

SEVEN MEADOWS GOLF CLUB, Netherton
Lane, Highley, Bridgnorth, **SHROPSHIRE**,
WV16 6HZ, **ENGLAND**.
(T) 01746 862212

- **Manager:** Mrs Janet Mayden

Course/s:
- **SEVERN MEADOWS**
  Number of Holes: 9

SHALDON APPROACH

SHALDON APPROACH GOLF COURSE,
Shaldon, Teignmouth, **DEVON**, TQ14 0EY,
ENGLAND.
(T) 01626 872484

Course/s:
- **SHALDON APPROACH**
  Number of Holes: 9

SHANDON PARK

SHANDON PARK GOLF CLUB, 73 Shandon
Pk, Belfast, **COUNTY ANTRIM**, BT5 6NY,
NORTHERN IRELAND.
(T) 028 90401856

Contact/s:
- **General Manager:** Mr M Corsar

Course/s:
- **SHANDON PARK**
  Number of Holes: 18

SHANKLIN & SANDOWN

SHANKLIN & SANDOWN GOLF CLUB, The
Fairway, Sandown, **ISLE OF WIGHT**, PO36
9PR, **ENGLAND**.
(T) 01983 403217

Membership: Members & Public
Size of Complex: 140 Acres

Contact/s:
- **Professional:** Mr Peter Hammond
  ☎ 01983 404424

Course/s:
- **SHANKLIN & SANDOWN**
  Description: Links, Heath Land
  Number of Holes: 18   **Par:** 70
  Yds: 6063   **F9 Yds:** 2824   **B9 Yds:** 3289

SHANNON

SHANNON GOLF CLUB, Shannon Airport,
Shannon, **COUNTY CLARE**, **IRELAND**.
(T) 061 471020

Course/s:
- **SHANNON**
  Number of Holes: 18
  Designer: John Harris

SHAW HILL

**SHAW HILL HOTEL GOLF & COUNTRY
CLUB,** Shaw Hill, Whittle-Le-Woods, Chorley,
LANCASHIRE, PR6 7PP, **ENGLAND**.
(T) 01257 269221
(E) info@shaw-hill.co.uk
(W) www.shaw-hill.co.uk

Contact/s:
- **Professional:** Mr David Clarke

Course/s:
- **SHAW HILL**
  Description: Parkland, Undulating
  Built: 1925
  Number of Holes: 18   **Par:** 73
  Yds: 6064   **F9 Yds:** 3059   **B9 Yds:** 3005

SHENDISH MANOR

SHENDISH MANOR, Shendish, Hemel
Hempstead, **HERTFORDSHIRE**, HP3 0AA,
ENGLAND.
(T) 01442 251806

Membership: Members & Public

Contact/s:
- **Club Secretary:** Mr Tom Concannon
  ☎ 01442 232220
- **Professional:** Mr M White
- **Pro Shop:** Mr A Stormont

Course/s:
- **SHENDISH MANOR**
  Description: Wooded, Parkland,
  Undulating, Tight
  Green Speed: Medium
  Built: 1995   **Built On:** Chalk/Soil
  Number of Holes: 18   **Par:** 70
  Designer: A Dancer, Donald Steel

SHERBORNE

SHERBORNE GOLF CLUB, Higher
Clatcombe, Sherborne, **DORSET**, DT9 4RN,
ENGLAND.
(T) 01935 814431

Contact/s:
- **Company Secretary:** Mr M Betteridge

Course/s:
- **SHERBORNE**
  Number of Holes: 18
  Designer: James Braid

SHERDLEY PARK MUNICIPAL

**SHERDLEY PARK MUNICIPAL GOLF
COURSE,** Sherdley Rd, St. Helens,
MERSEYSIDE, WA9 5DE, **ENGLAND**.
(T) 01744 813149

Membership: Public

Contact/s:
- **Professional:** Mr Daniel Jones

Course/s:
- **SHERDLEY PARK**
  Description: Parkland, Undulating, Open,
  Medium Length, Tends to Flood
  Green Speed: Medium
  Built: 1972
  Number of Holes: 18   **Par:** 71
  Par 3's: 3   **Par 4's:** 13   **Par 5's:** 2
  Yds: 5974   **F9 Yds:** 3424   **B9 Yds:** 2550
  Further Information:
  The course tends to flood in winter.

SHERDONS

SHERDONS GOLF CENTRE (THE), Manor
Farm, Tredington, Tewkesbury,
GLOUCESTERSHIRE, GL20 7BP, **ENGLAND**.
(T) 01684 274782

Membership: Members & Public
Size of Complex: 70 Acres

Contact/s:
- **Club Secretary:** Mr Richard Chatham
- **Professional:** Mr Philip Clark

Course/s:
- **THE MANOR**
  Description: Parkland, Undulating,
  Sheltered, Open, Medium Length, Tight,
  Drains Well, Ideal for the Elderly
  Green Speed: Medium
  Built: 1982   **Built On:** Clay
  Number of Holes: 9   **Par:** 34
  Yds: 2654
  Prevailing Wind: South/West
  Further Information:
  This flat 9 hole course can also be played
  as an 18 hole course.

SHERWOOD FOREST

SHERWOOD FOREST GOLF CLUB, Eakring
Rd, Mansfield, **NOTTINGHAMSHIRE**, NG18
3EW, **ENGLAND**.

(T) 01623 623327

Membership: Members & Public

Contact/s:
- **Club Secretary:** Mrs P Davies
  ☎ 01623 626689
- **Professional:** Mr K Hall
- **Pro Shop:** Mr Ken Hall
  ☎ 01623 627403

Course/s:
- 🏌 **SHERWOOD FOREST**
  Description: Heath Land, Undulating, Long, Tight, Drains Well
  Green Speed: Fast
  Built: 1895   **Built On:** Sand
  Number of Holes: 18   **Par:** 71
  Yds: 6849   **F9 Yds:** 3471   **B9 Yds:** 3378
  Designer: James Braid, W S Colt

SHETLAND

SHETLAND GOLF CLUB, Dale, Gott, Shetland, **SHETLAND ISLANDS**, ZE2 9SB, **SCOTLAND**.
(T) 01595 840369

Contact/s:
- **Manager:** Mr Colin Lobban

Course/s:
- 🏌 **DALE**
  Number of Holes: 18

SHIFNAL

SHIFNAL GOLF CLUB, Decker Hill, Shifnal, **SHROPSHIRE**, TF11 8QL, **ENGLAND**.
(T) 01952 460330

Membership: Members & Public

Contact/s:
- **Club Secretary:** Mr M J Vanner
- **Professional:** Mr J Flannigan
  ☎ 01952 460457

Course/s:
- 🏌 **SHIFNAL**
  Description: Parkland, Open, Tends to Flood, Ideal for the Elderly
  Green Speed: Medium/Fast
  Built: 1969   **Built On:** Soil
  Number of Holes: 18   **Par:** 71
  Yds: 6468   **F9 Yds:** 2503   **B9 Yds:** 2965
  Designer: Pennick

SHILLINGLEE PARK

SHILLINGLEE PARK GOLF COURSE, Chiddingfold, Godalming, **SURREY**, GU8 4TA, **ENGLAND**.
(T) 01428 653237

Contact/s:
- **Professional:** Mr Mark Dowdell

Course/s:
- 🏌 **SHILLINGLEE PARK**
  Built: 1980
  Number of Holes: 9   **Par:** 32
  Designer: Roger Mace
  Further Information:
  There are many water hazards throughout the course.

SHIPLEY

SHIPLEY GOLF CLUB, Beckfoot Lane, Bingley, **YORKSHIRE (WEST)**, BD16 1LX, **ENGLAND**.
(T) 01274 563674
(E) office@shipleygc.co.uk
(W) www.shipleygc.co.uk

Membership: Members & Public

Contact/s:
- **Professional:** Mr Bob Parry

Course/s:
- 🏌 **SHIPLEY**
  Description: Wooded, Parkland, Valley, Undulating, Sheltered, Medium Length, Tight, Drains Well, Ideal for the Elderly
  Green Speed: Fast
  Built: 1921   **Built On:** Clay
  Number of Holes: 18   **Par:** 71
  Record: 63 (Steven Bottomley)
  Yds: 6235   **F9 Yds:** 3337   **B9 Yds:** 2898
  Prevailing Wind: West
  Designer: Alistair MacKenzie
  Further Information:
  A very challenging course.

SHIPTON

SHIPTON GOLF COURSE, Near Frogmill, Andoversford, Cheltenham, **GLOUCESTERSHIRE**, GL54 4LJ, **ENGLAND**.
(T) 01242 890237

Membership: Public

Contact/s:
- **Club Secretary:** Mrs S Beaumont
- **Professional:** Mr N Boland
- **Book Lessons:**
  ☎ 07880 732065

Course/s:
- 🏌 **SHIPTON**
  Description: Parkland, Sheltered, Short, Drains Well, Ideal for the Elderly
  Green Speed: Medium
  Built: 1995   **Built On:** Soil
  Number of Holes: 9   **Par:** 34
  Further Information:
  This is a flat course.

SHIREHAMPTON PARK

SHIREHAMPTON PARK GOLF CLUB, Pk Hill, Shirehampton, Bristol, **BRISTOL**, BS11 0UL, **ENGLAND**.
(T) 01179 822488

Contact/s:
- **Professional:** Mr Brent Ellis

Course/s:
- 🏌 **SHIREHAMPTON PARK**
  Description: Parkland, Undulating
  Built: 1907
  Number of Holes: 18   **Par:** 67
  Further Information:
  A challenging course.

SHIRENEWTON

SHIRENEWTON GOLF & COUNTRY CLUB, Shirenewton, Chepstow, **MONMOUTHSHIRE**, NP16 6RL, **WALES**.
(T) 01291 641471

Membership: Members & Public

Contact/s:
- **Club Secretary:** Mrs Christine Leather
- **Professional:** Mr Lee Pagett

Course/s:
- 🏌 **SHIRENEWTON**
  Description: Wooded, Parkland, Hilltop, Valley, Undulating, Sheltered
  Green Speed: Medium
  Built: 1995   **Built On:** Clay
  Number of Holes: 18

SHIRLAND

SHIRLAND GOLF CLUB, Lower Delves, Shirland, Alfreton, **DERBYSHIRE**, DE55 6AU, **ENGLAND**.
(T) 01773 834935

Membership: Members & Public
Size of Complex: 200 Acres

Contact/s:
- **Club Secretary:** Mrs Carol Fincham
  ☎ 01773 832515
- **Professional:** Mr Neville Hallam

Course/s:
- 🏌 **SHIRLAND**
  Description: Wooded, Parkland, Undulating, Sheltered, Medium Length, Tight
  Green Speed: Medium
  Built: 1967   **Built On:** Clay
  Number of Holes: 18   **Par:** 70
  Record: 67 (Neville Hallam)
  Par 3's: 6   **Par 4's:** 8   **Par 5's:** 4
  Yds: 6072

SHIRLEY

SHIRLEY GOLF COURSE, Stratford Rd, Shirley, Solihull, **MIDLANDS (WEST)**, B90 4EW, **ENGLAND**.
(T) 0121 7446001
(E) shirleygolfclub@btclick.com

Membership: Members & Public

Contact/s:
- **Club Secretary:** Mrs V A Duggan
- **Professional:** Mr S Bottrill
  ☎ 0121 7454979

Course/s:
- 🏌 **SHIRLEY**
  Description: Parkland, Undulating, Medium Length
  Green Speed: Medium/Fast
  Built: 1955
  Number of Holes: 18   **Par:** 72
  Yds: 6507   **F9 Yds:** 3359   **B9 Yds:** 3148

SHIRLEY PARK

SHIRLEY PARK GOLF CLUB LTD, Addiscombe Rd, Croydon, **SURREY**, CR0 7LB, **ENGLAND**.
(T) 020 86541143
(E) secretary@shirleyparkgolfclub.co.uk
(W) www.shirleyparkgolfclub.co.uk

Contact/s:
- **General Manager:** Mr David Roy

Course/s:
- 🏌 **SHIRLEY PARK**
  Number of Holes: 18   **Par:** 71
  Par 3's: 4   **Par 4's:** 11   **Par 5's:** 3
  Yds: 6210   **F9 Yds:** 3222   **B9 Yds:** 2988

SHISKINE

SHISKINE GOLF AND TENNIS CLUB, Shore Rd, Blackwaterfoot, Isle Of Arran, **AYRSHIRE (NORTH)**, KA27 8EX, **SCOTLAND**.
(T) 01770 860226
(E) info@shiskinegolf.com
(W) www.shiskinegolf.com

Membership: Members & Public

Contact/s:
- **Book Tee Times:** Mrs Fiona Brown

Course/s:
- 🏌 **SHISKINE**
  Description: Links, Open, Drains Well
  Green Speed: Medium
  Built: 1896   **Built On:** Sand
  Number of Holes: 12   **Par:** 42
  Par 3's: 7   **Par 4's:** 4   **Par 5's:** 1
  Yds: 3050   **Designer:** William Fernie

SHOOTERS HILL

SHOOTERS HILL GOLF CLUB, Eaglesfield Rd, London, **LONDON (GREATER)**, SE18 3DA, **ENGLAND**.

(T) 020 88546368

Membership: Members & Public

Contact/s:
- **Club Secretary:** Ms Sandy Watt
- **Professional:** Mr David Brotherton

Course/s:
- **SHOOTERS HILL**
  Description: Parkland, Tends to Flood
  Green Speed: Medium
  Built: 1903 **Built On:** Clay
  Number of Holes: 18
  Prevailing Wind: South
  Designer: William Park

SHORTLANDS

SHORTLANDS GOLF CLUB, Meadow Rd, Bromley, **KENT**, BR2 0DX, **ENGLAND**.
(T) 020 84646182

Membership: Members & Public

Contact/s:
- **Club Secretary:** Mr Peter May
  ☎ 020 84608828
- **Professional:** Mr Mick Taylor

Course/s:
- **SHORTLANDS**
  Description: Wooded, Parkland, Sheltered, Short, Tight, Drains Well, Ideal for the Elderly
  Green Speed: Medium
  Built: 1894 **Built On:** Clay
  Number of Holes: 9 **Par:** 67 **Record:** 59 (Nick Haynes)
  Par 3's: 4 **Par 4's:** 3 **Par 5's:** 2
  Yds: 5261
  Prevailing Wind: West
  Further Information:
  River Ravenbourne runs through the course. This 9 hole course can be played as an 18 hole course, using 5 different tees for the second 9.

SHOTTS

SHOTTS GOLF CLUB, Blairhead, Benhar Rd, Shotts, **LANARKSHIRE (NORTH)**, ML7 5BJ, **SCOTLAND**.
(T) 01501 820431

Contact/s:
- **Professional:** Mr John Strachan

Course/s:
- **SHOTTS**
  Built: 1895
  Number of Holes: 18 **Par:** 70
  Designer: James Braid
  Further Information:
  Shotts' notorious 409 yard par 4 is aptly called the Devil's Elbow as it is extremely challenging.

SHREWBURY

SHREWSBURY GOLF CLUB, Grange Lane, Condover, Shrewsbury, **SHROPSHIRE**, SY5 7BL, **ENGLAND**.
(T) 01743 872976

Membership: Members & Public

Contact/s:
- **Club Secretary:** Ms Sylvia Kenney
  ☎ 01743 872977
- **Professional:** Mr Peter Seal
  ☎ 01743 874581

Course/s:
- **SHREWBURY**
  Description: Parkland, Undulating, Open, Tends to Flood, Ideal for the Elderly
  Green Speed: Fast
  Built: 1970 **Built On:** Gravel
  Number of Holes: 18 **Par:** 70

Record: 65
Yds: 6207 **F9 Yds:** 3079 **B9 Yds:** 3128
Further Information:
There are water features throughout the course.

SHRIGLEY HALL

SHRIGLEY HALL HOTEL, GOLF & COUNTRY CLUB, Shrigley Pk, Pott Shrigley, Macclesfield, **CHESHIRE**, SK10 5KB, **ENGLAND**.
(T) 01625 575626
(E) shrigleyhall@paramount-hotels.co.uk
(W) www.paramounthotels.co.uk

Contact/s:
- **Owner:** Granville Ogden

Course/s:
- **SHRIGLEY HALL GOLF**
  Description: Parkland
  Built: 1989 **Built On:** Soil
  Number of Holes: 18 **Par:** 71
  Designer: Donald Steel

SHRIVENHAM PARK

SHRIVENHAM PARK, Pennyhooks, Shrivenham, Swindon, **WILTSHIRE**, SN6 8EX, **ENGLAND**.
(T) 01793 783853

Membership: Members & Public

Contact/s:
- **Professional:** Mr T Pocock
- **Pro Shop:** Mr S Ash

Course/s:
- **SHRIVENHAM PARK**
  Description: Parkland, Undulating, Short, Tight, Drains Well
  Green Speed: Medium
  Built: 1980 **Built On:** Sand/Soil
  Number of Holes: 18 **Par:** 69
  Par 3's: 6 **Par 4's:** 9 **Par 5's:** 3
  Yds: 5769 **F9 Yds:** 3010 **B9 Yds:** 2759
  Further Information:
  A river runs through the course.

SHROPSHIRE

SHROPSHIRE (THE) GOLF COURSE, Granville Pk, Muxton, Telford, **SHROPSHIRE**, TF2 8PH, **ENGLAND**.
(T) 01952 677800

Course/s:
- **BLUE/GOLD**
  Number of Holes: 18
  Designer: Hawtree
- **BLUE/SILVER**
  Number of Holes: 18
  Designer: Hawtree
- **SILVER/GOLD**
  Number of Holes: 18
  Designer: Hawtree

SICKLEHOLME

SICKLEHOLME GOLF CLUB, Station Rd, Bamford, Hope Valley, **DERBYSHIRE**, S33 0BN, **ENGLAND**.
(T) 01433 651306
(W) www.sickleholme.co.uk
Size of Complex: 110 Acres

Contact/s:
- **Professional:** Mr P Taylor

Course/s:
- **SICKLEHOLME**
  Description: Parkland, Undulating, Medium Length, Tends to Flood
  Green Speed: Medium
  Built: 1899 **Built On:** Clay/Sand

Number of Holes: 18
Further Information:
Large ravines and rivers.

SIDCUP

SIDCUP GOLF CLUB (1926) LTD, 7 Hurst Rd, Sidcup, **KENT**, DA15 9AE, **ENGLAND**.
(T) 020 83090679

Course/s:
- **SIDCUP**
  Number of Holes: 9
  Designer: James Braid

SIDMOUTH

SIDMOUTH GOLF CLUB, Cotmaton Rd, Sidmouth, **DEVON**, EX10 8SX, **ENGLAND**.
(T) 01395 513451

Membership: Members & Public
Size of Complex: 85 Acres

Contact/s:
- **Club Secretary:** Mr Ian Smith
- **Professional:** Mr Gaele Tapper
  ☎ 01395 516407

Course/s:
- **SIDMOUTH**
  Description: Parkland, Moorland, Sheltered, Short, Tight
  Green Speed: Fast
  Built: 1889
  Number of Holes: 18 **Par:** 66
  Yds: 5068 **F9 Yds:** 2573 **B9 Yds:** 2495
  Prevailing Wind: South/West
  Designer: Taylor

SILECROFT

SILECROFT GOLF CLUB, Silecroft, Millom, **CUMBRIA**, LA18 4NX, **ENGLAND**.
(T) 01229 774250

Contact/s:
- **Honorary Secretary:** Mr David MacLardie
  ☎ 01229 774342

Course/s:
- **SILECROFT**
  Number of Holes: 9 **Par:** 68
  Par 3's: 2 **Par 4's:** 7
  Yds: 5877 **F9 Yds:** 2926 **B9 Yds:** 2951
  Further Information:
  9 hole course can be played as an 18 hole course

SILKSTONE

SILKSTONE GOLF CLUB, Elmhirst Lane, Silkstone, Barnsley, **YORKSHIRE (SOUTH)**, S75 4LD, **ENGLAND**.
(T) 01226 790328

Course/s:
- **SILKSTONE**
  Number of Holes: 18 **Par:** 70
  Yds: 5871 **F9 Yds:** 3100 **B9 Yds:** 2771

SILLOTH

SILLOTH ON SOLWAY GOLF CLUB, Golf Clubhouse, Station Sq, Silloth, Wigton, **CUMBRIA**, CA7 4BL, **ENGLAND**.
(T) 01697 331304

Membership: Members & Public

Contact/s:
- **Professional:** Mr J Graham
  ☎ 01697 332404

Course/s:
- **SILLOTH**
  Description: Links, Heath Land
  Built: 1892 **Built On:** Sand

Number of Holes: 18 Par: 72
Par 3's: 4 Par 4's: 10 Par 5's: 4
Yds: 6358 F9 Yds: 3007 B9 Yds: 3351
Designer: William Park ♟

SILSDEN

SILSDEN GOLF CLUB, High Brunthwaite, Silsden, Keighley, **YORKSHIRE (WEST)**, BD20 0NH, **ENGLAND**.
(T) 01535 652998

Contact/s:
● Manager: Mr John Chambers

Course/s:
● SILSDEN
Built: 1913
Number of Holes: 18 Par: 67
Yds: 5259 F9 Yds: 2501 B9 Yds: 2758
Further Information:
Views of Aire Valley.

SILVERDALE

SILVERDALE GOLF CLUB, Red Bridge Lane, Silverdale, Carnforth, **LANCASHIRE**, LA5 0SP, **ENGLAND**.
(T) 01524 701300

Contact/s:
● Club Secretary: Mr Keith Smith
☎ 01524 702074

Course/s:
● SILVERDALE
Number of Holes: 12 Par: 69
Yds: 5210 F9 Yds: 2550 B9 Yds: 2660
Further Information:
The course will become 18 holes by mid 2002.

SILVERKNOWES

SILVERKNOWES GOLF COURSE, 118 Silverknowes Rd, Parkway, Edinburgh, **EDINBURGH (CITY OF)**, EH4 5ET, **SCOTLAND**.
(T) 0131 3363843

Course/s:
● SILVERKNOWES
Built: 1947
Number of Holes: 18 Par: 71
Yds: 6070

SILVERMERE GOLF COMPLEX

SILVERMERE GOLF COMPLEX, Redhill Rd, Cobham, **SURREY**, KT11 1EF, **ENGLAND**.
(T) 01932 868122

Course/s:
● SILVERMERE
Number of Holes: 18

SILVERSTONE

SILVERSTONE GOLF CLUB, Silverstone Rd, Stowe, Buckingham, **BUCKINGHAMSHIRE**, MK18 5LH, **ENGLAND**.
(T) 01280 850005

Membership: Members & Public
Size of Complex: 180 Acres

Contact/s:
● Pro Shop: Mr Rodney Holt

Course/s:
● SILVERSTONE
Description: Parkland
Green Speed: Medium
Built: 1992 Built On: Clay
Number of Holes: 18 Par: 72
Yds: 6213 F9 Yds: 3135 B9 Yds: 3078
Designer: David Snell

SINFIN

SINFIN GOLF COURSE, Wilmore Rd, Sinfin, Derby, **DERBYSHIRE**, DE24 9HD, **ENGLAND**.
(T) 01332 766462

Course/s:
● SINFIN
Number of Holes: 18

SINGING HILLS

SINGING HILLS GOLF COURSE LTD, Off B2117, Albourne, **SUSSEX (WEST)**, BN6 9EB, **ENGLAND**.
(T) 01273 835353

Membership: Members & Public

Contact/s:
● Club Secretary: Mr Brian Hazelgrove
● Professional: Mr Wallace Street
● Pro Shop: Mr Merrick Trevaskis

Course/s:
● LAKE
Description: Championship, Parkland, Undulating, Open, Medium Length, Tends to Flood, Ideal for the Elderly
Green Speed: Medium
Built: 1992 Built On: Clay
Number of Holes: 9 Par: 34
Par 3's: 3 Par 4's: 5 Par 5's: 1
Yds: 2928
Prevailing Wind: East
Designer: Robert Sandow
Further Information:
Can play as a 18 hole course by using a combination of the 3 courses.

● RIVER
Number of Holes: 9 Par: 34
Par 3's: 3 Par 4's: 5 Par 5's: 1
Yds: 2861
Designer: Robert Sandow
Further Information:
Can play as a 18 hole course using a combination of the 3 courses.

● VALLEY
Number of Holes: 9 Par: 36
Par 3's: 1 Par 4's: 7 Par 5's: 1
Yds: 3362 F9 Yds: 3362
Designer: Robert Sandow
Further Information:
Can play as a 18 hole course by using a combination of the 3 courses.

SITTINGBOURNE & MILTON REGIS

SITTINGBOURNE & MILTON REGIS GOLF CLUB, Wormdale Hill, Newington, Sittingbourne, **KENT**, ME9 7PX, **ENGLAND**.
(T) 01795 842261
(E) sittingbourne@golfclub.totalserve.co.uk

Contact/s:
● Club Secretary: Mr H D G Wylie

Course/s:
● SITTINGBOURNE & MILTON REGIS
Number of Holes: 18 Par: 71
Yds: 6291 F9 Yds: 3082 B9 Yds: 3209
Designer: Donald Steel

SITWELL

SITWELL PARK GOLF CLUB, Shrogswood Rd, Rotherham, **YORKSHIRE (SOUTH)**, S60 4BY, **ENGLAND**.
(T) 01709 700799

Contact/s:
● Club Secretary: Mr G Simmonite
● Professional: Mr Nic Taylor

Course/s:

● SITWELL
Description: Parkland, Undulating
Built: 1913
Number of Holes: 18 Par: 71
Yds: 5960 F9 Yds: 2931 B9 Yds: 3029
Designer: Alistair MacKenzie

SIX HILLS LEISURE

SIX HILLS LEISURE, Six Hills Farm, Six Hills Rd, Six Hills, Melton Mowbray, **LEICESTERSHIRE**, LE14 3PR, **ENGLAND**.
(T) 01509 881225

Contact/s:
● Owner: Mr J A Hawley

Course/s:
● SIX HILLS
Number of Holes: 18

SKEABOST

SKEABOST GOLF COURSE, Skeabost House Hotel, Skeabost Bridge, Skeabost, **HIGHLANDS**, IV51 9NR, **SCOTLAND**.
(T) 01470 532202

Course/s:
● SKEABOST
Number of Holes: 9
Designer: John Stuart

SKELMORLIE

SKELMORLIE GOLF CLUB, Skelmorlie, **AYRSHIRE (NORTH)**, PA17 5ES, **SCOTLAND**.
(T) 01475 520152
(E) matchsec@skelmorliegolf.co.uk
(W) www.skelmorliegolf.co.uk

Course/s:
● SKELMORLIE
Number of Holes: 18 Par: 65
Yds: 5030 F9 Yds: 2434 B9 Yds: 2596
Designer: James Braid

SKERRIES

SKERRIES GOLF CLUB, Hacketstown, Skerries, **COUNTY DUBLIN**, **IRELAND**.
(T) 01 8491567

Course/s:
● SKERRIES
Number of Holes: 18

SKIBBEREEN & WEST CARBERY

SKIBBEREEN & WEST CARBERY GOLF CLUB, Skibbereen, **COUNTY CORK**, **IRELAND**.
(T) 02 821227

Course/s:
● SKIBBEREEN & WEST CARBERY
Number of Holes: 18

SKIPSEA

SKIPSEA GOLF CLUB, Hornsea Rd, Skipsea, Driffield, **YORKSHIRE (EAST)**, YO25 8SY, **ENGLAND**.
(T) 01262 468186

Contact/s:
● Owner: Mr C Voase

Course/s:
● SKIPSEA GOLF COURSE
Number of Holes: 9 Par: 27
Par 3's: 9
Yds: 3142 F9 Yds: 3142

SKIPTON

SKIPTON GOLF CLUB, Off North West By Passage, Skipton, **YORKSHIRE (NORTH)**, BD23 3LF, **ENGLAND**.
(T) 01756 795657
(E) enquiries@skiptongolfclub.co.uk
(W) www.skiptongolfclub.co.uk

Contact/s:
- Club Secretary: Mr Eric Paterson
- Professional: Mr Peter Robinson
  ☎ 01756 793257

Course/s:
- **SKIPTON**
  Description: Parkland, Undulating
  Built: 1893
  Number of Holes: 18 Par: 70
  Yds: 6076 F9 Yds: 3267 B9 Yds: 2809

SLADE VALLEY

SLADE VALLEY GOLF CLUB, Lynch Pk, Brittas, Brittas Bay, **COUNTY DUBLIN**, **IRELAND**.
(T) 01 4582183

Course/s:
- **SLADE VALLEY**
  Number of Holes: 18

SLALEY HALL GOLF COURSE

SLALEY HALL HOTEL & GOLF RESORT, De Vere Slaley Hall, Slaley, Hexham, **NORTHUMBERLAND**, NE47 0BY, **ENGLAND**.
(T) 01434 673154
(E) slaley.hall@devere-hotels.com
(W) www.devere-hotels.com

Contact/s:
- Head Teaching Professional: Mr Gordon Robinson

Course/s:
- **HUNTING**
  Description: Championship
  Built: 1990
  Number of Holes: 18 Par: 72
  Yds: 7021
  Designer: Peter Alliss

- **PRIESTMAN**
  Description: Championship
  Built: 1999
  Number of Holes: 18 Par: 72
  Yds: 6280
  Designer: Neil Coles

SLEAFORD

SLEAFORD GOLF CLUB, Willoughby Rd, South Rauceby, Sleaford, **LINCOLNSHIRE**, NG34 8PL, **ENGLAND**.
(T) 01529 488326
(E) sleafordgolfclub@btinternet.com

Membership: Members & Public

Contact/s:
- Professional: Mr James Wilson
  ☎ 01529 488644

Course/s:
- **SLEAFORD**
  Description: Championship, Heath Land, Medium Length, Drains Well, Ideal for the Elderly
  Green Speed: Medium
  Built: 1905 Built On: Sand
  Number of Holes: 18 Par: 72
  Record: 66 (S Emery)
  Par 3's: 3 Par 4's: 12 Par 5's: 3
  Yds: 6443 F9 Yds: 3230 B9 Yds: 3213
  Prevailing Wind: West
  Designer: T Williams

Further Information:
A challenging course.

SLIEVENAMON

SLIEVENAMON GOLF CLUB, Clonacody, Lisronagh, Clonmel, **COUNTY TIPPERARY**, **IRELAND**.
(T) 052 32213
(E) info@slievenamongolfclub.com
(W) www.slievenamongolfclub.com

Membership: Members & Public

Contact/s:
- Pro Shop: Mr John Mitchell
- Book Lessons: Mr Derry Kiley

Course/s:
- **SLIEVENAMON**
  Number of Holes: 18 Par: 62
  Par 3's: 10 Par 4's: 8
  Yds: 4135

SLIGO (COUNTY)

COUNTY SLIGO GOLF CLUB, Rossespoint, Sligo, **COUNTY SLIGO**, **IRELAND**.
(T) 071 77134
(E) cosligo@iol.ie
(W) www.countysligogolfclub.ie

Membership: Members & Public

Contact/s:
- Club Secretary: Ms Teresa Banks
- Professional: Mr Jim Robinson
  ☎ 071 77171

Course/s:
- **BOMORE 9 HOLE**
  Description: Links, Open, Medium Length, Drains Well
  Green Speed: Medium
  Number of Holes: 9
  Designer: H S Colt

- **CHAMPIONSHIP**
  Description: Championship, Links, Open
  Built: 1927
  Number of Holes: 18 Par: 71
  Yds: 5840 F9 Yds: 2897 B9 Yds: 2943
  Designer: H S Colt ♟

SLINFOLD PARK

SLINFOLD PARK GOLF & COUNTRY CLUB, Stane St, Slinfold, Horsham, **SUSSEX (WEST)**, RH13 7RE, **ENGLAND**.
(T) 01403 791555

Contact/s:
- Professional: Mr Tony Clingan

Course/s:
- **CHAMPIONSHIP**
  Description: Championship, Parkland
  Built: 1993
  Number of Holes: 18 Par: 72
  Par 3's: 4 Par 4's: 10 Par 5's: 4
  Yds: 6432 F9 Yds: 3094 B9 Yds: 3338
  Designer: John Fortune

- **SHORT**
  Number of Holes: 9
  Designer: John Fortune

SOLENT MEADS GOLF CTRE

SOLENT MEADS GOLF CENTRE, Rolls Drive, Hengistbury Head, Bournemouth, **DORSET**, BH6 4NA, **ENGLAND**.
(T) 01202 420795

Membership: Public

Contact/s:
- Managing Director: Mr A Tate

Course/s:
- **SOLENT MEADS PAR 3**
  Number of Holes: 18

SOLWAY LINKS

SOLWAY LINKS GOLF COURSE, East Preston Farm, Kirkbean, Dumfries, **DUMFRIES AND GALLOWAY**, DG2 8BE, **SCOTLAND**.
(T) 01387 880217

Membership: Members & Public
Size of Complex: 100 Acres

Contact/s:
- Club Secretary: Mr M B Clark

Course/s:
- **SOLWAY LINKS**
  Description: Links, Undulating, Open, Medium Length, Drains Well, Ideal for the Elderly
  Green Speed: Medium
  Built: 1992 Built On: Soil
  Number of Holes: 18 Par: 66
  Par 3's: 7 Par 4's: 10 Par 5's: 1
  Yds: 4701
  Prevailing Wind: South/West
  Designer: Gordon Cray
  Further Information:
  The course is near the coast and the Southerness Golf Club is also nearby.

SONNING

SONNING GOLF CLUB, Duffield Rd, Sonning, Reading, **BERKSHIRE**, RG4 6GJ, **ENGLAND**.
(T) 0118 9693332

Contact/s:
- Club Secretary: Mr Andrew Tanner
- Professional: Mr R McDougall

Course/s:
- **SONNING**
  Description: Wooded, Parkland
  Green Speed: Fast
  Number of Holes: 18 Par: 70
  Par 3's: 4 Par 4's: 12 Par 5's: 2
  Yds: 6366 F9 Yds: 3148 B9 Yds: 3218
  Designer: Hawtree

SOUTH BEDS

SOUTH BEDS GOLF CLUB, Warden Hill Rd, Luton, **BEDFORDSHIRE**, LU2 7AE, **ENGLAND**.
(T) 01582 591500

Membership: Members & Public

Contact/s:
- Club Secretary: Mr Ray Wright
- Professional: Mr Eddie Cogle

Course/s:
- **GALLEY HILL**
  Description: Wooded, Breckland, Undulating, Sheltered, Open, Medium Length, Tight, Drains Well, Ideal for the Elderly
  Green Speed: Medium
  Built: 1892 Built On: Chalk
  Number of Holes: 18 Par: 71
  Par 3's: 5 Par 4's: 9 Par 5's: 4
  Yds: 6397 F9 Yds: 3345 B9 Yds: 3052
  Prevailing Wind: South/West
  Designer: Harry Vardon
  Further Information:
  Excellent greens with good conditions all year round.

- **WARDEN HILL**
  Description: Heath Land, Breckland, Hilltop, Open, Short, Tight, Drains Well, Ideal for the Elderly
  Green Speed: Fast

Built: 1892 **Built On:** Chalk
Number of Holes: 18 **Par:** 64
Par 3's: 8 **Par 4's:** 10
Yds: 4914 **F9 Yds:** 2424 **B9 Yds:** 2490
Prevailing Wind: South/West
Further Information:
The greens are superb all year round on
this testing but fair course

SOUTH BRADFORD

SOUTH BRADFORD GOLF CLUB, Pearson
Rd, Bradford, **YORKSHIRE (WEST),** BD6
1BH, **ENGLAND.**
(T) 01274 679195

Contact/s:
● **Club Secretary:** Mr Ian Moody
  ☎ 01274 672231
● **Professional:** Mr Paul Cooke

Course/s:
⛳ **SOUTH BRADFORD**
  Number of Holes: 9 **Par:** 70
  Yds: 5696 **F9 Yds:** 2848 **B9 Yds:** 2848
  Further Information:
  9 hole course can be played as an 18 hole
  course

SOUTH ESSEX

AMERICAN GOLF CORPORATION,
Herongate, Brentwood, **ESSEX,** CM13 3LW,
ENGLAND.
(T) 01277 811289
(E) southessex@americangolf.uk.com
(W) www.americangolf.com

Membership: Members & Public

Contact/s:
● **Professional:** Mr Gary Stewart
● **Pro Shop:**
  ☎ 01277 811008
● **Book Tee Times:**
  ☎ 01277 811006

Course/s:
⛳ **HAWK (HAWK & VIXON)**
  Description: Wooded, Parkland,
  Undulating, Long, Drains Well
  Green Speed: Medium
  Built: 1992
  Number of Holes: 18 **Par:** 71
  Yds: 6471 **F9 Yds:** 3369 **B9 Yds:** 3102
  Designer: R Plumbridge
  Further Information:
  Built with nature in mind, the course uses
  beautiful bluebell carpeted woodlands to
  form the layout.

⛳ **HERON (HERON & HAWK)**
  Description: Wooded, Parkland,
  Undulating, Long, Drains Well
  Green Speed: Medium
  Built: 1992
  Number of Holes: 18 **Par:** 72
  Yds: 6851 **F9 Yds:** 3482 **B9 Yds:** 3369
  Designer: R Plumbridge
  Further Information:
  Built with nature in mind, the course uses
  beautiful bluebell carpeted woodlands to
  form the layout.

⛳ **VIXEN (VIXEN & HERON)**
  Description: Wooded, Parkland,
  Undulating, Long, Drains Well
  Green Speed: Medium
  Built: 1992
  Number of Holes: 18 **Par:** 71
  Yds: 6584 **F9 Yds:** 3102 **B9 Yds:** 3482
  Designer: R Plumbridge
  Further Information:
  Built with nature in mind, the course uses
  beautiful bluebell carpeted woodlands to
  form the layout.

SOUTH HEREFORDSHIRE

SOUTH HEREFORDSHIRE GOLF CLUB,
Twin Lakes, Upton Bishop, Ross-on-Wye,
HEREFORDSHIRE, HR9 7UA, **ENGLAND.**
(T) 01989 780535

Membership: Members & Public

Contact/s:
● **Club Secretary:** Mr R L A Lee
● **Professional:** Mr E Litchfield

Course/s:
⛳ **SOUTH HEREFORDSHIRE 18 HOLE**
  Number of Holes: 18
  Par 3's: 18
  Yds: 6672

⛳ **SOUTH HEREFORDSHIRE 9 HOLE COURSE**
  Number of Holes: 9
  Par 3's: 9

SOUTH HERTS

SOUTH HERTS GOLF CLUB, Links Drive,
London, **LONDON (GREATER),** N20 8QU,
ENGLAND.
(T) 020 84452035
(W) www.southherts.co.uk

Membership: Members & Public

Contact/s:
● **Club Secretary:** Mr Kevin Bravat
● **Professional:** Mr Bobby Mitchell
● **Pro Shop:**
  ☎ 020 84454633

Course/s:
⛳ **COURSE 2**
  Number of Holes: 9 **Par:** 56
  Yds: 1581

⛳ **SOUTH HERTS**
  Description: Wooded, Parkland,
  Undulating, Sheltered, Open, Medium
  Length, Drains Well
  Green Speed: Fast
  Built: 1899 **Built On:** Clay
  Number of Holes: 18 **Par:** 72
  Record: 65
  Yds: 6432
  Designer: Harry Vardon

SOUTH KYME

SOUTH KYME GOLF CLUB, Skinners Lane,
South Kyme, Lincoln, **LINCOLNSHIRE,** LN4
4AT, **ENGLAND.**
(T) 01526 861113
(W) www.skgc.co.uk

Membership: Members & Public

Contact/s:
● **Club Secretary:** Mr Peter Chamberlain

Course/s:
⛳ **SOUTH KYME**
  Description: Links
  Built: 1990
  Number of Holes: 18 **Par:** 72
  Par 3's: 4 **Par 4's:** 10 **Par 5's:** 4
  Yds: 6568 **F9 Yds:** 3121 **B9 Yds:** 3447
  Designer: G Bradley
  Further Information:
  An Inland Links course.

SOUTH LEEDS

SOUTH LEEDS GOLF CLUB, Parkside Links,
Gipsy Lane, Leeds, **YORKSHIRE (WEST),**
LS11 5TU, **ENGLAND.**
(T) 0113 2700479

Membership: Members & Public

Contact/s:
● **Club Secretary:** Mr John Neal
  ☎ 0113 2771676

● **Professional:** Mr Michael Lewis

Course/s:
⛳ **SOUTH LEEDS**
  Description: Championship, Wooded,
  Parkland, Undulating, Open, Short, Drains
  Well, Ideal for the Elderly
  Green Speed: Fast
  Built: 1914 **Built On:** Soil
  Number of Holes: 18 **Par:** 69
  Par 3's: 4 **Par 4's:** 13 **Par 5's:** 1
  Yds: 5865 **F9 Yds:** 2728 **B9 Yds:** 3137
  Prevailing Wind: West
  Designer: Robert Trent Jones
  Further Information:
  A very difficult course.

SOUTH MEATH

SOUTH MEATH GOLF CLUB, Calverstown,
Longwood Rd, Trim, **COUNTY MEATH,**
IRELAND.
(T) 04 631471

Membership: Members & Public

Contact/s:
● **Manager:** Mr Joe Kegan

Course/s:
⛳ **SOUTH MEATH COURSE**
  Description: Parkland, Undulating, Long,
  Drains Well, Ideal for the Elderly
  Green Speed: Slow
  Built: 1993 **Built On:** Clay
  Number of Holes: 9 **Par:** 70
  Designer: Edward Hackett
  Further Information:
  A couple of ponds along the course

SOUTH MOOR

SOUTH MOOR GOLF CLUB, The Middles,
Craghead, Stanley, **COUNTY DURHAM,** DH9
6AG, **ENGLAND.**
(T) 01207 232848

Contact/s:
● **Professional:** Mr Sean Cowell

Course/s:
⛳ **SOUTH MOOR**
  Description: Parkland, Moorland,
  Undulating **Built:** 1923
  Number of Holes: 18 **Par:** 72
  Yds: 6271 **Designer:** Alistair MacKenzie

SOUTH PEMBROKE

SOUTH PEMBROKESHIRE GOLF CLUB,
Military Rd, Pennar, Pembroke Dock,
PEMBROKESHIRE, SA72 6SE, **WALES.**
(T) 01646 621453

Membership: Members & Public
Size of Complex: 75 Acres

Contact/s:
● **Club Secretary:** Mr Don Owen

Course/s:
⛳ **SOUTH PEMBROKE**
  Description: Parkland, Cliff Top,
  Undulating, Open, Medium Length, Tight,
  Drains Well, Ideal for the Elderly
  Green Speed: Fast
  Built: 1970 **Built On:** Clay
  Number of Holes: 18
  Prevailing Wind: West
  Designer: Members
  Further Information:
  Breathtaking views over the coastline.

SOUTH SHIELDS

SOUTH SHIELDS GOLF CLUB LTD, Mens
Section, Cleadon Hill, South Shields, **TYNE**
AND WEAR, NE34 8EG, **ENGLAND.**

(T) 0191 4560475

Contact/s:
● **Accountant:** Mr Paul Stuart Lancaster

Course/s:
⛳ **SOUTH SHIELDS**
Number of Holes: 18 **Par:** 71
Yds: 6264
Designer: James Braid, Alistair MacKenzie

SOUTH STAFFORDSHIRE

SOUTH STAFFORDSHIRE GOLF CLUB,
Danescourt Rd, Wolverhampton, **MIDLANDS (WEST)**, WV6 9BQ, **ENGLAND**.
(T) 01902 754816

Contact/s:
● **Club Secretary:** Mr J A Macklin
● **Professional:** Mr J Rhodes

Course/s:
⛳ **SOUTH STAFFORDSHIRE**
Number of Holes: 18 **Par:** 71
Yds: 6500 **F9 Yds:** 3282 **B9 Yds:** 3218
Designer: Harry Vardon

SOUTH VIEW LEISURE

SOUTH VIEW LEISURE GOLF CLUB, Pro Shop, Burgh Rd, Skegness, **LINCOLNSHIRE**, PE25 2LA, **ENGLAND**.
(T) 01754 760589

Contact/s:
● **Owner:** Mr B Cole

Course/s:
⛳ **SOUTH VIEW GOLF COURSE**
Number of Holes: 9 **Par:** 66
Yds: 4544 **F9 Yds:** 2272
Further Information:
Can be played as an 18 hole course. The course is currently being restructured, and will be open for play from April 2002. Telephone for more details

SOUTH WALES

SOUTH WALES GOLF RANGE & COURSE,
Port Rd East, Barry, **GLAMORGAN (VALE OF)**, CF62 9PX, **WALES**.
(T) 01446 742434

Contact/s:
● **Owner:** Mr Simon Cox

Course/s:
⛳ **SOUTH WALES GOLF COURSE**
Number of Holes: 9 **Par:** 54
Par 3's: 9
Yds: 2180 **F9 Yds:** 1090
Further Information:
Can be played as an 18 hole course. Also has a driving range on site

SOUTH WINCHESTER

SOUTH WINCHESTER GOLF CLUB,
Romsey Rd, Pitt, Winchester, **HAMPSHIRE**, SO22 5QW, **ENGLAND**.
(T) 01962 840469
(E) w.sheffield@crownsportsplc.com
(W) www.southwinchester.com

Membership: Members & Public
Size of Complex: 210 Acres

Contact/s:
● **Club Secretary:** Mr Richard Adams
● **Book Tee Times:** Mrs Jan Morley

Course/s:
⛳ **SOUTH WINCHESTER**
Description: Championship, Links, Parkland, Open, Long, Drains Well
Green Speed: Medium

Built: 1993 **Built On:** Chalk
Number of Holes: 18 **Par:** 72
Record: 67 (Kevin Saunders)
Yds: 6729 **F9 Yds:** 3368 **B9 Yds:** 3361
Prevailing Wind: South/West
Designer: Peter Alliss, David Thomas
Further Information:
All year round golf.

SOUTHAMPTON MUNICIPAL

SOUTHAMPTON MUNICIPAL GOLF COURSE, 1 Golf Course Rd, Southampton, **HAMPSHIRE**, SO16 7LE, **ENGLAND**.
(T) 023 80760478
(E) golf.course@southampton.gov.uk

Membership: Public

Contact/s:
● **Club Secretary:** Mr Don Cambell
☎ 023 80768927
● **Professional:** Mr Ben Benfleet
☎ 023 80768407
● **Book Tee Times:** Mrs Lyn Davies
☎ 023 80760546

Course/s:
⛳ **SOUTHAMPTON MUNICIPAL 18 HOLE**
Description: Parkland, Undulating, Sheltered, Long, Tends to Flood
Green Speed: Medium
Built: 1935 **Built On:** Clay
Number of Holes: 18 **Par:** 69
Record: 62 (Mr Murray)
Par 3's: 4 **Par 4's:** 13 **Par 5's:** 1
Yds: 6213 **F9 Yds:** 2996 **B9 Yds:** 3217
Designer: Hockley, A P Taylor
Further Information:
Although the course is liable to flooding the drainage has been improved.

⛳ **SOUTHAMPTON MUNICIPAL 9 HOLE**
Number of Holes: 9 **Par:** 33
Par 3's: 4 **Par 4's:** 4 **Par 5's:** 1
Yds: 2395

SOUTHEND-ON-SEA

SOUTHEND-ON-SEA GOLF CLUB, Belfais Pk, Eastwood Rd North, Leigh-on-Sea, **ESSEX**, SS9 4LR, **ENGLAND**.
(T) 01702 524836

Course/s:
⛳ **SOUTHEND-ON-SEA**
Number of Holes: 18 **Par:** 70
Yds: 5840

SOUTHERN VALLEY

SOUTHERN VALLEY GOLF CLUB, Thong Lane, Gravesend, **KENT**, DA12 4LF, **ENGLAND**.
(T) 01474 740026
(E) info@southernvalley.co.uk
(W) www.southernvalley.co.uk

Membership: Members & Public

Contact/s:
● **Professional:** Mr Larry Batchelor
☎ 01474 568568

Course/s:
⛳ **SOUTHERN VALLEY**
Description: Links, Valley, Undulating, Open, Medium Length, Drains Well, Ideal for the Elderly
Green Speed: Medium/Fast
Built: 1997 **Built On:** Chalk
Number of Holes: 18 **Par:** 69
Yds: 6150
Prevailing Wind: West
Further Information:
This course overlooks the Thames.

SOUTHERNDOWN

SOUTHERNDOWN GOLF CLUB, Ogmore-by-Sea, Bridgend, **BRIDGEND**, CF32 0QP, **WALES**.
(T) 01656 880326
(E) southerndowngolf@btconnect.com
(W) www.southerndowngolfclub.com

Contact/s:
● **Chief Executive:** Mr A J Hughes
☎ 01656 880476

Course/s:
⛳ **SOUTHERNDOWN**
Number of Holes: 18 **Par:** 70
Par 3's: 4 **Par 4's:** 12 **Par 5's:** 2
Yds: 6449 **F9 Yds:** 3215 **B9 Yds:** 3234
Designer: William Fernie

SOUTHERNESS

SOUTHERNESS GOLF CLUB, Southerness, Dumfries, **DUMFRIES AND GALLOWAY**, DG2 8AZ, **SCOTLAND**.
(T) 01387 880677
(E) admin@southernessgc.sol.co.uk
(W) www.southernessgolfclub.com

Membership: Members & Public
Size of Complex: 200 Acres

Contact/s:
● **Club Secretary:** Mr Ian Robin
☎ 01387 252004
● **Pro Shop:** Mrs G Robison

Course/s:
⛳ **SOUTHERNESS**
Description: Championship, Links, Open, Long, Drains Well, Ideal for the Elderly
Built: 1947
Number of Holes: 18 **Par:** 69
Yds: 6566 **F9 Yds:** 3342 **B9 Yds:** 3224
Prevailing Wind: South/West
Designer: Alistair MacKenzie, L Ross 🏌

SOUTHFIELD

SOUTHFIELD GOLF CLUB LTD, Hill Top Rd, Oxford, **OXFORDSHIRE**, OX4 1PF, **ENGLAND**.
(T) 01865 244258

Contact/s:
● **Club Secretary:** Mrs Sheryl Mathews

Course/s:
⛳ **SOUTHFIELD**
Number of Holes: 18
Designer: Harry Shapland Colt

SOUTHPORT & AINSDALE

SOUTHPORT & AINSDALE GOLF CLUB LTD, Bradshaws Lane, Ainsdale, Southport, **MERSEYSIDE**, PR8 3LG, **ENGLAND**.
(T) 01704 578000
(W) www.sandagolfclub.co.uk

Membership: Members & Public
Size of Complex: 140 Acres

Contact/s:
● **Club Secretary:** Mr Richard Penley-Martin
● **Professional:** Mr Jim Payne
☎ 01704 577316

Course/s:
⛳ **SOUTHPORT & AINSDALE**
Description: Championship, Links, Medium Length, Tight, Drains Well
Green Speed: Fast
Built: 1906 **Built On:** Sand
Number of Holes: 18 **Par:** 71
Par 3's: 4 **Par 4's:** 12 **Par 5's:** 2
Yds: 6687 **F9 Yds:** 3206 **B9 Yds:** 3079
Prevailing Wind: South
Designer: James Braid

SOUTHPORT MUNICIPAL

SOUTHPORT MUNICIPAL GOLF COURSE,
Pk Rd West, Southport, **MERSEYSIDE**, PR9
0JS, **ENGLAND**.
(T) 01704 535286

Membership: Members & Public
Size of Complex: 94 Acres

Contact/s:
● **Professional:** Mr Bill Fletcher

Course/s:
🏌 **SOUTHPORT MUNICIPAL**
　Description: Links, Open, Medium
　Length, Tends to Flood, Ideal for the
　Elderly
　Green Speed: Medium **Built On:** Sand
　Number of Holes: 18 **Record:** 67 (Bill
　Fletcher)
　Prevailing Wind: North/East

SOUTHPORT OLD LINKS

SOUTHPORT OLD LINKS, Moss Lane,
Churchtown, Southport, **MERSEYSIDE**, PR9
7QS, **ENGLAND**.
(T) 01704 228207
Size of Complex: 54 Acres

Contact/s:
● **Club Secretary:** Mr B Kenyon
● **Professional:** Mr G Copeman

Course/s:
🏌 **SOUTHPORT OLD LINKS**
　Description: Championship, Links, Open,
　Drains Well, Ideal for the Elderly
　Green Speed: Medium
　Built: 1880 **Built On:** Soil
　Number of Holes: 18 **Par:** 72
　Par 3's: 4 **Par 4's:** 10 **Par 5's:** 4
　Yds: 6371

SOUTHWELL

SOUTHWELL GOLF CLUB, Rolleston,
Southwell, Newark, **NOTTINGHAMSHIRE**,
NG25 0TS, **ENGLAND**.
(T) 01636 814481

Membership: Members & Public
Size of Complex: 100 Acres

Contact/s:
● **Professional:** Mr S Meade
　☎ 01636 813706

Course/s:
🏌 **SOUTHWELL**
　Description: Parkland, Open, Medium
　Length, Drains Well
　Green Speed: Fast
　Built: 1994 **Built On:** Sand/Soil
　Number of Holes: 18 **Par:** 70
　Record: 63 (S Meade)
　Par 3's: 5 **Par 4's:** 10 **Par 5's:** 3
　Yds: 5768
　Designer: R Muddle
　Further Information:
　A flat course.

SOUTHWICK PARK

**SOUTHWICK PARK NAVAL RECREATION
CENTRE,** Pinsley Drive, Southwick, Fareham,
HAMPSHIRE, PO17 6EL, **ENGLAND**.
(T) 023 92370683

Course/s:
🏌 **SOUTHWICK PARK**
　Number of Holes: 18

SOUTHWOLD

SOUTHWOLD GOLF CLUB, The Common,
Southwold, **SUFFOLK**, IP18 6TB, **ENGLAND**.

(T) 01502 723234
Membership: Members & Public
Contact/s:
● **Club Secretary:** Mr Peter Oberne
● **Professional:** Mr Brian Alan

Course/s:
🏌 **SOUTHWOLD**
　Description: Heath Land, Open, Medium
　Length, Drains Well, Ideal for the Elderly
　Green Speed: Medium
　Built: 1884 **Built On:** Soil
　Number of Holes: 18 **Par:** 70
　Par 3's: 5 **Par 4's:** 10 **Par 5's:** 3
　Yds: 6052 **F9 Yds:** 3019 **B9 Yds:** 3033
　Prevailing Wind: North
　Designer: James Braid

SOUTHWOOD

SOUTHWOOD GOLF COURSE, Ively Rd,
Farnborough, **HAMPSHIRE**, GU14 0LJ,
ENGLAND.
(T) 01252 548700

Course/s:
🏌 **SOUTHWOOD**
　Number of Holes: 18
　Designer: Hawtree

SPA

SPA GOLF CLUB, 20 Grove Rd,
Ballynahinch, **COUNTY DOWN**, BT24 8PN,
NORTHERN IRELAND.
(T) 028 97562365
(E) spagolfclub@btconnect.com

Contact/s:
● **General Manager:** Mr Terry McGee

Course/s:
🏌 **SPA**
　Number of Holes: 18 **Par:** 72
　Yds: 6469 **F9 Yds:** 3187 **B9 Yds:** 3332
　Designer: F Ainsworth

SPALDING

SPALDING GOLF CLUB, Surfleet, Spalding,
LINCOLNSHIRE, PE11 4EA, **ENGLAND**.
(T) 01775 680386

Contact/s:
● **Club Secretary:** Mr Barry Walker

Course/s:
🏌 **SPALDING**
　Number of Holes: 18 **Par:** 72
　Par 3's: 3 **Par 4's:** 12 **Par 5's:** 3
　Yds: 6492 **F9 Yds:** 3306 **B9 Yds:** 3186
　Designer: Price, Spencer, Ward

SPANISH POINT

SPANISH POINT GOLF CLUB, Miltown
Malbay, **COUNTY CLARE**, **IRELAND**.
(T) 065 84198

Course/s:
🏌 **SPANISH POINT**
　Number of Holes: 9

SPARKWELL

SPARKWELL GOLF COURSE, Blacklands,
Sparkwell, Plymouth, **DEVON**, PL7 5DF,
ENGLAND.
(T) 01752 837219

Membership: Members & Public

Contact/s:
● **Club Secretary:** Mr George Adamson
　☎ 01752 87219
● **Professional:** Mr Neville Whitley

Course/s:

🏌 **WELBECK MANOR & SPARKWELL**
　Description: Parkland, Valley, Open,
　Tight, Drains Well
　Green Speed: Medium
　Built: 1993 **Built On:** Soil
　Number of Holes: 9
　Prevailing Wind: East
　Designer: John Gabb

SPEY BAY

SPEY BAY GOLF COURSE, Spey Bay,
Fochabers, **MORAY**, IV32 7PJ, **SCOTLAND**.
(T) 01343 820424

Course/s:
🏌 **SPEY BAY**
　Number of Holes: 18
　Designer: Ben Sayers

SPOFFORTH

SPOFFORTH GOLF COURSE, Manor Farm,
Haggs Rd, Follifoot, Harrogate, **YORKSHIRE
(NORTH)**, HG3 1EQ, **ENGLAND**.
(T) 01423 872543

Membership: Public

Contact/s:
● **Professional:** Mr M Simpson

Course/s:
🏌 **SPOFFORTH**
　Description: Wooded, Parkland, Valley,
　Undulating, Medium Length, Drains Well
　Green Speed: Medium
　Built: 1992
　Number of Holes: 18

SPRINGHEAD PARK MUNICIPAL

**SPRINGHEAD PARK GOLF CLUB
(MUNICIPAL),** Willerby Rd, Hull,
YORKSHIRE (EAST), HU5 5JE, **ENGLAND**.
(T) 01482 656309

Membership: Public

Course/s:
🏌 **SPRINGHEAD PARK MUNICIPAL**
　Number of Holes: 18

SPRINGHILL

SPRINGHILL GOLF & COUNTRY CLUB,
49B Gargadis Rd, Trillick, Omagh, **COUNTY
TYRONE**, BT78 3TS, **NORTHERN IRELAND**.
(T) 028 89561861

Membership: Members & Public

Contact/s:
● **Club Secretary:** Sara McCrystal
● **Professional:** Kevin McGirr
　☎ 028 89561547

Course/s:
🏌 **SPRINGHILL**
　Description: Drains Well
　Green Speed: Medium
　Built: 1996
　Number of Holes: 9

SPRINGMILL

SPRINGMILL GOLF COURSE, Queens
Drive, Ossett, **YORKSHIRE (WEST)**, WF5
0ND, **ENGLAND**.
(T) 01924 281781

Course/s:
🏌 **SPRINGMILL GOLF COURSE**
　Number of Holes: 9 **Par:** 54
　Par 3's: 9
　Yds: 2496 **F9 Yds:** 1248
　Further Information:
　Can be played as an 18 hole course

SPRINGWATER

SPRINGWATER GOLF CLUB, Moor Lane, Calverton, Nottingham, **NOTTINGHAMSHIRE**, NG14 6FZ, **ENGLAND**.
(T) 0115 9652129
(E) mooregrouppltd@aol.com
(W) www.springwatergolf.co.uk
Membership: Members & Public
Size of Complex: 120 Acres
Contact/s:
● **Club Secretary:** Mr Bill Turner
  ☎ 0115 9652565
● **Professional:** Mr Paul Drew
Course/s:
⛳ **SPRINGWATER**
  Description: Parkland, Undulating, Open, Long, Drains Well
  Green Speed: Medium
  Built: 1991 **Built On:** Clay
  Number of Holes: 18 **Par:** 71
  Par 3's: 5 **Par 4's:** 9 **Par 5's:** 4
  Yds: 6224 **F9 Yds:** 3020 **B9 Yds:** 3204

SPROWSTON MANOR

MARRIOTT SPROWSTON MANOR GOLF CLUB, Wroxham Rd, Norwich, **NORFOLK**, NR7 8RP, **ENGLAND**.
(T) 01603 410871
Membership: Members & Public
Contact/s:
● **Professional:** Mr Guy Ireson
● **Pro Shop:** Miss R Shubrook
Course/s:
⛳ **MARRIOT SPRAWSTON MANOR**
  Description: Parkland, Sheltered, Medium Length, Drains Well
  Green Speed: Fast
  Built: 1980 **Built On:** Soil
  Number of Holes: 18 **Par:** 70
  Par 3's: 5 **Par 4's:** 10 **Par 5's:** 3
  Yds: 5763 **F9 Yds:** 3250 **B9 Yds:** 2513
  Designer: Tony Mower
  Further Information:
  A flat course.

ST. AGUSTINES

ST. AGUSTINES GOLF CLUB, Cottington Rd, Cliffsend, Ramsgate, **KENT**, CT12 5JN, **ENGLAND**.
(T) 01843 590333
(E) sagc@golf9991.freeserve.co.uk
Membership: Members & Public
Size of Complex: 80 Acres
Contact/s:
● **Club Secretary:** Mr L P Dyke
● **Professional:** Mr Derek Scott
  ☎ 01843 590222
Course/s:
⛳ **ST AGUSTINES**
  Description: Parkland, Sheltered, Open, Medium Length, Tight, Tends to Flood, Ideal for the Elderly
  Green Speed: Fast
  Built: 1907 **Built On:** Chalk
  Number of Holes: 18 **Record:** 63 (Simon Page)
  Prevailing Wind: North
  Designer: Harry Vardon

ST. ANDREWS LINKS

ST. ANDREWS LINKS GOLF CLUB, The Links, West Sands Rd, St. Andrews, **FIFE**, KY16 9XL, **SCOTLAND**.
(T) 01334 466666
(E) reservations@standrews.org.uk
(W) www.standrews.org.uk
Membership: Public
Contact/s:
● **Club Secretary:** Mr A J R McGregor
Course/s:
⛳ **BALGOVE**
  Description: Short
  Built: 1993 **Built On:** Sand
  Number of Holes: 9 **Par:** 30
  Par 3's: 6 **Par 4's:** 3
  Yds: 1520
⛳ **EDEN**
  Description: Links
  Built: 1914 **Built On:** Sand
  Number of Holes: 18 **Par:** 70
  Par 3's: 4 **Par 4's:** 12 **Par 5's:** 2
  Yds: 6112 **F9 Yds:** 3012 **B9 Yds:** 3100
  Designer: Harry Shapland Colt
⛳ **JUBILEE**
  Description: Links
  Built: 1897 **Built On:** Sand
  Number of Holes: 18 **Par:** 72
  Par 3's: 4 **Par 4's:** 10 **Par 5's:** 4
  Yds: 6805 **F9 Yds:** 3301 **B9 Yds:** 3504
⛳ **NEW**
  Description: Championship, Links
  Built: 1895 **Built On:** Sand
  Number of Holes: 18 **Par:** 71
  Par 3's: 4 **Par 4's:** 11 **Par 5's:** 3
  Yds: 1520 **F9 Yds:** 3270 **B9 Yds:** 3334
  Designer: Tom Morris ♟
⛳ **OLD**
  Description: Championship, Links
  Built On: Sand
  Number of Holes: 18 **Par:** 72
  Par 3's: 2 **Par 4's:** 14 **Par 5's:** 2
  Yds: 7115 **F9 Yds:** 3545 **B9 Yds:** 3570
  Designer: D Anderson, Alistair MacKenzie, Tom Morris ♟
⛳ **STRATHTYRUM**
  Description: Parkland, Undulating
  Built: 1993
  Number of Holes: 18 **Par:** 69
  Par 3's: 5 **Par 4's:** 11 **Par 5's:** 2
  Yds: 5094 **F9 Yds:** 2457 **B9 Yds:** 2637
  Prevailing Wind: West
  Designer: Donald Steel

ST. ANDREWS MAJOR

ST. ANDREWS MAJOR GOLF COURSE, Coldbrook Rd, Off Barry Docks Link Rd, Barry, **GLAMORGAN (VALE OF)**, CF63 3RA, **WALES**.
(T) 01446 722227
Membership: Members & Public
Size of Complex: 95 Acres
Contact/s:
● **Professional:** Mr Jestyn Taylor
● **Pro Shop:** Mr J Edmunds
● **Book Lessons:**
  ☎ 07779 712164
Course/s:
⛳ **ST ANDREWS MAJOR**
  Description: Parkland, Undulating, Open, Short, Drains Well, Ideal for the Elderly
  Green Speed: Medium
  Built: 1993 **Built On:** Clay
  Number of Holes: 18 **Par:** 69
  Yds: 5425 **F9 Yds:** 2624 **B9 Yds:** 2801
  Prevailing Wind: West
  Designer: Edmunds, Richard Hurd

ST. ANNES

ST. ANNES GOLF CLUB, North Bull Island, Dollymount, Dublin, **COUNTY DUBLIN**, **IRELAND**.
(T) 01 8336471
(E) info@stanneslinkgolf.com
(W) www.stanneslinksgolf.com
Course/s:
⛳ **ST ANNE'S**
  Number of Holes: 18

ST. ANNES OLD LINKS

ST. ANNES OLD LINKS GOLF CLUB, Highbury Rd East, Lytham St. Annes, **LANCASHIRE**, FY8 2LD, **ENGLAND**.
(T) 01253 723597
(E) info@saolgc.uk.com
(W) www.saolgc.uk.com
Contact/s:
● **Club Secretary:** Mr Rod Beach
● **Professional:** Mr Daniel Webster
Course/s:
⛳ **ST ANNES OLD LINKS**
  Number of Holes: 18 **Par:** 72
  Yds: 6684 **F9 Yds:** 3267 **B9 Yds:** 3417
  Designer: G Lowe

ST. AUSTELL

ST. AUSTELL GOLF CLUB, Tregongeeves, St. Austell, **CORNWALL**, PL26 7DS, **ENGLAND**.
(T) 01726 74756
Membership: Members & Public
Size of Complex: 115 Acres
Contact/s:
● **Club Secretary:** Mr K Trahair
● **Professional:** Mr T Pitts
  ☎ 01726 68621
Course/s:
⛳ **ST AUSTELL**
  Description: Parkland, Heath Land, Drains Well
  Green Speed: Medium
  Built: 1911
  Number of Holes: 18 **Par:** 69
  Record: 67 (T Nash)
  Par 3's: 4 **Par 4's:** 13 **Par 5's:** 1
  Yds: 6097 **F9 Yds:** 3121 **B9 Yds:** 2976
  Designer: James Braid
  Further Information:
  With a tin mine situated in the centre of the course, St Austell is a good test for golfers of all abilities.

ST. BOSWELLS

ST. BOSWELLS GOLF CLUB, Braeheads Rd, St. Boswells, Melrose, **SCOTTISH BORDERS**, TD6 0DE, **SCOTLAND**.
(T) 01835 823527
Contact/s:
● **Manager:** Mr J G Phillips
Course/s:
⛳ **ST BOSWELLS**
  Number of Holes: 9
  Designer: William Park

ST. CLEMENT

ST. CLEMENT, Jersey Recreation Grounds, St. Clement, Jersey, **CHANNEL ISLANDS**, JE2 6PN, **ENGLAND**.
(T) 01534 721938
Course/s:
⛳ **ST CLEMENT**
  Number of Holes: 9 **Par:** 30
  Yds: 2244

ST. CLERES HALL

ST. CLERES HALL GOLF CLUB, London Rd, Stanford-Le-Hope, **ESSEX**, SS17 0LX, **ENGLAND**.
(T) 01375 673007

Contact/s:
● **Owner:** Mr M Valente

Course/s:
🏌 **ST CLERES HALL GOLF COURSE**
Description: Parkland, Long
Number of Holes: 18 **Par:** 72
Yds: 6474

ST. DAVIDS

ST. DAVIDS CITY GOLF CLUB, Whitesands Rd, St. Davids, Haverfordwest, **PEMBROKESHIRE**, SA62 6PT, **WALES**.
(T) 01437 721751

Membership: Members & Public

Contact/s:
● **Club Secretary:** Mr Rod Hatfield

Course/s:
🏌 **ST DAVID'S CITY**
Description: Links, Cliff Top, Open, Medium Length, Drains Well, Ideal for the Elderly
Green Speed: Fast
Built: 1903 **Built On:** Sand
Number of Holes: 9
Prevailing Wind: South/West
Further Information:
The course offers lovely sea views.

ST. DEINIOL

ST. DEINIOL GOLF CLUB, Bangor, **GWYNEDD**, LL57 1PX, **WALES**.
(T) 01248 353098

Contact/s:
● **Club Secretary:** Mr R D Thomas
☎ 01248 370792

Course/s:
🏌 **ST DEINIOL**
Number of Holes: 18 **Par:** 68
Yds: 5654 **F9 Yds:** 2761 **B9 Yds:** 2893
Designer: James Braid

ST. ENODOC

ST. ENODOC GOLF CLUB, Rock, Wadebridge, **CORNWALL**, PL27 6LD, **ENGLAND**.
(T) 01208 863216

Membership: Members & Public

Contact/s:
● **Professional:** Mr Nick Williams
☎ 01208 862402

Course/s:
🏌 **CHURCH**
Number of Holes: 18 **Par:** 69
Yds: 6243 **F9 Yds:** 3165 **B9 Yds:** 3078
Designer: James Braid 🏆

🏌 **HOLYWELL**
Number of Holes: 18 **Par:** 63
Yds: 4103 **F9 Yds:** 2200 **B9 Yds:** 1903
Designer: James Braid

ST. FILLANS

ST. FILLANS GOLF CLUB, S Lochearn Rd, St. Fillans, Loch Earn, **PERTH AND KINROSS**, PH6 2NJ, **SCOTLAND**.
(T) 01764 685312
(W) www.st-fillans-golf.com

Contact/s:
● **Starter:** Mr Gordon Hibbert

Course/s:
🏌 **ST FILLANS**
Built: 1903
Number of Holes: 9 **Par:** 35
Par 3's: 2 **Par 4's:** 6 **Par 5's:** 1
Yds: 3027
Designer: William Auchterlonie
Further Information:
9 hole course can be played as an 18 hole course

ST. GEORGE'S (ROYAL)

ROYAL ST GEORGES GOLF CLUB, Professionals Cottage, Royal St. Georges Golf Club, Sandwich Bay, Sandwich, **KENT**, CT13 9PB, **ENGLAND**.
(T) 01304 613090
(E) secretary@royalstgeorges.com
(W) www.royalstgeorges.com

Membership: Members & Public

Contact/s:
● **Club Secretary:** Mr C Gabby
● **Professional:** Mr Andrew Brooks
☎ 01304 615236

Course/s:
🏌 **ROYAL ST GEORGE'S**
Description: Championship, Links
Number of Holes: 18 **Par:** 70
Par 3's: 4 **Par 4's:** 12 **Par 5's:** 2
Yds: 6607 **F9 Yds:** 3216 **B9 Yds:** 3391
Designer: L Purves 🏆

ST. GEORGES HILL

ST. GEORGES HILL GOLF CLUB (THE), Clubhouse, Golf Club Rd, Weybridge, **SURREY**, KT13 0NL, **ENGLAND**.
(T) 01932 847758

Membership: Members & Public

Contact/s:
● **Club Secretary:** Mr J Robinson

Course/s:
🏌 **BLUE**
Number of Holes: 9 **Par:** 35
Par 3's: 2 **Par 4's:** 6 **Par 5's:** 1
Yds: 3303 **F9 Yds:** 3303
Designer: Harry Shapland Colt
Further Information:
Can also be played as an 18 hole course in combination with either of the other courses. 🏆

🏌 **GREEN**
Number of Holes: 9
Yds: 2897
Designer: Harry Shapland Colt
Further Information:
Can also be played as an 18 hole course in combination with either of the other courses. 🏆

🏌 **RED**
Number of Holes: 9 **Par:** 35
Par 3's: 2 **Par 4's:** 5 **Par 5's:** 1
Yds: 3193 **F9 Yds:** 3193
Designer: Harry Shapland Colt
Further Information:
Can also be played as an 18 hole course in combination with either of the other courses. 🏆

ST. GILES

ST. GILES GOLF CLUB, Pool Rd, Newtown, **POWYS**, SY16 3AJ, **WALES**.
(T) 01686 625844

Contact/s:
● **Professional:** Mr D P Owen

Course/s:

🏌 **ST GILES**
Built: 1895
Number of Holes: 9 **Par:** 70
Further Information:
This is a challenging riverside course which can be played as an 18 hole course.

ST. HELENS BAY

ST. HELENS BAY GOLF & COUNTRY CLUB, Kilrane, Rosslare Harbour, Rosslare, **COUNTY WEXFORD**, **IRELAND**.
(T) 05 333234
(E) sthelens@iol.ie
(W) www.sthelensbay.com

Contact/s:
● **Managing Director:** Mr Larry Byene

Course/s:
🏌 **ST HELEN'S BAY**
Description: Links, Parkland
Built: 1993
Number of Holes: 18 **Par:** 72
Yds: 6639 **F9 Yds:** 3201 **B9 Yds:** 3438
Designer: Philip Walton
Further Information:
Panoramic views of St Helens Bay.

ST. IDLOES

ST. IDLOES GOLF CLUB, Llanidloes, **POWYS**, SY18 6LG, **WALES**.
(T) 01686 412559

Course/s:
🏌 **ST IDLOES**
Number of Holes: 9

ST. IVES

ST. IVES GOLF CLUB, Westwood Rd, St. Ives, Huntingdon, **CAMBRIDGESHIRE**, PE17 4RS, **ENGLAND**.
(T) 01480 468392

Course/s:
🏌 **ST IVES**
Number of Holes: 9

ST. KEW

ST. KEW GOLF CLUB, St. Kew Golf Course, St. Kew Highway, Nr Wadebridge, Bodmin, **CORNWALL**, PL30 3EF, **ENGLAND**.
(T) 01208 841500

Membership: Members & Public

Contact/s:
● **Partner:** Mr J Brown

Course/s:
🏌 **ST KEW**
Description: Parkland, Short
Number of Holes: 9
Designer: David Derry

ST. MARGARETS

ST. MARGARETS GOLF & COUNTRY CLUB, St Margarets, **COUNTY DUBLIN**, **IRELAND**.
(T) 01 8640400
(E) strmarggc@indigo.ie

Course/s:
🏌 **ST MARGARET'S**
Number of Holes: 18
Designer: Craddock, Ruddy

ST. MARYS HOTEL

ST. MARYS HOTEL GOLF & COUNTRY CLUB, St. Mary Hill, Bridgend, **BRIDGEND**, CF35 5EA, **WALES**.

(T) 01656 861100

Course/s:

🌑 **SEVENOAKS**
Number of Holes: 9

🌑 **ST MARY'S**
Number of Holes: 18

ST. MEDAN

ST. MEDAN GOLF CLUB, Monreith, Newton Stewart, **DUMFRIES AND GALLOWAY**, DG8 9LJ, **SCOTLAND**.
(T) 01988 700358

Course/s:

🌑 **ST MEDAN**
Built: 1905 Built On: Sand
Number of Holes: 18 Par: 64
Par 3's: 8 Par 4's: 10
Yds: 4558 F9 Yds: 2279 B9 Yds: 2279
Designer: James Braid

ST. MELLION INTERNATIONAL

AMERICAN GOLF CORPORATION, St. Mellion, Saltash, **CORNWALL**, PL12 6SD, **ENGLAND**.
(T) 01579 351351
(E) stmellion@americangolf.uk.com
(W) www.st-mellion.co.uk

Membership: Nicklaus
● Club Secretary: Mr Roy Dransfield
● Professional: Mr David Moon
  ☎ 01579 352002
● Y:
  ☎ 450 🍴

ST. MELLONS

ST. MELLONS GOLF CLUB, St. Mellons, Cardiff, **GLAMORGAN (VALE OF)**, CF3 2XS, **WALES**.
(T) 01633 680408

Contact/s:
● Manageress: Mrs K Newling

Course/s:

🌑 **ST MELLONS**
Number of Holes: 18

ST. MELYD

ST. MELYD GOLF CLUB, The Paddock, Prestatyn, **DENBIGHSHIRE**, LL19 8NB, **WALES**.
(T) 01745 854405
(W) www.stmelydgolf.co.uk

Membership: Members & Public

Contact/s:
● Professional: Mr Richard Hughes

Course/s:

🌑 **ST MELYD**
Description: Parkland, Sheltered, Medium Length, Drains Well, Ideal for the Elderly
Green Speed: Medium
Built: 1922 Built On: Soil
Number of Holes: 9
Prevailing Wind: South/West
Further Information:
Beautiful views of Snowdon.

ST. MICHAELS

ST. MICHAELS GOLF CLUB, Leuchars, St. Andrews, **FIFE**, KY16 0DX, **SCOTLAND**.
(T) 01334 838666
(E) stmichaelsgc@btclick.com
(W) www.stmichaelsgolf.co.uk

Course/s:

🌑 **ST MICHAELS**
Description: Parkland, Undulating
Built: 1903
Number of Holes: 18 Par: 70
Par 3's: 4 Par 4's: 12 Par 5's: 2
Yds: 5802 F9 Yds: 2950 B9 Yds: 2852

ST. MICHAELS JUBILEE

ST. MICHAELS JUBILEE GOLF CLUB, Dundalk Rd, Widnes, **CHESHIRE**, WA8 8BS, **ENGLAND**.
(T) 0151 4246230

Contact/s:
● Manager: Mr Darren Chapman

Course/s:

🌑 **ST MICHAEL JUBILEE**
Number of Holes: 18

ST. NEOTS

ST. NEOTS GOLF CLUB, Crosshall Rd, Huntingdon, **CAMBRIDGESHIRE**, PE19 4AE, **ENGLAND**.
(T) 01480 472363
(W) www.stneots-golfclub.co.uk

Membership: Members & Public
Size of Complex: 124 Acres

Contact/s:
● Professional: Mr Peter Round
  ☎ 01480 476513

Course/s:

🌑 **ST NEOTS**
Description: Parkland, Undulating, Sheltered, Long, Tight, Tends to Flood, Ideal for the Elderly
Green Speed: Fast
Built: 1950 Built On: Clay
Number of Holes: 18 Par: 69
Par 3's: 5 Par 4's: 11 Par 5's: 2
Yds: 6033 F9 Yds: 3152 B9 Yds: 2881
Prevailing Wind: North/West
Designer: Harry Vardon
Further Information:
Close to Kym and Great Ouse rivers.

ST. NEWLYN EAST

ST. NEWLYN EAST GOLF COURSE, Barn Acres, St. Newlyn East, Newquay, **CORNWALL**, TR8 5HZ, **ENGLAND**.
(T) 01872 510317
(E) info@lappavalley.co.uk
(W) www.lappa-railway.co.uk

Course/s:

🌑 **ST NEWLYN EAST**
Description: Parkland
Number of Holes: 9
Further Information:
9 hole course can be played as an 18 hole course

ST. PIERRE

MARRIOTT SAINT PIERRE HOTEL & COUNTRY CLUB (THE), St. Pierre Pk, Chepstow, **MONMOUTHSHIRE**, NP16 6YA, **WALES**.
(T) 01291 625261

Membership: Public

Contact/s:
● Club Secretary: Mr Terry Cleary
● Professional: Mr Craig Dun
● Pro Shop: Mr Jon Moody
  ☎ 01291 635205

Course/s:

🌑 **MATHERN**
Description: Parkland
Green Speed: Medium

Built: 1962
Number of Holes: 18
Designer: B Cox

🌑 **OLD**
Description: Parkland
Green Speed: Medium
Built: 1962
Number of Holes: 18
Designer: C K Cotton, J J Frank Pennink

ST. PIERRE PARK

ST. PIERRE PARK GOLF CLUB, Rohais, St Peters Port, **GUERNSEY**, GY1 1FD, **ENGLAND**.
(T) 01481 728282

Membership: Members & Public

Course/s:

🌑 **ST PIERRE PARK**
Number of Holes: 9 Par: 54
Yds: 2610
Designer: Tony Jacklin
Further Information:
9 hole course can be played as an 18 hole course

ST. THOMAS' PRIORY

ST. THOMAS' PRIORY GOLF CLUB, Armitage Lane, Rugeley, **STAFFORDSHIRE**, WS15 1ED, **ENGLAND**.
(T) 01543 491116

Contact/s:
● Club Secretary: Mr John Bissell
● Professional: Mr Richard O'Hanlon
  ☎ 01543 492096

Course/s:

🌑 **ST THOMAS' PRIORY**
Description: Parkland, Undulating, Drains Well
Green Speed: Medium
Built: 1965
Number of Holes: 18

STACKSTOWN

STACKSTOWN GOLF CLUB, Kellystown Rd, Dublin, Dublin, **COUNTY DUBLIN**, **IRELAND**.
(T) 01 4942338

Course/s:

🌑 **STACKSTOWN**
Number of Holes: 18

STADDON HEIGHTS

STADDON HEIGHTS GOLF CLUB, Staddon Heights, Plystock, Plymouth, **DEVON**, PL9 9SP, **ENGLAND**.
(T) 01752 402475

Contact/s:
● Club Secretary: Mr Kevin Brabant

Course/s:

🌑 **STADDON HEIGHTS**
Number of Holes: 18
Designer: J Hamilton-Stutt

STAFFORD CASTLE

STAFFORD CASTLE GOLF CLUB, Newport Rd, Stafford, **STAFFORDSHIRE**, ST16 1BP, **ENGLAND**.
(T) 01785 212200

Contact/s:
● Administrator: Mr Charles Lightbrown
  ☎ 01785 223821

Course/s:

🌑 **STAFFORD CASTLE**

Number of Holes: 9 **Par:** 71
Yds: 6071 **F9 Yds:** 3071 **B9 Yds:** 3000

STAMFORD

STAMFORD GOLF CLUB, Oakfield, Huddersfield Rd, Carrbrook, Stalybridge, **CHESHIRE**, SK15 3PY, **ENGLAND**.
(T) 01457 832126

Contact/s:
● Club Secretary: Mr B D Matthews
  ☎ 0161 6335721

Course/s:
⛳ STAMFORD
  Number of Holes: 18 **Par:** 70
  Yds: 5701 **F9 Yds:** 3016 **B9 Yds:** 2685

STAND

STAND GOLF CLUB, Ashbourne Gr, Whitefield, Manchester, **MANCHESTER (GREATER)**, M45 7NL, **ENGLAND**.
(T) 0161 7662214

Contact/s:
● Professional: Mr Mark Dance

Course/s:
⛳ STAND
  Description: Parkland, Moorland, Undulating, Open
  Built: 1904
  Number of Holes: 18 **Par:** 72
  Yds: 6426 **F9 Yds:** 3199 **B9 Yds:** 3227
  Designer: A Herd, G Lowe

STANDISH COURT

STANDISH COURT GOLF CLUB, Rectory Lane, Standish, Wigan, **LANCASHIRE**, WN6 0XD, **ENGLAND**.
(T) 01257 425777

Contact/s:
● Professional: Mr Tim Kershaw

Course/s:
⛳ STANDISH COURT
  Description: Wooded, Parkland, Undulating
  Built: 1995 **Built On:** Soil
  Number of Holes: 18 **Par:** 68
  Designer: P Dawson

STANEDGE

STANEDGE GOLF CLUB, Walton Hay Farm, Stonedge, Ashover, Chesterfield, **DERBYSHIRE**, S45 0LW, **ENGLAND**.
(T) 01246 566156

Membership: Members & Public
Size of Complex: 90 Acres

Contact/s:
● Club Secretary: Mr Bill Tyzack

Course/s:
⛳ STANEDGE
  Description: Moorland, Hilltop, Medium Length, Tight, Drains Well
  Green Speed: Medium **Built On:** Soil
  Number of Holes: 18 **Par:** 69
  Par 3's: 5 **Par 4's:** 11 **Par 5's:** 2
  Yds: 5786
  Prevailing Wind: West
  Further Information:
  9 hole course can be played as an 18 hole course

STANMORE

STANMORE GOLF CLUB, Gordon Ave, Stanmore, **LONDON (GREATER)**, HA7 2RL, **ENGLAND**.
(T) 020 89542599

Contact/s:
● Club Secretary: Mr A W Schooling
● Pro Shop: Mr V R Law
  ☎ 020 89542646

Course/s:
⛳ STANMORE
  Number of Holes: 18

STANTON ON THE WOLDS

STANTON ON THE WOLDS GOLF CLUB, Golf Course Rd, Keyworth, Nottingham, **NOTTINGHAMSHIRE**, NG12 5BH, **ENGLAND**.
(T) 0115 9374885

Membership: Members & Public

Contact/s:
● Professional: Mr Nick Hernon
● Pro Shop:
  ☎ 0115 9372390

Course/s:
⛳ STANTON ON THE WOLDS
  Description: Parkland, Open, Medium Length, Drains Well
  Green Speed: Fast **Built On:** Soil
  Number of Holes: 18 **Par:** 73
  Par 3's: 4 **Par 4's:** 9 **Par 5's:** 5
  Yds: 6421
  Designer: Tom Williamson
  Further Information:
  A flat course.

STAPLEFORD ABBOTTS GOLF CLUB

AMERICAN GOLF CORPORATION, Horseman Side, Tysea Hill, Stapleford Abbotts, Romford, **ESSEX**, RM4 1JU, **ENGLAND**.
(T) 01708 381108

Membership: Members & Public

Contact/s:
● Pro Shop: Mr Alan Hall
  ☎ 01708 381278

Course/s:
⛳ ABBOTTS
  Description: Wooded, Parkland, Medium Length, Drains Well
  Number of Holes: 18 **Par:** 72
  Yds: 6501 **F9 Yds:** 3412 **B9 Yds:** 3089
  Designer: Henry Cotton, Howard Swan
  Further Information:
  No temporary greens

⛳ MONASTRY
  Description: Parkland
  Number of Holes: 9 **Par:** 27
  Yds: 1140
  Designer: Henry Cotton, Howard Swan

⛳ PRIORS
  Description: Parkland, Undulating, Medium Length, Drains Well
  Number of Holes: 18 **Par:** 70
  Yds: 5878 **F9 Yds:** 2971 **B9 Yds:** 2907
  Designer: Henry Cotton, Howard Swan

STAPLEHURST GOLFING PARK

STAPLEHURST GOLFING PARK, Cradducks Lane, Staplehurst, Tonbridge, **KENT**, TN12 0DR, **ENGLAND**.
(T) 01580 893362

Membership: Public
Size of Complex: 54 Acres

Contact/s:
● Professional: Mr Colin Jenkins

Course/s:
⛳ STAPLEHURST
  Description: Parkland, Undulating, Sheltered, Ideal for the Elderly

Green Speed: Fast
Built: 1995 **Built On:** Clay
Number of Holes: 9
Prevailing Wind: South/West
Designer: Jenkins, Sayner

STAVERTON PARK

STAVERTON PARK GOLF CLUB, Daventry Rd, Staverton, Daventry, **NORTHAMPTONSHIRE**, NN11 6JT, **ENGLAND**.
(T) 01327 705506

Contact/s:
● Club Secretary: Ms Anne Radford
● Professional: Mr Richard Mudge

Course/s:
⛳ STAVERTON PARK
  Description: Championship, Undulating
  Built: 1977
  Number of Holes: 18 **Par:** 71
  Par 3's: 4 **Par 4's:** 11 **Par 5's:** 3
  Yds: 6176 **F9 Yds:** 3097 **B9 Yds:** 3079
  Designer: Commander J Harris
  Further Information:
  The course has large greens.

STEPASIDE

STEPASIDE PUBLIC GOLF COURSE, Stepaside, **COUNTY DUBLIN**, **IRELAND**.
(T) 01 2952859

Course/s:
⛳ STEPASIDE
  Number of Holes: 18 **Par:** 74
  Par 3's: 2 **Par 4's:** 12 **Par 5's:** 4
  Yds: 6374

STEVENAGE

STEVENAGE GOLF CENTRE, 4 Aston Lane, Aston, Stevenage, **HERTFORDSHIRE**, SG2 7EL, **ENGLAND**.
(T) 01438 880424

Membership: Members & Public
Size of Complex: 22 Acres

Contact/s:
● Club Secretary: Mrs Sue Elwin
● Professional: Mr Stephen Barker

Course/s:
⛳ STEVENAGE
  Description: Parkland, Undulating, Sheltered, Medium Length, Tight, Tends to Flood
  Green Speed: Medium
  Built: 1982 **Built On:** Clay
  Number of Holes: 18 **Par:** 72
  Par 3's: 5 **Par 4's:** 8 **Par 5's:** 5
  Yds: 6341
  Prevailing Wind: East
  Designer: John Jacobs
  Further Information:
  A brook runs through the course forming two ponds. It has also had several new bunkers added to test lower handicaps.

STILTON OAKS

STILTON OAKS GOLF COURSE, 34 High St, Stilton, Peterborough, **CAMBRIDGESHIRE**, PE7 3RA, **ENGLAND**.
(T) 01733 245233

Membership: Members & Public

Contact/s:
● Club Secretary: Ms Marilyn Smith
  ☎ 01733 243354

Course/s:
⛳ STILTON OAKS
  Description: Undulating, Medium Length

Green Speed: Slow
Built: 1996
Number of Holes: 18

STINCHCOMBE HILL

STINCHCOMBE HILL GOLF CLUB,
Stinchcombe Hill, Dursley,
GLOUCESTERSHIRE, GL11 6AQ,
ENGLAND.
(T) 01453 542015

Contact/s:
● Professional: Mr Paul Bushell

Course/s:
🔸 STINCHCOMBE HILL
Description: Downland
Built: 1889
Number of Holes: 18 Par: 68
Designer: Arthur Hoare
Further Information:
The course is situated on the edge of the
Cotswold hills.

STIRLING

STIRLING GOLF CLUB, Kings Pk, Stirling,
STIRLING, FK8 3AA, **SCOTLAND**.
(T) 01786 475577

Course/s:
🔸 STIRLING
Number of Holes: 18
Designer: James Braid, Henry Cotton

STOCK BROOK MANOR

**STOCK BROOK MANOR GOLF &
COUNTRY CLUB,** Queens Pk Ave, Billericay,
ESSEX, CM12 0SP, **ENGLAND**.
(T) 01277 653616

Contact/s:
● Manager: Miss Z Denham

Course/s:
🔸 MANOR
Number of Holes: 9
Designer: Martin Gillett

🔸 STOCK & BROOKS
Number of Holes: 18
Designer: Martin Gillett

STOCKLEY PARK

STOCKLEY PARK GOLF CLUB, Stockley Pk,
Uxbridge, **LONDON (GREATER)**, UB11 1AQ,
ENGLAND.
(T) 020 85616339

Course/s:
🔸 STOCKLEY PARK
Description: Drains Well
Built: 1993
Number of Holes: 18 Par: 72
Yds: 6754 F9 Yds: 3303 B9 Yds: 3451
Designer: Robert Trent Jones

STOCKPORT

STOCKPORT GOLF CLUB, Offerton Rd,
Stockport, **CHESHIRE**, SK2 5HL, **ENGLAND**.
(T) 0161 4272421

Contact/s:
● Accountant: Mr John Oxton Bolt

Course/s:
🔸 STOCKPORT
Number of Holes: 18
Designer: P Barrie, A Herd

STOCKS HOTEL

**STOCKS HOTEL & GOLF & COUNTRY
CLUB,** Stocks Rd, Aldbury, Tring,

HERTFORDSHIRE, HP23 5RX, **ENGLAND**.
(T) 01442 851341

Contact/s:
● Operations Director: Mr J L Jegard

Course/s:
🔸 STOCKS HOTEL &
Number of Holes: 18 Par: 72
Yds: 6804 F9 Yds: 3455 B9 Yds: 3349
Designer: Mike Billcliffe

STOCKSBRIDGE

STOCKSBRIDGE GOLF CLUB, Royd Lane,
Deepcar, Sheffield, **YORKSHIRE (SOUTH)**,
S36 2RZ, **ENGLAND**.
(T) 0114 2882003
(E) stocksbridge@district.fsnet.co.uk

Course/s:
🔸 STOCKSBRIDGE
Number of Holes: 18 Par: 66
Yds: 5097 F9 Yds: 2746 B9 Yds: 2351
Designer: Peter Alliss

STOCKSFIELD

STOCKSFIELD GOLF CLUB LTD, New
Ridley Rd, New Ridley, Stocksfield,
NORTHUMBERLAND, NE43 7RE,
ENGLAND.
(T) 01661 843041
(E) info@sgcgold.co.uk
(W) www.sgcgolf.co.uk

Contact/s:
● Club Secretary: Mr B Slade
● Professional: Mr D Mather

Course/s:
🔸 STOCKSFIELD
Description: Wooded, Parkland,
Undulating, Short
Green Speed: Medium
Built: 1913 Built On: Clay/Soil
Number of Holes: 18 Par: 70
Record: 63 (S McKenna)
Par 3's: 4 Par 4's: 12 Par 5's: 2
Yds: 6015 F9 Yds: 3133 B9 Yds: 2882
Designer: Cotton Pennick Lawrie &
Partners
Further Information:
The course was relocated in 1948 to its
present location. The course is quite
undulating but not excessive.

STOCKWOOD PARK

STOCKWOOD PARK GOLF COURSE,
London Rd, Luton, **BEDFORDSHIRE**, LU1
4LX, **ENGLAND**.
(T) 01582 413704

Membership: Members & Public

Contact/s:
● Club Secretary: Mrs Bobby McMillan
● Professional: Mr Glynn McCarthy

Course/s:
🔸 STOCKWOOD PARK
Description: Parkland, Open, Medium
Length, Drains Well, Ideal for the Elderly
Green Speed: Medium
Built: 1973 Built On: Chalk/Soil
Number of Holes: 18 Par: 69
Par 3's: 5 Par 4's: 11 Par 5's: 2
Yds: 6113 F9 Yds: 3251 B9 Yds: 2862
Prevailing Wind: South/West
Further Information:
Interesting and rewarding game for
established players and beginners.

STOCKWOOD VALE

STOCKWOOD VALE GOLF CLUB,
Stockwood Lane, Keynsham, Bristol,

BRISTOL, BS18 2ER, **ENGLAND**.
(T) 01179 866505

Contact/s:
● Professional: Mr John Richards

Course/s:
🔸 STOCKWOOD VALE
Description: Parkland, Drains Well
Built: 1991
Number of Holes: 18 Par: 71
Further Information:
The course has many water features
throughout and the greens are built to
USGA standards.

STOKE ALBANY

STOKE ALBANY GOLF COURSE, Ashley
Rd, Stoke Albany, Market Harborough,
LEICESTERSHIRE, LE16 8PL, **ENGLAND**.
(T) 01858 535208
(E) info@stokealbanygolfclub.co.uk
(W) www.stokealbanygolfclub.co.uk

Membership: Members & Public

Contact/s:
● Club Secretary: Mr Roland Want
● Professional: Mr Adrian Clifford

Course/s:
🔸 STOKE ALBANY
Description: Parkland, Medium Length,
Drains Well, Ideal for the Elderly
Green Speed: Fast
Built: 1994
Number of Holes: 18
Designer: Hawtree

STOKE POGES

STOKE POGES GOLF CLUB, Stoke Pk, North
Drive, Stoke Poges, Slough, **BERKSHIRE**,
SL2 4PG, **ENGLAND**.
(T) 01753 717171

Course/s:
🔸 STOKE POGES
Number of Holes: 18
Designer: Harry Shapland Colt

STOKE ROCHFORD

STOKE ROCHFORD GOLF CLUB, Stoke
Rochford, Grantham, **LINCOLNSHIRE**, NG33
5EW, **ENGLAND**.
(T) 01476 530262

Contact/s:
● Professional: Mr Angus Dowe

Course/s:
🔸 STOKE ROCHFORD
Number of Holes: 18
Designer: Colonel Hotchkin

STOKE-BY-NAYLAND

STOKE-BY-NAYLAND GOLF CLUB, Golf
Shop, Keepers Lane, Leavenheath, Colchester,
ESSEX, CO6 4PZ, **ENGLAND**.
(T) 01206 262769

Contact/s:
● Manager: Mr K Lovelock

Course/s:
🔸 CONSTABLE
Number of Holes: 18

🔸 GAINSBOROUGH
Number of Holes: 18

STONE

STONE GOLF CLUB, The Fillybrooks, Stone,
STAFFORDSHIRE, ST15 0NB, **ENGLAND**.
(T) 01785 813103

Membership: Members & Public

Contact/s:
- **Captain:** Mick Weaver

Course/s:

STONE
Description: Wooded, Parkland, Hilltop, Medium Length, Drains Well, Ideal for the Elderly
Built: 1922 **Built On:** Soil
Number of Holes: 9 **Par:** 71
Further Information:
Can be played as an 18 hole course.

STONEBRIDGE

STONEBRIDGE GOLF CENTRE, Somers Rd, Meriden, Coventry, **MIDLANDS (WEST)**, CV7 7PL, **ENGLAND**.
(T) 01676 522442

Membership: Members & Public

Contact/s:
- **Club Secretary:** Mr Rob Grier
- **Pro Shop:**
  ☎ 01676 522334

Course/s:

STONEBRIDGE
Description: Parkland, Medium Length, Drains Well
Green Speed: Medium
Built: 1995
Number of Holes: 18
Designer: M Jones

STONEHAM

STONEHAM GOLF CLUB, Monks Wood Cl, Southampton, **HAMPSHIRE**, SO16 3TT, **ENGLAND**.
(T) 023 80768397

Contact/s:
- **Professional:** Mr Ian Young

Course/s:

STONEHAM
Number of Holes: 18 **Par:** 72
Yds: 6387 **F9 Yds:** 3114 **B9 Yds:** 3273
Designer: William Park

STONEHAVEN

STONEHAVEN GOLF CLUB, Golf Clubhouse, Stonehaven, **ABERDEENSHIRE**, AB39 3RH, **SCOTLAND**.
(T) 01569 762124
(W) www.stonehavengolfclub.co.uk

Membership: Members & Public
Size of Complex: 69 Acres

Contact/s:
- **Pro Shop:** Mr W Donald

Course/s:

STONEHAVEN
Description: Parkland, Cliff Top, Undulating, Short, Tight, Tends to Flood
Green Speed: Medium
Built: 1888 **Built On:** Clay
Number of Holes: 18 **Par:** 66
Prevailing Wind: East
Designer: Simpson
Further Information:
This course overlooks St Heron Bay and has natural gullies.

STONELEIGH DEER PARK

STONELEIGH DEER PARK GOLF CLUB, The Old Deer Pk, Coventry Rd, Stoneleigh, Coventry, **MIDLANDS (WEST)**, CV8 3DR, **ENGLAND**.
(T) 024 76639991

Membership: Members & Public

Contact/s:
- **Club Secretary:** Ms Cherry Reay
- **Professional:** Mr John Reay
  ☎ 024 76639912

Course/s:

AVON
Number of Holes: 9 **Par:** 27
Par 3's: 9
Yds: 1251
Designer: Ken Harrison

TANTARA
Description: Parkland
Built: 1991
Number of Holes: 18 **Par:** 71
Par 3's: 6 **Par 4's:** 7 **Par 5's:** 5
Yds: 6056 **F9 Yds:** 3390 **B9 Yds:** 2666

STONY HOLME

STONY HOLME THE PROFESSIONAL SHOP, St. Aidans Rd, Carlisle, **CUMBRIA**, CA1 1LS, **ENGLAND**.
(T) 01228 625511

Contact/s:
- **Manager:** Mr S Ling

Course/s:

STONY HOLME MUNICIPAL
Number of Holes: 18

STORNOWAY

STORNOWAY GOLF CLUB, Lady Lever Pk, Stornoway, **WESTERN ISLES**, HS2 0XP, **SCOTLAND**.
(T) 01851 702240
(W) www.stornowaygolfclub.co.uk

Membership: Members & Public
Size of Complex: 45 Acres

Contact/s:
- **Club Secretary:** Mr James D F Watson

Course/s:

STORNOWAY
Description: Wooded, Parkland, Undulating, Short, Tight
Green Speed: Medium
Built: 1950 **Built On:** Soil
Number of Holes: 18 **Par:** 68
Record: 64 (J C Farmer)
Par 3's: 6 **Par 4's:** 10 **Par 5's:** 2
Yds: 5252 **F9 Yds:** 2707 **B9 Yds:** 2545
Prevailing Wind: South/West
Further Information:
A short but tricky course set in the grounds of Lews Castle. The course has stunning views over the minch to the Scottish Highlands.

STORWS WEN

STORWS WEN GOLF CLUB, Clubhouse, Brynteg, **ISLE OF ANGLESEY**, LL78 8JY, **WALES**.
(T) 01248 852673

Membership: Members & Public

Contact/s:
- **Club Secretary:** Mr Colin Purves
- **Professional:** Mr Paul Brunt

Course/s:

STORWS WEN
Description: Parkland, Undulating
Green Speed: Medium
Built: 1996 **Built On:** Soil
Number of Holes: 9 **Par:** 34
Par 3's: 3 **Par 4's:** 5 **Par 5's:** 1
Yds: 2501
Prevailing Wind: West
Designer: Ken Jones

STOURBRIDGE

STOURBRIDGE GOLF CLUB, Worcester Lane, Stourbridge, **MIDLANDS (WEST)**, DY8 2RB, **ENGLAND**.
(T) 01384 395566

Contact/s:
- **Club Secretary:** Mrs M Betts
- **Professional:** Mr Mark Male

Course/s:

STOURBRIDGE
Number of Holes: 18 **Par:** 70
Yds: 6231

STOWMARKET

STOWMARKET GOLF CLUB LTD, Lower Rd, Onehouse, Stowmarket, **SUFFOLK**, IP14 3DA, **ENGLAND**.
(T) 01449 736473

Course/s:

STOWMARKET
Number of Holes: 18

STRABANE

STRABANE GOLF CLUB, 33 Ballycolman Rd, Strabane, **COUNTY TYRONE**, BT82 9PH, **NORTHERN IRELAND**.
(T) 028 71382271

Membership: Members & Public

Contact/s:
- **Club Secretary:** Mr Jerry Glover

Course/s:

STRABANE
Description: Parkland, Undulating, Sheltered, Long, Tight, Ideal for the Elderly
Green Speed: Medium
Built: 1908 **Built On:** Soil
Number of Holes: 18 **Par:** 69
Par 3's: 5 **Par 4's:** 11 **Par 5's:** 2
Yds: 5543
Designer: Edward Hackett, P Jones
Further Information:
River Mourne flows alongside the 9th hole.

STRANDHILL

STRANDHILL GOLF CLUB, Strandhill, **COUNTY SLIGO**, **IRELAND**.
(T) 07 168188

Course/s:

STRANDHILL
Number of Holes: 18

STRANRAER

STRANRAER GOLF CLUB, Creachmore, Leswalt, Stranraer, **DUMFRIES AND GALLOWAY**, DG9 0LF, **SCOTLAND**.
(T) 01776 870245

Membership: Members & Public
Size of Complex: 76 Acres

Contact/s:
- **Club Secretary:** Mr Bryce Kelly

Course/s:

CREACHMORE
Description: Parkland, Undulating, Medium Length
Green Speed: Slow
Built: 1952
Number of Holes: 18 **Par:** 70
Par 3's: 3 **Par 4's:** 14 **Par 5's:** 1
Yds: 6152 **F9 Yds:** 2956 **B9 Yds:** 3196
Designer: James Braid
Further Information:

Creachmore was the last course ever to be designed by James Braid.

STRATFORD OAKS

STRATFORD OAKS GOLF CLUB, Bearley Rd, Snitterfield, Stratford-upon-Avon, **WARWICKSHIRE**, CV37 0EZ, **ENGLAND**.
(T) 01789 731982

Course/s:
- **STRATFORD OAKS**
  Number of Holes: 18
  Designer: Howard Swan

STRATFORD ON AVON

STRATFORD ON AVON GOLF CLUB, Tiddington Rd, Stratford-upon-Avon, **WARWICKSHIRE**, CV37 7BA, **ENGLAND**.
(T) 01789 297296

Contact/s:
- Company Secretary: Mr R Hill

Course/s:
- **STRATFORD-UPON-AVON**
  Number of Holes: 18

STRATHAVEN

STRATHAVEN GOLF CLUB, Glasgow Rd, Strathaven, **LANARKSHIRE (SOUTH)**, ML10 6NL, **SCOTLAND**.
(T) 01357 520421

Course/s:
- **STRATHAVEN**
  Number of Holes: 18
  Designer: William Fernie, Stutt

STRATHCLYDE PARK

STRATHCLYDE PARK GOLF CENTRE, Mote Hill, Hamilton, **LANARKSHIRE (SOUTH)**, ML3 6BY, **SCOTLAND**.
(T) 01698 285511

Contact/s:
- Manager: Mr W Walker

Course/s:
- **STRATHCLYDE PARK**
  Number of Holes: 9

STRATHLENE

STRATHLENE GOLF CLUB, Portessie, Buckie, **MORAY**, AB56 4DJ, **SCOTLAND**.
(T) 01542 831798

Membership: Members & Public

Contact/s:
- Club Secretary: Mr George Jappy
- Book Tee Times: Miss Sally Reaich
- Book Lessons: Mr Brian Siorach

Course/s:
- **STRATHLENE**
  Description: Links, Open, Tends to Flood, Ideal for the Elderly
  Green Speed: Fast
  Built: 1877 Built On: Soil
  Number of Holes: 18 Par: 69
  Par 3's: 4 Par 4's: 13 Par 5's: 1
  Yds: 5977
  Designer: Bryson
  Further Information:
  One of the oldest courses in Scotland, with a particularly difficult 17th hole.

STRATHMORE GOLF CTRE

STRATHMORE GOLF CENTRE LTD, Leroch, Alyth, Blairgowrie, **PERTH AND KINROSS**, PH11 8NZ, **SCOTLAND**.
(T) 01828 633322

(E) enquiries@strathmoregolf.com
(W) www.strathmoregolf.com

Membership: Members & Public
Size of Complex: 150 Acres

Contact/s:
- Club Secretary: Ms Jane Taylor
- Professional: Mr Colin Smith
  ☎ 01575 573027

Course/s:
- **LEITFIE LINKS**
  Description: Parkland, Valley, Short, Drains Well, Ideal for the Elderly
  Built: 1994 Built On: Soil
  Number of Holes: 9 Par: 29
  Par 3's: 7 Par 4's: 2
  Yds: 1666
  Designer: Jeremy Barron, Daniel Scott
- **RANNALEROCH**
  Description: Championship, Wooded, Parkland, Valley, Undulating, Sheltered, Open, Long, Drains Well, Ideal for the Elderly
  Green Speed: Fast
  Built: 1994 Built On: Soil
  Number of Holes: 18 Par: 72
  Par 3's: 4 Par 4's: 10 Par 5's: 4
  Yds: 6454
  Prevailing Wind: South/West
  Designer: John Salverson

STRATHPEFFER SPA

STRATHPEFFER SPA GOLF CLUB, Golf Course Rd, Strathpeffer, **HIGHLANDS**, IV14 9AS, **SCOTLAND**.
(T) 01997 421219
(E) mail@strathpeffergolf.co.uk
(W) www.strathpeffergolf.co.uk

Membership: Members & Public

Contact/s:
- Club Secretary: Mr N Roxburgh
  ☎ 01997 421396

Course/s:
- **STRATHPEFFER SPA**
  Description: Moorland, Hilltop
  Built: 1888
  Number of Holes: 18 Par: 65
  Yds: 4794 F9 Yds: 2300 B9 Yds: 2494
  Designer: Tom Morris, William Park
  Further Information:
  The drive on the first hole from tee to green features the longest drop on any course in Scotland.

STRAWBERRY HILL

STRAWBERRY HILL GOLF CLUB, Wellesley Rd, Twickenham, **LONDON (GREATER)**, TW2 5SD, **ENGLAND**.
(T) 020 88940165

Contact/s:
- Manager: Mr Peter Buchan

Course/s:
- **STRAWBERRY HILL**
  Number of Holes: 9
  Designer: Taylor

STRESSHOLME

STRESSHOLME GOLF CENTRE, Snipe Lane, Darlington, **COUNTY DURHAM**, DL2 2SA, **ENGLAND**.
(T) 01325 461002

Membership: Members & Public

Contact/s:
- Professional: Mr Ralph Givens

Course/s:
- **STRESSHOLME**

Description: Parkland, Open, Long, Drains Well, Icleal for the Elderly
Green Speed: Medium
Built: 1976 Built On: Sand
Number of Holes: 18 Par: 71
Record: 64 (Neil Coles)
Yds: 6431 F9 Yds: 2955 B9 Yds: 3476
Further Information:
A river runs through course.

STROKESTOWN

STROKESTOWN GOLF COURSE, Cloonfinlough, Strokestown, **COUNTY ROSCOMMON**, **IRELAND**.
(T) 07 833323

Course/s:
- **STROKESTOWN**
  Number of Holes: 9

STROMNESS

STROMNESS GOLF CLUB, Stromness, Isle Of Orkney, Isle of Orkney, **ORKNEY ISLES**, KW16 3DW, **SCOTLAND**.
(T) 01856 850772

Course/s:
- **STROMNESS**
  Number of Holes: 18

STRUTT CLUB

STRUTT CLUB, 1 Gibfield Lane, Belper, **DERBYSHIRE**, DE56 1WA, **ENGLAND**.
(T) 01773 820088

Membership: Members & Public

Contact/s:
- Club Secretary: Mr Gordon Insley
- Book Tee Times: Mr Pete Durand

Course/s:
- **STRUTT CLUB**
  Built: 1999
  Number of Holes: 18
  Further Information:
  This golf simulator course is indoors and has 22 different courses.

STUDLEY WOOD

STUDLEY WOOD GOLF CLUB LTD, The Straight Mile, Horton-Cum-Studley, **OXFORDSHIRE**, OX33 1BF, **ENGLAND**.
(T) 01865 351144
(W) www.studleywoodgolf.co.uk

Membership: Members & Public
Size of Complex: 165 Acres

Contact/s:
- Club Secretary: Mr Barry Yates
- Professional: Mr Tony Williams
- Book Lessons:
  ☎ 01865 351122

Course/s:
- **STUDLEY WOOD**
  Description: Wooded, Parkland, Medium Length
  Green Speed: Medium
  Built: 1994 Built On: Clay
  Number of Holes: 18 Record: 65 (Leigh Sandford)

  Yds: 6315 F9 Yds: 3005
  Designer: Simon Gidman

STURMINSTER MARSHALL

STURMINSTER MARSHALL GOLF COURSE, Moor Lane, Sturminster Marshall, Wimborne, **DORSET**, BH21 4BD, **ENGLAND**.
(T) 01258 858444

Contact/s:
- **Owner:** Mr D Holdsworth

Course/s:
🏌 **STURMINSTER MARSHALL**
Number of Holes: 9
Designer: David Holdsworth, John Sharkey

STYAL

STYAL GOLF CLUB LTD, Station Rd, Styal, **CHESHIRE**, SK9 4JN, **ENGLAND**.
(T) 01625 531359

Membership: Members & Public
Size of Complex: 140 Acres

Contact/s:
- **Club Secretary:** Mr Alan Winn
  ☎ 01625 530063

Course/s:
🏌 **ACADEMY CHAMPIONSHIP PAR 3**
Description: Championship, Parkland, Medium Length
Green Speed: Medium
Built: 2000 **Built On:** Clay
Number of Holes: 9 **Par:** 27
Par 3's: 9
Yds: 1203
Designer: Glynn Traynor
Further Information:
USGA specified greens, unique tee design and fantastic layout.

🏌 **STYAL**
Description: Parkland, Sheltered, Medium Length, Ideal for the Elderly
Green Speed: Medium
Built: 1994 **Built On:** Clay
Number of Holes: 18 **Par:** 70
Par 3's: 4 **Par 4's:** 12 **Par 5's:** 2
Yds: 5768 **F9 Yds:** 3371 **B9 Yds:** 2610
Designer: Tony Holmes
Further Information:
The course has many interesting water hazards and USGA specified greens.

SUDBROOK MOOR

SUDBROOK MOOR GOLF CLUB, Charity St, Carlton Scroop, Grantham, **LINCOLNSHIRE**, NG32 3AT, **ENGLAND**.
(T) 01400 250796
(W) www.sudbrookmoor.co.uk

Membership: Members & Public

Contact/s:
- **Club Secretary:** Mrs Judith Hutton
- **Professional:** Mr Tim Hutton
- **Pro Shop:** Mr Mick Blankley

Course/s:
🏌 **SUDBROOK MOOR**
Description: Parkland, Moorland, Valley, Medium Length, Drains Well, Ideal for the Elderly
Built: 1990
Number of Holes: 9 **Par:** 66 **Record:** 61 (Ben Hutton)
Par 3's: 3 **Par 4's:** 6
Yds: 4827 **F9 Yds:** 2400 **B9 Yds:** 2427
Designer: Tim Hutton
Further Information:
9 hole course can be played as an 18 hole course

SUDBURY

SUDBURY GOLF CLUB LTD, Bridgewater Rd, Wembley, **LONDON (GREATER)**, HA0 1AL, **ENGLAND**.
(T) 020 89023713

Contact/s:
- **General Manager:** Mr A J Poole

Course/s:
🏌 **SUDBURY**
Number of Holes: 18

SUFFOLK GOLF

SUFFOLK GOLF & COUNTRY CLUB (THE), Fornham St Genevieve, Fornham St. Martin, Bury St. Edmunds, **SUFFOLK**, IP28 6JQ, **ENGLAND**.
(T) 01284 706777
(E) thelodge@the-suffolk.co.uk
(W) www.the-suffolk.co.uk

Contact/s:
- **Club Secretary:** Mr Mervyn Aho
- **Professional:** Mr Stephen Hall

Course/s:
🏌 **THE GENEVIEVE**
Description: Wooded, Parkland, Undulating, Sheltered, Open, Medium Length, Tight, Drains Well, Ideal for the Elderly
Built: 1969
Number of Holes: 18
Designer: Howard Swan

SUMMERHILL

SUMMERHILL GOLF CLUB, Isaacstown, Rathmolyon, **COUNTY MEATH**, **IRELAND**.
(T) 04 0557666

Course/s:
🏌 **SUMMERHILL**
Number of Holes: 9 **Par:** 70
Yds: 2929

SUMMERHILL

SUMMERHILL GOLF CLUB, Summer Hill House, Clifford, Hay-on-Wye, Hereford, **HEREFORDSHIRE**, HR3 5EW, **ENGLAND**.
(T) 01497 820451

Contact/s:
- **Professional:** Mr Andy Gealy

Course/s:
🏌 **SUMMERHILL**
Number of Holes: 9 **Par:** 70
Par 3's: 3 **Par 4's:** 4 **Par 5's:** 2
Yds: 5858 **F9 Yds:** 2929 **B9 Yds:** 2929
Further Information:
9 hole course can be played as an 18 hole course. Currently preparing an additional 3 hole pitch & put area

SUNBURY

AMERICAN GOLF CORPORATION, Charlton Lane, Shepperton, **SURREY**, TW17 8QA, **ENGLAND**.
(T) 01932 771414
(W) www.americangolf.com

Membership: Members & Public/Public

Contact/s:
- **Professional:** Mr Alistair Hardaway
  ☎ 01932 722898
- **Pro Shop:**
  ☎ 01932 772898

Course/s:
🏌 **SUNBURY 18 HOLE**
Description: Parkland, Undulating, Open, Drains Well, Ideal for the Elderly
Built On: Gravel
Number of Holes: 18 **Par:** 68
F9 Yds: 2541 **B9 Yds:** 2562
Further Information:
Holes 6 and 7 are signature holes, with a large lake which runs parallel to the fairway.

🏌 **SUNBURY 9 HOLE**

Description: Parkland, Undulating
Number of Holes: 9 **Par:** 33

SUNDRIDGE PARK

SUNDRIDGE PARK GOLF CLUB, Bar, Garden Rd, Bromley, **KENT**, BR1 3NE, **ENGLAND**.
(T) 020 84601822

Course/s:
🏌 **EAST**
Number of Holes: 18
Designer: William Park

🏌 **WEST**
Number of Holes: 18
Designer: William Park

SUNNINGDALE

SUNNINGDALE GOLF CLUB, Ridgemount Rd, Sunningdale, Ascot, **SURREY**, SL5 9RR, **ENGLAND**.
(T) 01344 621681
(W) www.sunningdale-golfclub.co.uk

Membership: Members & Public

Contact/s:
- **Professional:** Mr Keith Maxwell
  ☎ 01344 20128

Course/s:
🏌 **NEW**
Description: Heath Land
Built: 1923
Number of Holes: 18 **Par:** 70
Par 3's: 5 **Par 4's:** 10 **Par 5's:** 3
Yds: 6083 **F9 Yds:** 3082 **B9 Yds:** 3001
Designer: Harry Shapland Colt 🏆

🏌 **OLD**
Description: Championship, Heath Land
Built: 1901
Number of Holes: 18 **Par:** 70
Par 3's: 4 **Par 4's:** 12 **Par 5's:** 2
Yds: 6063 **F9 Yds:** 2885 **B9 Yds:** 3178
Designer: William Park (Jnr) 🏆

SUNNINGDALE LADIES

SUNNINGDALE LADIES GOLF CLUB, Cross Rd, Ascot, **BERKSHIRE**, SL5 9RX, **ENGLAND**.
(T) 01344 620507

Contact/s:
- **Club Secretary:** Mr John Darroch

Course/s:
🏌 **SUNNINGDALE LADIES**
Description: Heath Land, Sheltered, Short, Tight, Drains Well, Ideal for the Elderly **Green Speed:** Slow/Medium
Built: 1902 **Built On:** Sand/Soil
Number of Holes: 18
Designer: Harry Shapland Colt

SURBITON

SURBITON GOLF CLUB, Woodstock Lane, Chessington, **SURREY**, KT9 1UG, **ENGLAND**.
(T) 020 83983101

Contact/s:
- **Company Secretary:** Mr D Crockford

Course/s:
🏌 **SURBITON**
Number of Holes: 18
Designer: Tom Dunn

SURREY GOLF & FITNESS

SURREY GOLF & FITNESS, Moated Farm Drive, Addlestone, **SURREY**, KT15 2DW, **ENGLAND**.

(T) 01932 858551
(E) contact@surreygolfandfitness.co.uk
(W) www.surreygolfandfitness.co.uk
Membership: Public
Contact/s:
● **Professional:** Mr Neil Burke
● **Pro Shop:** Mr Paul Clarke
Course/s:
🏌 **SURREY GOLF & FITNESS**
Description: Short, Drains Well
Built: 1997
Number of Holes: 9

SUTTON

SUTTON GOLF CLUB, Cush Point, Sutton, Dublin, **COUNTY DUBLIN**, **IRELAND**.
(T) 01 8323013
Course/s:
🏌 **SUTTON**
Number of Holes: 9

SUTTON BRIDGE

SUTTON BRIDGE GOLF CLUB, New Rd, Sutton Bridge, Spalding, **LINCOLNSHIRE**, PE12 9RQ, **ENGLAND**.
(T) 01406 350323

Membership: Members & Public
Contact/s:
● **Club Secretary:** Mr Norman Davies
● **Book Tee Times:** Miss Alison Johns
● **Book Lessons:** Mr P Fields
  ☎ 01406 351422
Course/s:
🏌 **SUTTON BRIDGE** .
Description: Parkland, Undulating, Sheltered, Medium Length, Tight, Drains Well, Ideal for the Elderly
Green Speed: Fast
Built: 1914 **Built On:** Soil
Number of Holes: 9 **Par:** 70
Par 3's: 2 **Par 4's:** 6 **Par 5's:** 1
Yds: 5822 **F9 Yds:** 2911 **B9 Yds:** 2911
Prevailing Wind: South/West
Further Information:
9 hole course can be played as an 18 hole course

SUTTON COLDFIELD

SUTTON COLDFIELD GOLF CLUB, 110 Thornhill Rd, Sutton Coldfield, **MIDLANDS (WEST)**, B74 3ER, **ENGLAND**.
(T) 0121 3539633
Contact/s:
● **Professional:** Mr Jerry Hayes
● **Pro Shop:**
  ☎ 0121 5807878
Course/s:
🏌 **SUTTON COLDFIELD**
Number of Holes: 18 **Par:** 72
Yds: 6549 **F9 Yds:** 3304 **B9 Yds:** 3245
Designer: Alistair MacKenzie

SUTTON COLDFIELD LADIES

SUTTON COLDFIELD LADIES GOLF CLUB, Thornhill Rd, Sutton Coldfield, **MIDLANDS (WEST)**, B74 3ER, **ENGLAND**.
(T) 0121 3531682

Membership: Members & Public
Contact/s:
● **Club Secretary:** Barbara Fairclough
  ☎ 01543 480656
● **Professional:** Jerry Hayes
  ☎ 0121 580 7878
Course/s:

🏌 **SUTTON COLDFIELD**
Description: Parkland, Heath Land, Medium Length, Tight, Drains Well
Green Speed: Medium
Built: 1892
Number of Holes: 18
Designer: Alistair MacKenzie

SUTTON GREEN

SUTTON GREEN GOLF CLUB, New Lane, Sutton Green, Guildford, **SURREY**, GU4 7QF, **ENGLAND**.
(T) 01483 747898
(W) www.suttongreengc.co.uk
Contact/s:
● **Professional:** Mr P Tedder
● **Pro Shop:**
  ☎ 01483 766849
Course/s:
🏌 **SUTTON GREEN**
Description: Parkland, Open, Medium Length, Drains Well, Ideal for the Elderly
Green Speed: Fast
Built: 1994 **Built On:** Sand/Soil
Number of Holes: 18 **Par:** 71
Yds: 6307 **F9 Yds:** 3247 **B9 Yds:** 3060
Designer: L Davies, D Walker
Further Information:
A flat course.

SUTTON HALL

SUTTON HALL GOLF CLUB, Aston Lane, Sutton Weaver, Runcorn, **CHESHIRE**, WA7 3ED, **ENGLAND**.
(T) 01928 714872

Membership: Members & Public
Contact/s:
● **Club Secretary:** Mr Maxwell Faulkner
● **Professional:** Mr Ian Smith
Course/s:
🏌 **SUTTON HALL**
Description: Parkland, Undulating, Long, Drains Well
Green Speed: Medium
Built: 1994
Number of Holes: 18
Designer: Stephen Wundke

SUTTON PARK

SUTTON PARK GOLF CLUB, Salthouse Rd, Hull, **YORKSHIRE (EAST)**, HU8 9HF, **ENGLAND**.
(T) 01482 374242
Course/s:
🏌 **SUTTON PARK**
Number of Holes: 18

SWAFFHAM

SWAFFHAM GOLF CLUB, Cley Rd, Swaffham, **NORFOLK**, PE37 8AE, **ENGLAND**.
(T) 01760 721611
Contact/s:
● **Professional:** Mr Peter Field
Course/s:
🏌 **SWAFFHAM**
Number of Holes: 18 **Par:** 71
Yds: 6539 **F9 Yds:** 3348 **B9 Yds:** 3191

SWALLOW HALL

SWALLOW HALL GOLF COURSE, Crockey Hill, York, **YORKSHIRE (NORTH)**, YO19 4SG, **ENGLAND**.
(T) 01904 448889
(E) jtscores@hotmail.com

(W) www.swallowhall.co.uk
Membership: Members & Public
Contact/s:
● **Owner:** Mr Jonathan Scutt
  ☎ 01904 448219
Course/s:
🏌 **SWALLOW HALL**
Description: Open, Short, Drains Well, Ideal for the Elderly
Green Speed: Medium
Built: 1990 **Built On:** Sand
Number of Holes: 18 **Par:** 56
Par 3's: 16 **Par 4's:** 2
Yds: 3222 **F9 Yds:** 1438 **B9 Yds:** 1784
Designer: Brian Henry

SWANMORE GOLF CTRE

SWANMORE GOLF CENTRE, Bishopswood, Bishops Wood Rd, Mislingford, Fareham, **HAMPSHIRE**, PO17 5AT, **ENGLAND**.
(T) 01329 835300
Contact/s:
● **Owner:** Mr K Chalk
Course/s:
🏌 **SWANMORE GOLF COURSE**
Description: Parkland
Number of Holes: 9 **Par:** 60
Yds: 3244 **F9 Yds:** 1622 **B9 Yds:** 1622
Further Information:
Can be played as an 18 hole course. Also has a driving range on site

SWANSEA BAY GOLF SHOP

SWANSEA BAY GOLF SHOP, Jersey Marine, Neath, **NEATH PORT TALBOT**, SA10 6JP, **WALES**.
(T) 01792 812198
Contact/s:
● **Professional:** Mr Mike Day
Course/s:
🏌 **SWANSEA BAY**
Number of Holes: 18 **Par:** 72
Par 3's: 4 **Par 4's:** 10 **Par 5's:** 4
Yds: 6605 **F9 Yds:** 3258 **B9 Yds:** 3347

SWANSTON

SWANSTON GOLF CLUB, 111 Swanston Rd, Edinburgh, **EDINBURGH (CITY OF)**, EH10 7DS, **SCOTLAND**.
(T) 0131 4457165
(W) www.teamweb.co.uk/test_area/golf

Membership: Members & Public
Contact/s:
● **Club Secretary:** Mr John Allan
● **Professional:** Mr Richard Fyvie
  ☎ 0131 4454002
Course/s:
🏌 **SWANSTON**
Description: Medium Length, Drains Well
Green Speed: Fast
Built: 1927
Number of Holes: 18 **Par:** 66
Par 3's: 6 **Par 4's:** 12
Yds: 5004 **F9 Yds:** 2746 **B9 Yds:** 2258
Designer: Margaret Carswell
Further Information:
This is a short but challenging course with quality greens, great par 3's and fantastic views of Edinburgh and the surrounding area.

SWARLAND HALL

SWARLAND HALL GOLF CLUB, Coast View, Swarland, Morpeth, **NORTHUMBERLAND**, NE65 9JG, **ENGLAND**.

(T) 01670 787010

Course/s:

🏌 **SWARLAND HALL**
Description: Wooded, Parkland, Undulating
Built: 1993
Number of Holes: 18   **Par:** 72
Par 3's: 4   **Par 4's:** 10   **Par 5's:** 4
Yds: 6628   **F9 Yds:** 3266   **B9 Yds:** 3362

SWEETWOODS PARK

SWEETWOODS PARK GOLF CLUB, Cowden, Edenbridge, **KENT**, TN8 7JN, **ENGLAND**.
(T) 01342 850729
(E) sweetwoods1@cs.com
(W) www.sweetwoodspark.com

Membership: Members & Public
Size of Complex: 160 Acres

Contact/s:
● **Club Secretary:** Mr D Howe
  ☎ 01342 850942
● **Professional:** Mr Paul Lyons

Course/s:

🏌 **SWEETWOODS PARK**
Description: Championship, Parkland, Undulating, Sheltered, Medium Length, Ideal for the Elderly
Green Speed: Medium
Built: 1994 **Built On:** Clay
Number of Holes: 18   **Par:** 71
Record: 68
Par 3's: 4   **Par 4's:** 11   **Par 5's:** 3
Yds: 6439   **F9 Yds:** 3233   **B9 Yds:** 3206
Prevailing Wind: West
Designer: P Strand

SWIFTS

SWIFTS GOLF COURSE & DRIVING RANGE, Newmarket Rd, Carlisle, **CUMBRIA**, CA1 1JG, **ENGLAND**.
(T) 01228 625530

Contact/s:
● **Manager:** Mr John Hodgson

Course/s:

🏌 **SWIFTS GOLF COURSE**
Number of Holes: 9   **Par:** 54
Par 3's: 9
Yds: 2800   **F9 Yds:** 1400   **B9 Yds:** 1400
Further Information:
Can be played as an 18 hole course. Also has a driving range on site

SWINDON

SWINDON GOLF CLUB, Bridgnorth Rd, Blackhills, Swindon, Dudley, **MIDLANDS (WEST)**, DY3 4PU, **ENGLAND**.
(T) 01902 897031
(W) www.swindongolfclub.co.uk

Contact/s:
● **Manager:** Mr E Greenway

Course/s:

🏌 **NEW**
Number of Holes: 9

🏌 **OLD**
Number of Holes: 18   **Par:** 71
Yds: 6121   **F9 Yds:** 3170   **B9 Yds:** 2951

SWINFORD

SWINFORD GOLF CLUB, Brabazon Pk, Swinford, **COUNTY MAYO**, **IRELAND**.
(T) 094 51378

Course/s:

🏌 **SWINFORD**

Number of Holes: 9

SWINLEY FOREST

SWINLEY FOREST GOLF CLUB, Bodens Ride, Ascot, **BERKSHIRE**, SL5 9LE, **ENGLAND**.
(T) 01344 620197
(E) swinleyfgc@aol.com
(W) www.golfclubatlas.com/swinley000134.html

Membership: Members & Public
Size of Complex: 100 Acres

Contact/s:
● **Club Secretary:** Mr I L Pearce
  ☎ 01344 874979
● **Professional:** Mr Stuart Hill

Course/s:

🏌 **SWINLEY FOREST**
Description: Wooded, Heath Land, Sheltered, Medium Length, Drains Well, Ideal for the Elderly
Green Speed: Medium/Fast
Built: 1909 **Built On:** Sand
Number of Holes: 18   **Par:** 68
Par 3's: 5   **Par 4's:** 12   **Par 5's:** 1
Yds: 5751   **F9 Yds:** 2994   **B9 Yds:** 2757
Designer: Harry Shapland Colt 🏆

SWINTON PARK

SWINTON PARK GOLF CLUB, East Lancashire Rd, Swinton, Manchester, **MANCHESTER (GREATER)**, M27 5LX, **ENGLAND**.
(T) 0161 7941785

Membership: Members & Public

Contact/s:
● **Club Secretary:** Mr Trevor Glover
● **Professional:** Mr Jimmy Wilson

Course/s:

🏌 **SWINTON PARK**
Description: Parkland, Undulating, Sheltered, Long, Drains Well, Ideal for the Elderly
Green Speed: Fast **Built On:** Clay
Number of Holes: 18
Prevailing Wind: North/West
Designer: James Braid

SWORDS OPEN

SWORDS OPEN GOLF COURSE, Balheary Ave, Swords, **COUNTY DUBLIN**, **IRELAND**.
(T) 01 8409819
(E) swordsgc@indigo.ie
(W) www.swordsopengolfcourse.com

Membership: Members & Public

Contact/s:
● **Club Secretary:** Ms Orla McGuinness

Course/s:

🏌 **SWORDS OPEN**
Description: Parkland
Green Speed: Medium
Built: 1992
Number of Holes: 18
Designer: T Halpin

TADMARTON HEATH

TADMARTON HEATH GOLF CLUB, Tadmarton Heath, Banbury, **OXFORDSHIRE**, OX15 5HL, **ENGLAND**.
(T) 01608 737278

Course/s:

🏌 **TADMARTON HEATH**
Number of Holes: 18
Designer: Colonel Hutchinson

TAIN

TAIN GOLF CLUB, Chapel Rd, Tain, **HIGHLANDS**, IV19 1JE, **SCOTLAND**.
(T) 01862 892314
(E) info@tain-golfclub.co.uk
(W) www.tain-golfclub.co.uk

Membership: Members & Public

Course/s:

🏌 **TAIN**
Description: Links, Sheltered
Built: 1890
Number of Holes: 18   **Par:** 70
Par 3's: 4   **Par 4's:** 12   **Par 5's:** 2
Yds: 6404   **F9 Yds:** 3161   **B9 Yds:** 3243
Designer: Tom Morris
Further Information:
The course's length, the natural links turf, the water hazards and bunkers, all make Tain a course for the strategic golfer.

TALL PINES

TALL PINES GOLF COURSE, Cooks Bridle Path, Downside, Backwell, Bristol, **BRISTOL**, BS48 3DJ, **ENGLAND**.
(T) 01275 472076

Contact/s:
● **Professional:** Mr Alex Murray

Course/s:

🏌 **TALL PINES**
Description: Parkland, Drains Well
Built: 1990
Number of Holes: 18   **Par:** 70
Designer: T Murray

TAMWORTH MUNICIPAL

TAMWORTH MUNICIPAL GOLF CLUB, Eagle Drive, Amington, Tamworth, **STAFFORDSHIRE**, B77 4EG, **ENGLAND**.
(T) 01827 709303

Membership: Public

Contact/s:
● **Professional:** Mr Wayne Alcock

Course/s:

🏌 **TAMWORTH MUNICIPAL**
Number of Holes: 18   **Par:** 73
Yds: 6488   **F9 Yds:** 3099   **B9 Yds:** 3389
Designer: Hawtree

TANDRAGEE

TANDRAGEE GOLF CLUB, Markethill Rd, Tandragee, Craigavon, **COUNTY ARMAGH**, BT62 2ER, **NORTHERN IRELAND**.
(T) 028 38841272
(E) office@tandragee.co.uk
(W) www.tandragee.co.uk

Membership: Members & Public
Size of Complex: 130 Acres

Contact/s:
● **Club Secretary:** Mr Robert Cassells
● **Professional:** Mr Paul Stevenson
● **Pro Shop:** Mr Gary Mercer
  ☎ 028 38841761

Course/s:

🏌 **TANRAGEE**
Description: Parkland, Undulating, Medium Length, Drains Well
Green Speed: Medium
Built: 1911 **Built On:** Soil
Number of Holes: 18   **Par:** 70
Par 3's: 4   **Par 4's:** 12   **Par 5's:** 2
Yds: 6029   **F9 Yds:** 2960   **B9 Yds:** 3068
Prevailing Wind: West
Designer: Stone
Further Information:
Views of the mountains.

TANDRIDGE

TANDRIDGE GOLF CLUB, Godstone Rd, Oxted, **SURREY**, RH8 9NQ, **ENGLAND**.
(T) 01883 712274

Course/s:
- **TANDRIDGE**
  Number of Holes: 18
  Designer: Harry Shapland Colt

TANKERSLEY PARK

TANKERSLEY PARK GOLF CLUB, Westwood, High Green, Sheffield, **YORKSHIRE (SOUTH)**, S35 4LG, **ENGLAND**.
(T) 0114 2468247

Contact/s:
- Professional: Mr Ian Kirk
  ☎ 0114 2455583

Course/s:
- **TANKERSLEY PARK**
  Description: Parkland
  Built: 1907
  Number of Holes: 18 Par: 69
  Yds: 6168 F9 Yds: 3176 B9 Yds: 2992
  Designer: Hawtree

TANTALLON

TANTALLON GOLF CLUB, Clubhouse, Westgate, North Berwick, **LOTHIAN (EAST)**, EH39 4AH, **SCOTLAND**.
(T) 01620 892114

Contact/s:
- Club Secretary: Mr T Hill

Course/s:
- **COURSE #1**
  Description: Links
  Number of Holes: 18 Par: 70
  Yds: 4452

TAPTON PARK

TAPTON PARK GOLF COURSE, Murray House, Crow Lane, Chesterfield, **DERBYSHIRE**, S41 0EQ, **ENGLAND**.
(T) 01246 239500

Contact/s:
- Manageress: Mrs Deborah Wigmore

Course/s:
- **DOBBIN CLOUGH**
  Number of Holes: 9

- **TAPTON MAIN**
  Number of Holes: 18

TARA (ROYAL)

ROYAL TARA GOLF CLUB, Bellinter, Navan, **COUNTY MEATH, IRELAND**.
(T) 046 25244
(E) info@royaltaragolfclub.com
(W) www.royaltaragolfclub.com

Contact/s:
- Professional: Mr Adam Whiston

Course/s:
- **BELLINTER NINE**
  Number of Holes: 9

- **NEW**
  Number of Holes: 18 Par: 72
  Yds: 6456 F9 Yds: 3270 B9 Yds: 3186

TARA GLEN

TARA GLEN GOLF & COUNTRY CLUB, Tara Glen, Ballymoney, **COUNTY ANTRIM, NORTHERN IRELAND**.
(T) 05 525413

Contact/s:
- Club Secretary: Mr David Popplewell

Course/s:
- **TARA GLEN**
  Number of Holes: 9 Par: 72
  Yds: 6350 F9 Yds: 6350

TARBAT

TARBAT GOLF CLUB, Tarbatness Rd, Portmahomack, Fearn, **HIGHLANDS**, IV20 1YQ, **SCOTLAND**.
(T) 01862 871598
(E) motol@clara.co.uk

Contact/s:
- Club Secretary: Ms Morag Lane

Course/s:
- **TARBAT**
  Number of Holes: 9 Par: 68
  Yds: 5196 F9 Yds: 2616 B9 Yds: 2580
  Further Information:
  9 hole course can be played as an 18 hole course

TARBERT

TARBERT GOLF CLUB, Kilberry Rd, Tarbert, **ARGYLL AND BUTE**, PA29 6XX, **SCOTLAND**.
(T) 01880 820536

Contact/s:
- Club Secretary: Peter Cuples
  ☎ 01546 606896

Course/s:
- **TARBERT**
  Description: Parkland
  Number of Holes: 9 Par: 33
  Yds: 4460 F9 Yds: 4460
  Further Information:
  9 hole course can be played as an 18 hole course.

TARLAIR (ROYAL)

ROYAL TARLAIR GOLF CLUB, Buchan St, Macduff, **ABERDEENSHIRE**, AB44 1TA, **SCOTLAND**.
(T) 01261 832897
(W) www.royaltarlair.co.uk

Membership: Members & Public

Contact/s:
- Club Secretary: Mrs Caroline Davidson

Course/s:
- **ROYAL TARLAIR**
  Description: Parkland, Cliff Top, Short
  Built: 1926 Built On: Sand
  Number of Holes: 18 Par: 71
  Par 3's: 4 Par 4's: 11 Par 5's: 3
  Yds: 5866 F9 Yds: 2968 B9 Yds: 2898
  Further Information:
  The tee for the spectacular 13th hole is 100 feet above the green, with an imposing deep ravine dividing the two. It is perhaps the most fearsome hole anywhere along the coastline.

TARLAND

TARLAND GOLF CLUB, Aberdeen Rd, Tarland, Aboyne, **ABERDEENSHIRE**, AB34 4TB, **SCOTLAND**.
(T) 01339 881413

Contact/s:
- Treasurer: Mr T R Ward

Course/s:
- **TARLAND**
  Number of Holes: 9 Par: 67
  Yds: 5857 F9 Yds: 2896 B9 Yds: 2979
  Designer: Tom Morris

TAUNTON & PICKERIDGE

TAUNTON & PICKERIDGE GOLF CLUB, Corfe, Taunton, **SOMERSET**, TA3 7BY, **ENGLAND**.
(T) 01823 421537

Contact/s:
- Professional: G Milne
  ☎ 01823 421790

Course/s:
- **TAUNTON & PICKERIDGE**
  Number of Holes: 18
  Yds: 5927

TAUNTON VALE

TAUNTON VALE GOLF CLUB, Creech Heathfield, Taunton, **SOMERSET**, TA3 5EY, **ENGLAND**.
(T) 01823 412220
(E) tvgc@easynet.co.uk
(W) www.tauntonvalegolf.co.uk

Membership: Members & Public
Size of Complex: 156 Acres

Contact/s:
- Club Secretary: Mrs Joanne Wyatt
- Professional: Mr Martin Keitch
  ☎ 01823 412880

Course/s:
- **CHARLTON**
  Number of Holes: 18 Par: 70
  Par 3's: 4 Par 4's: 12 Par 5's: 2
  Yds: 6167 F9 Yds: 3051 B9 Yds: 3116
  Designer: John Payne

- **DURSTON**
  Number of Holes: 9 Par: 32
  Yds: 2004 F9 Yds: 2004
  Designer: John Payne

TAVISTOCK

TAVISTOCK GOLF CLUB, Down Rd, Tavistock, **DEVON**, PL19 9AQ, **ENGLAND**.
(T) 01822 612344

Membership: Members & Public

Contact/s:
- Club Secretary: Mr Michael O'Dowd
- Professional: Mr Domonic Rehaag

Course/s:
- **TAVISTOCK**
  Description: Moorland, Breckland, Open, Medium Length, Drains Well, Ideal for the Elderly
  Green Speed: Fast
  Built: 1890 Built On: Soil
  Number of Holes: 18
  Designer: Herbert Fowler
  Further Information:
  Situated in the Dartmoor National Park.

TAYMOUTH CASTLE

TAYMOUTH CASTLE GOLF COURSE, Taymouth Castle Est, Kenmore, **PERTH AND KINROSS**, PH15 2NT, **SCOTLAND**.
(T) 01887 830228
(E) golf@scotland-golfco.uk
(W) www.scotland-golf.co.uk

Membership: Members & Public

Contact/s:
- Professional: Mr Colin Dott
- Pro Shop: Mr Robert Ilesley

Course/s:
- **TAYMOUTH CASTLE**
  Description: Parkland, Valley, Sheltered, Medium Length, Drains Well
  Green Speed: Medium

Built: 1924
Number of Holes: 18   Par: 69
Par 3's: 4   Par 4's: 13   Par 5's: 1
Yds: 6066   F9 Yds: 3143   B9 Yds: 2923
Designer: James Braid
Further Information:
The course is situated amidst beautiful
Mountain and Loch scenery.

TED MCCARTHY MUNICIPAL

TED MCCARTHY MUNICIPAL, Bessboro
Rd, Mahon, **COUNTY CORK**, **IRELAND**.
(T) 021 4294280

Membership: Public

Course/s:
● TED MCCARTHY MUNICIPAL GOLF COURSE
  Description: Undulating
  Number of Holes: 18   Par: 67
  Yds: 5353
  Further Information:
  Extremely demanding greens.

TEESSIDE

TEESSIDE GOLF CLUB, Acklam Rd,
Thornaby, Stockton-on-Tees, **CLEVELAND**,
TS17 7JS, **ENGLAND**.
(T) 01642 616516

Course/s:
● TEESSIDE
  Number of Holes: 18   Par: 72
  Yds: 6472

TEHIDY

TEHIDY PARK GOLF CLUB, Tehidy,
Camborne, **CORNWALL**, TR14 0HH,
ENGLAND.
(T) 01209 842208

Membership: Members & Public

Contact/s:
● Club Secretary: Mr Ray Parker
● Professional: Mr James Dumbreck
  ☎ 01209 842914

Course/s:
● TEHIDY
  Description: Parkland, Sheltered, Open,
  Tight, Ideal for the Elderly
  Green Speed: Medium
  Built: 1922   Built On: Clay
  Number of Holes: 18

TEIGN VALLEY

TEIGN VALLEY GOLF CLUB, Christow,
Exeter, **DEVON**, EX6 7PA, **ENGLAND**.
(T) 01647 253026
(E) welcome@teignvalleygolf.co.uk
(W) www.teignvalleygolf.co.uk

Membership: Members & Public

Contact/s:
● Club Secretary: Mr Mike Daniels
● Professional: Mr Scott Amiet
  ☎ 01647 253127

Course/s:
● TEIGN VALLEY
  Description: Parkland, Hilltop, Valley,
  Medium Length
  Green Speed: Medium
  Number of Holes: 18
  Designer: Nicholson

TEIGNMOUTH

TEIGNMOUTH GOLF CLUB, Haldon Moor,
Teignmouth, **DEVON**, TQ14 9NY, **ENGLAND**.
(T) 01626 777070

Membership: Members & Public

Contact/s:
● Professional: Mr Peter Ward
  ☎ 01626 772894

Course/s:
● TEIGNMOUTH
  Description: Heath Land, Open, Long,
  Drains Well
  Built: 1924   Built On: Soil
  Number of Holes: 18   Par: 69
  Yds: 6083   F9 Yds: 3012   B9 Yds: 3071
  Prevailing Wind: South
  Designer: Alistair MacKenzie

TELFORD

TELFORD GOLF & COUNTRY CLUB, Great
Hay Drive, Sutton Heights, Telford,
SHROPSHIRE, TF7 4DT, **ENGLAND**.
(T) 01952 429977

Contact/s:
● Professional: Mr Dan Bateman

Course/s:
● TELFORD
  Description: Wooded
  Built: 1975
  Number of Holes: 18   Par: 72
  Designer: Peter Alliss, David Thomas
  Further Information:
  Mature course.

TEMPLE

TEMPLE GOLF CLUB, Henley Rd, Hurley,
Maidenhead, **BERKSHIRE**, SL6 5LH,
ENGLAND.
(T) 01628 824795
Size of Complex: 160 Acres

Contact/s:
● Club Secretary: Mr K G M Adderley
● Professional: Mr J Whiteley
  ☎ 01628 824254

Course/s:
● TEMPLE
  Description: Open, Medium Length,
  Drains Well
  Green Speed: Medium/Fast
  Built: 1909   Built On: Chalk
  Number of Holes: 18   Par: 70
  Par 3's: 5   Par 4's: 10   Par 5's: 3
  Yds: 6261   F9 Yds: 3296   B9 Yds: 2965
  Designer: William Park
  Further Information:
  Panoramic views of the Thames Valley.

TEMPLE CLUB

TEMPLE GOLF & COUNTRY CLUB, 60
Church Rd, Lisburn, **COUNTY ANTRIM**,
BT27 6UP, **NORTHERN IRELAND**.
(T) 028 92639213

Membership: Members & Public

Contact/s:
● Club Secretary: Mr David Kinnear
● Professional: Mr Joseph McBride

Course/s:
● TEMPLE CLUB
  Description: Parkland, Valley, Open,
  Medium Length, Tight, Drains Well, Ideal
  for the Elderly
  Green Speed: Fast
  Built: 1994   Built On: Soil
  Number of Holes: 9
  Further Information:
  A challenging course.

TEMPLE NEWSAM

TEMPLE NEWSAM GOLF CLUB, Temple
Newsam Rd, Leeds, **YORKSHIRE (WEST)**,
LS15 0NB, **ENGLAND**.

(T) 0113 2645624

Membership: Public

Contact/s:
● Club Secretary: Mr G Gower
● Pro Shop: Mr Alan Swaine
  ☎ 0113 2647362

Course/s:
● LADY DOROTHY
  Description: Parkland, Undulating
  Number of Holes: 18   Par: 70
  Yds: 6029
● LORD IRWIN
  Description: Parkland, Undulating
  Number of Holes: 18   Par: 71
  Yds: 6448

TEMPLEMORE

TEMPLEMORE GOLF CLUB, Manna South,
Templemore, **COUNTY TIPPERARY**,
IRELAND.
(T) 05 0432923

Membership: Members & Public
Size of Complex: 70 Acres

Contact/s:
● Club Secretary: Mr John Hackett
  ☎ 05043 1502

Course/s:
● TEMPLEMORE
  Description: Parkland, Open, Medium
  Length, Tight, Ideal for the Elderly
  Green Speed: Fast
  Built: 1968   Built On: Soil
  Number of Holes: 9   Par: 70
  Par 3's: 3   Par 4's: 4   Par 5's: 2
  Yds: 5933   F9 Yds: 3002   B9 Yds: 2931
  Further Information:
  This 9 hole course can be played as an 18
  hole course using different coloured
  markers.

TENBY

TENBY GOLF CLUB, The Burrows, Tenby,
PEMBROKESHIRE, SA70 7NP, **WALES**.
(T) 01834 842978
(E) tenbygolfclub@netscapeonline.co.uk
(W) www.tenbygolf.co.uk

Membership: Members & Public

Contact/s:
● Professional: Mr M Hawkey
  ☎ 01834 844447

Course/s:
● TENBY
  Description: Championship, Links,
  Undulating, Medium Length, Tight, Drains
  Well
  Green Speed: Medium/Fast
  Built: 1888   Built On: Sand
  Number of Holes: 18   Par: 69
  Par 3's: 4   Par 4's: 13   Par 5's: 1
  Yds: 6224   F9 Yds: 3125   B9 Yds: 3099
  Prevailing Wind: South/West
  Designer: James Braid
  Further Information:
  This challenging course has a natural
  layout with excellent greens.

TENTERDEN

TENTERDEN GOLF CLUB, Woodchurch Rd,
Tenterden, **KENT**, TN30 7DR, **ENGLAND**.
(T) 01580 763987
(E) tenterden-golf-club@lineone.net
(W) www.tenterdengolfclub.co.uk

Membership: Members & Public

Contact/s:
● Club Secretary: Mr Tug Wilson

- **Professional:** Mr Kyle Kelsall
  ☎ 01580 762409

Course/s:

🏌 **TENTERDEN**
  Description: Parkland, Undulating, Open,
  Medium Length
  Green Speed: Medium
  Built: 1905 **Built On:** Clay
  Number of Holes: 18 **Par:** 70
  Par 3's: 5 **Par 4's:** 10 **Par 5's:** 3
  Yds: 6073 **F9 Yds:** 2795 **B9 Yds:** 3278

TEST VALLEY

TEST VALLEY GOLF CLUB, Micheldever Rd,
Overton, Basingstoke, **HAMPSHIRE**, RG25
3DS, **ENGLAND**.
(T) 08707 459 021
(E) info@testvalleygolf.com
(W) www.testvalleygolf.com

Contact/s:

- **Professional:** Mr Alastair Briggs

Course/s:

🏌 **TEST VALLEY**
  Description: Downland, Drains Well
  Built: 1992 **Built On:** Chalk/Soil
  Number of Holes: 18 **Par:** 72
  Par 3's: 4 **Par 4's:** 10 **Par 5's:** 4
  Yds: 6622 **F9 Yds:** 3185 **B9 Yds:** 3437
  Designer: E Darcy, D Wright

TETNEY

TETNEY GOLF CLUB LTD, Station Rd,
Tetney, Grimsby, **LINCOLNSHIRE (NORTH
EAST)**, DN36 5HY, **ENGLAND**.
(T) 01472 211644

Contact/s:

- **Owner:** Mr Roy Caswell

Course/s:

🏌 **TETNEY GOLF CLUB**
  Number of Holes: 18 **Par:** 71
  Yds: 6100

TEWKESBURY PARK

TEWKESBURY PARK GOLF COURSE,
Lincoln Green Lane, Tewkesbury,
GLOUCESTERSHIRE, GL20 7DN,
ENGLAND.
(T) 01684 272320

Contact/s:

- **Professional:** Mr Charlie Boast

Course/s:

🏌 **TEWKESBURY PARK**
  Description: Parkland
  Built: 1976
  Number of Holes: 18 **Par:** 73
  Further Information:
  Overlooks Tewkesbury Abbey.

THAMES DITTON & ESHER

THAMES DITTON & ESHER GOLF CLUB,
Portsmouth Rd, Esher, **SURREY**, KT10 9AL,
ENGLAND.
(T) 020 83981551
(W) www.tdandegc.co.uk

Membership: Members & Public

Contact/s:

- **Club Secretary:** Mr A Barry
- **Professional:** Mr R Jones

Course/s:

🏌 **THAMES DITTON & ESHER**
  Description: Links, Wooded, Undulating,
  Sheltered, Short, Tight, Drains Well
  Green Speed: Medium
  Built: 1892 **Built On:** Sand/Soil

Number of Holes: 9 **Par:** 66
  Yds: 5149 **F9 Yds:** 2612 **B9 Yds:** 2537
  Further Information:
  9 hole course can be played as an 18 hole
  course

THAMESVIEW

THAMESVIEW GOLF CENTRE, Fairway
Drive, London, **LONDON (GREATER)**, SE28
8PP, **ENGLAND**.
(T) 020 83107975
(E) enquiries@thamesview-golf.fsnet.co.uk

Membership: Members & Public

Contact/s:

- **Club Secretary:** Ms Sara-Jane
  Springham

Course/s:

🏌 **RIVERSIDE**
  Number of Holes: 9 **Par:** 35
  Par 3's: 2 **Par 4's:** 6 **Par 5's:** 1
  Yds: 2791
  Designer: Heffernan

THEALE GOLF CTRE

THEALE GOLF CENTRE, North St, Theale,
Reading, **BERKSHIRE**, RG7 5EX, **ENGLAND**.
(T) 0118 9305331

Membership: Members & Public
Size of Complex: 137 Acres

Contact/s:

- **Club Secretary:** Mr Mike Lowe
- **Professional:** Mr Lee Newman
- **Book Tee Times:** Mr Alan Clarke

Course/s:

🏌 **THEALE**
  Description: Wooded, Parkland,
  Undulating, Sheltered, Long, Drains Well,
  Ideal for the Elderly
  Green Speed: Medium/Fast
  Built: 1996 **Built On:** Soil
  Number of Holes: 18 **Par:** 72
  Par 3's: 4 **Par 4's:** 10 **Par 5's:** 4
  Yds: 6395
  Designer: Mike Lowe
  Further Information:
  A flat course.

THETFORD

THETFORD GOLF CLUB, Brandon Rd,
Thetford, **NORFOLK**, IP24 3NE, **ENGLAND**.
(T) 01842 752169

Membership: Members & Public

Contact/s:

- **Club Secretary:** Mrs S A Redpath
- **Professional:** Mr Gary Kitley
  ☎ 01842 752662

Course/s:

🏌 **THETFORD**
  Description: Heath Land, Breckland,
  Sheltered, Long, Tight, Drains Well
  Green Speed: Medium
  Built: 1912 **Built On:** Sand/Soil
  Number of Holes: 18 **Par:** 72
  Par 3's: 4 **Par 4's:** 10 **Par 5's:** 4
  Yds: 6849 **F9 Yds:** 3269 **B9 Yds:** 3580
  Further Information:
  A flat course.

THEYDON BOIS

THEYDON BOIS GOLF CLUB, Secretary,
Theydon Rd, Epping, **ESSEX**, CM16 4EH,
ENGLAND.
(T) 01992 813054/ 812460

Contact/s:

- **Book Tee Times:**

  ☎ 01992 812460

Course/s:

🏌 **THEYDON BOIS**
  Number of Holes: 18 **Par:** 68
  Yds: 5480
  Designer: James Braid

THIRSK & NORTHALLERTON

THIRSK & NORTHALLERTON GOLF CLUB,
Northallerton Rd, Thornton Le Street, Thirsk,
YORKSHIRE (NORTH), YO7 4AB,
ENGLAND.
(T) 01845 522170

Contact/s:

- **Club Secretary:** Mr G S Batterbee

Course/s:

🏌 **THIRSK & NORTHALLERTON**
  Number of Holes: 18 **Par:** 72
  Yds: 6495 **F9 Yds:** 3321 **B9 Yds:** 3174

THORNBURY GOLF

THORNBURY GOLF CENTRE, Bristol Rd,
Thornbury, Bristol, **BRISTOL**, BS35 2AA,
ENGLAND.
(T) 01454 281144

Contact/s:

- **Professional:** Mr Simon Hubbard

Course/s:

🏌 **HIGH**
  Description: Parkland, Undulating
  Built: 1992
  Number of Holes: 18 **Par:** 71
  Designer: Hawtree
  Further Information:
  Challenging with some water hazards.

🏌 **LOW**
  Description: Parkland, Undulating
  Built: 1992
  Number of Holes: 18
  Designer: Hawtree
  Further Information:
  The course overlooks the Severn Estuary.

THORNDON PARK

THORNDON PARK GOLF CLUB LTD,
Thorndon Pk, Ingrave, Brentwood, **ESSEX**,
CM13 3RH, **ENGLAND**.
(T) 01277 810345
(W) www.thorndonparkgolfclub.com

Contact/s:

- **Club Secretary:** Lt Col R M Estcourt
- **Pro Shop:** Mr Brian White
  ☎ 01277 810736

Course/s:

🏌 **THORNDON PARK**
  Number of Holes: 18 **Par:** 71
  Yds: 6245 **F9 Yds:** 3057 **B9 Yds:** 3188
  Designer: Charles Hugh Alison, Harry
  Shapland Colt

THORNE

THORNE GOLF CLUB, Kirton Lane, Thorne,
Doncaster, **YORKSHIRE (SOUTH)**, DN8
5RE, **ENGLAND**.
(T) 01405 812084

Contact/s:

- **Club Secretary:** Mr P Kitteridge
  ☎ 01405 813827

Course/s:

🏌 **THORNE**
  Number of Holes: 18
  Yds: 5366
  Designer: R D Highfield

THORNEY

THORNEY GOLF CLUB, English Drove, Thorney, Peterborough, **CAMBRIDGESHIRE**, PE6 0TJ, **ENGLAND**.
(T) 01733 270570

Membership: Members & Public
Size of Complex: 250 Acres

Contact/s:
● Club Secretary: Ms J Hind
● Professional: Mr Mark Templeman

Course/s:
⛳ **FEN**
Description: Open, Medium Length, Tends to Flood, Ideal for the Elderly
Green Speed: Medium
Built: 1991 **Built On:** Clay
Number of Holes: 18 **Par:** 70
Record: 65 (Stuart Brown)
Par 3's: 5 **Par 4's:** 10 **Par 5's:** 3
Yds: 6104
Designer: Angus Dow
Further Information:
Challenging fen land, links course.

⛳ **LAKES**
Number of Holes: 18 **Par:** 71
Par 3's: 4 **Par 4's:** 11 **Par 5's:** 3
Yds: 6402

THORNEY PARK

THORNEY PARK GOLF COURSE, Thorney Mill Rd, Iver, **BUCKINGHAMSHIRE**, SL0 9AL, **ENGLAND**.
(T) 01895 422095

Membership: Members & Public
Size of Complex: 115 Acres

Contact/s:
● Professional: Mr Andrew Killing

Course/s:
⛳ **THORNEY PARK**
Description: Parkland, Undulating, Medium Length
Green Speed: Medium
Built: 1993 **Built On:** Soil
Number of Holes: 9 **Par:** 34
Par 3's: 3 **Par 4's:** 5 **Par 5's:** 1
Yds: 2834
Further Information:
9 hole course can be played as an 18 hole course

THORNHILL

THORNHILL GOLF CLUB, Blacknest, Thornhill, **DUMFRIES AND GALLOWAY**, DG3 5DW, **SCOTLAND**.
(T) 01848 331779

Membership: Members & Public
Size of Complex: 120 Acres

Contact/s:
● Club Secretary: Mr David Balfour
● Professional: Mr J T Davidson
● Pro Shop:
  ☎ 01848 330456
● Book Tee Times:
  ☎ 01848 330546

Course/s:
⛳ **THORNHILL**
Description: Parkland, Heath Land, Breckland, Open, Medium Length, Drains Well, Ideal for the Elderly
Built: 1893
Number of Holes: 18 **Par:** 71
Par 3's: 4 **Par 4's:** 11 **Par 5's:** 3
Yds: 6085 **F9 Yds:** 2917 **B9 Yds:** 3168
Prevailing Wind: West
Designer: James Braid
Further Information:

The Thornhill course is surrounded by hills and has breathtaking views.

THORNTON

THORNTON GOLF CLUB, Thornton, Kirkcaldy, **FIFE**, KY1 4DW, **SCOTLAND**.
(T) 01592 771111
(W) www.thorntongolfclubfife.co.uk

Membership: Members & Public
Size of Complex: 100 Acres

Contact/s:
● Club Secretary: Mr Brian Main

Course/s:
⛳ **THORNTON**
Description: Wooded, Parkland, Sheltered, Short, Drains Well, Ideal for the Elderly
Green Speed: Medium
Built: 1921
Number of Holes: 18 **Par:** 70
Yds: 6155 **F9 Yds:** 2925 **B9 Yds:** 3230
Prevailing Wind: West
Further Information:
River Ore runs through the course and is a water hazard on three of the holes.

THORPE HALL

THORPE HALL GOLF CLUB, Thorpe Hall Ave, Thorpe Bay, Southend-on-Sea, **ESSEX**, SS1 3AT, **ENGLAND**.
(T) 01702 582205

Size of Complex: 95 Acres

Contact/s:
● Club Secretary: K Sims
● Professional: Mr Bill McColl

Course/s:
⛳ **THORPE HALL**
Number of Holes: 18 **Par:** 71
Yds: 6286

THORPE WOOD

THORPE WOOD GOLF COURSE, Thorpe Wood, Peterborough, **CAMBRIDGESHIRE**, PE3 6SE, **ENGLAND**.
(T) 01733 267701
(E) enquiries@thorpewoodgolfcourse.co.uk
(W) www.thorpewoodgolfcourse.co.uk

Contact/s:
● Professional: Mr Lee Vaughn

Course/s:
⛳ **THORPE WOOD**
Description: Parkland, Undulating, Long, Drains Well
Green Speed: Medium
Built: 1975
Number of Holes: 18 **Par:** 73
Record: 70 (Gary Casey)
Par 3's: 3 **Par 4's:** 11 **Par 5's:** 4
Yds: 7086 **F9 Yds:** 3521 **B9 Yds:** 3565
Designer: Peter Alliss, David Thomas

THORPENESS

THORPENESS HOTEL AND GOLF CLUB, Thorpeness, Aldeburgh, **SUFFOLK**, IP16 4NH, **ENGLAND**.
(T) 01728 452176
(E) info@thorpeness.co.uk
(W) www.thorpeness.co.uk

Contact/s:
● Sales & Marketing Manager: Ms Emma Sharland

Course/s:
⛳ **THORPENESS HOTEL &**
Number of Holes: 18 **Par:** 69
Par 3's: 4 **Par 4's:** 13 **Par 5's:** 1

Yds: 6281 **F9 Yds:** 3178 **B9 Yds:** 3103
Designer: James Braid

THOULSTONE PARK

THOULSTONE PARK GOLF CLUB, Thoulstone, Chapmanslade, Westbury, **WILTSHIRE**, BA13 4AQ, **ENGLAND**.
(T) 01373 832825

Contact/s:
● Club Secretary: Mrs Jean Pierce
● Professional: Mr Tony Isaacs

Course/s:
⛳ **THOULSTONE PARK**
Description: Parkland
Built: 1992
Number of Holes: 18 **Par:** 71
Further Information:
This course caters for every standard of golfer.

THREE LOCKS

THREE LOCKS GOLF CLUB, Partridge Hse, Partridge Hill, Great Brickhill, Milton Keynes, **BUCKINGHAMSHIRE**, MK17 9BH, **ENGLAND**.
(T) 01525 270050

Contact/s:
● Partner: Mrs Patrice Critchley

Course/s:
⛳ **THREE LOCKS**
Number of Holes: 18 **Par:** 70
Yds: 6036 **F9 Yds:** 2900 **B9 Yds:** 3136

THREE RIVERS

THREE RIVERS GOLF & COUNTRY CLUB, Stow Rd, Cold Norton, Purleigh, Chelmsford, **ESSEX**, CM3 6RR, **ENGLAND**.
(T) 01621 828631

Contact/s:
● Professional: Mr Phil Green

Course/s:
⛳ **JUBILEE**
Description: Parkland
Built: 1971
Number of Holes: 18 **Par:** 64

⛳ **KINGS**
Description: Championship, Wooded, Parkland, Medium Length
Built: 1971
Number of Holes: 18 **Par:** 72
Designer: Hawtree

THURLES

THURLES GOLF CLUB LTD, Turtulla, Thurles, **COUNTY TIPPERARY**, **IRELAND**.
(T) 05 0421983

Course/s:
⛳ **THURLES**
Description: Wooded, Parkland
Number of Holes: 18 **Par:** 72
Yds: 6205

THURLESTONE

THURLESTONE GOLF CLUB, Thurlestone, Kingsbridge, **DEVON**, TQ7 3NZ, **ENGLAND**.
(T) 01548 560405
(W) www.thurlestonegc.co.uk

Membership: Members & Public
Size of Complex: 200 Acres

Contact/s:
● Club Secretary: Mr John Scott
● Professional: Mr Peter Laugher
  ☎ 01548 560715

Course/s:

🏌 **THURLESTONE**
Description: Open, Medium Length, Drains Well
Green Speed: Medium
Built: 1897 **Built On:** Sand/Soil
Number of Holes: 18 **Par:** 71
Yds: 6340 **F9 Yds:** 2724 **B9 Yds:** 3616
Prevailing Wind: South/West
Designer: Harry Shapland Colt

THURSO

THURSO GOLF CLUB, Newlands of Geise, Janetstown, Thurso, **HIGHLANDS**, KW14 7XD, **SCOTLAND**.
(T) 01847 893807

Contact/s:
● **Club Secretary:** Mr R Black
  ☎ 01847 892575

Course/s:

🏌 **THURSO**
Description: Parkland, Undulating
Built: 1893
Number of Holes: 18 **Par:** 69
Yds: 5853 **F9 Yds:** 2928 **B9 Yds:** 2925

TICKENHAM

TICKENHAM GOLF CENTRE, Clevedon Rd, Tickenham, Bristol, **BRISTOL**, BS21 6RY, **ENGLAND**.
(T) 01275 856626
(W) www.tickenhamgolf.co.uk

Membership: Members & Public

Contact/s:
● **Professional:** Mrs Sarah Jarrett

Course/s:

🏌 **TICKENHAM**
Description: Parkland, Undulating, Short, Drains Well, Ideal for the Elderly
Green Speed: Medium
Built: 1994 **Built On:** Clay/Sand
Number of Holes: 9 **Par:** 60
Par 3's: 6 **Par 4's:** 3
Yds: 3776 **F9 Yds:** 1888 **B9 Yds:** 1888
Designer: Andrew Sutcliffe
Further Information:
9 hole course can be played as an 18 hole course

TIDBURY GREEN

TIDBURY GREEN GOLF CLUB, Tilehse Lane, Tidbury Green, Solihull, **MIDLANDS (WEST)**, B90 1PT, **ENGLAND**.
(T) 01564 824460

Course/s:

🏌 **TIDBURY GREEN**
Number of Holes: 9 **Par:** 68
Yds: 4596 **F9 Yds:** 2298 **B9 Yds:** 2298

TIDWORTH GARRISON

TIDWORTH GARRISON GOLF CLUB, Bulford Rd, Tidworth, **WILTSHIRE**, SP9 7AF, **ENGLAND**.
(T) 01980 842301
(E) tidworth@garrison.fsnet.co.uk
Size of Complex: 153 Acres

Contact/s:
● **Professional:** Mr Terry Gosden
  ☎ 01980 842321

Course/s:

🏌 **TIDWORTH GARRISON**
Description: Undulating, Open, Medium Length, Drains Well, Ideal for the Elderly
Green Speed: Fast
Built: 1908 **Built On:** Chalk

Number of Holes: 18 **Par:** 70
Record: 63 (Scott Watson)
Yds: 6320 **F9 Yds:** 3123 **B9 Yds:** 3197
Prevailing Wind: South/West
Designer: Donald Steel
Further Information:
This course is situated on the edge of Salisbury Plain.

TILGATE FOREST

TILGATE FOREST GOLF CENTRE, Titmus Drive, Tilgate, Crawley, **SUSSEX (WEST)**, RH10 5EU, **ENGLAND**.
(T) 01293 530103

Membership: Members & Public
Size of Complex: 200 Acres

Contact/s:
● **Club Secretary:** Mr Alex Wilson
● **Professional:** Mr Sean Trussell

Course/s:

🏌 **TILGATE FOREST**
Description: Wooded, Parkland, Undulating, Sheltered, Medium Length, Tight, Tends to Flood, Ideal for the Elderly
Green Speed: Medium
Built: 1982 **Built On:** Clay
Number of Holes: 18 **Record:** 71
Prevailing Wind: South/East
Designer: Neil Coles, Brian Huggett

TILLICOULTRY

TILLICOULTRY GOLF CLUB, Alva Rd, Tillicoultry, **CLACKMANNANSHIRE**, FK13 6BL, **SCOTLAND**.
(T) 01259 750124

Course/s:

🏌 **TILLICOULTRY**
Number of Holes: 9

TILSWORTH

TILSWORTH GOLF CENTRE LTD, Dunstable Rd, Tilsworth, Leighton Buzzard, **BEDFORDSHIRE**, LU7 9PU, **ENGLAND**.
(T) 01525 210721
(E) info@tilsworthgolf.co.uk
(W) www.tilsworthgolf.co.uk

Membership: Members & Public
Size of Complex: 30 Acres

Contact/s:
● **Club Secretary:** Mr Alan Cant
● **Professional:** Mr Nick Webb
● **Pro Shop:** Mr Warwick Payne

Course/s:

🏌 **TILSWORTH GOLF CENTRE**
Description: Parkland, Undulating, Short, Tight
Green Speed: Fast
Built: 1975 **Built On:** Clay
Number of Holes: 18 **Par:** 69
Record: 65 (Nick Webb)
Par 3's: 5 **Par 4's:** 11 **Par 5's:** 2
Yds: 5306 **F9 Yds:** 2947 **B9 Yds:** 2359
Prevailing Wind: South/West
Further Information:
This course is ideal for beginners.

TINSLEY PARK

TINSLEY PARK GOLF CLUB, High Hazels Pk, Sheffield, **YORKSHIRE (SOUTH)**, S9 4PE, **ENGLAND**.
(T) 0114 2037435

Contact/s:
● **General Manager:** Mr T Hifield

Course/s:

🏌 **TINSLEY PARK MUNICIPAL**

Number of Holes: 18

TIPPERARY

TIPPERARY GOLF CLUB, Rathanny, Tipperary Town, **COUNTY TIPPERARY**, **IRELAND**.
(T) 06 251119

Course/s:

🏌 **TIPPERARY**
Number of Holes: 18

TIPPERARY (COUNTY)

COUNTY TIPPERARY GOLF COURSE, Dundrum Hse Hotel, Tipperary, Dundrum, **COUNTY TIPPERARY**, **IRELAND**.
(T) 062 71116

Course/s:

🏌 **TIPPERARY**
Number of Holes: 18
Designer: Philip Walton

TIVERTON

TIVERTON GOLF CLUB, Post Hill, Tiverton, **DEVON**, EX16 4NE, **ENGLAND**.
(T) 01884 252187

Membership: Members & Public
Size of Complex: 300 Acres

Contact/s:
● **Club Secretary:** Mrs Rosemary Parry
● **Professional:** Mr Michael Hawton

Course/s:

🏌 **TIVERTON**
Description: Wooded, Parkland, Sheltered, Open, Medium Length, Drains Well
Green Speed: Medium
Built: 1936 **Built On:** Clay
Number of Holes: 18 **Record:** 71 (Michael Hawton)
Prevailing Wind: South/West
Designer: James Braid

TOBERMORY

TOBERMORY GOLF CLUB, Isle Of Mull, Tobermory, **ARGYLL AND BUTE**, PA75 6PG, **SCOTLAND**.
(T) 01688 302338

Course/s:

🏌 **TOBERMORY**
Number of Holes: 9
Designer: David Adams

TODMORDEN

TODMORDEN GOLF CLUB, Rive Rocks, Cross Stone Rd, Todmorden, **YORKSHIRE (WEST)**, OL14 8RD, **ENGLAND**.
(T) 01706 812986

Contact/s:
● **Manager:** Mrs B Rudman

Course/s:

🏌 **TODMORDEN**
Number of Holes: 9

TOFT HOTEL

TOFT HOTEL GOLF COURSE, Toft, Bourne, **LINCOLNSHIRE**, PE10 0XX, **ENGLAND**.
(T) 01778 590616

Membership: Members & Public
Size of Complex: 95 Acres

Contact/s:
● **Club Secretary:** Mr Neil Frame
  ☎ 01778 590614
● **Professional:** Mr Mark Jackson

Course/s:

TOFT HOTEL
Description: Championship, Parkland, Hilltop, Undulating, Open
Green Speed: Medium
Built: 1984 **Built On:** Soil
Number of Holes: 18 **Par:** 72
Par 3's: 4 **Par 4's:** 10 **Par 5's:** 4
Yds: 6486
Prevailing Wind: West
Designer: Fitton

TOLLADINE

TOLLADINE GOLF CLUB, Tolladine Rd, Worcester, **WORCESTERSHIRE**, WR4 9BA, **ENGLAND**.
(T) 01905 21074

Course/s:

TOLLADINE
Number of Holes: 9

TOOT HILL

TOOT HILL GOLF CLUB, School Rd, Toot Hill, Ongar, **ESSEX**, CM5 9PU, **ENGLAND**.
(T) 01277 364509

Contact/s:

● **Owner:** Mrs C Cameron

Course/s:

TOOT HILL
Number of Holes: 18
Designer: Martin Gillett

TOP MEADOW

TOP MEADOW GOLF CLUB, Fen Lane, North Ockendon, Upminster, **ESSEX**, RM14 3PR, **ENGLAND**.
(T) 01708 852239

Membership: Members & Public

Contact/s:

● **Club Secretary:** Mr Danny Stock
● **Professional:** Mr Roy Porter

Course/s:

TOP MEADOW
Description: Open, Medium Length, Tight, Drains Well, Ideal for the Elderly
Green Speed: Medium
Built: 1990 **Built On:** Clay
Number of Holes: 18
Designer: Burns, Stock

TORPHIN HILL

TORPHIN HILL GOLF CLUB, Professional Shop, Torphin Rd, Edinburgh, **EDINBURGH (CITY OF)**, EH13 0PG, **SCOTLAND**.
(T) 0131 4417166

Contact/s:

● **Treasurer:** Mr A Hepburn

Course/s:

TORPHIN HILL
Number of Holes: 18

TORPHINS

TORPHINS GOLF CLUB, Bog Rd, Torphins, Banchory, **ABERDEENSHIRE**, AB31 4JU, **SCOTLAND**.
(T) 01339 882115

Membership: Members & Public

Contact/s:

● **Club Secretary:** Mr Stuart MacGregor
  ☎ 01339 882402

Course/s:

TORPHINS
Description: Parkland, Undulating, Short,

Tight, Drains Well
Green Speed: Medium
Built: 1896 **Built On:** Soil
Number of Holes: 9
Prevailing Wind: East
Further Information:
The course has magnificent views of the highlands.

TORQUAY

TORQUAY GOLF CLUB, 30 Petitor Rd, St. Marychurch, Torquay, **DEVON**, TQ1 4QF, **ENGLAND**.
(T) 01803 314591

Membership: Members & Public
Size of Complex: 150 Acres

Contact/s:

● **Club Secretary:** Mr Barry Long
● **Professional:** Mr Stuart Disney
  ☎ 01803 329113
● **Book Lessons:** Mr Martin Ruth

Course/s:

TORQUAY
Description: Championship, Wooded, Parkland, Cliff Top, Open, Medium Length, Tight, Drains Well, Tends to Flood
Green Speed: Medium
Built: 1910 **Built On:** Clay
Number of Holes: 18 **Record:** 63 (Martin Ruth)
Prevailing Wind: South/West
Further Information:
Beautiful views overlooking Babbacombe Bay.

TORRANCE HOUSE

TORRANCE HOUSE GOLF CLUB, Strathaven Rd, East Kilbride, Glasgow, **GLASGOW (CITY OF)**, G75 0QZ, **SCOTLAND**.
(T) 01355 249720

Course/s:

TORRANCE HOUSE
Number of Holes: 18

TORRINGTON

GREAT TORRINGTON GOLF CLUB, Weare Trees, Torrington, **DEVON**, EX38 7EZ, **ENGLAND**.
(T) 01805 622229

Membership: Members & Public

Contact/s:

● **Club Secretary:** Mrs Jeanette M Cudmore

Course/s:

TORRINGTON
Description: Heath Land, Open, Short, Tight, Drains Well, Ideal for the Elderly
Green Speed: Fast
Built: 1937 **Built On:** Soil
Number of Holes: 18 **Par:** 64
Par 3's: 8 **Par 4's:** 10
Yds: 4285 **F9 Yds:** 2110 **B9 Yds:** 2175
Prevailing Wind: West
Further Information:
Torrington is an easy walking course with breathtaking views.

TORWOODLEE

TORWOODLEE GOLF CLUB, Edinburgh Rd, Galashiels, **SCOTTISH BORDERS**, TD1 2NE, **SCOTLAND**.
(T) 01896 752260

Contact/s:

● **Club Secretary:** Mr George Donnelly
● **Book Tee Times:** Mr David Hogarth

Course/s:

TORWOODLEE
Description: Parkland, Undulating, Sheltered, Open, Medium Length, Drains Well
Green Speed: Medium
Built: 1895 **Built On:** Soil
Number of Holes: 18 **Par:** 69
Par 3's: 5 **Par 4's:** 11 **Par 5's:** 2
Yds: 6021 **F9 Yds:** 3000 **B9 Yds:** 3021
Prevailing Wind: East
Designer: William Park

TOURNERBURY GOLF CTRE

TOURNERBURY GOLF CENTRE, Tournerbury Lane, Hayling Island, **HAMPSHIRE**, PO11 9DL, **ENGLAND**.
(T) 023 92462266

Membership: Members & Public

Contact/s:

● **Professional:** Mr Phillip Bryden
● **Pro Shop:** Mr Robert Brown

Course/s:

TOURNERBURY
Description: Parkland, Open, Medium Length, Drains Well, Ideal for the Elderly
Green Speed: Medium
Built: 1991
Number of Holes: 9 **Par:** 70 **Record:** 32 (Phillip Bryden)
Par 3's: 3 **Par 4's:** 4 **Par 5's:** 2
Yds: 5912 **F9 Yds:** 2956 **B9 Yds:** 2956
Prevailing Wind: South/West
Further Information:
9 hole course can be played as an 18 hole course

TOWERLANDS

TOWERLANDS GOLF CLUB, Panfield Rd, Braintree, **ESSEX**, CM7 5BJ, **ENGLAND**.
(T) 01376 326802

Course/s:

TOWERLANDS
Number of Holes: 9
Designer: G Shiels

TOWNELEY MUNICIPAL

TOWNELEY MUNICIPAL GOLF COURSE, Todmorden Rd, Burnley, **LANCASHIRE**, BB11 3ED, **ENGLAND**.
(T) 01282 438473

Membership: Public

Contact/s:

● **Club Secretary:** Mr Nigel Clarke
● **Pro Shop:** Mr Derrick Garside

Course/s:

TOWNELEY MUNICIPAL
Description: Parkland, Undulating, Sheltered, Open, Medium Length, Drains Well
Green Speed: Medium
Built: 1932 **Built On:** Soil
Number of Holes: 18 **Par:** 70
Par 3's: 4 **Par 4's:** 12 **Par 5's:** 2
Yds: 5810 **F9 Yds:** 2999 **B9 Yds:** 2811
Prevailing Wind: West
Further Information:
This course has been built on the grounds of a stately home.

TOWNLEY HALL

TOWNLEY HALL GOLF COURSE & DRIVING RANGE, Townley Hall, Tullyallen, **COUNTY LOUTH**, **IRELAND**.
(T) 041 9842229

Membership: Members & Public

Size of Complex: 43 Acres

Contact/s:
- **Owner:** Mr John Gilmore

Course/s:

TOWNLEY HALL
Description: Wooded, Parkland, Sheltered, Medium Length, Drains Well
Green Speed: Medium
Built: 1994 **Built On:** Soil
Number of Holes: 9 **Par:** 71
Yds: 5865 **F9 Yds:** 3000 **B9 Yds:** 2865
Designer: Philip Carolan
Further Information:
The course has 2 reservoirs. 9 hole course can be played as an 18 hole course

---

TRACY PARK

TRACY PARK GOLF & COUNTRY CLUB, Bath Rd, Wick, Bristol, **BRISTOL**, BS1 5BJ, **ENGLAND**.
(T) 01179 374288
(E) golf@tracypark.com
(W) www.tracypark.com

Membership: Members & Public
Size of Complex: 240 Acres

Contact/s:
- **Club Secretary:** Mr David Knipe
- **Professional:** Mr Tim Thompson-Green

Course/s:

CROMWELL
Description: Championship, Parkland, Hilltop, Undulating, Long, Tight, Drains Well
Green Speed: Medium/Fast
Built: 1976 **Built On:** Clay/Soil
Number of Holes: 18 **Par:** 70
Par 3's: 5 **Par 4's:** 10 **Par 5's:** 3
Yds: 6020 **F9 Yds:** 3144 **B9 Yds:** 2876
Prevailing Wind: South/West
Designer: Golf Design
Further Information:
This challenging course has stunning views of the surrounding countryside.

CROWN
Description: Championship, Parkland, Open, Long, Drains Well, Ideal for the Elderly
Green Speed: Medium
Built: 1976 **Built On:** Clay/Soil
Number of Holes: 18 **Par:** 70
Par 3's: 4 **Par 4's:** 12 **Par 5's:** 2
Yds: 6443 **F9 Yds:** 3352 **B9 Yds:** 3091
Prevailing Wind: South/West
Designer: Golf Design
Further Information:
Mentioned in the Doomsday Book, this course is home to spectacular 400 year old trees.

TRADITIONS GOLF COURSE

AMERICAN GOLF CORPORATION, Pyrford Rd, Pyrford, Woking, **SURREY**, GU22 8UE, **ENGLAND**.
(T) 01932 350355
(E) traditions@americangolf.uk.com
(W) www.americangolf.com

Membership: Members & Public
Size of Complex: 189 Acres

Contact/s:
- **Professional:** Mr Darren Brewer
- **Pro Shop:**
  ☎ 01932 350353

Course/s:

TRADITIONS
Description: Championship, Links, Wooded, Parkland, Undulating, Open, Medium Length, Drains Well, Ideal for the

---

Elderly
Green Speed: Medium
Built: 1999 **Built On:** Soil
Number of Holes: 18 **Par:** 71
Record: 67 (Darren Brewer)
Par 3's: 4 **Par 4's:** 11 **Par 5's:** 3
Yds: 6304 **F9 Yds:** 3112 **B9 Yds:** 3192
Prevailing Wind: North
Designer: Peter Alliss
Further Information:
This is a truly challenging course.

TRAIGH

TRAIGH GOLF COURSE, Traigh, Arisaig, **HIGHLANDS**, PH39 4NT, **SCOTLAND**.
(T) 01687 450337
(W) www.traighgolf.co.uk

Contact/s:
- **Manager:** Mr W Henderson
  ☎ 01687 450645

Course/s:

TRAIGH
Number of Holes: 9 **Par:** 68
Yds: 4912 **F9 Yds:** 2456 **B9 Yds:** 2456
Designer: John Salverson
Further Information:
9 hole course can be played as an 18 hole course

TRALEE

TRALEE GOLF CLUB, West Barrow, Ardfert, **COUNTY KERRY**, **IRELAND**.
(T) 066 7136379

Course/s:

TRALEE
Number of Holes: 18
Designer: Arnold Palmer

TRAMORE

TRAMORE GOLF CLUB, Newtown Hill, Tramore, **COUNTY WATERFORD**, **IRELAND**.
(T) 051 386170
(E) tragolf@iol.ie
(W) www.tramoregolfclub.com

Contact/s:
- **Professional:** Mr Derry Kiely

Course/s:

TRAMORE
Number of Holes: 18 **Par:** 72
Yds: 6600 **F9 Yds:** 3287 **B9 Yds:** 3313
Designer: Captain Tippet

TREDEGAR & RHYMNEY

TREDEGAR AND RHYMNEY GOLF CLUB, Cwmtysswg, Rhymney, Tredegar, **BLAENAU GWENT**, NP2 3BQ, **WALES**.
(T) 01685 840743 & 843400

Course/s:

TREDEGAR & RHYMNEY
Number of Holes: 9

TREDEGAR PARK

TREDEGAR PARK GOLF CLUB LTD, Parc-Y-Brain Rd, Rogerstone, Newport, **NEWPORT**, NP10 9TG, **WALES**.
(T) 01633 894433
(E) tpgc@btinternet.com

Membership: Members & Public

Contact/s:
- **Club Secretary:** Mr Anthony Trickett
- **Professional:** Merfyn Morgan
  ☎ 01633 894517

Course/s:

TREDEGAR PARK GOLF
Description: Parkland, Undulating, Medium Length
Green Speed: Medium
Built: 1999
Number of Holes: 18
Designer: Robert Sandow

TREFLOYNE

TREFLOYNE GOLF COURSE, Trefloyne Pk, Trefloyne Lane, Penally, Tenby, **PEMBROKESHIRE**, SA70 7RG, **WALES**.
(T) 01834 842165
(W) www.walesholidays.co.uk/trefloyne.html

Membership: Members & Public
Size of Complex: 150 Acres

Contact/s:
- **Professional:** Mr Steven Laidler

Course/s:

TREFLOYNE
Description: Parkland, Undulating, Open, Medium Length, Drains Well, Ideal for the Elderly
Green Speed: Medium
Built: 1996 **Built On:** Soil
Number of Holes: 18 **Par:** 72
Par 3's: 4 **Par 4's:** 10 **Par 5's:** 4
Yds: 6635 **F9 Yds:** 3504 **B9 Yds:** 3131
Prevailing Wind: North
Designer: F Gilman
Further Information:
Mature course with challenging holes and excellent views of Carnavon Bay.

TREGENNA CASTLE

TREGENNA CASTLE HOTEL, GOLF & COUNTRY CLUB, St. Ives, **CORNWALL**, TR26 2DE, **ENGLAND**.
(T) 01736 797381

Course/s:

TREGENNA CASTLE
Description: Parkland
Built: 1982
Number of Holes: 18 **Par:** 60
Further Information:
Views of St Ives town.

TRELOY

TRELOY GOLF CLUB, Newquay, **CORNWALL**, TR8 4JN, **ENGLAND**.
(T) 01637 878554

Contact/s:
- **Club Secretary:** Mr Jim Reid

Course/s:

TRELOY
Description: Parkland, Short
Number of Holes: 9 **Par:** 32
Yds: 2143
Designer: Robert Sandow
Further Information:
This is an executive golf course.

TRENT LOCK

TRENT LOCK GOLF CENTRE, Lock Lane, Sawley, Long Eaton, Nottingham, **NOTTINGHAMSHIRE**, NG10 2FY, **ENGLAND**.
(T) 0115 9464398

Membership: Members & Public

Contact/s:
- **Professional:** Mr J Clay
- **Pro Shop:** Mr Mark Taylor

Course/s:

TRENT LOCK GOLF CENTRE 18 HOLE
Description: Parkland, Open, Medium

Length, Tends to Flood
Green Speed: Medium
Built: 1990 **Built On:** Clay
Number of Holes: 18 **Par:** 69
Par 3's: 5 **Par 4's:** 11 **Par 5's:** 2
Yds: 5717
Designer: E McCausland
Further Information:
A flat course.

🍂 **TRENT LOCK GOLF CENTRE 9 HOLE**
Description: Tight
Number of Holes: 9 **Par:** 36
Par 3's: 2 **Par 4's:** 5 **Par 5's:** 2
Yds: 2908

TRENT PARK GOLF CLUB

AMERICAN GOLF CORPORATION,
Bramley Rd, Southgate, London, **LONDON
(GREATER)**, N14 4UT, **ENGLAND**.
(T) 020 8367 4653
(E) trentpark@americangolf.uk.com
(W) www.americangolf.com

Membership: Members & Public/Public

Contact/s:
● **Professional:** Mr Simon Squires
● **Pro Shop:**
  ☎ 020 8363 8909

Course/s:
🍂 **TRENT PARK**
Description: Wooded, Parkland, Valley,
Undulating, Tight, Drains Well
Green Speed: Medium
Built: 1972 **Built On:** Clay
Number of Holes: 18 **Par:** 70
Yds: 6200 **F9 Yds:** 3165 **B9 Yds:** 3035
Prevailing Wind: South
Designer: D McGibbon

TRENTHAM

TRENTHAM GOLF CLUB, Barlaston Old Rd,
Stoke-on-Trent, **STAFFORDSHIRE**, ST4 8HB,
ENGLAND.
(T) 01782 658109
(W) www.trenthamgolf.org

Contact/s:
● **Club Secretary:** Mr R N Portas
● **Professional:** Mr Sandy Wilson

Course/s:
🍂 **TRENTHAM**
Number of Holes: 18 **Par:** 72
Yds: 6619 **F9 Yds:** 3327 **B9 Yds:** 3292
Designer: Charles Hugh Alison, Harry
Shapland Colt

TRETHORNE

TRETHORNE GOLF CLUB, Kennards Hse,
Launceston, **CORNWALL**, PL15 8QE,
ENGLAND.
(T) 01566 86903

Membership: Members & Public
Size of Complex: 150 Acres

Contact/s:
● **Club Secretary:** Mr Mike Davey
● **Professional:** Mr Mark Boundy

Course/s:
🍂 **TRETHORNE**
Description: Parkland, Undulating, Long
Green Speed: Medium
Built: 1993 **Built On:** Sand/Soil
Number of Holes: 18 **Par:** 71
Yds: 6432 **F9 Yds:** 3163 **B9 Yds:** 3269
Designer: Frank Frayne

TREVOSE

TREVOSE GOLF & COUNTRY CLUB,

Constantine Bay, Padstow, **CORNWALL**,
PL28 8JB, **ENGLAND**.
(T) 01841 520208
(E) reception@trevose-gc.co.uk
(W) www.trevose-gc.co.uk

Membership: Members & Public

Contact/s:
● **Club Secretary:** Mr Patrick O'Shea
  ☎ 01841 520733
● **Professional:** Mr Gary Alliss
  ☎ 01841 520261

Course/s:
🍂 **CHAMPIONSHIP**
Number of Holes: 18 **Par:** 71
Par 3's: 4 **Par 4's:** 11 **Par 5's:** 3
Yds: 6435 **F9 Yds:** 3167 **B9 Yds:** 3268
Designer: Harry Shapland Colt

🍂 **NEW**
Number of Holes: 9 **Par:** 35
Par 3's: 2 **Par 4's:** 6 **Par 5's:** 1
Yds: 3031
Designer: Peter Alliss, T Bennett, P
Gannon
Further Information:
Can be played as an 18 hole.

🍂 **SHORT**
Built: 1970
Number of Holes: 9 **Par:** 29
Par 3's: 7 **Par 4's:** 2
Yds: 1360

TROON (ROYAL)

ROYAL TROON GOLF CLUB, Craigend Rd,
Troon, **AYRSHIRE (SOUTH)**, KA10 6EP,
SCOTLAND.
(T) 01292 311555
(W) www.royaltroon.com

Membership: Public

Contact/s:
● **Club Secretary:** Mr M J Chandler
● **Professional:** Mr R B Anderson
  ☎ 01292 313281

Course/s:
🍂 **OLD**
Description: Championship, Links, Open,
Long, Drains Well
Built: 1878 **Built On:** Sand
Number of Holes: 18 **Par:** 71
Record: 64 (Tiger Woods)
Par 3's: 4 **Par 4's:** 11 **Par 5's:** 3
Yds: 6641 **F9 Yds:** 3260 **B9 Yds:** 3381
Prevailing Wind: North/West
Designer: William Fernie 🏆

🍂 **PAR 3**
Description: Short
Number of Holes: 9 **Par:** 27
Par 3's: 9
Yds: 1191

🍂 **PORTLAND**
Description: Medium Length
Built: 1895
Number of Holes: 18 **Par:** 71
Par 3's: 5 **Par 4's:** 9 **Par 5's:** 4
Yds: 6289 **F9 Yds:** 3128 **B9 Yds:** 3161

TROON MUNICIPAL

TROON MUNICIPAL GOLF COURSE,
Harling Drive, Troon, **AYRSHIRE (SOUTH)**,
KA10 6NE, **SCOTLAND**.
(T) 01292 312464

Membership: Public

Contact/s:
● **Manager:** Mr J McCloughlin

Course/s:
🍂 **DARLEY**

Number of Holes: 18

🍂 **FULLARTON**
Number of Holes: 18

🍂 **LOCHGREEN**
Number of Holes: 18

TROON PORTLAND

TROON PORTLAND GOLF CLUB, 1 Crosbie
Rd, Troon, **AYRSHIRE (SOUTH)**, KA10 6HE,
SCOTLAND.
(T) 01292 313488

Contact/s:
● **Club Secretary:** Mr G Clark

Course/s:
🍂 **COURSE #1**
Number of Holes: 18
Yds: 6274

TRURO

TRURO GOLF CLUB, Tresawls Rd, Treliske,
Truro, **CORNWALL**, TR1 3LG, **ENGLAND**.
(T) 01872 278684

Contact/s:
● **Professional:** Mr Nigel Bicknell

Course/s:
🍂 **TRURO**
Description: Parkland, Undulating
Built: 1937
Number of Holes: 18 **Par:** 66
Designer: Charles Hugh Alison, Harry
Shapland Colt, J S F Morrison
Further Information:
Views over Truro and surrounding
countryside.

TUAM

TUAM GOLF CLUB, Barnacurragh, Tuam,
COUNTY GALWAY, **IRELAND**.
(T) 093 28993

Course/s:
🍂 **TUAM**
Number of Holes: 18
Designer: Edward Hackett

TUBBERCURRY

TUBBERCURRY GOLF CLUB, Tubbercurry,
COUNTY SLIGO, **IRELAND**.
(T) 071 85849

Course/s:
🍂 **TOBERCURRY**
Number of Holes: 9
Designer: Edward Hackett

TUDOR PARK

**MARRIOTT TUDOR PARK HOTEL &
COUNTRY CLUB,** Ashford Rd, Bearsted,
Maidstone, **KENT**, ME14 4NQ, **ENGLAND**.
(T) 01622 734334

Membership: Members & Public

Contact/s:
● **Club Secretary:** Mr J Ladbrook
● **Professional:** Mr Nick McNally
● **Book Tee Times:** Mr Simon Nairn

Course/s:
🍂 **TUDOR PARK**
Description: Wooded, Undulating,
Sheltered, Medium Length, Drains Well,
Ideal for the Elderly
Green Speed: Medium
Built: 1988
Number of Holes: 18 **Par:** 70
Par 3's: 4 **Par 4's:** 12 **Par 5's:** 2
Yds: 5988 **Designer:** Donald Steel

TULFARRIS HOUSE

TULFARRIS HOTEL & GOLF RESORT, Blessington, **COUNTY WICKLOW, IRELAND.**
(T) 045 867555

Contact/s:
● **Marketing Manager:** Ms Catherine Hayes

Course/s:
🦢 **TULFARRIS HOUSE**
 Number of Holes: 18 **Par:** 72
 Yds: 7116 **F9 Yds:** 3632 **B9 Yds:** 3484
 Designer: P Merrigan

TULLAMORE

TULLAMORE GOLF CLUB, Brookfield, Tullamore, **COUNTY OFFALY, IRELAND.**
(T) 050 623316

Course/s:
🦢 **TULLAMORE**
 Number of Holes: 18
 Designer: James Braid, Paddy Merrigan

TULLIALLAN

TULLIALLAN GOLF CLUB, Clubhouse, Kincardine, Alloa, **CLACKMANNANSHIRE,** FK10 4BB, **SCOTLAND.**
(T) 01259 730396

Contact/s:
● **Administrator:** Mr Noel Raleigh

Course/s:
🦢 **TULLIALLAN**
 Number of Holes: 18 **Par:** 69
 Yds: 5459 **F9 Yds:** 2750 **B9 Yds:** 2709

TUNBRIDGE WELLS

TUNBRIDGE WELLS GOLF CLUB (THE), Langton Rd, Tunbridge Wells, **KENT,** TN4 8XH, **ENGLAND.**
(T) 01892 536918

Contact/s:
● **Club Secretary:** Mr R Mealing
● **Professional:** Mr Mike Barton

Course/s:
🦢 **TUNBRIDGE WELLS**
 Description: Parkland
 Built: 1889
 Number of Holes: 9 **Par:** 32
 Yds: 2355 **F9 Yds:** 2355
 Further Information:
 9 hole course can be played as an 18 hole course

TUNSHILL

TUNSHILL GOLF CLUB LTD, Tunshill Lane, Milnrow, Rochdale, **LANCASHIRE,** OL16 3TS, **ENGLAND.**
(T) 01706 342095

Contact/s:
● **Club Secretary:** Mr G Hurst
 ☎ 01706 650566

Course/s:
🦢 **TUNSHILL**
 Number of Holes: 18 **Par:** 70
 Par 3's: 6 **Par 4's:** 8 **Par 5's:** 4
 Yds: 5745 **F9 Yds:** 2863 **B9 Yds:** 2882

TURNBERRY

WESTIN TURNBERRY RESORT (THE), Turnberry, Girvan, **AYRSHIRE (SOUTH),** KA26 9LT, **SCOTLAND.**
(T) 01655 331000
(E) turnberry@westin.com
(W) www.turnberry.co.uk

Contact/s:
● **Marketing Executive:** Mr Jamie Paxton
 ☎ 01655 334036

Course/s:
🦢 **AILSA**
 Number of Holes: 18 **Par:** 70
 Yds: 6976 **F9 Yds:** 3494 **B9 Yds:** 3482
 Designer: Alistair MacKenzie, L Ross
 Further Information:
 The Ailsa is a course that Colin Montgomerie called 'The finest links course in the world.' 🏆

🦢 **ARRAN ACADEMY**
 Number of Holes: 9

🦢 **CULZEAN PITCH AND PUTT**
 Number of Holes: 12

🦢 **KINTYRE**
 Number of Holes: 18 **Par:** 72
 Yds: 6976 **F9 Yds:** 3215 **B9 Yds:** 3638
 Designer: Alistair MacKenzie, L Ross, Donald Steel

TURNHOUSE

TURNHOUSE GOLF CLUB LTD, 154 Turnhouse Rd, Edinburgh, **EDINBURGH (CITY OF),** EH12 0AD, **SCOTLAND.**
(T) 0131 3391014
(E) turnhouse@aol.com
(W) www.turnhousegolfclub.co.uk

Contact/s:
● **Club Secretary:** Mr Archibald Brown Hay
● **Professional:** Mr John Murray

Course/s:
🦢 **TURNHOUSE**
 Number of Holes: 18 **Par:** 69
 Yds: 6155 **F9 Yds:** 3187 **B9 Yds:** 2968
 Designer: James Braid

TURRIFF

TURRIFF GOLF CLUB, Rosehall, Turriff, **ABERDEENSHIRE,** AB53 4HD, **SCOTLAND.**
(T) 01888 562982
(E) grace@turriffgolf.sol.co.uk
(W) www.turriffgolfclub.free-online.co.uk

Membership: Members & Public

Contact/s:
● **Professional:** Mr Robin Smith
 ☎ 01888 53025
● **Pro Shop:**
 ☎ 01888 563025

Course/s:
🦢 **TURRIFF**
 Description: Wooded, Parkland
 Green Speed: Medium
 Built: 1896 **Built On:** Soil
 Number of Holes: 18 **Par:** 70
 Par 3's: 5 **Par 4's:** 11 **Par 5's:** 2
 Yds: 5899 **F9 Yds:** 3165 **B9 Yds:** 2734
 Further Information:
 The course is situated next to a river.

TURTON

TURTON GOLF CLUB LTD, Chapeltown Rd, Bromley Cross, Bolton, **LANCASHIRE,** BL7 9QH, **ENGLAND.**
(T) 01204 852235

Membership: Members & Public

Contact/s:
● **Club Secretary:** Mr D Fairclough

Course/s:
🦢 **TURTON**
 Description: Parkland, Hilltop, Open, Medium Length, Drains Well, Ideal for the Elderly
 Green Speed: Fast
 Built: 1908 **Built On:** Clay
 Number of Holes: 18 **Par:** 70
 Par 3's: 4 **Par 4's:** 12 **Par 5's:** 2
 Yds: 6124 **F9 Yds:** 2922 **B9 Yds:** 3202
 Prevailing Wind: West
 Designer: A Herd

TURVEY

TURVEY GOLF & COUNTRY CLUB PLC, Turvey Hse Hotel, Turvey Ave, Donabute, Dublin, **COUNTY DUBLIN, IRELAND.**
(T) 01 8435169

Membership: Members & Public

Contact/s:
● **Club Secretary:** Ms Moira Hegarty

Course/s:
🦢 **TURVEY**
 Description: Wooded, Parkland, Undulating, Open, Long, Drains Well
 Green Speed: Medium
 Built: 1994
 Number of Holes: 18
 Designer: P McGuirk

TWICKENHAM PARK

TWICKENHAM PARK GOLF COURSE, Staines Rd, Twickenham, **LONDON (GREATER),** TW2 5JD, **ENGLAND.**
(T) 020 87831698

Course/s:
🦢 **TWICKENHAM GOLF CENTRE**
 Number of Holes: 9

TYDD ST GILES

TYDD ST GILES GOLF & LEISURE LTD, Kirkgate, Tydd St. Giles, Wisbech, **CAMBRIDGESHIRE,** PE13 5NZ, **ENGLAND.**
(T) 01945 871007
(E) enquiries@tyddstgilesgolfcentre.com
(W) www.tyddstgilesgolfcentre.com

Membership: Members & Public
Size of Complex: 140 Acres

Contact/s:
● **Professional:** Mr Martin Perkins
● **Book Tee Times:** Mrs Carol Fowler

Course/s:
🦢 **TYDD ST GILES**
 Description: Open, Medium Length, Drains Well **Green Speed:** Fast
 Built: 1995 **Built On:** Soil
 Number of Holes: 18 **Par:** 70
 Par 3's: 4 **Par 4's:** 12 **Par 5's:** 2
 Yds: 5880 **F9 Yds:** 2940 **B9 Yds:** 2940
 Designer: Adrian Hurst
 Further Information:
 Unique setting in the heart of the Fens.

TYLNEY PARK

TYLNEY PARK GOLF CLUB, Rotherwick, Hook, **HAMPSHIRE,** RG27 9AY, **ENGLAND.**
(T) 01256 762079

Contact/s:
● **Professional:** Mr Chris De Bruin

Course/s:
🦢 **TYLNEY PARK**
 Number of Holes: 18 **Par:** 70
 Yds: 6109 **F9 Yds:** 2938 **B9 Yds:** 3171

TYNEDALE

TYNEDALE GOLF CLUB, Tyne Green, Hexham, **NORTHUMBERLAND,** NE46 3HQ, **ENGLAND.**

(T) 01434 608154
(W) www.tynedale-golf-club.co.uk

Membership: Members & Public

Contact/s:
- **Club Secretary:** Mr S Plember
- **Professional:** Mr Ian Waugh

Course/s:
🏌 **TYNEDALE**
  Description: Parkland, Valley, Undulating, Sheltered, Medium Length, Drains Well, Ideal for the Elderly
  Green Speed: Medium
  Built: 1908 **Built On:** Soil
  Number of Holes: 9 **Par:** 69
  Par 3's: 2 **Par 4's:** 6 **Par 5's:** 1
  Yds: 5383 **F9 Yds:** 2777 **B9 Yds:** 2606
  Prevailing Wind: East
  Further Information:
  9 hole course can be played as an 18 hole course. River runs through some holes.

TYNEMOUTH

TYNEMOUTH GOLF CLUB LTD, North Shields, **TYNE AND WEAR,** NE30 2ER, **ENGLAND.**
(T) 0191 2574578

Course/s:
🏌 **TYNEMOUTH**
  Number of Holes: 18
  Designer: William Park

TYNESIDE

TYNESIDE GOLF CLUB LTD, Westfield Lane, Ryton, **TYNE AND WEAR,** NE40 3QE, **ENGLAND.**
(T) 0191 4132742

Contact/s:
- **Project Manager:** Mr Michael Andrew Brown

Course/s:
🏌 **TYNESIDE**
  Number of Holes: 18
  Designer: Harry Shapland Colt

TYRRELLS WOOD

TYRRELLS WOOD GOLF CLUB, Tyrrells Wood, Leatherhead, **SURREY,** KT22 8QP, **ENGLAND.**
(T) 01372 376025

Contact/s:
- **Manager:** Mr C Kidd

Course/s:
🏌 **TYRRELLS WOOD**
  Number of Holes: 18
  Designer: James Braid

TYTHERINGTON

TYTHERINGTON GOLF & COUNTRY CLUB, Manchester Rd, Macclesfield, **CHESHIRE,** SK10 2JP, **ENGLAND.**
(T) 01625 506000

Contact/s:
- **Professional:** Mr Gordon McLeod

Course/s:
🏌 **THE TYTHERINGTON CLUB**
  Description: Wooded, Parkland
  Built: 1986
  Number of Holes: 18 **Par:** 72
  Designer: Patrick Dawson, Peter Alliss
  Further Information:
  Headquarters of the Womens European Tour.

UFFORD PARK

UFFORD PARK HOTEL GOLF & LEISURE, Yarmouth Rd, Ufford, Woodbridge, **SUFFOLK,** IP13 6EP, **ENGLAND.**
(T) 01394 383555
(E) uffordparkltd@btinternet.com
(W) www.uffordpark.co.uk

Contact/s:
- **Professional:** Mr Stuart Robertson
  ☎ 01394 382836

Course/s:
🏌 **UFFORD PARK**
  Description: Parkland, Undulating, Drains Well
  Built: 1991
  Number of Holes: 18 **Par:** 71
  Yds: 6485 **F9 Yds:** 3340 **B9 Yds:** 3145
  Designer: Philip Pilgrim
  Further Information:
  Overlooks Deben Valley.

ULLAPOOL

ULLAPOOL GOLF CLUB, North Rd, Morefield, Ullapool, **HIGHLANDS,** IV26 2TH, **SCOTLAND.**
(T) 01854 613323
(E) info@ullapool.golf.co.uk
(W) www.ullapool.golf.co.uk

Membership: Members & Public

Contact/s:
- **Club Secretary:** Mr Alan Paterson
  ☎ 01854 612609

Course/s:
🏌 **ULLAPOOL**
  Description: Links, Parkland, Undulating
  Green Speed: Fast
  Built: 1997
  Number of Holes: 9 **Par:** 70
  Further Information:
  Views out to the Summer Isles. 9 hole course can be played as an 18 hole course

ULLESTHORPE

ULLESTHORPE GOLF CLUB, Frolesworth Rd, Ullesthorpe, Lutterworth, **LEICESTERSHIRE,** LE17 5BZ, **ENGLAND.**
(T) 01455 209023

Course/s:
🏌 **ULLESTHORPE**
  Number of Holes: 18

ULVERSTON

ULVERSTON GOLF CLUB, Bardsea, Ulverston, **CUMBRIA,** LA12 9QJ, **ENGLAND.**
(T) 01229 582824

Contact/s:
- **Professional:** Mr Mike Smith

Course/s:
🏌 **ULVERSTON**
  Description: Parkland, Undulating
  Built: 1909
  Number of Holes: 18 **Par:** 71
  Designer: Harry Shapland Colt

UPAVON

UPAVON GOLF CLUB, Andover Rd, Upavon, Pewsey, **WILTSHIRE,** SN9 6BQ, **ENGLAND.**
(T) 01980 630281

Membership: Members & Public

Contact/s:
- **Club Secretary:** Mr Les Mitchell
- **Professional:** Mr Richard Blake

Course/s:
🏌 **UPAVON**
  Description: Hilltop, Undulating, Open, Medium Length, Drains Well
  Green Speed: Medium
  Built: 1995 **Built On:** Chalk
  Number of Holes: 18 **Par:** 71
  Record: 69 (Andy Beal)
  Par 3's: 5 **Par 4's:** 9 **Par 5's:** 4
  Yds: 6402 **F9 Yds:** 3279 **B9 Yds:** 3123
  Prevailing Wind: South/West
  Designer: Richard Blake
  Further Information:
  The 18th hole is a challenging par 3 across a deep valley.

UPCHURCH RIVER VALLEY

UPCHURCH RIVER VALLEY GOLF COURSE, Oak Lane, Upchurch, Sittingbourne, **KENT,** ME9 7AY, **ENGLAND.**
(T) 01634 379592

Membership: Members & Public

Contact/s:
- **Professional:** Mr Roger Cornwell

Course/s:
🏌 **RIVER VALLEY 9 HOLE**
  Description: Short, Ideal for the Elderly
  Number of Holes: 9
  Prevailing Wind: South/West
  Further Information:
  9 hole course can be played as an 18 hole course

🏌 **UPCHURCH RIVER VALLEY**
  Description: Parkland, Undulating, Open, Medium Length, Drains Well
  Green Speed: Medium **Built On:** Chalk
  Number of Holes: 18
  Prevailing Wind: South/West
  Designer: David Smart

UPHALL

UPHALL GOLF CLUB, Uphall, Broxburn, **LOTHIAN (WEST),** EH52 6JT, **SCOTLAND.**
(T) 01506 855553

Course/s:
🏌 **UPHALL**
  Number of Holes: 18

UPMINSTER

UPMINSTER GOLF CLUB, 114 Hall Lane, Upminster, **ESSEX,** RM14 1AU, **ENGLAND.**
(T) 01708 222788

Contact/s:
- **Financial Director:** Mr John Richard Potticary

Course/s:
🏌 **UPMINSTER**
  Number of Holes: 18 **Par:** 69
  Yds: 6075

UPTON-BY-CHESTER

UPTON-BY-CHESTER GOLF CLUB, Upton Lane, Upton, Chester, **CHESHIRE,** CH2 1EE, **ENGLAND.**
(T) 01244 381183

Contact/s:
- **Professional:** Mr Peter Gardner

Course/s:
🏌 **UPTON-BY-CHESTER**
  Description: Wooded, Parkland, Medium Length, Tight, Tends to Flood, Ideal for the Elderly
  Green Speed: Medium
  Built: 1934 **Built On:** Clay
  Number of Holes: 18 **Par:** 69

Par 3's: 6 Par 4's: 9 Par 5's: 3
Yds: 5850 F9 Yds: 2731 B9 Yds: 3119
Designer: Bill Davies

UTTOXETER

UTTOXETER GOLF CLUB, Woodgate Farm, Wood Lane, Uttoxeter, **STAFFORDSHIRE**, ST14 8JR, **ENGLAND**.
(T) 01889 564884
(E) uttoxetergolfclub@talk21.com
Membership: Members & Public
Contact/s:
• Club Secretary: Mr Simon Large
• Professional: Mr Adam McCandless
Course/s:
⛳ **UTTOXETER**
Description: Parkland, Undulating, Medium Length, Tight
Green Speed: Medium
Built: 1972 Built On: Clay
Number of Holes: 18 Par: 69
Yds: 5455 F9 Yds: 2692 B9 Yds: 2763

UXBRIDGE

UXBRIDGE GOLF COURSE, The Drive, Uxbridge, **LONDON (GREATER)**, UB10 8AQ, **ENGLAND**.
(T) 01895 231169
Contact/s:
• Manager: Mr G Charlton
Course/s:
⛳ **UXBRIDGE**
Number of Holes: 18

VALE

VALE GOLF & COUNTRY CLUB (THE), Hill Furze Rd, Bishampton, Pershore, **WORCESTERSHIRE**, WR10 2LZ, **ENGLAND**.
(T) 01386 462781
Contact/s:
• General Manager: Mr D Gutteridge
Course/s:
⛳ **INTERNATIONAL**
Number of Holes: 18
Designer: Robert Sandow
⛳ **LENCHES**
Number of Holes: 9
Designer: Robert Sandow

VALE OF GLAMORGAN

VALE HOTEL GOLF & COUNTRY CLUB, Hensol Pk, Hensol, **GLAMORGAN (VALE OF)**, CF72 8JY, **WALES**.
(T) 01443 667800
(W) www.vale-hotel.com
Size of Complex: 220 Acres
Contact/s:
• Professional: Mr Peter Johnson
Course/s:
⛳ **HENSOL**
Description: Parkland
Built: 1993
Number of Holes: 9 Par: 36
Yds: 3115
⛳ **THE LAKE**
Description: Championship, Parkland
Built: 1993
Number of Holes: 18 Par: 72

VALE OF LEVEN

VALE OF LEVEN GOLF CLUB, Northfield Rd, Alexandria, **ARGYLL AND BUTE**, G83

9ET, **SCOTLAND**.
(T) 01389 752351
Contact/s:
• Manager: Mr David Chalmers
Course/s:
⛳ **VALE OF LEVEN**
Number of Holes: 18 Par: 67
Par 3's: 6 Par 4's: 11 Par 5's: 1
Yds: 5172 F9 Yds: 2803 B9 Yds: 2369

VALE OF LLANGOLLEN

VALE OF LLANGOLLEN GOLF CLUB, Holyhead, Llangollen, **DENBIGHSHIRE**, LL20 7PR, **WALES**.
(T) 01978 860906
Membership: Members & Public
Size of Complex: 132 Acres
Contact/s:
• Club Secretary: Mr A D Bluck
• Professional: Mr David Thorne
Course/s:
⛳ **VALE OF LLANGOLLEN**
Description: Championship, Wooded, Parkland, Breckland, Valley, Sheltered, Medium Length, Drains Well, Tends to Flood, Ideal for the Elderly
Green Speed: Medium
Built: 1908 Built On: Clay
Number of Holes: 18 Par: 72
Record: 67 (David Thorne)
Par 3's: 3 Par 4's: 12 Par 5's: 3
Yds: 6377 F9 Yds: 3357 B9 Yds: 3020
Further Information:
This is an easy course to play, in a picturesque setting.

VALE ROYAL ABBEY

VALE ROYAL ABBEY GOLF CLUB, Whitegate, Northwich, **CHESHIRE**, CW8 2BA, **ENGLAND**.
(T) 01606 301291
(E) vragc@crownsportsplc.com
(W) www.crownsportsplc.com
Membership: Members & Public
Contact/s:
• Professional: Mr Richard Stockdale
  ☎ 01606 301702
• Pro Shop: Mr Neil Clarkson
Course/s:
⛳ **VALE ROYAL ABBEY**
Description: Championship, Wooded, Parkland, Undulating, Open, Medium Length, Drains Well, Ideal for the Elderly
Green Speed: Medium
Built: 1998
Number of Holes: 18 Par: 71
Yds: 6357 F9 Yds: 3247 B9 Yds: 3110
Designer: Simon Gidman

VALLEY

VALLEY GOLF COURSE, Spencers Farm, 155 Sewardstone Rd, London, **LONDON (GREATER)**, E4 7PA, **ENGLAND**.
(T) 020 85594381
Course/s:
⛳ **VALLEY**
Number of Holes: 9

VAUL

VAUL GOLF CLUB, Vaul, Scarinish, **ARGYLL AND BUTE**, PA77 6TP, **SCOTLAND**.
(T) 01879 220848
Course/s:
⛳ **VAUL**

Number of Holes: 9 Par: 70
Yds: 2911

VENTNOR

VENTNOR GOLF CLUB, Steephill Down Rd, Ventnor, **ISLE OF WIGHT**, PO38 1BP, **ENGLAND**.
(T) 01983 853326
Contact/s:
• Principal: Mr W Thomson
Course/s:
⛳ **VENTNOR**
Number of Holes: 12
Further Information:
Holes have different tees, so can be played as an 18 hole course.

VERULAM

VERULAM GOLF CLUB, London Rd, St. Albans, **HERTFORDSHIRE**, AL1 1JG, **ENGLAND**.
(T) 01727 853327
(W) www.verulamgolf.co.uk
Contact/s:
• Sales Manager: Mr David John Cliffe
Course/s:
⛳ **VERULAM**
Description: Championship
Number of Holes: 18
Designer: James Braid

VICARS CROSS

VICARS CROSS GOLF CLUB, Tarvin Rd, Great Barrow, Chester, **CHESHIRE**, CH3 7HN, **ENGLAND**.
(T) 01244 335595
Contact/s:
• Club Secretary: Mrs K Hunt
  ☎ 01244 335174
Course/s:
⛳ **VICARS CROSS**
Number of Holes: 18 Par: 72
Yds: 6428
Designer: J Richardson

VILLA

VILLA GOLF CLUB, Villa Farm, Blackham, Tunbridge Wells, **KENT**, TN3 9UN, **ENGLAND**.
(T) 01892 740344
Membership: Public
Size of Complex: 40 Acres
Contact/s:
• Professional: Mr Brian Slade
Course/s:
⛳ **VILLA**
Description: Valley, Open, Medium Length, Tends to Flood, Ideal for the Elderly
Green Speed: Medium
Built: 1989 Built On: Clay
Number of Holes: 9 Par: 33
Par 3's: 4 Par 4's: 4 Par 5's: 1
Yds: 2473
Prevailing Wind: South/East
Further Information:
This 9 hole course is situated alongside a tributary of River Medway and can also be played as an 18 hole course.

VIRGINIA

VIRGINIA GOLF CLUB, Virginia, Cavan, **COUNTY CAVAN**, **IRELAND**.
(T) 049 8548066

Course/s:
VIRGINIA
Number of Holes: 9

VIRGINIA PARK

VIRGINIA PARK GOLF CLUB, Virginia Pk,
Caerphilly, **CAERPHILLY**, CF83 3SW,
WALES.
(T) 029 20863113

Contact/s:
● **Manager:** Mr D Llewellin

Course/s:
VIRGINIA PARK
Number of Holes: 9

VIVARY PARK

VIVARY PARK GOLF COURSE, Vivary Rd,
Taunton, **SOMERSET**, TA1 3JW, **ENGLAND**.
(T) 01823 333875

Membership: Public
Size of Complex: 66 Acres

Contact/s:
● **Club Secretary:** Mr Alan Stone
☎ 01823 289274
● **Professional:** Mr Michael Steadman

Course/s:
VIVARY PARK MUNICIPAL
Description: Wooded, Parkland,
Sheltered, Short, Tight, Ideal for the
Elderly
Green Speed: Medium
Built: 1928 **Built On:** Clay
Number of Holes: 18 **Par:** 63
Record: 60 (Michael Steadman)
Yds: 4620 **F9 Yds:** 2179 **B9 Yds:** 2441
Prevailing Wind: South/West
Designer: W Herbert Fowler

VOGRIE

VOGRIE GOLF COURSE, Vogrie Grange,
Gorebridge, **LOTHIAN (MID)**, EH23 4NT,
SCOTLAND.
(T) 01875 821716

Course/s:
VOGRIE
Number of Holes: 9

WAKEFIELD

WAKEFIELD GOLF CLUB, 28 Woodthorpe
Lane, Wakefield, **YORKSHIRE (WEST)**, WF2
6JH, **ENGLAND**.
(T) 01924 258778

Membership: Members & Public
Size of Complex: 120 Acres

Contact/s:
● **Club Secretary:** Mr Anthony McVicar
● **Professional:** Mr Ian Wright
☎ 01924 255380

Course/s:
WAKEFIELD
Description: Wooded, Parkland, Open,
Medium Length, Drains Well, Ideal for the
Elderly
Green Speed: Medium
Built: 1912 **Built On:** Clay
Number of Holes: 18 **Par:** 72
Par 3's: 3 **Par 4's:** 12 **Par 5's:** 3
Yds: 6653 **F9 Yds:** 3274 **B9 Yds:** 3379
Prevailing Wind: West
Designer: Herd, Alistair MacKenzie
Further Information:
A very challenging and picturesque
course.

WAKEFIELD

CITY OF WAKEFIELD GOLF CLUB, Horbury
Rd, Wakefield, **YORKSHIRE (WEST)**, WF2
8QS, **ENGLAND**.
(T) 01924 360282

Course/s:
CITY OF WAKEFIELD
Number of Holes: 18

WALDRINGFIELD HEATH

WALDRINGFIELD HEATH GOLF CLUB,
Newbourn Rd, Waldringfield, Woodbridge,
SUFFOLK, IP12 4PT, **ENGLAND**.
(T) 01473 736426

Contact/s:
● **Company Secretary:** Mr L J McWade

Course/s:
WALDRINGFIELD HEATH
Number of Holes: 18
Designer: Philip Pilgrim

WALLASEY

WALLASEY GOLF CLUB LTD, Bayswater Rd,
Wallasey, **MERSEYSIDE**, CH45 8LA,
ENGLAND.
(T) 0151 6911024

Membership: Members & Public

Contact/s:
● **Professional:** Mr M Adams
☎ 0151 6383 888

Course/s:
WALLASEY
Description: Championship, Links,
Undulating, Long, Drains Well
Green Speed: Medium
Built: 1891 **Built On:** Sand
Number of Holes: 18 **Par:** 72
Record: 65 (Andrew Marshall)
Yds: 6503 **F9 Yds:** 3304 **B9 Yds:** 3199
Designer: Tom Morris

WALLSEND

WALLSEND GOLF COURSE, Rheydt Ave,
Wallsend, **TYNE AND WEAR**, NE28 8SU,
ENGLAND.
(T) 0191 2624231

Course/s:
WALLSEND
Number of Holes: 18

WALMER & KINGSDOWN

WALMER & KINGSDOWN GOLF CLUB,
The Leas, Kingsdown, Deal, **KENT**, CT14 8EP,
ENGLAND.
(T) 01304 373256

Membership: Members & Public

Contact/s:
● **Club Secretary:** Mr Reg Harrison
● **Professional:** Mr Mathew Paget
☎ 01304 363017

Course/s:
WALMER & KINGSDOWN
Description: Cliff Top, Open, Medium
Length, Drains Well
Green Speed: Fast
Built: 1948 **Built On:** Chalk
Number of Holes: 18 **Par:** 72
Par 3's: 4 **Par 4's:** 10 **Par 5's:** 4
Yds: 6444 **F9 Yds:** 3309 **B9 Yds:** 3135
Prevailing Wind: North
Designer: James Braid
Further Information:
There are views of the sea from the

course.

WALMERSLEY

WALMERSLEY GOLF CLUB, Garrets Cl,
White Carr Lane, Bury, **LANCASHIRE**, BL9
6TE, **ENGLAND**.
(T) 0161 7641429

Contact/s:
● **Club Secretary:** Mr R O Goldstein
☎ 0161 7647770
● **Pro Shop:** Mr P Thorpe
☎ 0161 7639050

Course/s:
WALMERSLEY
Description: Moorland, Undulating
Built: 1906
Number of Holes: 18 **Par:** 69
Yds: 5341 **F9 Yds:** 2779 **B9 Yds:** 2562
Designer: S Marnoch

WALMLEY

**WALMLEY GOLF CLUB (WYLDE GREEN)
LTD,** Brooks Rd, Wylde Green, Sutton
Coldfield, **MIDLANDS (WEST)**, B72 1HR,
ENGLAND.
(T) 0121 373 7103
(W) www.walmleygolfclub.org.uk

Membership: Members & Public
Size of Complex: 140 Acres

Contact/s:
● **Professional:** Mr C J Wicketts
● **Book Tee Times:** Mrs Ann Clibbery
☎ 0121 3777272
● **Book Lessons:**
☎ 0121 3737108

Course/s:
WALMLEY
Description: Wooded, Parkland, Valley,
Medium Length, Tight, Drains Well, Ideal
for the Elderly
Green Speed: Fast
Built: 1902 **Built On:** Clay/Soil
Number of Holes: 18 **Par:** 68
Record: 66 (Darren Prosser)
Par 3's: 3 **Par 4's:** 11 **Par 5's:** 3
Yds: 6139

WALSALL

WALSALL GOLF CLUB, Broadway, Walsall,
MIDLANDS (WEST), WS1 3EY, **ENGLAND**.
(T) 01922 613512
(E) golfclub@walsallgolf.freeserve.co.uk
(W) www.walsallgolf.freeserve.co.uk

Course/s:
WALSALL
Number of Holes: 18 **Par:** 70
Yds: 6259 **F9 Yds:** 2870 **B9 Yds:** 3389
Designer: Alistair MacKenzie

WALTHAM WINDMILL

WALTHAM WINDMILL GOLF CLUB,
Cheapside, Waltham, Grimsby,
LINCOLNSHIRE (NORTH EAST), DN37
0HT, **ENGLAND**.
(T) 01472 824109

Contact/s:
● **Club Secretary:** Mr George W Fielding
● **Professional:** Mr Nigel Burkitt
☎ 01472 823963

Course/s:
WALTHAM WINDMILL
Description: Parkland
Number of Holes: 18
Yds: 6333

WALTON HALL

WALTON HALL GOLF COURSE, Warrington Rd, Higher Walton, Warrington, **CHESHIRE**, WA4 5LU, **ENGLAND**.
(T) 01925 263061
Course/s:
🏌 **WALTON HALL**
   Number of Holes: 18

WALTON HEATH

WALTON HEATH GOLF CLUB, Deans Lane, Tadworth, **SURREY**, KT20 7TP, **ENGLAND**.
(T) 01737 812380
(W) www.whgc.co.uk
Membership: Members & Public
Contact/s:
● **Club Secretary:** Mrs Janice Owen
● **Professional:** Mr Ken McPherson
Course/s:
🏌 **NEW**
   Built: 1913
   Number of Holes: 18 **Par:** 72
   Par 3's: 3 **Par 4's:** 12 **Par 5's:** 3
   Yds: 6613 **F9 Yds:** 3077 **B9 Yds:** 3536
   Designer: Herbert Fowler
🏌 **OLD**
   Description: Heath Land, Long, Drains Well
   Green Speed: Fast
   Built: 1904 **Built On:** Clay
   Number of Holes: 18 **Par:** 72
   Par 3's: 4 **Par 4's:** 10 **Par 5's:** 4
   Yds: 6817 **F9 Yds:** 3309 **B9 Yds:** 3508
   Designer: Herbert Fowler
   Further Information:
   This is a flat but challenging course. 🏌

WANSTEAD

WANSTEAD GOLF CLUB, Overton Drive, Wanstead, **LONDON (GREATER)**, E11 2LW, **ENGLAND**.
(T) 020 89893938
(E) wgclub@aol.com
Membership: Members & Public
Size of Complex: 55 Acres
Contact/s:
● **Professional:** Mr David Hawkins
   ☎ 020 89899876
● **Book Tee Times:** Mr Keith Jones
Course/s:
🏌 **WANSTEAD**
   Description: Championship, Parkland, Medium Length, Tight, Drains Well, Ideal for the Elderly
   Green Speed: Fast
   Built: 1893 **Built On:** Soil
   Number of Holes: 18 **Par:** 69
   Record: 64 (N Coles, P Brown)
   Par 3's: 4 **Par 4's:** 13 **Par 5's:** 1
   Yds: 5791 **F9 Yds:** 3307 **B9 Yds:** 2484
   Prevailing Wind: West
   Designer: James Braid

WAREHAM

WAREHAM GOLF CLUB (THE), Sandford Rd, Wareham, **DORSET**, BH20 4DH, **ENGLAND**.
(T) 01929 554147
Contact/s:
● **Manager:** Mr M Yeager
Course/s:
🏌 **WAREHAM**
   Number of Holes: 18

WARKWORTH

WARKWORTH GOLF CLUB, Warkworth, Morpeth, **NORTHUMBERLAND**, NE65 0SW, **ENGLAND**.
(T) 01665 711596
(E) warkworth.golfclub@tiscali.co.uk
(W) www.warkworthgolf.co.uk
Membership: Members & Public
Contact/s:
● **Club Secretary:** Mr J A Gray
Course/s:
🏌 **WARKWORTH**
   Description: Links, Undulating, Open, Medium Length, Drains Well
   Green Speed: Fast **Built On:** Sand
   Number of Holes: 9 **Par:** 70
   Par 3's: 2 **Par 4's:** 6 **Par 5's:** 1
   Yds: 5986 **F9 Yds:** 2931 **B9 Yds:** 3055
   Prevailing Wind: North
   Designer: Tom Morris
   Further Information:
   9 hole course can be played as an 18 hole course

WARLEY

WARLEY GOLF COURSE, Lightwoods Hill, Smethwick, **MIDLANDS (WEST)**, B67 5ED, **ENGLAND**.
(T) 0121 4292440
Contact/s:
● **Manager:** Mr D Owen
Course/s:
🏌 **WARLEY**
   Number of Holes: 9

WARLEY PARK

WARLEY PARK GOLF CLUB, Magpie Lane, Little Warley, Brentwood, **ESSEX**, CM13 3DX, **ENGLAND**.
(T) 01277 231352
Contact/s:
● **Professional:** Mr Jason Groat
Course/s:
🏌 **COURSE 1**
   Description: Parkland
   Built: 1975
   Number of Holes: 9 **Par:** 35
   Par 3's: 2 **Par 4's:** 6 **Par 5's:** 1
   Yds: 3006
   Designer: R Plumbridge
   Further Information:
   Three nine hole courses which can be played in any combination.
🏌 **COURSE 2**
   Description: Parkland
   Built: 1975
   Number of Holes: 9 **Par:** 34
   Par 3's: 3 **Par 4's:** 5 **Par 5's:** 1
   Yds: 2979
   Designer: R Plumbridge
   Further Information:
   Three nine hole courses which can be played in any combination.
🏌 **COURSE 3**
   Description: Parkland
   Built: 1975
   Number of Holes: 9 **Par:** 36
   Par 3's: 2 **Par 4's:** 5 **Par 5's:** 2
   Yds: 3244
   Designer: R Plumbridge
   Further Information:
   Three nine hole courses which can be played in any combination.

WARREN

WARREN GOLF CLUB (THE), Woodham Walter, Maldon, **ESSEX**, CM9 6RW, **ENGLAND**.
(T) 01245 223198
Membership: Members & Public
Size of Complex: 200 Acres
Contact/s:
● **Club Secretary:** Mr Mark Durham
● **Professional:** Miss Nicky Walker (OBE)
● **Pro Shop:** Mr David Brookes
Course/s:
🏌 **WARREN**
   Description: Wooded, Hilltop, Sheltered, Short, Tight, Drains Well, Ideal for the Elderly
   Green Speed: Medium/Fast
   Built: 1902 **Built On:** Clay/Sand
   Number of Holes: 18 **Record:** 62 (Bill McCaul)
   Prevailing Wind: South/West

WARREN

WARREN GOLF COURSE, Grove Rd, Wallasey, **MERSEYSIDE**, CH45 0JA, **ENGLAND**.
(T) 0151 6395730
Contact/s:
● **Manager:** Mr S Conrad
Course/s:
🏌 **WARREN**
   Number of Holes: 9

WARREN

WARREN GOLF CLUB, Dawlish Warren, Dawlish, **DEVON**, EX7 0NF, **ENGLAND**.
(T) 01626 862255
Membership: Members & Public
Contact/s:
● **Club Secretary:** Mr Tim Aggett
● **Professional:** Mr Darren Prowse
Course/s:
🏌 **WARREN**
   Description: Links, Open, Medium Length, Drains Well, Ideal for the Elderly
   Green Speed: Fast
   Built: 1892 **Built On:** Sand
   Number of Holes: 18 **Par:** 69
   Yds: 5965 **F9 Yds:** 2764 **B9 Yds:** 3201
   Prevailing Wind: South/West

WARRENPOINT

WARRENPOINT GOLF CLUB, Lower Dromore Rd, Warrenpoint, Newry, **COUNTY DOWN**, BT34 3LN, **NORTHERN IRELAND**.
(T) 028 41753695
(E) warrenpointgolfclub@talk21.com
(W) www.globalgolf.com
Size of Complex: 94 Acres
Contact/s:
● **Club Secretary:** Mrs Marian Trainor
● **Professional:** Mr Nigel Shaw
   ☎ 028 41752371
Course/s:
🏌 **WARRENPOINT**
   Description: Championship, Parkland, Sheltered, Long, Drains Well, Ideal for the Elderly
   Green Speed: Medium
   Built: 1893 **Built On:** Soil
   Number of Holes: 18 **Par:** 71
   Yds: 6001 **F9 Yds:** 3220 **B9 Yds:** 2781
   Prevailing Wind: South/West

WARWICK GOLF CTRE

WARWICK GOLF CENTRE, Warwick Racecourse, Warwick, **WARWICKSHIRE**, CV34 6HW, **ENGLAND**.
(T) 01926 494316

Course/s:

🏌 **WARWICK**
Number of Holes: 9 **Par:** 34
Par 3's: 3 **Par 4's:** 5 **Par 5's:** 1
Yds: 2682
Designer: D G Dunkley

WARWICKSHIRE

WARWICKSHIRE (THE), Leek Wootton, Warwick, **WARWICKSHIRE**, CV35 7QT, **ENGLAND**.
(T) 01926 409409
(W) www.clubhaus.com

Membership: Members & Public

Contact/s:
● **Professional:** Mr Danny Peck
● **Pro Shop:** Mr Blair Fogering

Course/s:

🏌 **NORTH WEST**
Number of Holes: 18
Designer: Karl Litten

🏌 **SOUTH EAST**
Description: Parkland, Undulating, Open, Medium Length, Drains Well
Number of Holes: 18
Designer: Colin Snape

WATER ROCK

WATER ROCK GOLF COURSE, Water Rock, Midleton, **COUNTY CORK**, **IRELAND**.
(T) 021 4613499

Course/s:

🏌 **WATER ROCK GOLF COURSE**
Description: Parkland, Drains Well
Built On: Sand
Number of Holes: 18 **Par:** 70
Yds: 6223
Designer: Paddy Merrigan

WATERBRIDGE

WATERBRIDGE GOLF COURSE, Down St Mary, Crediton, **DEVON**, EX17 5LG, **ENGLAND**.
(T) 01363 85111

Contact/s:
● **Owner:** Mr G W Wren
☎ 07855 145507

Course/s:

🏌 **WATERBRIDGE**
Number of Holes: 9 **Par:** 64
Yds: 3910 **F9 Yds:** 1955 **B9 Yds:** 1955
Designer: Taylor
Further Information:
9 hole course can be played as an 18 hole course

WATERFORD

WATERFORD GOLF CLUB, Newrath, Waterford, **COUNTY WATERFORD**, **IRELAND**.
(T) 051 876748

Course/s:

🏌 **WATERFORD**
Number of Holes: 18 **Par:** 71
Par 3's: 5 **Par 4's:** 9 **Par 5's:** 4
Yds: 5985 **F9 Yds:** 2872 **B9 Yds:** 3113
Designer: William Park, James Braid

WATERFORD CASTLE

WATERFORD CASTLE HOTEL & GOLF CLUB, The Island, Ballinakill, Waterford, **COUNTY WATERFORD**, **IRELAND**.
(T) 051 871633
(E) golf@waterfordcastle.com
(W) www.waterfordcastle.com

Course/s:

🏌 **WATERFORD CASTLE**
Number of Holes: 18 **Par:** 72
Yds: 6842 **F9 Yds:** 3421 **B9 Yds:** 3421
Designer: D Smyth

WATERHALL

WATERHALL GOLF CLUB, Waterhall Rd, Brighton, **SUSSEX (EAST)**, BN1 8YN, **ENGLAND**.
(T) 01273 508658

Membership: Public
Size of Complex: 200 Acres

Contact/s:
● **Club Secretary:** Mr Les Allen
● **Professional:** Mr Paul Charman

Course/s:

🏌 **WATERHALL**
Description: Downland, Hilltop, Undulating, Open, Medium Length, Tight, Drains Well, Ideal for the Elderly
Green Speed: Fast
Built: 1923 **Built On:** Chalk
Number of Holes: 18 **Par:** 69
Par 3's: 5 **Par 4's:** 11 **Par 5's:** 2
Yds: 5773
Designer: Boddington

WATERLOOVILLE

WATERLOOVILLE GOLF CLUB, Cherry Tree Ave, Waterlooville, **HAMPSHIRE**, PO8 8AP, **ENGLAND**.
(T) 023 92263388
(W) www.waterlooville.co.uk

Contact/s:
● **General Manager:** Mr David Nairne

Course/s:

🏌 **WATERLOOVILLE**
Number of Holes: 18 **Par:** 72
Yds: 6602 **F9 Yds:** 3194 **B9 Yds:** 3408
Designer: Henry Cotton

WATERSTOCK

WATERSTOCK GOLF COURSE & DRIVING RANGE, Thame Rd, Waterstock, Oxford, **OXFORDSHIRE**, OX33 1HT, **ENGLAND**.
(T) 01844 338093

Contact/s:
● **Professional:** Mr Julian Goodman

Course/s:

🏌 **WATERSTOCK**
Description: Parkland, Drains Well
Built: 1994
Number of Holes: 18 **Par:** 73
Yds: 6535 **F9 Yds:** 3266 **B9 Yds:** 3269
Designer: Donald Steel
Further Information:
High quality USGA standard greens.

WATERTON PARK

WATERTON PARK (GOLF CLUB) PLC, The Balk, Walton, Wakefield, **YORKSHIRE (WEST)**, WF2 6QL, **ENGLAND**.
(T) 01924 259525
(W) www.watertonpark.co.uk

Course/s:

🏌 **WATERTON PARK**

Number of Holes: 18 **Par:** 72
Par 3's: 4 **Par 4's:** 11 **Par 5's:** 3
Yds: 6559 **F9 Yds:** 3401 **B9 Yds:** 3158

WATERVILLE HOUSE & GOLF LINKS

WATERVILLE HOUSE & GOLF LINKS, Waterville, **COUNTY KERRY**, **IRELAND**.
(T) 066 9474102
(E) wvgolf@iol.ie
(W) www.waterville-insight.com/golf.html

Membership: Members & Public

Contact/s:
● **Club Secretary:** Mr Noel Cronin
● **Professional:** Mr Liam Higgins

Course/s:

🏌 **WATERVILLE HOUSE**
Description: Championship, Links
Number of Holes: 18 **Par:** 72
Yds: 7225 **F9 Yds:** 3535 **B9 Yds:** 3690
Designer: Edward Hackett 🏆

WATH

WATH GOLF CLUB, Professional Shop, Abdy Lane, Rawmarsh, Rotherham, **YORKSHIRE (SOUTH)**, S62 7SJ, **ENGLAND**.
(T) 01709 878609

Contact/s:
● **Manager:** Mr Chris Bassett

Course/s:

🏌 **WATH**
Number of Holes: 18

WAVENDON GOLF CTRE

WAVENDON GOLF CENTRE, Lower End Rd, Wavendon, Milton Keynes, **BUCKINGHAMSHIRE**, MK17 8DA, **ENGLAND**.
(T) 01908 281296

Contact/s:
● **Professional:** Mr Greg Iron
☎ 01908 281811

Course/s:

🏌 **FAMILY**
Description: Parkland
Built: 1990
Number of Holes: 9 **Par:** 27

🏌 **WAVENDON GOLF CTRE**
Description: Parkland
Built: 1990
Number of Holes: 18 **Par:** 69
Yds: 5570
Designer: J Drake, N Elmer
Further Information:
This is a gently sloping course.

WEALD OF KENT

WEALD OF KENT (THE), Maidstone Rd, Headcorn, Ashford, **KENT**, TN27 9PT, .
(T) 01622 890866

Contact/s:
● **Manager:** Mr William Lodders

Course/s:

🏌 **WEALD OF KENT**
Number of Holes: 18
Designer: John Millen

WEALD PARK GOLF CLUB

AMERICAN GOLF (UK) LTD, Coxtie Green Rd, South Weald, Brentwood, **ESSEX**, CM14 3RJ, **ENGLAND**.
(T) 01277 375101
(W) www.americangolf.com

Membership: Members & Public

Size of Complex: 210 Acres
Contact/s:
* Pro Shop:
  ☎ 01277 375484
Course/s:
🏌 WEALD
Description: Parkland, Undulating
Number of Holes: 18 Par: 72
Yds: 6600

WEARSIDE

WEARSIDE GOLF CLUB, Coxgreen, Sunderland, **TYNE AND WEAR**, SR4 9JT, **ENGLAND**.
(T) 0191 5342518
Course/s:
🏌 WEARSIDE
Number of Holes: 18

WELCOMBE HOTEL

WELCOMBE HOTEL & GOLF COURSE (THE), Golf Shop, Warwick Rd, Stratford-upon-Avon, **WARWICKSHIRE**, CV37 0NR, **ENGLAND**.
(T) 01789 413800
(W) www.welcombe.co.uk
Contact/s:
* Head Professional: Mr Karl Hayer
Course/s:
🏌 WELCOMBE HOTEL AND
Number of Holes: 18 Par: 70
Yds: 6288 F9 Yds: 2943 B9 Yds: 3345
Designer: T McCauley

WELLINGBOROUGH

WELLINGBOROUGH GOLF CLUB, Harrowden Hall, Great Harrowden, Wellingborough, **NORTHAMPTONSHIRE**, NN9 5AD, **ENGLAND**.
(T) 01933 677234
Membership: Members & Public
Size of Complex: 170 Acres
Contact/s:
* Club Secretary: Mr Roy Tomlin
* Professional: Mr David Clifford
  ☎ 01933 678752
Course/s:
🏌 WELLINGBOROUGH
Description: Parkland, Undulating, Medium Length
Green Speed: Fast
Built: 1975 Built On: Clay
Number of Holes: 18 Par: 72
Record: 68 (Mike Gallagher)
Yds: 6617 F9 Yds: 3207 B9 Yds: 3410
Designer: Hawtree

WELLOW

WELLOW GOLF CLUB LTD, Ryedown Lane, East Wellow, Romsey, **HAMPSHIRE**, SO51 6BD, **ENGLAND**.
(T) 01794 322872
Size of Complex: 210 Acres
Contact/s:
* Club Secretary: Mrs Christine Gurd
* Professional: Mr Neil Bratley
  ☎ 01794 323833
Course/s:
🏌 BLACKWATER
Number of Holes: 9 Par: 36
Par 3's: 2 Par 4's: 5 Par 5's: 2
Yds: 3074
Further Information:
There are 27 holes made up of 3 different

9 hole courses. Two courses can be played in any combination in order to play an 18 hole round.

🏌 EMBLEY
Description: Parkland, Sheltered, Medium Length, Drains Well, Ideal for the Elderly
Green Speed: Medium Built On: Clay
Number of Holes: 9 Par: 36
Par 3's: 2 Par 4's: 5 Par 5's: 2
Yds: 3221
Prevailing Wind: South
Further Information:
There are 27 holes made up of 3 different 9 hole courses. Two courses can be played in any combination in order to play an 18 hole round.

🏌 RYEDOWN
Description: Parkland, Sheltered, Medium Length, Drains Well, Ideal for the Elderly
Green Speed: Medium Built On: Clay
Number of Holes: 9 Par: 34
Par 3's: 3 Par 4's: 5 Par 5's: 1
Yds: 2718
Prevailing Wind: South
Designer: W Wiltshire
Further Information:
There are 27 holes made up of 3 different 9 hole courses. Two courses can be played in any combination in order to play an 18 hole round.

WELLS

WELLS GOLF CLUB LTD, Secretary, Blackheath Lane, East Horrington, Wells, **SOMERSET**, BA5 3DS, **ENGLAND**.
(T) 01749 679059
Membership: Members & Public
Size of Complex: 100 Acres
Contact/s:
* Club Secretary: Mrs Christine Seare
* Professional: Mr Adrian Bishop
Course/s:
🏌 WELLS (SOMERSET)
Description: Wooded, Parkland, Undulating, Sheltered, Open, Medium Length, Drains Well, Ideal for the Elderly
Green Speed: Medium
Built: 1893 Built On: Soil
Number of Holes: 18
Prevailing Wind: South/West
Further Information:
Trolleys are never banned from the course.

WELLSHURST

WELLSHURST GOLF & COUNTRY CLUB, North St, Hellingly, Hailsham, **SUSSEX (EAST)**, BN27 4EE, **ENGLAND**.
(T) 01435 813636
(W) www.wellshurst.com
Membership: Members & Public
Size of Complex: 150 Acres
Contact/s:
* Professional: Mr Mark Wood
  ☎ 01435 813456
Course/s:
🏌 WELLSHURST
Description: Wooded, Parkland, Undulating, Medium Length, Drains Well, Ideal for the Elderly
Green Speed: Medium
Built: 1991 Built On: Clay/Soil
Number of Holes: 18 Par: 70
Par 3's: 4 Par 4's: 12 Par 5's: 2
Yds: 5771 F9 Yds: 2894 B9 Yds: 2877
Designer: The Golf Corporation

Further Information:
With no winter greens, this course is in good condition all year round.

WELSH BORDER GOLF COMPLEX

WELSH BORDER GOLF COMPLEX, Bulthy Farm, Middleton, Welshpool, **POWYS**, SY21 8ER, **WALES**.
(T) 01743 884247
Membership: Members & Public
Contact/s:
* Club Secretary: Mr D Roberts
Course/s:
🏌 WELSH BORDER
Description: Parkland, Tends to Flood
Green Speed: Medium
Number of Holes: 9

WELSHPOOL

WELSHPOOL GOLF CLUB, Y Golfa, Welshpool, **POWYS**, SY21 9AQ, **WALES**.
(T) 01938 850249
(E) info@welshpoolgolfclub.co.uk
(W) www.welshpoolgolfclub.co.uk
Contact/s:
* Professional: Mr Bob Barlow
Course/s:
🏌 WELSHPOOL
Description: Heath Land
Built: 1894
Number of Holes: 18 Par: 70
Designer: James Braid

WELTON MANOR GOLF CTRE

WELTON MANOR GOLF CENTRE, Hackthorn Rd, Welton, Lincoln, **LINCOLNSHIRE**, LN2 3PA, **ENGLAND**.
(T) 01673 862827
Membership: Members & Public
Contact/s:
* Professional: Mr Gary Leslie
Course/s:
🏌 WELTON MANOR GOLF COURSE
Number of Holes: 18 Par: 70
Yds: 5601

WELWYN GARDEN CITY

WELWYN GARDEN CITY GOLF CLUB LTD, Mannicotts, High Oak Rd, Welwyn Garden City, **HERTFORDSHIRE**, AL8 7BP, **ENGLAND**.
(T) 01707 322722
Contact/s:
* Club Secretary: Mr G Eastwood
Course/s:
🏌 WELWYN GARDEN CITY
Number of Holes: 18

WENSUM VALLEY

WENSUM VALLEY GOLF CLUB, Beech Ave, Taverham, Norwich, **NORFOLK**, NR8 6HP, **ENGLAND**.
(T) 01603 261012
(W) www.wensumvalley.freeserve.co.uk
Membership: Members & Public
Contact/s:
* Professional: Mr Peter Whittle
* Pro Shop: Mr Peter White
Course/s:
🏌 WENSUM VALLEY
Description: Parkland, Valley, Undulating, Open, Medium Length, Drains Well
Green Speed: Medium
Built: 1991 Built On: Sand

Number of Holes: 18 Record: 68 (A Collison)
Designer: B Todd
Further Information:
The course has large undulating greens.

WENTWORTH

WENTWORTH CLUB LTD, Wentworth Drive, Virginia Water, **SURREY**, GU25 4LS, **ENGLAND**.
(T) 01344 842201
(W) www.wentworthclub.com
Membership: Members & Public
Contact/s:
● Professional: Mr David Rennie
☎ 01344 846306
Course/s:
🌑 EAST
   Description: Wooded, Heath Land
   Built: 1924
   Number of Holes: 18 Par: 68
   Record: 62 (Doug N Sewell)
   Yds: 6201
   Designer: Harry Shapland Colt ⅃
🌑 EDINBURGH
   Description: Wooded, Heath Land
   Number of Holes: 18 Par: 72
   Record: 67 (Gary Orr)
   Yds: 7004
   Designer: Bernhard Gallagher, John Jacobs, Gary Player
🌑 EXECUTIVE
   Number of Holes: 9 Par: 27
   Par 3's: 9
   Yds: 951
🌑 WEST
   Description: Championship, Wooded, Heath Land
   Number of Holes: 18 Par: 73
   Record: 63 (Wayne Riley)
   Yds: 6201
   Designer: Harry Shapland Colt ⅃

WENVOE CASTLE

WENVOE CASTLE GOLF CLUB, Wenvoe Castle, Wenvoe, Cardiff, **GLAMORGAN (VALE OF)**, CF5 6BE, **WALES**.
(T) 029 20594371
Contact/s:
● Club Secretary: Mrs N Sims
● Professional: Mr Jason Harris
Course/s:
🌑 WENVOE CASTLE
   Description: Parkland, Open
   Built: 1936
   Number of Holes: 18 Par: 72

WEPRE

WEPRE GOLF COURSE, Wepre Pk, Connah's Quay, Deeside, **FLINTSHIRE**, CH5 4HW, **WALES**.
(T) 01244 822090
Contact/s:
● Pro Shop: Mr Peter Davies
Course/s:
🌑 WEPRE
   Description: Hilltop, Undulating, Open, Short, Drains Well, Ideal for the Elderly
   Green Speed: Medium Built On: Soil
   Number of Holes: 9

WERGS

WERGS GOLF CLUB, Keepers Lane, Tettenhall, Wolverhampton, **MIDLANDS (WEST)**, WV6 8UA, **ENGLAND**.

(T) 01902 742225
Membership: Members & Public
Contact/s:
● Club Secretary: Mrs G L Parsons
Course/s:
🌑 WERGS
   Description: Parkland, Undulating, Open, Long, Drains Well, Ideal for the Elderly
   Built: 1990
   Number of Holes: 18 Par: 72
   Yds: 6949 F9 Yds: 3502 B9 Yds: 3447
   Designer: C W Moseley

WERNDDU

WERNDDU GOLF CENTRE, Wernddu Farm, Ross Rd, Abergavenny, **MONMOUTHSHIRE**, NP7 8NG, **WALES**.
(T) 01873 856223
(W) www.wernddugolfclub.co.uk
Membership: Members & Public
Size of Complex: 120 Acres
Contact/s:
● Club Secretary: Mrs Lyn Turvey
● Professional: Mr Alan Ashmead
● Pro Shop: Mr Graham Watkins
Course/s:
🌑 WERNDDU
   Description: Parkland, Undulating, Open, Medium Length, Drains Well, Ideal for the Elderly
   Green Speed: Medium
   Built: 1994 Built On: Sand
   Number of Holes: 18 Par: 68
   Yds: 5413 F9 Yds: 2986 B9 Yds: 2427
   Prevailing Wind: South/West
   Designer: G Watkins

WERNETH

WERNETH GOLF CLUB, Clubhouse, Green Lane, Garden Suburbs, Oldham, **MANCHESTER (GREATER)**, OL8 3AZ, **ENGLAND**.
(T) 0161 6241190
Membership: Members & Public
Contact/s:
● Club Secretary: Mr John Barlow
● Professional: Mr Roy Penny
Course/s:
🌑 WERNETH
   Description: Parkland, Short, Tight
   Green Speed: Medium
   Built: 1908 Built On: Clay
   Number of Holes: 18 Par: 68
   Yds: 5364 F9 Yds: 2751 B9 Yds: 2613

WERNETH LOW

WERNETH LOW GOLF CLUB, Werneth Low Rd, Hyde, **CHESHIRE**, SK14 3AF, **ENGLAND**.
(T) 0161 3682503
(E) mel.gregg@btinternet.com
Membership: Members & Public
Contact/s:
● Club Secretary: Mr Mel John Gregg
☎ 0161 3369496
Course/s:
🌑 WERNETH LOW
   Number of Holes: 11 Par: 70
   Par 3's: 2 Par 4's: 8 Par 5's: 1
   Yds: 6184 F9 Yds: 3112 B9 Yds: 3072
   Further Information:
   11 hole course can be played as an 18 hole course

WESSEX GOLF CTRE

WESSEX GOLF CENTRE, Radipole Lane, Weymouth, **DORSET**, DT4 9XH, **ENGLAND**.
(T) 01305 784737
Membership: Public
Contact/s:
● Professional: N Statham
Course/s:
🌑 WESSEX GOLF COURSE
   Number of Holes: 9
   Yds: 1432

WEST BERKSHIRE

WEST BERKSHIRE GOLF CLUB (THE), Chaddleworth, Newbury, **BERKSHIRE**, RG20 7DU, **ENGLAND**.
(T) 01488 638574
Membership: Members & Public
Size of Complex: 120 Acres
Contact/s:
● Club Secretary: Mrs C M Clayton
● Professional: Mr Paul Simpson
☎ 01488 638851
Course/s:
🌑 WEST BERKSHIRE
   Description: Downland, Undulating, Open, Long, Ideal for the Elderly
   Green Speed: Medium
   Built: 1975 Built On: Soil
   Number of Holes: 18 Par: 73
   Par 3's: 4 Par 4's: 9 Par 5's: 5
   Yds: 6712
   Designer: Robin Stagg
   Further Information:
   This course has various water hazards.

WEST BOWLING

WEST BOWLING GOLF CLUB, Professional Shop/Newall Hall, Rooley Lane, Bradford, **YORKSHIRE (WEST)**, BD5 8LB, **ENGLAND**.
(T) 01274 728036
Contact/s:
● Manager: Mr I Marshall
Course/s:
🌑 WEST BOWLING
   Number of Holes: 18

WEST BRADFORD

WEST BRADFORD GOLF CLUB, Chellow Grange Rd, Off Howarth Rd, Bradford, **YORKSHIRE (WEST)**, BD9 6NP, **ENGLAND**.
(T) 01274 542767
Contact/s:
● Professional: Mr Nigel Barber
☎ 01274 542102
Course/s:
🌑 WEST BRADFORD
   Description: Parkland
   Built: 1900
   Number of Holes: 18 Par: 69
   Par 3's: 6 Par 4's: 9 Par 5's: 3
   Yds: 5718 F9 Yds: 2939 B9 Yds: 2779

WEST BYFLEET

WEST BYFLEET GOLF CLUB, Sheerwater Rd, West Byfleet, **SURREY**, KT14 6AA, **ENGLAND**.
(T) 01932 343433
Contact/s:
● Club Secretary: Mr D G Lee
● Professional: Mr David Regan
Course/s:
🌑 WEST BYFLEET

Number of Holes: 18   Par: 70
Yds: 6211   F9 Yds: 3165   B9 Yds: 3046
Designer: C S Butchart

WEST CHILTINGTON

WEST CHILTINGTON GOLF CLUB,
Broadford Bridge Rd, West Chiltington,
Pulborough, **SUSSEX (WEST)**, RH20 2YA,
ENGLAND.
(T) 01798 813574

Membership: Members & Public
Size of Complex: 100 Acres

Contact/s:
- **Club Secretary:** Ms Christine Howell
- **Professional:** Mr Ian Williams
  ☎ 01798 812115

Course/s:
- **WEST CHILTINGTON**
  Description: Links, Heath Land,
  Undulating, Open, Short, Drains Well,
  Ideal for the Elderly
  Green Speed: Fast
  Built: 1988   **Built On:** Chalk/Sand
  Number of Holes: 18
  Yds: 5877
  Prevailing Wind: South/West
  Designer: Brian Barnes, Max Faulkner

WEST CORNWALL

WEST CORNWALL GOLF CLUB,
Professional Shop, Church Lane, Lelant, St.
Ives, **CORNWALL**, TR26 3DZ, **ENGLAND**.
(T) 01736 753401

Contact/s:
- **Club Secretary:** Mr M Lack

Course/s:
- **WEST CORNWALL**
  Number of Holes: 18
  Designer: Reverend Tyack

WEST DERBY

WEST DERBY GOLF CLUB, Yew Tree Lane,
Liverpool, **MERSEYSIDE**, L12 9HQ,
ENGLAND.
(T) 0151 2205478

Course/s:
- **WEST DERBY**
  Number of Holes: 18

WEST END

WEST END GOLF CLUB, Pro Shop, Paddock
Lane, Halifax, **YORKSHIRE (WEST)**, HX2
0NT, **ENGLAND**.
(T) 01422 341878

Contact/s:
- **Manager:** Mr D Rishworth

Course/s:
- **WEST END**
  Number of Holes: 18

WEST ESSEX

WEST ESSEX GOLF CLUB LTD, Bury Rd,
Sewardstonebury, Chingford, **LONDON
(GREATER)**, E4 7QL, **ENGLAND**.
(T) 020 8529 7558
(E) sec@westessexgolfclub.co.uk
(W) www.westessexgolfclub.co.uk

Membership: Members & Public
Size of Complex: 150 Acres

Contact/s:
- **Club Secretary:** Mr David Wilson
- **Professional:** Mr Robert Joyce
  ☎ 020 85294367

Course/s:

- **WEST ESSEX**
  Description: Wooded, Parkland,
  Undulating, Medium Length
  Green Speed: Fast
  Built: 1900   **Built On:** Clay
  Number of Holes: 18   **Par:** 71
  Record: 63 (Graham Burroughs)
  Par 3's: 4   **Par 4's:** 11   **Par 5's:** 3
  Yds: 6289
  Designer: James Braid

WEST HERTS

WEST HERTS GOLF CLUB, Cassiobury Pk,
Watford, **HERTFORDSHIRE**, WD1 7SL,
ENGLAND.
(T) 01923 236866

Contact/s:
- **General Manager:** Mr Clive Dodman

Course/s:
- **WEST HERTS**
  Number of Holes: 18
  Designer: Tom Morris

WEST HILL

WEST HILL GOLF CLUB, Bagshot Rd,
Brookwood, Woking, **SURREY**, GU24 0BH,
ENGLAND.
(T) 01483 474365
(W) www.westhill-golfclub.co.uk

Contact/s:
- **Club Secretary:** Mr M C Swatton

Course/s:
- **WEST HILL**
  Number of Holes: 18   **Par:** 69
  Yds: 6368   **F9 Yds:** 3098   **B9 Yds:** 3270
  Designer: C Butchart, William Parke

WEST HOVE

WEST HOVE GOLF CLUB, Church Farm,
Hove, **SUSSEX (EAST)**, BN3 8AN,
ENGLAND.
(T) 01273 419738
(W) www.westhovegolf.co.uk

Membership: Members & Public
Size of Complex: 150 Acres

Contact/s:
- **Professional:** Mr D Cook

Course/s:
- **WEST HOVE**
  Description: Downland, Valley, Medium
  Length, Drains Well
  Green Speed: Fast
  Built: 1990   **Built On:** Chalk
  Number of Holes: 18   **Par:** 71
  Record: 66 (J Partridge)
  Yds: 6020   **F9 Yds:** 2958   **B9 Yds:** 3062
  Prevailing Wind: South/West
  Designer: Hawtree

WEST KENT

WEST KENT GOLF CLUB, West Hill, Downe,
Orpington, **KENT**, BR6 7JJ, **ENGLAND**.
(T) 01689 851323
(E) golf@wkgc.co.uk
(W) www.wkgc.co.uk

Contact/s:
- **Professional:** Mr Roger Fidler
- **Book Tee Times:**
  ☎ 01689 856863

Course/s:
- **WEST KENT**
  Description: Parkland
  Built: 1916
  Number of Holes: 18   **Par:** 70
  Par 3's: 3   **Par 4's:** 14   **Par 5's:** 1

Yds: 6385   F9 Yds: 3251   B9 Yds: 3134
Further Information:
A testing course.

WEST KILBRIDE

WEST KILBRIDE GOLF CLUB, Fullerton
Drive, Seamill, West Kilbride, **AYRSHIRE
(NORTH)**, KA23 9HT, **SCOTLAND**.
(T) 01294 823911
(E) golf@westkilbridegolfclub.com
(W) www.westkilbridegolfclub.com

Contact/s:
- **Club Secretary:** Mr H Armour
  ☎ 01294 823991
- **Professional:** Mr Graham Ross
  ☎ 01294 823042

Course/s:
- **WEST KILBRIDE**
  Description: Championship, Links, Open,
  Ideal for the Elderly
  Green Speed: Medium
  Built: 1893   **Built On:** Sand
  Number of Holes: 18   **Par:** 71
  Record: 63 (Jason McReadie, Frazer
  Mann)
  Par 3's: 3   **Par 4's:** 13   **Par 5's:** 2
  Yds: 6452   **F9 Yds:** 3271   **B9 Yds:** 3181
  Prevailing Wind: North/West
  Designer: James Braid
  Further Information:
  Views of Isle of Arran.

WEST LANCASHIRE

WEST LANCASHIRE GOLF CLUB, Hall Rd
West, Liverpool, **MERSEYSIDE**, L23 8SZ,
ENGLAND.
(T) 0151 9243306
(E) golf@westlancashiregolf.co.uk
(W) www.westlancashiregolf.co.uk

Contact/s:
- **Club Secretary:** Mr Donald Wilson
  ☎ 0151 924 1076
- **Professional:** Mr Tim Hastings
  ☎ 0151 9245662
- **Book Tee Times:** Mr Stewart King

Course/s:
- **WEST LANCASHIRE**
  Number of Holes: 18   **Par:** 72
  Yds: 6862
  Designer: C K Cotton ♟

WEST LINTON

WEST LINTON GOLF CLUB, Medwyn Rd,
West Linton, **SCOTTISH BORDERS**, EH46
7HN, **SCOTLAND**.
(T) 01968 660970
(W) www.wlgc.co.uk

Membership: Members & Public

Contact/s:
- **Club Secretary:** Mr Alex Mitchell
- **Professional:** Mr Ian Wright
  ☎ 01968 660256

Course/s:
- **WEST LINTON**
  Description: Moorland, Open, Medium
  Length, Drains Well, Ideal for the Elderly
  Green Speed: Fast
  Built: 1890   **Built On:** Sand
  Number of Holes: 18   **Par:** 69
  Par 3's: 5   **Par 4's:** 11   **Par 5's:** 2
  Yds: 6132
  Prevailing Wind: West
  Designer: Robert Miller

WEST LOTHIAN

WEST LOTHIAN GOLF CLUB, Airngarth Hill, Linlithgow, **LOTHIAN (WEST)**, EH49 7RH, **SCOTLAND**.
(T) 01506 826030
Size of Complex: 120 Acres

Contact/s:
- **Professional:** Mr Ian Taylor
- **Book Tee Times:**
  ☎ 01506 825060

Course/s:
- **WEST LOTHIAN**
  Description: Championship, Parkland, Undulating, Open, Medium Length, Drains Well, Ideal for the Elderly
  Green Speed: Medium
  Built: 1892 **Built On:** Soil
  Number of Holes: 18 **Par:** 71
  Prevailing Wind: South/West
  Designer: Fraser Middleton
  Further Information:
  The course can be played all year round.

WEST MALLING

WEST MALLING GOLF CLUB, London Rd, Addington, West Malling, **KENT**, ME19 5AR, **ENGLAND**.
(T) 01732 844785
(W) www.westmallinggolf.com
Size of Complex: 210 Acres

Contact/s:
- **Club Secretary:** Mr W Ellis
- **Professional:** Mr Duncan Lambert
  ☎ 01732 844022

Course/s:
- **HURRICANE**
  Description: Parkland, Valley, Medium Length, Drains Well, Ideal for the Elderly
  Built: 1974
  Number of Holes: 18 **Par:** 70
  Par 3's: 6 **Par 4's:** 8 **Par 5's:** 4
  Yds: 6281
  Designer: Max Falconer

- **SPITFIRE**
  Description: Parkland, Sheltered, Medium Length, Drains Well
  Green Speed: Fast
  Built: 1974 **Built On:** Soil
  Number of Holes: 18 **Par:** 70
  Par 3's: 5 **Par 4's:** 10 **Par 5's:** 3
  Yds: 6142
  Designer: Max Falconer

WEST MIDDLESEX

WEST MIDDLESEX GOLF CLUB, Greenford Rd, Southall, **LONDON (GREATER)**, UB1 3EE, **ENGLAND**.
(T) 020 88430224

Contact/s:
- **General Manager:** Mr P J Furness

Course/s:
- **WEST MIDDLESEX**
  Number of Holes: 18

WEST MONMOUTHSHIRE

WEST MONMOUTHSHIRE GOLF CLUB, Golf Rd, Nantyglo, Ebbw Vale, **BLAENAU GWENT**, NP23 4QT, **WALES**.
(T) 01495 310233

Contact/s:
- **Club Secretary:** Mr S Williams

Course/s:
- **WEST MONMOUTHSHIRE**
  Number of Holes: 18

WEST NORFOLK (ROYAL)

ROYAL WEST NORFOLK GOLF CLUB, Beach Rd, Brancaster, King's Lynn, **NORFOLK**, PE31 8AX, **ENGLAND**.
(T) 01485 210087

Membership: Members & Public

Contact/s:
- **Club Secretary:** Maj N Carrington-Smith
- **Professional:** Mr Simon Rayner
  ☎ 01485 210616

Course/s:
- **ROYAL WEST NORFOLK**
  Number of Holes: 18 **Par:** 71
  Par 3's: 4 **Par 4's:** 11 **Par 5's:** 3
  Yds: 6427 **F9 Yds:** 3379 **B9 Yds:** 3048
  Designer: Holcombe-Ingleby ♟

WEST PARK

WEST PARK GOLF CENTRE, Waterhouse Lane, Chelmsford, **ESSEX**, CM1 2RY, **ENGLAND**.
(T) 01245 257682

Contact/s:
- **Professional:** Mr D Bugg

Course/s:
- **WEST PARK**
  Description: Short **Built On:** Soil
  Number of Holes: 18 **Par:** 54
  Yds: 1400 **F9 Yds:** 625 **B9 Yds:** 775
  Designer: Graham Wade
  Further Information:
  The course is situated close to the town centre.

WEST SURREY

WEST SURREY GOLF CLUB, Enton Green, Enton, Godalming, **SURREY**, GU8 5AF, **ENGLAND**.
(T) 01483 421275
(W) www.wsgc.co.uk

Membership: Members & Public

Contact/s:
- **Professional:** Mr A Tawse
- **Pro Shop:**
  ☎ 01483 417278

Course/s:
- **WEST SURREY**
  Description: Parkland, Undulating, Sheltered, Medium Length, Tight, Drains Well
  Green Speed: Medium
  Built: 1910
  Number of Holes: 18 **Record:** 65 (Gary Orr)
  Yds: 6300
  Designer: Fowler

WEST SUSSEX

WEST SUSSEX GOLF CLUB, Clubhouse, Hurston Lane, Pulborough, **SUSSEX (WEST)**, RH20 2EN, **ENGLAND**.
(T) 01798 872563
(W) www.westsussexgolf.co.uk

Membership: Members & Public
Size of Complex: 150 Acres

Contact/s:
- **Club Secretary:** Mr Colin Simpson
- **Professional:** Mr Tim Packham

Course/s:
- **WEST SUSSEX**
  Description: Wooded, Heath Land, Sheltered, Medium Length, Drains Well
  Built: 1930 **Built On:** Sand/Soil
  Number of Holes: 18 **Par:** 68

Par 3's: 5 **Par 4's:** 12 **Par 5's:** 1
Yds: 6223 **F9 Yds:** 2987 **B9 Yds:** 3236
Prevailing Wind: South/West
Designer: Campbell, Hutchinson ♟

WEST WATERFORD

WEST WATERFORD GOLF & COUNTRY CLUB, Dungarvan, **COUNTY WATERFORD**, **IRELAND**.
(T) 058 43216/41475
(E) info@westwaterfordgolf.com
(W) www.westwaterfordgolf.com

Membership: Members & Public
Size of Complex: 150 Acres

Contact/s:
- **Club Secretary:** Mr Tom Whelan

Course/s:
- **WEST WATERFORD**
  Description: Championship, Parkland, Medium Length, Drains Well, Ideal for the Elderly
  Green Speed: Fast
  Built: 1992 **Built On:** Sand/Soil
  Number of Holes: 18 **Par:** 72
  Par 3's: 4 **Par 4's:** 10 **Par 5's:** 4
  Yds: 6557 **F9 Yds:** 3186 **B9 Yds:** 3371
  Designer: Edward Hackett

WEST WILTS

WEST WILTS GOLF CLUB LTD, Elm Hill, Warminster, **WILTSHIRE**, BA12 0AU, **ENGLAND**.
(T) 01985 212110

Contact/s:
- **Accountant:** Mr Thomas William Meehan

Course/s:
- **WEST WILTS**
  Number of Holes: 18
  Designer: Taylor

WESTERHOPE

WESTERHOPE GOLF CLUB, Whorlton Grange, Newcastle Upon Tyne, **TYNE AND WEAR**, NE5 1PP, **ENGLAND**.
(T) 0191 2867636

Contact/s:
- **Club Secretary:** Mr R Pears

Course/s:
- **WESTERHOPE**
  Number of Holes: 18

WESTERN

WESTERN GOLF COURSE, Scudamore Rd, Braunstone Frith, Leicester, **LEICESTERSHIRE**, LE3 1UQ, **ENGLAND**.
(T) 0116 2995566

Contact/s:
- **Golf Professional:** Mr David Butler

Course/s:
- **WESTERN**
  Number of Holes: 18 **Par:** 72
  Yds: 6518 **F9 Yds:** 3338 **B9 Yds:** 3180

WESTERN GAILES

WESTERN GAILES GOLF CLUB, Gailes By Irvine, Irvine, **AYRSHIRE (NORTH)**, KA11 5AE, **SCOTLAND**.
(T) 01294 311649
(E) enquiries@westerngailes.com
(W) www.westerngailes.com

Membership: Members & Public

Course/s:
- **WESTERN GAILES**

Number of Holes: 18 Par: 71
Par 3's: 3 Par 4's: 13 Par 5's: 2
Yds: 6639 F9 Yds: 3289 B9 Yds: 3350
♀

WESTERWOOD

WESTERWOOD HOTEL, GOLF & COUNTRY CLUB, 1 St Andrews Drive, Cumbernauld, Glasgow, **GLASGOW (CITY OF)**, G68 0EW, **SCOTLAND**.
(T) 01236 725281
(E) westerwood@morton-hotels.com
(W) www.morton-hotels.com
Size of Complex: 400 Acres

Contact/s:
● Professional: Mr Alan Tait

Course/s:
⛳ **WESTERWOOD**
Description: Heath Land
Built: 1989
Number of Holes: 18 Par: 72
Yds: 6616 F9 Yds: 3142 B9 Yds: 3474
Designer: S Ballesteros, Thomas
Further Information:
The 6th hole is called Seve's Trap, a bottle-neck shaped hole demanding a good drive over a burn. The 15th Waterfall hole features an elevated tee and plateau green with a rockface behind it.

WESTGATE & BIRCHINGTON

WESTGATE & BIRCHINGTON GOLF CLUB LTD, Canterbury Rd, Westgate-on-Sea, **KENT**, CT8 8LT, **ENGLAND**.
(T) 01843 831115

Contact/s:
● Club Secretary: Mr John Wood

Course/s:
⛳ **WESTGATE AND BIRCHINGTON**
Number of Holes: 18

WESTHILL

WESTHILL GOLF CLUB, Clubhouse Office, Westhill Heights, Westhill, **ABERDEENSHIRE**, AB32 6RY, **SCOTLAND**.
(T) 01224 743361

Contact/s:
● Administrator: Miss A Barrett

Course/s:
⛳ **WESTHILL**
Number of Holes: 18

WESTHOUGHTON

WESTHOUGHTON GOLF CLUB, School St, Long Island, Westhoughton, Bolton, **LANCASHIRE**, BL5 2BR, **ENGLAND**.
(T) 01942 811085 or 840545
(E) westhoughton.gc@virgin.net

Contact/s:
● Club Secretary: Mr F Donohue

Course/s:
⛳ **WESTHOUGHTON**
Number of Holes: 9 Par: 70
Yds: 5772 B9 Yds: 2638
Further Information:
9 hole course can be played as an 18 hole course

WESTHOUGHTON

WESTHOUGHTON GOLF CENTRE, Hart Common Golf Club, Wigan Rd, Westhoughton, Bolton, **LANCASHIRE**, BL5 2BX, **ENGLAND**.
(T) 01942 813195
Membership: Members & Public

Size of Complex: 160 Acres

Contact/s:
● Club Secretary: Mr Bernard Hill
● Professional: Mr Gareth Benson
● Book Tee Times: Ms Joan Roberts

Course/s:
⛳ **ACADEMY**
Description: Parkland, Undulating
Green Speed: Medium
Built: 1998 Built On: Soil
Number of Holes: 9 Par: 27

⛳ **HART COMMON**
Description: Parkland, Undulating, Long
Green Speed: Medium
Built: 1995 Built On: Soil
Number of Holes: 18 Par: 72
Yds: 6300 F9 Yds: 2950 B9 Yds: 3350
Prevailing Wind: South/West
Designer: Michael Shattocks

WESTMINSTER PARK MUNICIPAL

WESTMINSTER PARK MUNICIPAL GOLF COURSE, Hough Green, Chester, **CHESHIRE**, CH4 8JQ, **ENGLAND**.
(T) 01244 680231
Membership: Public

Contact/s:
● Manager: Mr Matt Edwards

Course/s:
⛳ **WESTMINSTER PARK GOF COURSE**
Number of Holes: 9 Par: 27
Yds: 983

WESTON

WESTON SUPER MARE GOLF CLUB, Uphill Rd North, Weston-Super-Mare, **SOMERSET (NORTH)**, BS23 4NQ, **ENGLAND**.
(T) 01934 626968

Contact/s:
● Professional: Mr Mike Laband
☎ 01934 633360

Course/s:
⛳ **WESTON-SUPER-MARE**
Description: Links, Open, Drains Well, Ideal for the Elderly
Green Speed: Medium Built On: Sand
Number of Holes: 18 Par: 70
Par 3's: 5 Par 4's: 10 Par 5's: 3
Yds: 6208 F9 Yds: 3093 B9 Yds: 3115
Designer: Tom Dunn, Alistair MacKenzie

WESTON PARK

WESTON PARK GOLF CLUB, Weston Hse, Weston Longville, Norwich, **NORFOLK**, NR9 5JW, **ENGLAND**.
(T) 01603 872368
(W) www.weston-park.co.uk
Membership: Members & Public

Contact/s:
● Club Secretary: Mr R Wright
● Professional: Mr Michael Few
☎ 01603 827998

Course/s:
⛳ **WESTERN PARK**
Description: Wooded, Parkland, Undulating, Sheltered, Long, Tight, Drains Well
Green Speed: Medium
Built: 1992 Built On: Sand
Number of Holes: 18 Par: 72
Record: 71
Par 3's: 4 Par 4's: 10 Par 5's: 4
Yds: 6648 F9 Yds: 3272 B9 Yds: 3376
Prevailing Wind: North/West

Further Information:
An EGU approved course set amongst mature woodland.

WESTON TURVILLE

WESTON TURVILLE GOLF & SQUASH CLUB, New Rd, Weston Turville, Aylesbury, **BUCKINGHAMSHIRE**, HP22 5QT, **ENGLAND**.
(T) 01296 424084

Contact/s:
● Pro Shop: Ross Jenner

Course/s:
⛳ **WESTON TURVILLE**
Number of Holes: 18

WESTPORT

WESTPORT GOLF CLUB, Carrowholly, Westport, **COUNTY MAYO**, **IRELAND**.
(T) 098 25113
(E) wpgolf@iol.ie
(W) www.golfwestport.com

Contact/s:
● Manager: Mr Paul Neill

Course/s:
⛳ **WESTPORT**
Number of Holes: 18 Par: 73
Yds: 7072 F9 Yds: 3391 B9 Yds: 3681
Designer: Hawtree

WESTRAY

WESTRAY GOLF CLUB, Rosevale, Westray, Orkney Islands, Westray, **ORKNEY ISLES**, KW17 2DH, **SCOTLAND**.
(T) 01857 677373

Course/s:
⛳ **WESTRAY**
Number of Holes: 9

WESTRIDGE

WESTRIDGE GOLF CLUB, Brading Rd, Ryde, **ISLE OF WIGHT**, PO33 1QS, **ENGLAND**.
(T) 01983 613131
(W) www.westridgegc.co.uk
Membership: Members & Public

Contact/s:
● Club Secretary: Mr Simon Haywood

Course/s:
⛳ **WESTRIDGE**
Description: Parkland, Open, Medium Length, Tight, Drains Well, Ideal for the Elderly Green Speed: Fast
Built: 1980 Built On: Clay/Soil
Number of Holes: 9
Prevailing Wind: South
Further Information:
The course features many water hazards.

WESTWOOD

WESTWOOD GOLF CLUB, Newcastle Rd, Leek, **STAFFORDSHIRE**, ST13 7AA, **ENGLAND**.
(T) 01538 398385
Membership: Members & Public

Contact/s:
● Club Secretary: Mr Colin Plant
● Professional: Mr Neale Hyde
☎ 01538 398897

Course/s:
⛳ **WESTWOOD (LEEK)**
Description: Parkland, Undulating, Drains Well

Green Speed: Fast
Built: 1899 Built On: Sand
Number of Holes: 18 Par: 70
Yds: 6086 F9 Yds: 2794 B9 Yds: 3322
Further Information:
River.

WETHERBY

WETHERBY GOLF CLUB, Linton Lane, Linton, Wetherby, **YORKSHIRE (WEST)**, LS22 4JF, **ENGLAND**.
(T) 01937 582527

Membership: Members & Public

Contact/s:
● Manager: Mr M Dorbnay

Course/s:
◉ WETHERBY
  Number of Holes: 18

WEXFORD

WEXFORD GOLF CLUB, Mulgannon, Wexford, **COUNTY WEXFORD**, **IRELAND**.
(T) 053 42238

Course/s:
◉ WEXFORD
  Number of Holes: 18

WEXHAM PARK

WEXHAM PARK GOLF CLUB, Wexham St, Wexham, Slough, **BERKSHIRE**, SL3 6ND, **ENGLAND**.
(T) 01753 663425
(W) www.wexhamparkgolfcourse.co.uk

Contact/s:
● Professional: Mr John Kennedy

Course/s:
◉ BLUE
  Number of Holes: 18 Par: 68
  Yds: 5251 F9 Yds: 2556 B9 Yds: 2695
◉ GREEN
  Number of Holes: 9
◉ RED
  Number of Holes: 9

WEYBROOK PARK

WEYBROOK PARK GOLF CLUB, Rooksdown Lane, Basingstoke, **HAMPSHIRE**, RG24 9NT, **ENGLAND**.
(T) 01256 333232

Contact/s:
● Company Secretary: Mr G E Carpenter

Course/s:
◉ WEYBROOK PARK
  Number of Holes: 18

WEYMOUTH

WEYMOUTH GOLF CLUB, Links Rd, Weymouth, **DORSET**, DT4 0PF, **ENGLAND**.
(T) 01305 773997
(E) weymouthgolfclub@aol.com
(W) www.weymouthgc.co.uk

Contact/s:
● Professional: Mr Des Lochrie

Course/s:
◉ WEYMOUTH
  Description: Parkland
  Built: 1909
  Number of Holes: 18 Par: 70
  Par 3's: 4 Par 4's: 12 Par 5's: 2
  Yds: 5981 F9 Yds: 3050 B9 Yds: 2931
  Designer: James Braid
  Further Information:
  There are views of the coast and the

downs from the course.

WHADDON

WHADDON GOLF CENTRE, Church St, Whaddon, Royston, **HERTFORDSHIRE**, SG8 5RX, **ENGLAND**.
(T) 01223 207325

Membership: Public

Contact/s:
● Club Secretary: Mr K Green
● Professional: Mr Geoff Huggett

Course/s:
◉ WHADDON
  Description: Wooded, Sheltered, Short, Drains Well
  Green Speed: Medium
  Built: 1989 Built On: Chalk/Clay
  Number of Holes: 9

  Yds: 895
  Designer: Ken Green, Jeff Huggett
  Further Information:
  A flat course.

WHALLEY

WHALLEY GOLF CLUB, Long Leese Barn, Clerk Hill Rd, Whalley, Clitheroe, **LANCASHIRE**, BB7 9DR, **ENGLAND**.
(T) 01254 822236

Membership: Members & Public

Contact/s:
● Club Secretary: Mr Peter Lord
● Professional: Mr Jamie Hunt
● Book Tee Times:
  ☎ 01254 824766

Course/s:
◉ WHALLEY
  Description: Wooded, Parkland, Valley, Undulating, Sheltered, Open, Medium Length, Drains Well, Ideal for the Elderly
  Green Speed: Medium
  Built: 1912 Built On: Clay
  Number of Holes: 9 Par: 72
  Yds: 6258 F9 Yds: 3135 B9 Yds: 3123
  Further Information:
  9 hole course can be played as an 18 hole course

WHALSAY

WHALSAY GOLF CLUB, Skaw Taing, Whalsay, Shetland, **SHETLAND ISLANDS**, ZE2 9AA, **SCOTLAND**.
(T) 01806 566450&566481

Course/s:
◉ WHALSAY
  Number of Holes: 18

WHARTON PARK

WHARTON PARK GOLF CLUB, W.P.G.C., Longbank, Bewdley, **WORCESTERSHIRE**, DY12 2QW, **ENGLAND**.
(T) 01299 405163

Membership: Members & Public

Contact/s:
● Professional: Mr Angus Hoare

Course/s:
◉ WHARTON PARK
  Description: Wooded, Parkland, Medium Length
  Green Speed: Medium Built On: Soil
  Number of Holes: 18 Par: 72
  Yds: 6435 F9 Yds: 3229 B9 Yds: 3206

WHEATHILL

WHEATHILL GOLF CLUB, Wheathill, Somerton, **SOMERSET**, TA11 7HG, **ENGLAND**.
(T) 01963 240667

Contact/s:
● Professional: Mr John Goymer

Course/s:
◉ WHEATHILL
  Description: Parkland
  Built: 1993
  Number of Holes: 9 Par: 68
  Yds: 5351 F9 Yds: 2853 B9 Yds: 2498
  Designer: J Pain
  Further Information:
  This easy walking 9 hole course can be played as an 18 hole course.

WHEATLEY

WHEATLEY GOLF CLUB, Armthorpe Rd, Doncaster, **YORKSHIRE (SOUTH)**, DN2 5QB, **ENGLAND**.
(T) 01302 834085

Contact/s:
● Manager: Mr S Fox

Course/s:
◉ WHEATLEY
  Number of Holes: 18

WHETSTONE

WHETSTONE GOLF CLUB & DRIVING RANGE, Cambridge Rd, Cosby, Leicester, **LEICESTERSHIRE**, LE9 1SJ, **ENGLAND**.
(T) 0116 2861424

Membership: Members & Public

Contact/s:
● Professional: Mr David Raitt

Course/s:
◉ WHETSTONE
  Description: Parkland, Undulating, Open, Short, Tight, Drains Well, Ideal for the Elderly
  Green Speed: Medium
  Built: 1980 Built On: Soil
  Number of Holes: 18 Record: 63 (David Raitt)
  Prevailing Wind: South/West

WHICKHAM

WHICKHAM GOLF CLUB LTD, Hollinside Pk, Fellside Rd, Whickham, Newcastle Upon Tyne, **TYNE AND WEAR**, NE16 5BA, **ENGLAND**.
(T) 0191 4887309/ 0191 4881576
(E) enquiries@whickhamgolfclub.co.uk

Contact/s:
● Club Secretary: Mr Bruce Johnson

Course/s:
◉ WHICKHAM
  Number of Holes: 18 Par: 68
  Par 3's: 5 Par 4's: 12 Par 5's: 1
  Yds: 5878 F9 Yds: 2756 B9 Yds: 3122

WHINHILL

WHINHILL GOLF CLUB, Beith Rd, Greenock, **INVERCLYDE**, PA16 9LN, **SCOTLAND**.
(T) 01475 724694

Membership: Public

Contact/s:
● Club Secretary: Mr Peter Harris

Course/s:
◉ GREENOCK WHINHILL
  Description: Hilltop, Undulating, Open,

Short, Drains Well
Green Speed: Medium
Built: 1911 **Built On:** Soil
Number of Holes: 18

WHIPSNADE PARK

WHIPSNADE PARK GOLF CLUB, Studham Lane, Dagnall, Berkhamsted, **HERTFORDSHIRE**, HP4 1RH, **ENGLAND**.
(T) 01442 842330
(W) www.whipsnadeparkgc.co.uk
Membership: Members & Public

Contact/s:
- **Club Secretary:** Mr D Whalley
- **Professional:** Mr Roland Perry

Course/s:
- **WHIPSNADE PARK**
  Description: Parkland, Sheltered, Long, Tends to Flood, Ideal for the Elderly
  Green Speed: Medium
  Built: 1974 **Built On:** Clay
  Number of Holes: 18 **Par:** 73
  Yds: 6800
  Further Information:
  There are 2 ponds on this flat course.

WHISTON HALL

WHISTON HALL GOLF CLUB, Whiston, Stoke-on-Trent, **STAFFORDSHIRE**, ST10 2HZ, **ENGLAND**.
(T) 01538 266260
(E) enquiries@whistonhall.com
(W) www.whistonhall.com

Contact/s:
- **Co Owner:** Mr R Cliff

Course/s:
- **WHISTON HALL**
  Number of Holes: 18 **Par:** 71
  Par 3's: 4 **Par 4's:** 11 **Par 5's:** 3
  Yds: 5784 **F9 Yds:** 2982 **B9 Yds:** 2802

WHITBURN

WHITBURN GOLF CLUB, Lizard Lane, South Shields, **TYNE AND WEAR**, NE34 7AF, **ENGLAND**.
(T) 0191 5292144

Contact/s:
- **Club Secretary:** Mrs V Atkinson

Course/s:
- **WHITBURN**
  Number of Holes: 18 **Par:** 70
  Yds: 5899 **F9 Yds:** 3068 **B9 Yds:** 2831
  Designer: Charles Hugh Alison, Harry Shapland Colt, J S F Morrison

WHITBY

WHITBY GOLF CLUB, Sandsend Rd, Whitby, **YORKSHIRE (NORTH)**, YO21 3SR, **ENGLAND**.
(T) 01947 600660

Contact/s:
- **Club Secretary:** Mr T Graham
- **Professional:** Mr Tony Mason
  ☎ 01947 602719

Course/s:
- **WHITBY**
  Description: Links, Cliff Top
  Built: 1892 **Built On:** Clay
  Number of Holes: 18 **Par:** 71
  Yds: 6134 **F9 Yds:** 3065 **B9 Yds:** 3069
  Prevailing Wind: North

WHITCHURCH

WHITCHURCH GOLF CLUB, Pantmawr Rd,

Cardiff, **GLAMORGAN (VALE OF)**, CF14 7TD, **WALES**.
(T) 029 20620985
Membership: Members & Public

Contact/s:
- **Club Secretary:** Mr J W King
- **Professional:** Mr Eddie Clark
- **Pro Shop:**
  ☎ 029 20614660

Course/s:
- **WHITCHURCH**
  Description: Parkland, Undulating, Open, Medium Length, Drains Well
  Green Speed: Fast
  Built: 1915 **Built On:** Soil
  Number of Holes: 18 **Record:** 62 (Ian Woosnam)
  Designer: Fred Johns

WHITECRAIGS

WHITECRAIGS GOLF CLUB (THE), 72 Ayr Rd, Giffnock, Glasgow, **GLASGOW (CITY OF)**, G46 6SW, **SCOTLAND**.
(T) 0141 6392140

Course/s:
- **THE WHITECRAIGS**
  Number of Holes: 18

WHITEFIELD

WHITEFIELD GOLF CLUB, Higher Lane, Whitefield, Manchester, **MANCHESTER (GREATER)**, M45 7EZ, **ENGLAND**.
(T) 0161 3512700

Contact/s:
- **Professional:** Mr Paul Reeves

Course/s:
- **WHITEFIELD**
  Description: Parkland
  Built: 1932
  Number of Holes: 18 **Par:** 69

WHITEFIELDS

WHITEFIELDS HOTEL & GOLF COUNTRY CLUB, Coventry Rd, Thurlaston, Rugby, **WARWICKSHIRE**, CV23 9JR, **ENGLAND**.
(T) 01788 815555

Contact/s:
- **Professional:** Mr Darren Price

Course/s:
- **WHITEFIELDS**
  Description: Wooded, Parkland
  Built: 1992
  Number of Holes: 18 **Par:** 71
  Par 3's: 3 **Par 4's:** 13 **Par 5's:** 2
  Yds: 6223 **F9 Yds:** 3314 **B9 Yds:** 2909
  Designer: R Mason
  Further Information:
  The course borders Draycote Water, with many water hazards featuring on the course.

WHITEHALL

WHITEHALL GOLF CLUB, The Pavilion, Nelson, Treharris, **GLAMORGAN (VALE OF)**, CF46 6ST, **WALES**.
(T) 01443 740245

Contact/s:
- **Club Secretary:** Mr M Wilde

Course/s:
- **WHITEHALL**
  Number of Holes: 9

WHITEHEAD

WHITEHEAD GOLF CLUB, McCrea's Brae,

Whitehead, Carrickfergus, **COUNTY ANTRIM**, BT38 9NZ, **NORTHERN IRELAND**.
(T) 028 93370820
Size of Complex: 95 Acres

Contact/s:
- **Club Secretary:** Mr J M Niblock
- **Professional:** Mr Colin Farr

Course/s:
- **WHITEHEAD**
  Description: Parkland, Hilltop, Undulating, Open, Medium Length, Drains Well
  Green Speed: Medium
  Built: 1975 **Built On:** Clay
  Number of Holes: 18 **Par:** 70
  Par 3's: 5 **Par 4's:** 10 **Par 5's:** 3
  Yds: 6050 **F9 Yds:** 2985 **B9 Yds:** 3065
  Prevailing Wind: North/West
  Designer: A B Armstrong
  Further Information:
  This challenging course offers magnificent views of the coast of Scotland.

WHITEHILL GOLF CTRE

WHITEHILL GOLF CENTRE, Whitehill, Dane End, Ware, **HERTFORDSHIRE**, SG12 0JS, **ENGLAND**.
(T) 01920 438326

Contact/s:
- **Owner:** Mrs S Smith

Course/s:
- **WHITEHILL**
  Number of Holes: 18

WHITEKIRK

WHITEKIRK GOLF AND COUNTRY CLUB, Whitekirk, North Berwick, **LOTHIAN (EAST)**, EH39 5PR, **SCOTLAND**.
(T) 01620 870300
(E) countryclub@whitekirk.com
(W) www.whitekirk.com

Contact/s:
- **Club Secretary:** Mr David Brodie
- **Professional:** Mr Paul Wardell

Course/s:
- **WHITEKIRK**
  Description: Championship, Heath Land, Hilltop, Medium Length, Drains Well
  Green Speed: Medium
  Built: 1995
  Number of Holes: 18 **Par:** 72
  Yds: 6225 **F9 Yds:** 2920 **B9 Yds:** 3305
  Designer: C Sinclair

WHITELEAF

WHITELEAF GOLF CLUB, Whiteleaf, Princes Risborough, **BUCKINGHAMSHIRE**, HP27 0LY, **ENGLAND**.
(T) 01844 343097

Contact/s:
- **Club Secretary:** Mr Derek Hill
  ☎ 01844 274058
- **Professional:** Mr Ken Ward
  ☎ 01844 345472
- **Book Tee Times:**
  ☎ 01844 270058

Course/s:
- **WHITELEAF**
  Description: Parkland, Hilltop, Undulating, Short, Tight, Drains Well
  Green Speed: Medium
  Built: 1904 **Built On:** Chalk
  Number of Holes: 9 **Par:** 66
  Par 3's: 3 **Par 4's:** 6
  Yds: 5391 **F9 Yds:** 2732 **B9 Yds:** 2659

Further Information:
This challenging 9 hole course is well established, and can also be played as an 18 hole course.

WHITEMOSS

WHITEMOSS GOLF COURSE & CLUB, Whitemoss, Dunning, Perth, **PERTH AND KINROSS**, PH2 0QX, **SCOTLAND**.
(T) 01738 730300

Contact/s:
• Book Tee Times: Mr V Westwood

Course/s:
🏌 **COURSE #1**
Number of Holes: 18   Par: 69
Yds: 5968   F9 Yds: 3320   B9 Yds: 2648

WHITEWEBBS

WHITEWEBBS GOLF CLUB, Whitewebbs Lane, Beggars Hollow Clay Hill, Enfield, **LONDON (GREATER)**, EN2 9JN, **ENGLAND**.
(T) 020 8363 4454

Contact/s:
• Club Secretary: Mr Victor Van Graan
  ☎ 020 8363 2951
• Professional: D Lewis

Course/s:
🏌 **WHITEWEBBS MUNICIPAL**
Number of Holes: 18
Yds: 5863

WHITING BAY

WHITING BAY GOLF CLUB, Whiting Bay, Brodick, **AYRSHIRE (NORTH)**, KA27 8QT, **SCOTLAND**.
(T) 01770 700775

Contact/s:
• Club Secretary: Mr Jim Meechan

Course/s:
🏌 **WHITING BAY**
Number of Holes: 18

WHITLEY

WHITLEY GOLF COURSE, Corsham Rd, Whitley, Melksham, **WILTSHIRE**, SN12 8QE, **ENGLAND**.
(T) 01225 790099

Membership: Members & Public

Contact/s:
• Professional: Mr T Valentine

Course/s:
🏌 **WHITLEY**
Description: Parkland, Sheltered, Medium Length, Tight, Drains Well
Green Speed: Medium
Built: 1993   Built On: Clay
Number of Holes: 9   Par: 66
Yds: 4450   F9 Yds: 2710   B9 Yds: 2240
Designer: L Ross
Further Information:
This flat 9 hole course can also be played as an 18 holes course, using separate tees.

WHITLEY BAY

WHITLEY BAY GOLF CLUB LTD, Claremont Rd, Whitley Bay, **TYNE AND WEAR**, NE26 3UF, **ENGLAND**.
(T) 0191 2520180
(E) secretarywbgolf@netscapeonline.co.uk
(W) www.wbgolf.free-online.co.uk

Contact/s:
• Club Secretary: Mr H.C Hanover

Course/s:

🏌 **WHITLEY BAY**
Number of Holes: 18   Par: 71
Yds: 6261   F9 Yds: 3093   B9 Yds: 3168

WHITSAND BAY

WHITSAND BAY HOTEL GOLF AND COUNTRY CLUB, Portwrinkle, Torpoint, **CORNWALL**, PL11 3BP, **ENGLAND**.
(T) 01503 230276

Contact/s:
• Club Secretary: Mr G Dyer
  ☎ 01508 230164
• Professional: Mr D Poole
  ☎ 01503 230778

Course/s:
🏌 **WHITSAND BAY**
Description: Cliff Top
Built: 1905
Number of Holes: 18   Par: 69
Par 3's: 6   Par 4's: 9   Par 5's: 3
Yds: 5885   F9 Yds: 3226   B9 Yds: 2659
Designer: William Fernie

WHITSTABLE & SEASALTER

WHITSTABLE & SEASALTER GOLF CLUB, Collingwood Rd, Whitstable, **KENT**, CT5 1EB, **ENGLAND**.
(T) 01227 272020

Membership: Members & Public

Contact/s:
• Society Contact: Mr C Chapman

Course/s:
🏌 **WHITSTABLE & SEASALTER**
Description: Links, Open, Short, Tends to Flood, Ideal for the Elderly
Green Speed: Medium
Built: 1911   Built On: Clay
Number of Holes: 9
Prevailing Wind: South/West
Further Information:
Flat course with dykes throughout.

WHITTAKER

WHITTAKER GOLF CLUB, Shore Lane, Littleborough, **LANCASHIRE**, OL15 0LH, **ENGLAND**.
(T) 01706 378310

Course/s:
🏌 **WHITTAKER**
Number of Holes: 9

WHITTINGTON HEATH

WHITTINGTON HEATH GOLF CLUB, Tamworth Rd, Whittington, Lichfield, **STAFFORDSHIRE**, WS14 9PW, **ENGLAND**.
(T) 01543 432212

Contact/s:
• Manager: Mrs J Burton

Course/s:
🏌 **WHITTINGTON HEATH**
Number of Holes: 18   Par: 70
Par 3's: 4   Par 4's: 12   Par 5's: 2
Yds: 6490   F9 Yds: 3246   B9 Yds: 3244
Designer: Harry Shapland Colt

WHITTLEBURY PARK

WHITTLEBURY PARK GOLF & COUNTRY CLUB, Whittlebury, Towcester, **NORTHAMPTONSHIRE**, NN12 8XW, **ENGLAND**.
(T) 01327 858588

Course/s:
🏌 **1905**
Number of Holes: 9

Designer: C Sinclair

🏌 **GRAND PRIX**
Description: Parkland
Built: 1992
Number of Holes: 9   Par: 72
Designer: C Sinclair
Further Information:
The Grand Prix course can be linked with either of the other two 9 hole courses to make up an 18 hole course.

🏌 **ROYAL WHITTLEWOOD**
Number of Holes: 9
Designer: C Sinclair

WHITWOOD

WHITWOOD GOLF CLUB, Altofts Lane, Castleford, **YORKSHIRE (WEST)**, WF10 5PZ, **ENGLAND**.
(T) 01977 512835

Membership: Public

Contact/s:
• Club Secretary: Mr S Hicks
• Professional: Mr R Holland

Course/s:
🏌 **COURSE #1**
Built: 1987
Number of Holes: 9
Yds: 6176
Further Information:
9 hole course can be played as an 18 hole course.

WICK

WICK GOLF CLUB, Reiss, Wick, **HIGHLANDS**, KW1 4RW, **SCOTLAND**.
(T) 01955 602726

Contact/s:
• Manager: Mr John Hunter

Course/s:
🏌 **WICK**
Number of Holes: 18
Designer: James Braid

WICKHAM PARK

WICKHAM PARK GOLF CLUB, Titchfield Lane, Wickham, Fareham, **HAMPSHIRE**, PO17 5PJ, **ENGLAND**.
(T) 01329 833342
(W) www.wickhampark.co.uk

Membership: Members & Public
Size of Complex: 150 Acres

Contact/s:
• Professional: Mr Scott Edwards
• Pro Shop: Mr Ian Onions

Course/s:
🏌 **WICKHAM PARK**
Description: Parkland, Open, Medium Length, Drains Well, Ideal for the Elderly
Green Speed: Medium
Built: 1994   Built On: Clay/Soil
Number of Holes: 18   Par: 70
Par 3's: 4   Par 4's: 12   Par 5's: 2
Yds: 5898   F9 Yds: 2922   B9 Yds: 2976

WICKLOW

WICKLOW GOLF CLUB, Dunbur Rd, Wicklow, **COUNTY WICKLOW**, **IRELAND**.
(T) 040 467379

Contact/s:
• Professional: Mr David Daly

Course/s:
🏌 **WICKLOW**
Description: Parkland
Built: 1904

Number of Holes: 18 Par: 71
Designer: Craddock, Ruddy

WIDNES

WIDNES GOLF CLUB, Highfield Rd, Widnes, **CHESHIRE**, WA8 7DT, **ENGLAND**.
(T) 0151 4242440
(W) www.widnes-golfclub.co.uk

Contact/s:
● **Club Secretary:** Mr V A Rudder
  ☎ 0151 4242995

Course/s:
● **WIDNES**
  Number of Holes: 18 **Par:** 69
  Yds: 5729 **F9 Yds:** 2903 **B9 Yds:** 2826

WIDNEY MANOR

WIDNEY MANOR GOLF CLUB, Saintbury Drive, Solihull, **MIDLANDS (WEST)**, B91 3SZ, **ENGLAND**.
(T) 0121 7040704
(W) www.widneymanorgolfclub.co.uk

Membership: Members & Public

Contact/s:
● **Professional:** Mr Tim Atkinson

Course/s:
● **WIDNEY MANOR**
  Description: Parkland, Undulating, Sheltered, Open, Medium Length, Tight, Drains Well, Ideal for the Elderly
  Green Speed: Medium/Fast
  Built: 1992 **Built On:** Sand/Soil
  Number of Holes: 18 **Par:** 69
  Yds: 5284 **F9 Yds:** 2567 **B9 Yds:** 2717
  Prevailing Wind: North/West
  Further Information:
  This course has been refurbished and now has USGA greens.

WIGAN

WIGAN GOLF CLUB, Arley Hall, Arley Lane, Haigh, Wigan, **LANCASHIRE**, WN1 2UH, **ENGLAND**.
(T) 01257 421360

Membership: Members & Public

Contact/s:
● **Club Secretary:** Mr E Warmsley
  ☎ 01942 244429

Course/s:
● **WIGAN**
  Number of Holes: 18 **Par:** 70
  Yds: 6008 **F9 Yds:** 2773 **B9 Yds:** 3235

WIGTOWN & BLADNOCH

WIGTOWN & BLADNOCH GOLF CLUB, Lightlands Trce, Wigtown, Newton Stewart, **DUMFRIES AND GALLOWAY**, DG8 9DY, **SCOTLAND**.
(T) 01988 403354

Course/s:
● **WIGTOWN & BLADNOCH**
  Description: Parkland, Undulating
  Built: 1960
  Number of Holes: 9 **Par:** 68
  Yds: 5462 **F9 Yds:** 2731 **B9 Yds:** 2731
  Designer: Muir
  Further Information:
  9 hole course can be played as an 18 hole course

WIGTOWNSHIRE

WIGTOWNSHIRE COUNTY GOLF CLUB, Mains Of Pk, Glenluce, Newton Stewart, **DUMFRIES AND GALLOWAY**, DG8 0NN,

SCOTLAND.
(T) 01581 300420
(E) wcgc@glenluce.org.uk
(W) www.glenluce.org.uk/countygolfclub.htm

Membership: Members & Public
Size of Complex: 120 Acres

Contact/s:
● **Club Secretary:** Mrs Margaret Benson
● **Book Tee Times:** Mr Robert McKnight

Course/s:
● **COUNTY**
  Description: Links, Open, Medium Length, Drains Well, Ideal for the Elderly
  Green Speed: Medium
  Built: 1894 **Built On:** Sand
  Number of Holes: 18 **Par:** 70
  Par 3's: 3 **Par 4's:** 14 **Par 5's:** 1
  Yds: 5843 **F9 Yds:** 3042 **B9 Yds:** 2801
  Designer: G Cunningham

WILDERNESSE

WILDERNESSE GOLF CLUB, Park Lane, Seal, Sevenoaks, **KENT**, TN15 0JE, **ENGLAND**.
(T) 01732 761199

Contact/s:
● **Club Secretary:** Mr R Foster

Course/s:
● **COURSE #1**
  Number of Holes: 18 **Par:** 72
  Yds: 6440 **F9 Yds:** 3303 **B9 Yds:** 3137

WILDWOOD COUNTRY CLUB

WILDWOOD COUNTRY CLUB (THE), Horsham Rd, Alfold, Cranleigh, **SURREY**, GU6 8JE, **ENGLAND**.
(T) 01403 753255
(W) www.wildwoodgolf.co.uk

Membership: Members & Public

Contact/s:
● **Professional:** Mr S Andrews
● **Pro Shop:** Mr W Berry

Course/s:
● **WILDWOOD**
  Description: Parkland, Open, Long, Tight, Drains Well, Ideal for the Elderly
  Green Speed: Fast
  Built: 1991 **Built On:** Chalk/Clay
  Number of Holes: 18
  Designer: Hawtree
  Further Information:
  A flat course.

WILLESLEY PARK

WILLESLEY PARK GOLF CLUB LTD, Measham Rd, Ashby-De-La-Zouch, **LEICESTERSHIRE**, LE65 2PF, **ENGLAND**.
(T) 01530 414820

Contact/s:
● **Sales Manager:** Mr Keith William Keller

Course/s:
● **WILLESLEY PARK**
  Number of Holes: 18

WILLIAM WROE

WILLIAM WROE GOLF COURSE, Penny Bridge Lane, Flixton, Urmston, Manchester, **MANCHESTER (GREATER)**, M41 5DX, **ENGLAND**.
(T) 0161 7488680

Course/s:
● **WILLIAM WROE MUNICIPAL**
  Number of Holes: 18

WILLIAMWOOD

WILLIAMWOOD GOLF CLUB, Clarkston Rd, Glasgow, **GLASGOW (CITY OF)**, G44 3YR, **SCOTLAND**.
(T) 0141 6371783
(E) secretary@williamwoodgc.fsnet.co.uk

Contact/s:
● **Club Secretary:** Mr Thomas Hepburn
● **Professional:** Mr Stewart Marshall

Course/s:
● **WILLIAMWOOD**
  Number of Holes: 18 **Par:** 68
  Par 3's: 5 **Par 4's:** 12 **Par 5's:** 1
  Yds: 5878 **F9 Yds:** 2837 **B9 Yds:** 3041
  Designer: James Braid

WILLINGCOTT

WILLINGCOTT GOLF COURSE, Willingcott Valley, Woolacombe, **DEVON**, EX34 7HN, **ENGLAND**.
(T) 01271 870173
(W) www.willingcott.co.uk

Membership: Members & Public
Size of Complex: 120 Acres

Contact/s:
● **Club Secretary:** Mr Andrew Hodge
● **Professional:** Mr Jimmy McGhee

Course/s:
● **WILLINGCOTT**
  Description: Parkland, Valley, Open, Medium Length, Tight, Drains Well, Ideal for the Elderly
  Green Speed: Medium
  Built: 1995 **Built On:** Soil
  Number of Holes: 9
  Prevailing Wind: North/West
  Designer: Hawtree
  Further Information:
  Planned to be extended to an 18 hole course by mid 2002.

WILLINGDON

WILLINGDON GOLF CLUB, Southdown Rd, Eastbourne, **SUSSEX (EAST)**, BN20 9AA, **ENGLAND**.
(T) 01323 410983
(W) www.wgc.demon.co.uk

Membership: Members & Public
Size of Complex: 100 Acres

Contact/s:
● **Club Secretary:** Mrs J Packham
● **Professional:** Mr Troy Moore
  ☎ 01323 410984

Course/s:
● **WILLINGDON**
  Description: Undulating, Sheltered, Medium Length, Drains Well
  Green Speed: Medium
  Built: 1898 **Built On:** Clay
  Number of Holes: 18
  Designer: Alistair MacKenzie

WILLOW VALLEY

WILLOW VALLEY GOLF & COUNTRY CLUB LTD, Highmoor Lane, Clifton, Brighouse, **YORKSHIRE (WEST)**, HD6 4JB, **ENGLAND**.
(T) 01274 878624
(W) www.wvgc.co.uk

Membership: Members & Public

Contact/s:
● **Club Secretary:** Mrs Lynette Stone
● **Professional:** Mr Julian Haworth
● **Pro Shop:** Mr Clive Swain

Course/s:

⛳ FOUNTAIN
Number of Holes: 9   Par: 31
Par 3's: 5   Par 4's: 4
Yds: 2040

⛳ T.P.C
Description: Championship, Parkland, Undulating, Long, Tight, Drains Well
Green Speed: Medium
Built: 1997   Built On: Sand/Soil
Number of Holes: 18   Par: 72
Par 3's: 4   Par 4's: 10   Par 5's: 4
Yds: 6496
Designer: Jonathan Gaunt
Further Information:
A very exciting layout with 11 lakes on the course.

WILMSLOW

WILMSLOW GOLF CLUB (THE), Great Warford, Mobberley, Knutsford, **CHESHIRE**, WA16 7AY, **ENGLAND**.
(T) 01565 872148
Course/s:
⛳ WILMSLOW
Number of Holes: 18

WILPSHIRE

WILPSHIRE GOLF CLUB LTD, 72 Whalley Rd, Wilpshire, Blackburn, **LANCASHIRE**. BB1 9LF, **ENGLAND**.
(T) 01254 248260
Contact/s:
● Sales Director: Mr John Neil Pullen
Course/s:
⛳ WILPSHIRE
Number of Holes: 18
Designer: James Braid

WILTON

WILTON GOLF CLUB, Wilton Castle, Wilton, Redcar, **CLEVELAND**, TS10 4QY, **ENGLAND**.
(T) 01642 465265
Contact/s:
● Club Secretary: Mr J Elder
Course/s:
⛳ WILTON
Number of Holes: 18

WILTSHIRE

WILTSHIRE GOLF CLUB (THE), Vastern, Wootton Bassett, Swindon, **WILTSHIRE**, SN4 7PB, **ENGLAND**.
(T) 01793 849999
Contact/s:
● Professional: Mr Andy Gray
  ☎ 01793 851360
Course/s:
⛳ THE WILTSHIRE
Description: Championship, Downland
Built: 1991
Number of Holes: 18   Par: 72
Designer: Peter Alliss, Clive Clark
Further Information:
The course has many water hazards.

WIMBLEDON (ROYAL)

ROYAL WIMBLEDON GOLF CLUB, 29 Camp Rd, London, **LONDON (GREATER)**, SW19 4UW, **ENGLAND**.
(T) 020 89462125
(W) www.rwgc.co.uk
Contact/s:
● Club Secretary: Mr N I Smith
● Professional: Mr Hugh Boyle

Course/s:
⛳ ROYAL WIMBLEDON
Number of Holes: 18   Par: 70
Yds: 6348   F9 Yds: 3083   B9 Yds: 3265

WIMBLEDON COMMON

WIMBLEDON COMMON GOLF CLUB, 19 Camp Rd, London, **LONDON (GREATER)**, SW19 4UW, **ENGLAND**.
(T) 020 89467571
(E) secretary@wcgc.co.uk
(W) www.wcgc.co.uk
Membership: Members & Public
Contact/s:
● Club Secretary: Mr Raymond Pierce
● Professional: Mr Jeff Jukes
Course/s:
⛳ WIMBLEDON COMMON
Description: Heath Land, Open, Short, Tight, Drains Well, Ideal for the Elderly
Built: 1908
Number of Holes: 18   Par: 68
Record: 67 (Chris Emsley)
Yds: 5460   F9 Yds: 2606   B9 Yds: 2832
Further Information:
Golfers must wear a red outer garment on the course, but no red is allowed in the bar.

WIMBLEDON PARK

WIMBLEDON PARK GOLF CLUB LTD, Home Pk Rd, London, **LONDON (GREATER)**, SW19 7HR, **ENGLAND**.
(T) 020 89461250
Membership: Members & Public
Contact/s:
● Club Secretary: Mr Peter Dowl
● Professional: Mr Dean Windgrove
Course/s:
⛳ WIMBLEDON PARK
Description: Wooded, Parkland, Short, Tight, Tends to Flood, Ideal for the Elderly
Green Speed: Medium
Built: 1898   Built On: Clay
Number of Holes: 18
Designer: C Brown

WINCANTON

WINCANTON GOLF CLUB, The Race Course, Wincanton, **SOMERSET**, BA9 8BJ, **ENGLAND**.
(T) 01963 34606
Membership: Members & Public
Size of Complex: 60 Acres
Contact/s:
● Club Secretary: Mr Ian Chandler
● Professional: Mr Andrew England
Course/s:
⛳ WINCANTON
Description: Parkland, Open, Drains Well, Ideal for the Elderly
Green Speed: Fast
Built: 1994   Built On: Soil
Number of Holes: 9
Prevailing Wind: South
Designer: Eagle Golf

WINCHESTER (ROYAL)

ROYAL WINCHESTER GOLF CLUB, Sarum Rd, Winchester, **HAMPSHIRE**, SO22 5QE, **ENGLAND**.
(T) 01962 852462
Membership: Members & Public
Contact/s:

● Club Secretary: Mr Derek Thomson
● Professional: Mr Finlay Young
● Pro Shop: Mr Kevin Caplehorn
Course/s:
⛳ ROYAL WINCHESTER
Description: Wooded, Parkland, Undulating, Open, Medium Length, Tight, Drains Well
Green Speed: Medium
Built: 1888   Built On: Chalk
Number of Holes: 18
Designer: Harry Shapland Colt

WINDERMERE

WINDERMERE GOLF CLUB, Cleabarrow, Windermere, **CUMBRIA**, LA23 3NB, **ENGLAND**.
(T) 01539 443550
Contact/s:
● Club Secretary: Mr K R Moffat
  ☎ 01539 443123
● Professional: Mr W S M Rooke
Course/s:
⛳ WINDERMERE
Description: Undulating
Built: 1891
Number of Holes: 18   Par: 71
Yds: 5633
Designer: G Lowe

WINDLERMERE

WINDLEMERE GOLF COURSE, Windlesham Rd, West End, Woking, **SURREY**, GU24 9QL, **ENGLAND**.
(T) 01276 858727
(W) www.pineridgegolf.co.uk
Membership: Public
Contact/s:
● Professional: Mr David Thomas
Course/s:
⛳ WINDLEMERE
Description: Heath Land, Undulating, Sheltered, Short, Tends to Flood
Green Speed: Slow
Built: 1979   Built On: Clay/Sand
Number of Holes: 9   Par: 34
Par 3's: 2   Par 4's: 7
Yds: 2673
Designer: Clive Smith

WINDLESHAM

WINDLESHAM GOLF CLUB, Grove End, Bagshot, **SURREY**, GU19 5HY, **ENGLAND**.
(T) 01276 451122
Contact/s:
● Professional: Mr Lee Mucklow
Course/s:
⛳ WINDLESHAM
Description: Parkland, Undulating
Built: 1994
Number of Holes: 18   Par: 72
Par 3's: 4   Par 4's: 10   Par 5's: 4
Yds: 6650   F9 Yds: 3344   B9 Yds: 3306
Designer: Tommy Horton
Further Information:
This is a challenging course.

WINDMILL HILL

WINDMILL HILL GOLF CENTRE, Tattenhoe Lane, Bletchley, Milton Keynes, **BUCKINGHAMSHIRE**, MK3 7RB, **ENGLAND**.
(T) 01908 631113
Membership: Members & Public
Contact/s:

- **Club Secretary:** Mr Brian Smith
  ☎ 01908 366457
- **Professional:** Mr Colin Clingan
  ☎ 01908 378623

Course/s:
🏌 **WINDMILL HILL**
   Description: Championship, Parkland, Sheltered, Ideal for the Elderly
   Green Speed: Medium **Built On:** Soil
   Number of Holes: 18 **Par:** 73
   Par 3's: 4 **Par 4's:** 9 **Par 5's:** 5
   Yds: 6720 **F9 Yds:** 3443 **B9 Yds:** 3277
   Designer: Henry Cotton

WINDMILL VILLAGE

WINDMILL VILLAGE HOTEL GOLF & LEISURE CLUB, Birmingham Rd, Allesley, Coventry, **MIDLANDS (WEST)**, CV5 9AL, **ENGLAND**.
(T) 01203 404041
(E) reservations@windmillvillagehotel.co.uk

Contact/s:
- **Golf Manager:** Mr Robert Hunter

Course/s:
🏌 **WINDMILL VILLAGE**
   Number of Holes: 18 **Par:** 70
   Yds: 5186 **F9 Yds:** 2732 **B9 Yds:** 2452
   Designer: Robert Hunter

WINDWHISTLE

WINDWHISTLE GOLF & COUNTRY CLUB LTD, Cricket St Thomas, Chard, **SOMERSET**, TA20 4DG, **ENGLAND**.
(T) 01460 30231
(W) www.windwhistlegolf.com

Membership: Members & Public

Contact/s:
- **Club Secretary:** Mr Ian Dodd
- **Professional:** Mr Duncan Driver

Course/s:
🏌 **WINDWHISTLE**
   Description: Parkland, Undulating, Open, Drains Well, Ideal for the Elderly
   Green Speed: Medium
   Built: 1932 **Built On:** Soil
   Number of Holes: 18 **Par:** 72
   Par 3's: 2 **Par 4's:** 13 **Par 5's:** 3
   Yds: 6510 **F9 Yds:** 3331 **B9 Yds:** 3179
   Prevailing Wind: South/West
   Designer: James Braid, Fisher, Taylor
   Further Information:
   This is a challenging course with exceptional views.

WINDYHILL

WINDYHILL GOLF CLUB, Baljaffray Rd, Bearsden, Glasgow, **GLASGOW (CITY OF)**, G61 4QQ, **SCOTLAND**.
(T) 0141 9422349

Contact/s:
- **Club Secretary:** Mr W Proven
- **Professional:** Mr Chris Duffy

Course/s:
🏌 **WINDYHILL**
   Description: Moorland, Undulating
   Built: 1908
   Number of Holes: 18 **Par:** 71
   Yds: 6171 **F9 Yds:** 3164 **B9 Yds:** 3007
   Designer: James Braid

WINTER HILL

WINTER HILL GOLF CLUB, Grange Lane, Cookham, Maidenhead, **BERKSHIRE**, SL6 9RP, **ENGLAND**.
(T) 01628 527610

Contact/s:
- **Club Secretary:** Mr M B Goodenhough
  ☎ 01628 527613

Course/s:
🏌 **WINTER HILL**
   Number of Holes: 18 **Par:** 72
   Yds: 6408 **F9 Yds:** 3246 **B9 Yds:** 3162
   Designer: Charles Lawrie

WINTERFIELD

WINTERFIELD GOLF & RECREATIONAL CLUB, St. Margaret's, North Rd, Dunbar, **LOTHIAN (EAST)**, EH42 1AU, **SCOTLAND**.
(T) 01368 863562
(W) www.winterfieldgolfclub.net

Contact/s:
- **Club Secretary:** Ms Liz Goodall
  ☎ 01368 862280
- **Professional:** Mr Kevin Phillips

Course/s:
🏌 **WINTERFIELD**
   Number of Holes: 18 **Par:** 65
   Yds: 5155 **F9 Yds:** 2587 **B9 Yds:** 2568

WIRRAL LADIES

WIRRAL LADIES GOLF CLUB LTD, 93 Bidston Rd, Prenton, **MERSEYSIDE**, CH43 6TS, **ENGLAND**.
(T) 0151 6521255

Course/s:
🏌 **WIRRAL LADIES**
   Number of Holes: 18

WISHAW

WISHAW GOLF CLUB, Bulls Lane, Wishaw, Sutton Coldfield, **MIDLANDS (WEST)**, B76 9QW, **ENGLAND**.
(T) 0121 3513221

Membership: Members & Public

Contact/s:
- **Professional:** Mr Alan Partridge

Course/s:
🏌 **COURSE #1**
   Number of Holes: 18 **Par:** 69
   Yds: 5700

WISHAW

WISHAW GOLF CLUB, 55 Cleland Rd, Wishaw, **LANARKSHIRE (NORTH)**, ML2 7PH, **SCOTLAND**.
(T) 01698 372869

Course/s:
🏌 **WISHAW**
   Number of Holes: 18
   Designer: James Braid

WISLEY

WISLEY GOLF CLUB (THE), Ripley, Woking, **SURREY**, GU23 6QU, **ENGLAND**.
(T) 01483 211022

Membership: Members & Public

Contact/s:
- **Professional:** Mr Denis Pugh

Course/s:
🏌 **THE CHURCH**
   Number of Holes: 9 **Par:** 72
   Yds: 3356 **F9 Yds:** 36
   Further Information:
   Holes are rotated and mixed on a daily basis to determine the 18 hole course and the 9 hole course.

🏌 **THE GARDEN**

   Number of Holes: 9 **Par:** 72
   Yds: 3385
   Further Information:
   Holes are rotated and mixed on a daily basis to determine the 18 hole course and the 9 hole course.

🏌 **THE MILL**
   Number of Holes: 9 **Par:** 72
   Yds: 3473 **F9 Yds:** 36 **B9 Yds:** 36
   Further Information:
   Holes are rotated and mixed on a daily basis to determine the 18 hole course and the 9 hole course.

WITHERNSEA

WITHERNSEA GOLF CLUB, Chestnut Ave, Withernsea, **YORKSHIRE (EAST)**, HU19 2PG, **ENGLAND**.
(T) 01964 612258

Membership: Members & Public

Contact/s:
- **Administrator:** Mr K Purdue
  ☎ 01964 612078/ 670658

Course/s:
🏌 **WITHERNSEA**
   Description: Parkland, Undulating, Open, Medium Length, Tight, Tends to Flood
   Green Speed: Medium
   Built: 1909 **Built On:** Clay
   Number of Holes: 9 **Par:** 72
   Par 3's: 2 **Par 4's:** 5 **Par 5's:** 2
   Yds: 6207 **F9 Yds:** 3118 **B9 Yds:** 3089
   Prevailing Wind: West
   Further Information:
   9 hole course can be played as an 18 hole course

WITHINGTON

WITHINGTON GOLF CLUB, Palatine Rd, West Didsbury, Manchester, **MANCHESTER (GREATER)**, M20 2UE, **ENGLAND**.
(T) 0161 4453912

Course/s:
🏌 **WITHINGTON**
   Description: Parkland
   Built: 1892
   Number of Holes: 18 **Par:** 71

WITNEY LAKES

WITNEY LAKES GOLF CLUB, Downs Rd, Witney, **OXFORDSHIRE**, OX8 5SY, **ENGLAND**.
(T) 01993 779000

Membership: Members & Public

Contact/s:
- **Professional:** Mr Adam Souter

Course/s:
🏌 **WHITNEY LAKES**
   Description: Parkland, Undulating, Open, Medium Length, Drains Well, Ideal for the Elderly
   Green Speed: Medium
   Built: 1994 **Built On:** Clay
   Number of Holes: 18
   Designer: Simon Gidman

WOBURN

WOBURN GOLF & COUNTRY CLUB, Little Brickhill, Milton Keynes, **BUCKINGHAMSHIRE**, MK17 9LJ, **ENGLAND**.
(T) 01908 370756
(E) enquiries@woburngolf.com
(W) www.woburngolf.com

Membership: Members & Public

Contact/s:
- **Club Secretary:** Mrs Glenna Beasley
- **Professional:** Mr Luther Blacklock
  ☎ 01908 626600

Course/s:

DUCHESS
Description: Championship, Wooded, Undulating, Sheltered, Long, Tight, Drains Well
Green Speed: Fast
Built: 1974 **Built On:** Sand
Number of Holes: 18 **Par:** 72
Par 3's: 4 **Par 4's:** 10 **Par 5's:** 4
Yds: 6651
Designer: Charles Lawrie ▼

DUKES
Description: Championship, Wooded, Undulating, Sheltered, Long, Tight, Drains Well
Green Speed: Fast
Built: 1976 **Built On:** Sand
Number of Holes: 18 **Par:** 72
Record: 62 (Gary Orr)
Par 3's: 4 **Par 4's:** 10 **Par 5's:** 4
Yds: 6973
Designer: Charles Lawrie
Further Information:
Some 460 feet above sea level, with superb views across the county, the course's free draining, sandy sub soil ensures perfect playing conditions. ▼

MARQUESS
Description: Championship, Wooded, Long, Tight, Drains Well
Green Speed: Fast
Built: 2000 **Built On:** Sand
Number of Holes: 18 **Par:** 72
Par 3's: 4 **Par 4's:** 10 **Par 5's:** 4
Yds: 6744
Designer: Peter Alliss, Ross McMurry
Further Information:
The Marquess course has been designed to provide an enjoyable challenge for golfers of all abilities. All holes possess their own distinctive characteristics.

WOKEFIELD PARK

WOKEFIELD PARK GOLF CLUB, Mortimer, Reading, **BERKSHIRE**, RG7 3AE, **ENGLAND**.
(T) 01189 334013
(W) www.wokefieldgolf.co.uk

Membership: Members & Public
Size of Complex: 250 Acres

Contact/s:
- **Club Secretary:** Mr John Lafferty
- **Professional:** Mr Gary Smith
  ☎ 0118 9334078

Course/s:

WOKEFIELD PARK
Description: Parkland, Open, Long, Drains Well
Green Speed: Medium/Fast
Built: 1996
Number of Holes: 18 **Par:** 72
Record: 65 (Martin Thomson)
Par 3's: 4 **Par 4's:** 10 **Par 5's:** 4
Yds: 6588 **F9 Yds:** 3230 **B9 Yds:** 3358
Designer: Jonathan Gaunt
Further Information:
This American styled course, with long bunkers and lakes, is in excellent condition for its age.

WOKING

WOKING GOLF CLUB, Pond Rd, Woking, **SURREY**, GU22 0JZ, **ENGLAND**.
(T) 01483 760053

Membership: Members & Public

Contact/s:
- **Professional:** Mr Carl Bianco

Course/s:

WOKING
Description: Heath Land, Open, Ideal for the Elderly
Number of Holes: 18 **Par:** 70
Yds: 6340
Designer: Tom Dunn ▼

WOLL

WOLL GOLF COURSE, Ashkirk, Selkirk, **SCOTTISH BORDERS**, TD7 4NY, **SCOTLAND**.

Membership: Members & Public

Contact/s:
- **Book Tee Times:** Mr Nicholas Brown

Course/s:

COURSE #1
Description: Parkland
Built: 1993
Number of Holes: 9 **Par:** 72
Yds: 6408 **F9 Yds:** 3204 **B9 Yds:** 3204
Further Information:
9 hole course can be played as an 18 hole course.

WOLLATON PARK

WOLLATON PARK GOLF CLUB, Wollaton Pk, Nottingham, **NOTTINGHAMSHIRE**, NG8 1BT, **ENGLAND**.
(T) 0115 9787574

Membership: Members & Public

Contact/s:
- **Club Secretary:** Mr Michael Harvey
- **Professional:** Mr J Lower
- **Pro Shop:**
  ☎ 0115 9784834

Course/s:

WOLLATON PARK
Description: Parkland, Sheltered, Medium Length, Tight
Green Speed: Medium **Built On:** Soil
Number of Holes: 18
Designer: W Williamson
Further Information:
A flat course.

WOLSTANTON

WOLSTANTON GOLF CLUB, Dimsdale Old Hall, Hassam Prde, Newcastle, **STAFFORDSHIRE**, ST5 9DR, **ENGLAND**.
(T) 01782 616995

Contact/s:
- **Professional:** Mr Simon Arnold

Course/s:

WOLSTANTON
Description: Wooded, Parkland
Built: 1904
Number of Holes: 18 **Par:** 68
Yds: 5574 **F9 Yds:** 2879 **B9 Yds:** 2695
Further Information:
Wolstanton is a compact course.

WOODBRIDGE

WOODBRIDGE GOLF CLUB, Bromeswell, Woodbridge, **SUFFOLK**, IP12 2PF, **ENGLAND**.
(T) 01394 382038

Membership: Members & Public

Contact/s:
- **Club Secretary:** Mr A Thenissen
- **Professional:** Mr Adrian Hubert

Course/s:

FOREST
Number of Holes: 9 **Par:** 35
Yds: 3191 **F9 Yds:** 3191
Designer: D Grant

WOODBRIDGE
Description: Heath Land, Undulating, Open, Medium Length, Drains Well, Ideal for the Elderly
Green Speed: Medium
Built: 1893 **Built On:** Soil
Number of Holes: 18 **Par:** 70
Record: 64
Yds: 6299 **F9 Yds:** 3167 **B9 Yds:** 3132
Prevailing Wind: North/East
Designer: D Grant

WOODBROOK

WOODBROOK GOLF CLUB, Dublin Rd, Bray, **COUNTY WICKLOW**, **IRELAND**.
(T) 01 2824799
(E) woodbrook@internet-ireland.ie
(W) www.woodbrook.ie

Course/s:

WOODBROOK
Number of Holes: 18
Designer: P McEvoy

WOODBURY PARK

WOODBURY PARK HOTEL GOLF & COUNTRY CLUB, Woodbury Castle, Woodbury, Exeter, **DEVON**, EX5 1JJ, **ENGLAND**.
(T) 01395 233382
(E) golf@woodburypark.co.uk
(W) www.woodburypark.co.uk

Membership: Members & Public
Size of Complex: 500 Acres

Contact/s:
- **Professional:** Mr Alan Richards

Course/s:

ACORN
Description: Wooded, Parkland, Heath Land, Breckland, Hilltop, Open, Long, Tight, Tends to Flood, Ideal for the Elderly
Green Speed: Medium
Built: 1981 **Built On:** Clay
Number of Holes: 9
Prevailing Wind: East
Designer: J Hamilton-Stutt

OAKS
Description: Championship, Wooded, Parkland, Heath Land, Breckland, Hilltop, Open, Long, Tight, Tends to Flood
Green Speed: Medium
Built: 1981 **Built On:** Clay
Number of Holes: 18 **Record:** 69
(David Clements)
Prevailing Wind: East
Designer: J Hamilton-Stutt

WOODCOTE PARK

WOODCOTE PARK GOLF CLUB LTD, Meadow Hill, Bridle Way, Coulsdon, **SURREY**, CR5 2QQ, **ENGLAND**.
(T) 020 8668 2788
(E) woodcotepgc@ic24.net

Contact/s:
- **Professional:** Mr Ian Golding
- **Book Lessons:**
  ☎ 020 86681843

Course/s:

WOODCOTE PARK
Number of Holes: 18 **Par:** 71
Yds: 6669 **F9 Yds:** 3136 **B9 Yds:** 3533

WOODCRAY MANOR

WOODCRAY MANOR GOLF COURSE, Finchampstead Rd, Wokingham, **BERKSHIRE**, RG40 3HG, **ENGLAND**.
(T) 0118 9771073

Membership: Members & Public

Contact/s:
- **Professional:** Mr Mike Mannion

Course/s:
- **COURSE #1**
  Number of Holes: 18 **Par:** 72
  Yds: 6452

WOODENBRIDGE

WOODENBRIDGE GOLF CLUB, Vale Of Avoca, Arklow, **COUNTY WICKLOW**, **IRELAND**.
(T) 040 235202
(E) wgc@eircom.net

Contact/s:
- **Club Secretary:** Mr Henry Crummy

Course/s:
- **WOODENBRIDGE**
  Number of Holes: 18 **Par:** 71
  Yds: 6400 **F9 Yds:** 3140 **B9 Yds:** 3260
  Designer: P Merrigan

WOODFARM GOLF COMPLEX

WOODFARM GOLF COMPLEX, Broad Lane, Essington, Wolverhampton, **MIDLANDS (WEST)**, WV11 2RJ, **ENGLAND**.
(T) 01922 404888

Contact/s:
- **Owner:** Mr R Brown

WOODFORD

WOODFORD GOLF CLUB, 2 Sunset Ave, Woodford Green, **ESSEX**, IG8 0ST, **ENGLAND**.
(T) 020 85044254

Course/s:
- **WOODFORD**
  Number of Holes: 9
  Designer: Tom Dunn

WOODHALL HILLS

WOODHALL HILLS GOLF CLUB LTD, Woodhall Rd, Calverley, Pudsey, **YORKSHIRE (WEST)**, LS28 5UN, **ENGLAND**.
(T) 0113 2554594

Membership: Members & Public

Contact/s:
- **Professional:** Mr Warren Lockett
  ☎ 0113 2562857

Course/s:
- **WOODHALL HILLS**
  Description: Parkland, Hilltop, Medium Length, Tight, Drains Well
  Green Speed: Fast
  Built: 1905 **Built On:** Clay
  Number of Holes: 18 **Par:** 71
  Yds: 6184 **F9 Yds:** 3195 **B9 Yds:** 2989
  Further Information:
  This is a challenging course with an excellent variety of holes.

WOODHALL SPA

WOODHALL SPA GOLF CLUB, The Broadway, Woodhall Spa, **LINCOLNSHIRE**, LN10 6PU, **ENGLAND**.
(T) 01526 352511

Membership: Members & Public/Public

Contact/s:
- **Club Secretary:** B H Fawcett
- **Professional:** Mr Campbell Elliot

Course/s:
- **BRACKEN**
  Number of Holes: 18 **Par:** 73
  Par 3's: 3 **Par 4's:** 11 **Par 5's:** 4
  Yds: 6747 **F9 Yds:** 3308 **B9 Yds:** 3439
  Designer: Donald Steel
- **HOTCHKIN**
  Number of Holes: 18 **Par:** 73
  Par 3's: 3 **Par 4's:** 11 **Par 5's:** 4
  Yds: 6921 **F9 Yds:** 3443 **B9 Yds:** 3478
  Designer: Colonel Hotchkin ♟

WOODHAM

WOODHAM GOLF & COUNTRY CLUB LTD, Burnhill Way, Newton Aycliffe, **COUNTY DURHAM**, DL5 4PN, **ENGLAND**.
(T) 01325 318346

Contact/s:
- **Professional:** Mr Ernie Wilson
- **Book Tee Times:**
  ☎ 01325 315257

Course/s:
- **WOODHAM**
  Description: Wooded, Parkland
  Built: 1981
  Number of Holes: 18 **Par:** 73
  Designer: J Hamilton-Stutt

WOODLAKE PARK

WOODLAKE PARK GOLF CLUB, Glascoed, Usk, **MONMOUTHSHIRE**, NP4 0TE, **WALES**.
(T) 01291 673933
(W) www.woodlake.co.uk

Membership: Members & Public
Size of Complex: 150 Acres

Contact/s:
- **Club Secretary:** Mr M J Wood
- **Professional:** Mr A Pritchard

Course/s:
- **WOODLAKE PARK**
  Description: Championship, Parkland, Undulating, Open, Drains Well
  Green Speed: Fast
  Built: 1993 **Built On:** Sand/Soil
  Number of Holes: 18 **Par:** 71
  Record: 67 (M Wooton)
  Yds: 5906 **F9 Yds:** 3058 **B9 Yds:** 2848
  Further Information:
  This course has superb greens, built to USGA specification.

WOODLANDS

WOODLANDS GOLF & COUNTRY CLUB, Woodlands Lane, Bradley Stoke, Almondsbury, Bristol, **BRISTOL**, BS32 4JZ, **ENGLAND**.
(T) 01454 618121
(E) society@woodlands-golf.co.uk
(W) www.woodlands-golf.com

Contact/s:
- **Managing Director:** Mr David Knipe
  ☎ 0117 9372251

Course/s:
- **WOODLANDS**
  Number of Holes: 18 **Par:** 70
  Yds: 6068 **F9 Yds:** 3349 **B9 Yds:** 2719
  Designer: Golf Design

WOODLANDS

WOODLANDS GOLF CLUB, Cooleragh, Coill Dubh, Naas, **COUNTY KILDARE**, **IRELAND**.
(T) 045 860777

Course/s:
- **WOODLANDS**
  Number of Holes: 9
  Designer: T Halpin

WOODLANDS MANOR

WOODLANDS MANOR GOLF CLUB, Woodlands, West Kingsdown, **KENT**, TN15 6AB, **ENGLAND**.
(T) 01959 523806&524161
(E) woodlandsgolf@aol.com

Contact/s:
- **Club Secretary:** Mr Colin Robins

Course/s:
- **WOODLANDS MANOR**
  Number of Holes: 18 **Par:** 69
  Par 3's: 5 **Par 4's:** 11 **Par 5's:** 2
  Yds: 6015 **F9 Yds:** 3215 **B9 Yds:** 2800
  Designer: Coles, Lyons

WOODSOME HALL

WOODSOME HALL GOLF CLUB (THE), Fenay Bridge, Huddersfield, **YORKSHIRE (WEST)**, HD8 0LQ, **ENGLAND**.
(T) 01484 602034

Membership: Members & Public
Size of Complex: 340 Acres

Contact/s:
- **Club Secretary:** Mr Robert Shaw
- **Professional:** Mr Michael Higginbottom

Course/s:
- **WOODSOME HALL**
  Description: Parkland, Undulating, Sheltered, Open, Medium Length, Drains Well
  Green Speed: Medium
  Built: 1922 **Built On:** Clay
  Number of Holes: 18 **Record:** 65 (Matthew Broadbent)
  Prevailing Wind: East

WOODSPRING

WOODSPRING GOLF & COUNTRY CLUB, Yanley Lane, Long Ashton, Bristol, **BRISTOL**, BS41 9LR, **ENGLAND**.
(T) 01275 394378

Contact/s:
- **Professional:** Mr Nigel Beer

Course/s:
- **AVON**
  Description: Championship, Parkland, Undulating
  Built: 1994
  Number of Holes: 9 **Par:** 35
  Designer: Peter Alliss, Clive Clarke, Donald Steel
  Further Information:
  There are views of Bristol and the surrounding countryside from the course.
- **BRUNEL**
  Number of Holes: 9 **Par:** 37
  Designer: Peter Alliss, Clive Clarke, Donald Steel
- **SEVERN**
  Number of Holes: 9 **Par:** 36
  Designer: Peter Alliss, Clive Clarke, Donald Steel

WOODSTOCK

WOODSTOCK GOLF & COUNTRY CLUB, Woodstock House, Ennis, **COUNTY CLARE**, **IRELAND**.
(T) 065 6829463

(E) woodstock.ennis@eircom.net
(W) www.golfeurope.com/clubs/woodstock.
Membership: Members & Public
Contact/s:
● **General Manager:** Mr Andrew Griffith
Course/s:
WOODSTOCK
Description: Parkland, Undulating, Drains Well
Number of Holes: 18
Yds: 6432

WOODTHORPE HALL

WOODTHORPE HALL GOLF CLUB, Woodthorpe, Alford, **LINCOLNSHIRE,** LN13 0DD, **ENGLAND.**
(T) 01507 450000
Membership: Public
Contact/s:
● **Club Secretary:** Mr Eddie Burton
Course/s:
WOODTHORPE HALL
Description: Parkland, Open, Short, Tends to Flood, Ideal for the Elderly
Green Speed: Medium
Built: 1986 Built On: Clay
Number of Holes: 18 Par: 67
Yds: 5140 F9 Yds: 2380 B9 Yds: 2760
Prevailing Wind: East
Designer: Charles Stubbs

WOOLER

WOOLER GOLF CLUB, Dod Law, Doddington, Wooler, **NORTHUMBERLAND,** NE71 6EA, **ENGLAND.**
(T) 01668 281137
Course/s:
WOOLER
Description: Parkland
Built: 1975
Number of Holes: 9 Par: 72
Further Information:
9 hole course can be played as an 18 hole course using different coloured markers. Attractive water hazards and much wildlife including grouse and deer.

WOOLTON

WOOLTON GOLF CLUB, Doe Pk, Speke Rd, Woolton, Liverpool, **MERSEYSIDE,** L25 7TZ, **ENGLAND.**
(T) 0151 4861601
Contact/s:
● **Club Secretary:** Mr K Hamilton
Course/s:
WOOLTON
Number of Holes: 18 Par: 69
Par 3's: 5 Par 4's: 11 Par 5's: 2
Yds: 5724 F9 Yds: 2799 B9 Yds: 2925

WORCESTER

WORCESTER GOLF & COUNTRY CLUB, Boughton Pk, Bransford Rd, Worcester, **WORCESTERSHIRE,** WR2 4EZ, **ENGLAND.**
(T) 01905 422555
Course/s:
WORCESTER
Number of Holes: 18
Designer: Alistair MacKenzie

WORCESTERSHIRE

WORCESTERSHIRE GOLF CLUB, Woodfarm Rd, Malvern, **WORCESTERSHIRE,** WR14 4PP, **ENGLAND.**

(T) 01684 575992
Contact/s:
● **General Manager:** Mr T Duke
Course/s:
THE WORCESTERSHIRE (MALVERN WELLS)
Number of Holes: 18 Par: 71
Par 3's: 4 Par 4's: 11 Par 5's: 3
Yds: 6500 F9 Yds: 2918 B9 Yds: 3582
Designer: James Braid, Harry Shapland Colt

WORFIELD

WORFIELD GOLF CLUB, Roughton, Bridgnorth, **SHROPSHIRE,** WV15 5HE, **ENGLAND.**
(T) 01746 716372
Contact/s:
● **Professional:** Mr Stephen Russell
Course/s:
WORFIELD
Description: Parkland, Drains Well
Built: 1991
Number of Holes: 18 Par: 73
Designer: T Williams

WORKINGTON

WORKINGTON GOLF CLUB LTD, Branthwaite Rd, Workington, **CUMBRIA,** CA14 4SS, **ENGLAND.**
(T) 01900 603460
Membership: Members & Public
Contact/s:
● **Club Secretary:** Mr Tom Stout
Course/s:
WORKINGTON
Number of Holes: 18 Par: 72
Yds: 6247 F9 Yds: 3213 B9 Yds: 3034
Designer: James Braid

WORKSOP

WORKSOP GOLF CLUB, Windmill Lane, Worksop, **NOTTINGHAMSHIRE,** S80 2SQ, **ENGLAND.**
(T) 01909 477731
Membership: Members & Public
Contact/s:
● **Club Secretary:** Mr David Dufall
● **Professional:** Mr Carl Weatherhead
● **Pro Shop:**
  ☎ 01909 477732
Course/s:
WORKSOP
Description: Heath Land, Sheltered, Long, Tight, Drains Well
Green Speed: Fast
Built: 1914 Built On: Sand
Number of Holes: 18 Par: 72
Record: 66 (A Coltart)
Yds: 6640
Prevailing Wind: South/West
Designer: Tom Williamson
Further Information:
This is a flat course.

WORLDHAM PARK

WORLDHAM PARK GOLF COURSE, Cakers Lane, East Worldham, Alton, **HAMPSHIRE,** GU34 3BF, **ENGLAND.**
(T) 01420 544606
Contact/s:
● **Partner:** Mrs M R Whidborne
Course/s:
WORLDHAM PARK
Number of Holes: 18

Designer: F J Whidborne

WORLEBURY

WORLEBURY GOLF CLUB, Worlebury Hill Rd, Weston-Super-Mare, **SOMERSET (NORTH),** BS22 9SX, **ENGLAND.**
(T) 01934 418473
Contact/s:
● **Owner:** Mr G Marks
Course/s:
WORLEBURY
Number of Holes: 18
Designer: Hawtree

WORLINGTON & NEWMARKET (ROYAL)

ROYAL WORLINGTON & NEWMARKET GOLF CLUB, Worlington, Bury St. Edmunds, **SUFFOLK,** IP28 8SD, **ENGLAND.**
(T) 01638 712216
Membership: Members & Public
Contact/s:
● **Club Secretary:** Mr Ken Weston
  ☎ 01638 717787
● **Professional:** Mr Malcolm Hawkins
Course/s:
ROYAL WORLINGTON & NEWMARKET
Description: Open, Medium Length, Tight, Drains Well, Ideal for the Elderly
Green Speed: Fast
Built: 1893 Built On: Sand
Number of Holes: 9 Par: 70
Yds: 6210 F9 Yds: 3105 B9 Yds: 3105
Prevailing Wind: West
Designer: Harry Shapland Colt
Further Information:
9 hole course can be played as an 18 hole course ⛳

WORPLESDON

WORPLESDON GOLF CLUB, Heath House Rd, Woking, **SURREY,** GU22 0RA, **ENGLAND.**
(T) 01483 473287
Contact/s:
● **Club Secretary:** Mr J T Christine
● **Professional:** Mr Jim Christine
Course/s:
WORPLESDON
Description: Wooded, Heath Land
Number of Holes: 18 Par: 71
Yds: 6440 F9 Yds: 3180 B9 Yds: 3260
Designer: J F Abercromby ⛳

WORSLEY

WORSLEY GOLF CLUB, Stableford Ave, Eccles, Manchester, **MANCHESTER (GREATER),** M30 8AP, **ENGLAND.**
(T) 0161 7894202
Membership: Members & Public
Contact/s:
● **Professional:** Honourable Ceri Cousin
Course/s:
WORSLEY
Description: Wooded, Parkland, Undulating, Sheltered, Medium Length, Drains Well
Green Speed: Medium
Built: 1894 Built On: Soil
Number of Holes: 18 Par: 72
Record: 66 (Ceri Cousin)
Par 3's: 4 Par 4's: 10 Par 5's: 4
Yds: 6257 F9 Yds: 3158 B9 Yds: 3099
Designer: James Braid

WORSLEY PARK

MARRIOTT WORSLEY PARK HOTEL & COUNTRY CLUB, Worsley Pk, Worsley, **MANCHESTER (GREATER)**, M28 2QT, **ENGLAND**.
(T) 0161 9752000
(W) www.marriotthotels.com

Membership: Members & Public
Size of Complex: 135 Acres

Contact/s:
● **Professional:** Mr David Screeton
● **Book Tee Times:**
☎ 0161 9752043

Course/s:
⛳ **WORSLEY PARK**
Built: 1999
Number of Holes: 18 Par: 71
Designer: European Golf Design
Further Information:
135 acres of nondescript farmland has been transformed into a thing of wonder: visually interesting, exciting to play and full of movement, with holes that embrace the heroic and the delightful, all with plenty of options.

WORTHING

WORTHING GOLF CLUB CO LTD, Links Rd, Worthing, **SUSSEX (WEST)**, BN14 9QZ, **ENGLAND**.
(T) 01903 260717

Membership: Members & Public
Size of Complex: 330 Acres

Contact/s:
● **Club Secretary:** Mr Ian Evans
● **Professional:** Mr Steven Rolley
● **Book Lessons:**
☎ 01903 260718

Course/s:
⛳ **LOWER**
Description: Downland, Undulating, Open, Long, Drains Well
Green Speed: Fast
Built: 1905 Built On: Chalk
Number of Holes: 18 Par: 71
Yds: 6530 F9 Yds: 3111 B9 Yds: 3419
Prevailing Wind: South/West
Designer: Harry Shapland Colt

⛳ **UPPER**
Number of Holes: 18 Par: 66
Yds: 5243 F9 Yds: 2509 B9 Yds: 2714
Designer: Harry Shapland Colt

WORTLEY

WORTLEY GOLF CLUB, Hermit Hill Lane, Wortley, Sheffield **YORKSHIRE (SOUTH)**, S35 7DF, **ENGLAND**.
(T) 0114 2885294

Contact/s:
● **Club Secretary:** Mr W Hoyland

Course/s:
⛳ **WORTLEY**
Number of Holes: 18

WRAG BARN

WRAG BARN GOLF CLUB, Shrivenham Rd, Highworth, Swindon, **WILTSHIRE**, SN6 7QQ, **ENGLAND**.
(T) 01793 861327
(W) www.wragbarn.com

Membership: Members & Public
Size of Complex: 150 Acres

Contact/s:
● **Club Secretary:** Mrs Rosemary Castle

● **Professional:** Mr Barry Loughrey
☎ 01793 766027

Course/s:
⛳ **WRAG BARN**
Description: Wooded, Hilltop, Medium Length, Drains Well, Ideal for the Elderly
Green Speed: Medium Built On: Soil
Number of Holes: 18 Par: 72
Par 3's: 4 Par 4's: 10 Par 5's: 4
Yds: 6595
Designer: Hawtree

WRANGATON

WRANGATON GOLF CLUB, Golf Links Rd, Wrangaton, South Brent, **DEVON**, TQ10 9HJ, **ENGLAND**.
(T) 01364 73229

Membership: Members & Public

Contact/s:
● **Club Secretary:** Mr Graham Williams
☎ 01364 72161
● **Professional:** Mr Glenn Richards

Course/s:
⛳ **WRANGATON (S DEVON)**
Description: Parkland, Moorland, Open, Medium Length, Drains Well, Ideal for the Elderly
Built: 1900
Number of Holes: 18 Par: 70
Yds: 6083 F9 Yds: 3240 B9 Yds: 2843
Designer: Donald Steel

WREKIN

WREKIN GOLF CLUB LTD, Ercall Woods, Wrekin, Telford, **SHROPSHIRE**, TF6 5BX, **ENGLAND**.
(T) 01952 244032

Membership: Members & Public

Contact/s:
● **Club Secretary:** Mr D Briscoe
● **Professional:** Mr Keith Housden

Course/s:
⛳ **WREKIN**
Description: Parkland, Undulating, Sheltered, Open, Short, Tight, Drains Well
Green Speed: Medium/Fast
Built: 1905 Built On: Soil
Number of Holes: 18 Par: 66
Yds: 5570 F9 Yds: 2660 B9 Yds: 2910

WREXHAM

WREXHAM GOLF CLUB, Holt Rd, Llan-Y-Pwll, Wrexham, **WREXHAM**, LL13 9SB, **WALES**.
(T) 01978 261033

Contact/s:
● **Club Secretary:** Mr Jim Johnson
● **Professional:** Mr Paul Williams

Course/s:
⛳ **WREXHAM**
Number of Holes: 18 Par: 70
Yds: 6246 F9 Yds: 3368 B9 Yds: 2878
Designer: James Braid

WROTHAM HEATH

WROTHAM HEATH GOLF CLUB, Seven Mile Lane, Borough Green, Sevenoaks, **KENT**, TN15 8QZ, **ENGLAND**.
(T) 01732 883854

Contact/s:
● **Manager:** Mr L J Bryne

Course/s:
⛳ **WROTHAM HEATH**
Number of Holes: 18

Designer: Donald Steel

WROTTESLEY

WROTTESLEY GOLF CLUB, 83 Wergs Rd, Wolverhampton, **MIDLANDS (WEST)**, WV6 9BP **ENGLAND**.
(T) 01902 846499

Course/s:
⛳ **WROTTESLEY GOLF CLUB**
Built: 1990
Number of Holes: 18

WYBOSTON

WYBOSTON GOLF & LEISURE PARK, Wyboston Lakes, Great North Rd, Wyboston, Bedford, **BEDFORDSHIRE**, MK44 3AL, **ENGLAND**.
(T) 01480 223004

Membership: Members & Public

Course/s:
⛳ **WYBOSTON LAKES**
Description: Parkland
Number of Holes: 18 Par: 70
Yds: 5955
Designer: N Oakden

WYCHNOR PARK

WYCHNOR PARK COUNTRY CLUB, Wychnor Hall, Wychnor, Burton-on-Trent, **STAFFORDSHIRE**, DE13 8BU, **ENGLAND**.
(T) 01283 791391

Contact/s:
● **General Manager:** Mr J Hodson

Course/s:
⛳ **WYCHNOR PARK PAR 3**
Description: Short
Number of Holes: 9 Par: 27
Par 3's: 9
Yds: 1297

WYCOMBE HEIGHTS GOLF CTRE

WYCOMBE HEIGHTS GOLF CENTRE, Rayners Ave, Loudwater, High Wycombe, **BUCKINGHAMSHIRE**, HP10 9SZ, **ENGLAND**.
(T) 01494 816686

Membership: Members & Public

Contact/s:
● **Manager:** Mr D Lunniss

Course/s:
⛳ **FAMILY**
Number of Holes: 18 Par: 54
Par 3's: 18
Yds: 1955 F9 Yds: 1009 B9 Yds: 946
Designer: John Jacobs

⛳ **MAIN**
Number of Holes: 18 Par: 70
Par 3's: 4 Par 4's: 12 Par 5's: 2
Yds: 6265 F9 Yds: 3242 B9 Yds: 3023
Designer: John Jacobs

WYKE GREEN

WYKE GREEN GOLF CLUB, Secretary, Syon Lane, Isleworth, **LONDON (GREATER)**, TW7 5PT, **ENGLAND**.
(T) 020 88471956
(E) office@wykegreen.golfagent.co.uk

Contact/s:
● **Professional:** Mr Neil Smith
☎ 020 88470685

Course/s:
⛳ **WYKE GREEN**
Description: Wooded, Parkland, Medium

Length, Drains Well
Green Speed: Fast
Built: 1928 **Built On:** Clay
Number of Holes: 18
Prevailing Wind: West
Designer: Hawtree

WYNYARD CLUB

WYNYARD CLUB (THE), Wellington Drive,
Wynyard, Billingham, **CLEVELAND**, TS22
5QJ, **ENGLAND**.
(T) 01740 644399

Membership: Members & Public

Contact/s:
● **Professional:** Mr Andrew Oliphant

Course/s:
🔴 **THE WELLINGTON**
Description: Championship, Parkland,
Ideal for the Elderly
Green Speed: Fast **Built On:** Soil
Number of Holes: 18 **Par:** 72
Par 3's: 4 **Par 4's:** 10 **Par 5's:** 4
Yds: 6653 **Designer:** Hawtree
Further Information:
Situated on an old country estate.

WYRE FOREST

WYRE FOREST GOLF CENTRE LTD,
Zortech Ave, Kidderminster,
WORCESTERSHIRE, DY11 7EX, **ENGLAND**.
(T) 01299 822682
(W) www.wyreforestgolf.co.uk

Membership: Members & Public

Contact/s:
● **Professional:** Mr Simon Price

Course/s:
🔴 **WYRE FOREST**
Description: Links, Open, Medium
Length, Drains Well, Ideal for the Elderly
Green Speed: Medium
Built: 1995
Number of Holes: 18

YARROW VALLEY

YARROW VALLEY GOLF COURSE, Iddon
House Farm, Church Lane, Charnock Richard,
Chorley, **LANCASHIRE**, PR7 3RB,
ENGLAND.
(T) 01257 276652

Course/s:
🔴 **YARROW VALLEY 9 HOLE**
Number of Holes: 9

YELVERTON

YELVERTON GOLF CLUB, Golf Links Rd,
Yelverton, **DEVON**, PL20 6BN, **ENGLAND**.
(T) 01822 855658

Membership: Members & Public

Contact/s:
● **Club Secretary:** Mr Stewart Barnes
● **Professional:** Mr Tim McSherry
● **Book Lessons:**
☎ 01822 852824

Course/s:
🔴 **YELVERTON**
Description: Moorland, Open, Medium
Length, Ideal for the Elderly
Green Speed: Fast
Built: 1904
Number of Holes: 18 **Par:** 71
Par 3's: 4 **Par 4's:** 11 **Par 5's:** 3
Yds: 6353 **F9 Yds:** 3146 **B9 Yds:** 3207
Designer: Fowler
Further Information:
Views of Dartmoor and the River Tamar.

YEOVIL

YEOVIL GOLF CLUB, Club Secretary,
Sherborne Rd, Yeovil, **SOMERSET**, BA21
5BW, **ENGLAND**.
(T) 01935 422965
(E) yeovilgolfclub@yeovilgc.fsnet.co.uk

Membership: Members & Public

Contact/s:
● **Club Secretary:** Mr Graham Dodd
● **Professional:** Mr Geoff Kite
☎ 01935 473763

Course/s:
🔴 **NEWTON**
Number of Holes: 9
Designer: Charles Hugh Alison, Herbert
Fowler

🔴 **OLD**
Description: Parkland, Medium Length,
Drains Well
Green Speed: Medium
Built: 1907 **Built On:** Sand
Number of Holes: 18 **Par:** 72
Record: 64 (Alan Evans, Ian Harrison)
Yds: 6150 **F9 Yds:** 3182 **B9 Yds:** 2968
Prevailing Wind: South/West
Designer: Charles Carter

YORK

YORK GOLF CLUB, Lords Moor Lane,
Strensall, York, **YORKSHIRE (NORTH)**,
YO32 5XF, **ENGLAND**.
(T) 01904 491840

Course/s:
🔴 **YORK**
Number of Holes: 18
Designer: Taylor

YORK GOLF CTRE

SKELTON PARK GOLF COURSE, Shipton
Rd, York, **YORKSHIRE (NORTH)**, YO30
1XW, **ENGLAND**.
(T) 01904 470549

Membership: Members & Public

Contact/s:
● **Owner:** Mr Ricky Pearson-Adams

Course/s:
🔴 **YORK GOLF CTRE**
Description: Parkland, Open, Short,
Tends to Flood, Ideal for the Elderly
Green Speed: Medium
Built: 1990 **Built On:** Clay
Number of Holes: 9 **Par:** 30 **Record:** 70
(Martin Keitch)
Par 3's: 6 **Par 4's:** 3
Yds: 1558
Prevailing Wind: West
Designer: Astham Biyan College, RNBS,
RSPA
Further Information:
9 hole course can be played as an 18 hole
course

YOUGHAL

YOUGHAL GOLF CLUB, Knockaverry,
Youghal, **COUNTY CORK**, **IRELAND**.
(T) 024 92787
(E) youghalgolfclub@eircom.net

Course/s:
🔴 **YOUGHAL**
Number of Holes: 18
Designer: Commander J Harris

SECTION 2

This section helps you to locate clubs by county and town of your choice.
This is the conventional way most directories display information. The counties are also categorised by country.

eg. England, **Cheshire, Chester,** Aldersey Green

Once you have located a club using this section, you can then refer to the detailed profile of the club in Section 1, or search for specific details in other sections.

GolfWorld Directory

BATH & SOMERSET (NORTH EAST)

BATH

- APPROACH
- BATH
- COMBE GROVE MANOR
- ENTRY HILL
- FOSSEWAY
- LANSDOWN
- MENDIP

FROME

- FROME GOLF CLUB
- ORCHARDLEIGH

BEDFORDSHIRE

BEDFORD

- BEDFORD
- BEDFORD & COUNTY
- BEDFORDSHIRE
- COLMWORTH & NORTH BEDFORDSHIRE
- LYSHOTT HEATH
- MOWSBURY
- OUSE VALLEY
- PAVENHAM
- WYBOSTON

DUNSTABLE

- CHALGRAVE MANOR
- DUNSTABLE DOWNS

HENLOW

- MOUNT PLEASANT

LEIGHTON BUZZARD

- AYLESBURY VALE
- IVINGHOE
- LEIGHTON BUZZARD
- MENTMORE
- TILSWORTH

LUTON

- GRIFFIN
- LUTON GOLF CTRE
- SOUTH BEDS
- STOCKWOOD PARK

SANDY

- JOHN O'GAUNT

SHEFFORD

- BARON & BARONESS

BERKSHIRE

ASCOT

- ASCOT (ROYAL)
- BERKSHIRE
- LAVENDER PARK
- MILL RIDE
- SUNNINGDALE LADIES
- SWINLEY FOREST

BRACKNELL

- BLUE MOUNTAIN GOLF CENTRE

CROWTHORNE

- EAST BERKSHIRE

MAIDENHEAD

- BIRD HILLS
- MAIDENHEAD
- TEMPLE
- WINTER HILL

NEWBURY

- DEANWOOD PARK
- DONNINGTON VALLEY
- NEWBURY & CROOKHAM
- NEWBURY RACECOURSE
- PARASAMPIA
- WEST BERKSHIRE

READING

- CALCOT PARK
- CASTLE ROYLE
- CAVERSHAM HEATH
- GORING AND STREATLEY
- HURST
- MAPLEDURHAM
- READING
- SONNING
- THEALE GOLF CTRE
- WOKEFIELD PARK

SINDLESHAM

- BEARWOOD

SLOUGH

- BURNHAM BEECHES
- DATCHET
- FARNHAM PARK
- LAMBOURNE CLUB
- LANES
- STOKE POGES
- WEXHAM PARK

WARGRAVE

- HENNERTON

WOKINGHAM

- BEARWOOD LAKES
- BILLINGBEAR PARK
- DOWNSHIRE
- SAND MARTINS
- WOODCRAY MANOR

BRISTOL

BRISTOL

- ASHTON COURT
- BRISTOL & CLIFTON
- CHIPPING SODBURY
- FARRINGTON
- FILTON
- HENBURY
- KENDLESHIRE
- KNOWLE
- LONG ASHTON
- MANGOTSFIELD
- MENDIP SPRING
- SALTFORD
- SHIREHAMPTON PARK
- STOCKWOOD VALE
- TALL PINES
- THORNBURY GOLF
- TICKENHAM
- TRACY PARK
- WOODLANDS
- WOODSPRING

BUCKINGHAMSHIRE

AYLESBURY

- AYLESBURY
- AYLESBURY PARK
- CHILTERN FOREST

- ELLESBOROUGH
- WESTON TURVILLE

BEACONSFIELD

- BEACONSFIELD

BOARDSTALL

- MAGNOLIA PARK

BUCKINGHAM

- SILVERSTONE

CHALFONT ST. GILES

- HAREWOOD DOWNS
- LITTLE CHALFONT
- OAKLAND PARK

CHESHAM

- CHARTRIDGE PARK
- CHESHAM & LEY HILL

GERRARDS CROSS

- GERRARDS CROSS

HIGH WYCOMBE

- FLACKWELL HEATH
- HAZLEMERE
- WYCOMBE HEIGHTS GOLF CTRE

IVER

- IVER
- RICHINGS PARK
- THORNEY PARK

MARLOW

- HARLEYFORD

MILTON KEYNES

- ABBEY HILL
- ASPLEY GUISE & WOBURN SANDS
- KINGFISHER
- THREE LOCKS
- WAVENDON GOLF CTRE
- WINDMILL HILL
- WOBURN

PRINCES RISBOROUGH

- PRINCES RISBOROUGH
- WHITELEAF

TINGEWICK

- BUCKINGHAM

WOOBURN GREEN

- HEDSOR

CAMBRIDGESHIRE

CAMBRIDGE

- BOURN
- CAMBRIDGE
- CAMBRIDGE LAKES
- CAMBRIDGE MERIDIAN
- CAMBRIDGESHIRE MOAT HOUSE
- GIRTON
- GOG MAGOG

ELY

- ELY CITY

HUNTINGDON

- ABBOTSLEY
- BRAMPTON PARK
- HEMINGFORD ABBOT
- LAKESIDE LODGE
- RAMSEY CLUB
- ST. IVES

- ST. NEOTS

MARCH
- MARCH

PETERBOROUGH
- ELTON FURZE
- ORTON MEADOWS
- OUNDLE
- PETERBOROUGH MILTON
- STILTON OAKS
- THORNEY
- THORPE WOOD

RAMSEY
- OLD NENE

WISBECH
- TYDD ST GILES

CHANNEL ISLANDS
ALDERNEY
- ALDERNEY

GUERNSEY
- LA GRANDE MARE

JERSEY
- ST. CLEMENT

CHESHIRE
ALDERLEY EDGE
- ALDERLEY EDGE

ALTRINCHAM
- ALTRINCHAM
- DUNHAM FOREST
- HALE
- RINGWAY

CHEADLE
- CHEADLE
- GATLEY

CHESTER
- ALDERSEY GREEN
- CARDEN PARK
- CHESTER
- EATON
- MOLLINGTON GRANGE
- PRYORS HAYES
- UPTON-BY-CHESTER
- VICARS CROSS
- WESTMINSTER PARK MUNICIPAL

CONGLETON
- ASTBURY
- CONGLETON

CREWE
- CREWE
- ONNELEY
- QUEENS PARK

DUKINFIELD
- DUKINFIELD

FRODSHAM
- FRODSHAM
- HELSBY

HYDE
- WERNETH LOW

KNUTSFORD
- HEYROSE
- HIGH LEGH PARK

- KNUTSFORD
- MERE
- MOBBERLEY
- PEOVER
- WILMSLOW

LYMM
- LYMM

MACCLESFIELD
- ADLINGTON
- MACCLESFIELD
- MARTON MEADOWS
- MOTTRAM HALL
- PRESTBURY
- SHRIGLEY HALL
- TYTHERINGTON

NANTWICH
- ALVASTON HALL
- REASEHEATH

NORTHWICH
- ANTROBUS
- SANDIWAY
- VALE ROYAL ABBEY

RUNCORN
- RUNCORN
- SUTTON HALL

SALE
- ASHTON-ON-MERSEY
- SALE

SANDBACH
- MALKINS BANK
- SANDBACH

STALYBRIDGE
- STAMFORD

STOCKPORT
- AVRO
- BRAMALL PARK
- BRAMHALL
- DAVENPORT
- DISLEY
- HAZEL GROVE
- HEATON MOOR
- HOULDSWORTH
- MARPLE
- MELLOR & TOWNSCLIFFE
- NEW MILLS
- REDDISH VALE
- ROMILEY
- STOCKPORT

STYAL
- STYAL

TARPORLEY
- PORTAL
- PORTAL PREMIER

WARRINGTON
- ALDER ROOT
- BIRCHWOOD
- LEIGH
- WALTON HALL

WIDNES
- MERSEY VALLEY
- ST. MICHAELS JUBILEE
- WIDNES

WINSFORD
- KNIGHTS GRANGE

CLEVELAND
BILLINGHAM
- BILLINGHAM
- WYNYARD CLUB

HARTLEPOOL
- CASTLE EDEN
- HARTLEPOOL
- HIGH THROSTON
- SEATON CAREW

MIDDLESBROUGH
- MIDDLESBROUGH
- MIDDLESBROUGH MUNICIPAL

REDCAR
- CLEVELAND
- WILTON

SALTBURN-BY-THE-SEA
- HUNLEY HALL
- SALTBURN

STOCKTON-ON-TEES
- EAGLESCLIFFE
- KNOTTY HILL GOLF CTRE
- NORTON
- TEESSIDE

CORNWALL
BODMIN
- LANHYDROCK
- ST. KEW

BUDE
- BUDE & NORTH CORNWALL
- IVYLEAF

CAMBORNE
- TEHIDY

CAMELFORD
- BOWOOD

FALMOUTH
- BUDOCK VEAN
- FALMOUTH

HAYLE
- GREENACRES

HELSTON
- HELSTON
- MULLION

LAUNCESTON
- LAUNCESTON
- TRETHORNE

LOOE
- LOOE

LOSTWITHIEL
- LOSTWITHIEL

NEWQUAY
- HOLYWELL BAY
- MERLIN
- NEWQUAY
- ST. NEWLYN EAST
- TRELOY

PADSTOW
- TREVOSE

PENZANCE
- CAPE CORNWALL
- PRAA SANDS

PERRANPORTH
- PERRANPORTH

REDRUTH
- RADNOR GOLF & SKI CTRE

SALTASH
- CHINA FLEET
- ST. MELLION INTERNATIONAL

ST. AUSTELL
- CARLYON BAY
- PORTHPEAN
- ST. AUSTELL

ST. IVES
- TREGENNA CASTLE
- WEST CORNWALL

TORPOINT
- WHITSAND BAY

TRURO
- KILLIOW PARK
- TRURO

WADEBRIDGE
- ROSERROW
- ST. ENODOC

COUNTY DURHAM

BARNARD CASTLE
- BARNARD CASTLE

BISHOP AUCKLAND
- BISHOP AUCKLAND

CHESTER LE STREET
- BIRTLEY
- CHESTER-LE-STREET
- ROSEBERRY GRANGE

CONSETT
- CONSETT & DISTRICT

CROOK
- CROOK

DARLINGTON
- BLACKWELL GRANGE
- DARLINGTON
- DINSDALE SPA
- HALLGARTH
- STRESSHOLME

DURHAM
- BRANCEPETH CASTLE
- DURHAM CITY
- MOUNT OSWALD MANOR
- RAMSIDE

NEWTON AYCLIFFE
- AYCLIFFE
- OAK LEAF
- WOODHAM

SEAHAM
- SEAHAM HARBOUR

STANLEY
- BEAMISH PARK
- SOUTH MOOR

CUMBRIA

ALSTON
- ALSTON MOOR

APPLEBY-IN-WESTMORLAND
- APPLEBY

ASKAM-IN-FURNESS
- DUNNERHOLME

BARROW-IN-FURNESS
- BARROW
- FURNESS

BRAMPTON
- BRAMPTON
- HALTWHISTLE

CARLISLE
- CARLISLE
- EDEN
- STONY HOLME
- SWIFTS

COCKERMOUTH
- COCKERMOUTH

GRANGE-OVER-SANDS
- GRANGE FELL
- GRANGE-OVER-SANDS

KENDAL
- BECKSIDE
- CARUS GREEN
- KENDAL

KESWICK
- KESWICK

KIRKBY LONSDALE
- CASTERTON

MARYPORT
- MARYPORT

MILLOM
- SILECROFT

PENRITH
- PENRITH

SEASCALE
- SEASCALE

SEDBERGH
- SEDBURGH

ULVERSTON
- ULVERSTON

WIGTON
- SILLOTH

WINDERMERE
- WINDERMERE

WORKINGTON
- DISTINGTON GOLF
- WORKINGTON

DERBYSHIRE

ALFRETON
- ALFRETON
- SHIRLAND

ASHBOURNE
- ASHBOURNE
- BRAILSFORD

BAKEWELL
- BAKEWELL

BELPER
- CHEVIN
- STRUTT CLUB

BUXTON
- BUXTON & HIGH PEAK
- CAVENDISH

CHESTERFIELD
- BARLBOROUGH LINKS
- CHESTERFIELD
- GRASSMOOR GOLF CTRE
- STANEDGE
- TAPTON PARK

DERBY
- ALLESTREE
- BREEDON PRIORY
- BROUGHTON HEATH
- DERBY
- HORSLEY LODGE
- KEDLESTON PARK
- MAYWOOD
- MICKLEOVER
- SINFIN

DRONFIELD
- BIRCH HALL
- HALLOWES

GLOSSOP
- GLOSSOP & DISTRICT

HIGH PEAK
- CHAPEL-EN-LE-FRITH

HOPE VALLEY
- SICKLEHOLME

ILKESTON
- BREADSALL PRIORY
- EREWASH VALLEY
- MORLEY HAYES
- PEWIT

RIPLEY
- ORMONDE FIELDS

DEVON

BARNSTAPLE
- PORTMORE GOLF PARK

BIDEFORD
- HARTLAND FOREST
- NORTH DEVON (ROYAL)

BRAUNTON
- SAUNTON

BRIXHAM
- CHURSTON

BUDLEIGH SALTERTON
- EAST DEVON

CHULMLEIGH
- CHULMLEIGH

CREDITON
- CREDITON
- WATERBRIDGE

CULLOMPTON
- PADBROOK PARK

by COUNTY by TOWN in England

Devon — Essex

DAWLISH
- DAWLISH APPROACH
- WARREN

EXETER
- EXETER
- FINGLE GLEN
- OAK MEADOW
- TEIGN VALLEY
- WOODBURY PARK

HOLSWORTHY
- HOLSWORTHY

HONITON
- HONITON
- OTTER VALLEY GOLF CTRE

ILFRACOMBE
- ILFRACOMBE

IVYBRIDGE
- DINNATON

KINGSBRIDGE
- BIGBURY
- THURLESTONE

NEWTON ABBOT
- DAINTON PARK
- HELE PARK GOLF CTRE
- MANOR HOUSE
- NEWTON ABBOT

OKEHAMPTON
- ASHBURY
- OKEHAMPTON

PLYMOUTH
- CENTRAL PARK
- ELFORDLEIGH
- SPARKWELL
- STADDON HEIGHTS

SEATON
- AXE CLIFF

SIDMOUTH
- SIDMOUTH

SOUTH BRENT
- WRANGATON

TAVISTOCK
- HURDWICK
- TAVISTOCK

TEIGNMOUTH
- SHALDON APPROACH
- TEIGNMOUTH

TIVERTON
- TIVERTON

TORQUAY
- TORQUAY

TORRINGTON
- TORRINGTON

TOTNES
- DARTMOUTH

UMBERLEIGH
- HIGHBULLEN HOTEL
- LIBBATON

WOOLACOMBE
- MORTEHOE & WOOLACOMBE
- WILLINGCOTT

YELVERTON
- YELVERTON

DORSET

BEAMINSTER
- CHEDINGTON COURT

BLANDFORD FORUM
- ASHLEY WOOD
- DORSET HEIGHTS

BOURNEMOUTH
- BOSCOMBE LADIES
- BOURNEMOUTH & MEYRICK
- KNIGHTON HEATH
- QUEENS PARK
- SOLENT MEADS GOLF CTRE

BRIDPORT
- BRIDPORT & WEST DORSET

BROADSTONE
- BROADSTONE

CHRISTCHURCH
- DUDMOOR
- HIGHCLIFFE CASTLE
- IFORD BRIDGE
- PARLEY

DORCHESTER
- CAME DOWN
- LYONS GATE

FERNDOWN
- DUDSBURY
- FERNDOWN
- FERNDOWN FOREST

GILLINGHAM
- BULLPITS

LYME REGIS
- LYME REGIS

POOLE
- BULBURY
- PARKSTONE

SHERBORNE
- FOLKE GOLF CTRE
- SHERBORNE

SWANAGE
- ISLE OF PURBECK

VERWOOD
- CRANE VALLEY

WAREHAM
- EAST DORSET
- WAREHAM

WEYMOUTH
- WESSEX GOLF CTRE
- WEYMOUTH

WIMBORNE
- CANFORD MAGNA
- STURMINSTER MARSHALL

ESSEX

BASILDON
- BASILDON

BENFLEET
- BOYCE HILL

BILLERICAY
- BURSTEAD
- STOCK BROOK MANOR

BRAINTREE
- BRAINTREE
- TOWERLANDS

BRENTWOOD
- BENTLEY
- DUNTON HILLS
- HARTSWOOD
- PRIORS
- SOUTH ESSEX
- THORNDON PARK
- WARLEY PARK
- WEALD PARK GOLF CLUB

BURNHAM-ON-CROUCH
- BURNHAM-ON-CROUCH

CANVEY ISLAND
- CASTLE POINT

CHELMSFORD
- CHANNELS
- CHELMSFORD
- REGIMENT
- THREE RIVERS
- WEST PARK

CHIGWELL
- CHIGWELL
- EPPING FOREST
- HAINAULT FOREST

CLACTON-ON-SEA
- CLACTON
- MILLERS BARN GOLF PARK

COLCHESTER
- BIRCH GROVE
- COLCHESTER
- COLNE VALLEY
- ESSEX
- LEXDEN
- STOKE-BY-NAYLAND

EPPING
- EPPING
- HOBBS CROSS
- NORTH WEALD
- NORTH WEALD PAR 3
- THEYDON BOIS

FRINTON-ON-SEA
- FRINTON

GRAYS
- ORSETT

HALSTEAD
- GOSFIELD LAKE

HARLOW
- CANONS BROOK

HARWICH
- HARWICH & DOVERCOURT

ILFORD
- ILFORD

INGATESTONE
- CRONDON PARK
- HYLANDS GOLF COMPLEX

LEIGH-ON-SEA
- BELFAIRS PARK
- SOUTHEND-ON-SEA

LOUGHTON
- HIGH BEECH
- LOUGHTON

MALDON
- BUNSAY DOWNS
- FIVE LAKES HOTEL
- FORRESTER PARK
- MALDON
- WARREN

ONGAR
- TOOT HILL

RAYLEIGH
- HANOVER

ROCHFORD
- BALLARDS GORE
- ROCHFORD HUNDRED

ROMFORD
- ABRIDGE
- MAYLANDS
- RISEBRIDGE
- ROMFORD
- STAPLEFORD ABBOTTS GOLF CLUB

SAFFRON WALDEN
- SAFFRON WALDEN

SOUTH OCKENDON
- BELHUS PARK
- MARDYKE VALLEY GOLF CTRE

SOUTHEND-ON-SEA
- ESSEX
- THORPE HALL

STANFORD-LE-HOPE
- ST. CLERES HALL

UPMINSTER
- LANGDON HILLS GOLF CTRE
- TOP MEADOW
- UPMINSTER

WALTHAM ABBEY
- NAZEING

WITHAM
- BENTON HALL
- BRAXTED PARK
- NOTLEYS
- RIVENHALL OAKS

WOODFORD GREEN
- WOODFORD

GLOUCESTERSHIRE

CHELTENHAM
- CLEEVE HILL
- COTSWOLD HILLS
- LILLEY BROOK
- NAUNTON DOWNS
- SHIPTON

CHURCH DOWN
- BRICKHAMPTON COURT

CIRENCESTER
- CIRENCESTER

COLEFORD
- FOREST HILLS
- FOREST OF DEAN

DURSLEY
- STINCHCOMBE HILL

DYMOCK
- DYMOCK GRANGE

GLOUCESTER
- GLOUCESTER
- ORCHARD
- RAMADA HOTEL
- RODWAY HILL

LYDNEY
- LYDNEY

NEWENT
- NEWENT

STROUD
- MINCHINHAMPTON
- PAINSWICK

TEWKESBURY
- HILTON PUCKRUP HALL
- SHERDONS
- TEWKESBURY PARK

WOTTON-UNDER-EDGE
- CANNONS COURT
- COTSWOLD EDGE

GUERNSEY

L'ANCRESSE VALE
- GUERNSEY (ROYAL)

ST PETERS PORT
- ST. PIERRE PARK

HAMPSHIRE

ALDERSHOT
- ARMY

ALRESFORD
- ALRESFORD

ALTON
- ALTON
- BLACKNEST
- FOUR MARKS
- WORLDHAM PARK

ANDOVER
- ANDOVER
- HAMPSHIRE

BASINGSTOKE
- BASINGSTOKE
- BASINGSTOKE
- DUMMER
- TEST VALLEY
- WEYBROOK PARK

BORDON
- BLACKMOOR
- DEAN FARM

BROCKENHURST
- BROKENHURST MANOR

DENMEAD
- FURZELEY

EASTLEIGH
- EAST HORTON GOLF CTRE

- FLEMING PARK

FAREHAM
- CAMS HALL ESTATE GOLF CLUB
- FAREHAM WOODS
- SOUTHWICK PARK
- SWANMORE GOLF CTRE
- WICKHAM PARK

FARNBOROUGH
- SOUTHWOOD

FLEET
- NORTH HANTS FLEET

GOSPORT
- GOSPORT & STOKES BAY

HAYLING ISLAND
- HAYLING
- TOURNERBURY GOLF CTRE

HOOK
- BLACKWATER VALLEY
- HARTLEY WINTNEY
- TYLNEY PARK

LEE-ON-THE-SOLENT
- LEE ON THE SOLENT

LIPHOOK
- LIPHOOK
- OLD THORNS

LISS
- PETERSFIELD

LYNDHURST
- BRAMSHAW
- NEW FOREST

NEW MILTON
- BARTON-ON-SEA
- CHEWTON GLEN

PETERSFIELD
- PETERSFIELD

PORTSMOUTH
- GREAT SALTERNS

RINGWOOD
- BURLEY
- MOORS VALLEY GOLF CTRE

ROMSEY
- AMPFIELD PAR-THREE
- DUNWOOD MANOR
- PAULTONS GOLF CENTRE
- WELLOW

ROWLANDS CASTLE
- ROWLANDS CASTLE

SOUTHAMPTON
- BOTLEY PARK
- BRAMSHOTT HILL
- CHILWORTH
- CORHAMPTON
- COUNTY
- DIBDEN GOLF CTRE
- FAIRTHORNE MANOR
- MEON VALLEY
- ROMSEY
- SOUTHAMPTON MUNICIPAL
- STONEHAM

STOCKBRIDGE
- LECKFORD

TADLEY
- BISHOPSWOOD
- SANDFORD SPRINGS

WATERLOOVILLE
- PORTSMOUTH
- WATERLOOVILLE

WINCHESTER
- HOCKLEY
- OTTERBOURNE
- PARK
- SOUTH WINCHESTER
- WINCHESTER (ROYAL)

HEREFORDSHIRE

HEREFORD
- BELMONT
- BRAMPTON GOLF
- BROCKINGTON
- BURGHILL VALLEY
- HEREFORD MUNICIPAL
- HEREFORDSHIRE
- SUMMERHILL

KINGTON
- KINGTON

LEOMINSTER
- GROVE
- LEOMINSTER

ROSS-ON-WYE
- ROSS-ON-WYE
- SOUTH HEREFORDSHIRE

HERTFORDSHIRE

BARNET
- ARKLEY
- BRIDGEDOWN
- DYRHAM PARK
- EAST BARNET
- HADLEY WOOD
- OAK HILL PARK
- OLD FOLD MANOR

BERKHAMSTED
- ASHRIDGE
- BERKHAMSTED
- WHIPSNADE PARK

BISHOP'S STORTFORD
- BISHOPS STORTFORD

BROXBOURNE
- HERTFORDSHIRE

BUNTINGFORD
- EAST HERTS

BUSHEY
- BUSHEY HALL

HARPENDEN
- ALDWICKBURY PARK
- HARPENDEN
- HARPENDEN COMMON

HATFIELD
- BROOKMANS PARK
- HATFIELD LONDON

HEMEL HEMPSTEAD
- BOXMOOR
- LITTLE HAY

- SHENDISH MANOR

HERTFORD
- BRICKENDON GRANGE

HITCHIN
- CHESFIELD DOWNS

KNEBWORTH
- KNEBWORTH

LETCHWORTH
- LETCHWORTH

MUCH HADHAM
- ASH VALLEY GOLF CLUB
- GREAT HADHAM

POTTERS BAR
- POTTERS BAR

RADLETT
- PORTER'S PARK

RICKMANSWORTH
- BATCHWORTH PARK
- CHORLEYWOOD
- MOOR PARK
- RICKMANSWORTH

ROYSTON
- BARKWAY PARK
- HEYDON GRANGE
- KINGSWAY
- MALTON
- ROYSTON
- WHADDON

SAWBRIDGEWORTH
- MANOR OF GROVES

ST. ALBANS
- ABBEY VIEW
- BATCHWOOD
- MID-HERTS
- REDBOURN
- VERULAM

STEVENAGE
- STEVENAGE

TRING
- STOCKS HOTEL

WALTHAM CROSS
- CHESHUNT PARK GOLF COURSE

WARE
- BRIGGENS HOUSE
- CHADWELL SPRINGS
- HANBURY MANOR
- WHITEHILL GOLF CTRE

WATFORD
- ALDENHAM
- BUSHEY GOLF COURSE
- HARTSBOURNE COUNTRY CLUB
- OXHEY PARK
- PENFOLD PARK
- WEST HERTS

WELWYN
- DANESBURY PARK

WELWYN GARDEN CITY
- BROCKET HALL
- MILL GREEN GOLF CLUB
- PANSHANGER GOLF COMPLEX
- WELWYN GARDEN CITY

ISLE OF MAN

CASTLETOWN
- CASTLETOWN GOLF LINKS

DOUGLAS
- DOUGLAS
- MOUNT MURRAY

ONCHAN
- KING EDWARD BAY

PEEL
- PEEL

PORT ERIN
- ROWANY

PORT ST MARY
- PORT ST MARY

RAMSEY
- RAMSEY

ISLE OF WIGHT

COWES
- COWES

EAST COWES
- OSBORNE

FRESHWATER
- FRESHWATER BAY

NEWPORT
- NEWPORT

RYDE
- RYDE
- WESTRIDGE

SANDOWN
- SHANKLIN & SANDOWN

VENTNOR
- VENTNOR

ISLES OF SCILLY

ST. MARYS
- ISLES OF SCILLY

JERSEY

GROUVILLE
- JERSEY (ROYAL)

ST BRELADE
- LA MOYE

KENT

ASHFORD
- ASHFORD
- ASHFORD
- CHART HILLS
- HOMELANDS

BECKENHAM
- BECKENHAM PLACE PARK
- LANGLEY PARK

BEXLEYHEATH
- BARNEHURST
- BEXLEYHEATH

BROADSTAIRS
- NORTH FORELAND

BROMLEY
- BROMLEY
- SHORTLANDS

SUNDRIDGE PARK

CANTERBURY
BROOME PARK
CANTERBURY

CHISLEHURST
CHISLEHURST

CRANBROOK
HAWKHURST
HEMSTED FOREST GOLF CLUB

DARTFORD
AUSTIN LODGE
BIRCHWOOD PARK
DARTFORD
PRINCES GOLF & LEISURE CLUB

DEAL
CINQUE PORTS (ROYAL)
WALMER & KINGSDOWN

EDENBRIDGE
EDENBRIDGE
HEVER
HOLTYE
SWEETWOODS PARK

FAVERSHAM
BOUGHTON
FAVERSHAM

FOLKESTONE
ETCHINGHILL
ROUNDWOOD HALL
SENE VALLEY

GILLINGHAM
GILLINGHAM

GRAVESEND
MID KENT
SOUTHERN VALLEY

HERNE BAY
HERNE BAY

HYTHE
HYTHE IMPERIAL

LONGFIELD
FAWKHAM VALLEY GOLF CLUB

MAIDSTONE
BEARSTED
COBTREE MANOR PARK
LEEDS CASTLE
MOTE PARK GOLF HUT
RIDGE GOLF CLUB
TUDOR PARK

NEW ROMNEY
LITTLESTONE
ROMNEY WARREN

ORPINGTON
CHELSFIELD LAKES GOLF CTRE
CRAY VALLEY
HIGH ELMS
LULLINGSTONE PARK
RUXLEY PARK
WEST KENT

RAMSGATE
ST. AGUSTINES

ROCHESTER
ALLHALLOWS

DEANGATE RIDGE
ROCHESTER & COBHAM

ROMNEY MARSH
LYDD

SANDWICH
PRINCES
ST. GEORGE'S (ROYAL)

SEVENOAKS
BROKE HILL
DARENTH VALLEY
KNOLE PARK
LONDON
REDLIBBETS
WILDERNESSE
WROTHAM HEATH

SIDCUP
SIDCUP

SITTINGBOURNE
OAST GOLF CTRE
SITTINGBOURNE & MILTON REGIS
UPCHURCH RIVER VALLEY

SNODLAND
OAST PARK

SWANLEY
PEDHAM PLACE GOLF CTRE

TENTERDEN
LONDON BEACH
TENTERDEN

TONBRIDGE
HILDEN EUROPRO
MOATLANDS
NIZELS
POULT WOOD GOLF CTRE
STAPLEHURST GOLFING PARK

TUNBRIDGE WELLS
LAMBERHURST
NEVILL
TUNBRIDGE WELLS
VILLA

WEST KINGSDOWN
WOODLANDS MANOR

WEST MALLING
KINGS HILL
WEST MALLING

WESTERHAM
CHERRY LODGE
PARK WOOD

WESTGATE-ON-SEA
WESTGATE & BIRCHINGTON

WHITSTABLE
CHESTFIELD
WHITSTABLE & SEASALTER

LANCASHIRE

ACCRINGTON
ACCRINGTON & DISTRICT
BAXENDEN & DISTRICT
GREEN HAWORTH

ASHTON-UNDER-LYNE
ASHTON-UNDER-LYNE

BACUP
BACUP

BARNOLDSWICK
GHYLL

BLACKBURN
BLACKBURN
GREAT HARWOOD
MYTTON FOLD
PLEASINGTON
RISHTON
WILPSHIRE

BLACKPOOL
BLACKPOOL NORTH SHORE
BLACKPOOL PARK
HERONS REACH

BOLTON
BOLTON
BOLTON
BREIGHTMET
DEANE
DUNSCAR
GREAT LEVER & FARNWORTH
HARWOOD
HORWICH
MANOR
OLD LINKS
REGENT PARK
TURTON
WESTHOUGHTON
WESTHOUGHTON

BURNLEY
BRUNSHAW
BURNLEY
TOWNELEY MUNICIPAL

BURY
BURY
GREENMOUNT
LOWES PARK
PIKEFOLD
WALMERSLEY

CARNFORTH
KIRKBY LONSDALE
SILVERDALE

CHORLEY
CHARNOCK RICHARD
CHORLEY
DUXBURY JUBILEE PARK
EUXTON PARK GOLF CTRE
HIGHFIELD
SHAW HILL
YARROW VALLEY

CLITHEROE
CLITHEROE
WHALLEY

COLNE
COLNE

DARWEN
DARWEN

FLEETWOOD
FLEETWOOD

LANCASTER
ASHTON

- BENTHAM
- LANCASTER
- LANCASTER
- LANSIL

LEIGH
- PENNINGTON

LITTLEBOROUGH
- WHITTAKER

LYTHAM ST. ANNES
- FAIRHAVEN
- LYTHAM & ST ANNES (ROYAL)
- LYTHAM GREEN
- ST. ANNES OLD LINKS

MORECAMBE
- HEYSHAM
- MORECAMBE

NELSON
- MARSDEN PARK PUBLIC
- NELSON

ORMSKIRK
- HURLSTON
- MOSSOCK HALL
- ORMSKIRK

POULTON-LE-FYLDE
- KNOTT END
- POULTON LE FYLDE

PRESTON
- ASHTON & LEA
- FISHWICK HALL
- GARSTANG
- INGOL
- LEYLAND
- LONGRIDGE
- PENWORTHAM
- PRESTON

ROCHDALE
- CASTLE HAWK
- LOBDEN
- MARLAND
- ROCHDALE
- TUNSHILL

ROSSENDALE
- ROSENDALE GOLF CLUB

SKELMERSDALE
- DEAN WOOD

WIGAN
- ASHTON IN MAKERFIELD
- BEACON PARK
- GATHURST
- HAIGH HALL
- HINDLEY HALL
- STANDISH COURT
- WIGAN

LEICESTERSHIRE

ASHBY-DE-LA-ZOUCH
- WILLESLEY PARK

HINCKLEY
- HINCKLEY

LEICESTER
- BEEDLES LAKE
- BIRSTALL

- COSBY
- ENDERBY GOLF CLUB
- FOREST HILL
- GLEN GORSE
- HUMBERSTONE HEIGHTS
- KIBWORTH
- KIRBY MUXLOE
- LEICESTER
- OADBY
- ROTHLEY PARK
- SCRAPTOFT
- WESTERN
- WHETSTONE

LOUGHBOROUGH
- CHARNWOOD FOREST
- LINGDALE
- LONGCLIFFE
- PARK HILL
- RUSHCLIFFE

LUTTERWORTH
- KILWORTH SPRINGS
- LUTTERWORTH
- ULLESTHORPE

MARKET HARBOROUGH
- BLACKTHORN WOOD
- MARKET HARBOROUGH
- STOKE ALBANY

MELTON MOWBRAY
- MELTON MOWBRAY
- MELTON MOWBRAY TOWN EST
- SIX HILLS LEISURE

LINCOLNSHIRE

ALFORD
- WOODTHORPE HALL

BOSTON
- BOSTON
- KIRTON HOLME

BOURNE
- TOFT HOTEL

GAINSBOROUGH
- GAINSBOROUGH

GRANTHAM
- BELTON PARK
- BELTON WOODS
- ROPSLEY
- STOKE ROCHFORD
- SUDBROOK MOOR

HORNCASTLE
- HORNCASTLE

LINCOLN
- BLANKNEY
- CANWICK PARK
- CARHOLME
- LINCOLN
- MARTIN MOOR
- MILLFIELD GOLF
- POTTERGATE
- SOUTH KYME
- WELTON MANOR GOLF CTRE

LOUTH
- KENWICK PARK
- LOUTH

MABLETHORPE
- SANDILANDS & LEISURE

MARKET RASEN
- MARKET RASEN & DISTRICT
- OWMBY

SKEGNESS
- ADDLETHORPE
- NORTH SHORE
- SEACROFT
- SOUTH VIEW LEISURE

SLEAFORD
- SLEAFORD

SPALDING
- GEDNEY HILL
- SPALDING
- SUTTON BRIDGE

STAMFORD
- BURGHLEY PARK
- LUFFENHAM HEATH
- RUTLAND COUNTY

WOODHALL SPA
- WOODHALL SPA

LINCOLNSHIRE (NORTH EAST)

CLEETHORPES
- CLEETHORPES

GRIMSBY
- GRIMSBY
- HUMBERSTON PARK
- MANOR
- TETNEY
- WALTHAM WINDMILL

IMMINGHAM
- IMMINGHAM

LINCOLNSHIRE (NORTH)

BRIGG
- ELSHAM
- FOREST PINES

SCUNTHORPE
- ASHBY DECOY
- GRANGE PARK
- HOLME HALL
- KINGSWAY
- NORMANBY HALL

LONDON (GREATER)

CHINGFORD
- EPPING FOREST (ROYAL)
- WEST ESSEX

DENHAM
- BUCKINGHAMSHIRE

EDGWARE
- EDGWAREBURY

ENFIELD
- CREWS HILL
- ENFIELD
- WHITEWEBBS

GREENFORD
- EALING
- HORSENDEN HILL
- PERIVALE PARK

HAMPTON
- FULWELL

HARROW
- HARROW HILL

HILLINGDON
- HASTE HILL

HOUNSLOW
- AIRLINKS
- HOUNSLOW HEATH

ISLEWORTH
- WYKE GREEN

KINGSTON UPON THAMES
- COOMBE HILL
- COOMBE WOOD
- HAMPTON COURT PALACE GOLF CLUB

LONDON
- AQUARIUS
- BETHUNE PARK
- BLACKHEATH (ROYAL)
- BRENT VALLEY
- BRENT VALLEY PUBLIC
- BUSH HILL PARK
- CENTRAL LONDON
- CHINGFORD
- DUKES MEADOW
- DULWICH & SYDENHAM HILL
- ELTHAM WARREN
- FINCHLEY
- HAMPSTEAD
- HENDON
- HIGHGATE
- HUMAX
- LEE VALLEY
- LONDON SCOTTISH
- MILL HILL
- MUSWELL HILL
- NORTH MIDDLESEX
- RICHMOND PARK
- SHOOTERS HILL
- SOUTH HERTS
- THAMESVIEW
- TRENT PARK GOLF CLUB
- VALLEY
- WIMBLEDON (ROYAL)
- WIMBLEDON COMMON
- WIMBLEDON PARK

NORTHOLT
- C & L
- LIME TREES PARK
- RECTORY

NORTHWOOD
- NORTHWOOD
- SANDY LODGE

PINNER
- GRIMSDYKE

RUISLIP
- RUISLIP GOLF CTRE

SOUTHALL
- WEST MIDDLESEX

STANMORE
- STANMORE

TWICKENHAM
- STRAWBERRY HILL
- TWICKENHAM PARK

UXBRIDGE
- DENHAM
- HILLINGDON
- STOCKLEY PARK
- UXBRIDGE

WANSTEAD
- WANSTEAD

WEMBLEY
- SUDBURY

WEST DRAYTON
- HEATHPARK

MANCHESTER (GREATER)

MANCHESTER
- ACREGATE
- BLACKLEY
- BOYSNOPE PARK
- BRACKLEY
- BROOKDALE
- CHORLTON-CUM-HARDY
- DAVYHULME PARK
- DENTON
- DIDSBURY
- ELLESMERE
- FAIRFIELD GOLF & SAILING CLUB
- FLIXTON
- HEATON PARK
- MANCHESTER
- NEW NORTH MANCHESTER
- NORTHENDEN
- PRESTWICH
- STAND
- SWINTON PARK
- WHITEFIELD
- WILLIAM WROE
- WITHINGTON
- WORSLEY

OLDHAM
- CROMPTON & ROYTON
- OLDHAM
- SADDLEWORTH
- WERNETH

WORSLEY
- WORSLEY PARK

MERSEYSIDE

BIRKENHEAD
- PRENTON

BOOTLE
- BOOTLE

ELLESMERE PORT
- ELLESMERE PORT

LIVERPOOL
- AINTREE
- ALLERTON
- BOWRING PARK
- CHILDWALL
- FORMBY
- FORMBY HALL
- FORMBY LADIES
- HUYTON & PRESCOT

- LEE PARK
- LIVERPOOL MUNICIPAL
- WEST DERBY
- WEST LANCASHIRE
- WOOLTON

NEWTON-LE-WILLOWS
- HAYDOCK PARK

PRENTON
- WIRRAL LADIES

PRESCOT
- BLUNDELLS HILL

SOUTHPORT
- BIRKDALE (ROYAL)
- HESKETH
- HILLSIDE
- PARK
- SOUTHPORT & AINSDALE
- SOUTHPORT MUNICIPAL
- SOUTHPORT OLD LINKS

ST. HELENS
- GRANGE PARK
- HOUGHWOOD
- SHERDLEY PARK MUNICIPAL

WALLASEY
- BIDSTON
- WALLASEY
- WARREN

WIRRAL
- ARROWE PARK
- BRACKENWOOD
- BRACKENWOOD MUNICIPAL
- BROMBOROUGH
- CALDY
- EASTHAM LODGE
- HESWALL
- HOYLAKE MUNICIPAL
- LEASOWE
- LIVERPOOL (ROYAL)

MIDLANDS (WEST)

BIRMINGHAM
- COCKS MOORS WOODS
- EDGBASTON
- FULFORD HEATH
- GAY HILL
- GREAT BARR
- HANDSWORTH
- HARBORNE
- HARBORNE CHURCH FARM
- HATCHFORD BROOK
- HILLTOP
- KINGS NORTON
- LICKEY HILLS
- MAXSTOKE PARK
- MOSELEY
- NORTH WORCESTERSHIRE

COVENTRY
- ANSTY GOLF CTRE
- BRANDON WOOD MUNICIPAL
- COVENTRY
- FOREST OF ARDEN
- HAWKESBURY GOLF CENTRE
- HEARSALL
- NORTH WARWICKSHIRE

- STONEBRIDGE
- STONELEIGH DEER PARK
- WINDMILL VILLAGE

CRADLEY HEATH

- CORNGREAVES

DUDLEY

- DUDLEY
- HIMLEY HALL GOLF CTRE
- SEDGLEY GOLF CTRE
- SWINDON

HALESOWEN

- HALESOWEN

SMETHWICK

- WARLEY

SOLIHULL

- COPT HEATH
- HAVEN PASTURES
- HENLEY
- LADBROOK PARK
- OLTON
- ROBIN HOOD
- SHIRLEY
- TIDBURY GREEN
- WIDNEY MANOR

STOURBRIDGE

- ENVILLE
- HAGLEY
- STOURBRIDGE

SUTTON COLDFIELD

- ASTON WOOD
- BELFRY
- BOLDMERE
- LEA MARSTON
- LITTLE ASTON
- MOOR HALL
- PYPE HAYES
- SUTTON COLDFIELD
- SUTTON COLDFIELD LADIES
- WALMLEY
- WISHAW

WALSALL

- BLOXWICH
- CALDERFIELDS
- DRUIDS HEATH
- WALSALL

WARLEY

- BRANDHALL

WEST BROMWICH

- DARTMOUTH
- SANDWELL PARK

WOLVERHAMPTON

- OXLEY PARK
- PATSHULL PARK
- PENN
- PERTON PARK
- SOUTH STAFFORDSHIRE
- WERGS
- WOODFARM GOLF COMPLEX
- WROTTESLEY

NORFOLK

CROMER

- CROMER (ROYAL)

DEREHAM

- DEREHAM
- MATTISHALL

DISS

- DISS

DOWNHAM MARKET

- RYSTON PARK

FAKENHAM

- FAKENHAM

GREAT YARMOUTH

- CALDECOTT HALL
- GORLESTON
- GREAT YARMOUTH & CAISTER

HUNSTANTON

- HUNSTANTON

KING'S LYNN

- DUNHAM
- EAGLES
- KING'S LYNN
- MIDDLETON HALL
- WEST NORFOLK (ROYAL)

NORWICH

- BARNHAM BROOM
- BAWBURGH
- COSTESSEY PARK
- EATON
- MUNDESLEY
- NORFOLK
- NORWICH (ROYAL)
- SPROWSTON MANOR
- WENSUM VALLEY
- WESTON PARK

SWAFFHAM

- SWAFFHAM

THETFORD

- FELTWELL
- RICHMOND PARK
- THETFORD

NORTHAMPTONSHIRE

CORBY

- CORBY PUBLIC

DAVENTRY

- DAVENTRY & DISTRICT
- STAVERTON PARK

KETTERING

- KETTERING
- PYTCHLEY GOLF LODGE

NORTHAMPTON

- BRAMPTON HEATH
- COLD ASHBY
- COLLINGTREE PARK
- DELAPRE PARK GOLF COMPLEX
- KINGSTHORPE
- NORTHAMPTON
- NORTHAMPTONSHIRE COUNTY
- OVERSTONE PARK

TOWCESTER

- FARTHINGSTONE
- WHITTLEBURY PARK

WELLINGBOROUGH

- RUSHDEN

- WELLINGBOROUGH

NORTHUMBERLAND

ALNWICK

- ALNMOUTH
- ALNMOUTH VILLAGE
- ALNWICK
- DUNSTANBURGH CASTLE

BAMBURGH

- BAMBURGH CASTLE

BEDLINGTON

- BEDLINGTONSHIRE

BELFORD

- BELFORD

BERWICK-UPON-TWEED

- BERWICK
- HAGGERSTON CASTLE
- MAGDALENE FIELDS

BLYTH

- BLYTH

CRAMLINGTON

- ARCOT HALL

HEXHAM

- ALLENDALE
- BELLINGHAM
- HEXHAM
- SLALEY HALL GOLF COURSE
- TYNEDALE

MORPETH

- BURGHAM
- LINDEN HALL
- LONGHIRST HALL
- MORPETH
- ROTHBURY
- SWARLAND HALL
- WARKWORTH

NEWBIGGIN-BY-THE-SEA

- NEWBIGGIN

PRUDHOE

- PRUDHOE

SEAHOUSES

- SEAHOUSES

STOCKSFIELD

- STOCKSFIELD

WOOLER

- WOOLER

NOTTINGHAMSHIRE

MANSFIELD

- MANSFIELD WOODHOUSE
- SHERWOOD FOREST

NEWARK

- NEWARK
- SOUTHWELL

NOTTINGHAM

- BEESTON FIELDS
- BRAMCOTE HILLS
- BULWELL FOREST
- CHILWELL MANOR
- COTGRAVE PLACE
- EDWALTON MUNICIPAL
- LEE VALLEY GOLF CTRE

- MAPPERLEY
- NOTTINGHAM CITY
- NOTTS
- RADCLIFFE-ON-TRENT
- RAMSDALE PARK
- RIVERSIDE
- RUDDINGTON GRANGE
- SPRINGWATER
- STANTON ON THE WOLDS
- TRENT LOCK
- WOLLATON PARK

OLLERTON
- RUFFORD PARK GOLF CTRE

RETFORD
- RETFORD

SOUTHWELL
- NORWOOD PARK
- OAKMERE PARK

SUTTON-IN-ASHFIELD
- BRIERLEY FOREST
- COXMOOR

WORKSOP
- BONDHAY GOLF & FISHING CLUB
- COLLEGE PINES
- KILTON FOREST
- LINDRICK
- WORKSOP

OXFORDSHIRE

ABINGDON
- DRAYTON PARK
- FRILFORD HEATH

BANBURY
- BANBURY GOLF CTRE
- BRAILES
- CHERWELL EDGE
- RYE HILL
- TADMARTON HEATH

BICESTER
- BICESTER GOLF & COUNRTY CLUB

BURFORD
- BURFORD

CHIPPING NORTON
- CHIPPING NORTON
- LYNEHAM

DIDCOT
- HADDEN HILL

FARINGDON
- CARSWELL
- FARINGDON

HENLEY-ON-THAMES
- ASPECT PARK
- DOG
- GREYS GREEN
- HENLEY
- HUNTERCOMBE

HORTON-CUM-STUDLEY
- STUDLEY WOOD

KIDLINGTON
- KIRTLINGTON

OXFORD
- HINKSEY HEIGHTS
- NORTH OXFORD
- SOUTHFIELD
- WATERSTOCK

THAME
- OXFORDSHIRE

WITNEY
- WITNEY LAKES

RUTLAND

OAKHAM
- GREETHAM VALLEY
- RUTLAND WATER

SHROPSHIRE

BRIDGNORTH
- BRIDGNORTH
- CHESTERTON VALLEY
- SEVEN MEADOWS
- WORFIELD

CHURCH STRETTON
- CHURCH STRETTON

CLEOBURY MORTIMER
- CLEOBURY MORTIMER

ELLESMERE
- BROW

LUDLOW
- LUDLOW

MARKET DRAYTON
- MARKET DRAYTON

NEWPORT
- LILLESHALL HALL

OSWESTRY
- LLANYMYNECH
- MILE END
- OSWESTRY

SHIFNAL
- SHIFNAL

SHREWSBURY
- ARSCOTT
- HAWKSTONE PARK
- MEOLE BRACE
- SHREWBURY

TELFORD
- SHROPSHIRE
- TELFORD
- WREKIN

WHITCHURCH
- HILL VALLEY

SOMERSET

BRIDGWATER
- CANNINGTON
- ENMORE PARK

BURNHAM-ON-SEA
- BREAN
- BURNHAM & BERROW

CHARD
- WINDWHISTLE

LANGPORT
- LONG SUTTON

MINEHEAD
- MINEHEAD & WEST SOMERSET

SOMERTON
- WHEATHILL

TAUNTON
- OAKE MANOR
- TAUNTON & PICKERIDGE
- TAUNTON VALE
- VIVARY PARK

WEDMORE
- ISLE OF WEDMORE

WELLS
- WELLS

WINCANTON
- WINCANTON

YEOVIL
- HALSTOCK
- YEOVIL

SOMERSET (NORTH)

CLEVEDON
- CLEVEDON

WESTON-SUPER-MARE
- WESTON
- WORLEBURY

STAFFORDSHIRE

BURTON-ON-TRENT
- BRANSTON
- BURTON ON TRENT
- CRAYTHORNE
- WYCHNOR PARK

CANNOCK
- BEAU DESERT
- CANNOCK PARK

LEEK
- LEEK
- WESTWOOD

LICHFIELD
- SEEDY MILL
- WHITTINGTON HEATH

NEWCASTLE
- NEWCASTLE-UNDER-LYME
- WOLSTANTON

RUGELEY
- ST. THOMAS' PRIORY

STAFFORD
- BROCTON HALL
- CHASE
- INGESTRE PARK
- STAFFORD CASTLE

STOKE-ON-TRENT
- ALSAGER
- BURSLEM
- GOLDENHILL
- GREENWAY HALL
- PARKHALL
- TRENTHAM
- WHISTON HALL

STONE
- BARLASTON
- IZAAK WALTON
- STONE

TAMWORTH
- DRAYTON PARK
- TAMWORTH MUNICIPAL

UTTOXETER
- MANOR
- UTTOXETER

SUFFOLK

ALDEBURGH
- ALDEBURGH
- THORPENESS

BECCLES
- BECCLES

BUNGAY
- BUNGAY & WAVENEY VALLEY

BURY ST. EDMUNDS
- BURY ST EDMUNDS
- FLEMPTON
- SUFFOLK GOLF
- WORLINGTON & NEWMARKET (ROYAL)

FELIXSTOWE
- FELIXSTOWE FERRY

HALESWORTH
- HALESWORTH

HAVERHILL
- HAVERHILL

IPSWICH
- ALNESBOURNE PRIORY
- BRETTVALE
- FYNN VALLEY
- HINTLESHAM HALL
- IPSWICH
- RUSHMERE

LOWESTOFT
- DIP FARM
- ROOKERY PARK

NEWMARKET
- LINKS

SAXMUNDHAM
- HIGH LODGE

SOUTHWOLD
- SOUTHWOLD

STOWMARKET
- STOWMARKET

SUDBURY
- CLARE PARK LAKE
- NEWTON GREEN

WOODBRIDGE
- CRETINGHAM
- SECKFORD
- UFFORD PARK
- WALDRINGFIELD HEATH
- WOODBRIDGE

SURREY

ADDLESTONE
- ABBEYMOOR
- NEW ZEALAND
- SURREY GOLF & FITNESS

ASCOT
- SUNNINGDALE

ASHFORD
- ASHFORD MANOR

BAGSHOT
- PENNYHILL PARK
- WINDLESHAM

BANSTEAD
- CUDDINGTON

CAMBERLEY
- CAMBERLEY HEATH
- PINE RIDGE GOLF CTRE

CARSHALTON
- OAKS SPORTS CTRE

CATERHAM
- DUKES DENE
- HAPPY VALLEY
- NORTH DOWNS

CHERTSEY
- BARROW HILLS
- FOXHILLS GOLF
- LALEHAM

CHESSINGTON
- CHESSINGTON
- SURBITON

COBHAM
- SILVERMERE GOLF COMPLEX

COULSDON
- CHIPSTEAD
- COULSDON MANOR
- WOODCOTE PARK

CRANLEIGH
- CRANLEIGH
- WILDWOOD COUNTRY CLUB

CROYDON
- ADDINGTON
- ADDINGTON COURT GOLF CLUB
- ADDINGTON PALACE
- SELSDON PARK
- SHIRLEY PARK

DORKING
- BETCHWORTH PARK
- DORKING
- GATTON MANOR

EPSOM
- EPSOM
- HORTON PARK GOLF

ESHER
- MOORE PLACE
- SANDOWN GOLF CTRE
- THAMES DITTON & ESHER

FARNHAM
- BOWENHURST
- FARNHAM
- FARNHAM PARK PAR 3
- HANKLEY COMMON
- OAK PARK GOLF CLUB

GODALMING
- BROADWATER PARK
- CHIDDINGFOLD
- HURTMORE
- MILFORD GOLF CLUB
- SHILLINGLEE PARK
- WEST SURREY

GODSTONE
- HORNE PARK

GUILDFORD
- BRAMLEY
- CLANDON REGIS
- GUILDFORD
- MERRIST WOOD
- PUTTENHAM
- ROKER PARK
- SUTTON GREEN

HINDHEAD
- HINDHEAD

LEATHERHEAD
- DRIFT
- EFFINGHAM
- LEATHERHEAD
- PACHESHAM PARK GOLF CTRE
- TYRRELLS WOOD

LINGFIELD
- LINGFIELD PARK

MITCHAM
- MITCHAM

NEW MALDEN
- MALDEN

NEWDIGATE
- RUSPER

OXTED
- LIMPSFIELD CHART
- TANDRIDGE

REDHILL
- BLETCHINGLEY
- REDHILL & REIGATE
- REDHILL GOLF CTRE

REIGATE
- REIGATE HEATH
- REIGATE HILL

RICHMOND
- MID-SURREY (ROYAL)
- RICHMOND

SHEPPERTON
- SUNBURY

SOUTH CROYDON
- CROHAM HURST
- PURLEY DOWNS

SUNBURY-ON-THAMES
- HAZELWOOD GOLF CTRE

SUTTON
- BANSTEAD DOWNS

TADWORTH
- KINGSWOOD
- WALTON HEATH

VIRGINIA WATER
- WENTWORTH

WALTON-ON-THAMES
- BURHILL
- HERSHAM VILLAGE

WARLINGHAM
- FARLEIGH COURT

WEST BYFLEET
- WEST BYFLEET

WEYBRIDGE
- ST. GEORGES HILL

WOKING
- CHOBHAM
- GOAL FARM
- HOEBRIDGE
- PYRFORD GOLF CLUB
- TRADITIONS GOLF COURSE
- WEST HILL
- WINDLERMERE
- WISLEY
- WOKING
- WORPLESDON

SUSSEX (EAST)

BATTLE
- BATTLE
- SEDLESCOMBE

BEXHILL-ON-SEA
- COODEN BEACH
- HIGHWOODS

BRIGHTON
- BRIGHTON & HOVE
- DYKE
- EAST BRIGHTON
- HOLLINGBURY PARK
- WATERHALL

CROWBOROUGH
- BOARS HEAD
- CROWBOROUGH BEACON
- DEWLANDS MANOR

DITCHLING
- MID SUSSEX

EASTBOURNE
- EASTBOURNE DOWNS
- EASTBOURNE GOLFING PARK
- WILLINGDON

FOREST ROW
- ASHDOWN FOREST
- ASHDOWN FOREST (ROYAL)

HAILSHAM
- WELLSHURST

HEATHFIELD
- HORAM PARK

HOVE
- BENFIELD VALLEY
- WEST HOVE

LEWES
- LEWES

NEWHAVEN
- PEACEHAVEN

RYE
- RYE

SEAFORD
- SEAFORD
- SEAFORD HEAD

ST. LEONARDS-ON-SEA
- HASTINGS

UCKFIELD
- EAST SUSSEX NATIONAL

WADHURST
- DALE HILL

SUSSEX (WEST)

ALBOURNE
- SINGING HILLS

ARUNDEL
- AVISFORD PARK

BILLINGSHURST
- FOXBRIDGE

BOGNOR REGIS
- BOGNOR REGIS

BURGESS HILL
- BURGESS HILL

CHICHESTER
- CHICHESTER
- GOODWOOD
- SELSEY

CRAWLEY
- COPTHORNE
- COTTESMORE
- EFFINGHAM PARK
- IFIELD
- TILGATE FOREST

EAST GRINSTEAD
- CHARTHAM PARK

HASSOCKS
- HASSOCKS

HAYWARDS HEATH
- CUCKFIELD
- HAYWARDS HEATH
- PAXHILL PARK

HORSHAM
- HORSHAM GOLF
- MANNINGS HEATH
- ROOKWOOD
- SLINFOLD PARK

LITTLEHAMPTON
- HAM MANOR
- LITTLEHAMPTON GOLF
- RUSTINGTON

MIDHURST
- COWDRAY PARK

PETWORTH
- OSIERS FARM
- PETWORTH

PULBOROUGH
- WEST CHILTINGTON
- WEST SUSSEX

WORTHING
- BROOKLANDS PARK
- HILLBARN
- WORTHING

TYNE AND WEAR

EAST BOLDON
- BOLDON

GATESHEAD
- HEWORTH
- RAVENSWORTH

HOUGHTON LE SPRING
- ELEMORE
- HOUGHTON LE SPRING

NEWCASTLE UPON TYNE
- BACKWORTH
- GARESFIELD
- GOSFORTH
- HOBSON
- NEWCASTLE
- NEWCASTLE UNITED
- NORTHUMBERLAND
- PARKLANDS
- PONTELAND
- WESTERHOPE
- WHICKHAM

NORTH SHIELDS
- TYNEMOUTH

RYTON
- RYTON
- TYNESIDE

SOUTH SHIELDS
- SOUTH SHIELDS
- WHITBURN

SUNDERLAND
- RYHOPE
- WEARSIDE

WALLSEND
- WALLSEND

WASHINGTON
- GEORGE WASHINGTON

WHITLEY BAY
- WHITLEY BAY

WARWICKSHIRE

ALCESTER
- BIDFORD GRANGE

KENILWORTH
- KENILWORTH

LEAMINGTON SPA
- LEAMINGTON & COUNTY
- NEWBOLD COMYN

NUNEATON
- ATHERSTONE
- BRAMCOTE WATERS
- NUNEATON
- OAKRIDGE
- PURLEY CHASE

RUGBY
- RUGBY
- WHITEFIELDS

STRATFORD-UPON-AVON
- STRATFORD OAKS
- STRATFORD ON AVON
- WELCOMBE HOTEL

WARWICK
- WARWICK GOLF CTRE
- WARWICKSHIRE

WILTSHIRE

BATH
- CUMBERWELL

BRADFORD-ON-AVON
- BRADFORD-ON-AVON

CALNE
- BOWOOD

CHIPPENHAM
- BRINKWORTH
- CHIPPENHAM
- MANOR HOUSE
- MONKTON PARK PAR 3

CORSHAM
- KINGSDOWN

CRICKLADE
- CRICKLADE

DEVIZES
- ERLESTOKE SANDS
- NORTH WILTS

MALMESBURY
- OAKSEY

MARLBOROUGH
- MARLBOROUGH
- OGBOURNE DOWNS

MELKSHAM
- WHITLEY

PEWSEY
- UPAVON

SALISBURY
- HAMPTWORTH
- HIGH POST
- RUSHMORE PARK
- SALISBURY & SOUTH WILTS

SWINDON
- BROOME MANOR
- HIGHWORTH GOLF CENTRE
- SHRIVENHAM PARK
- WILTSHIRE
- WRAG BARN

TIDWORTH
- TIDWORTH GARRISON

WARMINSTER
- WEST WILTS

WESTBURY
- THOULSTONE PARK

WORCESTERSHIRE

BEWDLEY
- BEWDLEY PINES
- WHARTON PARK

BROADWAY
- BROADWAY

BROMSGROVE
- BLACKWELL
- BROMSGROVE

DROITWICH
- DROITWICH
- LITTLE LAKES
- OMBERSLEY

KIDDERMINSTER
- CHURCHILL & BLAKEDOWN
- HABBERLEY
- KIDDERMINSTER
- WYRE FOREST

MALVERN
- WORCESTERSHIRE

PERSHORE
- EVESHAM
- VALE

REDDITCH
- ABBEY HOTEL
- PITCHEROAK
- REDDITCH

TENBURY WELLS
- CADMORE LODGE

WORCESTER
- BANK HOUSE
- LITTLE LAKES
- PERDISWELL PARK GOLF COURSE
- RAVENMEADOW
- SAPEY
- TOLLADINE
- WORCESTER

YORKSHIRE (EAST)

BEVERLEY
- BEVERLEY & EAST RIDING
- CHERRY BURTON

BRIDLINGTON
- BRIDLINGTON
- BRIDLINGTON
- FLAMBOROUGH HEAD

BROUGH
- BROUGH
- CAVE CASTLE

COTTINGHAM
- HESSLE

DRIFFIELD
- DRIFFIELD
- HAINSWORTH PARK
- SKIPSEA

GOOLE
- BOOTHFERRY PARK

HORNSEA
- HORNSEA

HULL
- GANSTEAD PARK
- HULL
- SPRINGHEAD PARK MUNICIPAL
- SUTTON PARK

WITHERNSEA
- WITHERNSEA

YORKSHIRE (NORTH)

BEDALE
- BEDALE

CATTERICK GARRISON
- CATTERICK

FILEY
- FILEY

HARROGATE
- CRIMPLE VALLEY
- HARROGATE
- OAKDALE
- PANNAL
- RUDDING PARK
- SPOFFORTH

KNARESBOROUGH
- KNARESBOROUGH

MALTON
- MALTON & NORTON

NORTHALLERTON
- ROMANBY

RICHMOND
- RICHMOND

RIPON
- MASHAM
- RIPON CITY

SCARBOROUGH
- GANTON
- NORTH CLIFF
- RAVEN HALL
- SCARBOROUGH SOUTH CLIFF

SELBY
- SELBY

SETTLE
- SETTLE

SKIPTON
- SKIPTON

TADCASTER
- COCKSFORD
- SCARTHINGWELL

THIRSK
- THIRSK & NORTHALLERTON

WHITBY
- WHITBY

YORK
- ALDWARK MANOR
- ALLERTHORPE
- EASINGWOLD
- FOREST OF GALTRES
- FOREST PARK
- FULFORD
- HEWORTH
- KILNWICK PERCY
- KIRKBYMOORSIDE
- OAKS
- SWALLOW HALL
- YORK
- YORK GOLF CTRE

YORKSHIRE (SOUTH)

BARNSLEY
- BARNSLEY
- HILLIES PAVILION
- SANDHILL
- SILKSTONE

DONCASTER
- AUSTERFIELD
- CROOKHILL PARK MUNICIPAL
- DONCASTER TOWN MOOR
- HICKLETON

- KINGSWOOD
- OWSTON PARK
- ROBIN HOOD
- SERLBY PARK
- THORNE
- WHEATLEY

ROTHERHAM
- GRANGE PARK
- PHOENIX
- ROTHERHAM
- SITWELL
- WATH

SHEFFIELD
- ABBEYDALE
- BEAUCHIEF MUNICIPAL
- BIRLEY WOOD
- CONCORD GOLF CTRE
- DORE & TOTLEY
- HALLAMSHIRE
- HILLSBOROUGH
- LEES HALL
- RENISHAW PARK
- ROTHER VALLEY GOLF
- STOCKSBRIDGE
- TANKERSLEY PARK
- TINSLEY PARK
- WORTLEY

YORKSHIRE (WEST)

BINGLEY
- BINGLEY ST IVES
- SHIPLEY

BRADFORD
- BAILDON
- BRADFORD MOOR
- CLAYTON
- EAST BIERLEY
- HEADLEY
- HOLLINS HALL
- MANOR
- QUEENSBURY
- SOUTH BRADFORD
- WEST BOWLING
- WEST BRADFORD

BRIGHOUSE
- CROW NEST PARK
- WILLOW VALLEY

CASTLEFORD
- WHITWOOD

CLECKHEATON
- CLECKHEATON & DISTRICT

DEWSBURY
- HANGING HEATON

ELLAND
- ELLAND

HALIFAX
- BRADLEY HALL
- HALIFAX
- LIGHTCLIFFE
- WEST END

HEBDEN BRIDGE
- HEBDEN BRIDGE

HUDDERSFIELD
- BAGDEN HALL
- BRADLEY PARK
- CROSLAND HEATH
- HUDDERSFIELD
- LONGLEY PARK
- MARSDEN
- MELTHAM
- OUTLANE
- WOODSOME HALL

ILKLEY
- BEN RHYDDING
- BRACKEN GHYLL
- ILKLEY

KEIGHLEY
- BRANSHAW
- FARDEW
- KEIGHLEY
- RIDDLESDEN
- SILSDEN

LEEDS
- ALWOODLEY
- BRADFORD
- BRANDON
- COOKRIDGE HALL GOLF CLUB
- GARFORTH
- HEADINGLEY
- HORSFORTH
- HOWLEY HALL
- LEEDS
- LEEDS GOLF CTRE
- MIDDLETON PARK MUNICIPAL
- MOOR ALLERTON
- MOORTOWN
- OULTON PARK
- RAWDON
- ROUNDHAY
- SAND MOOR
- SCARCROFT
- SOUTH LEEDS
- TEMPLE NEWSAM

MIRFIELD
- DEWSBURY DISTRICT

OSSETT
- LOW LAITHES
- SPRINGMILL

OTLEY
- OTLEY

PONTEFRACT
- MID YORKSHIRE
- PONTEFRACT
- PONTEFRACT & DISTRICT

PUDSEY
- CALVERLEY
- FULNECK
- WOODHALL HILLS

SHIPLEY
- NORTHCLIFFE

SOWERBY BRIDGE
- RYBURN

TODMORDEN
- TODMORDEN

WAKEFIELD
- LOFTHOUSE HILL
- NORMANTON
- PAINTHORPE HOUSE
- WAKEFIELD
- WAKEFIELD
- WATERTON PARK

WETHERBY
- WETHERBY

by **COUNTY** by **TOWN** in **England**

Yorkshire (South) — Yorkshire (West)

COUNTY CARLOW

BORRIS
- BORRIS

CARLOW
- CARLOW
- QUINNAGH HOUSE PAR 3

TULLOW
- MOUNT WOLSELEY HOTEL

COUNTY CAVAN

BELTURBET
- BELTURBET

BLACKLION
- BLACKLION

CAVAN
- CAVAN (COUNTY)
- VIRGINIA

COUNTY CLARE

CLONLARA
- CLONLARA GOLF & LEISURE

DOONBEG
- DOONBEG

ENNIS
- ENNIS
- WOODSTOCK

KILKEE
- KILKEE

KILRUSH
- KILRUSH

LAHINCH
- LAHINCH

MILTOWN MALBAY
- SPANISH POINT

NEWMARKET ON FERGUS
- DROMOLAND CASTLE ESTATE

SCARIFF
- EAST CLARE

SHANNON
- SHANNON

COUNTY CORK

BANDON
- BANDON

BANTRY
- BANTRY BAY

BLARNEY
- BLARNEY

CARRIGALINE
- FERNHILL

CARRIGROHANE
- MUSKERRY

CARRIGTWOHILL
- FOTA ISLAND

CASTLETOWNBERE
- BEREHAVEN

COBH
- COBH

CORK
- CHARLEVILLE
- MAHON MUNICIPAL

DONERAILE
- DONERAILE

DOUGLAS
- DOUGLAS
- FRANKFIELD

FERMOY
- FERMOY

GLENGARRIFF
- GLENGARRIFF

KANTURK
- KANTURK

KINSALE
- KINSALE
- OLD HEAD GOLF LINKS

LISSELAN
- LISSELAN

LITTLE ISLAND
- CORK
- HARBOUR POINT

MACROOM
- MAHON MUNICIPAL

MAHON
- TED MCCARTHY MUNICIPAL

MALLOW
- MALLOW

MIDLETON
- EAST CORK
- WATER ROCK

MITCHELSTOWN
- MITCHELSTOWN

MONKSTOWN
- MONKSTOWN

MUCKROSS
- DUNMORE

OVENS
- LEE VALLEY

SCHULL
- COOSHEEN GOLF LINKS

SKIBBEREEN
- SKIBBEREEN & WEST CARBERY

TIVOLI
- FITZPATRICK FITNESS CTRE

YOUGHAL
- YOUGHAL

COUNTY DONEGAL

BALLYBOFEY
- BALLYBOFEY & STRANORLAR

BUNCRANA
- BUNCRANA
- NORTH WEST

BUNDORAN
- BUNDORAN

CARDONAGH
- BALLYLIFFIN

CRUIT ISLAND
- CRUIT ISLAND

FALCARRAGH
- CLOUGHANEELY

GREENCASTLE
- GREENCASTLE

LAGHEY
- DONEGAL

LETTERKENNY
- DUNFANAGHY
- GWEEDORE
- LETTERKENNY
- PORTSALON

MOVILLE
- REDCASTLE

NARIN
- NARIN/PORTNOO

RATHMULLAN
- OTWAY

ROSAPENNA
- ROSAPENNA

COUNTY DUBLIN

BALBRIGGAN
- BALBRIGGAN

BALLINASCORNEY
- BALLINASCORNEY

BALLYBOUGHAL
- HOLLYWOOD LAKES

BRITTAS BAY
- SLADE VALLEY

CASTLEKNOCK
- ELMGREEN

CLONDALKIN
- GRANGE CASTLE

DELGANY
- DELGANY

DONABATE
- BALCARRICK
- BEAVERSTOWN
- CORBALLIS PUBLIC LINKS
- DONABATE
- ISLAND

DUBLIN
- CARRICKMINES
- CHRISTY O'CONNOR
- CLONTARF
- DEER PARK HOTEL
- DUBLIN (ROYAL)
- DUBLIN MOUNTAIN
- ELM PARK GOLF & SPORTS CLUB
- FINNSTOWN FAIRWAYS
- FORREST LITTLE
- GRANGE
- HOLLYSTOWN GOLF
- LUTTRELLSTOWN CASTLE
- NEWLANDS
- OLDFIELD
- PINE VALLEY PAR 3
- RATHFARNHAM
- ST. ANNES

- STACKSTOWN
- SUTTON
- TURVEY

DUN LAOGHAIRE
- DUN LAOGHAIRE

FOX ROCK
- FOXROCK
- LEOPARDSTOWN

JOBSTOWN
- HAZEL GROVE

KILCOOLE
- KILCOOLE

KILLINEY
- KILLINEY

KILSALLAGHAN
- CORRSTOWN

KILTERNAN
- KILTERNAN

LUCAN
- HERMITAGE
- LUCAN

MALAHIDE
- MALAHIDE

MILLTOWN
- MILLTOWN

PORTMARNOCK
- PORTMARNOCK
- PORTMARNOCK HOTEL

RATHCOOLE
- BEECH PARK

RATHFARNHAM
- CASTLE
- EDMONDSTOWN

RUSH
- RUSH

SKERRIES
- SKERRIES

ST MARGARETS
- OPEN
- ST. MARGARETS

STEPASIDE
- BURROW
- STEPASIDE

SUTTON
- HOWTH

SWORDS
- SWORDS OPEN

COUNTY GALWAY

BALLINASLOE
- BALLINASLOE
- MOUNTBELLEW

BEARNA
- BEARNA

CLIFDEN
- CONNEMARA

CONNEMARA
- RENVYLE HOUSE

DUNMORE
- DUNMORE DEMESNE

GALWAY
- GLENLO ABBEY

GORT
- GORT

LETTERMORE
- CONNEMARA ISLES

LOUGHREA
- CURRA WEST
- LOUGHREA

ORANMORE
- ATHENRY
- GALWAY BAY

OUGHTERARD
- OUGHTERARD

PORTUMNA
- PORTUMNA

ROSSHILL
- ROSSHILL PAR 3

SALTHILL
- GALWAY

TUAM
- TUAM

COUNTY KERRY

ARDFERT
- TRALEE

BALLYBUNION
- BALLYBUNION

BALLYFERRITER
- CEANN SIBEAL

BALLYHEIGUE
- BALLYHEIGUE CASTLE

CASTLEGREGORY
- CASTLEGREGORY

GLENBEIGH
- DOOKS

KENMARE
- KENMARE
- RING OF KERRY

KILLARNEY
- BEAUFORT
- CASTLEROSSE
- DUNLOE
- KILLARNEY
- ROSS GOLF

KILLORGLIN
- KILLORGLIN

LISTOWEL
- LISTOWEL

PARKNASILLA
- PARKNASILLA

TRALEE
- KERRIES

WATERVILLE
- WATERVILLE HOUSE & GOLF LINKS

COUNTY KILDARE

ATHY
- ATHY

BODENSTOWN
- BODENSTOWN

CARBURY
- HIGHFIELD

CASTLEDERMOT
- KILKEA CASTLE

CELBRIDGE
- CELBRIDGE ELM HALL

CURRAGH
- CURRAGH

DONADEA
- KNOCKANALLY

KILCOCK
- KILCOCK

KILL
- KILLEEN

LLANDEILO
- CILL-DARA

NAAS
- CRADDOCKSTOWN
- NAAS
- WOODLANDS

NEWBRIDGE
- NEWBRIDGE

SAGGART
- CITYWEST

STRAFFAN
- CASTLEWARDEN
- K CLUB

COUNTY KILKENNY

BALLYHALE
- MOUNTAIN VIEW

CALLAN
- CALLAN

CASTLECOMER
- CASTLECOMER

GOWRAN
- GOWRAN PARK GOLF & LEISURE

GRAIGUENAMANAGH
- CARRIGLEADE

KILKENNY
- KILKENNY
- POCOCKE

THOMASTOWN
- MOUNT JULIET

COUNTY LAOIS

ABBEYLEIX
- ABBEYLEIX

MOUNTRATH
- MOUNTRATH

PORTARLINGTON
- PORTARLINGTON

PORTLAOISE
- HEATH

PORTLAOISE PAR 3

RATHDOWNEY

RATHDOWNEY

COUNTY LEITRIM

CARRICK-ON-SHANNON

BALLINAMORE

CARRICK-ON-SHANNON

COUNTY LIMERICK

ABBEYFEALE

ABBEYFEALE

ADARE

ADARE MANOR

ARDAGH

NEWCASTLE WEST

FOYNES

FOYNES

LIMERICK

CASTLETROY

LIMERICK

LIMERICK (COUNTY)

NEWCASTLEWEST

KILLELINE GOLF

RATHBANE

RATHBANE

COUNTY LONGFORD

LONGFORD

LONGFORD (COUNTY)

COUNTY LOUTH

ARDEE

ARDEE

BLACKROCK

DUNDALK

DROGHEDA

LOUTH (COUNTY)

DUNDALK

BALLYMASCANLON HOUSE

KILLIN PARK

KILLINBEG

GREENORE

GREENORE

KILCURRY

CARNBEG

TERMONFECKIN

SEAPOINT

TULLYALLEN

TOWNLEY HALL

COUNTY MAYO

ACHILL ISLAND

ACHILL ISLAND

BALLA

BALLA

BALLINA

BALLINA

MOY BALLEY PAR 3

BALLINROBE

BALLINROBE

BALLYHAUNIS

BALLYHAUNIS

BELMULLET

CARNE

CASTLEBAR

CASTLEBAR

CLAREMORRIS

CLAREMORRIS

ENNISCRONE

ENNISCRONE

SWINFORD

SWINFORD

WESTPORT

CLEWBAY

MULRANNY

WESTPORT

COUNTY MEATH

ASHBOURNE

ASHBOURNE

BETTYSTOWN

LAYTOWN & BETTYSTOWN

DUNSHAUGHLIN

BLACK BUSH

KELLS

HEADFORT

MOORTOWN

MOOR-PARK

NAVAN

TARA (ROYAL)

RATHMOLYON

SUMMERHILL

TRIM

GLEBE

MEATH (COUNTY)

SOUTH MEATH

COUNTY MONAGHAN

CARRICKMACROSS

NUREMORE HOTEL

CASTLEBLAYNEY

CASTLEBLAYNEY

CLONES

CLONES

MANNAN

MANNAN CASTLE

ROSSMORE

ROSSMORE

COUNTY OFFALY

BIRR

BIRR

DAINGEAN

CASTLE BARNA

EDENDERRY

EDENDERRY

TULLAMORE

ESKER HILLS

TULLAMORE

COUNTY ROSCOMMON

ATHLONE

ATHLONE

BALLAGHADERREEN

BALLAGHADERREEN

BOYLE

BOYLE

CASTLEREA

CASTLEREA

ROSCOMMON

ROSCOMMON

STROKESTOWN

STROKESTOWN

COUNTY SLIGO

BALLYMOTE

BALLYMOTE

SLIGO

SLIGO (COUNTY)

STRANDHILL

STRANDHILL

TUBBERCURRY

TUBBERCURRY

COUNTY TIPPERARY

CAHIR

CAHIR PARK

CARRICK-ON-SUIR

CARRICK-ON-SUIR

CASHEL

CASHEL GOLF RANGE

CLONMEL

CLONMEL

SLIEVENAMON

DUNDRUM

TIPPERARY (COUNTY)

LIMERICK JUNCTION

BALLYKISTEEN

NENAGH

NENAGH

ROSCREA

ROSCREA

TEMPLEMORE

TEMPLEMORE

THURLES

THURLES

TIPPERARY TOWN

TIPPERARY

COUNTY WATERFORD

DUNGARVAN

DUNGARVAN

GOLD COAST

WEST WATERFORD

DUNMORE

DUNMORE EAST

FAITHLEGG

FAITHLEGG

LISMORE	DUNLAVIN
(LISMORE	(RATHSALLAGH
TRAMORE	**ENNISKERRY**
(TRAMORE	(ENNISKERRY PAR 3
WATERFORD	(POWERSCOURT
(WATERFORD	**GREYSTONES**
(WATERFORD CASTLE	(CHARLESLAND
COUNTY WESTMEATH	(GREYSTONES
DELVIN	**NEWCASTLE**
(DELVIN CASTLE	(GLEN MILL
MOATE	**NEWTOWNMOUNTKENNEDY**
(MOATE	(DRUIDS GLEN
(MOUNT TEMPLE	(ROUNDWOOD
MULLINGAR	**RATHDRUM**
(MULLINGAR	(GLENMALURE
COUNTY WEXFORD	**ROUNDWOOD**
BALLINTESKIN	(DJOUCE MOUNTAIN
(BALLINTESKIN PAR 3	**WICKLOW**
ENNISCORTHY	(PUCKS CASTLE PAR 3
(ENNISCORTHY	(WICKLOW
(GARRYLOUGH	
GOREY	
(BALLYMONEY	
(COURTOWN	
NEW ROSS	
(NEW ROSS	
RATHASPECK	
(RATHASPECK MANOR	
ROSSLARE	
(ROSSLARE	
(ST. HELENS BAY	
SCARKE	
(SCARKE	
WEXFORD	
(WEXFORD	
COUNTY WICKLOW	
ARKLOW	
(ARKLOW	
(COOLATTIN	
(WOODENBRIDGE	
BALTINGLASS	
(BALTINGLASS	
BLAINROE	
(BLAINROE	
BLESSINGTON	
(BOYSTOWN	
(TULFARRIS HOUSE	
BRAY	
(BRAY	
(OLD CONNA	
(WOODBROOK	
BRITTAS BAY	
(EUROPEAN CLUB	
COOLLATTIN	
(COOLLATTIN	
DELGANY	
(GLEN OF THE DOWNS	

by **COUNTY** by **TOWN** in **Ireland**

County Waterford — County Wicklow

by **COUNTY** by **TOWN** in **N.Ireland**

County Antrim — County Tyrone

COUNTY ANTRIM

ANTRIM
- ALLEN PARK
- MASSEREENE

BALLYCASTLE
- BALLYCASTLE

BALLYCLARE
- BALLYCLARE
- GREENACRES GOLF CTRE

BALLYMENA
- BALLYMENA
- CUSHENDALL
- GALGORM CASTLE

BALLYMONEY
- GRACEHILL
- TARA GLEN

BELFAST
- BALMORAL
- BELVOIR PARK
- CLIFTONVILLE
- DUNMURRY
- FORT WILLIAM
- GILNAHIRK
- KNOCK
- MALONE
- MOUNT OBER
- ORMEAU
- SHANDON PARK

BUSHMILLS
- BUSHFOOT

CARRICKFERGUS
- BENTRA MUNICIPAL
- CARRICKFERGUS
- GREENISLAND
- WHITEHEAD

LARNE
- CAIRNDHU
- LARNE

LISBURN
- ABERDELGHY
- DOWN ROYAL PARK
- LISBURN
- TEMPLE CLUB

NEWTOWNABBEY
- BELFAST
- BURNFIELD HOUSE

PORTRUSH
- BALLYREAGH
- PORTRUSH (ROYAL)
- RATHMORE

COUNTY ARMAGH

ARMAGH
- ARMAGH (COUNTY)

CRAIGAVON
- EDENMORE
- LURGAN
- PORTADOWN
- TANDRAGEE

LURGAN
- CRAIGAVON

COUNTY DOWN

BALLYNAHINCH
- SPA

BANBRIDGE
- BANBRIDGE

BANGOR
- BANGOR
- BLACKWOOD GOLF CTRE
- CARNALEA
- HELENS BAY

BELFAST
- ROCKMOUNT

DONAGHADEE
- DONAGHADEE

DOWNPATRICK
- ARDGLASS
- BRIGHT CASTLE
- DOWNPATRICK
- RINGDUFFERIN

HOLYWOOD
- BELFAST (ROYAL)
- HOLYWOOD

NEWCASTLE
- DOWN (ROYAL COUNTY)

NEWRY
- CLOVERHILL
- KILKEEL
- NEWRY
- WARRENPOINT

NEWTOWNARDS
- ARDMINNAN
- CLANDEBOYE
- KIRKISTOWN CASTLE
- MAHEE ISLAND
- SCRABO

COUNTY FERMANAGH

ENNISKILLEN
- ASHWOODS
- CASTLE HUME
- ENNISKILLEN

COUNTY LONDONDERRY

COLERAINE
- BROWN TROUT

KILREA
- KILREA

LIMAVADY
- BENONE
- RADISSON ROE PARK

LONDONDERRY
- DERRY
- FAUGHAN VALLEY
- FOYLE

MAGHERAFELT
- MOYOLA PARK
- RONAN VALLEY

PORTSTEWART
- PORTSTEWART

COUNTY TYRONE

COOKSTOWN
- KILLYMOON

DUNGANNON
- BENBURB VALLEY
- DUNGANNON

OMAGH
- CLARE COUNTRY
- FINTONA
- NEWTOWNSTEWART
- OMAGH
- SPRINGHILL

STRABANE
- HILL VALLEY GOLF CTRE
- STRABANE

ABERDEEN (CITY OF)

ABERDEEN
- ABERDEEN (ROYAL)
- AUCHMILL
- BALNAGASK
- BON-ACCORD
- CALEDONIAN
- CRAIBSTONE
- DEESIDE
- EAST ABERDEENSHIRE
- HAZLEHEAD
- HUNTLY
- KINGS LINKS GOLF CTRE
- MELDRUM HOUSE
- MURCAR
- NEWMACHAR
- NIGG BAY
- NORTHERN
- PORTLETHEN

ABERDEENSHIRE

ABOYNE
- ABOYNE
- TARLAND

ALFORD
- ALFORD

BALLATER
- BALLATER
- BRAEMAR

BANCHORY
- BANCHORY
- INCHMARLO GOLF CTRE
- TORPHINS

BANFF
- DUFF HOUSE ROYAL

DUFFTOWN
- DUFFTOWN

ELLON
- NEWBURGH-ON-YTHAN

FRASERBURGH
- FRASERBURGH
- INVERALLOCHY

INSCH
- INSCH

INVERURIE
- INVERURIE
- KINTORE

KEMNAY
- KEMNAY

LAURENCEKIRK
- AUCHENBLAE

MACDUFF
- TARLAIR (ROYAL)

OLDMELDRUM
- OLDMELDRUM

PETERCULTER
- PETERCULTER

PETERHEAD
- CRUDEN BAY
- PETERHEAD

STONEHAVEN
- STONEHAVEN

TURRIFF
- TURRIFF

WESTHILL
- WESTHILL

ANGUS

ARBROATH
- ARBROATH
- LETHAM GRANGE RESORT

BRECHIN
- BRECHIN GOLF & SQUASH CLUB

CARNOUSTIE
- CARNOUSTIE
- PANMURE

DUNDEE
- CAIRD PARK
- CAMPERDOWN
- DOWNFIELD
- LADIES PANMURE
- MONIFIETH GOLF LINKS
- PIPERDAM GOLF

EDZELL
- EDZELL

FORFAR
- FORFAR

KIRRIEMUIR
- KIRRIEMUIR

MONTROSE
- MONTROSE (ROYAL)
- MONTROSE LINKS TRUST

ARGYLL AND BUTE

ALEXANDRIA
- LOCH LOMOND
- VALE OF LEVEN

CAMPBELTOWN
- CARRADALE
- DUNAVERTY
- MACHRIHANISH

CLYDEBANK
- CLYDEBANK & DISTRICT
- DALMUIR MUNICIPAL

DALMALLY
- DALMALLY

DUMBARTON
- CARDROSS
- DUMBARTON
- MARTIN

DUNOON
- COWAL
- INNELLAN

HELENSBURGH
- HELENSBURGH

ISLE OF BUTE
- PORT BANNATYNE

ISLE OF COLONSAY
- COLONSAY

ISLE OF GIGHA
- GIGHA

ISLE OF ISLAY
- MACHRIE

ISLE OF MULL
- CRAIGNURE

LOCHGILPHEAD
- LOCHGILPHEAD

OBAN
- GLENCRUITTEN

ROTHESAY
- BUTE
- ROTHESAY

SCARINISH
- VAUL

TARBERT
- TARBERT

TIGHNABRUAICH
- KYLES OF BUTE

TOBERMORY
- TOBERMORY

AYRSHIRE (EAST)

GALSTON
- LOUDOUN

KILMARNOCK
- ANNANHILL
- CAPRINGTON

LOCHHILL
- NEW CUMNOCK

MAUCHLINE
- BALLOCHMYLE

AYRSHIRE (NORTH)

BEITH
- BEITH

BRODICK
- BRODICK
- CORRIE
- WHITING BAY

IRVINE
- GLASGOW GAILES
- IRVINE
- RAVENSPARK
- WESTERN GAILES

ISLE OF ARRAN
- SHISKINE

KILBIRNIE
- KILBIRNIE PLACE

LARGS
- LARGS
- ROUTENBURN

MILLPORT
- MILLPORT

SKELMORLIE
- SKELMORLIE

STEVENSTON
- ARDEER
- AUCHENHARVIE

WEST KILBRIDE
- WEST KILBRIDE

AYRSHIRE (SOUTH)

AYR
- BELLEISLE & SEAFIELD
- DALMILLING
- DOON VALLEY
- ROODLEA

DAILLY
- BRUNSTON CASTLE

GIRVAN
- GIRVAN
- TURNBERRY

MAYBOLE
- MAYBOLE MUNICIPAL

PRESTWICK
- PRESTWICK
- PRESTWICK ST CUTHBERT
- PRESTWICK ST NICHOLAS

TROON
- KILMARNOCK
- TROON (ROYAL)
- TROON MUNICIPAL
- TROON PORTLAND

CLACKMANNANSHIRE

ALLOA
- ALLOA
- BRAEHEAD
- TULLIALLAN

ALVA
- ALVA

BRIDGE OF ALLAN
- BRIDGE OF ALLAN

DOLLAR
- DOLLAR
- MUCKHART

TILLICOULTRY
- TILLICOULTRY

DUMFRIES AND GALLOWAY

ANNAN
- POWFOOT

CASTLE DOUGLAS
- CASTLE DOUGLAS
- GATEHOUSE
- NEW GALLOWAY

DALBEATTIE
- COLVEND
- CRAIGIEKNOWES

DUMFRIES
- CRICHTON
- DUMFRIES & COUNTY
- GALLOWAY
- PINES
- SOLWAY LINKS
- SOUTHERNESS

GRETNA
- GRETNA

KIRKCUDBRIGHT
- BRIGHOUSE BAY
- KIRKCUDBRIGHT
- PARK TONGLAND

LANGHOLM
- LANGHOLM

LOCKERBIE
- LOCKERBIE

LOCKMABEN
- LOCHMABEN

MOFFAT
- MOFFAT

NEWTON STEWART
- NEWTON STEWART
- ST. MEDAN
- WIGTOWN & BLADNOCH
- WIGTOWNSHIRE

SANQUHAR
- SANQUHAR

STRANRAER
- LAGGANMORE
- PORTPATRICK - DUNSKEY
- STRANRAER

THORNHILL
- THORNHILL

EDINBURGH (CITY OF)

EDINBURGH
- BABERTON
- BRAID HILLS
- BRUNTSFIELD GOLF CLUB
- BURGESS (ROYAL)
- CARRICK KNOWE
- CARRICK KNOWE
- CARRICKVALE
- CRAIGENTINNY
- CRAIGMILLAR PARK
- DALMAHOY
- DUDDINGSTON
- EDINBURGH WESTERN
- HARRISON
- LIBERTON
- LOCHEND
- LOTHIANBURN
- MERCHANTS OF EDINBURGH
- MORTONHALL
- MURRAYFIELD
- PORTOBELLO
- PRESTONFIELD
- RAVELSTON
- SILVERKNOWES
- SWANSTON
- TORPHIN HILL
- TURNHOUSE

NEWBRIDGE
- GOGARBURN
- RATHO PARK

FALKIRK

BONNYBRIDGE
- BONNYBRIDGE

CAMELON
- FALKIRK

LARBERT
- FALKIRK TRYST
- GLENBERVIE

MADDISTON
- POLMONT

POLMONT
- GRANGEMOUTH

FIFE

ANSTRUTHER
- ANSTRUTHER
- CRAIL

BURNTISLAND
- ABERDOUR
- BURNTISLAND

COLINSBURGH
- CHARLETON

COWDENBEATH
- COWDENBEATH

CUPAR
- CUPAR
- ELMWOOD
- FALKLAND
- LADYBANK

DUNFERMLINE
- CANMORE
- DUNFERMLINE
- PITREAVIE
- SALINE

GLENROTHES
- BALBIRNIE PARK
- GLENROTHES
- LESLIE

KINGHORN
- KINGHORN

KIRKCALDY
- DUNNIKIER
- KIRKCALDY
- THORNTON

LEVEN
- ELIE GOLF
- LEVEN LINKS
- LEVEN THISTLE
- LUNDIN
- LUNDIN LADIES
- SCOONIE

LOCHGELLY
- AUCHTERDERRAN
- LOCHGELLY
- LOCHORE MEADOWS

ST. ANDREWS
- DRUMOIG
- DUKES
- KINGSBARNS GOLF LINKS
- NEW
- ST. ANDREWS LINKS
- ST. MICHAELS

TAYPORT
- SCOTSCRAIG

GLASGOW (CITY OF)

GLASGOW
- ALEXANDRA
- BALMORE
- BEARSDEN

- BISHOPBRIGGS
- BLAIRBETH
- BONNYTON
- BOTHWELL CASTLE
- CALDERBRAES
- CALDWELL
- CAMBUSLANG
- CAMPSIE
- CATHCART CASTLE
- CATHKIN BRAES
- CAWDER
- CLOBER
- COWGLEN
- CROW WOOD
- DOUGLAS PARK
- DULLATUR
- EAST KILBRIDE
- EAST RENFREWSHIRE
- EASTWOOD
- FERENEZE
- GLASGOW
- HAGGS CASTLE
- HAYSTON
- HILTON PARK
- KILSYTH LENNOX
- KIRKHILL
- KIRKINTILLOCH
- KNIGHTSWOOD
- LANGLANDS
- LENZIE
- LETHAMHILL
- LINN PARK
- LITTLEHILL
- MILNGAVIE
- MOUNT ELLEN
- POLLOK
- SANDYHILLS
- TORRANCE HOUSE
- WESTERWOOD
- WHITECRAIGS
- WILLIAMWOOD
- WINDYHILL

MILNGAVIE
- ESPORTA DOUGALSTON

HIGHLANDS
ALNESS
- ALNESS
ARDGAY
- BONAR BRIDGE/ARDGAY
ARISAIG
- TRAIGH
AVIEMORE
- DALFABER
BEAULY
- AIGAS
BOAT OF GARTEN
- BOAT OF GARTEN
BRORA
- BRORA
CARRBRIDGE
- CARRBRIDGE
DORNOCH
- CARNEGIE

- DORNOCH (ROYAL)
FEARN
- TARBAT
FORT AUGUSTUS
- FORT AUGUSTUS
FORTROSE
- FORTROSE & ROSEMARKIE
GAIRLOCH
- GAIRLOCH
GOLSPIE
- GOLSPIE
HELMSDALE
- HELMSDALE
INVERGORDON
- INVERGORDON
INVERNESS
- INVERNESS
- LOCH NESS
ISLE OF SKYE
- ISLE OF SKYE
KINGUSSIE
- KINGUSSIE
LAIRG
- DURNESS
LOCHCARRON
- LOCHCARRON
LYBSTER
- LYBSTER
MUIR OF ORD
- MUIR OF ORD
NAIRN
- NAIRN
- NAIRN DUNBAR
NETHY BRIDGE
- ABERNETHY
NEWTONMORE
- NEWTONMORE
SKEABOST
- SKEABOST
STRATHPEFFER
- STRATHPEFFER SPA
TAIN
- TAIN
THURSO
- REAY
- THURSO
ULLAPOOL
- ULLAPOOL
WICK
- WICK

INVERCLYDE
GOUROCK
- GOUROCK
GREENOCK
- WHINHILL
KILMACOLM
- KILMACOLM

ISLE OF ARRAN
LAMLASH
- LAMLASH
LOCHRANZA
- LOCHRANZA GOLF
MACHRIE
- MACHRIE BAY

LANARKSHIRE (NORTH)
AIRDRIE
- AIRDRIE
- EASTER MOFFAT
BELLSHILL
- BELLSHILL
COATBRIDGE
- COATBRIDGE
- DRUMPELLIER
CUMBERNAULD
- PALACERIGG
MOTHERWELL
- COLVILLE PARK
- DALZIEL
SHOTTS
- SHOTTS
WISHAW
- WISHAW

LANARKSHIRE (SOUTH)
BIGGAR
- BIGGAR
- LEADHILLS
CARLUKE
- CARLUKE
HAMILTON
- RICCARTON
- STRATHCLYDE PARK
LANARK
- CARNWATH
- DOUGLAS WATER
- HOLLANDBUSH
- KAMES GOLF
- LANARK
LARKHALL
- LARKHALL
STRATHAVEN
- STRATHAVEN

LOTHIAN (EAST)
DUNBAR
- DUNBAR
- WINTERFIELD
GULLANE
- GULLANE
- MUIRFIELD
HADDINGTON
- CASTLE PARK
- GIFFORD
- HADDINGTON
LONGNIDDRY
- KILSPINDIE
- LONGNIDDRY

- LUFFNESS

MUSSELBURGH
- MUSSELBURGH LINKS

NORTH BERWICK
- GLEN
- NORTH BERWICK
- TANTALLON
- WHITEKIRK

PRESTONPANS
- MUSSELBURGH (ROYAL)

LOTHIAN (MID)

BONNYRIGG
- BROOMIEKNOWE

DALKEITH
- NEWBATTLE

GOREBRIDGE
- VOGRIE

LASSWADE
- KINGS ACRE

MUSSELBURGH
- MUSSELBURGH

PENICUIK
- GLENCORSE

SOUTH QUEENSFERRY
- DUNDAS PARKS

LOTHIAN (WEST)

BATHGATE
- BATHGATE
- BRIDGECASTLE
- GREENBURN
- POLKEMMET

BROXBURN
- NIDDRY CASTLE
- UPHALL

LINLITHGOW
- BRIDGEND
- LINLITHGOW
- WEST LOTHIAN

LIVINGSTON
- DEER PARK
- PUMPHERSTON

WEST CALDER
- HARBURN

MORAY

ABERLOUR
- ROTHES

BUCKIE
- BUCKPOOL
- CULLEN
- STRATHLENE

ELGIN
- HOPEMAN

FOCHABERS
- GARMOUTH & KINGSTON
- SPEY BAY

FORRES
- FORRES
- KINLOSS

GRANTOWN ON SPEY
- GRANTOWN-ON-SPEY

KEITH
- KEITH

LOSSIEMOUTH
- MORAY

ORKNEY ISLES

ISLE OF ORKNEY
- STROMNESS

KIRKWALL
- ORKNEY

WESTRAY
- WESTRAY

PERTH AND KINROSS

ABERFELDY
- ABERFELDY
- KENMORE

AUCHTERARDER
- AUCHTERARDER
- GLENEAGLES

BLAIRGOWRIE
- ALYTH
- BLAIRGOWRIE
- DALMUNZIE
- GLENISLA
- STRATHMORE GOLF CTRE

CALLANDER
- CALLANDER

CRIEFF
- COMRIE
- CRIEFF

DUNBLANE
- DUNBLANE NEW

DUNKELD
- DUNKELD

KENMORE
- TAYMOUTH CASTLE

KILLIN
- KILLIN

KINROSS
- GREEN HOTEL
- KINROSS
- MILNATHORT

LOCH EARN
- ST. FILLANS

MUTHILL
- MUTHILL

PERTH
- CRAIGIE HILL
- DUNNING
- KING JAMES VI
- LYNEDOCH & MURRAYSHALL
- NORTH INCH MUNICIPAL
- WHITEMOSS

PITLOCHRY
- BLAIR ATHOLL
- PITLOCHRY

RENFREWSHIRE

BISHOPTON
- ERSKINE

BRIDGE OF WEIR
- RANFURLY
- RANFURLY CASTLE

JOHNSTONE
- COCHRANE CASTLE
- ELDERSLIE

LOCHWINNOCH
- LOCHWINNOCH

PAISLEY
- BARSHAW
- PAISLEY
- RALSTON

PORT GLASGOW
- GLEDDOCH
- PORT GLASGOW

RENFREW
- RENFREW

SCOTTISH BORDERS

COLDSTREAM
- HIRSEL

DUNS
- DUNS

EYEMOUTH
- EYEMOUTH

GALASHIELS
- GALASHIELS
- TORWOODLEE

HAWICK
- HAWICK
- MINTO

INNERLEITHEN
- INNERLEITHEN

JEDBURGH
- JEDBURGH

KELSO
- KELSO
- ROXBURGHE

LAUDER
- LAUDER

MELROSE
- MELROSE
- ST. BOSWELLS

NEWCASTLETON
- NEWCASTLETON

PEEBLES
- CARDRONA
- PEEBLES

SELKIRK
- SELKIRK
- WOLL

WEST LINTON
- RUTHERFORD CASTLE
- WEST LINTON

SHETLAND ISLANDS
SHETLAND
- SHETLAND
- WHALSAY

STIRLING
DRYMEN
- BUCHANAN CASTLE
STIRLING
- ABERFOYLE
- STIRLING

WESTERN ISLES
LOCHBOISDALE
- ASKERNISH
STORNOWAY
- STORNOWAY

by **COUNTY** by **TOWN** in **Scotland**

Shetland Islands — Western Isles

BLAENAU GWENT

EBBW VALE
- WEST MONMOUTHSHIRE

TREDEGAR
- TREDEGAR & RHYMNEY

BRIDGEND

BRIDGEND
- GROVE
- PYLE & KENFIG
- SOUTHERNDOWN
- ST. MARYS HOTEL

MAESTEG
- MAESTEG

PORTHCAWL
- PORTHCAWL (ROYAL)

CAERPHILLY

BARGOED
- BARGOED

BLACKWOOD
- BLACKWOOD
- OAKDALE

CAERPHILLY
- CAERPHILLY
- CASTELL HEIGHTS
- VIRGINIA PARK

HENGOED
- BRYN MEADOWS

CARMARTHENSHIRE

AMMANFORD
- GARNANT PARK
- GLYNHIR

BURRY PORT
- ASHBURNHAM

CARMARTHEN
- CARMARTHEN
- DERLLYS COURT
- LLANSTEFFAN
- PANTYDDERWEN

KIDWELLY
- GLYN ABBEY

LAMPETER
- CILGWYN

LLANDYSUL
- SARON

CEREDIGION

ABERYSTWYTH
- ABERYSTWYTH
- CAPEL BANGOR
- PENLANLAS

BORTH
- BORTH & YNYSLAS

CARDIGAN
- CARDIGAN
- CLIFF HOTEL

LLANDYSUL
- CWMRHYDNEUADD

LLANRHYSTUD
- PENRHOS

CONWY

ABERGELE
- ABERGELE

BETWS-Y-COED
- BETWS-Y-COED

COLWYN BAY
- OLD COLWYN

LLANDUDNO
- MAESDU
- NORTH WALES
- RHOS-ON-SEA

MORFA
- CONWY

PENMAENMAWR
- PENMAENMAWR

DENBIGHSHIRE

DENBIGH
- BRYN MORFYDD
- DENBIGH

LLANGOLLEN
- VALE OF LLANGOLLEN

PRESTATYN
- PRESTATYN
- ST. MELYD

RHYL
- KINMEL PARK GOLF
- RHUDDLAN
- RHYL

RUTHIN
- RUTHIN-PWLLGLAS

FLINTSHIRE

DEESIDE
- HAWARDEN
- WEPRE

FLINT
- FLINT

HOLYWELL
- HOLYWELL
- KINSALE
- PENNANT PARK

MOLD
- ALLT-GYMBYD
- CAERWYS NINE OF CLUBS
- MOLD
- NORTHOP
- OLD PADESWOOD
- PADESWOOD & BUCKLEY

GLAMORGAN (VALE OF)

ABERDARE
- ABERDARE

BARRY
- BRYNHILL
- RAF ST ATHAN
- SOUTH WALES
- ST. ANDREWS MAJOR

CARDIFF
- CARDIFF
- CASTLECOCH
- COTTRELL PARK
- CREIGIAU
- LLANISHEN
- PETERSTONE LAKES
- RADYR
- ST. MELLONS
- WENVOE CASTLE
- WHITCHURCH

DINAS POWYS
- DINAS POWYS

HENSOL
- VALE OF GLAMORGAN

MERTHYR TYDFIL
- MERTHYR CILSANWS
- MERTHYR TYDFIL
- MORLAIS CASTLE

PENARTH
- GLAMORGANSHIRE

TREHARRIS
- WHITEHALL

GWYNEDD

ABERDOVEY
- ABERDOVEY

BALA
- BALA

BANGOR
- ST. DEINIOL

BLAENAU FFESTINIOG
- FFESTINIOG

CAERNARFON
- CAERNARFON (ROYAL TOWN OF)

CRICCIETH
- CRICCIETH

DOLGELLAU
- DOLGELLAU

FAIRBOURNE
- FAIRBOURNE

HARLECH
- HARLECH

LLANFAIRFECHAN
- LLANFAIRFECHAN

PORTHMADOG
- PORTHMADOG

PWLLHELI
- ABERSOCH
- NEFYN & DISTRICT
- PWLLHELI

ISLE OF ANGLESEY

AMLWCH
- BULL BAY

BEAUMARIS
- BARON HILL
- PRINCE'S

BRYNTEG
- STORWS WEN

HOLYHEAD
- HOLYHEAD

LLANGEFNI
- LLANGEFNI PUBLIC

RHOSNEIGR
- ANGLESEY

MONMOUTHSHIRE

ABERGAVENNY
- MONMOUTHSHIRE
- WERNDDU

CALDICOT
- DEWSTOW

CHEPSTOW
- SHIRENEWTON
- ST. PIERRE

MONMOUTH
- MONMOUTH
- ROLLS OF MONMOUTH

PONTYPOOL
- PONTYPOOL

USK
- ALICE SPRINGS
- RAGLAN PARC
- WOODLAKE PARK

NEATH PORT TALBOT

NEATH
- EARLSWOOD
- GLYNNEATH
- NEATH
- SWANSEA BAY GOLF SHOP

PORT TALBOT
- BRITISH STEEL PORT TALBOT
- LAKESIDE
- PORT TALBOT

NEWPORT

NEWPORT
- CAERLEON
- CELTIC MANOR
- LLANWERN
- NEWPORT GOLF
- PARC
- TREDEGAR PARK

PEMBROKESHIRE

HAVERFORDWEST
- HAVERFORDWEST
- PRISKILLY
- ST. DAVIDS

MILFORD HAVEN
- DAWN 'TIL DUSK
- MILFORD HAVEN

NARBERTH
- HERONS BROOK

NEWPORT
- NEWPORT

PEMBROKE DOCK
- SOUTH PEMBROKE

TENBY
- TENBY
- TREFLOYNE

POWYS

BRECON
- BRECON

BUILTH WELLS
- BUILTH WELLS
- RHOSGOCH GOLF

CAERSWS
- MID WALES GOLF CTRE

CRICKHOWELL
- OLD RECTORY

KNIGHTON
- KNIGHTON

LLANDRINDOD WELLS
- LLANDRINDOD WELLS

LLANIDLOES
- ST. IDLOES

MACHYNLLETH
- MACHYNLLETH

NEWTOWN
- ST. GILES

WELSHPOOL
- WELSH BORDER GOLF COMPLEX
- WELSHPOOL

RHONDDA CYNON TAFF

FERNDALE
- RHONDDA

MOUNTAIN ASH
- MOUNTAIN ASH

PONTYCLUN
- LLANTRISANT & PONTYCLUN

PONTYPRIDD
- PONTYPRIDD

SWANSEA

SWANSEA
- ALLT-Y-GRABAN
- CLYNE
- FAIRWOOD PARK
- GOWER
- LANGLAND BAY
- MORRISTON
- PALLEG
- PENNARD
- PONTARDAWE

TORFAEN

CWMBRAN
- GREEN MEADOW
- LLANYRAFON
- PONTNEWYDD

WREXHAM

WREXHAM
- CHIRK
- CLAYS GOLF CTRE
- MOSS VALLEY
- PLASSEY
- WREXHAM

by **COUNTY** by **TOWN** in **Wales**

Isle of Anglesey — Wrexham

by Nearest Location

SECTION 3

This section helps you to locate golf clubs by their nearest location. For example, you may be passing through a town or village and want to know if a golf course is nearby.

eg. England, **Stone,** Barlaston

Once you have located a club using this section you can then refer to the detailed profile of the club in Section 1, or search for specific details in other sections.

ABINGDON
- DRAYTON PARK Oxfordshire
- FRILFORD HEATH Oxfordshire

ABRIDGE
- ABRIDGE Essex

ACCRINGTON
- ACCRINGTON & DISTRICT Lancashire
- BAXENDEN & DISTRICT Lancashire
- GREEN HAWORTH Lancashire

ADDINGTON VILLAGE
- ADDINGTON Surrey

ADDLESTONE
- ABBEYMOOR Surrey
- SURREY GOLF & FITNESS Surrey

ALDEBURGH
- ALDEBURGH Suffolk
- THORPENESS Suffolk

ALDERLEY EDGE
- ALDERLEY EDGE Cheshire

ALDERSHOT
- ARMY Hampshire

ALFRETON
- ALFRETON Derbyshire
- SHIRLAND Derbyshire

ALNWICK
- ALNMOUTH Northumberland
- ALNMOUTH VILLAGE Northumberland
- ALNWICK Northumberland
- DUNSTANBURGH CASTLE Northumberland

ALRESFORD
- ALRESFORD Hampshire

ALSTON
- ALSTON MOOR Cumbria

ALTON
- ALTON Hampshire
- BLACKNEST Hampshire
- FOUR MARKS Hampshire
- WORLDHAM PARK Hampshire

ALTRINCHAM
- ALTRINCHAM Cheshire
- DUNHAM FOREST Cheshire
- HALE Cheshire
- RINGWAY Cheshire

ANDOVER
- ANDOVER Hampshire
- HAMPSHIRE Hampshire

APPLEBY
- APPLEBY Cumbria

ARUNDEL
- AVISFORD PARK Sussex (West)

ASCOT
- ASCOT (ROYAL) Berkshire
- BERKSHIRE Berkshire
- LAVENDER PARK Berkshire
- SUNNINGDALE Surrey
- SUNNINGDALE LADIES Berkshire
- SWINLEY FOREST Berkshire

ASHBOURNE
- ASHBOURNE Derbyshire

ASHBY-DE-LA-ZOUCH
- WILLESLEY PARK Leicestershire

ASHFORD
- ASHFORD Kent
- ASHFORD Kent
- ASHFORD MANOR Surrey
- HOMELANDS Kent
- LONDON BEACH Kent
- TENTERDEN Kent

ASHTON-UNDER-LYNE
- ASHTON-UNDER-LYNE Lancashire

ASKAM-IN-FURNESS
- DUNNERHOLME Cumbria

AVELEY
- BELHUS PARK Essex

AYLESBURY
- AYLESBURY Buckinghamshire
- AYLESBURY PARK Buckinghamshire
- CHILTERN FOREST Buckinghamshire
- ELLESBOROUGH Buckinghamshire
- PRINCES RISBOROUGH Buckinghamshire
- WESTON TURVILLE Buckinghamshire

BACUP
- BACUP Lancashire

BAGSHOT
- PENNYHILL PARK Surrey
- WINDLESHAM Surrey

BAKEWELL
- BAKEWELL Derbyshire

BAMBURGH
- BAMBURGH CASTLE Northumberland

BANBURY
- BANBURY GOLF CTRE Oxfordshire
- BRAILES Oxfordshire
- CHERWELL EDGE Oxfordshire
- RYE HILL Oxfordshire
- TADMARTON HEATH Oxfordshire

BANSTEAD
- CUDDINGTON Surrey

BARLBOROUGH
- BARLBOROUGH LINKS Derbyshire

BARNARD CASTLE
- BARNARD CASTLE County Durham

BARNET
- ARKLEY Hertfordshire
- BRIDGEDOWN Hertfordshire
- DYRHAM PARK Hertfordshire
- EAST BARNET Hertfordshire
- HADLEY WOOD Hertfordshire
- OAK HILL PARK Hertfordshire
- OLD FOLD MANOR Hertfordshire

BARNOLDSWICK
- GHYLL Lancashire

BARNSLEY
- BARNSLEY Yorkshire (South)

- HILLIES PAVILION Yorkshire (South)
- SANDHILL Yorkshire (South)
- SILKSTONE Yorkshire (South)

BARNSTAPLE
- PORTMORE GOLF PARK Devon
- SAUNTON Devon

BARROW-IN-FURNESS
- BARROW Cumbria
- FURNESS Cumbria

BASILDON
- BASILDON Essex

BASINGSTOKE
- BASINGSTOKE Hampshire
- BASINGSTOKE Hampshire
- DUMMER Hampshire
- TEST VALLEY Hampshire
- WEYBROOK PARK Hampshire

BATH
- APPROACH Bath & Somerset (North East)
- BATH Bath & Somerset (North East)
- COMBE GROVE MANOR Bath & Somerset (North East)
- CUMBERWELL Wiltshire
- ENTRY HILL Bath & Somerset (North East)
- FOSSEWAY Bath & Somerset (North East)
- KINGSDOWN Wiltshire
- LANSDOWN Bath & Somerset (North East)
- TRACY PARK Bristol

BATTLE
- BATTLE Sussex (East)
- SEDLESCOMBE Sussex (East)

BEACONSFIELD
- BEACONSFIELD Buckinghamshire

BECCLES
- BECCLES Suffolk

BEDALE
- BEDALE Yorkshire (North)

BEDFORD
- BEDFORD Bedfordshire
- BEDFORD & COUNTY Bedfordshire
- BEDFORDSHIRE Bedfordshire
- CHALGRAVE MANOR Bedfordshire
- COLMWORTH & NORTH BEDFORDSHIRE Bedfordshire
- LYSHOTT HEATH Bedfordshire
- MOWSBURY Bedfordshire
- OUSE VALLEY Bedfordshire
- PAVENHAM Bedfordshire
- WYBOSTON Bedfordshire

BEDLINGTON
- BEDLINGTONSHIRE Northumberland

BELFORD
- BELFORD Northumberland

BELPER
- CHEVIN Derbyshire
- STRUTT CLUB Derbyshire

BENFLEET
- BOYCE HILL Essex

BERKHAMSTEAD
- WHIPSNADE PARK Hertfordshire

BERKHAMSTEAD
- ASHRIDGE Hertfordshire
- BERKHAMSTED Hertfordshire

BERWICK-UPON-TWEED
- BERWICK Northumberland
- HAGGERSTON CASTLE Northumberland
- MAGDALENE FIELDS Northumberland

BEVERLEY
- BEVERLEY & EAST RIDING Yorkshire (East)
- CHERRY BURTON Yorkshire (East)

BEWDLEY
- BEWDLEY PINES Worcestershire
- LITTLE LAKES Worcestershire
- WHARTON PARK Worcestershire

BEXHILL-ON-SEA
- COODEN BEACH Sussex (East)
- HIGHWOODS Sussex (East)

BEXLEYHEATH
- BARNEHURST Kent
- BEXLEYHEATH Kent

BICESTER
- BICESTER GOLF & COUNRTY CLUB Oxfordshire

BIDEFORD
- HARTLAND FOREST Devon
- NORTH DEVON (ROYAL) Devon

BIGGLESWADE
- JOHN O'GAUNT Bedfordshire

BILLERICAY
- BURSTEAD Essex
- STOCK BROOK MANOR Essex

BILLINGHAM
- BILLINGHAM Cleveland
- WYNYARD CLUB Cleveland

BILLINGSHURST
- FOXBRIDGE Sussex (West)

BINGLEY
- BINGLEY ST IVES Yorkshire (West)
- SHIPLEY Yorkshire (West)

BIRKENHEAD
- ARROWE PARK Merseyside
- BIDSTON Merseyside
- BROMBOROUGH Merseyside
- HESWALL Merseyside
- PRENTON Merseyside
- WALLASEY Merseyside

BIRMINGHAM
- COCKS MOORS WOODS Midlands (West)
- EDGBASTON Midlands (West)
- FULFORD HEATH Midlands (West)
- GAY HILL Midlands (West)
- GREAT BARR Midlands (West)
- HANDSWORTH Midlands (West)
- HARBORNE Midlands (West)
- HARBORNE CHURCH FARM Midlands (West)
- HATCHFORD BROOK Midlands (West)
- HILLTOP Midlands (West)
- KINGS NORTON Midlands (West)
- LICKEY HILLS Midlands (West)
- LITTLE ASTON Midlands (West)
- MAXSTOKE PARK Midlands (West)
- MOSELEY Midlands (West)
- NORTH WORCESTERSHIRE Midlands (West)

BISHOP AUCKLAND
- BISHOP AUCKLAND County Durham

BISHOP'S STORTFORD
- BISHOPS STORTFORD Hertfordshire

BLACKBURN
- BLACKBURN Lancashire
- GREAT HARWOOD Lancashire
- MYTTON FOLD Lancashire
- PLEASINGTON Lancashire
- RISHTON Lancashire
- WILPSHIRE Lancashire

BLACKPOOL
- BLACKPOOL NORTH SHORE Lancashire
- BLACKPOOL PARK Lancashire
- FLEETWOOD Lancashire
- HERONS REACH Lancashire
- KNOTT END Lancashire

BLAMFORD
- RUSHMORE PARK Wiltshire

BLANDFORD FORUM
- ASHLEY WOOD Dorset
- DORSET HEIGHTS Dorset

BLYTH
- BLYTH Northumberland

BODMIN
- LANHYDROCK Cornwall

BOGNOR
- BOGNOR REGIS Sussex (West)

BOLTON
- BOLTON Lancashire
- BOLTON Lancashire
- BREIGHTMET Lancashire
- DEANE Lancashire
- DUNSCAR Lancashire
- GREAT LEVER & FARNWORTH Lancashire
- HARWOOD Lancashire
- HORWICH Lancashire
- OLD LINKS Lancashire
- REGENT PARK Lancashire
- TURTON Lancashire
- WESTHOUGHTON Lancashire
- WESTHOUGHTON Lancashire

BORDON
- BLACKMOOR Hampshire
- DEAN FARM Hampshire

BOSTON
- BOSTON Lincolnshire
- KIRTON HOLME Lincolnshire

BOTLEY VILLAGE
- BOTLEY PARK Hampshire

BOURNE
- TOFT HOTEL Lincolnshire

BOURNEMOUTH
- BARTON-ON-SEA Hampshire
- BOSCOMBE LADIES Dorset
- BOURNEMOUTH & MEYRICK Dorset
- DUDSBURY Dorset
- KNIGHTON HEATH Dorset
- QUEENS PARK Dorset
- SOLENT MEADS GOLF CTRE Dorset

BRACKNELL
- BLUE MOUNTAIN GOLF CENTRE Berkshire

BRADFORD
- BAILDON Yorkshire (West)
- BRADFORD MOOR Yorkshire (West)
- CLAYTON Yorkshire (West)
- EAST BIERLEY Yorkshire (West)
- HEADLEY Yorkshire (West)
- HOLLINS HALL Yorkshire (West)
- QUEENSBURY Yorkshire (West)
- SOUTH BRADFORD Yorkshire (West)
- WEST BOWLING Yorkshire (West)
- WEST BRADFORD Yorkshire (West)

BRADFORD ON AVON
- BRADFORD-ON-AVON Wiltshire

BRAINTREE
- TOWERLANDS Essex

BRAMPTON
- BRAMPTON Cumbria
- HALTWHISTLE Cumbria

BRANSTON
- NOTLEYS Essex

BRENTWOOD
- BENTLEY Essex
- DUNTON HILLS Essex
- HARTSWOOD Essex
- SOUTH ESSEX Essex
- THORNDON PARK Essex
- WARLEY PARK Essex
- WEALD PARK GOLF CLUB Essex

BRIDGNORTH
- BRIDGNORTH Shropshire
- CHESTERTON VALLEY Shropshire
- SEVEN MEADOWS Shropshire
- WORFIELD Shropshire

BRIDGWATER
- CANNINGTON Somerset
- ENMORE PARK Somerset

BRIDLINGTON
- BRIDLINGTON Yorkshire (East)
- BRIDLINGTON Yorkshire (East)
- FLAMBOROUGH HEAD Yorkshire (East)

BRIDPORT
- BRIDPORT & WEST DORSET Dorset

BRIGG
- FOREST PINES Lincolnshire (North)

BRIGHOUSE
- CROW NEST PARK Yorkshire (West)
- WILLOW VALLEY Yorkshire (West)

BRIGHTON
- BRIGHTON & HOVE Sussex (East)
- DYKE Sussex (East)
- EAST BRIGHTON Sussex (East)
- HOLLINGBURY PARK Sussex (East)
- SEAFORD Sussex (East)
- SINGING HILLS Sussex (West)
- WATERHALL Sussex (East)

BRISTOL
- ASHTON COURT Bristol
- BRISTOL & CLIFTON Bristol
- CHIPPING SODBURY Bristol
- FILTON Bristol
- HENBURY Bristol
- KENDLESHIRE Bristol
- KNOWLE Bristol
- MANGOTSFIELD Bristol
- SALTFORD Bristol
- SHIREHAMPTON PARK Bristol
- STOCKWOOD VALE Bristol
- TALL PINES Bristol
- THORNBURY GOLF Bristol
- TICKENHAM Bristol
- WOODLANDS Bristol
- WOODSPRING Bristol

BROAD
- NORTH FORELAND Kent

BROADWAY
- BROADWAY Worcestershire

BROCKENHURST
- BROKENHURST MANOR Hampshire

BROMLEY
- BECKENHAM PLACE PARK Kent
- BROMLEY Kent
- SHORTLANDS Kent
- SUNDRIDGE PARK Kent

BROMSGROVE
- BLACKWELL Worcestershire
- BROMSGROVE Worcestershire

BROUGH
- BROUGH Yorkshire (East)

BUCKINGHAM
- BUCKINGHAM Buckinghamshire
- SILVERSTONE Buckinghamshire

BUDE
- BUDE & NORTH CORNWALL Cornwall
- IVYLEAF Cornwall

BUDLEIGH SALTERTON
- EAST DEVON Devon

BUNGAY
- BUNGAY & WAVENEY VALLEY Suffolk

BUNTINGFORD
- EAST HERTS Hertfordshire

BURFORD
- BURFORD Oxfordshire

BURGESS HILL
- BURGESS HILL Sussex (West)
- HASSOCKS Sussex (West)
- MID SUSSEX Sussex (East)

BURNHAM-ON-CROUCH
- BURNHAM-ON-CROUCH Essex

BURNHAM-ON-SEA
- BREAN Somerset
- BURNHAM & BERROW Somerset

BURNLEY
- BRUNSHAW Lancashire
- BURNLEY Lancashire
- COLNE Lancashire
- TOWNELEY MUNICIPAL Lancashire

BURTON-ON-TRENT
- BRANSTON Staffordshire
- BROUGHTON HEATH Derbyshire
- BURTON ON TRENT Staffordshire
- CRAYTHORNE Staffordshire
- WYCHNOR PARK Staffordshire

BURY
- BURY Lancashire
- GREENMOUNT Lancashire
- LOWES PARK Lancashire
- PIKEFOLD Lancashire
- WALMERSLEY Lancashire

BURY ST EDMUNDS
- BURY ST EDMUNDS Suffolk
- FLEMPTON Suffolk
- SUFFOLK GOLF Suffolk

BUXTON
- BUXTON & HIGH PEAK Derbyshire
- CAVENDISH Derbyshire

CALNE
- BOWOOD Wiltshire

CAMBERLEY
- CAMBERLEY HEATH Surrey
- PINE RIDGE GOLF CTRE Surrey
- WINDLERMERE Surrey

CAMBORNE
- TEHIDY Cornwall

CAMBRIDGE
- BOURN Cambridgeshire
- CAMBRIDGE Cambridgeshire
- CAMBRIDGE LAKES Cambridgeshire
- CAMBRIDGE MERIDIAN Cambridgeshire
- CAMBRIDGESHIRE MOAT HOUSE Cambridgeshire
- GIRTON Cambridgeshire
- GOG MAGOG Cambridgeshire
- MALTON Hertfordshire

CAMELFORD
- BOWOOD Cornwall

CANNOCK
- BEAU DESERT Staffordshire
- CANNOCK PARK Staffordshire
- CHASE Staffordshire

CANTERBURY
- BOUGHTON Kent
- BROOME PARK Kent
- CANTERBURY Kent

CANVEY ISLAND
- CASTLE POINT Essex

CARCROFT
- ROBIN HOOD Yorkshire (South)

CARLISLE
- CARLISLE Cumbria
- EDEN Cumbria
- STONY HOLME Cumbria
- SWIFTS Cumbria

CARNFORTH
- KIRKBY LONSDALE Lancashire
- SILVERDALE Lancashire

CARSHALTON
- OAKS SPORTS CTRE Surrey

CASTLEFORD
- WHITWOOD Yorkshire (West)

CASTLETOWN
- CASTLETOWN GOLF LINKS Isle of Man

CATERHAM
- DUKES DENE Surrey
- HAPPY VALLEY Surrey
- NORTH DOWNS Surrey

CATTERICK GARRISON
- CATTERICK Yorkshire (North)

CHALFONT ST. GILES
- HAREWOOD DOWNS Buckinghamshire
- LITTLE CHALFONT Buckinghamshire
- OAKLAND PARK Buckinghamshire

CHAPEL-EN-LE-FRITH
- CHAPEL-EN-LE-FRITH Derbyshire

CHARD
- WINDWHISTLE Somerset

CHEADLE
- CHEADLE Cheshire
- GATLEY Cheshire

CHELMSFORD
- CHANNELS Essex
- CHELMSFORD Essex
- REGIMENT Essex
- WEST PARK Essex

CHELTENHAM
- CLEEVE HILL Gloucestershire
- COTSWOLD HILLS Gloucestershire
- LILLEY BROOK Gloucestershire
- NAUNTON DOWNS Gloucestershire
- SHIPTON Gloucestershire

CHERTSEY
- BARROW HILLS Surrey
- LALEHAM Surrey

CHESHAM
- CHARTRIDGE PARK Buckinghamshire
- CHESHAM & LEY HILL Buckinghamshire

CHESSINGTON
- SURBITON Surrey

CHESTER
- ALDERSEY GREEN Cheshire
- CARDEN PARK Cheshire
- CHESTER Cheshire
- EATON Cheshire
- MOLLINGTON GRANGE Cheshire
- PRYORS HAYES Cheshire
- UPTON-BY-CHESTER Cheshire
- VICARS CROSS Cheshire
- WESTMINSTER PARK MUNICIPAL Cheshire

CHESTER LE STREET
- BEAMISH PARK County Durham
- BIRTLEY County Durham
- ROSEBERRY GRANGE County Durham

CHESTERFIELD
- CHESTERFIELD Derbyshire
- GRASSMOOR GOLF CTRE Derbyshire
- STANEDGE Derbyshire
- TAPTON PARK Derbyshire

CHICHESTER
- CHICHESTER Sussex (West)
- GOODWOOD Sussex (West)
- SELSEY Sussex (West)

CHIGWELL
- EPPING FOREST Essex

CHINGFORD
- CHINGFORD London (Greater)
- EPPING FOREST (ROYAL) London (Greater)
- WEST ESSEX London (Greater)

CHIPPENHAM
- CHIPPENHAM Wiltshire
- MANOR HOUSE Wiltshire
- MONKTON PARK PAR 3 Wiltshire

CHIPPING NORTON
- CHIPPING NORTON Oxfordshire
- LYNEHAM Oxfordshire

CHISLEHURST
- CHISLEHURST Kent

CHISWELL
- CHIGWELL Essex

CHORLEY
- CHARNOCK RICHARD Lancashire
- CHORLEY Lancashire
- DUXBURY JUBILEE PARK Lancashire
- EUXTON PARK GOLF CTRE Lancashire
- HIGHFIELD Lancashire
- SHAW HILL Lancashire
- YARROW VALLEY Lancashire

CHRISTCHURCH
- DUDMOOR Dorset
- HIGHCLIFFE CASTLE Dorset
- IFORD BRIDGE Dorset
- PARLEY Dorset

CHULMLEIGH
- CHULMLEIGH Devon

CHURCH DOWN
- BRICKHAMPTON COURT Gloucestershire

CHURCH STRETTON
- CHURCH STRETTON Shropshire

CIRENCESTER
- CIRENCESTER Gloucestershire

CLACTON-ON-SEA
- CLACTON Essex
- MILLERS BARN GOLF PARK Essex

CLECKHEATON
- CLECKHEATON & DISTRICT Yorkshire (West)

CLEETHORPES
- CLEETHORPES Lincolnshire (North East)

CLEOBURY MORTIMER
- CLEOBURY MORTIMER Shropshire

CLEVEDON
- CLEVEDON Somerset (North)

CLITHEROE
- CLITHEROE Lancashire
- WHALLEY Lancashire

COBHAM
- SILVERMERE GOLF COMPLEX Surrey

COCKERMOUTH
- COCKERMOUTH Cumbria

COLCHESTER
- BIRCH GROVE Essex
- COLNE VALLEY Essex
- ESSEX Essex
- LEXDEN Essex
- STOKE-BY-NAYLAND Essex

COLEFORD
- FOREST HILLS Gloucestershire
- FOREST OF DEAN Gloucestershire

CONGLETON
- ASTBURY Cheshire
- CONGLETON Cheshire

CONGRESBURY
- MENDIP SPRING Bristol

CORBRIDGE
- SLALEY HALL GOLF COURSE Northumberland

CORBY
- CORBY PUBLIC Northamptonshire

COTTINGHAM
- HESSLE Yorkshire (East)

COULSDON
- CHIPSTEAD Surrey
- COULSDON MANOR Surrey
- WOODCOTE PARK Surrey

COVENTRY
- ANSTY GOLF CTRE Midlands (West)
- BRANDON WOOD MUNICIPAL Midlands (West)
- COVENTRY Midlands (West)
- FOREST OF ARDEN Midlands (West)
- HAWKESBURY GOLF CENTRE Midlands (West)
- HEARSALL Midlands (West)
- NORTH WARWICKSHIRE Midlands (West)
- STONEBRIDGE Midlands (West)
- STONELEIGH DEER PARK Midlands (West)
- WINDMILL VILLAGE Midlands (West)

COWES
- COWES Isle of Wight

CRADLEY HEATH
- CORNGREAVES Midlands (West)

CRAMLINGTON
- ARCOT HALL Northumberland

CRANBROOK
- HEMSTED FOREST GOLF CLUB Kent
- LAMBERHURST Kent
- STAPLEHURST GOLFING PARK Kent

CRANLEIGH
- WILDWOOD COUNTRY CLUB Surrey

CRAWLEY
- COPTHORNE Sussex (West)
- COTTESMORE Sussex (West)
- EFFINGHAM PARK Sussex (West)
- IFIELD Sussex (West)
- TILGATE FOREST Sussex (West)

CREDITON
- WATERBRIDGE Devon

CREECH HEATHFIELD
- TAUNTON VALE Somerset

CREW KERNE
- CHEDINGTON COURT Dorset

CREWE
- CREWE Cheshire
- ONNELEY Cheshire
- QUEENS PARK Cheshire

CRICKLADE
- CRICKLADE Wiltshire

CROMER
- CROMER (ROYAL) Norfolk

CROOK
- CROOK County Durham

CROWBOROUGH
- BOARS HEAD Sussex (East)
- CROWBOROUGH BEACON Sussex (East)
- DEWLANDS MANOR Sussex (East)

CROWTHORNE
- EAST BERKSHIRE Berkshire

CROYDON
- ADDINGTON COURT GOLF CLUB Surrey
- ADDINGTON PALACE Surrey
- PARK WOOD Kent
- SELSDON PARK Surrey
- SHIRLEY PARK Surrey

CULLOMPTON
- PADBROOK PARK Devon

DAGENHAM
- HAINAULT FOREST Essex

DARLINGTON
- BLACKWELL GRANGE County Durham
- DARLINGTON County Durham
- DINSDALE SPA County Durham
- HALLGARTH County Durham
- STRESSHOLME County Durham

DARTFORD
- AUSTIN LODGE Kent
- DARTFORD Kent
- PRINCES GOLF & LEISURE CLUB Kent

DARWEN
- DARWEN Lancashire

DAVENTRY
- DAVENTRY & DISTRICT Northamptonshire
- STAVERTON PARK Northamptonshire

DAWLISH
- DAWLISH APPROACH Devon
- WARREN Devon

DEAL
- CINQUE PORTS (ROYAL) Kent
- WALMER & KINGSDOWN Kent

DENHAM
- BUCKINGHAMSHIRE London (Greater)

DERBY
- ALLESTREE Derbyshire
- BRAILSFORD Derbyshire
- BREEDON PRIORY Derbyshire
- DERBY Derbyshire
- MAYWOOD Derbyshire
- MICKLEOVER Derbyshire
- SINFIN Derbyshire

DEREHAM
- DEREHAM Norfolk
- MATTISHALL Norfolk

DEVIZES
- ERLESTOKE SANDS Wiltshire
- NORTH WILTS Wiltshire
- UPAVON Wiltshire

DEWSBURY
- HANGING HEATON Yorkshire (West)

DIDCOT
- HADDEN HILL Oxfordshire

DISS
- DISS Norfolk

DONCASTER
- AUSTERFIELD Yorkshire (South)
- CROOKHILL PARK MUNICIPAL Yorkshire (South)
- DONCASTER TOWN MOOR Yorkshire (South)
- HICKLETON Yorkshire (South)
- KINGSWOOD Yorkshire (South)
- OWSTON PARK Yorkshire (South)
- SERLBY PARK Yorkshire (South)
- THORNE Yorkshire (South)
- WHEATLEY Yorkshire (South)

DORCHESTER
- CAME DOWN Dorset
- LYONS GATE Dorset

DORKING
- BETCHWORTH PARK Surrey
- DORKING Surrey
- GATTON MANOR Surrey

DOUGLAS
- DOUGLAS Isle of Man
- MOUNT MURRAY Isle of Man

DOWNE
- WEST KENT Kent

DOWNHAM MARKET
- RYSTON PARK Norfolk

DRIFFIELD
- DRIFFIELD Yorkshire (East)
- HAINSWORTH PARK Yorkshire (East)
- SKIPSEA Yorkshire (East)

DROITWICH
- DROITWICH Worcestershire
- OMBERSLEY Worcestershire

DROITWICH SPA
- LITTLE LAKES Worcestershire

DRONFIELD
- BIRCH HALL Derbyshire
- HALLOWES Derbyshire

DUDLEY
- DUDLEY Midlands (West)
- HIMLEY HALL GOLF CTRE Midlands (West)
- SEDGLEY GOLF CTRE Midlands (West)
- SWINDON Midlands (West)

DUKINFIELD
- DUKINFIELD Cheshire

DUNSTABLE
- DUNSTABLE DOWNS Bedfordshire

DURHAM
- BRANCEPETH CASTLE County Durham
- CHESTER-LE-STREET County Durham
- DURHAM CITY County Durham
- MOUNT OSWALD MANOR County Durham
- RAMSIDE County Durham

DURSLEY
- STINCHCOMBE HILL Gloucestershire

DYMOCK
- DYMOCK GRANGE Gloucestershire

EALING
- BRENT VALLEY PUBLIC London (Greater)

EAST BOLDON
- BOLDON Tyne And Wear

EAST COWES
- OSBORNE Isle of Wight

EAST GRINSTEAD
- CHARTHAM PARK Sussex (West)
- HOLTYE Kent

- HORNE PARK Surrey
- VILLA Kent

EASTBOURNE
- EASTBOURNE DOWNS Sussex (East)
- EASTBOURNE GOLFING PARK Sussex (East)
- WILLINGDON Sussex (East)

EASTLEIGH
- EAST HORTON GOLF CTRE Hampshire
- FLEMING PARK Hampshire

EDENBRIDGE
- EDENBRIDGE Kent
- HEVER Kent
- SWEETWOODS PARK Kent

EDGWARE
- EDGWAREBURY London (Greater)

ELLAND
- ELLAND Yorkshire (West)

ELLESMERE
- BROW Shropshire

ELLESMERE PORT
- ELLESMERE PORT Merseyside

ELSHAM
- ELSHAM Lincolnshire (North)

ELTHAM
- BLACKHEATH (ROYAL) London (Greater)

ELY
- ELY CITY Cambridgeshire

ENFIELD
- BUSH HILL PARK London (Greater)
- CREWS HILL London (Greater)
- ENFIELD London (Greater)
- WHITEWEBBS London (Greater)

EPPING
- EPPING Essex
- HOBBS CROSS Essex
- NORTH WEALD Essex
- NORTH WEALD PAR 3 Essex
- THEYDON BOIS Essex

EPSOM
- EPSOM Surrey
- HORTON PARK GOLF Surrey
- WALTON HEATH Surrey

ESHER
- MOORE PLACE Surrey
- SANDOWN GOLF CTRE Surrey
- THAMES DITTON & ESHER Surrey

EXETER
- CREDITON Devon
- EXETER Devon
- FINGLE GLEN Devon
- OAK MEADOW Devon
- TEIGN VALLEY Devon

EXMOUTH
- WOODBURY PARK Devon

FAKENHAM
- FAKENHAM Norfolk

FALMOUTH
- BUDOCK VEAN Cornwall
- FALMOUTH Cornwall

FAREHAM
- CAMS HALL ESTATE GOLF CLUB Hampshire
- FAREHAM WOODS Hampshire
- SOUTHWICK PARK Hampshire
- SWANMORE GOLF CTRE Hampshire
- WICKHAM PARK Hampshire

FARINGDON
- CARSWELL Oxfordshire
- FARINGDON Oxfordshire

FARNBOROUGH
- SOUTHWOOD Hampshire

FARNHAM
- FARNHAM Surrey
- FARNHAM PARK PAR 3 Surrey
- HANKLEY COMMON Surrey
- OAK PARK GOLF CLUB Surrey

FARNWORTH
- MANOR Lancashire

FAVERSHAM
- FAVERSHAM Kent

FELIXSTOWE
- FELIXSTOWE FERRY Suffolk

FERNDOWN
- FERNDOWN Dorset
- FERNDOWN FOREST Dorset

FILEY
- FILEY Yorkshire (North)

FLEET
- BOWENHURST Surrey
- NORTH HANTS FLEET Hampshire

FOLKESTONE
- ETCHINGHILL Kent
- LITTLESTONE Kent
- ROMNEY WARREN Kent
- ROUNDWOOD HALL Kent

FOREST HILL
- AQUARIUS London (Greater)

FOREST ROW
- ASHDOWN FOREST Sussex (East)
- ASHDOWN FOREST (ROYAL) Sussex (East)

FRESHWATER
- FRESHWATER BAY Isle of Wight

FRINTON-ON-SEA
- FRINTON Essex

FRODSHAM
- FRODSHAM Cheshire
- HELSBY Cheshire

FROME
- FROME GOLF CLUB Bath & Somerset (North East)
- ORCHARDLEIGH Bath & Somerset (North East)

GAINSBOROUGH
- GAINSBOROUGH Lincolnshire
- LINCOLN Lincolnshire

GATESHEAD
- HEWORTH Tyne And Wear
- RAVENSWORTH Tyne And Wear

GERRARDS CROSS
- GERRARDS CROSS Buckinghamshire

GILLINGHAM
- BULLPITS Dorset
- GILLINGHAM Kent

GLOSSOP
- GLOSSOP & DISTRICT Derbyshire

GLOUCESTER
- GLOUCESTER Gloucestershire
- ORCHARD Gloucestershire
- RAMADA HOTEL Gloucestershire

GODALMING
- BROADWATER PARK Surrey
- SHILLINGLEE PARK Surrey
- WEST SURREY Surrey

GOSPORT
- GOSPORT & STOKES BAY Hampshire

GRANGE-OVER-SANDS
- GRANGE FELL Cumbria
- GRANGE-OVER-SANDS Cumbria

GRANTHAM
- BELTON PARK Lincolnshire
- BELTON WOODS Lincolnshire
- ROPSLEY Lincolnshire
- STOKE ROCHFORD Lincolnshire
- SUDBROOK MOOR Lincolnshire

GRAVESEND
- MID KENT Kent
- SOUTHERN VALLEY Kent

GRAYS
- ORSETT Essex

GREAT YARMOUTH
- CALDECOTT HALL Norfolk
- GORLESTON Norfolk
- GREAT YARMOUTH & CAISTER Norfolk

GREENFORD
- EALING London (Greater)
- HORSENDEN HILL London (Greater)
- PERIVALE PARK London (Greater)

GRIMSBY
- GRIMSBY Lincolnshire (North East)
- HUMBERSTON PARK Lincolnshire (North East)
- MANOR Lincolnshire (North East)
- TETNEY Lincolnshire (North East)
- WALTHAM WINDMILL Lincolnshire (North East)

GROUVILLE
- JERSEY (ROYAL) Jersey

GUILDFORD
- BRAMLEY Surrey
- CLANDON REGIS Surrey
- CRANLEIGH Surrey
- GUILDFORD Surrey
- HURTMORE Surrey
- MERRIST WOOD Surrey
- PUTTENHAM Surrey
- ROKER PARK Surrey
- WORPLESDON Surrey

GUILFORD
- MILFORD GOLF CLUB Surrey

HADDESDON
- HERTFORDSHIRE Hertfordshire

HAILSHAM
- WELLSHURST Sussex (East)

HALESOWEN
- HALESOWEN Midlands (West)

HALESWORTH
- HIGH LODGE Suffolk

HALIFAX
- BRADLEY HALL Yorkshire (West)
- HALIFAX Yorkshire (West)
- LIGHTCLIFFE Yorkshire (West)
- WEST END Yorkshire (West)

HALSTEAD
- GOSFIELD LAKE Essex

HAMPSTEAD
- HAMPSTEAD London (Greater)

HAMPTON
- FULWELL London (Greater)

HARLOW
- CANONS BROOK Essex

HARPENDEN
- ALDWICKBURY PARK Hertfordshire
- HARPENDEN Hertfordshire
- HARPENDEN COMMON Hertfordshire

HARROGATE
- CRIMPLE VALLEY Yorkshire (North)
- HARROGATE Yorkshire (North)
- OAKDALE Yorkshire (North)
- PANNAL Yorkshire (North)
- RUDDING PARK Yorkshire (North)
- SPOFFORTH Yorkshire (North)

HARROW
- HARROW HILL London (Greater)

HARTLEPOOL
- CASTLE EDEN Cleveland
- HARTLEPOOL Cleveland
- HIGH THROSTON Cleveland
- SEATON CAREW Cleveland

HARWICH
- HARWICH & DOVERCOURT Essex

HASLEMERE
- PETWORTH Sussex (West)

HATFIELD
- HATFIELD LONDON Hertfordshire

HAVANT
- ROWLANDS CASTLE Hampshire

HAVERHILL
- HAVERHILL Suffolk

HAWKHURST
- HAWKHURST Kent

HAYLE
- GREENACRES Cornwall

HAYLING
- TOURNERBURY GOLF CTRE Hampshire

HAYLING ISLAND
- HAYLING Hampshire

HAYWARDS HEATH
- CUCKFIELD Sussex (West)
- HAYWARDS HEATH Sussex (West)
- PAXHILL PARK Sussex (West)

HAZELMERE
- HINDHEAD Surrey

HEATHFIELD
- HORAM PARK Sussex (East)

HEBDEN BRIDGE
- HEBDEN BRIDGE Yorkshire (West)

HELSTON
- HELSTON Cornwall
- MULLION Cornwall

HEMEL HEMPSTEAD
- BOXMOOR Hertfordshire
- LITTLE HAY Hertfordshire
- SHENDISH MANOR Hertfordshire

HENLEY
- HENNERTON Berkshire
- HUNTERCOMBE Oxfordshire

HENLEY-ON-THAMES
- ASPECT PARK Oxfordshire
- DOG Oxfordshire
- GREYS GREEN Oxfordshire
- HENLEY Oxfordshire

HEREFORD
- BELMONT Herefordshire
- BRAMPTON GOLF Herefordshire
- BROCKINGTON Herefordshire
- BURGHILL VALLEY Herefordshire
- HEREFORD MUNICIPAL Herefordshire
- HEREFORDSHIRE Herefordshire
- SUMMERHILL Herefordshire

HERNE BAY
- HERNE BAY Kent

HERTFORD
- BRICKENDON GRANGE Hertfordshire

HEXHAM
- ALLENDALE Northumberland
- BELLINGHAM Northumberland
- HEXHAM Northumberland
- STOCKSFIELD Northumberland
- TYNEDALE Northumberland

HIGH WYCOMBE
- FLACKWELL HEATH Buckinghamshire
- HAZLEMERE Buckinghamshire
- WYCOMBE HEIGHTS GOLF CTRE Buckinghamshire

HIGHNAM
- RODWAY HILL Gloucestershire

HINCKLEY
- HINCKLEY Leicestershire

HITCHIN
- CHESFIELD DOWNS Hertfordshire
- MOUNT PLEASANT Bedfordshire

HOLSWORTHY
- HOLSWORTHY Devon

HONITON
- HONITON Devon
- OTTER VALLEY GOLF CTRE Devon

HOOK
- BLACKWATER VALLEY Hampshire
- HARTLEY WINTNEY Hampshire
- TYLNEY PARK Hampshire

HOPE VALLEY
- SICKLEHOLME Derbyshire

HORNCASTLE
- HORNCASTLE Lincolnshire
- WOODHALL SPA Lincolnshire

HORNSEA
- HORNSEA Yorkshire (East)

HORSHAM
- HORSHAM GOLF Sussex (West)
- MANNINGS HEATH Sussex (West)
- ROOKWOOD Sussex (West)
- RUSPER Surrey
- SLINFOLD PARK Sussex (West)

HOUGHTON LE SPRING
- ELEMORE Tyne And Wear
- HOUGHTON LE SPRING Tyne And Wear

HOUNSLOW
- AIRLINKS London (Greater)
- HOUNSLOW HEATH London (Greater)

HOVE
- BENFIELD VALLEY Sussex (East)
- WEST HOVE Sussex (East)

HOWDEN
- BOOTHFERRY PARK Yorkshire (East)

HUDDERSFIELD
- BAGDEN HALL Yorkshire (West)
- BRADLEY PARK Yorkshire (West)
- CROSLAND HEATH Yorkshire (West)
- HUDDERSFIELD Yorkshire (West)
- LONGLEY PARK Yorkshire (West)
- MARSDEN Yorkshire (West)
- MELTHAM Yorkshire (West)
- OUTLANE Yorkshire (West)
- WOODSOME HALL Yorkshire (West)

HULL
- CAVE CASTLE Yorkshire (East)
- GANSTEAD PARK Yorkshire (East)
- HULL Yorkshire (East)
- SPRINGHEAD PARK MUNICIPAL Yorkshire (East)
- SUTTON PARK Yorkshire (East)

HUNTINGDON
- ABBOTSLEY Cambridgeshire
- BRAMPTON PARK Cambridgeshire
- HEMINGFORD ABBOT Cambridgeshire
- LAKESIDE LODGE Cambridgeshire
- RAMSEY CLUB Cambridgeshire
- ST. IVES Cambridgeshire
- ST. NEOTS Cambridgeshire

HYDE
- WERNETH LOW Cheshire

HYTHE
- HYTHE IMPERIAL Kent
- SENE VALLEY Kent

ILFORD
- ILFORD Essex

ILFRACOOMBE
- ILFRACOMBE Devon

ILKESTON
- BREADSALL PRIORY Derbyshire
- EREWASH VALLEY Derbyshire
- HORSLEY LODGE Derbyshire
- MORLEY HAYES Derbyshire
- PEWIT Derbyshire

ILKLEY
- BEN RHYDDING Yorkshire (West)
- BRACKEN GHYLL Yorkshire (West)
- ILKLEY Yorkshire (West)

IMMINGHAM
- IMMINGHAM Lincolnshire (North East)

INGATESTONE
- CRONDON PARK Essex
- HYLANDS GOLF COMPLEX Essex

IPSWICH
- ALNESBOURNE PRIORY Suffolk
- FYNN VALLEY Suffolk
- HINTLESHAM HALL Suffolk
- IPSWICH Suffolk
- RUSHMERE Suffolk

IVYBRIDGE
- DINNATON Devon
- WRANGATON Devon

KEIGHLEY
- BRANSHAW Yorkshire (West)
- FARDEW Yorkshire (West)
- KEIGHLEY Yorkshire (West)
- RIDDLESDEN Yorkshire (West)
- SILSDEN Yorkshire (West)

KENDAL
- BECKSIDE Cumbria
- CARUS GREEN Cumbria
- CASTERTON Cumbria
- KENDAL Cumbria

KENILWORTH
- KENILWORTH Warwickshire

KESWICK
- KESWICK Cumbria

KETTERING
- KETTERING Northamptonshire
- PYTCHLEY GOLF LODGE Northamptonshire

KIDDERMINSTER
- CHURCHILL & BLAKEDOWN Worcestershire
- HABBERLEY Worcestershire
- KIDDERMINSTER Worcestershire
- WYRE FOREST Worcestershire

KIDLINGTON
- KIRTLINGTON Oxfordshire

KING'S LYNN
- DUNHAM Norfolk
- EAGLES Norfolk
- KING'S LYNN Norfolk

- MIDDLETON HALL Norfolk
- SUTTON BRIDGE Lincolnshire
- WEST NORFOLK (ROYAL) Norfolk

KINGSBRIDGE

- BIGBURY Devon
- THURLESTONE Devon

KINGSTON UPON THAMES

- COOMBE HILL London (Greater)
- COOMBE WOOD London (Greater)

KINGSTON-UPON-THAMES

- HAMPTON COURT PALACE GOLF CLUB London (Greater)

KINGTON

- KINGTON Herefordshire

KIRBY

- MOSSOCK HALL Lancashire

KIRKBY IN ASHFIELD

- NOTTS Nottinghamshire

KNARESBOROUGH

- KNARESBOROUGH Yorkshire (North)

KNEBWORTH

- KNEBWORTH Hertfordshire

KNUTSFORD

- HEYROSE Cheshire
- HIGH LEGH PARK Cheshire
- KNUTSFORD Cheshire
- MERE Cheshire
- MOBBERLEY Cheshire
- PEOVER Cheshire
- WILMSLOW Cheshire

LANCASTER

- ASHTON Lancashire
- BENTHAM Lancashire
- LANCASTER Lancashire
- LANCASTER Lancashire
- LANSIL Lancashire

L'ANCRESSE VALE

- GUERNSEY (ROYAL) Guernsey

LANGLEY

- IVER Buckinghamshire
- RICHINGS PARK Buckinghamshire

LANGPORT

- LONG SUTTON Somerset

LAUNCESTON

- LAUNCESTON Cornwall
- TRETHORNE Cornwall

LEAMINGTON SPA

- LEAMINGTON & COUNTY Warwickshire
- NEWBOLD COMYN Warwickshire

LEATHERHEAD

- DRIFT Surrey
- EFFINGHAM Surrey
- LEATHERHEAD Surrey
- PACHESHAM PARK GOLF CTRE Surrey
- TYRRELLS WOOD Surrey

LEEDS

- ALWOODLEY Yorkshire (West)
- BRADFORD Yorkshire (West)
- BRANDON Yorkshire (West)
- CALVERLEY Yorkshire (West)

- COOKRIDGE HALL GOLF CLUB Yorkshire (West)
- GARFORTH Yorkshire (West)
- HEADINGLEY Yorkshire (West)
- HORSFORTH Yorkshire (West)
- HOWLEY HALL Yorkshire (West)
- LEEDS Yorkshire (West)
- LEEDS GOLF CTRE Yorkshire (West)
- MANOR Yorkshire (West)
- MIDDLETON PARK MUNICIPAL Yorkshire (West)
- MOOR ALLERTON Yorkshire (West)
- MOORTOWN Yorkshire (West)
- OULTON PARK Yorkshire (West)
- RAWDON Yorkshire (West)
- ROUNDHAY Yorkshire (West)
- SAND MOOR Yorkshire (West)
- SCARCROFT Yorkshire (West)
- SOUTH LEEDS Yorkshire (West)
- TEMPLE NEWSAM Yorkshire (West)

LEEK

- LEEK Staffordshire
- WESTWOOD Staffordshire

LEE-ON-THE-SOLENT

- LEE ON THE SOLENT Hampshire

LEICESTER

- BIRSTALL Leicestershire
- COSBY Leicestershire
- ENDERBY GOLF CLUB Leicestershire
- FOREST HILL Leicestershire
- GLEN GORSE Leicestershire
- HUMBERSTONE HEIGHTS Leicestershire
- KIBWORTH Leicestershire
- KIRBY MUXLOE Leicestershire
- LEICESTER Leicestershire
- OADBY Leicestershire
- ROTHLEY PARK Leicestershire
- SCRAPTOFT Leicestershire
- WESTERN Leicestershire
- WHETSTONE Leicestershire

LEIGH

- PENNINGTON Lancashire

LEIGH-ON-SEA

- BELFAIRS PARK Essex
- SOUTHEND-ON-SEA Essex

LEIGHTON BUZZARD

- AYLESBURY VALE Bedfordshire
- IVINGHOE Bedfordshire
- LEIGHTON BUZZARD Bedfordshire
- MENTMORE Bedfordshire
- TILSWORTH Bedfordshire

LEOMINSTER

- GROVE Herefordshire
- LEOMINSTER Herefordshire

LETCHWORTH

- LETCHWORTH Hertfordshire

LEWES

- LEWES Sussex (East)

LICHFIELD

- SEEDY MILL Staffordshire

- WHITTINGTON HEATH Staffordshire

LINCOLN

- BLANKNEY Lincolnshire
- CANWICK PARK Lincolnshire
- CARHOLME Lincolnshire
- MILLFIELD GOLF Lincolnshire
- POTTERGATE Lincolnshire
- SOUTH KYME Lincolnshire
- WELTON MANOR GOLF CTRE Lincolnshire

LINGFIELD

- LINGFIELD PARK Surrey

LIPHOOK

- LIPHOOK Hampshire
- OLD THORNS Hampshire

LISS

- PETERSFIELD Hampshire

LITTLEBOROUGH

- WHITTAKER Lancashire

LITTLEHAMPTON

- HAM MANOR Sussex (West)
- LITTLEHAMPTON GOLF Sussex (West)
- RUSTINGTON Sussex (West)

LIVERPOOL

- AINTREE Merseyside
- ALLERTON Merseyside
- BOOTLE Merseyside
- BOWRING PARK Merseyside
- CHILDWALL Merseyside
- FORMBY Merseyside
- FORMBY LADIES Merseyside
- HUYTON & PRESCOT Merseyside
- LEE PARK Merseyside
- LIVERPOOL MUNICIPAL Merseyside
- WEST DERBY Merseyside
- WEST LANCASHIRE Merseyside
- WOOLTON Merseyside

LONDON

- BETHUNE PARK London (Greater)
- BRENT VALLEY London (Greater)
- CENTRAL LONDON London (Greater)
- DUKES MEADOW London (Greater)
- DULWICH & SYDENHAM HILL London (Greater)
- ELTHAM WARREN London (Greater)
- FINCHLEY London (Greater)
- HENDON London (Greater)
- HIGHGATE London (Greater)
- LEE VALLEY London (Greater)
- LONDON SCOTTISH London (Greater)
- MAYLANDS Essex
- MILL HILL London (Greater)
- NORTH MIDDLESEX London (Greater)
- SOUTH HERTS London (Greater)
- THAMESVIEW London (Greater)
- VALLEY London (Greater)
- WIMBLEDON (ROYAL) London (Greater)
- WYKE GREEN London (Greater)

LONG ASHTON
- LONG ASHTON Bristol

LONG EATON
- TRENT LOCK Nottinghamshire

LONG SUTTON
- TYDD ST GILES Cambridgeshire

LONGFIELD
- FAWKHAM VALLEY GOLF CLUB Kent

LONGTON
- PARKHALL Staffordshire

LOOE
- LOOE Cornwall

LOSTWITHIEL
- LOSTWITHIEL Cornwall

LOUGH
- CHARNWOOD FOREST Leicestershire

LOUGHBOROUGH
- LINGDALE Leicestershire
- LONGCLIFFE Leicestershire
- PARK HILL Leicestershire
- RUSHCLIFFE Leicestershire

LOUGHTON
- HIGH BEECH Essex
- LOUGHTON Essex

LOUTH
- KENWICK PARK Lincolnshire
- LOUTH Lincolnshire

LOWESTOFT
- DIP FARM Suffolk
- HALESWORTH Suffolk
- ROOKERY PARK Suffolk

LUDLOW
- LUDLOW Shropshire

LUTON
- GRIFFIN Bedfordshire
- LUTON GOLF CTRE Bedfordshire
- SOUTH BEDS Bedfordshire
- STOCKWOOD PARK Bedfordshire

LUTTERWORTH
- KILWORTH SPRINGS Leicestershire
- LUTTERWORTH Leicestershire
- ULLESTHORPE Leicestershire

LYDNEY
- LYDNEY Gloucestershire

LYME REGIS
- LYME REGIS Dorset

LYMM
- LYMM Cheshire

LYNDHURST
- BRAMSHAW Hampshire
- NEW FOREST Hampshire

LYTHAM ST ANNES
- LYTHAM & ST ANNES (ROYAL) Lancashire

LYTHAM ST. ANNES
- FAIRHAVEN Lancashire
- LYTHAM GREEN Lancashire
- ST. ANNES OLD LINKS Lancashire

MABLETHORPE
- SANDILANDS & LEISURE Lincolnshire
- WOODTHORPE HALL Lincolnshire

MACCLESFIELD
- ADLINGTON Cheshire
- DAVENPORT Cheshire
- MACCLESFIELD Cheshire
- MARTON MEADOWS Cheshire
- PRESTBURY Cheshire
- SHRIGLEY HALL Cheshire
- TYTHERINGTON Cheshire

MAIDENHEAD
- BIRD HILLS Berkshire
- MAIDENHEAD Berkshire
- TEMPLE Berkshire
- WINTER HILL Berkshire

MAIDSTONE
- BEARSTED Kent
- CHART HILLS Kent
- COBTREE MANOR PARK Kent
- LEEDS CASTLE Kent
- MOTE PARK GOLF HUT Kent
- RIDGE GOLF CLUB Kent
- TUDOR PARK Kent

MALDON
- BUNSAY DOWNS Essex
- FIVE LAKES HOTEL Essex
- FORRESTER PARK Essex
- MALDON Essex
- WARREN Essex

MALMESBURY
- OAKSEY Wiltshire

MALTON
- MALTON & NORTON Yorkshire (North)

MALVERN
- WORCESTERSHIRE Worcestershire

MANCHESTER
- ACREGATE Manchester (Greater)
- BOYSNOPE PARK Manchester (Greater)
- BRACKLEY Manchester (Greater)
- BROOKDALE Manchester (Greater)
- CHORLTON-CUM-HARDY Manchester (Greater)
- DAVYHULME PARK Manchester (Greater)
- DENTON Manchester (Greater)
- DIDSBURY Manchester (Greater)
- FAIRFIELD GOLF & SAILING CLUB Manchester (Greater)
- FLIXTON Manchester (Greater)
- HEATON PARK Manchester (Greater)
- MANCHESTER Manchester (Greater)
- NEW NORTH MANCHESTER Manchester (Greater)
- NORTHENDEN Manchester (Greater)
- PRESTWICH Manchester (Greater)
- STAND Manchester (Greater)
- SWINTON PARK Manchester (Greater)

- WHITEFIELD Manchester (Greater)
- WILLIAM WROE Manchester (Greater)
- WITHINGTON Manchester (Greater)
- WORSLEY Manchester (Greater)

MANSFIELD
- MANSFIELD WOODHOUSE Nottinghamshire
- SHERWOOD FOREST Nottinghamshire

MARCH
- MARCH Cambridgeshire

MARKET DRAYTON
- MARKET DRAYTON Shropshire

MARKET HARBOROUGH
- BLACKTHORN WOOD Leicestershire
- COLD ASHBY Northamptonshire
- MARKET HARBOROUGH Leicestershire
- STOKE ALBANY Leicestershire

MARKET RASEN
- MARKET RASEN & DISTRICT Lincolnshire
- OWMBY Lincolnshire

MARLBOROUGH
- MARLBOROUGH Wiltshire
- OGBOURNE DOWNS Wiltshire

MARLOW
- HARLEYFORD Buckinghamshire

MARYPORT
- MARYPORT Cumbria

MELKSHAM
- WHITLEY Wiltshire

MELTON
- UFFORD PARK Suffolk

MELTON MOWBRAY
- MELTON MOWBRAY Leicestershire
- MELTON MOWBRAY TOWN EST Leicestershire
- SIX HILLS LEISURE Leicestershire

METHERINGHAM
- MARTIN MOOR Lincolnshire

MIDDLESBROUGH
- MIDDLESBROUGH Cleveland
- MIDDLESBROUGH MUNICIPAL Cleveland

MIDHURST
- COWDRAY PARK Sussex (West)

MIDSOMER NORTON
- FARRINGTON Bristol

MILFORD
- CHIDDINGFOLD Surrey

MILLOM
- SILECROFT Cumbria

MILTON KEYNES
- ABBEY HILL Buckinghamshire
- ASPLEY GUISE & WOBURN SANDS Buckinghamshire
- KINGFISHER Buckinghamshire
- THREE LOCKS Buckinghamshire
- WAVENDON GOLF CTRE Buckinghamshire

- WINDMILL HILL Buckinghamshire
- WOBURN Buckinghamshire

MINEHEAD
- MINEHEAD & WEST SOMERSET Somerset

MIRFIELD
- DEWSBURY DISTRICT Yorkshire (West)

MITCHAM
- MITCHAM Surrey

MORECAMBE
- HEYSHAM Lancashire
- MORECAMBE Lancashire

MORPETH
- BURGHAM Northumberland
- LINDEN HALL Northumberland
- LONGHIRST HALL Northumberland
- MORPETH Northumberland
- ROTHBURY Northumberland
- SWARLAND HALL Northumberland

MORTEHOE
- MORTEHOE & WOOLACOMBE Devon

MUCH HADHAM
- ASH VALLEY GOLF CLUB Hertfordshire
- GREAT HADHAM Hertfordshire

MUSWELL HILL
- MUSWELL HILL London (Greater)

NANTWICH
- ALVASTON HALL Cheshire
- REASEHEATH Cheshire

NELSON
- MARSDEN PARK PUBLIC Lancashire
- NELSON Lancashire

NEW MALDEN
- MALDEN Surrey

NEW MILTON
- CHEWTON GLEN Hampshire

NEWARK
- NEWARK Nottinghamshire
- SOUTHWELL Nottinghamshire

NEWBIGGIN-BY-THE-SEA
- NEWBIGGIN Northumberland

NEWBURY
- DEANWOOD PARK Berkshire
- DONNINGTON VALLEY Berkshire
- NEWBURY & CROOKHAM Berkshire
- NEWBURY RACECOURSE Berkshire
- PARASAMPIA Berkshire
- WEST BERKSHIRE Berkshire

NEWCASTLE
- NEWCASTLE-UNDER-LYME Staffordshire
- WOLSTANTON Staffordshire

NEWCASTLE UPON TYNE
- BACKWORTH Tyne And Wear
- CONSETT & DISTRICT County Durham
- GARESFIELD Tyne And Wear

- GOSFORTH Tyne And Wear
- HOBSON Tyne And Wear
- NEWCASTLE Tyne And Wear
- NEWCASTLE UNITED Tyne And Wear
- NORTHUMBERLAND Tyne And Wear
- PARKLANDS Tyne and Wear
- PONTELAND Tyne And Wear
- WESTERHOPE Tyne And Wear
- WHICKHAM Tyne And Wear

NEWENT
- NEWENT Gloucestershire

NEWHAVEN
- PEACEHAVEN Sussex (East)

NEWMARKET
- LINKS Suffolk
- WORLINGTON & NEWMARKET (ROYAL) Suffolk

NEWPORT
- LILLESHALL HALL Shropshire
- NEWPORT Isle of Wight

NEWQUAY
- HOLYWELL BAY Cornwall
- MERLIN Cornwall
- NEWQUAY Cornwall
- ST. NEWLYN EAST Cornwall
- TRELOY Cornwall

NEWTON ABBOT
- DAINTON PARK Devon
- HELE PARK GOLF CTRE Devon
- MANOR HOUSE Devon
- NEWTON ABBOT Devon

NEWTON AYCLIFFE
- AYCLIFFE County Durham
- OAK LEAF County Durham
- WOODHAM County Durham

NORTH SHIELDS
- TYNEMOUTH Tyne And Wear

NORTHALLERTON
- ROMANBY Yorkshire (North)

NORTHAMPTON
- BRAMPTON HEATH Northamptonshire
- COLLINGTREE PARK Northamptonshire
- DELAPRE PARK GOLF COMPLEX Northamptonshire
- KINGSTHORPE Northamptonshire
- NORTHAMPTON Northamptonshire
- NORTHAMPTONSHIRE COUNTY Northamptonshire
- OVERSTONE PARK Northamptonshire

NORTHOLT
- C & L London (Greater)
- LIME TREES PARK London (Greater)
- RECTORY London (Greater)

NORTHWICH
- ANTROBUS Cheshire
- SANDIWAY Cheshire
- VALE ROYAL ABBEY Cheshire

NORTHWOOD
- HASTE HILL London (Greater)
- NORTHWOOD London (Greater)
- SANDY LODGE London (Greater)

NORWICH
- BARNHAM BROOM Norfolk
- BAWBURGH Norfolk
- COSTESSEY PARK Norfolk
- EATON Norfolk
- MUNDESLEY Norfolk
- NORFOLK Norfolk
- NORWICH (ROYAL) Norfolk
- SPROWSTON MANOR Norfolk
- WENSUM VALLEY Norfolk
- WESTON PARK Norfolk

NOTTINGHAM
- BEESTON FIELDS Nottinghamshire
- BRAMCOTE HILLS Nottinghamshire
- BULWELL FOREST Nottinghamshire
- CHILWELL MANOR Nottinghamshire
- COTGRAVE PLACE Nottinghamshire
- EDWALTON MUNICIPAL Nottinghamshire
- LEE VALLEY GOLF CTRE Nottinghamshire
- MAPPERLEY Nottinghamshire
- NOTTINGHAM CITY Nottinghamshire
- OAKMERE PARK Nottinghamshire
- RADCLIFFE-ON-TRENT Nottinghamshire
- RAMSDALE PARK Nottinghamshire
- RIVERSIDE Nottinghamshire
- RUDDINGTON GRANGE Nottinghamshire
- SPRINGWATER Nottinghamshire
- STANTON ON THE WOLDS Nottinghamshire
- WOLLATON PARK Nottinghamshire

NUNEATON
- ATHERSTONE Warwickshire
- BRAMCOTE WATERS Warwickshire
- NUNEATON Warwickshire
- OAKRIDGE Warwickshire
- PURLEY CHASE Warwickshire

OAKHAM
- GREETHAM VALLEY Rutland
- RUTLAND WATER Rutland

OKEHAMPTON
- ASHBURY Devon
- OKEHAMPTON Devon

OLD HUNSTANTON
- HUNSTANTON Norfolk

OLDHAM
- BLACKLEY Manchester (Greater)
- CROMPTON & ROYTON Manchester (Greater)
- OLDHAM Manchester (Greater)
- SADDLEWORTH Manchester (Greater)

WERNETH Manchester (Greater)

OLLERTON

RUFFORD PARK GOLF CTRE Nottinghamshire

ONCHAN

KING EDWARD BAY Isle of Man

ONGAR

TOOT HILL Essex

ORMSKIRK

HURLSTON Lancashire

ORMSKIRK Lancashire

ORPINGTON

CHELSFIELD LAKES GOLF CTRE Kent

CRAY VALLEY Kent

HIGH ELMS Kent

LULLINGSTONE PARK Kent

RUXLEY PARK Kent

OSSETT

LOW LAITHES Yorkshire (West)

SPRINGMILL Yorkshire (West)

OSWESTRY

LLANYMYNECH Shropshire

MILE END Shropshire

OSWESTRY Shropshire

OTLEY

OTLEY Yorkshire (West)

OUNDLE

OUNDLE Cambridgeshire

OXFORD

HINKSEY HEIGHTS Oxfordshire

MAGNOLIA PARK Buckinghamshire

NORTH OXFORD Oxfordshire

SOUTHFIELD Oxfordshire

STUDLEY WOOD Oxfordshire

WATERSTOCK Oxfordshire

OXTED

LIMPSFIELD CHART Surrey

TANDRIDGE Surrey

PADSTOW

TREVOSE Cornwall

PAIGNTON

CHURSTON Devon

PEEL

PEEL Isle of Man

PENRITH

PENRITH Cumbria

PENZANCE

CAPE CORNWALL Cornwall

PRAA SANDS Cornwall

PERRANPORTH

PERRANPORTH Cornwall

PERSHORE

EVESHAM Worcestershire

VALE Worcestershire

PETERBOROUGH

ELTON FURZE Cambridgeshire

ORTON MEADOWS Cambridgeshire

PETERBOROUGH MILTON Cambridgeshire

STILTON OAKS Cambridgeshire

THORNEY Cambridgeshire

THORPE WOOD Cambridgeshire

PETERSFIELD

PETERSFIELD Hampshire

PETWORTH

OSIERS FARM Sussex (West)

PINNER

GRIMSDYKE London (Greater)

PLYMOUTH

CENTRAL PARK Devon

SPARKWELL Devon

STADDON HEIGHTS Devon

PLYMPTON

ELFORDLEIGH Devon

PONTEFRACT

MID YORKSHIRE Yorkshire (West)

PONTEFRACT & DISTRICT Yorkshire (West)

POOLE

BROADSTONE Dorset

BULBURY Dorset

PARKSTONE Dorset

PORT ERIN

ROWANY Isle of Man

PORT ST MARY

PORT ST MARY Isle of Man

PORTSMOUTH

GREAT SALTERNS Hampshire

POTTERS BAR

BROOKMANS PARK Hertfordshire

POTTERS BAR Hertfordshire

POULTON-LE-FYLDE

POULTON LE FYLDE Lancashire

PRENTON

WIRRAL LADIES Merseyside

PRESTON

ASHTON & LEA Lancashire

FISHWICK HALL Lancashire

GARSTANG Lancashire

INGOL Lancashire

LEYLAND Lancashire

LONGRIDGE Lancashire

PENWORTHAM Lancashire

PRESTON Lancashire

PRINCES RISBOROUGH

WHITELEAF Buckinghamshire

PRUDHOE

PRUDHOE Northumberland

PUDSEY

FULNECK Yorkshire (West)

WOODHALL HILLS Yorkshire (West)

PULBOROUGH

WEST CHILTINGTON Sussex (West)

QUARNDON

KEDLESTON PARK Derbyshire

RADLETT

PORTER'S PARK Hertfordshire

RAINHAM

UPCHURCH RIVER VALLEY Kent

RAMSEY

OLD NENE Cambridgeshire

RAMSEY Isle of Man

RAMSGATE

ST. AGUSTINES Kent

RAYDON

BRETTVALE Suffolk

RAYLEIGH

HANOVER Essex

READING

CALCOT PARK Berkshire

CASTLE ROYLE Berkshire

CAVERSHAM HEATH Berkshire

GORING AND STREATLEY Berkshire

HURST Berkshire

MAPLEDURHAM Berkshire

READING Berkshire

THEALE GOLF CTRE Berkshire

WOKEFIELD PARK Berkshire

REDCAR

CLEVELAND Cleveland

WILTON Cleveland

REDDITCH

ABBEY HOTEL Worcestershire

PITCHEROAK Worcestershire

REDDITCH Worcestershire

REDHILL

BLETCHINGLEY Surrey

REDHILL & REIGATE Surrey

REDHILL GOLF CTRE Surrey

REDRUTH

RADNOR GOLF & SKI CTRE Cornwall

REIGATE

REIGATE HEATH Surrey

REIGATE HILL Surrey

RETFORD

RETFORD Nottinghamshire

RICHMOND

MID-SURREY (ROYAL) Surrey

RICHMOND Yorkshire (North)

RICHMOND Surrey

RICHMOND PARK London (Greater)

RICKMANSWORTH

BATCHWORTH PARK Hertfordshire

CHORLEYWOOD Hertfordshire

MOOR PARK Hertfordshire

RICKMANSWORTH Hertfordshire

RINGWOOD

BURLEY Hampshire

MOORS VALLEY GOLF CTRE Hampshire

RIPLEY

ORMONDE FIELDS Derbyshire

RIPON

MASHAM Yorkshire (North)

RIPON CITY Yorkshire (North)

ROCHDALE

CASTLE HAWK Lancashire

LOBDEN Lancashire

by **NEAREST LOCATION** in England

Oldham — Rochdale

- MARLAND Lancashire
- ROCHDALE Lancashire
- TUNSHILL Lancashire

ROCHESTER
- ALLHALLOWS Kent
- DEANGATE RIDGE Kent

ROCHFORD
- BALLARDS GORE Essex
- ROCHFORD HUNDRED Essex

ROMFORD
- PRIORS Essex
- RISEBRIDGE Essex
- ROMFORD Essex

ROMNEY MARSH
- LYDD Kent

ROMSEY
- AMPFIELD PAR-THREE Hampshire
- DUNWOOD MANOR Hampshire
- PAULTONS GOLF CENTRE Hampshire
- WELLOW Hampshire

ROSSENDALE
- ROSENDALE GOLF CLUB Lancashire

ROSS-ON-WYE
- ROSS-ON-WYE Herefordshire
- SOUTH HEREFORDSHIRE Herefordshire

ROTHERHAM
- GRANGE PARK Yorkshire (South)
- PHOENIX Yorkshire (South)
- ROTHERHAM Yorkshire (South)
- SITWELL Yorkshire (South)
- WATH Yorkshire (South)

ROYSTON
- BARKWAY PARK Hertfordshire
- HEYDON GRANGE Hertfordshire
- KINGSWAY Hertfordshire
- ROYSTON Hertfordshire

RUGBY
- RUGBY Warwickshire
- WHITEFIELDS Warwickshire

RUGELEY
- ST. THOMAS' PRIORY Staffordshire

RUISLIP
- RUISLIP GOLF CTRE London (Greater)

RUNCORN
- RUNCORN Cheshire
- SUTTON HALL Cheshire

RYDE
- RYDE Isle of Wight
- WESTRIDGE Isle of Wight

RYE
- RYE Sussex (East)

RYTON
- RYTON Tyne And Wear
- TYNESIDE Tyne And Wear

SAFFRON WALDEN
- SAFFRON WALDEN Essex

SALE
- ASHTON-ON-MERSEY Cheshire
- SALE Cheshire

SALISBURY
- HAMPTWORTH Wiltshire
- HIGH POST Wiltshire
- SALISBURY & SOUTH WILTS Wiltshire

SALTASH
- CHINA FLEET Cornwall
- ST. MELLION INTERNATIONAL Cornwall

SALTBURN-BY-THE-SEA
- HUNLEY HALL Cleveland
- SALTBURN Cleveland

SANDBACH
- MALKINS BANK Cheshire
- SANDBACH Cheshire

SANDOWN
- SHANKLIN & SANDOWN Isle of Wight

SANDWICH
- PRINCES Kent
- ST. GEORGE'S (ROYAL) Kent

SAWBRIDGEWORTH
- MANOR OF GROVES Hertfordshire

SCARBOROUGH
- GANTON Yorkshire (North)
- NORTH CLIFF Yorkshire (North)
- RAVEN HALL Yorkshire (North)
- SCARBOROUGH SOUTH CLIFF Yorkshire (North)

SCUNTHORPE
- ASHBY DECOY Lincolnshire (North)
- GRANGE PARK Lincolnshire (North)
- HOLME HALL Lincolnshire (North)
- KINGSWAY Lincolnshire (North)
- NORMANBY HALL Lincolnshire (North)

SEAFORD
- SEAFORD HEAD Sussex (East)

SEAHAM
- SEAHAM HARBOUR County Durham

SEAHOUSES
- SEAHOUSES Northumberland

SEASCALE
- SEASCALE Cumbria

SEATON
- AXE CLIFF Devon

SEDBERGH
- SEDBURGH Cumbria

SEDGEFIELD
- KNOTTY HILL GOLF CTRE Cleveland

SELBY
- SELBY Yorkshire (North)

SETTLE
- SETTLE Yorkshire (North)

SEVENOAKS
- BROKE HILL Kent
- DARENTH VALLEY Kent
- KNOLE PARK Kent
- LONDON Kent

- REDLIBBETS Kent
- WILDERNESSE Kent
- WROTHAM HEATH Kent

SHEFFIELD
- ABBEYDALE Yorkshire (South)
- BEAUCHIEF MUNICIPAL Yorkshire (South)
- BIRLEY WOOD Yorkshire (South)
- CONCORD GOLF CTRE Yorkshire (South)
- DORE & TOTLEY Yorkshire (South)
- HALLAMSHIRE Yorkshire (South)
- HILLSBOROUGH Yorkshire (South)
- LEES HALL Yorkshire (South)
- RENISHAW PARK Yorkshire (South)
- ROTHER VALLEY GOLF Yorkshire (South)
- STOCKSBRIDGE Yorkshire (South)
- TANKERSLEY PARK Yorkshire (South)
- TINSLEY PARK Yorkshire (South)
- WORTLEY Yorkshire (South)

SHEFFORD
- BARON & BARONESS Bedfordshire

SHEPPERTON
- SUNBURY Surrey

SHEPTON MALLET
- MENDIP Bath & Somerset (North East)

SHERBORNE
- FOLKE GOLF CTRE Dorset
- SHERBORNE Dorset

SHIFNAL
- SHIFNAL Shropshire

SHIPLEY
- NORTHCLIFFE Yorkshire (West)

SHREWSBURY
- ARSCOTT Shropshire
- HAWKSTONE PARK Shropshire
- MEOLE BRACE Shropshire
- SHREWBURY Shropshire

SIDCUP
- SIDCUP Kent

SIDMOUTH
- SIDMOUTH Devon

SINDLESHAM
- BEARWOOD Berkshire

SITTINGBOURNE
- OAST GOLF CTRE Kent
- SITTINGBOURNE & MILTON REGIS Kent

SKEGNESS
- ADDLETHORPE Lincolnshire
- NORTH SHORE Lincolnshire
- SEACROFT Lincolnshire
- SOUTH VIEW LEISURE Lincolnshire

SKELMERSDALE
- DEAN WOOD Lancashire

SKIPTON
- SKIPTON Yorkshire (North)

SLEAFORD
- SLEAFORD Lincolnshire

SLOUGH
- BURNHAM BEECHES Berkshire
- DATCHET Berkshire
- FARNHAM PARK Berkshire
- LAMBOURNE CLUB Berkshire
- LANES Berkshire
- STOKE POGES Berkshire
- THORNEY PARK Buckinghamshire
- WEXHAM PARK Berkshire

SMETHWICK
- WARLEY Midlands (West)

SNODLAND
- OAST PARK Kent

SOLIHULL
- COPT HEATH Midlands (West)
- HAVEN PASTURES Midlands (West)
- HENLEY Midlands (West)
- LADBROOK PARK Midlands (West)
- OLTON Midlands (West)
- ROBIN HOOD Midlands (West)
- SHIRLEY Midlands (West)
- TIDBURY GREEN Midlands (West)
- WIDNEY MANOR Midlands (West)

SOMERTON
- WHEATHILL Somerset

SONNING
- SONNING Berkshire

SOUTH CROYDON
- CROHAM HURST Surrey
- PURLEY DOWNS Surrey

SOUTH OCKENDON
- MARDYKE VALLEY GOLF CTRE Essex

SOUTH SHIELDS
- SOUTH SHIELDS Tyne And Wear
- WHITBURN Tyne And Wear

SOUTH WOODHAM
- THREE RIVERS Essex

SOUTHALL
- WEST MIDDLESEX London (Greater)

SOUTHAMPTON
- BRAMSHOTT HILL Hampshire
- CHILWORTH Hampshire
- CORHAMPTON Hampshire
- DIBDEN GOLF CTRE Hampshire
- FAIRTHORNE MANOR Hampshire
- MEON VALLEY Hampshire
- ROMSEY Hampshire
- SOUTHAMPTON MUNICIPAL Hampshire
- STONEHAM Hampshire

SOUTHEND-ON-SEA
- ESSEX Essex
- THORPE HALL Essex

SOUTHGATE
- TRENT PARK GOLF CLUB London (Greater)

SOUTHPORT
- BIRKDALE (ROYAL) Merseyside

- FORMBY HALL Merseyside
- HESKETH Merseyside
- HILLSIDE Merseyside
- PARK Merseyside
- SOUTHPORT & AINSDALE Merseyside
- SOUTHPORT MUNICIPAL Merseyside
- SOUTHPORT OLD LINKS Merseyside

SOUTHWELL
- NORWOOD PARK Nottinghamshire

SOUTHWOLD
- SOUTHWOLD Suffolk

SOWERBY BRIDGE
- RYBURN Yorkshire (West)

SPALDING
- GEDNEY HILL Lincolnshire
- SPALDING Lincolnshire

ST ANNES
- ALDERNEY Channel Islands

ST BRELADE
- LA MOYE Jersey

ST HELIER
- ST. CLEMENT Channel Islands

ST PETER PORT
- LA GRANDE MARE Channel Islands

ST PETERS PORT
- ST. PIERRE PARK Guernsey

ST. ALBANS
- ABBEY VIEW Hertfordshire
- BATCHWOOD Hertfordshire
- MID-HERTS Hertfordshire
- REDBOURN Hertfordshire
- VERULAM Hertfordshire

ST. AUSTELL
- CARLYON BAY Cornwall
- PORTHPEAN Cornwall
- ST. AUSTELL Cornwall

ST. HELENS
- GRANGE PARK Merseyside
- SHERDLEY PARK MUNICIPAL Merseyside

ST. IVES
- TREGENNA CASTLE Cornwall
- WEST CORNWALL Cornwall

ST. LEONARDS-ON-SEA
- HASTINGS Sussex (East)

ST. MARYS
- ISLES OF SCILLY Isles of Scilly

STAFFORD
- BROCTON HALL Staffordshire
- INGESTRE PARK Staffordshire
- STAFFORD CASTLE Staffordshire

STALYBRIDGE
- STAMFORD Cheshire

STAMFORD
- BURGHLEY PARK Lincolnshire
- LUFFENHAM HEATH Lincolnshire
- RUTLAND COUNTY Lincolnshire

STANFORD-LE-HOPE
- ST. CLERES HALL Essex

STANLEY
- SOUTH MOOR County Durham

STANMORE
- STANMORE London (Greater)

STAPLEFORD ABBOT
- STAPLEFORD ABBOTTS GOLF CLUB Essex

STEVENAGE
- STEVENAGE Hertfordshire

STISTED
- BRAINTREE Essex

STOCKBRIDGE
- LECKFORD Hampshire

STOCKPORT
- AVRO Cheshire
- BRAMALL PARK Cheshire
- BRAMHALL Cheshire
- DISLEY Cheshire
- HAZEL GROVE Cheshire
- HEATON MOOR Cheshire
- HOULDSWORTH Cheshire
- MARPLE Cheshire
- MELLOR & TOWNSCLIFFE Cheshire
- NEW MILLS Cheshire
- REDDISH VALE Cheshire
- ROMILEY Cheshire
- STOCKPORT Cheshire

STOCKTON
- NORTON Cleveland

STOCKTON-ON-TEES
- EAGLESCLIFFE Cleveland
- TEESSIDE Cleveland

STOKE-ON-TRENT
- ALSAGER Staffordshire
- BURSLEM Staffordshire
- GOLDENHILL Staffordshire
- GREENWAY HALL Staffordshire
- TRENTHAM Staffordshire
- WHISTON HALL Staffordshire

STONE
- BARLASTON Staffordshire
- IZAAK WALTON Staffordshire
- STONE Staffordshire

STOURBRIDGE
- ENVILLE Midlands (West)
- HAGLEY Midlands (West)
- STOURBRIDGE Midlands (West)

STOWMARKET
- STOWMARKET Suffolk

STRATFORD-UPON-AVON
- BIDFORD GRANGE Warwickshire
- STRATFORD OAKS Warwickshire
- STRATFORD ON AVON Warwickshire
- WELCOMBE HOTEL Warwickshire

STROOD
- ROCHESTER & COBHAM Kent

STROUD
- MINCHINHAMPTON Gloucestershire
- PAINSWICK Gloucestershire

STYAL
- STYAL Cheshire

SUDBURY
- CLARE PARK LAKE Suffolk
- NEWTON GREEN Suffolk

SUNBURY-ON-THAMES
- HAZELWOOD GOLF CTRE Surrey

SUNDERLAND
- RYHOPE Tyne And Wear
- WEARSIDE Tyne And Wear

SURBITON
- CHESSINGTON Surrey

SUTTON
- BANSTEAD DOWNS Surrey

SUTTON COLDFIELD
- ASTON WOOD Midlands (West)
- BELFRY Midlands (West)
- BOLDMERE Midlands (West)
- LEA MARSTON Midlands (West)
- MOOR HALL Midlands (West)
- PYPE HAYES Midlands (West)
- SUTTON COLDFIELD Midlands (West)
- SUTTON COLDFIELD LADIES Midlands (West)
- WALMLEY Midlands (West)
- WISHAW Midlands (West)

SUTTON-IN-ASHFIELD
- BRIERLEY FOREST Nottinghamshire
- COXMOOR Nottinghamshire

SWAFFHAM
- SWAFFHAM Norfolk

SWANAGE
- ISLE OF PURBECK Dorset

SWANLEY
- BIRCHWOOD PARK Kent
- PEDHAM PLACE GOLF CTRE Kent

SWINDON
- BRINKWORTH Wiltshire
- BROOME MANOR Wiltshire
- HIGHWORTH GOLF CENTRE Wiltshire
- SHRIVENHAM PARK Wiltshire
- WRAG BARN Wiltshire

SYSTON
- BEEDLES LAKE Leicestershire

TADCASTER
- COCKSFORD Yorkshire (North)
- SCARTHINGWELL Yorkshire (North)

TADLEY
- BISHOPSWOOD Hampshire
- SANDFORD SPRINGS Hampshire

TADWORTH
- KINGSWOOD Surrey

TAMWORTH
- DRAYTON PARK Staffordshire
- TAMWORTH MUNICIPAL Staffordshire

TARPORLEY
- PORTAL Cheshire
- PORTAL PREMIER Cheshire

TAUNTON
- OAKE MANOR Somerset
- TAUNTON & PICKERIDGE Somerset
- VIVARY PARK Somerset

TAVISTOCK
- HURDWICK Devon
- TAVISTOCK Devon

TEIGNMOUTH
- SHALDON APPROACH Devon
- TEIGNMOUTH Devon

TELFORD
- SHROPSHIRE Shropshire
- TELFORD Shropshire

TENBURY WELLS
- CADMORE LODGE Worcestershire

TEWKESBURY
- HILTON PUCKRUP HALL Gloucestershire
- SHERDONS Gloucestershire
- TEWKESBURY PARK Gloucestershire

THAME
- OXFORDSHIRE Oxfordshire

THETFORD
- FELTWELL Norfolk
- RICHMOND PARK Norfolk
- THETFORD Norfolk

THIRSK
- THIRSK & NORTHALLERTON Yorkshire (North)

TIDWORTH
- TIDWORTH GARRISON Wiltshire

TIVERTON
- TIVERTON Devon

TODMORDEN
- TODMORDEN Yorkshire (West)

TONBRIDGE
- HILDEN EUROPRO Kent
- MOATLANDS Kent
- NIZELS Kent
- POULT WOOD GOLF CTRE Kent

TORPOINT
- WHITSAND BAY Cornwall

TORQUAY
- TORQUAY Devon

TORRINGTON
- TORRINGTON Devon

TOTNES
- DARTMOUTH Devon

TOWCESTER
- FARTHINGSTONE Northamptonshire
- WHITTLEBURY PARK Northamptonshire

TRING
- STOCKS HOTEL Hertfordshire

TRURO
- KILLIOW PARK Cornwall
- TRURO Cornwall

TUNBRIDGE WELLS
- NEVILL Kent

- TUNBRIDGE WELLS Kent

TWICKENHAM
- STRAWBERRY HILL London (Greater)
- TWICKENHAM PARK London (Greater)

UCKFIELD
- EAST SUSSEX NATIONAL Sussex (East)

ULVERSTON
- ULVERSTON Cumbria

UMBERLEIGH
- HIGHBULLEN HOTEL Devon
- LIBBATON Devon

UPMINSTER
- LANGDON HILLS GOLF CTRE Essex
- TOP MEADOW Essex
- UPMINSTER Essex

UTTOXETER
- MANOR Staffordshire
- UTTOXETER Staffordshire

UXBRIDGE
- DENHAM London (Greater)
- HILLINGDON London (Greater)
- STOCKLEY PARK London (Greater)
- UXBRIDGE London (Greater)

VENTNOR
- VENTNOR Isle of Wight

VERWOOD
- CRANE VALLEY Dorset

VIRGINIA WATERS
- WENTWORTH Surrey

WADEBRIDGE
- ROSERROW Cornwall
- ST. ENODOC Cornwall
- ST. KEW Cornwall

WADHURST
- DALE HILL Sussex (East)

WAKEFIELD
- LOFTHOUSE HILL Yorkshire (West)
- NORMANTON Yorkshire (West)
- PAINTHORPE HOUSE Yorkshire (West)
- PONTEFRACT Yorkshire (West)
- WAKEFIELD Yorkshire (West)
- WAKEFIELD Yorkshire (West)
- WATERTON PARK Yorkshire (West)

WALKDEN
- ELLESMERE Manchester (Greater)

WALLASEY
- LEASOWE Merseyside
- WARREN Merseyside

WALLSEND
- WALLSEND Tyne And Wear

WALSALL
- BLOXWICH Midlands (West)
- CALDERFIELDS Midlands (West)
- DRUIDS HEATH Midlands (West)
- WALSALL Midlands (West)

WALTHAM ABBEY
- NAZEING Essex

WALTHAM CROSS
- CHESHUNT PARK GOLF COURSE Hertfordshire

WALTON ON THAMES
- BURHILL Surrey
- HERSHAM VILLAGE Surrey

WANSTEAD
- WANSTEAD London (Greater)

WARE
- BRIGGENS HOUSE Hertfordshire
- CHADWELL SPRINGS Hertfordshire
- HANBURY MANOR Hertfordshire
- WHITEHILL GOLF CTRE Hertfordshire

WAREHAM
- EAST DORSET Dorset
- WAREHAM Dorset

WARKWOTH
- WARKWORTH Northumberland

WARLEY
- BRANDHALL Midlands (West)

WARLINGHAM
- FARLEIGH COURT Surrey

WARMINSTER
- WEST WILTS Wiltshire

WARRINGTON
- ALDER ROOT Cheshire
- BIRCHWOOD Cheshire
- HAYDOCK PARK Merseyside
- LEIGH Cheshire
- WALTON HALL Cheshire

WARWICK
- WARWICK GOLF CTRE Warwickshire
- WARWICKSHIRE Warwickshire

WASHINGTON
- GEORGE WASHINGTON Tyne and Wear

WATERLOOVILLE
- FURZELEY Hampshire
- PORTSMOUTH Hampshire
- WATERLOOVILLE Hampshire

WATFORD
- ALDENHAM Hertfordshire
- BUSHEY GOLF COURSE Hertfordshire
- BUSHEY HALL Hertfordshire
- HARTSBOURNE COUNTRY CLUB Hertfordshire
- OXHEY PARK Hertfordshire
- PENFOLD PARK Hertfordshire
- WEST HERTS Hertfordshire

WEDMORE
- ISLE OF WEDMORE Somerset

WELLING
- SHOOTERS HILL London (Greater)

WELLINGBOROUGH
- RUSHDEN Northamptonshire
- WELLINGBOROUGH Northamptonshire

WELLINGTON
- WREKIN Shropshire

WELLS
- WELLS Somerset

WELWYN
- DANESBURY PARK Hertfordshire

WELWYN GARDEN CITY
- BROCKET HALL Hertfordshire
- MILL GREEN GOLF CLUB Hertfordshire
- PANSHANGER GOLF COMPLEX Hertfordshire
- WELWYN GARDEN CITY Hertfordshire

WEMBLEY
- SUDBURY London (Greater)

WEST BROMWICH
- DARTMOUTH Midlands (West)
- SANDWELL PARK Midlands (West)

WEST BURGHOLT
- COLCHESTER Essex

WEST BYFLEET
- WEST BYFLEET Surrey

WEST DRAYTON
- HEATHPARK London (Greater)

WEST END
- COUNTY Hampshire

WEST KINGSDOWN
- WOODLANDS MANOR Kent

WEST KIRBY
- CALDY Merseyside

WEST MALLING
- KINGS HILL Kent
- WEST MALLING Kent

WEST WICKHAM
- LANGLEY PARK Kent

WESTBURY
- THOULSTONE PARK Wiltshire

WESTERHAM
- CHERRY LODGE Kent

WESTGATE-ON-SEA
- WESTGATE & BIRCHINGTON Kent

WESTON-SUPER-MARE
- WESTON Somerset (North)
- WORLEBURY Somerset (North)

WETHERBY
- WETHERBY Yorkshire (West)

WEYBRIDGE
- ST. GEORGES HILL Surrey

WEYMOUTH
- WESSEX GOLF CTRE Dorset
- WEYMOUTH Dorset

WHADDON
- WHADDON Hertfordshire

WHEAT HAMPSTEAD
- HUMAX London (Greater)

WHITBY
- WHITBY Yorkshire (North)

WHITCHURCH
- HILL VALLEY Shropshire

WHITLEY BAY
- WHITLEY BAY Tyne And Wear

WHITSTABLE
- CHESTFIELD Kent
- WHITSTABLE & SEASALTER Kent

WIDNES
- MERSEY VALLEY Cheshire
- ST. MICHAELS JUBILEE Cheshire
- WIDNES Cheshire

WIDNESS
- BLUNDELLS HILL Merseyside

WIGAN
- ASHTON IN MAKERFIELD Lancashire
- BEACON PARK Lancashire
- GATHURST Lancashire
- HAIGH HALL Lancashire
- HINDLEY HALL Lancashire
- HOUGHWOOD Merseyside
- STANDISH COURT Lancashire
- WIGAN Lancashire

WIGTON
- SILLOTH Cumbria

WILMSLOW
- MOTTRAM HALL Cheshire

WIMBLEDON
- WIMBLEDON COMMON London (Greater)

WIMBLEDON PARK
- WIMBLEDON PARK London (Greater)

WIMBORNE
- CANFORD MAGNA Dorset
- STURMINSTER MARSHALL Dorset

WINCANTON
- WINCANTON Somerset

WINCHESTER
- HOCKLEY Hampshire
- OTTERBOURNE Hampshire
- PARK Hampshire
- SOUTH WINCHESTER Hampshire
- WINCHESTER (ROYAL) Hampshire

WINDERMERE
- WINDERMERE Cumbria

WINDSOR
- MILL RIDE Berkshire

WINSFORD
- KNIGHTS GRANGE Cheshire

WIRRAL
- BRACKENWOOD Merseyside
- BRACKENWOOD MUNICIPAL Merseyside
- EASTHAM LODGE Merseyside
- HOYLAKE MUNICIPAL Merseyside
- LIVERPOOL (ROYAL) Merseyside

WITHAM
- BENTON HALL Essex
- BRAXTED PARK Essex
- RIVENHALL OAKS Essex

WITHERNSEA
- WITHERNSEA Yorkshire (East)

WITNEY
- WITNEY LAKES Oxfordshire

WOKING
- CHOBHAM Surrey

- FOXHILLS GOLF Surrey
- GOAL FARM Surrey
- HOEBRIDGE Surrey
- NEW ZEALAND Surrey
- PYRFORD GOLF CLUB Surrey
- SUTTON GREEN Surrey
- TRADITIONS GOLF COURSE Surrey
- WEST HILL Surrey
- WISLEY Surrey
- WOKING Surrey

WOKINGHAM
- BEARWOOD LAKES Berkshire
- BILLINGBEAR PARK Berkshire
- DOWNSHIRE Berkshire
- SAND MARTINS Berkshire
- WOODCRAY MANOR Berkshire

WOLVERHAMPTON
- OXLEY PARK Midlands (West)
- PATSHULL PARK Midlands (West)
- PENN Midlands (West)
- PERTON PARK Midlands (West)
- SOUTH STAFFORDSHIRE Midlands (West)
- WERGS Midlands (West)
- WOODFARM GOLF COMPLEX Midlands (West)
- WROTTESLEY Midlands (West)

WOOBURN GREEN
- HEDSOR Buckinghamshire

WOODBRIDGE
- CRETINGHAM Suffolk
- SECKFORD Suffolk
- WALDRINGFIELD HEATH Suffolk
- WOODBRIDGE Suffolk

WOODFORD GREEN
- WOODFORD Essex

WOOLACOOMBE
- WILLINGCOTT Devon

WOOLER
- WOOLER Northumberland

WOOTTON BASSETT
- WILTSHIRE Wiltshire

WORCESTER
- BANK HOUSE Worcestershire
- PERDISWELL PARK GOLF COURSE Worcestershire
- RAVENMEADOW Worcestershire
- SAPEY Worcestershire
- TOLLADINE Worcestershire
- WORCESTER Worcestershire

WORKINGTON
- DISTINGTON GOLF Cumbria
- WORKINGTON Cumbria

WORKSOP
- BONDHAY GOLF & FISHING CLUB Nottinghamshire
- COLLEGE PINES Nottinghamshire
- KILTON FOREST Nottinghamshire
- LINDRICK Nottinghamshire
- WORKSOP Nottinghamshire

WORSLEY
- WORSLEY PARK Manchester (Greater)

WORTHING
- BROOKLANDS PARK Sussex (West)
- HILLBARN Sussex (West)
- WEST SUSSEX Sussex (West)
- WORTHING Sussex (West)

WOTTON-UNDER-EDGE
- CANNONS COURT Gloucestershire
- COTSWOLD EDGE Gloucestershire

YELVERTON
- YELVERTON Devon

YEOVIL
- HALSTOCK Somerset
- YEOVIL Somerset

YORK
- ALDWARK MANOR Yorkshire (North)
- ALLERTHORPE Yorkshire (North)
- EASINGWOLD Yorkshire (North)
- FOREST OF GALTRES Yorkshire (North)
- FOREST PARK Yorkshire (North)
- FULFORD Yorkshire (North)
- HEWORTH Yorkshire (North)
- KILNWICK PERCY Yorkshire (North)
- KIRKBYMOORSIDE Yorkshire (North)
- OAKS Yorkshire (North)
- SWALLOW HALL Yorkshire (North)
- YORK Yorkshire (North)
- YORK GOLF CTRE Yorkshire (North)

ABBEYFEALE
- ABBEYFEALE County Limerick
ABBEYLEIX
- ABBEYLEIX County Laois
ACHILL ISLAND
- ACHILL ISLAND County Mayo
ADARE
- ADARE MANOR County Limerick
ARDAGH
- NEWCASTLE WEST County Limerick
ARDEE
- ARDEE County Louth
ARDFERT
- TRALEE County Kerry
ARKLOW
- ARKLOW County Wicklow
- COOLATTIN County Wicklow
- WOODENBRIDGE County Wicklow
ASHBOURNE
- ASHBOURNE County Meath
ATHENRY
- ATHENRY County Galway
ATHLONE
- ATHLONE County Roscommon
ATHY
- ATHY County Kildare
BALBRIGGAN
- BALBRIGGAN County Dublin
BALLA
- BALLA County Mayo
BALLAGHADERREEN
- BALLAGHADERREEN County Roscommon
BALLINA
- BALLINA County Mayo
- MOY BALLEY PAR 3 County Mayo
BALLINASCORNEY
- BALLINASCORNEY County Dublin
BALLINASLOE
- BALLINASLOE County Galway
- MOUNTBELLEW County Galway
BALLINROBE
- BALLINROBE County Mayo
BALLINTESKIN
- BALLINTESKIN PAR 3 County Wexford
BALLYBOFEY
- BALLYBOFEY & STRANORLAR County Donegal
BALLYBOUGHAL
- HOLLYWOOD LAKES County Dublin
BALLYBUNION
- BALLYBUNION County Kerry
BALLYFERRITER
- CEANN SIBEAL County Kerry
BALLYHALE
- MOUNTAIN VIEW County Kilkenny
BALLYHAUNIS
- BALLYHAUNIS County Mayo

BALLYHEIGUE
- BALLYHEIGUE CASTLE County Kerry
BALLYMOTE
- BALLYMOTE County Sligo
BALTINGLASS
- BALTINGLASS County Wicklow
BANDON
- BANDON County Cork
BANTRY
- BANTRY BAY County Cork
BEARNA
- BEARNA County Galway
BELMULLET
- CARNE County Mayo
BELTURBET
- BELTURBET County Cavan
BETTYSTOWN
- LAYTOWN & BETTYSTOWN County Meath
BIRR
- BIRR County Offaly
BLACKLION
- BLACKLION County Cavan
BLACKROCK
- DUNDALK County Louth
BLAINROE
- BLAINROE County Wicklow
BLESSINGTON
- BOYSTOWN County Wicklow
- TULFARRIS HOUSE County Wicklow
BODENSTOWN
- BODENSTOWN County Kildare
BORRIS
- BORRIS County Carlow
BOYLE
- BOYLE County Roscommon
BRAY
- BRAY County Wicklow
- OLD CONNA County Wicklow
- POWERSCOURT County Wicklow
- WOODBROOK County Wicklow
BRITTAS BAY
- SLADE VALLEY County Dublin
BUNCRANA
- BUNCRANA County Donegal
- NORTH WEST County Donegal
BUNDORAN
- BUNDORAN County Donegal
CAHIR
- CAHIR PARK County Tipperary
CALLAN
- CALLAN County Kilkenny
CARDONAGH
- BALLYLIFFIN County Donegal
CARLOW
- CARLOW County Carlow
- QUINNAGH HOUSE PAR 3 County Carlow

CARRICKMACROSS
- NUREMORE HOTEL County Monaghan
CARRICK-ON-SHANNON
- BALLINAMORE County Leitrim
- CARRICK-ON-SHANNON County Leitrim
CARRICK-ON-SUIR
- CARRICK-ON-SUIR County Tipperary
CARRIGALINE
- FERNHILL County Cork
CARRIGROHANE
- MUSKERRY County Cork
CARRIGTWOHILL
- FOTA ISLAND County Cork
CASHEL
- CASHEL GOLF RANGE County Tipperary
CASTLEBAR
- CASTLEBAR County Mayo
CASTLEBLAYNEY
- CASTLEBLAYNEY County Monaghan
CASTLEDERMOT
- KILKEA CASTLE County Kildare
CASTLEGREGORY
- CASTLEGREGORY County Kerry
CASTLEKNOCK
- ELMGREEN County Dublin
CASTLEREA
- CASTLEREA County Roscommon
CASTLETOWNBERE
- BEREHAVEN County Cork
CAVAN
- CAVAN (COUNTY) County Cavan
- VIRGINIA County Cavan
CELBRIDGE
- CELBRIDGE ELM HALL County Kildare
CLAREMORRIS
- CLAREMORRIS County Mayo
CLIFDEN
- CONNEMARA County Galway
CLONDALKIN
- GRANGE CASTLE County Dublin
CLONES
- CLONES County Monaghan
CLONLARA
- CLONLARA GOLF & LEISURE County Clare
CLONMEL
- CLONMEL County Tipperary
- SLIEVENAMON County Tipperary
COBH
- COBH County Cork
CONNEMARA
- RENVYLE HOUSE County Galway
COOLATTIN
- COOLATTIN County Wicklow

CORK
- CHARLEVILLE County Cork

CORK CITY
- BLARNEY County Cork

CRUIT ISLAND
- CRUIT ISLAND County Donegal

CURRAGH
- CURRAGH County Kildare

DAINGEAN
- CASTLE BARNA County Offaly

DELGANY
- DELGANY County Dublin
- GLEN OF THE DOWNS County Wicklow

DELVIN
- DELVIN CASTLE County Westmeath

DONABATE
- BALCARRICK County Dublin
- BEAVERSTOWN County Dublin
- CORBALLIS PUBLIC LINKS County Dublin
- DONABATE County Dublin
- ISLAND County Dublin

DONADEA
- KNOCKANALLY County Kildare

DONERAILE
- DONERAILE County Cork

DOONBEG
- DOONBEG County Clare

DOUGLAS
- DOUGLAS County Cork
- FRANKFIELD County Cork

DROGHEDA
- LOUTH (COUNTY) County Louth
- TOWNLEY HALL County Louth

DUBLIN
- CARRICKMINES County Dublin
- CASTLE County Dublin
- CASTLEWARDEN County Kildare
- CHRISTY O'CONNOR County Dublin
- CLONTARF County Dublin
- DEER PARK HOTEL County Dublin
- DRUIDS GLEN County Wicklow
- DUBLIN (ROYAL) County Dublin
- DUBLIN MOUNTAIN County Dublin
- ELM PARK GOLF & SPORTS CLUB County Dublin
- FINNSTOWN FAIRWAYS County Dublin
- FORREST LITTLE County Dublin
- HOLLYSTOWN GOLF County Dublin
- LONGFORD (COUNTY) County Longford
- LUTTRELLSTOWN CASTLE County Dublin
- MALAHIDE County Dublin
- NEWLANDS County Dublin
- OLDFIELD County Dublin
- OPEN County Dublin
- PINE VALLEY PAR 3 County Dublin
- PORTMARNOCK County Dublin
- RATHFARNHAM County Dublin

- ST. ANNES County Dublin
- STACKSTOWN County Dublin
- SUTTON County Dublin
- TURVEY County Dublin

DUN LAOGHAIRE
- DUN LAOGHAIRE County Dublin

DUNDALK
- BALLYMASCANLON HOUSE County Louth
- KILLIN PARK County Louth
- KILLINBEG County Louth

DUNDRUM
- TIPPERARY (COUNTY) County Tipperary

DUNGARVAN
- GOLD COAST County Waterford
- WEST WATERFORD County Waterford

DUNLAVIN
- RATHSALLAGH County Wicklow

DUNMORE
- DUNMORE DEMESNE County Galway
- DUNMORE EAST County Waterford

DUNSHAUGHLIN
- BLACK BUSH County Meath

EDENDERRY
- EDENDERRY County Offaly
- HIGHFIELD County Kildare

ENNIS
- ENNIS County Clare
- LAHINCH County Clare
- WOODSTOCK County Clare

ENNISCORTHY
- ENNISCORTHY County Wexford
- GARRYLOUGH County Wexford

ENNISCRONE
- ENNISCRONE County Mayo

ENNISKERRY
- ENNISKERRY PAR 3 County Wicklow

FALCARRAGH
- CLOUGHANEELY County Donegal

FERMOY
- FERMOY County Cork

FOX ROCK
- FOXROCK County Dublin
- LEOPARDSTOWN County Dublin

FOYNES
- FOYNES County Limerick

GALWAY
- GLENLO ABBEY County Galway

GLENGARRIFF
- GLENGARRIFF County Cork

GOREY
- BALLYMONEY County Wexford
- COURTOWN County Wexford

GORT
- GORT County Galway

GOWRAN
- GOWRAN PARK GOLF & LEISURE County Kilkenny

GRAIGUENAMANAGH
- CARRIGLEADE County Kilkenny

GREENCASTLE
- GREENCASTLE County Donegal

GREENORE
- GREENORE County Louth

GREYSTONES
- CHARLESLAND County Wicklow
- GREYSTONES County Wicklow

JOBSTOWN
- HAZEL GROVE County Dublin

KANTURK
- KANTURK County Cork

KELLS
- HEADFORT County Meath

KENMARE
- KENMARE County Kerry
- RING OF KERRY County Kerry

KILCOCK
- KILCOCK County Kildare

KILCOOLE
- KILCOOLE County Dublin

KILCURRY
- CARNBEG County Louth

KILKEE
- KILKEE County Clare

KILKENNY
- CASTLECOMER County Kilkenny
- KILKENNY County Kilkenny
- MOUNT JULIET County Kilkenny
- POCOCKE County Kilkenny

KILL
- KILLEEN County Kildare

KILLARNEY
- BEAUFORT County Kerry
- CASTLEROSSE County Kerry
- DUNLOE County Kerry
- KILLARNEY County Kerry
- ROSS GOLF County Kerry

KILLINEY
- KILLINEY County Dublin

KILLORGLIN
- DOOKS County Kerry
- KILLORGLIN County Kerry

KILRUSH
- KILRUSH County Clare

KILSALLAGHAN
- CORRSTOWN County Dublin

KILTERNAN
- KILTERNAN County Dublin

KINSALE
- KINSALE County Cork
- OLD HEAD GOLF LINKS County Cork

LAGHEY
- DONEGAL County Donegal

LETTERKENNY
- DUNFANAGHY County Donegal
- GWEEDORE County Donegal
- LETTERKENNY County Donegal
- PORTSALON County Donegal

LETTERMORE
- CONNEMARA ISLES County Galway

LIMERICK
- CASTLETROY County Limerick
- LIMERICK County Limerick
- LIMERICK (COUNTY) County Limerick

LIMERICK JUNCTION
- BALLYKISTEEN County Tipperary

LISMORE
- LISMORE County Waterford

LISSELAN
- LISSELAN County Cork

LISTOWEL
- LISTOWEL County Kerry

LITTLE ISLAND
- CORK County Cork
- HARBOUR POINT County Cork

LLANDEILO
- CILL-DARA County Kildare

LOUGHREA
- CURRA WEST County Galway
- LOUGHREA County Galway

LUCAN
- HERMITAGE County Dublin
- LUCAN County Dublin

MACROOM
- MAHON MUNICIPAL County Cork
- MAHON MUNICIPAL County Cork

MAHON
- TED MCCARTHY MUNICIPAL County Cork

MALAHIDE
- PORTMARNOCK HOTEL County Dublin

MALLOW
- MALLOW County Cork

MANNAN
- MANNAN CASTLE County Monaghan

MIDLETON
- EAST CORK County Cork
- WATER ROCK County Cork

MILLTOWN
- MILLTOWN County Dublin

MILTOWN MALBAY
- SPANISH POINT County Clare

MITCHELSTOWN
- MITCHELSTOWN County Cork

MOATE
- MOATE County Westmeath
- MOUNT TEMPLE County Westmeath

MONKSTOWN
- MONKSTOWN County Cork

MOORTOWN
- MOOR-PARK County Meath

MOUNTRATH
- MOUNTRATH County Laois

MOVILLE
- REDCASTLE County Donegal

MUCKROSS
- DUNMORE County Cork

MULLINGAR
- MULLINGAR County Westmeath

NAAS
- CRADDOCKSTOWN County Kildare
- NAAS County Kildare
- WOODLANDS County Kildare

NARIN
- NARIN/PORTNOO County Donegal

NAVAN
- TARA (ROYAL) County Meath

NENAGH
- NENAGH County Tipperary

NEW ROSS
- NEW ROSS County Wexford

NEWBRIDGE
- NEWBRIDGE County Kildare

NEWCASTLE
- GLEN MILL County Wicklow

NEWCASTLEWEST
- KILLELINE GOLF County Limerick

NEWMARKET ON FERGUS
- DROMOLAND CASTLE ESTATE County Clare

NEWTOWNMOUNTKENNEDY
- ROUNDWOOD County Wicklow

ORANMORE
- GALWAY BAY County Galway

OUGHTERARD
- OUGHTERARD County Galway

OVENS
- LEE VALLEY County Cork

PARKNASILLA
- PARKNASILLA County Kerry

PORTARLINGTON
- PORTARLINGTON County Laois

PORTLAOISE
- HEATH County Laois
- PORTLAOISE PAR 3 County Laois

PORTUMNA
- PORTUMNA County Galway

RATHASPECK
- RATHASPECK MANOR County Wexford

RATHBANE
- RATHBANE County Limerick

RATHCOOLE
- BEECH PARK County Dublin

RATHDOWNEY
- RATHDOWNEY County Laois

RATHDRUM
- GLENMALURE County Wicklow

RATHFARNHAM
- EDMONDSTOWN County Dublin
- GRANGE County Dublin

RATHMOLYON
- SUMMERHILL County Meath

RATHMULLAN
- OTWAY County Donegal

ROSAPENNA
- ROSAPENNA County Donegal

ROSCOMMON
- ROSCOMMON County Roscommon

ROSCREA
- ROSCREA County Tipperary

ROSSHILL
- ROSSHILL PAR 3 County Galway

ROSSLARE
- ROSSLARE County Wexford
- ST. HELENS BAY County Wexford

ROSSMORE
- ROSSMORE County Monaghan

ROUNDWOOD
- DJOUCE MOUNTAIN County Wicklow

RUSH
- RUSH County Dublin

SAGGART
- CITYWEST County Kildare

SALTHILL
- GALWAY County Galway

SCARIFF
- EAST CLARE County Clare

SCARKE
- SCARKE County Wexford

SCHULL
- COOSHEEN GOLF LINKS County Cork

SHANNON
- SHANNON County Clare

SKERRIES
- SKERRIES County Dublin

SKIBBEREEN
- SKIBBEREEN & WEST CARBERY County Cork

SLIGO TOWN
- SLIGO (COUNTY) County Sligo

ST MARGARETS
- ST. MARGARETS County Dublin

STEPASIDE
- BURROW County Dublin
- STEPASIDE County Dublin

STRAFFAN
- K CLUB County Kildare

STRANDHILL
- STRANDHILL County Sligo

STROKESTOWN
- STROKESTOWN County Roscommon

SUTTON
- HOWTH County Dublin

SWINFORD
- SWINFORD County Mayo

SWORDS
- SWORDS OPEN County Dublin

TEMPLEMORE
- TEMPLEMORE County Tipperary

TERMONFECKIN
- SEAPOINT County Louth

THURLES
- THURLES County Tipperary

TIPPERARY TOWN
- TIPPERARY County Tipperary

TIVOLI
- FITZPATRICK FITNESS CTRE County Cork

TRALEE
- KERRIES County Kerry

TRAMORE
- TRAMORE County Waterford

TRIM
- GLEBE County Meath
- MEATH (COUNTY) County Meath
- SOUTH MEATH County Meath

TUAM
- TUAM County Galway

TUBBERCURRY
- TUBBERCURRY County Sligo

TULLAMORE
- ESKER HILLS County Offaly
- TULLAMORE County Offaly

TULLOW
- MOUNT WOLSELEY HOTEL County Carlow

WATERFORD
- DUNGARVAN County Waterford
- FAITHLEGG County Waterford
- WATERFORD County Waterford
- WATERFORD CASTLE County Waterford

WATERVILLE
- WATERVILLE HOUSE & GOLF LINKS County Kerry

WESTPORT
- CLEWBAY County Mayo
- MULRANNY County Mayo
- WESTPORT County Mayo

WEXFORD
- WEXFORD County Wexford

WICKLOW
- EUROPEAN CLUB County Wicklow
- PUCKS CASTLE PAR 3 County Wicklow
- WICKLOW County Wicklow

YOUGHAL
- YOUGHAL County Cork

ANTRIM
- ALLEN PARK County Antrim
- MASSEREENE County Antrim

ARMAGH
- ARMAGH (COUNTY) County Armagh

BALLYCASTLE
- BALLYCASTLE County Antrim

BALLYCLARE
- BALLYCLARE County Antrim
- GREENACRES GOLF CTRE County Antrim

BALLYGALLY
- CAIRNDHU County Antrim

BALLYMENA
- BALLYMENA County Antrim
- GALGORM CASTLE County Antrim

BALLYMONEY
- GRACEHILL County Antrim
- TARA GLEN County Antrim

BALLYNAHINCH
- SPA County Down

BANBRIDGE
- BANBRIDGE County Down

BANGOR
- BANGOR County Down
- BLACKWOOD GOLF CTRE County Down
- CARNALEA County Down
- DONAGHADEE County Down
- HELENS BAY County Down
- HOLYWOOD County Down

BELFAST
- BALMORAL County Antrim
- BELFAST County Antrim
- BELVOIR PARK County Antrim
- CLIFTONVILLE County Antrim
- DOWN (ROYAL COUNTY) County Down
- DUNMURRY County Antrim
- FORT WILLIAM County Antrim
- GILNAHIRK County Antrim
- KIRKISTOWN CASTLE County Down
- KNOCK County Antrim
- MALONE County Antrim
- MOUNT OBER County Antrim
- ORMEAU County Antrim
- ROCKMOUNT County Down
- SHANDON PARK County Antrim

BUSHMILLS
- BUSHFOOT County Antrim

CARRICKFERGUS
- BENTRA MUNICIPAL County Antrim
- CARRICKFERGUS County Antrim
- GREENISLAND County Antrim

COOKSTOWN
- KILLYMOON County Tyrone

CRAIGAVON
- EDENMORE County Armagh
- LURGAN County Armagh
- PORTADOWN County Armagh

CUSHENDALL
- CUSHENDALL County Antrim

DOWNPATRICK
- ARDGLASS County Down
- BRIGHT CASTLE County Down
- DOWNPATRICK County Down
- RINGDUFFERIN County Down

DUNGANNON
- BENBURB VALLEY County Tyrone
- DUNGANNON County Tyrone

ENNISKILLEN
- ASHWOODS County Fermanagh
- CASTLE HUME County Fermanagh
- ENNISKILLEN County Fermanagh

HOLYWOOD
- BELFAST (ROYAL) County Down

KILKEEL
- KILKEEL County Down

KILREA
- BROWN TROUT County Londonderry
- KILREA County Londonderry

LARNE
- LARNE County Antrim

LIMAVADY
- BENONE County Londonderry
- RADISSON ROE PARK County Londonderry

LISBURN
- ABERDELGHY County Antrim
- DOWN ROYAL PARK County Antrim
- LISBURN County Antrim
- TEMPLE CLUB County Antrim

LONDONDERRY
- DERRY County Londonderry
- FAUGHAN VALLEY County Londonderry
- FOYLE County Londonderry

LURGAN
- CRAIGAVON County Armagh

MAGHERAFELT
- MOYOLA PARK County Londonderry
- RONAN VALLEY County Londonderry

NEWRY
- CLOVERHILL County Down
- NEWRY County Down
- WARRENPOINT County Down

NEWTOWNABBEY
- BURNFIELD HOUSE County Antrim

NEWTOWNARDS
- ARDMINNAN County Down
- CLANDEBOYE County Down
- MAHEE ISLAND County Down
- SCRABO County Down

OMAGH
- CLARE COUNTRY County Tyrone
- FINTONA County Tyrone
- NEWTOWNSTEWART County Tyrone
- OMAGH County Tyrone
- SPRINGHILL County Tyrone

PORTADOWN
- TANDRAGEE County Armagh

PORTRUSH
- BALLYREAGH County Antrim
- PORTRUSH (ROYAL) County Antrim
- RATHMORE County Antrim

PORTSTEWART
- PORTSTEWART County Londonderry

STRABANE
- HILL VALLEY GOLF CTRE County Tyrone
- STRABANE County Tyrone

WHITEHEAD
- WHITEHEAD County Antrim

by NEAREST LOCATION in Scotland

Aberdeen — Dalmally

ABERDEEN
- ABERDEEN (ROYAL) Aberdeen (City of)
- AUCHMILL Aberdeen (City of)
- BALNAGASK Aberdeen (City of)
- BANCHORY Aberdeenshire
- BON-ACCORD Aberdeen (City of)
- CALEDONIAN Aberdeen (City of)
- CRAIBSTONE Aberdeen (City of)
- DEESIDE Aberdeen (City of)
- DUFF HOUSE ROYAL Aberdeenshire
- EAST ABERDEENSHIRE Aberdeen (City of)
- HAZLEHEAD Aberdeen (City of)
- HUNTLY Aberdeen (City of)
- INSCH Aberdeenshire
- KINGS LINKS GOLF CTRE Aberdeen (City of)
- MURCAR Aberdeen (City of)
- NEWMACHAR Aberdeen (City of)
- NIGG BAY Aberdeen (City of)
- NORTHERN Aberdeen (City of)

ABERFELDY
- ABERFELDY Perth And Kinross
- KENMORE Perth And Kinross

ABERLOUR
- ROTHES Moray

ABOYNE
- ABOYNE Aberdeenshire
- TARLAND Aberdeenshire

AIRDRIE
- AIRDRIE Lanarkshire (North)
- EASTER MOFFAT Lanarkshire (North)

ALEXANDRIA
- LOCH LOMOND Argyll and Bute
- VALE OF LEVEN Argyll and Bute

ALFORD
- ALFORD Aberdeenshire

ALLOA
- ALLOA Clackmannanshire
- BRAEHEAD Clackmannanshire
- TULLIALLAN Clackmannanshire

ALNESS
- ALNESS Highlands

ALVA
- ALVA Clackmannanshire

ANNAN
- POWFOOT Dumfries And Galloway

ANSTRUTHER
- ANSTRUTHER Fife
- CRAIL Fife

ARBROATH
- ARBROATH Angus
- LETHAM GRANGE RESORT Angus

ARDGAY
- BONAR BRIDGE/ARDGAY Highlands

ARISAIG
- TRAIGH Highlands

AUCHTERARDER
- AUCHTERARDER Perth And Kinross
- GLENEAGLES Perth And Kinross

AVIEMORE
- DALFABER Highlands

AYR
- BELLEISLE & SEAFIELD Ayrshire (South)
- DALMILLING Ayrshire (South)
- DOON VALLEY Ayrshire (South)
- ROODLEA Ayrshire (South)
- TROON (ROYAL) Ayrshire (South)

BALLATER
- BALLATER Aberdeenshire
- BRAEMAR Aberdeenshire

BANCHORY
- INCHMARLO GOLF CTRE Aberdeenshire
- TORPHINS Aberdeenshire

BATHGATE
- BATHGATE Lothian (West)
- BRIDGECASTLE Lothian (West)
- GREENBURN Lothian (West)
- POLKEMMET Lothian (West)

BEARSDEN
- DOUGLAS PARK Glasgow (City of)

BEAULY
- AIGAS Highlands

BEITH
- BEITH Ayrshire (North)

BELLSHILL
- BELLSHILL Lanarkshire (North)

BIGGAR
- BIGGAR Lanarkshire (South)
- LEADHILLS Lanarkshire (South)

BISHOPTON
- ERSKINE Renfrewshire

BLACKWATERFOOT
- SHISKINE Ayrshire (North)

BLAIRGOWRIE
- ALYTH Perth And Kinross
- BLAIRGOWRIE Perth And Kinross
- DALMUNZIE Perth And Kinross
- GLENISLA Perth And Kinross
- STRATHMORE GOLF CTRE Perth And Kinross

BONNYBRIDGE
- BONNYBRIDGE Falkirk

BONNYRIGG
- BROOMIEKNOWE Lothian (Mid)

BRECHIN
- BRECHIN GOLF & SQUASH CLUB Angus
- EDZELL Angus

BRIDGE OF ALLAN
- BRIDGE OF ALLAN Clackmannanshire

BRIDGE OF WEIR
- RANFURLY Renfrewshire
- RANFURLY CASTLE Renfrewshire

BRODICK
- BRODICK Ayrshire (North)
- CORRIE Ayrshire (North)
- WHITING BAY Ayrshire (North)

BROXBURN
- NIDDRY CASTLE Lothian (West)
- UPHALL Lothian (West)

BUCKIE
- BUCKPOOL Moray
- CULLEN Moray
- STRATHLENE Moray

BURNTISLAND
- BURNTISLAND Fife

CALLANDER
- CALLANDER Perth and Kinross

CAMPBELTOWN
- CARRADALE Argyll and Bute
- DUNARVERTY Argyll and Bute

CARLUKE
- CARLUKE Lanarkshire (South)

CARNOUSTIE
- CARNOUSTIE Angus
- PANMURE Angus

CARNWATH
- CARNWATH Lanarkshire (South)

CARRBRIDGE
- CARRBRIDGE Highlands

CASTLE DOUGLAS
- CASTLE DOUGLAS Dumfries And Galloway
- GATEHOUSE Dumfries And Galloway

CLYDEBANK
- CLYDEBANK & DISTRICT Argyll and Bute
- DALMUIR MUNICIPAL Argyll and Bute

COATBRIDGE
- COATBRIDGE Lanarkshire (North)
- DRUMPELLIER Lanarkshire (North)

COLDSTREAM
- HIRSEL Scottish Borders

COWDENBEATH
- COWDENBEATH Fife

CRIEFF
- COMRIE Perth and Kinross
- CRIEFF Perth And Kinross

CUMBERNAULD
- PALACERIGG Lanarkshire (North)

CUPAR
- CUPAR Fife
- ELMWOOD Fife
- FALKLAND Fife
- LADYBANK Fife

DAILLY
- BRUNSTON CASTLE Ayrshire (South)

DALBEATTIE
- COLVEND Dumfries And Galloway
- CRAIGIEKNOWES Dumfries And Galloway

DALKEITH
- NEWBATTLE Lothian (Mid)

DALMALLY
- DALMALLY Argyll and Bute

DOLLAR
- MUCKHART Clackmannanshire

DORNOCH
- CARNEGIE Highlands
- DORNOCH (ROYAL) Highlands

DRYMEN
- BUCHANAN CASTLE Stirling

DUMBARTON
- CARDROSS Argyll and Bute
- DUMBARTON Argyll and Bute
- MARTIN Argyll and Bute

DUMFERMLINE
- SALINE Fife

DUMFRIES
- CRICHTON Dumfries And Galloway
- DUMFRIES & COUNTY Dumfries And Galloway
- GALLOWAY Dumfries And Galloway
- PINES Dumfries And Galloway
- SOLWAY LINKS Dumfries And Galloway
- SOUTHERNESS Dumfries And Galloway
- THORNHILL Dumfries And Galloway

DUNBAR
- DUNBAR Lothian (East)
- WINTERFIELD Lothian (East)

DUNBLANE
- DUNBLANE NEW Perth And Kinross

DUNDEE
- CAIRD PARK Angus
- CAMPERDOWN Angus
- DOWNFIELD Angus
- LADIES PANMURE Angus
- MONIFIETH GOLF LINKS Angus
- PIPERDAM GOLF Angus
- SCOTSCRAIG Fife

DUNFERMLINE
- AUCHTERDERRAN Fife
- CANMORE Fife
- DUNFERMLINE Fife
- PITREAVIE Fife

DUNKELD
- DUNKELD Perth And Kinross

DUNOON
- COWAL Argyll and Bute
- INNELLAN Argyll and Bute

DUNS
- DUNS Scottish Borders

EDINBURGH
- BABERTON Edinburgh (City of)
- BRAID HILLS Edinburgh (City of)
- BRUNTSFIELD GOLF CLUB Edinburgh (City of)
- BURGESS (ROYAL) Edinburgh (City of)
- CARRICK KNOWE Edinburgh (City of)
- CARRICK KNOWE Edinburgh (City of)
- CARRICKVALE Edinburgh (City of)

CRAIGENTINNY Edinburgh (City of)
- CRAIGENTINNY Edinburgh (City of)
- CRAIGMILLAR PARK Edinburgh (City of)
- DALMAHOY Edinburgh (City of)
- DUDDINGSTON Edinburgh (City of)
- EDINBURGH WESTERN Edinburgh (City of)
- GLEN Lothian (East)
- GULLANE Lothian (East)
- HARRISON Edinburgh (City of)
- LIBERTON Edinburgh (City of)
- LOCHEND Edinburgh (City of)
- LOTHIANBURN Edinburgh (City of)
- LUFFNESS Lothian (East)
- MERCHANTS OF EDINBURGH Edinburgh (City of)
- MORTONHALL Edinburgh (City of)
- MURRAYFIELD Edinburgh (City of)
- PORTOBELLO Edinburgh (City of)
- PRESTONFIELD Edinburgh (City of)
- RAVELSTON Edinburgh (City of)
- SILVERKNOWES Edinburgh (City of)
- SWANSTON Edinburgh (City of)
- TORPHIN HILL Edinburgh (City of)
- TURNHOUSE Edinburgh (City of)

ELGIN
- HOPEMAN Moray

ELLON
- NEWBURGH-ON-YTHAN Aberdeenshire

EYEMOUTH
- EYEMOUTH Scottish Borders

FALKIRK
- FALKIRK Falkirk
- FALKIRK TRYST Falkirk
- POLMONT Falkirk

FEARN
- TARBAT Highlands

FOCHABERS
- GARMOUTH & KINGSTON Moray
- SPEY BAY Moray

FORFAR
- FORFAR Angus

FORRES
- KINLOSS Moray

FORRES (HIGH ST)
- FORRES Moray

FORT AUGUSTUS
- FORT AUGUSTUS Highlands

FORTROSE
- FORTROSE & ROSEMARKIE Highlands

FRASERBURGH
- FRASERBURGH Aberdeenshire
- INVERALLOCHY Aberdeenshire

GAIRLOCH
- GAIRLOCH Highlands

GALASHIELS
- GALASHIELS Scottish Borders
- TORWOODLEE Scottish Borders

GALSTON
- LOUDOUN Ayrshire (East)

GIRVAN
- GIRVAN Ayrshire (South)
- TURNBERRY Ayrshire (South)

GLASGOW
- ALEXANDRA Glasgow (City of)
- BALMORE Glasgow (City of)
- BEARSDEN Glasgow (City of)
- BISHOPBRIGGS Glasgow (City of)
- BLAIRBETH Glasgow (City of)
- BONNYTON Glasgow (City of)
- BOTHWELL CASTLE Glasgow (City of)
- CALDERBRAES Glasgow (City of)
- CALDWELL Glasgow (City of)
- CAMBUSLANG Glasgow (City of)
- CAMPSIE Glasgow (City of)
- CATHCART CASTLE Glasgow (City of)
- CATHKIN BRAES Glasgow (City of)
- CAWDER Glasgow (City of)
- CLOBER Glasgow (City of)
- COWGLEN Glasgow (City of)
- CROW WOOD Glasgow (City of)
- DULLATUR Glasgow (City of)
- EAST KILBRIDE Glasgow (City of)
- EAST RENFREWSHIRE Glasgow (City of)
- FERENEZE Glasgow (City of)
- GLASGOW Glasgow (City of)
- HAGGS CASTLE Glasgow (City of)
- HAYSTON Glasgow (City of)
- HILTON PARK Glasgow (City of)
- KILSYTH LENNOX Glasgow (City of)
- KIRKHILL Glasgow (City of)
- KIRKINTILLOCH Glasgow (City of)
- KNIGHTSWOOD Glasgow (City of)
- LANGLANDS Glasgow (City of)
- LENZIE Glasgow (City of)
- LETHAMHILL Glasgow (City of)
- LINN PARK Glasgow (City of)
- LITTLEHILL Glasgow (City of)
- MILNGAVIE Glasgow (City of)
- MOUNT ELLEN Glasgow (City of)
- POLLOK Glasgow (City of)
- SANDYHILLS Glasgow (City of)
- TORRANCE HOUSE Glasgow (City of)
- WESTERWOOD Glasgow (City of)
- WHITECRAIGS Glasgow (City of)
- WILLIAMWOOD Glasgow (City of)
- WINDYHILL Glasgow (City of)

GLENROTHES
- BALBIRNIE PARK Fife
- GLENROTHES Fife
- LESLIE Fife

GOLSPIE
- GOLSPIE Highlands

GOREBRIDGE
- VOGRIE Lothian (Mid)

GOUROCK
- GOUROCK Inverclyde

GRANTOWN ON SPEY
- GRANTOWN-ON-SPEY Moray

GREENOCK
- WHINHILL Inverclyde

GRETNA
- GRETNA Dumfries And Galloway

GULLANE
- MUIRFIELD Lothian (East)

HADDINGTON
- GIFFORD Lothian (East)
- HADDINGTON Lothian (East)

HADDINTON
- CASTLE PARK Lothian (East)

HAMILTON
- RICCARTON Lanarkshire (South)
- STRATHCLYDE PARK Lanarkshire (South)

HAWICK
- HAWICK Scottish Borders
- MINTO Scottish Borders

HEITON
- ROXBURGHE Scottish Borders

HELENSBURGH
- HELENSBURGH Argyll and Bute

HELMSDALE
- HELMSDALE Highlands

HUNTLY
- DUFFTOWN Aberdeenshire

INVERGORDON
- INVERGORDON Highlands

INVERNESS
- BOAT OF GARTEN Highlands
- BRORA Highlands
- INVERNESS Highlands
- LOCH NESS Highlands
- NEWTONMORE Highlands

INVERURIE
- KINTORE Aberdeenshire

IRVINE
- GLASGOW GAILES Ayrshire (North)
- IRVINE Ayrshire (North)
- RAVENSPARK Ayrshire (North)

ISLE OF COLONSAY
- COLONSAY Argyll and Bute

ISLE OF GIGHA
- GIGHA Argyll and Bute

ISLE OF ISLAY
- MACHRIE Argyll and Bute

ISLE OF MULL
- CRAIGNURE Argyll and Bute

ISLE OF ORKNEY
- STROMNESS Orkney Isles

JEDBURGH
- JEDBURGH Scottish Borders

JOHNSTONE
- COCHRANE CASTLE Renfrewshire
- ELDERSLIE Renfrewshire

KEITH
- KEITH Moray

KELSO
- KELSO Scottish Borders

KEMNAY
- KEMNAY Aberdeenshire

KENMORE
- TAYMOUTH CASTLE Perth And Kinross

KILBIRNIE
- KILBIRNIE PLACE Ayrshire (North)

KILLIN
- KILLIN Perth And Kinross

KILMACOLM
- KILMACOLM Inverclyde

KILMARNOCK
- ANNANHILL Ayrshire (East)
- CAPRINGTON Ayrshire (East)

KINGHORN
- KINGHORN Fife

KINGUSSIE
- KINGUSSIE Highlands

KINROSS
- GREEN HOTEL Perth And Kinross
- KINROSS Perth And Kinross
- MILNATHORT Perth And Kinross

KIRKCALDY
- ABERDOUR Fife
- DUNNIKIER Fife
- KIRKCALDY Fife
- THORNTON Fife

KIRKCUDBRIGHT
- BRIGHOUSE BAY Dumfries And Galloway
- KIRKCUDBRIGHT Dumfries And Galloway
- PARK TONGLAND Dumfries And Galloway

KIRKWALL
- ORKNEY Orkney Isles

KIRRIEMUIR
- KIRRIEMUIR Angus

LAIRG
- DURNESS Highlands

LAMLASH
- LAMLASH Isle of Arran

LANARK
- DOUGLAS WATER Lanarkshire (South)
- HOLLANDBUSH Lanarkshire (South)
- KAMES GOLF Lanarkshire (South)
- LANARK Lanarkshire (South)

LANGHOLM
- LANGHOLM Dumfries And Galloway

LARBERT
- GLENBERVIE Falkirk

LARGS
- LARGS Ayrshire (North)
- ROUTENBURN Ayrshire (North)

LARKHALL
- LARKHALL Lanarkshire (South)

LASSWADE
- KINGS ACRE Lothian (Mid)

LAUDER
- LAUDER Scottish Borders

LAURENCEKIRK
- AUCHENBLAE Aberdeenshire

LEVEN
- ELIE GOLF Fife
- LEVEN LINKS Fife
- LEVEN THISTLE Fife
- LUNDIN Fife
- LUNDIN LADIES Fife
- SCOONIE Fife

LINLITHGOW
- BRIDGEND Lothian (West)
- LINLITHGOW Lothian (West)
- WEST LOTHIAN Lothian (West)

LIVINGSTON
- DEER PARK Lothian (West)
- PUMPHERSTON Lothian (West)

LOCH EARN
- ST. FILLANS Perth and Kinross

LOCHBOISDALE
- ASKERNISH Western Isles

LOCHCARRON
- LOCHCARRON Highlands

LOCHGELLY
- LOCHGELLY Fife
- LOCHORE MEADOWS Fife

LOCHGILPHEAD
- LOCHGILPHEAD Argyll and Bute

LOCHHILL
- NEW CUMNOCK Ayrshire (East)

LOCHRANZA
- LOCHRANZA GOLF Isle of Arran

LOCHWINNOCH
- LOCHWINNOCH Renfrewshire

LOCKERBIE
- LOCHMABEN Dumfries And Galloway
- LOCKERBIE Dumfries And Galloway

LONGNIDDRY
- KILSPINDIE Lothian (East)
- LONGNIDDRY Lothian (East)

LOSSIEMOUTH
- MORAY Moray

LYBSTER
- LYBSTER Highlands

MACDUFF
- TARLAIR (ROYAL) Aberdeenshire

MACHRIE
- MACHRIE BAY Isle of Arran

MAUCHLINE
- BALLOCHMYLE Ayrshire (East)

MAYBOLE
- MAYBOLE MUNICIPAL Ayrshire (South)

MELROSE
- MELROSE Scottish Borders
- ST. BOSWELLS Scottish Borders

MILLPORT
- MILLPORT Ayrshire (North)

MILNGAVIE
- ESPORTA DOUGALSTON Glasgow (City of)

MOFFAT
- MOFFAT Dumfries And Galloway

MONTROSE
- MONTROSE (ROYAL) Angus
- MONTROSE LINKS TRUST Angus

MOTHERWELL
- COLVILLE PARK Lanarkshire (North)
- DALZIEL Lanarkshire (North)

MUIR OF ORD
- MUIR OF ORD Highlands

MUSSELBURGH
- MUSSELBURGH Lothian (Mid)
- MUSSELBURGH LINKS Lothian (East)

MUTHILL
- MUTHILL Perth And Kinross

NAIRN
- NAIRN Highlands
- NAIRN DUNBAR Highlands

NETHY BRIDGE
- ABERNETHY Highlands

NEW GALLOWAY
- NEW GALLOWAY Dumfries And Galloway

NEWBRIDGE
- GOGARBURN Edinburgh (City of)
- RATHO PARK Edinburgh (City of)

NEWCASTLETON
- NEWCASTLETON Scottish Borders

NEWTON MEARNS
- EASTWOOD Glasgow (City of)

NEWTON STEWART
- NEWTON STEWART Dumfries And Galloway
- ST. MEDAN Dumfries And Galloway
- WIGTOWN & BLADNOCH Dumfries And Galloway

NORTH BERWICK
- NORTH BERWICK Lothian (East)
- TANTALLON Lothian (East)
- WHITEKIRK Lothian (East)

OBAN
- GLENCRUITTEN Argyll and Bute

OLD MELDRUM
- MELDRUM HOUSE Aberdeen (City of)

OLDMELDRUM
- INVERURIE Aberdeenshire
- OLDMELDRUM Aberdeenshire

PAISLEY
- BARSHAW Renfrewshire
- PAISLEY Renfrewshire
- RALSTON Renfrewshire

PEEBLES
- CARDRONA Scottish Borders
- INNERLEITHEN Scottish Borders
- PEEBLES Scottish Borders

PENICUIK
- GLENCORSE Lothian (Mid)

- WEST LINTON Scottish Borders

PERTH
- CRAIGIE HILL Perth And Kinross
- DUNNING Perth And Kinross
- KING JAMES VI Perth And Kinross
- LYNEDOCH & MURRAYSHALL Perth And Kinross
- NORTH INCH MUNICIPAL Perth And Kinross
- WHITEMOSS Perth And Kinross

PETERCULTER
- PETERCULTER Aberdeenshire

PETERHEAD
- CRUDEN BAY Aberdeenshire
- PETERHEAD Aberdeenshire

PITLOCHRY
- BLAIR ATHOLL Perth And Kinross
- PITLOCHRY Perth And Kinross

POLMONT
- GRANGEMOUTH Falkirk

PORT GLASGOW
- GLEDDOCH Renfrewshire
- PORT GLASGOW Renfrewshire

PORTLETHAN
- PORTLETHEN Aberdeen (City of)

PORTREE
- ISLE OF SKYE Highlands

PRESTONPANS
- MUSSELBURGH (ROYAL) Lothian (East)

PRESTWICK
- PRESTWICK Ayrshire (South)
- PRESTWICK ST CUTHBERT Ayrshire (South)
- PRESTWICK ST NICHOLAS Ayrshire (South)

RENFREW
- RENFREW Renfrewshire

ROTHESAY
- BUTE Argyll and Bute
- PORT BANNATYNE Argyll and Bute
- ROTHESAY Argyll and Bute

SANQUHAR
- SANQUHAR Dumfries And Galloway

SCARINISH
- VAUL Argyll and Bute

SEAMILL
- WEST KILBRIDE Ayrshire (North)

SELKIRK
- SELKIRK Scottish Borders
- WOLL Scottish Borders

SHETLAND
- SHETLAND Shetland Islands
- WHALSAY Shetland Islands

SHOTTS
- SHOTTS Lanarkshire (North)

SKEABOST
- SKEABOST Highlands

SKELMORLIE
- SKELMORLIE Ayrshire (North)

SOUTH QUEENSFERRY
- DUNDAS PARKS Lothian (Mid)

SOUTHEND
- MACHRIHANISH Argyll and Bute

ST ANDREWS
- ST. ANDREWS LINKS Fife

ST. ANDREWS
- CHARLETON Fife
- DRUMOIG Fife
- DUKES Fife
- KINGSBARNS GOLF LINKS Fife
- NEW Fife
- ST. MICHAELS Fife

STEVENSTON
- ARDEER Ayrshire (North)
- AUCHENHARVIE Ayrshire (North)

STIRLING
- ABERFOYLE Stirling
- DOLLAR Clackmannanshire
- STIRLING Stirling

STONEHAVEN
- STONEHAVEN Aberdeenshire

STORNOWAY
- STORNOWAY Western Isles

STRANRAER
- LAGGANMORE Dumfries And Galloway
- PORTPATRICK - DUNSKEY Dumfries And Galloway
- STRANRAER Dumfries And Galloway
- WIGTOWNSHIRE Dumfries And Galloway

STRATHAVEN
- STRATHAVEN Lanarkshire (South)

STRATHPEFFER
- STRATHPEFFER SPA Highlands

TAIN
- TAIN Highlands

TARBERT
- TARBERT Argyll and Bute

THURSO
- REAY Highlands
- THURSO Highlands

TIGHNABRUAICH
- KYLES OF BUTE Argyll and Bute

TILLICOULTRY
- TILLICOULTRY Clackmannanshire

TOBERMORY
- TOBERMORY Argyll and Bute

TROON
- KILMARNOCK Ayrshire (South)
- TROON MUNICIPAL Ayrshire (South)
- TROON PORTLAND Ayrshire (South)
- WESTERN GAILES Ayrshire (North)

TURRIFF
- TURRIFF Aberdeenshire

ULLAPOOL
- ULLAPOOL Highlands

by **NEAREST LOCATION** in **Scotland**

Milngavie — Ullapool

WEST CALDER
- HARBURN Lothian (West)

WEST LINTON
- RUTHERFORD CASTLE Scottish Borders

WESTHILL
- WESTHILL Aberdeenshire

WESTRAY
- WESTRAY Orkney Isles

WICK
- WICK Highlands

WISHAW
- WISHAW Lanarkshire (North)

ABERDARE
- ABERDARE Glamorgan (Vale of)

ABERDOVEY
- ABERDOVEY Gwynedd

ABERGAVENNY
- ALICE SPRINGS Monmouthshire
- MONMOUTHSHIRE Monmouthshire
- RAGLAN PARC Monmouthshire
- WERNDDU Monmouthshire

ABERGELE
- ABERGELE Conwy

ABERYSTWYTH
- ABERYSTWYTH Ceredigion
- BORTH & YNYSLAS Ceredigion
- CAPEL BANGOR Ceredigion
- PENLANLAS Ceredigion
- PENRHOS Ceredigion

AMLWCH
- BULL BAY Isle of Anglesey

AMMANFORD
- GARNANT PARK Carmarthenshire
- GLYNHIR Carmarthenshire

BALA
- BALA Gwynedd

BANGOR
- ST. DEINIOL Gwynedd

BARGOED
- BARGOED Caerphilly

BARRY
- BRYNHILL Glamorgan (Vale of)
- RAF ST ATHAN Glamorgan (Vale of)
- SOUTH WALES Glamorgan (Vale of)
- ST. ANDREWS MAJOR Glamorgan (Vale of)

BEAUMARIS
- BARON HILL Isle of Anglesey
- PRINCE'S Isle of Anglesey

BENLLECH
- STORWS WEN Isle of Anglesey

BLACKWOOD
- BLACKWOOD Caerphilly
- OAKDALE Caerphilly

BLAENAU FFESTINIOG
- FFESTINIOG Gwynedd

BRECON
- BRECON Powys

BRIDGEND
- GROVE Bridgend
- PYLE & KENFIG Bridgend
- SOUTHERNDOWN Bridgend
- ST. MARYS HOTEL Bridgend

BUCKLEY
- OLD PADESWOOD Flintshire

BUILTH WELLS
- BUILTH WELLS Powys
- RHOSGOCH GOLF Powys

BURRY PORT
- ASHBURNHAM Carmarthenshire

CAERNARFON
- CAERNARFON (ROYAL TOWN OF) Gwynedd

CAERPHILLY
- CAERPHILLY Caerphilly
- CASTELL HEIGHTS Caerphilly
- VIRGINIA PARK Caerphilly

CAERSWS
- MID WALES GOLF CTRE Powys

CALDICOT
- DEWSTOW Monmouthshire

CARDIFF
- CARDIFF Glamorgan (Vale of)
- CASTLECOCH Glamorgan (Vale of)
- COTTRELL PARK Glamorgan (Vale of)
- LLANISHEN Glamorgan (Vale of)
- PETERSTONE LAKES Glamorgan (Vale of)
- RADYR Glamorgan (Vale of)
- ST. MELLONS Glamorgan (Vale of)
- WENVOE CASTLE Glamorgan (Vale of)
- WHITCHURCH Glamorgan (Vale of)

CARDIGAN
- CARDIGAN Ceredigion
- CLIFF HOTEL Ceredigion
- CWMRHYDNEUADD Ceredigion

CARMARTHEN
- CARMARTHEN Carmarthenshire
- DERLLYS COURT Carmarthenshire
- LLANSTEFFAN Carmarthenshire
- PANTYDDERWEN Carmarthenshire

CHEPSTOW
- SHIRENEWTON Monmouthshire
- ST. PIERRE Monmouthshire

COLWYN BAY
- OLD COLWYN Conwy

CONWY
- BETWS-Y-COED Conwy
- PENMAENMAWR Conwy

CREIGIAU
- CREIGIAU Glamorgan (Vale of)

CRICCIETH
- CRICCIETH Gwynedd

CRICKHOWELL
- OLD RECTORY Powys

CWMBRAN
- GREEN MEADOW Torfaen
- LLANYRAFON Torfaen
- PONTNEWYDD Torfaen
- WOODLAKE PARK Monmouthshire

DEESIDE
- HAWARDEN Flintshire
- WEPRE Flintshire

DENBIGH
- BRYN MORFYDD Denbighshire
- DENBIGH Denbighshire

DINAS POWYS
- DINAS POWYS Glamorgan (Vale of)

DOLGELLAU
- DOLGELLAU Gwynedd

EBBW VALE
- WEST MONMOUTHSHIRE Blaenau Gwent

FAIRBOURNE
- FAIRBOURNE Gwynedd

FERNDALE
- RHONDDA Rhondda Cynon Taff

FISHGUARD
- PRISKILLY Pembrokeshire

FLINT
- FLINT Flintshire

GOWERTON
- GOWER Swansea

HARLECH
- HARLECH Gwynedd

HAVERFORD WEST
- DAWN 'TIL DUSK Pembrokeshire
- HAVERFORDWEST Pembrokeshire

HENGOED
- BRYN MEADOWS Caerphilly

HENSOL
- VALE OF GLAMORGAN Glamorgan (Vale of)

HOLYHEAD
- HOLYHEAD Isle of Anglesey

HOLYWELL
- HOLYWELL Flintshire
- KINSALE Flintshire
- PENNANT PARK Flintshire

KNIGHTON
- KNIGHTON Powys

LAMPETER
- CILGWYN Carmarthenshire

LLANDRINDOD WELLS
- LLANDRINDOD WELLS Powys

LLANDUDNO
- MAESDU Conwy
- NORTH WALES Conwy
- RHOS-ON-SEA Conwy

LLANDYSUL
- SARON Carmarthenshire

LLANFAELOG
- ANGLESEY Isle of Anglesey

LLANFAIRFECHAN
- LLANFAIRFECHAN Gwynedd

LLANGEFNI
- LLANGEFNI PUBLIC Isle of Anglesey

LLANGOLLEN
- VALE OF LLANGOLLEN Denbighshire

LLANIDLOES
- ST. IDLOES Powys

MACHYNLLETH
- MACHYNLLETH Powys

MAESTEG
- MAESTEG Bridgend

MERTHYR TYDFIL
- MERTHYR CILSANWS Glamorgan (Vale of)
- MERTHYR TYDFIL Glamorgan (Vale of)
- MORLAIS CASTLE Glamorgan (Vale of)

MIDDLETOWN
- WELSH BORDER GOLF COMPLEX Powys

MILFORD HAVEN
- MILFORD HAVEN Pembrokeshire

MOLD
- ALLT-GYMBYD Flintshire
- CAERWYS NINE OF CLUBS Flintshire
- MOLD Flintshire
- NORTHOP Flintshire
- PADESWOOD & BUCKLEY Flintshire

MONMOUTH
- MONMOUTH Monmouthshire
- ROLLS OF MONMOUTH Monmouthshire

MORFA
- CONWY Conwy

MOUNTAIN ASH
- MOUNTAIN ASH Rhondda Cynon Taff

NARBERTH
- HERONS BROOK Pembrokeshire

NEATH
- EARLSWOOD Neath Port Talbot
- GLYNNEATH Neath Port Talbot
- NEATH Neath Port Talbot
- SWANSEA BAY GOLF SHOP Neath Port Talbot

NEWPORT
- CAERLEON Newport
- CELTIC MANOR Newport
- LLANWERN Newport
- NEWPORT Pembrokeshire
- NEWPORT GOLF Newport
- PARC Newport
- TREDEGAR PARK Newport

NEWTOWN
- ST. GILES Powys

PENARTH
- GLAMORGANSHIRE Glamorgan (Vale of)

PENNAR
- SOUTH PEMBROKE Pembrokeshire

PONTYCLUN
- LLANTRISANT & PONTYCLUN Rhondda Cynon Taff

PONTYPOOL
- PONTYPOOL Monmouthshire

PONTYPRIDD
- PONTYPRIDD Rhondda Cynon Taff

PORT TALBOT
- BRITISH STEEL PORT TALBOT Neath Port Talbot
- LAKESIDE Neath Port Talbot
- PORT TALBOT Neath Port Talbot

PORTHCAWL
- PORTHCAWL (ROYAL) Bridgend

PORTHMADOG
- PORTHMADOG Gwynedd

PRESTATYN
- PRESTATYN Denbighshire
- ST. MELYD Denbighshire

PWLLHELI
- ABERSOCH Gwynedd
- NEFYN & DISTRICT Gwynedd
- PWLLHELI Gwynedd

RHYL
- KINMEL PARK GOLF Denbighshire
- RHYL Denbighshire

RUTHIN
- RUTHIN-PWLLGLAS Denbighshire

ST ASAPH
- RHUDDLAN Denbighshire

ST DAVIDS TOWN
- ST. DAVIDS Pembrokeshire

SWANSEA
- ALLT-Y-GRABAN Swansea
- CLYNE Swansea
- FAIRWOOD PARK Swansea
- LANGLAND BAY Swansea
- MORRISTON Swansea
- PALLEG Swansea
- PENNARD Swansea
- PONTARDAWE Swansea

TENBY
- TENBY Pembrokeshire
- TREFLOYNE Pembrokeshire

TREDEGAR
- TREDEGAR & RHYMNEY Blaenau Gwent

TREHARRIS
- WHITEHALL Glamorgan (Vale of)

TRIMSARAN
- GLYN ABBEY Carmarthenshire

WELSHPOOL
- WELSHPOOL Powys

WREXHAM
- CHIRK Wrexham
- CLAYS GOLF CTRE Wrexham
- MOSS VALLEY Wrexham
- PLASSEY Wrexham
- WREXHAM Wrexham

SECTION 4

Within a grid format, this section allows you to search for clubs by the key characteristics of the course. clubs are listed by country, then by county.

e.g Built on Chalk, Wooded, Lakes, Large Bunkers, Ideal for the Elderly

Once you have located a club using this section you can then refer to the detailed profile of the club in Section 1, or search for specific details in other sections.

GolfWorld Directory

Course descriptions and features

Golf Club/Courses by County

ENGLAND

BATH & SOMERSET (NORTH EAST)

BEDFORDSHIRE

Feature	Combe Grove Manor	Entry Hill	Fosseway	Frome Golf Club	Mendip	Orchardleigh	Aylesbury Vale	Baron & Baroness: Baron Manhattan	Baron & Baroness: Baroness Manhattan	Bedford	Bedford & County	Bedfordshire	Chalgrave Manor	Colmworth & North Bedfordshire	Dunstable Downs	Griffin	John O'Gaunt: Carthagena	John O'Gaunt: John O'Gaunt	Leighton Buzzard	Lyshott Heath	Mentmore: Rosebery	Mentmore: Rothschild	Mount Pleasant	Mowsbury	Pavenham	South Beds: Galley Hill	South Beds: Warden Hill	Stockwood Park	Tilsworth	Wyboston
Views	●	●	●	●	●	●		●	●				●	●							●		●	●	●	●	●		●	
Streams				●				●	●											●	●			●	●					●
Lakes				●				●					●				●						●	●				●		●
Deep Bunkers										●																		●		
Large Bunkers										●														●				●		
Ideal for the Elderly				●				●				●	●				●		●			●		●			●			
Tends to Flood																														
Drains Well	●			●	●			●		●			●	●					●			●			●					
Tight				●																	●			●	●			●		
Short	●	●															●								●			●		
Medium Length		●			●			●	●			●					●					●		●	●	●	●			
Long										●			●	●					●				●							
Open										●				●									●	●	●	●				
Sheltered																	●					●								
Championship								●	●	●							●				●	●								
Undulating						●		●	●				●								●	●	●	●				●		
Cliff Top																														
Valley			●																											
Hilltop	●	●		●																					●					
Downland															●															
Breckland																									●	●				
Moorland																														
Heath Land				●																										
Links															●		●													
Wooded		●												●		●		●					●							
Parkland		●	●	●	●	●		●		●		●	●	●		●	●	●	●	●	●	●	●	●				●	●	●
Built of Gravel										●																				
Built on Clay								●	●				●	●								●	●		●			●		
Built on Soil				●																●						●				
Built on Sand										●							●													
Built on Chalk																				●						●	●			
Green Speed Slow	●																													
Green Speed Medium		●		●	●			●		●			●		●	●		●					●	●	●					
Green Speed Fast				●				●		●												●				●		●		●

www.hccgolfworld.com

Course descriptions and features

Golf Club/Courses by County

Golf Club	Views	Streams	Lakes	Deep Bunkers	Large Bunkers	Ideal for the Elderly	Tends to Flood	Drains Well	Tight	Short	Medium Length	Long	Open	Sheltered	Championship	Undulating	Cliff Top	Valley	Hilltop	Downland	Breckland	Moorland	Heath Land	Links	Wooded	Parkland	Built of Gravel	Built on Clay	Built on Soil	Built on Sand	Built on Chalk	Green Speed Slow	Green Speed Medium	Green Speed Fast
BERKSHIRE																																		
ASCOT (ROYAL)	●					●		●	●		●		●										●						●	●			●	
BEARWOOD LAKES	●	●	●					●				●		●	●	●									●	●		●						●
BERKSHIRE: BLUE																							●											
BERKSHIRE: RED																							●											
BILLINGBEAR PARK: THE OLD	●							●			●			●		●									●			●					●	
BLUE MOUNTAIN GOLF CENTRE		●									●					●									●	●		●				●	●	
CALCOT PARK	●		●					●				●				●										●			●				●	●
CASTLE ROYLE				●	●			●								●									●	●			●				●	●
CAVERSHAM HEATH	●			●	●			●							●								●	●		●		●		●			●	
DATCHET						●				●																●		●					●	
DEANWOOD PARK						●				●															●	●		●	●			●	●	
EAST BERKSHIRE																							●								●	●	●	
HENNERTON										●						●										●		●			●	●		
HURST	●																									●	●						●	●
LAMBOURNE CLUB	●		●									●	●		●									●		●			●				●	
LAVENDER PARK	●	●	●			●				●				●												●							●	
MAIDENHEAD	●	●	●	●	●			●						●	●	●										●	●	●					●	●
MAPLEDURHAM											●		●													●		●	●				●	
MILL RIDE		●													●	●										●		●	●				●	●
NEWBURY & CROOKHAM										●															●	●							●	
PARASAMPIA															●	●										●			●					
READING			●	●		●						●			●	●										●				●			●	●
SAND MARTINS			●			●									●											●				●				
SONNING											●			●												●			●				●	●
SUNNINGDALE LADIES	●																						●	●								●	●	●
SWINLEY FOREST	●									●				●										●						●			●	●
TEMPLE	●				●								●	●		●				●										●	●		●	●
THEALE GOLF CTRE	●					●					●															●							●	
WEST BERKSHIRE	●	●	●		●	●						●	●			●										●			●					●
WOKEFIELD PARK	●	●										●	●			●			●							●								
BRISTOL																																		
BRISTOL & CLIFTON	●					●		●			●				●	●			●							●							●	●
FARRINGTON: EXECUTIVE	●		●		●	●		●				●	●			●										●			●				●	

Course descriptions and features

Golf Club/Courses by County

Feature	FILTON	HENBURY	KENDLESHIRE	KNOWLE	LONG ASHTON	MENDIP SPRING: BRINSEA	MENDIP SPRING: LAKESIDE	SHIREHAMPTON PARK	STOCKWOOD VALE	TALL PINES	THORNBURY GOLF: HIGH	THORNBURY GOLF: LOW	TICKENHAM	TRACY PARK: CROMWELL	TRACY PARK: CROWN	WOODSPRING: AVON	ABBEY HILL GOLF CENTRE: ABBEY HILL	ASPLEY GUISE & WOBURN SANDS	AYLESBURY	AYLESBURY PARK	BUCKINGHAM	CHILTERN FOREST	HEDSOR	IVER	MAGNOLIA PARK	OAKLAND PARK	PRINCES RISBOROUGH	RICHINGS PARK	SILVERSTONE	THORNEY PARK	WAVENDON GOLF CTRE: FAMILY	WAVENDON GOLF CTRE: WAVENDON GOLF CTRE	WHITELEAF
Views	●			●	●	●			●						●	●			●	●	●	●				●		●	●				●
Streams					●	●	●	●						●	●							●					●						
Lakes	●		●		●	●	●							●	●		●					●			●	●	●		●	●	●		
Deep Bunkers	●																								●								
Large Bunkers	●			●										●	●		●							●	●	●							
Ideal for the Elderly	●			●	●	●	●					●					●	●		●	●		●			●							
Tends to Flood																				●													
Drains Well			●	●	●				●	●			●	●	●		●																●
Tight														●				●															●
Short												●											●	●									●
Medium Length	●	●	●	●	●												●		●	●			●	●		●	●		●				
Long						●	●							●	●																		
Open						●	●								●		●		●	●				●	●								
Sheltered																		●				●											
Championship						●	●							●	●	●						●											
Undulating	●		●		●			●			●	●	●	●			●	●				●			●	●	●		●				●
Cliff Top																																	
Valley																						●											
Hilltop				●									●					●															●
Downland																																	
Breckland																																	
Moorland																																	
Heath Land																		●															
Links																																	
Wooded																						●	●	●									
Parkland	●	●	●	●	●	●	●	●	●	●	●	●	●	●	●		●		●	●				●	●	●	●	●	●	●	●	●	●
Built of Gravel																																	
Built on Clay	●	●										●	●	●				●							●			●		●			
Built on Soil													●	●	●											●				●			
Built on Sand												●					●																
Built on Chalk																											●						●
Green Speed Slow																				●													
Green Speed Medium	●			●	●								●	●	●		●							●		●	●		●	●			●
Green Speed Fast	●	●		●										●										●		●							●

Course descriptions and features

www.hccgolfworld.com

Features (columns): Views · Streams · Lakes · Deep Bunkers · Large Bunkers · Ideal for the Elderly · Tends to Flood · Drains Well · Tight · Short · Medium Length · Long · Open · Sheltered · Championship · Undulating · Cliff Top · Valley · Hilltop · Downland · Breckland · Moorland · Heath Land · Links · Wooded · Parkland · Built of Gravel · Built on Clay · Built on Soil · Built on Sand · Built on Chalk · Green Speed Slow · Green Speed Medium · Green Speed Fast

Golf Club / Courses by County

- **WINDMILL HILL** — Ideal for the Elderly; Parkland; Built on Soil; Green Speed Medium
- **WOBURN: DUCHESS** — Views; Deep Bunkers; Drains Well; Tight; Long; Sheltered; Championship; Undulating; Wooded; Built on Sand; Green Speed Fast
- **WOBURN: DUKES** — Views; Drains Well; Tight; Long; Sheltered; Championship; Undulating; Wooded; Built on Sand; Green Speed Fast
- **WOBURN: MARQUESS** — Views; Streams; Lakes; Large Bunkers; Drains Well; Tight; Long; Championship; Wooded; Built on Sand; Green Speed Fast

CAMBRIDGESHIRE

- **ABBOTSLEY: ABBOTSLEY** — Views; Streams; Ideal for the Elderly; Drains Well; Medium Length; Open; Undulating; Parkland; Built on Soil; Green Speed Medium
- **ABBOTSLEY: CROMWELL** — Views; Streams; Ideal for the Elderly; Medium Length; Open; Parkland; Built on Clay; Built on Soil; Green Speed Medium
- **BOURN** — Views; Streams; Drains Well; Undulating; Parkland; Green Speed Medium
- **BRAMPTON PARK** — Streams; Sheltered; Medium Length; Parkland
- **CAMBRIDGE** — Views; Streams; Lakes; Ideal for the Elderly; Drains Well; Long; Open; Undulating; Parkland; Green Speed Medium; Green Speed Fast
- **CAMBRIDGE LAKES** — Lakes; Ideal for the Elderly; Medium Length; Open; Parkland; Green Speed Medium
- **CAMBRIDGE MERIDIAN** — Streams; Lakes; Medium Length; Undulating; Parkland; Built on Clay; Green Speed Medium
- **ELTON FURZE** — Lakes; Drains Well; Tight; Wooded; Parkland; Built on Chalk
- **ELY CITY** — Deep Bunkers; Tight; Open; Undulating; Parkland; Built on Clay; Built on Chalk; Green Speed Medium
- **GOG MAGOG: THE OLD** — Views; Drains Well; Long; Open; Undulating; Downland; Parkland; Green Speed Medium
- **GOG MAGOG: WANDLEBURY** — Views; Long; Open; Undulating; Parkland; Green Speed Medium
- **LAKESIDE LODGE: LODGE** — Views; Lakes; Large Bunkers; Long; Open; Parkland; Built on Clay; Green Speed Fast
- **MARCH** — Views; Medium Length; Sheltered; Parkland; Built on Clay
- **ORTON MEADOWS** — Views; Lakes; Deep Bunkers; Large Bunkers; Ideal for the Elderly; Long; Open; Sheltered; Parkland; Built on Clay; Green Speed Medium
- **OUNDLE** — Views; Ideal for the Elderly; Long; Open; Sheltered; Championship; Parkland; Built on Clay; Green Speed Medium
- **PETERBOROUGH MILTON** — Views; Ideal for the Elderly; Medium Length; Open; Sheltered; Undulating; Parkland; Built on Clay; Green Speed Medium
- **RAMSEY CLUB** — Views; Streams; Large Bunkers; Deep Bunkers; Ideal for the Elderly; Tight; Long; Parkland; Built on Clay; Green Speed Fast
- **ST. NEOTS** — Views; Tight; Medium Length; Undulating; Parkland; Green Speed Fast
- **STILTON OAKS** — Short; Parkland; Green Speed Slow
- **THORNEY: FEN** — Tends to Flood; Drains Well; Open; Medium Length; Built on Soil; Green Speed Fast
- **THORPE WOOD** — Views; Tends to Flood; Medium Length; Undulating; Parkland; Green Speed Medium
- **TYDD ST GILES** — Streams; Lakes; Drains Well; Long; Medium Length; Parkland; Built on Soil; Green Speed Fast

CHANNEL ISLANDS

- **LA GRANDE MARE** — Lakes; Medium Length; Parkland; Built on Clay; Green Speed Medium

CHESHIRE

- **ADLINGTON** — Short

- **ALDER ROOT** — Parkland; Built on Soil; Green Speed Medium
- **ALDERLEY EDGE** — Views; Undulating; Parkland; Built on Soil; Green Speed Medium
- **ALDERSEY GREEN** — Views; Streams; Lakes; Drains Well; Tight; Wooded; Parkland; Built on Clay; Green Speed Medium

Course descriptions and features

The columns are the golf clubs/courses listed by county. Column labels (left to right):

1. ANTROBUS
2. ASHTON-ON-MERSEY
3. DAVENPORT
4. DUNHAM FOREST
5. EATON
6. FRODSHAM
7. GATLEY
8. LEIGH
9. LYMM
10. MACCLESFIELD
11. MARTON MEADOWS
12. MELLOR & TOWNSCLIFFE: OLD
13. MELLOR & TOWNSCLIFFE: VALLEY
14. MERE
15. MERSEY VALLEY
16. MOBBERLEY
17. MOLLINGTON GRANGE
18. MOTTRAM HALL
19. ONNELEY
20. PEOVER
21. PORTAL: CHAMPIONSHIP
22. PORTAL: PREMIER
23. PORTAL PREMIER
24. PRYORS HAYES
25. REDDISH VALE
26. RINGWAY
27. RUNCORN
28. SHRIGLEY HALL
29. STYAL: ACADEMY CHAMPIONSHIP PAR 3
30. STYAL: STYAL
31. SUTTON HALL
32. TYTHERINGTON
33. UPTON-BY-CHESTER
34. VALE ROYAL ABBEY

Feature	1	2	3	4	5	6	7	8	9	10	11	12	13	14	15	16	17	18	19	20	21	22	23	24	25	26	27	28	29	30	31	32	33	34
Views		•		•		•					•	•	•	•				•			•	•	•	•		•		•	•	•	•	•		•
Streams	•									•		•						•	•			•	•	•	•		•							•
Lakes	•				•							•						•			•	•	•	•						•		•		•
Deep Bunkers				•														•			•							•			•	•		
Large Bunkers				•														•			•							•			•	•		
Ideal for the Elderly				•						•					•	•	•							•		•					•		•	
Tends to Flood																																	•	
Drains Well				•						•				•	•	•					•			•		•					•			
Tight	•							•	•									•								•						•		
Short										•														•										
Medium Length				•						•		•						•	•			•		•	•					•	•		•	•
Long																		•											•					
Open			•										•			•		•																•
Sheltered				•																											•			
Championship														•				•										•			•			
Undulating	•		•	•		•			•		•		•	•	•			•	•	•			•	•		•						•		
Cliff Top																																		
Valley																										•								
Hilltop																																		
Downland																																		
Breckland																																		
Moorland													•	•												•								
Heath Land			•							•																								
Links																																		
Wooded	•	•			•			•	•								•															•	•	•
Parkland	•	•	•	•	•	•	•	•	•					•	•	•	•	•		•	•		•	•	•	•	•	•	•	•	•		•	•
Built of Gravel																																		
Built on Clay	•		•						•	•																•			•	•		•		
Built on Soil	•			•	•			•	•						•										•		•							
Built on Sand								•																										
Built on Chalk																																		
Green Speed Slow																																		
Green Speed Medium	•						•	•	•	•		•		•	•	•	•			•				•			•			•	•	•		•
Green Speed Fast			•	•					•																•									

www.hccgolfworld.com

Course descriptions and features

Golf Club/Courses by County

Golf Club/Courses by County	Views	Streams	Lakes	Deep Bunkers	Large Bunkers	Ideal for the Elderly	Tends to Flood	Drains Well	Tight	Short	Medium Length	Long	Open	Sheltered	Championship	Undulating	Cliff Top	Valley	Hilltop	Downland	Breckland	Moorland	Heath Land	Links	Wooded	Parkland	Built of Gravel	Built on Clay	Built on Soil	Built on Sand	Built on Chalk	Green Speed Slow	Green Speed Medium	Green Speed Fast
CLEVELAND																																		
BILLINGHAM		●					●				●			●														●					●	
CASTLE EDEN	●															●										●				●			●	●
CLEVELAND													●											●						●				
HARTLEPOOL	●												●										●							●			●	
HUNLEY HALL	●	●	●	●	●	●		●	●	●	●	●	●	●	●	●	●	●							●	●			●				●	
KNOTTY HILL GOLF CTRE: BISHOPS	●		●			●		●				●	●		●	●		●							●	●			●				●	
KNOTTY HILL GOLF CTRE: PRINCES						●							●			●									●	●			●				●	
MIDDLESBROUGH MUNICIPAL						●																				●			●			●		
NORTON	●					●					●															●							●	
WYNYARD CLUB	●		●												●											●								●
CORNWALL																																		
BOWOOD															●											●								
BUDE & NORTH CORNWALL	●	●																						●						●				●
CARLYON BAY	●																									●								●
HELSTON										●																●								
LAUNCESTON																										●								
LOOE																										●								
LOSTWITHIEL	●	●	●					●	●		●		●	●	●	●	●								●	●			●				●	
MERLIN																	●																	
MULLION																			●					●										
PERRANPORTH	●																		●					●		●								
PORTHPEAN																										●								
PRAA SANDS																										●								
ROSERROW	●							●																		●			●					
ST. AUSTELL	●																						●			●							●	
ST. KEW	●		●																							●							●	
ST. MELLION INTERNATIONAL: NICKLAUS															●											●								
ST. MELLION INTERNATIONAL: THE OLD	●																									●								
ST. NEWLYN EAST	●									●			●			●										●								
TEHIDY	●					●			●					●												●		●					●	
TREGENNA CASTLE	●				●																					●								
TRELOY			●							●			●													●							●	
TRETHORNE	●	●	●	●	●							●				●										●			●	●			●	

Course descriptions and features

Golf Club/Courses by County

Feature	TRURO	WHITSAND BAY	BARNARD CASTLE	BEAMISH PARK	BISHOP AUCKLAND	CHESTER-LE-STREET	CONSETT & DISTRICT	DARLINGTON	DURHAM CITY	OAK LEAF	RAMSIDE: BISHOPS	RAMSIDE: CATHEDRAL	RAMSIDE: PRINCES	ROSEBERRY GRANGE	SEAHAM HARBOUR	SOUTH MOOR	STRESSHOLME	WOODHAM	APPLEBY	BARROW	BECKSIDE	BRAMPTON	CARLISLE	CARUS GREEN	CASTERTON	COCKERMOUTH	DISTINGTON GOLF	DUNNEHOLME	EDEN	GRANGE-OVER-SANDS	HALTWHISTLE	KENDAL
Views	•	•																		•	•				•	•	•	•	•	•	•	•
Streams		•							•	•																				•		
Lakes					•						•	•	•	•				•	•				•					•	•	•		
Deep Bunkers																																
Large Bunkers								•																								
Ideal for the Elderly			•		•	•	•			•	•	•	•	•	•		•						•	•	•							•
Tends to Flood					•	•																										
Drains Well			•						•	•				•									•	•	•							•
Tight										•																						
Short																												•				
Medium Length			•	•	•			•	•			•	•			•				•	•		•	•	•	•						•
Long					•		•				•	•	•	•			•															•
Open			•		•	•	•				•	•		•	•	•	•															•
Sheltered																							•		•							
Championship												•	•							•			•					•				
Undulating	•								•					•	•	•	•			•			•	•	•							•
Cliff Top	•																															
Valley																																
Hilltop																							•					•				•
Downland																																
Breckland																																
Moorland																	•		•													
Heath Land			•																							•	•	•				
Links																												•				
Wooded			•	•		•		•										•										•	•			
Parkland	•			•	•	•	•	•	•	•	•	•	•	•	•	•	•	•		•		•	•	•	•				•	•	•	
Built of Gravel																																
Built on Clay						•					•	•	•	•												•						
Built on Soil			•	•	•																			•	•							
Built on Sand											•	•	•				•		•	•			•					•				
Built on Chalk																																
Green Speed Slow								•																				•				
Green Speed Medium			•	•	•				•	•	•						•			•	•	•	•	•	•							•
Green Speed Fast				•											•				•				•					•				

Course descriptions and features

Feature column key: Vi = Views · St = Streams · La = Lakes · DB = Deep Bunkers · LB = Large Bunkers · IE = Ideal for the Elderly · TF = Tends to Flood · DW = Drains Well · Ti = Tight · Sh = Short · ML = Medium Length · Lo = Long · Op = Open · Sh̄ = Sheltered · Ch = Championship · Un = Undulating · CT = Cliff Top · Va = Valley · Hi = Hilltop · Do = Downland · Br = Breckland · Mo = Moorland · HL = Heath Land · Li = Links · Wo = Wooded · Pa = Parkland · BG = Built of Gravel · BC = Built on Clay · BS = Built on Soil · BSa = Built on Sand · BCh = Built on Chalk · GSS = Green Speed Slow · GSM = Green Speed Medium · GSF = Green Speed Fast

Golf Club/Courses by County	Vi	St	La	DB	LB	IE	TF	DW	Ti	Sh	ML	Lo	Op	Sh̄	Ch	Un	CT	Va	Hi	Do	Br	Mo	HL	Li	Wo	Pa	BG	BC	BS	BSa	BCh	GSS	GSM	GSF
KESWICK	●		●													●														●				
MARYPORT	●												●			●								●						●				
SEASCALE	●	●														●								●	●									
SEDBURGH	●																									●				●				
SILLOTH		●																					●	●										
ULVERSTON	●															●										●								
WINDERMERE	●	●														●										●								
DERBYSHIRE																																		
ALFRETON	●	●							●				●													●				●		●		
ALLESTREE PARK	●							●		●	●		●			●										●		●					●	
ASHBOURNE	●		●			●		●			●		●		●							●				●		●					●	●
BARLBOROUGH LINKS			●				●				●		●															●						
BRAILSFORD			●								●		●			●													●					
BREADSALL PRIORY: MOORLAND					●																													
BREADSALL PRIORY: PRIORY			●																															
BROUGHTON HEATH																						●												
BUXTON & HIGH PEAK								●		●						●									●	●			●				●	
CHAPEL-EN-LE-FRITH			●					●						●												●		●						
CHESTERFIELD	●	●									●															●		●		●				
CHEVIN	●	●														●										●		●						
HALLOWES	●	●									●		●		●	●			●															
HORSLEY LODGE	●	●		●	●	●					●	●	●	●	●				●							●		●					●	
MAYWOOD	●			●	●	●						●		●											●	●			●	●				●
MORLEY HAYES: MANOR	●											●														●								●
MORLEY HAYES: TOWER	●																									●								●
ORMONDE FIELDS							●							●											●	●		●					●	
PEWIT							●																			●		●						●
SHIRLAND	●										●			●		●												●					●	
SICKLEHOLME	●	●							●		●					●			●											●			●	
STANEDGE	●										●					●						●							●				●	
DEVON																																		
ASHBURY: OAKWOOD	●	●	●	●	●	●		●	●	●	●		●	●		●		●							●	●		●	●	●			●	
CENTRAL PARK						●		●																		●						●	●	
CHURSTON	●																●		●												●			

Course descriptions and features

Golf Club/Courses by County	Views	Streams	Lakes	Deep Bunkers	Large Bunkers	Ideal for the Elderly	Tends to Flood	Drains Well	Tight	Short	Medium Length	Long	Open	Sheltered	Championship	Undulating	Cliff Top	Valley	Hilltop	Downland	Breckland	Moorland	Heath Land	Links	Wooded	Parkland	Built of Gravel	Built on Clay	Built on Soil	Built on Sand	Built on Chalk	Green Speed Slow	Green Speed Medium	Green Speed Fast
CREDITON		•	•		•			•			•			•											•	•			•				•	
DAINTON PARK	•		•		•						•		•			•										•			•	•			•	•
DARTMOUTH: CHAMPIONSHIP	•		•		•	•		•			•			•	•	•		•								•								•
DINNATON	•		•	•				•	•	•			•									•			•				•				•	
ELFORDLEIGH	•	•	•											•	•											•								
EXETER		•									•					•										•							•	
FINGLE GLEN	•	•						•					•													•				•				
HARTLAND FOREST	•				•						•	•														•								
HELE PARK GOLF CTRE			•																							•								
HOLSWORTHY		•	•					•			•															•		•					•	
ILFRACOMBE	•					•		•					•				•				•					•							•	
MORTEHOE & WOOLACOMBE	•					•			•																									
NEWTON ABBOT		•	•		•			•	•	•																•								
NORTH DEVON (ROYAL)	•							•			•													•						•			•	
OKEHAMPTON	•			•	•			•				•	•						•			•				•			•				•	
OTTER VALLEY GOLF CTRE	•							•		•																•								•
PADBROOK PARK	•									•																•								
PORTMORE GOLF PARK: BARUM	•																								•					•				
PORTMORE GOLF PARK: LANDKEY	•	•			•			•			•			•											•	•				•				•
SAUNTON: EAST	•				•						•			•	•									•	•	•				•			•	•
SAUNTON: WEST	•				•										•									•	•					•				•
SIDMOUTH	•									•									•							•			•					
SPARKWELL	•					•					•					•		•	•			•				•							•	
TAVISTOCK									•		•																		•					•
TEIGN VALLEY									•				•																•				•	
TEIGNMOUTH	•			•									•	•	•			•			•		•			•		•		•			•	
THURLESTONE	•	•											•																	•				
TIVERTON	•			•	•						•		•									•	•	•	•	•		•		•			•	
TORQUAY	•										•		•				•	•					•		•	•			•				•	
TORRINGTON	•		•	•	•			•			•		•					•								•			•					•
WARREN	•			•							•		•					•								•								•
WILLINGCOTT																																		
WOODBURY PARK: ACORN	•	•	•	•	•	•	•				•	•	•						•		•	•	•		•	•		•					•	
WOODBURY PARK: OAKS	•	•	•	•	•	•	•				•	•	•	•	•			•	•		•	•	•		•	•		•					•	

Course descriptions and features

Golf Club/Courses by County

Feature	WRANGATON	YELVERTON	DORSET	ASHLEY WOOD	BOSCOMBE LADIES	BOURNEMOUTH & MEYRICK	BRIDPORT & WEST DORSET	BROADSTONE	CAME DOWN	CHEDINGTON COURT	CRANE VALLEY: VALLEY 18 HOLE	DUDSBURY	EAST DORSET: LAKELAND	EAST DORSET: WOODLAND	FERNDOWN: PRESIDENTS	FERNDOWN: THE OLD COURSE	FERNDOWN FOREST	ISLE OF PURBECK: DENE	ISLE OF PURBECK: PURBECK	LYME REGIS	PARKSTONE	PARLEY	WEYMOUTH	ESSEX	ABRIDGE	BELFAIRS PARK	BELHUS PARK	BENTON HALL	BIRCH GROVE	BOYCE HILL	BRAINTREE	BRAXTED PARK	BUNSAY DOWNS: BUNSAY DOWNS	BUNSAY DOWNS: PAR 3
Views	●	●					●	●			●	●		●							●		●		●	●	●	●	●				●	●
Streams								●			●	●	●			●						●	●		●	●	●	●	●				●	●
Lakes								●			●		●	●		●					●				●				●				●	●
Deep Bunkers						●						●																					●	●
Large Bunkers													●	●											●	●	●							
Ideal for the Elderly	●	●		●					●		●	●				●					●					●	●			●			●	
Tends to Flood																				●														
Drains Well	●			●	●	●		●				●	●	●	●	●	●					●								●			●	
Tight					●			●				●							●															
Short																	●												●			●		
Medium Length	●	●		●	●	●			●	●			●				●	●				●	●		●	●							●	●
Long													●	●																			●	●
Open	●	●							●				●	●	●		●				●				●	●	●						●	●
Sheltered						●				●				●					●						●	●	●							
Championship									●			●	●			●					●				●			●						
Undulating				●					●	●	●	●	●	●							●	●			●	●	●	●	●		●			
Cliff Top								●												●														
Valley											●																							
Hilltop										●																					●		●	●
Downland										●																								
Breckland																																		
Moorland	●	●																																
Heath Land							●						●			●	●		●															
Links							●													●														
Wooded				●	●	●			●					●														●	●	●				
Parkland	●				●	●				●	●	●				●						●	●		●	●	●	●	●	●	●			
Built of Gravel																																		
Built on Clay										●						●									●	●	●							
Built on Soil											●					●				●									●				●	●
Built on Sand						●	●				●									●									●					
Built on Chalk				●				●					●	●																				
Green Speed Slow																																		
Green Speed Medium				●	●				●	●			●	●			●					●	●		●	●	●	●	●			●	●	●
Green Speed Fast	●			●		●		●			●	●	●	●	●	●												●		●				

Course descriptions and features

Golf Club/Courses by County	BURNHAM-ON-CROUCH	CANONS BROOK	CHANNELS: BELSTEAD	CHANNELS: CHANNELS	CHELMSFORD	CHIGWELL	CLACTON	COLCHESTER	COLNE VALLEY	CRONDON PARK: CRONDON PARK	DUNTON HILLS: DUNTON HILLS 18 HOLE PAR 3	DUNTON HILLS: MAIN	EPPING	EPPING FOREST	FORRESTER PARK	HAINAULT FOREST: TOP	HYLANDS GOLF COMPLEX: HANBURY	HYLANDS GOLF COMPLEX: PRYORS	LANGDON HILLS GOLF CTRE: BULPHAN	LANGDON HILLS GOLF CTRE: HORNDON	LANGDON HILLS GOLF CTRE: LANGDON	LEXDEN	MARDYKE VALLEY GOLF CTRE: THE VALLEY	MAYLANDS	MILLERS BARN GOLF PARK	NAZEING	NOTLEYS	ORSETT	PRIORS	REGIMENT	ROMFORD	SOUTH ESSEX: HAWK (HAWK & VIXON)	SOUTH ESSEX: HERON (HERON & HAWK)	SOUTH ESSEX: VIXEN (VIXEN & HERON)
Views	•			•	•			•	•			•	•			•	•	•						•	•			•	•		•	•	•	•
Streams		•	•	•				•	•			•										•		•			•		•			•		
Lakes		•	•	•			•		•	•	•	•	•	•	•				•				•	•				•			•		•	
Deep Bunkers		•	•																•	•											•			
Large Bunkers		•						•				•						•									•	•			•			
Ideal for the Elderly		•			•		•		•			•	•			•	•	•				•			•				•	•				
Tends to Flood							•																											
Drains Well		•	•	•	•		•	•	•	•	•	•	•															•	•	•	•	•	•	•
Tight			•	•									•		•												•							
Short																							•					•						
Medium Length			•	•	•			•					•				•	•				•						•			•			
Long	•										•																						•	•
Open	•	•		•	•	•	•					•			•	•	•	•				•						•	•	•	•	•	•	
Sheltered				•				•	•					•				•																
Championship	•									•			•			•												•		•				
Undulating	•	•	•	•	•	•		•				•	•	•		•	•	•	•	•	•		•					•	•			•	•	•
Cliff Top																																		
Valley							•	•				•						•				•												
Hilltop	•																																	
Downland																																		
Breckland																																		
Moorland																																		
Heath Land																											•							
Links																																		
Wooded						•							•																					
Parkland	•	•	•	•	•	•		•	•	•	•	•	•	•	•	•	•	•	•	•	•	•	•	•	•			•	•	•	•	•	•	•
Built of Gravel																																		
Built on Clay	•	•		•	•			•	•			•		•			•										•							
Built on Soil			•	•																•									•	•	•			
Built on Sand														•											•									
Built on Chalk																																		
Green Speed Slow																																		
Green Speed Medium	•	•				•			•	•	•	•			•	•	•					•	•		•			•	•	•	•	•	•	•
Green Speed Fast		•	•	•	•			•				•			•			•																

www.hccgolfworld.com

Course descriptions and features

Golf Club/Courses by County

Feature	THREE RIVERS: JUBILEE	THREE RIVERS: KINGS	TOP MEADOW	WARLEY PARK: COURSE 1	WARLEY PARK: COURSE 2	WARLEY PARK: COURSE 3	WARREN	WEALD PARK GOLF CLUB	WEST PARK	BRICKHAMPTON COURT: SPA	CIRENCESTER	COTSWOLD EDGE	COTSWOLD HILLS	DYMOCK GRANGE	FOREST HILLS	FOREST OF DEAN	GLOUCESTER	LILLEY BROOK	MINCHINHAMPTON: AVENING	MINCHINHAMPTON: CHERINGTON	NAUNTON DOWNS	NEWENT	ORCHARD	PAINSWICK	RODWAY HILL	SHERDONS	SHIPTON	STINCHCOMBE HILL	TEWKESBURY PARK	ALTON	ARMY	BARTON-ON-SEA: BECTON
Views		●					●			●	●	●	●	●		●	●	●	●	●	●	●	●	●	●	●	●	●	●	●		
Streams							●	●		●																	●	●		●		
Lakes			●	●	●	●					●		●		●		●		●	●				●			●	●				
Deep Bunkers																						●										
Large Bunkers		●																				●										
Ideal for the Elderly		●					●			●						●										●	●			●	●	●
Tends to Flood																														●	●	
Drains Well		●					●				●				●		●	●								●	●	●		●		
Tight		●									●		●			●	●	●								●				●		
Short							●		●															●	●	●						
Medium Length	●	●									●				●	●	●		●	●		●	●				●					
Long																											●			●	●	
Open		●													●		●							●			●			●		●
Sheltered							●				●					●		●			●						●	●		●		
Championship	●																															
Undulating								●		●	●						●						●	●		●	●			●		
Cliff Top																																●
Valley																																
Hilltop							●							●									●									
Downland																												●				
Breckland																																
Moorland																																
Heath Land																														●		
Links																																
Wooded	●						●																●			●						
Parkland	●	●		●	●	●	●			●	●		●		●	●		●	●			●				●			●	●		
Built of Gravel																																
Built on Clay			●				●					●				●		●									●			●	●	
Built on Soil									●				●	●											●		●					
Built on Sand							●															●										
Built on Chalk																			●	●										●		
Green Speed Slow																																
Green Speed Medium		●					●			●		●	●					●	●		●					●	●			●	●	●
Green Speed Fast		●													●	●							●	●								

Section headers (county bands): **GLOUCESTERSHIRE** (between WEST PARK and BRICKHAMPTON COURT: SPA), **HAMPSHIRE** (between TEWKESBURY PARK and ALTON).

WIN BEN SAYERS CLUBS £2,000 WORTH OF PRIZES

GOLF
WORLD

Verdict
on the
BIG
HITTERS
NEW DRIVERS FOR 2002
- TAYLOR MADE
- PING ● MIZUNO
- CALLAWAY
- SRIXON ● WILSON

"I have rising
**damp but lots
of character"**
round with Nick Faldo
es, he can still play a bit]

**THE SEX
MACHINE**
ow women golfers
e spicing up their act

**-FORE!-1
GREEN FEES**
.ay half-price golf at
former Open venue

**IPS FROM
THE TOUR**
uick and easy ways
shape your shots

MONTY
The man, his mind
and his method...

SHOOT
LOWER
SCORES
AND YOU DON'T
EVEN HAVE TO
PRACTISE!

A ROUND EVERY MONTH

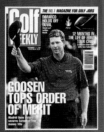

Improve your Golf

EXCLUSIVE DRIVER TESTS: MIZUNO ● PING ● SRIXON ● WILSON

Today's Golfer

INCORPORATING **FORE!**

SLASH 9 SHOTS OFF YOUR NEXT ROUND

(Sounds silly, right? But you're curious)

HALF-PRICE GREEN FEES!

Play quality courses – even in winter

YOU CAN JOIN THAT SWANKY CLUB

How to jump the waiting list & save money

'DO I GET A FREE DROP OFF THIS PARK BENCH?'

7 simple rules that'll help you score better

READERS' MID-ROUND PROBLEMS SOLVED p118

OUT EVERY MONTH

Another Next Generation Directory

The Ultimate Guide to Golf Courses

On CD-ROM

Order the Golf World CD-ROM
on
0870 754 1678

www.hccgolfworld.com

Course descriptions and features

Golf Club/Courses by County

Feature	BASINGSTOKE	BLACKMOOR	BLACKNEST	BOTLEY PARK	BURLEY	CAMS HALL ESTATE GOLF CLUB: CREEK	CAMS HALL ESTATE GOLF CLUB: PARK	COUNTY	DIBDEN GOLF CTRE: DIBDEN 18 HOLE	DUNWOOD MANOR	EAST HORTON GOLF CTRE: GREENWOOD	EAST HORTON GOLF CTRE: PARKLAND	FOUR MARKS	FURZELEY	GREAT SALTERNS	HAMPSHIRE: HAMPSHIRE 9 HOLE	HAYLING	LEE ON THE SOLENT	MEON VALLEY: MEON	MOORS VALLEY GOLF CTRE	NEW FOREST	NORTH HANTS FLEET	OLD THORNS	OTTERBOURNE	PARK	PAULTONS GOLF CENTRE: PAULTONS 18 HOLE MASTER	PORTSMOUTH	ROMSEY	ROWLANDS CASTLE	SOUTH WINCHESTER	SOUTHAMPTON MUNICIPAL: SOUTHAMPTON MUNICIPAL 18 HOLE	TEST VALLEY	TOURNERBURY GOLF CTRE	WELLOW: EMBLEY
Views			●	●	●	●	●			●	●	●		●			●	●	●		●	●		●	●			●			●	●	●	●
Streams			●								●	●		●					●			●	●											
Lakes			●			●					●	●		●				●				●	●					●						
Deep Bunkers			●											●								●							●					
Large Bunkers			●																			●												
Ideal for the Elderly	●		●		●	●	●	●			●		●				●		●	●				●	●			●					●	●
Tends to Flood																							●											
Drains Well	●		●	●		●	●	●			●																		●		●			●
Tight		●																				●					○							
Short	●												●	●				●		●			●											
Medium Length		●		●		●	●	●		●							●				●			●	●		●	○			●			●
Long																			●											●	●	●		
Open				●		●	●						●				●	●	●	●					●			●			●		●	
Sheltered																			●										○					
Championship		●			●			●									●				●													
Undulating	●		●	●	●					●	●	●							●	●		●	●		●		●	●						
Cliff Top																																		
Valley																																		
Hilltop													●																					
Downland																																	●	
Breckland																																		
Moorland		●			●																													
Heath Land																		●		●	●	●												
Links					●												●													●				
Wooded							●	●						●				●	●		●				●			○	●					
Parkland	●	●	●	●		●	●	●	●	●	●	●		●	●	●				●		●		●	●	●			●			●	●	●
Built of Gravel																																		
Built on Clay				●							●	●							●	●										●		●		●
Built on Soil	●																					●	●								●			
Built on Sand		●				●		●									●	●			●	●												
Built on Chalk													●												●					●	●			
Green Speed Slow																																		
Green Speed Medium		●				●	●	●			●	●	●			●			●	●			●	●	●	●		●	●	●	●		●	●
Green Speed Fast	●			●										●				●																

© HCC Publishing Ltd

www.hccgolfworld.com

Course descriptions and features

Golf Club/Courses by County

Course	Views	Streams	Lakes	Deep Bunkers	Large Bunkers	Ideal for the Elderly	Tends to Flood	Drains Well	Tight	Short	Medium Length	Long	Open	Sheltered	Championship	Undulating	Cliff Top	Valley	Hilltop	Downland	Breckland	Moorland	Heath Land	Links	Wooded	Parkland	Built of Gravel	Built on Clay	Built on Soil	Built on Sand	Built on Chalk	Green Speed Slow	Green Speed Medium	Green Speed Fast
WELLOW: RYEDOWN						●		●			●			●												●		●	●				●	
WICKHAM PARK	●					●		●			●		●													●		●					●	
WINCHESTER (ROYAL)	●			●	●			●	●		●		●			●									●	●					●		●	
HEREFORDSHIRE																																		
BRAMPTON GOLF	●					●				●				●																				
BROCKINGTON	●		●			●			●							●										●	●						●	
GROVE		●							●	●						●																	●	
LEOMINSTER											●		●																			●		
HERTFORDSHIRE																																		
ALDWICKBURY PARK	●	●	●					●			●			●		●		●							●	●								●
ARKLEY	●					●		●			●					●																		●
ASH VALLEY GOLF CLUB	●							●			●		●			●			●						●	●		●	●		●		●	
ASHRIDGE	●	●	●	●	●			●			●	●														●		●	●	●	●		●	●
BARKWAY PARK	●										●													●									●	
BATCHWORTH PARK	●							●			●														●								●	
BERKHAMSTED		●		●	●																		●		●			●					●	
BISHOPS STORTFORD																●										●								
BRICKENDON GRANGE			●								●		●	●	●	●																		
BRIGGENS HOUSE						●						●			●											●								
BROCKET HALL: MELBOURNE	●	●						●				●	●	●		●									●	●							●	●
BROCKET HALL: PALMERSTON	●							●						●												●								●
BROOKMANS PARK	●				●			●			●	●	●												●	●								
BUSHEY GOLF COURSE	●																									●							●	●
BUSHEY HALL							●	●							●													●			●		●	
CHADWELL SPRINGS																												●	●		●			
CHESFIELD DOWNS	●	●	●					●								●							●			●								
CHORLEYWOOD					●			●		●				●	●	●									●									
EAST HERTS																																	●	
HADLEY WOOD	●							●																		●		●	●					
HANBURY MANOR							●							●	●																			
HARPENDEN COMMON	●												●																					
HERTFORDSHIRE	●																								●	●		●		●	●		●	
LITTLE HAY	●	●	●	●	●	●					●															●		●					●	
MALTON	●	●	●								●					●										●		●					●	

Course descriptions and features

www.hccgolfworld.com

Feature	MANOR OF GROVES	MILL GREEN GOLF CLUB	OLD FOLD MANOR	OXHEY PARK	PANSHANGER GOLF COMPLEX	PENFOLD PARK	RICKMANSWORTH	ROYSTON	SHENDISH MANOR	STEVENAGE	VERULAM	WHADDON	WHIPSNADE PARK	ISLE OF MAN	CASTLETOWN GOLF LINKS	MOUNT MURRAY	ISLE OF WIGHT	FRESHWATER BAY	RYDE	SHANKLIN & SANDOWN	WESTRIDGE	JERSEY (ROYAL)	KENT	ALLHALLOWS	ASHFORD	ASHFORD	AUSTIN LODGE	BEARSTED	BECKENHAM PLACE PARK	BIRCHWOOD PARK	BOUGHTON	BROMLEY	BROOME PARK
Views	●			●	●		●	●	●	●		●	●		●	●		●	●		●			●		●		●		●		●	●
Streams				●								●													●	●		●		●			
Lakes	●	●	●	●	●							●				●								●			●	●	●	●		●	●
Deep Bunkers				●	●							●																					
Large Bunkers					●							●																●					
Ideal for the Elderly				●		●							●					●			●				●				●		●		
Tends to Flood											●		●																				
Drains Well	●	●	●	●	●			●				●						●			●			●	●			●					
Tight							●	●	●	●	●										●				●								
Short					●		●	●				●												●	●						●		
Medium Length	●		●		●				●										●					●	●		●		●				
Long		●											●																				
Open		●						●										●			●			●		●		●		●	●	●	
Sheltered				●	●		●			●		●	●						●									●					
Championship	●										●				●	●									●	●				●			●
Undulating	●	●		●	●			●		●					●				●					●			●	●	●	●	●		●
Cliff Top																																	
Valley				●					●																						●		
Hilltop									●																								
Downland																		●															
Breckland																																	
Moorland																																	
Heath Land		●					●													●													
Links															●					●				●									
Wooded		●		●	●	●			●		●																●						
Parkland	●					●			●	●	●		●					●		●				●	●	●	●	●	●	●	●	●	
Built of Gravel																																	
Built on Clay	●		●	●							●		●					●		●						●		●	●	●			
Built on Soil	●								●											●				●		●		●					
Built on Sand															●											●							
Built on Chalk				●			●	●	●			●																					
Green Speed Slow																																	
Green Speed Medium				●	●	●	●	●	●	●		●	●					●						●	●	●		●					●
Green Speed Fast	●	●	●		●		●														●									●		●	

www.hccgolfworld.com

Course descriptions and features

Golf Club/Courses by County	Views	Streams	Lakes	Deep Bunkers	Large Bunkers	Ideal for the Elderly	Tends to Flood	Drains Well	Tight	Short	Medium Length	Long	Open	Sheltered	Championship	Undulating	Cliff Top	Valley	Hilltop	Downland	Breckland	Moorland	Heath Land	Links	Wooded	Parkland	Built of Gravel	Built on Clay	Built on Soil	Built on Sand	Built on Chalk	Green Speed Slow	Green Speed Medium	Green Speed Fast
CANTERBURY								•	•		•			•	•											•					•		•	•
CHART HILLS	•	•				•		•							•	•										•		•					•	
CHELSFIELD LAKES GOLF CTRE			•										•													•								
CHERRY LODGE	•		•			•					•	•	•			•										•		•			•		•	•
CHESTFIELD					•	•			•	•				•		•										•		•					•	•
CINQUE PORTS (ROYAL)																																		•
COBTREE MANOR PARK								•					•			•		•					•			•		•					•	
CRAY VALLEY: CRAY VALLEY 18 HOLES	•	•	•			•	•				•					•										•		•					•	
CRAY VALLEY: CRAY VALLEY 9 HOLE	•	•	•			•							•													•								
DARENTH VALLEY						•												•								•			•					
DARTFORD						•					•															•							•	
DEANGATE RIDGE: DEANGATE RIDGE						•					•		•			•										•						•		
EDENBRIDGE: NEW											•		•			•		•														•		
ETCHINGHILL					•									•					•							•								•
FAWKHAM VALLEY GOLF CLUB																									•									
HAWKHURST																									•					•				
HILDEN EUROPRO			•			•			•							•										•				•			•	
HOLTYE			•						•		•												•										•	
HOMELANDS							•		•	•											•		•			•							•	
KINGS HILL							•		•																									
KNOLE PARK	•	•				•		•	•			•	•	•		•										•		•						•
LAMBERHURST	•		•								•			•		•										•		•						•
LANGLEY PARK	•										•			•		•																		
LEEDS CASTLE	•															•										•		•		•				•
LITTLESTONE	•					•						•	•			•								•		•								•
LONDON BEACH	•																									•		•						
LULLINGSTONE PARK: LULLINGSTONE PARK 18 HOLE	•											•	•													•							•	•
LULLINGSTONE PARK: LULLINGSTONE PARK 9 HOLE	•												•																				•	•
LYDD	•							•			•													•						•				•
MOATLANDS																										•								
MOTE PARK GOLF HUT: MOTE PARK 18 HOLE PUTTING GREEN	•		•			•																				•							•	
MOTE PARK GOLF HUT: MOTE PARK PITCH AND PUT PAR 3	•		•			•																				•							•	
NORTH FORELAND: MAIN						•		•			•		•				•							•							•		•	
PARK WOOD	•					•		•					•		•											•							•	

Course descriptions and features

Golf Club/Courses by County

Course column key:
1. PEDHAM PLACE GOLF CTRE: RED
2. PEDHAM PLACE GOLF CTRE: YELLOW
3. PRINCES: HIMALAYAS
4. REDLIBBETS
5. RIDGE GOLF CLUB
6. ROCHESTER & COBHAM
7. ROMNEY WARREN
8. ROUNDWOOD HALL
9. RUXLEY PARK: RUXLEY PARK 18 HOLE
10. RUXLEY PARK: RUXLEY PARK 9 HOLE
11. SENE VALLEY
12. SHORTLANDS
13. SOUTHERN VALLEY
14. ST. AGUSTINES
15. ST. GEORGE'S (ROYAL)
16. STAPLEHURST GOLFING PARK
17. SWEETWOODS PARK
18. TENTERDEN
19. TUDOR PARK
20. TUNBRIDGE WELLS
21. UPCHURCH RIVER VALLEY: RIVER VALLEY 9 HOLE
22. UPCHURCH RIVER VALLEY: UPCHURCH RIVER VALLEY
23. VILLA
24. WALMER & KINGSDOWN
25. WEST KENT
26. WEST MALLING: HURRICANE
27. WEST MALLING: SPITFIRE
28. WHITSTABLE & SEASALTER

LANCASHIRE
29. ACCRINGTON & DISTRICT
30. ASHTON
31. ASHTON & LEA
32. ASHTON-UNDER-LYNE
33. BACUP

Feature	Courses marked (•)
Views	1, 2, 4, 5, 6, 7, 9, 11, 16, 17, 18, 22, 23, 24, 25, 27, 29, 33
Streams	16, 17, 18, 26, 27, 32, 33
Lakes	1, 4, 5, 16, 17, 18, 19, 20, 22, 26, 27, 31
Deep Bunkers	2, 11, 16, 22
Large Bunkers	11, 16
Ideal for the Elderly	2, 5, 8, 12, 13, 17, 20, 23, 26, 28, 31, 33
Tends to Flood	14, 22
Drains Well	1, 2, 4, 5, 8, 9, 10, 11, 13, 18, 23, 29, 30, 33
Tight	2, 13, 14
Short	8, 9, 11, 13, 20, 33
Medium Length	1, 4, 5, 8, 11, 13, 14, 16, 17, 18, 22, 23, 24, 26, 27, 29, 33
Long	2, 5
Open	2, 5, 7, 8, 9, 10, 12, 13, 17, 22, 23, 24, 28, 29, 30, 33
Sheltered	3, 4, 5, 12, 16, 17, 18, 20, 27, 33
Championship	2, 3, 4, 5, 15, 18, 33
Undulating	2, 3, 4, 5, 16, 22, 29, 33
Cliff Top	
Valley	3, 13, 22
Hilltop	9, 10
Downland	
Breckland	
Moorland	29, 33
Heath Land	
Links	1, 2, 3, 6, 13, 15, 28
Wooded	3, 7, 13, 19, 32, 33
Parkland	4, 5, 6, 7, 8, 9, 11, 13, 16, 17, 18, 20, 23, 24, 25, 26, 31, 32
Built of Gravel	
Built on Clay	6, 12, 13, 16, 17, 18, 23, 29, 31, 32
Built on Soil	3, 4, 28, 30, 33
Built on Sand	2, 6
Built on Chalk	2, 7, 11, 13, 14, 22, 23
Green Speed Slow	30
Green Speed Medium	1, 2, 3, 4, 6, 8, 11, 12, 16, 17, 18, 22, 23, 28, 31, 32
Green Speed Fast	3, 5, 16, 17, 20, 23, 27, 29, 33

Course descriptions and features

Golf Club/Courses by County

Feature	BENTHAM	BLACKPOOL NORTH SHORE	BOLTON	BREIGHTMET	BRUNSHAW	CASTLE HAWK: OLD	CHARNOCK RICHARD	CLITHEROE	COLNE	DEAN WOOD	DEANE	DUNSCAR	FISHWICK HALL	FLEETWOOD	GREAT LEVER & FARNWORTH	GREENMOUNT: OLD	GREENMOUNT: WHITE	HAIGH HALL: HAIGH HALL	HAIGH HALL: HIMALAYAN PUTTING GREEN	HEYSHAM	HIGHFIELD	HINDLEY HALL	HORWICH	HURLSTON	INGOL	KIRKBY LONSDALE	KNOTT END	LANCASTER	LANSIL	LEYLAND	LYTHAM & ST ANNES (ROYAL)	LYTHAM GREEN	MOSSOCK HALL	MYTTON FOLD
Views	●	●	●		●		●	●	●	●	●		●		●	●				●	●	●	●		●			●			●	●	●	●
Streams			●	●			●	●				●	●	●						●	●		●			●	●						●	●
Lakes		●	●	●				●	●											●	●				●	●	●						●	●
Deep Bunkers		●	●			●			●					●						●	●		●							●				
Large Bunkers																				●			●							●				
Ideal for the Elderly	●	●			●			●	●		●					●	●			●	●							●			●		●	
Tends to Flood	●				●																													
Drains Well		●	●	●			●	●		●	●		●							●	●	●						●	●					
Tight			●				●				●					●	●							●						●				
Short			●			●						●										●	●											
Medium Length	●	●				●	●	●	●		●									●	●				●	●	●			●			●	
Long					●						●																●							
Open	●	●					●	●	●	●	●									●	●									●	●	●		
Sheltered			●			●	●				●					●				●				●								●		
Championship							●		●							●																●		
Undulating		●	●	●			●	●	●		●					●	●	●	●	●	●	●	●		●	●	●			●				●
Cliff Top																																		
Valley								●	●																									
Hilltop												●	●								●													
Downland																																		
Breckland																																		
Moorland																●		●								●	●							
Heath Land																								●										
Links		●							●					●						●					●						●			
Wooded			●	●			●		●		●										●												●	●
Parkland	●	●	●	●	●	●	●	●	●	●	●	●	●			●	●			●			●		●			●	●	●	●		●	●
Built of Gravel																																		
Built on Clay	●	●			●	●		●		●	●									●			●		●	●							●	●
Built on Soil			●	●		●		●			●									●			●						●				●	●
Built on Sand																●				●														
Built on Chalk																																		
Green Speed Slow					●																													
Green Speed Medium		●	●	●			●	●		●	●	●				●	●			●					●	●	●			●			●	●
Green Speed Fast	●						●																●	●						●			●	●

Course descriptions and features

Golf Club/Courses by County	NELSON	PIKEFOLD	PLEASINGTON	PRESTON	SHAW HILL	STANDISH COURT	TOWNELEY MUNICIPAL	TURTON	WALMERSLEY	WESTHOUGHTON: ACADEMY	WESTHOUGHTON: HART COMMON	WHALLEY	BEEDLES LAKE	BIRSTALL	BLACKTHORN WOOD	CHARNWOOD FOREST	GLEN GORSE	HINCKLEY	KIBWORTH	KIRBY MUXLOE	LEICESTER	LINGDALE	LONGCLIFFE	MELTON MOWBRAY	OADBY	PARK HILL	SCRAPTOFT	STOKE ALBANY	WHETSTONE	ADDLETHORPE	BELTON PARK: ANCASTER	BELTON PARK: BROWNLOW
Views	●	●	●	●	●	●	●		●			●		●		●		●	●	●	●	●						●			●	●
Streams					●	●	●		●		●	●		●		●		●				●									●	●
Lakes		●	●		●						●	●				●		●			●				●						●	●
Deep Bunkers			●					●				●						●							●	●			●			
Large Bunkers			●					●				●														●	●		●			
Ideal for the Elderly	●				●			●				●		●	●			●								●		●	●			●
Tends to Flood																	●															
Drains Well	●	●					●	●				●						●			●								●			●
Tight																																
Short																						●	●						●			
Medium Length				●			●	●				●	●			●			●			●	●				●				●	
Long	●	●							●											●	●											
Open	●	●					●	●				●		●		●		●			●							●				
Sheltered			●	●			●					●						●				●	●						●			
Championship			●																							●	●					
Undulating	●	●	●	●	●			●	●	●	●	●										●										
Cliff Top																																
Valley												●																				
Hilltop								●																								
Downland																																
Breckland																																
Moorland	●							●																								
Heath Land																	●								●							
Links																																
Wooded				●	●							●				●	●	●			●	●									●	●
Parkland	●	●	●	●	●	●	●	●			●	●		●	●	●		●	●	●	●	●				●	●	●		●	●	●
Built of Gravel																																
Built on Clay	●		●					●				●		●				●		●												
Built on Soil	●					●	●				●	●									●		●	●					●			
Built on Sand		●																														
Built on Chalk																																
Green Speed Slow																																
Green Speed Medium		●	●				●			●	●	●			●	●		●			●				●				●			●
Green Speed Fast	●							●												●			●	●				●		●		

www.hccgolfworld.com

Course descriptions and features

Golf Club/Courses by County	Views	Streams	Lakes	Deep Bunkers	Large Bunkers	Ideal for the Elderly	Tends to Flood	Drains Well	Tight	Short	Medium Length	Long	Open	Sheltered	Championship	Undulating	Cliff Top	Valley	Hilltop	Downland	Breckland	Moorland	Heath Land	Links	Wooded	Parkland	Built of Gravel	Built on Clay	Built on Soil	Built on Sand	Built on Chalk	Green Speed Slow	Green Speed Medium	Green Speed Fast
BELTON WOODS: THE LAKES			•		•																				•									•
BELTON WOODS: THE WOODSIDE					•																								•					
BOSTON									•		•		•													•							•	
CANWICK PARK																										•							•	
CARHOLME																										•							•	
GEDNEY HILL																								•		•								•
KENWICK PARK	•	•	•			•		•			•		•			•									•	•								
KIRTON HOLME			•			•		•			•		•			•										•				•				•
LINCOLN																										•								
LOUTH																							•			•								•
LUFFENHAM HEATH	•		•					•			•		•													•							•	
MARTIN MOOR	•	•		•	•	•		•	•		•			•		•												•		•	•			•
NORTH SHORE	•					•		•			•		•			•		•						•		•		•						
OWMBY	•	•		•	•			•			•			•	•	•						•				•				•				•
POTTERGATE												•			•														•	•	•		•	
RUTLAND COUNTY	•	•	•	•	•	•		•			•		•	•	•	•		•						•		•				•			•	•
SANDILANDS & LEISURE																								•					•	•				•
SEACROFT	•	•	•	•	•	•		•			•		•	•	•	•			•				•	•		•				•				•
SLEAFORD	•			•	•	•		•	•		•				•	•										•			•				•	
SOUTH KYME																																		•
SUDBROOK MOOR																			•							•			•					
SUTTON BRIDGE		•	•	•		•		•		•	•			•										•		•			•				•	•
TOFT HOTEL	•	•	•	•	•	•	•		•	•	•		•			•										•		•					•	
WOODTHORPE HALL	•		•		•			•		•	•		•		•											•							•	
LINCOLNSHIRE (NORTH EAST)																																		
HUMBERSTON PARK		•	•	•	•	•		•	•	•				•												•		•					•	
IMMINGHAM									•	•	•		•	•												•				•				
LINCOLNSHIRE (NORTH)																																		
ASHBY DECOY	•			•	•			•	•	•			•			•										•				•			•	
ELSHAM																										•								
FOREST PINES: BEECHES													•										•											
FOREST PINES: FOREST													•										•											
FOREST PINES: PINES													•										•											
GRANGE PARK		•	•		•	•		•	•	•	•		•													•				•			•	

© HCC Publishing Ltd

Course descriptions and features

Golf Club/Courses by County

LONDON (GREATER)

Feature	AQUARIUS	BETHUNE PARK	BLACKHEATH (ROYAL)	BRENT VALLEY PUBLIC	BUSH HILL PARK	CENTRAL LONDON	CHINGFORD	COOMBE HILL	COOMBE WOOD	DUKES MEADOW	ELTHAM WARREN	ENFIELD	EPPING FOREST (ROYAL)	FINCHLEY	HAMPSTEAD	HASTE HILL	HENDON	HIGHGATE	HUMAX	LEE VALLEY	LONDON SCOTTISH	MILL HILL	MUSWELL HILL	NORTHWOOD	RICHMOND PARK: DUKES	RICHMOND PARK: PRINCES	SHOOTERS HILL	SOUTH HERTS	STOCKLEY PARK	TRENT PARK GOLF CLUB	WANSTEAD	WEST ESSEX	WIMBLEDON COMMON
Views		●		●			●	●	●						●	●	●	●		●		●			●	●		●		●			●
Streams				●					●						●	●	●								●	●	●	●					
Lakes		●		●	●						●						●									●					●		
Deep Bunkers	●	●	●	●							●				●	●	●	●				●			●	●							
Large Bunkers	●	●													●		●	●	●			●											
Ideal for the Elderly				●		●			●						●	●												●			●		
Tends to Flood		●															●									●							
Drains Well	●		●	●		●		●							●			●	●	●	●							●	●	●		●	
Tight					●	●	●	●	●		●				●			●		●											●		●
Short				●	●	●	●		●	●								●		●		●											●
Medium Length	●	●		●	●			●							●	●	●	●	●									●				●	
Long																																	
Open	●	●		●		●													●									●					●
Sheltered			●		●			●							●	●	●	●															
Championship				●															●														
Undulating		●		●	●			●							●	●	●	●					●								●		
Cliff Top																																	
Valley				●																													
Hilltop	●	●																															
Downland																																	
Breckland		●																															
Moorland																					●												
Heath Land																																	●
Links																																	
Wooded				●	●	●		●		●				●		●	●	●	●				●										
Parkland	●	●	●	●	●	●		●		●	●	●	●	●	●	●	●	●		●	●	●	●			●	●	●		●	●	●	●
Built of Gravel									●																								
Built on Clay	●	●	●	●	●	●			●					●	●	●	●	●	●		●		●			●	●	●			●		●
Built on Soil		●		●				●												●	●			●	●			●			●		
Built on Sand				●																				●									
Built on Chalk																																	
Green Speed Slow				●																													
Green Speed Medium	●	●	●	●	●	●	●								●	●	●		●		●				●	●	●			●			
Green Speed Fast			●					●	●	●								●	●	●		●						●			●	●	

www.hccgolfworld.com

www.hccgolfworld.com

Course descriptions and features

Golf Club/Courses by County

The chart below records, for each golf club, the course-description features marked with a dot. Features (columns) read: Views · Streams · Lakes · Deep Bunkers · Large Bunkers · Ideal for the Elderly · Tends to Flood · Drains Well · Tight · Short · Medium Length · Long · Open · Sheltered · Championship · Undulating · Cliff Top · Valley · Hilltop · Downland · Breckland · Moorland · Heath Land · Links · Wooded · Parkland · Built of Gravel · Built on Clay · Built on Soil · Built on Sand · Built on Chalk · Green Speed Slow · Green Speed Medium · Green Speed Fast.

Golf Club	Marked features
WIMBLEDON PARK	Lakes; Deep Bunkers; Large Bunkers; Ideal for the Elderly; Tends to Flood; Tight; Short; Wooded; Parkland; Built on Clay; Green Speed Medium
WYKE GREEN	Drains Well; Medium Length; Wooded; Parkland; Built on Clay; Green Speed Fast
MANCHESTER (GREATER)	
BLACKLEY	Drains Well; Medium Length; Moorland; Parkland; Built on Soil; Green Speed Fast
BOYSNOPE PARK	Lakes; Deep Bunkers; Ideal for the Elderly; Drains Well; Long; Open; Undulating; Built on Soil; Green Speed Medium
BROOKDALE	Streams; Lakes; Short; Open; Sheltered; Undulating; Wooded; Parkland; Green Speed Medium
CHORLTON-CUM-HARDY	Views; Streams; Medium Length; Sheltered; Wooded; Parkland; Built on Soil; Green Speed Medium
CROMPTON & ROYTON	Views; Streams; Lakes; Ideal for the Elderly; Drains Well; Medium Length; Open; Undulating; Wooded; Parkland; Built on Clay; Green Speed Medium
DAVYHULME PARK	Views; Streams; Deep Bunkers; Ideal for the Elderly; Tight; Medium Length; Sheltered; Undulating; Wooded; Parkland; Built on Clay; Built on Sand; Green Speed Medium
DENTON	Views; Streams; Large Bunkers; Ideal for the Elderly; Medium Length; Open; Undulating; Wooded; Parkland; Built on Soil; Green Speed Medium
ELLESMERE	Views; Large Bunkers; Ideal for the Elderly; Medium Length; Open; Undulating; Wooded; Parkland; Built on Clay; Green Speed Medium
HEATON PARK	Views; Streams; Lakes; Deep Bunkers; Large Bunkers; Ideal for the Elderly; Tends to Flood; Short; Open; Undulating; Parkland; Green Speed Medium
MANCHESTER	Streams; Short; Open; Parkland
OLDHAM	Streams; Long; Open; Championship; Hilltop; Moorland; Green Speed Medium
STAND	Streams; Open; Undulating; Moorland; Parkland; Built on Clay; Green Speed Fast
SWINTON PARK	Views; Streams; Short; Ideal for the Elderly; Undulating; Parkland; Built on Clay; Green Speed Fast
WERNETH	Views; Streams
WHITEFIELD	Streams; Parkland; Built on Clay
WITHINGTON	Streams; Drains Well; Tight; Parkland; Green Speed Medium
WORSLEY	Views; Streams; Lakes; Deep Bunkers; Large Bunkers; Medium Length; Open; Sheltered; Undulating; Wooded; Parkland; Built on Soil
MERSEYSIDE	
AINTREE	Streams; Large Bunkers; Ideal for the Elderly; Drains Well; Short; Long; Open; Sheltered; Heath Land; Parkland; Built on Sand; Green Speed Medium
ALLERTON: ALLERTON 18 HOLE	Views; Ideal for the Elderly; Tends to Flood; Drains Well; Medium Length; Long; Open; Green Speed Medium
ARROWE PARK: LONG	Ideal for the Elderly; Green Speed Medium
BIDSTON	Views; Ideal for the Elderly; Drains Well; Medium Length; Open; Sheltered; Parkland; Built on Clay
BIRKDALE (ROYAL)	Views; Open; Championship; Hilltop; Links; Built on Clay; Built on Sand; Green Speed Fast
BLUNDELLS HILL	Parkland
BROMBOROUGH	Open; Parkland; Built on Sand
CALDY	Streams; Lakes; Large Bunkers; Medium Length; Long; Open; Heath Land; Links; Parkland; Green Speed Medium
CHILDWALL	Streams; Lakes; Large Bunkers; Long; Wooded; Parkland; Green Speed Medium
EASTHAM LODGE	Large Bunkers; Tends to Flood; Wooded; Parkland; Built on Soil; Green Speed Fast
FORMBY	Lakes; Deep Bunkers; Large Bunkers; Ideal for the Elderly; Drains Well; Open; Championship; Links; Parkland; Built on Sand; Green Speed Slow
FORMBY HALL	Views; Large Bunkers; Built on Soil; Green Speed Fast
HAYDOCK PARK	Views; Streams; Large Bunkers; Ideal for the Elderly; Drains Well; Medium Length; Long; Sheltered; Wooded; Parkland; Built on Soil; Green Speed Medium

Course descriptions and features

Feature categories (listed across the top of the chart):
Views · Streams · Lakes · Deep Bunkers · Large Bunkers · Ideal for the Elderly · Tends to Flood · Drains Well · Tight · Short · Medium Length · Long · Open · Sheltered · Championship · Undulating · Cliff Top · Valley · Hilltop · Downland · Breckland · Moorland · Heath Land · Links · Wooded · Parkland · Built of Gravel · Built on Clay · Built on Soil · Built on Sand · Built on Chalk · Green Speed Slow · Green Speed Medium · Green Speed Fast

Golf Club/Courses by County	Features marked (•)
HESKETH	Drains Well; Long; Championship; Links; Parkland; Built on Sand; Green Speed Fast
HESWALL	Views; Large Bunkers; Ideal for the Elderly; Drains Well; Medium Length; Open; Hilltop; Parkland; Built on Clay; Green Speed Medium
HOUGHWOOD	Views; Streams; Lakes; Drains Well; Medium Length; Open; Undulating; Parkland; Built on Clay; Built on Soil; Green Speed Medium
LEASOWE	Views; Deep Bunkers; Large Bunkers; Ideal for the Elderly; Drains Well; Medium Length; Open; Links; Built on Sand; Green Speed Medium
LEE PARK	Views; Deep Bunkers; Large Bunkers; Ideal for the Elderly; Drains Well; Medium Length; Undulating; Links; Parkland; Built on Clay; Green Speed Medium
LIVERPOOL (ROYAL)	Views; Deep Bunkers; Championship; Links
LIVERPOOL MUNICIPAL	Lakes; Large Bunkers; Tends to Flood; Sheltered; Parkland; Built on Clay
PRENTON	Streams; Undulating; Parkland; Built on Soil; Green Speed Fast
SHERDLEY PARK MUNICIPAL	Tends to Flood; Undulating; Parkland; Built on Soil; Green Speed Medium
SOUTHPORT & AINSDALE	Deep Bunkers; Tight; Long; Open; Championship; Links; Built on Sand; Green Speed Medium
SOUTHPORT MUNICIPAL	Views; Ideal for the Elderly; Medium Length; Long; Open; Links; Built on Sand; Green Speed Medium
SOUTHPORT OLD LINKS	Views; Ideal for the Elderly; Open; Championship; Links; Built on Soil
WALLASEY	Views; Medium Length; Long; Championship; Links; Built on Sand; Green Speed Medium
MIDLANDS (WEST)	
ASTON WOOD	Streams; Ideal for the Elderly; Drains Well; Medium Length; Open; Parkland; Green Speed Medium
BOLDMERE	Views; Streams; Lakes; Ideal for the Elderly; Short; Undulating; Parkland; Green Speed Medium
BRANDON WOOD MUNICIPAL	Streams; Parkland
DARTMOUTH	Views; Wooded; Parkland
EDGBASTON	Streams; Lakes; Deep Bunkers; Tight; Medium Length; Open; Sheltered; Undulating; Wooded; Parkland; Built on Soil; Green Speed Medium
FOREST OF ARDEN: AYLESFORD	Parkland
FOREST OF ARDEN: CHAMPIONSHIP - ARDEN	Championship; Parkland; Green Speed Fast
HAWKESBURY GOLF CENTRE	Short; Parkland; Green Speed Medium
LITTLE ASTON	Views; Streams; Short; Championship; Undulating; Valley; Parkland
MOOR HALL	Long; Parkland
NORTH WORCESTERSHIRE	Views; Tight; Undulating; Parkland; Green Speed Medium
PERTON PARK	Open; Undulating; Parkland
PYPE HAYES	Large Bunkers; Sheltered; Parkland
ROBIN HOOD	Drains Well; Short; Sheltered; Undulating; Heath Land; Wooded; Parkland; Green Speed Medium
SANDWELL PARK	Deep Bunkers; Medium Length; Wooded; Parkland; Built on Clay
SHIRLEY	Streams; Medium Length; Heath Land; Parkland; Built on Clay; Built on Soil; Green Speed Medium
STONEBRIDGE	Lakes; Medium Length; Parkland; Green Speed Medium
STONELEIGH DEER PARK: TANTARA	Views; Parkland
SUTTON COLDFIELD LADIES	Views; Medium Length; Parkland; Green Speed Medium
WALMLEY	Views; Ideal for the Elderly; Medium Length; Valley; Wooded; Parkland; Green Speed Fast

www.hccgolfworld.com

www.hccgolfworld.com

Course descriptions and features

Golf Club/Courses by County	Views	Streams	Lakes	Deep Bunkers	Large Bunkers	Ideal for the Elderly	Tends to Flood	Drains Well	Tight	Short	Medium Length	Long	Open	Sheltered	Championship	Undulating	Cliff Top	Valley	Hilltop	Downland	Breckland	Moorland	Heath Land	Links	Wooded	Parkland	Built of Gravel	Built on Clay	Built on Soil	Built on Sand	Built on Chalk	Green Speed Slow	Green Speed Medium	Green Speed Fast
WERGS		•	•			•		•	•		•	•	•	•		•										•			•	•			•	•
WIDNEY MANOR	•					•		•					•			•										•								
NORFOLK																																		
BARNHAM BROOM: HILL	•																								•	•			•				•	
BARNHAM BROOM: VALLEY																		•								•				•				
BAWBURGH	•							•			•			•		•							•			•			•	•			•	
CALDECOTT HALL	•	•	•	•	•			•				•				•										•							•	
COSTESSEY PARK	•								•	•						•										•				•			•	
CROMER (ROYAL)	•							•				•	•				•	•								•							•	
DEREHAM			•								•					•									•	•			•					
EAGLES	•										•			•												•								
EATON	•							•	•							•										•			•					
FAKENHAM							•			•				•																				•
FELTWELL				•										•										•							•			
KING'S LYNN	•							•	•		•														•	•				•			•	
MIDDLETON HALL	•								•					•		•										•			•					
MUNDESLEY																										•							•	
NORWICH (ROYAL)					•				•	•					•										•					•				
RICHMOND PARK	•										•			•		•									•	•								
RYSTON PARK	•											•		•		•										•			•					•
SPROWSTON MANOR	•	•						•			•	•		•							•								•	•			•	•
THETFORD	•							•			•		•			•							•		•					•			•	
WENSUM VALLEY																										•								
WESTON PARK																										•								
NORTHAMPTONSHIRE																																		
BRAMPTON HEATH: MAIN	•		•			•		•	•		•		•			•		•								•				•			•	
COLD ASHBY	•		•					•			•															•			•				•	
COLLINGTREE PARK	•	•	•			•		•							•	•										•		•					•	
CORBY PUBLIC	•		•	•		•		•		•		•			•											•		•					•	
DELAPRE PARK GOLF COMPLEX: HARDING STONE						•							•															•						
DELAPRE PARK GOLF COMPLEX: MAIN											•	•																						
FARTHINGSTONE	•						•																			•						•		
KINGSTHORPE		•						•	•							•										•				•			•	
NORTHAMPTON	•	•	•					•	•				•	•		•										•				•			•	•

Course descriptions and features

Golf Club/Courses by County	Views	Streams	Lakes	Deep Bunkers	Large Bunkers	Ideal for the Elderly	Tends to Flood	Drains Well	Tight	Short	Medium Length	Long	Open	Sheltered	Championship	Undulating	Cliff Top	Valley	Hilltop	Downland	Breckland	Moorland	Heath Land	Links	Wooded	Parkland	Built of Gravel	Built on Clay	Built on Soil	Built on Sand	Built on Chalk	Green Speed Slow	Green Speed Medium	Green Speed Fast
NORTHAMPTONSHIRE COUNTY	●	●				●		●		●	●		●			●							●			●							●	
PYTCHLEY GOLF LODGE															●	●										●								
STAVERTON PARK			●	●	●										●	●												●						●
WELLINGBOROUGH			●								●					●										●								
WHITTLEBURY PARK: GRAND PRIX			●																							●								
NORTHUMBERLAND																																		
ALNWICK	●																									●								
BELFORD																										●			●					●
BELLINGHAM	●					●		●				●	●			●										●							●	
BERWICK	●					●		●				●	●			●								●		●		●					●	●
BURGHAM	●																									●		●		●			●	
DUNSTANBURGH CASTLE	●																							●		●				●				
HAGGERSTON CASTLE	●																									●								
HEXHAM																									●	●								
LINDEN HALL			●																							●			●					
LONGHIRST HALL: THE NEW			●																							●								
LONGHIRST HALL: THE OLD			●																							●								
MAGDALENE FIELDS	●	●				●																				●		●					●	
MORPETH																●										●								
PRUDHOE																										●								
SEAHOUSES																								●						●				
SLALEY HALL GOLF COURSE: HUNTING	●														●										●	●		●					●	
SLALEY HALL GOLF COURSE: PRIESTMAN	●														●										●	●								
STOCKSFIELD	●									●						●			●							●								
SWARLAND HALL																●										●			●				●	
TYNEDALE		●				●		●			●			●		●		●						●		●				●			●	
WARKWORTH	●										●		●	●		●		●								●			●					●
WOOLER	●										●															●								
NOTTINGHAMSHIRE																																		
BRAMCOTE HILLS	●									●			●						●							●			●				●	●
BRIERLEY FOREST	●									●	●		●													●			●	●			●	
BULWELL FOREST	●	●						●			●			●		●							●			●				●			●	
CHILWELL MANOR	●							●		●	●			●		●										●							●	
COLLEGE PINES																							●			●								

Course descriptions and features

Golf Club/Courses by County	Views	Streams	Lakes	Deep Bunkers	Large Bunkers	Ideal for the Elderly	Tends to Flood	Drains Well	Tight	Short	Medium Length	Long	Open	Sheltered	Championship	Undulating	Cliff Top	Valley	Hilltop	Downland	Breckland	Moorland	Heath Land	Links	Wooded	Parkland	Built of Gravel	Built on Clay	Built on Soil	Built on Sand	Built on Chalk	Green Speed Slow	Green Speed Medium	Green Speed Fast
COTGRAVE PLACE: MASTERS	●	●	●		●								●		●	●										●		●					●	
COTGRAVE PLACE: OPEN	●	●	●												●											●		●					●	
EDWALTON MUNICIPAL	●							●	●		●		●			●										●			●				●	
KILTON FOREST			●					●			●		●			●							●			●				●			●	●
LINDRICK								●															●									●		
MANSFIELD WOODHOUSE	●		●		●	●		●			●		●												●	●				●			●	
NORWOOD PARK	●		●			●		●				●		●									●			●								●
NOTTS	●	●		●								●	●			●														●				●
OAKMERE PARK	●							●				●				●										●								
RADCLIFFE-ON-TRENT	●							●			●		●			●										●		●		●			●	
RAMSDALE PARK: RAMSDALE PARK MAIN	●		●								●					●										●		●		●			●	
RETFORD	●												●			●										●								●
RUDDINGTON GRANGE		●	●		●			●			●															●				●			●	
RUFFORD PARK GOLF CTRE	●		●								●	●													●				●	●				
SHERWOOD FOREST	●		●					●	●			●		●		●							●			●				●			●	●
SOUTHWELL	●		●					●			●		●			●										●		●	●	●			●	●
SPRINGWATER	●	●					●	●			●		●			●										●			●	●				●
STANTON ON THE WOLDS	●		●					●			●		●			●										●		●	●				●	
TRENT LOCK: TRENT LOCK GOLF CENTRE 18 HOLE	●		●						●				●	●		●										●							●	
TRENT LOCK: TRENT LOCK GOLF CENTRE 9 HOLE									●	●			●	●																			●	
WOLLATON PARK	●	●							●		●			●												●								
WORKSOP								●				●	●		●								●			●			●	●			●	●
OXFORDSHIRE																																		
ASPECT PARK						●		●			●		●	●		●		●							●	●				●			●	
BANBURY GOLF CTRE: BLUE	●	●	●			●					●		●	●		●		●								●				●			●	
BANBURY GOLF CTRE: RED	●	●				●					●		●	●		●		●								●				●			●	
BANBURY GOLF CTRE: YELLOW						●				●	●		●	●		●		●								●								
BRAILES	●	●	●			●								●		●							●			●		●		●			●	
CARSWELL	●	●				●			●		●		●			●																●	●	●
CHERWELL EDGE			●								●		●			●										●		●	●				●	●
FARINGDON								●	●		●		●	●		●										●				●			●	
FRILFORD HEATH: BLUE			●									●			●	●																		
FRILFORD HEATH: GREEN		●							●	●			●	●									●			●				●			●	
FRILFORD HEATH: RED										●		●	●	●	●																			

Course descriptions and features

Golf Club/Courses by County

Feature	HADDEN HILL	HINKSEY HEIGHTS	HUNTERCOMBE	LYNEHAM	RYE HILL	STUDLEY WOOD	WATERSTOCK	WITNEY LAKES	GREETHAM VALLEY: LAKES	GREETHAM VALLEY: VALLEY	RUTLAND WATER	ARSCOTT	BRIDGNORTH	CHURCH STRETTON	CLEOBURY MORTIMER: DEER PARK	CLEOBURY MORTIMER: FOXES RUN	LUDLOW	MILE END	OSWESTRY	SHIFNAL	SHREWSBURY	TELFORD	WORFIELD	WREKIN	BREAN	CANNINGTON	ENMORE PARK	HALSTOCK	ISLE OF WEDMORE	LONG SUTTON	MINEHEAD & WEST SOMERSET
Views	●	●	●	●	●	●			●	●	●	●	●	●	●					●	●			●	●	●			●	●	●
Streams					●	●	●																			●					
Lakes	●	●			●	●	●	●									●									●	●			●	
Deep Bunkers						●																									
Large Bunkers		●				●	●	●																	●		●		●		●
Ideal for the Elderly	●	●	●	●				●					●							●	●	●				●		●			
Tends to Flood															●							●	●								
Drains Well	●	●	●	●	●	●		●	●	●							●					●		●							
Tight		●	●									●							●												
Short				●							●													●				●			
Medium Length	●					●		●							●	●								●	●				●	●	
Long		●				●																									
Open	●	●			●	●			●	●								●	●	●				●	●	●					●
Sheltered			●																				●								
Championship			●																												
Undulating	●	●							●	●	●		●							●	●			●		●	●				
Cliff Top																															
Valley									●	●																					
Hilltop	●													●	●	●															
Downland																															
Breckland																															
Moorland																															
Heath Land		●			●												●														
Links		●																								●					●
Wooded			●			●					●		●		●	●						●			●						
Parkland	●			●		●	●	●	●	●			●		●	●			●	●	●			●	●	●	●	●	●		
Built of Gravel																					●										
Built on Clay	●	●		●		●		●				●																●			
Built on Soil						●	●		●	●		●			●	●			●				●		●	●	●			●	●
Built on Sand	●			●											●				●												●
Built on Chalk			●																												
Green Speed Slow																															
Green Speed Medium	●		●	●		●		●				●	●		●	●			●	●				●	●	●				●	●
Green Speed Fast	●			●					●	●										●	●			●		●					

© HCC Publishing Ltd

www.hccgolfworld.com

www.hccgolfworld.com

Course descriptions and features

Golf Club/Courses by County	Views	Streams	Lakes	Deep Bunkers	Large Bunkers	Ideal for the Elderly	Tends to Flood	Drains Well	Tight	Short	Medium Length	Long	Open	Sheltered	Championship	Undulating	Cliff Top	Valley	Hilltop	Downland	Breckland	Moorland	Heath Land	Links	Wooded	Parkland	Built of Gravel	Built on Clay	Built on Soil	Built on Sand	Built on Chalk	Green Speed Slow	Green Speed Medium	Green Speed Fast
OAKE MANOR	●	●	●						●	●				●												●		●					●	
VIVARY PARK		●	●			●								●											●	●							●	
WELLS						●		●			●		●			●									●	●			●					
WHEATHILL																										●								●
WINCANTON	●			●	●	●		●					●													●			●					
WINDWHISTLE	●				●	●		●			●		●			●										●			●				●	
YEOVIL: OLD								●																		●				●			●	
SOMERSET (NORTH)																																		
WESTON	●					●		●					●											●						●			●	
STAFFORDSHIRE																																		
ALSAGER	●																									●								
BARLASTON			●							●																●								
BRANSTON: BRANSTON		●	●			●	●	●			●		●		●	●		●								●			●				●	●
BROCTON HALL			●			●		●								●										●	●							●
CANNOCK PARK						●		●	●	●		●														●							●	●
CHASE			●										●	●		●										●				●			●	
CRAYTHORNE																							●			●		●						●
GOLDENHILL																										●								
GREENWAY HALL	●		●								●		●			●							●		●	●								
NEWCASTLE-UNDER-LYME																										●								
PARKHALL																										●								
SEEDY MILL: MILL						●		●			●					●										●								
SEEDY MILL: SPIRES								●			●															●								
ST. THOMAS' PRIORY																●			●							●							●	
STONE								●								●									●	●			●					
UTTOXETER									●																	●							●	●
WESTWOOD																										●								
WOLSTANTON																									●	●				●				
SUFFOLK																																		
ALDEBURGH: ALDEBURGH	●	●						●															●	●						●				●
ALDEBURGH: RIVER	●	●				●		●															●	●						●				●
BRETTVALE	●					●		●		●															●					●			●	
BURY ST EDMUNDS: BURY ST EDMUNDS	●		●	●	●	●						●	●	●		●									●	●					●		●	
BURY ST EDMUNDS: BURY ST EDMUNDS 9 HOLE	●					●																			●	●					●			

Course descriptions and features

Golf Club/Courses by County	Green Speed Fast	Green Speed Medium	Green Speed Slow	Built on Chalk	Built on Sand	Built on Soil	Built on Clay	Built of Gravel	Parkland	Wooded	Links	Heath Land	Moorland	Breckland	Downland	Hilltop	Valley	Cliff Top	Undulating	Championship	Sheltered	Open	Long	Medium Length	Short	Tight	Drains Well	Tends to Flood	Ideal for the Elderly	Large Bunkers	Deep Bunkers	Lakes	Streams	Views
CLARE PARK LAKE			●		●	●			●								●		●		●	●			●	●	●	●	●			●	●	●
CRETINGHAM		●				●				●									●		●	●			●	●	●	●	●					
DIP FARM	●	●				●	●		●		●					●		●	●			●		●			●		●			●	●	●
FELIXSTOWE FERRY		●				●					●											●		●			●		●			●	●	●
FLEMPTON		●				●			●			●												●			●			●			●	●
FYNN VALLEY: FYNN VALLEY 18 HOLE		●					●		●										●					●			●							●
FYNN VALLEY: FYNN VALLEY 9 HOLE			●				●		●																●	●	●		●					
HALESWORTH: HALESWORTH							●		●													●	●				●		●	●	●	●		●
HAVERHILL	●					●	●		●	●									●			●				●	●			●			●	
HIGH LODGE		●					●		●	●						●			●	●	●	●	●	●	●		●		●	●	●	●		●
HINTLESHAM HALL		●			●	●			●											●											●	●		
IPSWICH		●										●												●			●							
NEWTON GREEN		●				●			●													●		●				●	●			●	●	
RUSHMERE	●				●							●							●			●		●			●		●	●	●	●		
SOUTHWOLD		●				●						●										●		●			●		●		●			●
SUFFOLK GOLF									●	●									●		●	●		●		●	●		●	●		●	●	●
UFFORD PARK									●										●								●							●
WOODBRIDGE: WOODBRIDGE		●				●						●							●			●		●			●		●					●
WORLINGTON & NEWMARKET (ROYAL)	●				●																	●		●		●	●		●					●
SURREY																																		
ABBEYMOOR									●																									
ADDINGTON									●			●																						
ADDINGTON COURT GOLF CLUB: CHAMPIONSHIP									●										●								●							
ADDINGTON COURT GOLF CLUB: FALCONWOOD									●										●															
ADDINGTON PALACE							●		●	●						●			●					●				●		●	●			
ASHFORD MANOR									●																									
BANSTEAD DOWNS		●		●							●				●									●		●	●		●					
BOWENHURST		●					●		●	●															●	●						●		●
BRAMLEY										●									●		●				●	●	●					●		●
BROADWATER PARK	●					●			●												●				●	●	●		●			●		●
BURHILL: BURHILL (NEW)									●														●				●		●					●
BURHILL: BURHILL (OLD)		●					●		●														●				●		●					●
CAMBERLEY HEATH												●							●		●			●		●	●					●		●
CHESSINGTON		●				●			●																●		●		●					●

www.hcgolfworld.com

Course descriptions and features

Golf Club/Courses by County

Feature	CHIDDINGFOLD	CHIPSTEAD	CHOBHAM	CRANLEIGH	CROHAM HURST	DRIFT	EFFINGHAM	EPSOM	FARNHAM	FOXHILLS GOLF: BERNARD HUNT	GATTON MANOR	GOAL FARM	HANKLEY COMMON	HAPPY VALLEY	HERSHAM VILLAGE	HINDHEAD	HOEBRIDGE: MAIN	HORNE PARK	HORTON PARK GOLF	HURTMORE	KINGSWOOD	LIMPSFIELD CHART	LINGFIELD PARK	MID-SURREY (ROYAL): OUTER	MILFORD GOLF CLUB	MOORE PLACE	NEW ZEALAND	NORTH DOWNS	OAK PARK GOLF CLUB: VILLAGE	OAK PARK GOLF CLUB: WOODLAND	PINE RIDGE GOLF CTRE	PUTTENHAM	PYRFORD GOLF CLUB	REDHILL & REIGATE
Views	•	•		•	•	•	•	•			•					•		•	•	•		•	•	•	•		•				•	•	•	•
Streams				•								•						•				•											•	
Lakes			•									•						•	•				•								•		•	
Deep Bunkers																																		
Large Bunkers																								•										
Ideal for the Elderly							•								•			•					•											
Tends to Flood	•					•			•									•	•															
Drains Well				•	•	•		•	•																						•	•	•	•
Tight	•			•	•	•		•																								•	•	•
Short				•				•					•																					
Medium Length	•					•	•	•	•							•	•							•										
Long																					•													
Open							•				•							•	•	•									•			•		
Sheltered											•										•					•	•							
Championship			•										•																					
Undulating	•			•	•													•																
Cliff Top																																		
Valley								•							•																			
Hilltop						•										•												•						
Downland						•																												
Breckland																																		
Moorland																																		
Heath Land									•					•						•							•					•		
Links																																		•
Wooded	•	•	•									•				•													•	•		•	•	•
Parkland	•		•	•	•	•		•	•	•							•	•	•	•		•	•	•		•								
Built of Gravel																																		
Built on Clay	•			•		•			•	•								•	•	•														
Built on Soil															•	•			•	•						•						•		
Built on Sand									•							•		•																
Built on Chalk					•		•	•																								•		
Green Speed Slow																																		
Green Speed Medium	•			•	•		•		•									•	•	•	•			•							•	•	•	•
Green Speed Fast						•										•																		

Course descriptions and features

A feature-by-course matrix ("•" indicates the feature applies to that course).

Golf Club/Courses by County	Views	Streams	Lakes	Deep Bunkers	Large Bunkers	Ideal for the Elderly	Tends to Flood	Drains Well	Tight	Short	Medium Length	Long	Open	Sheltered	Championship	Undulating	Cliff Top	Valley	Hilltop	Downland	Breckland	Moorland	Heath Land	Links	Wooded	Parkland	Built of Gravel	Built on Clay	Built on Soil	Built on Sand	Built on Chalk	Green Speed Slow	Green Speed Medium	Green Speed Fast
REDHILL GOLF CTRE	•					•			•	•			•													•		•		•			•	
REIGATE HILL	•								•		•		•			•									•	•		•		•			•	
RUSPER			•					•			•														•	•		•					•	
SANDOWN GOLF CTRE: PAR 3	•		•			•	•				•		•															•					•	
SELSDON PARK			•			•					•												•			•								
SHILLINGLEE PARK	•							•							•											•								
SUNBURY: SUNBURY 18 HOLE																										•								
SUNBURY: SUNBURY 9 HOLE																•										•			•					
SUNNINGDALE: NEW	•															•							•						•	•				
SUNNINGDALE: OLD	•														•								•						•	•				
SURREY GOLF & FITNESS																													•					
SUTTON GREEN	•		•			•		•		•	•		•													•								•
THAMES DITTON & ESHER	•		•					•	•							•								•	•	•		•					•	
TRADITIONS GOLF COURSE	•	•						•	•	•	•		•	•		•								•	•								•	
WALTON HEATH: OLD	•					•		•							•								•											•
WENTWORTH CLUB: EAST								•				•											•		•									
WENTWORTH CLUB: EDINBURGH																							•		•									
WENTWORTH CLUB: WEST															•								•		•									
WEST SURREY	•							•	•		•															•							•	
WILDWOOD COUNTRY CLUB	•		•					•				•		•		•							•			•		•			•			
WINDLERMERE	•	•	•			•		•					•			•										•		•						
WINDLESHAM		•	•				•			•				•		•							•			•				•		•		
WOKING						•																	•											
WORPLESDON													•												•									
SUSSEX (EAST)																																		
ASHDOWN FOREST (ROYAL)	•	•						•					•			•							•			•		•		•			•	
BATTLE	•	•						•		•	•		•	•		•										•		•		•			•	•
BOARS HEAD	•							•				•	•	•		•										•		•					•	
COODEN BEACH	•	•	•					•				•											•	•					•				•	
CROWBOROUGH BEACON	•											•	•		•	•							•					•					•	
DALE HILL: THE IAN WOOSNAM															•											•			•					•
DALE HILL: THE OLD					•																				•									•
DEWLANDS MANOR						•				•						•			•															•
EAST BRIGHTON	•							•					•							•								•						

Course descriptions and features

GolfWorld Directory — Golf Club/Courses by County

Features tracked (column headings, top to bottom): Views, Streams, Lakes, Deep Bunkers, Large Bunkers, Ideal for the Elderly, Tends to Flood, Drains Well, Tight, Short, Medium Length, Long, Open, Sheltered, Championship, Undulating, Cliff Top, Valley, Hilltop, Downland, Breckland, Moorland, Heath Land, Links, Wooded, Parkland, Built of Gravel, Built on Clay, Built on Soil, Built on Sand, Built on Chalk, Green Speed Slow, Green Speed Medium, Green Speed Fast.

East Sussex

Course	Features marked (●)
EAST SUSSEX NATIONAL: EAST	Views, Streams, Long, Championship, Undulating, Green Speed Fast
EAST SUSSEX NATIONAL: WEST	Views, Streams, Long, Championship, Undulating, Green Speed Fast
EASTBOURNE DOWNS	Views, Downland, Green Speed Fast
EASTBOURNE GOLFING PARK	Tight, Short, Ideal for the Elderly, Undulating, Wooded, Parkland, Built on Clay, Built on Soil, Green Speed Medium
HIGHWOODS	Views, Streams, Lakes, Large Bunkers, Ideal for the Elderly, Drains Well, Medium Length, Undulating, Parkland, Green Speed Medium, Green Speed Fast
LEWES	Views, Ideal for the Elderly, Drains Well, Open, Downland, Parkland
MID SUSSEX	Views, Streams, Drains Well, Medium Length, Open, Undulating, Parkland, Green Speed Fast
PEACEHAVEN	Views, Open, Downland
RYE: JUBILEE	Open, Links
RYE: OLD	Open, Links
SEAFORD	Views, Drains Well, Medium Length, Open, Undulating, Built on Chalk, Green Speed Medium
SEDLESCOMBE	Views, Streams, Lakes, Ideal for the Elderly, Drains Well, Medium Length, Tight, Undulating, Parkland, Built on Clay, Green Speed Medium
WATERHALL	Views, Ideal for the Elderly, Medium Length, Undulating, Valley, Hilltop, Green Speed Fast
WELLSHURST	Views, Streams, Drains Well, Medium Length, Undulating, Hilltop, Wooded, Parkland, Built on Soil, Built on Chalk, Green Speed Medium
WEST HOVE	Views, Drains Well, Medium Length, Open, Built on Chalk, Green Speed Medium
WILLINGDON	Views, Drains Well, Medium Length, Sheltered, Undulating, Built on Clay, Green Speed Medium, Green Speed Fast

Sussex (West)

Course	Features marked (●)
AVISFORD PARK	Streams, Tends to Flood, Drains Well, Short, Open, Valley, Parkland, Built on Clay, Green Speed Medium
BOGNOR REGIS	Views, Ideal for the Elderly, Short, Medium Length, Open, Wooded, Parkland, Built on Soil, Green Speed Medium
BROOKLANDS PARK	Ideal for the Elderly, Medium Length, Parkland, Green Speed Medium
CHARTHAM PARK	Lakes, Deep Bunkers, Large Bunkers, Drains Well, Long, Sheltered, Championship, Undulating, Parkland, Built on Sand, Green Speed Fast
CHICHESTER: CHICHESTER	Views, Streams, Lakes, Deep Bunkers, Ideal for the Elderly, Medium Length, Tight, Open, Parkland, Green Speed Medium
COTTESMORE: GRIFFIN	Views, Streams, Lakes, Drains Well, Medium Length, Open, Undulating, Wooded, Parkland, Green Speed Medium
COTTESMORE: PHOENIX	Lakes, Open, Parkland, Green Speed Medium
CUCKFIELD	Wooded, Parkland, Green Speed Medium
EFFINGHAM PARK	Parkland, Green Speed Medium
FOXBRIDGE	Views, Deep Bunkers, Ideal for the Elderly, Drains Well, Medium Length, Open, Undulating, Parkland, Green Speed Medium
GOODWOOD	Views, Streams, Deep Bunkers, Long, Open, Hilltop, Downland, Parkland, Built on Chalk, Green Speed Medium
HAM MANOR	Views, Lakes, Large Bunkers, Ideal for the Elderly, Drains Well, Medium Length, Open, Sheltered, Parkland, Green Speed Medium
HASSOCKS	Views, Streams, Drains Well, Medium Length, Open, Moorland, Parkland, Built on Clay, Green Speed Medium
HILLBARN	Views, Deep Bunkers, Large Bunkers, Short, Medium Length, Open, Tight, Links, Wooded, Built on Clay, Built on Chalk, Green Speed Medium
HORSHAM GOLF	Views, Streams, Ideal for the Elderly, Drains Well, Medium Length, Open, Wooded, Parkland, Built on Clay, Green Speed Medium
IFIELD	Large Bunkers, Medium Length, Open, Parkland, Green Speed Medium
MANNINGS HEATH: KINGFISHER	Views, Large Bunkers, Drains Well, Medium Length, Open, Built on Clay, Green Speed Fast

Course descriptions and features

Columns (left to right): 1 MANNINGS HEATH: WATERFALL, 2 PAXHILL PARK, 3 PETWORTH, 4 ROOKWOOD, 5 RUSTINGTON, 6 SELSEY, 7 SINGING HILLS: LAKE, 8 SLINFOLD PARK: CHAMPIONSHIP, 9 TILGATE FOREST, 10 WEST CHILTINGTON, 11 WEST SUSSEX, 12 WORTHING: LOWER, 13 TYNE AND WEAR, 14 RYTON, 15 WARWICKSHIRE, 16 ATHERSTONE, 17 BIDFORD GRANGE, 18 BRAMCOTE WATERS, 19 LEAMINGTON & COUNTY, 20 NEWBOLD COMYN, 21 NUNEATON, 22 WARWICKSHIRE: SOUTH EAST, 23 WHITEFIELDS, 24 WILTSHIRE, 25 BOWOOD, 26 BRADFORD ON AVON, 27 BRINKWORTH, 28 BROOME MANOR, 29 CUMBERWELL: WOODLANDS, 30 ERLESTOKE SANDS, 31 HAMPTWORTH, 32 HIGH POST, 33 KINGSDOWN, 34 MANOR HOUSE

Feature	1	2	3	4	5	6	7	8	9	10	11	12	13	14	15	16	17	18	19	20	21	22	23	24	25	26	27	28	29	30	31	32	33	34
Views		•	•	•	•	•	•	•	•		•				•			•	•	•						•	•	•			•	•	•	•
Streams	•		•			•	•		•					•			•		•	•								•			•			
Lakes	•			•	•	•	•		•		•						•	•										•	•	•				
Deep Bunkers			•	•						•	•	•					•										•			•				
Large Bunkers			•	•	•					•	•	•					•										•			•	•			
Ideal for the Elderly			•			•	•	•									•													•				
Tends to Flood					•	•	•										•																	
Drains Well		•	•					•	•	•	•						•	•	•	•					•	•		•						
Tight		•				•	•						•		•		•			•					•									
Short									•				•		•		•			•														
Medium Length	•	•	•		•		•	•	•						•		•	•	•						•			•		•	•	•		
Long											•																		•					
Open	•	•	•	•	•			•		•					•		•	•	•		•				•			•			•		•	
Sheltered							•			•		•			•		•																	
Championship							•	•							•										•							•		•
Undulating	•		•												•				•						•	•	•	•	•		•		•	
Cliff Top																																		
Valley																																		
Hilltop																•																		
Downland												•																					•	
Breckland																																		
Moorland														•																				
Heath Land									•	•																								
Links				•						•																								
Wooded	•		•	•					•		•								•				•						•					
Parkland	•		•					•	•	•				•		•	•	•	•	•	•	•	•		•	•	•	•	•	•	•			
Built of Gravel																																		
Built on Clay		•	•		•	•		•										•	•	•								•	•	•				
Built on Soil				•							•					•									•			•		•		•		
Built on Sand								•	•																	•		•		•				
Built on Chalk							•	•			•	•																•		•	•			
Green Speed Slow				•																														
Green Speed Medium	•	•	•		•		•								•		•	•										•	•	•		•		
Green Speed Fast							•		•											•						•	•	•			•	•	•	•

Course descriptions and features

Golf Club/Courses by County	Green Speed Fast	Green Speed Medium	Green Speed Slow	Built on Chalk	Built on Sand	Built on Soil	Built on Clay	Built of Gravel	Parkland	Wooded	Links	Heath Land	Moorland	Breckland	Downland	Hilltop	Valley	Cliff Top	Undulating	Championship	Sheltered	Open	Long	Medium Length	Short	Tight	Drains Well	Tends to Flood	Ideal for the Elderly	Large Bunkers	Deep Bunkers	Lakes	Streams	Views
OAKSEY									●																									
OGBOURNE DOWNS				●											●				●								●							
RUSHMORE PARK		●		●					●	●									●		●			●		●	●					●		●
SALISBURY & SOUTH WILTS: MAIN		●		●											●				●			●		●			●							●
SHRIVENHAM PARK		●			●	●			●										●						●	●	●					●		●
THOULSTONE PARK									●																							●		●
TIDWORTH GARRISON	●			●															●			●		●			●		●					●
UPAVON		●		●												●			●			●		●			●							●
WHITLEY		●					●		●												●			●		●	●					●		●
WILTSHIRE															●					●														
WRAG BARN		●				●				●						●								●			●		●	●			●	●
WORCESTERSHIRE																																		
ABBEY HOTEL									●											●														
BANK HOUSE		●							●																					●		●	●	●
BLACKWELL									●																									
BROMSGROVE		●			●				●										●		●	●		●			●		●	●		●		●
CADMORE LODGE																	●															●		
CHURCHILL & BLAKEDOWN	●				●														●		●						●		●					
LITTLE LAKES		●					●		●															●										
LITTLE LAKES									●										●															●
PERDISWELL PARK GOLF COURSE		●							●																●		●		●					
PITCHEROAK		●					●		●										●						●	●	●							
REDDITCH		●							●	●											●	●		●		●	●						●	
SAPEY: THE ROWAN					●				●													●					●		●					●
WHARTON PARK		●				●			●	●														●										●
WYRE FOREST		●									●											●		●			●		●					●
YORKSHIRE (EAST)																																		
BOOTHFERRY PARK		●					●															●												
BRIDLINGTON		●					●		●	●												●		●			●		●			●		●
CAVE CASTLE		●				●	●		●										●					●										
CHERRY BURTON		●				●			●										●			●	●				●					●	●	●
HAINSWORTH PARK		●					●		●	●									●			●		●			●		●				●	
HESSLE: HEXHAM	●					●			●															●			●							
HORNSEA	●					●			●	●									●			●		●		●	●							●

Course descriptions and features

Golf Club/Courses by County	Views	Streams	Lakes	Deep Bunkers	Large Bunkers	Ideal for the Elderly	Tends to Flood	Drains Well	Tight	Short	Medium Length	Long	Open	Sheltered	Championship	Undulating	Cliff Top	Valley	Hilltop	Downland	Breckland	Moorland	Heath Land	Links	Wooded	Parkland	Built of Gravel	Built on Clay	Built on Soil	Built on Sand	Built on Chalk	Green Speed Slow	Green Speed Medium	Green Speed Fast
WITHERNSEA			●				●		●		●		●			●										●		●					●	
YORKSHIRE (NORTH)																																		
ALDWARK MANOR	●	●	●			●		●			●			●	●										●	●		●					●	
COCKSFORD	●	●	●			●		●			●			●				●							●	●							●	
CRIMPLE VALLEY	●							●					●													●			●	●			●	●
FOREST PARK								●															●		●	●							●	
GANTON	●				●	●		●			●			●	●									●		●							●	
HEWORTH																										●		●					●	
KILNWICK PERCY	●	●				●					●		●						●							●							●	
KIRKBYMOORSIDE	●	●				●					●					●									●	●		●					●	●
OAKS		●	●				●	●								●									●	●								●
PANNAL												●										●				●							●	●
RUDDING PARK	●																								●	●		●						
SCARBOROUGH SOUTH CLIFF	●		●												●	●						●				●							●	
SCARTHINGWELL	●											●				●		●								●			●				●	
SKIPTON	●															●	●								●	●								
SPOFFORTH	●				●	●		●			●															●							●	
SWALLOW HALL		●								●																●				●			●	
WHITBY	●					●		●		●			●				●							●				●						
YORK GOLF CTRE	●				●			●	●	●			●													●		●					●	
YORKSHIRE (SOUTH)																																		
DONCASTER TOWN MOOR	●							●																		●							●	
HICKLETON	●	●						●			●		●			●										●		●					●	
HILLSBOROUGH	●	●	●			●		●				●														●		●					●	
KINGSWOOD			●									●				●										●		●					●	
ROBIN HOOD	●		●									●	●			●										●							●	
ROTHER VALLEY GOLF: ROTHER VALLEY	●		●		●	●											●									●								
SITWELL																										●			●					
TANKERSLEY PARK	●												●													●								
YORKSHIRE (WEST)																																		
ALWOODLEY	●		●					●				●	●	●	●	●							●						●				●	
BAGDEN HALL			●								●			●												●								
BAILDON	●							●				●	●	●	●	●						●				●		●					●	
BINGLEY ST IVES	●	●																				●			●	●								

Course descriptions and features

Golf Club/Courses by County

Feature	BRACKEN GHYLL	BRADLEY HALL	BRADLEY PARK	CALVERLEY	COOKRIDGE HALL GOLF CLUB	CROSLAND HEATH	CROW NEST PARK	EAST BIERLEY	ELLAND	FARDEW	HALIFAX	HEADLEY	HEBDEN BRIDGE	HOLLINS HALL	HORSFORTH	HOWLEY HALL	HUDDERSFIELD	KEIGHLEY	LEEDS	LEEDS GOLF CTRE: THE OAKS	LEEDS GOLF CTRE: WIKE RIDGE	LIGHTCLIFFE	LOFTHOUSE HILL	LONGLEY PARK	MANOR	MARSDEN	MELTHAM	MID YORKSHIRE	MOORTOWN	NORTHCLIFFE	OTLEY	OULTON PARK: MAIN	OUTLANE	PONTEFRACT
Views		●	●			●	●		●	●	●	●		●	●		●		●						●	●	●	●			●	●	●	●
Streams		●	●						●	●			●					●							●	●	●						●	●
Lakes			●																						●			●	●			●		●
Deep Bunkers		●	●			●	●				●														●	●								●
Large Bunkers			●			●	●																		●	●								●
Ideal for the Elderly									●				●						●						●	●	●							
Tends to Flood			●	●					●																						●			
Drains Well		●				●	●				●	●				●			●						●	●			●			●		
Tight	●						●															●												
Short									●				●						●															
Medium Length	●	●	●			●	●	●			●					●			●						●	●	●	●			●		●	
Long									●								●								●						●			
Open		●				●	●	●			●		●			●			●						●	●	●			●		●	●	●
Sheltered		●	●				●				●								●						●						●			●
Championship																																		
Undulating		●	●			●	●		●	●	●	●		●	●		●		●						●		●	●	●			●		
Cliff Top																																		
Valley													●									●												
Hilltop												●	●				●																	
Downland																																		
Breckland																																		
Moorland								●				●	●													●				●			●	
Heath Land					●							●		●								●												
Links																																		
Wooded						●		●	●							●	●	●		●	●	●	●	●		●					●		●	●
Parkland	●	●	●	●	●		●		●	●				●	●	●	●	●	●	●	●		●		●		●		●		●	●	●	●
Built of Gravel																																		
Built on Clay		●	●				●		●								●															●	●	●
Built on Soil				●				●	●	●		●				●									●		●	●	●		●	●		
Built on Sand					●																		●	●	●									
Built on Chalk																														●				●
Green Speed Slow																																		
Green Speed Medium	●	●	●						●	●	●	●					●			●	●				●		●	●	●			●	●	●
Green Speed Fast		●				●		●								●	●								●	●					●			

Course descriptions and features

Golf Club/Courses by County	RIDDLESDEN	ROUNDHAY	SHIPLEY	SILSDEN	SOUTH LEEDS	WAKEFIELD	WEST BRADFORD	WILLOW VALLEY: T.P.C	WOODHALL HILLS	WOODSOME HALL
Views	●	●	●	●	●	●			●	
Streams		●		●	●				●	●
Lakes		●					●			
Deep Bunkers	●			●	●				●	●
Large Bunkers	●	●		●	●					●
Ideal for the Elderly	●	●		●	●					
Tends to Flood										
Drains Well	●	●		●	●			●	●	●
Tight	●	●						●	●	
Short	●			●						
Medium Length		●			●				●	●
Long							●			
Open				●	●					●
Sheltered	●	●								●
Championship				●						
Undulating	●	●	●		●					
Cliff Top										
Valley		●								
Hilltop								●		
Downland										
Breckland										
Moorland										
Heath Land										
Links										
Wooded	●	●		●	●					
Parkland	●	●		●	●	●	●		●	●
Built of Gravel										
Built on Clay		●			●				●	●
Built on Soil				●			●			
Built on Sand	●						●			
Built on Chalk										
Green Speed Slow	●									
Green Speed Medium						●		●		●
Green Speed Fast		●		●				●		

Course descriptions and features

Golf Club/Courses by County

IRELAND

Features (rows) with the golf clubs (columns) marked ●:

Feature	Clubs marked (●)
Views	Doonbeg, Kilkee, Kilrush, Bantry Bay, Berehaven, Cobh, Kinsale: Farrangalway, Kinsale: Ringenane, Lisselan, Cloughaneely, Clontarf, Malahide, Open: Blue Nine, Open: Red Nine, Portmarnock, Portmarnock Hotel, Swords Open
Streams	Water Rock, Clontarf, Malahide, Portmarnock Hotel, Swords Open
Lakes	Kilkee, Blarney, Kinsale: Farrangalway, Lisselan, Clontarf, Open: Red Nine, Portmarnock
Deep Bunkers	Doonbeg, Kinsale: Farrangalway, Clontarf, Portmarnock
Large Bunkers	Doonbeg, Clontarf, Portmarnock Hotel
Ideal for the Elderly	Blarney, Cobh, Kinsale: Ringenane, Mallow, Leopardstown, Open: Blue Nine
Tends to Flood	—
Drains Well	Kilkee, Woodstock, Blarney, Cobh, Kinsale: Farrangalway, Mallow, Clontarf, Open: Blue Nine
Tight	Cobh, Kinsale: Farrangalway, Kinsale: Ringenane, Clontarf
Short	Kinsale: Farrangalway, Lisselan, Leopardstown, Open: Blue Nine
Medium Length	Kilkee, Kinsale: Farrangalway, Lisselan, Muskerry, Clontarf, Malahide, Open: Blue Nine, Open: Red Nine, Portmarnock
Long	Kinsale: Ringenane, Portmarnock Hotel
Open	Kilkee, Kinsale: Farrangalway, Open: Red Nine
Sheltered	Narin/Portnoo, Clontarf
Championship	Bantry Bay, Kinsale: Farrangalway
Undulating	Kilrush, Woodstock, Blarney, Cobh, Portmarnock
Cliff Top	Kilkee, Bantry Bay
Valley	Blarney, Clontarf
Hilltop	—
Downland	—
Breckland	—
Moorland	—
Heath Land	—
Links	Doonbeg, Kilkee, Bantry Bay, Ballyliffin: Glashedy Links, Ballyliffin: Old Links, Narin/Portnoo, Island, Portmarnock, Portmarnock Hotel
Wooded	Kinsale: Farrangalway, Kinsale: Ringenane, Narin/Portnoo
Parkland	Woodstock, Blarney, Cobh, Kinsale: Farrangalway, Kinsale: Ringenane, Lisselan, Mallow, Water Rock, Narin/Portnoo, Clontarf, Leopardstown, Malahide, Open: Blue Nine, Open: Red Nine, Portmarnock, Swords Open
Built of Gravel	—
Built on Clay	Kilkee, Bantry Bay, Clontarf, Open: Red Nine
Built on Soil	Blarney, Cobh
Built on Sand	Muskerry, Water Rock, Narin/Portnoo, Open: Blue Nine, Portmarnock, Portmarnock Hotel
Built on Chalk	—
Green Speed Slow	Cloughaneely
Green Speed Medium	Doonbeg, Kilkee, Blarney, Lisselan, Clontarf, Malahide, Open: Red Nine, Portmarnock, Swords Open
Green Speed Fast	Doonbeg, Kinsale: Farrangalway, Kinsale: Ringenane, Portmarnock, Portmarnock Hotel

County groupings:
- **COUNTY CLARE:** Doonbeg, Kilkee, Kilrush, Woodstock
- **COUNTY CORK:** Bantry Bay, Berehaven, Blarney, Cobh, Kinsale: Farrangalway, Kinsale: Ringenane, Lisselan, Mallow, Muskerry, Water Rock
- **COUNTY DONEGAL:** Ballyliffin: Glashedy Links, Ballyliffin: Old Links, Cloughaneely, Narin/Portnoo
- **COUNTY DUBLIN:** Clontarf, Hollywood Lakes, Island, Leopardstown, Malahide, Open: Blue Nine, Open: Red Nine, Portmarnock, Portmarnock Hotel, Swords Open

Course descriptions and features

Golf Club/Courses by County

Feature	TURVEY	ATHENRY	BALLINASLOE	BEARNA	CONNEMARA: CONNEMARA	BALLYBUNION: CASHEN	BALLYBUNION: OLD	BALLYHEIGUE CASTLE	CASTLEROSSE	DOOKS	KERRIES	RING OF KERRY	WATERVILLE HOUSE & GOLF LINKS	CELBRIDGE ELM HALL	CRADDOCKSTOWN	HIGHFIELD	K CLUB	KILKEA CASTLE	CARRIGLEADE	GOWRAN PARK GOLF & LEISURE	MOUNT JULIET	MOUNTAIN VIEW	POCOCKE	ABBEYFEALE GOLF CTRE	LIMERICK	LIMERICK (COUNTY)	NEWCASTLE WEST	RATHBANE
Views	●	●			●	●	●	●	●	●	●		●	●					●	●	●	●		●		●		●
Streams												●									●		●	●			●	
Lakes					●				●	●				●	●		●			●	●			●	●	●		
Deep Bunkers					●																●							
Large Bunkers					●			●						●							●				●			●
Ideal for the Elderly		●			●						●				●	●			●					●	●			
Tends to Flood																												
Drains Well	●	●		●	●			●			●				●						●		●	●				
Tight																				●					●			
Short											●												●	●				
Medium Length		●									●	●			●		●		●					●		●		●
Long	●				●			●																				
Open	●				●										●				●				●					
Sheltered																			●		●							
Championship				●	●								●		●		●	●		●						●		
Undulating	●				●	●	●															●	●					
Cliff Top																												
Valley																												
Hilltop																					●							
Downland																												
Breckland																												
Moorland			●																									
Heath Land		●										●																
Links					●	●	●			●			●															
Wooded	●	●							●	●									●	●	●							
Parkland	●	●	●					●			●	●		●	●	●		●	●	●	●	●		●	●			●
Built of Gravel																												
Built on Clay																									●			
Built on Soil		●																●			●		●					
Built on Sand		●			●				●														●					
Built on Chalk																												
Green Speed Slow																												
Green Speed Medium	●	●	●								●	●		●	●								●		●		●	
Green Speed Fast				●						●						●			●		●							

County headers within list: COUNTY GALWAY, COUNTY KERRY, COUNTY KILDARE, COUNTY KILKENNY, COUNTY LIMERICK

Course descriptions and features

Golf Club/Courses by County

Golf Club	Views	Streams	Lakes	Deep Bunkers	Large Bunkers	Ideal for the Elderly	Tends to Flood	Drains Well	Tight	Short	Medium Length	Long	Open	Sheltered	Championship	Undulating	Cliff Top	Valley	Hilltop	Downland	Breckland	Moorland	Heath Land	Links	Wooded	Parkland	Built of Gravel	Built on Clay	Built on Soil	Built on Sand	Built on Chalk	Green Speed Slow	Green Speed Medium	Green Speed Fast
COUNTY LOUTH								•		•																•							•	
KILLIN PARK		•			•																									•				•
LOUTH (COUNTY)											•													•										
SEAPOINT	•							•							•	•								•		•								
TOWNLEY HALL	•		•					•			•			•	•										•	•			•				•	
COUNTY MAYO	•	•																								•								
BALLINA											•													•		•			•				•	
MULRANNY											•																							
COUNTY MEATH	•	•			•			•								•			•							•								
GLEBE												•				•										•						•		•
SOUTH MEATH												•														•		•						
COUNTY MONAGHAN	•	•				•		•																										
CLONES								•			•															•								
COUNTY OFFALY																																		
CASTLE BARNA											•															•			•				•	
COUNTY ROSCOMMON	•	•	•			•																												
ROSCOMMON								•			•	•			•	•										•			•	•				
COUNTY SLIGO	•												•																				•	
SLIGO (COUNTY): BOMORE 9 HOLE	•												•											•										
SLIGO (COUNTY): CHAMPIONSHIP													•		•									•										
COUNTY TIPPERARY											•																							
BALLYKISTEEN									•				•													•								•
TEMPLEMORE						•																				•			•					•
COUNTY WATERFORD	•	•	•		•			•	•			•	•	•	•	•										•								
DUNGARVAN	•	•									•						•									•		•						
DUNMORE EAST	•	•											•		•											•			•					
FAITHLEGG	•	•	•		•	•		•			•				•		•									•		•	•	•			•	
GOLD COAST	•	•	•		•	•		•							•													•	•	•				
WEST WATERFORD											•																							•
COUNTY WESTMEATH																																		
MOATE						•																											•	
COUNTY WEXFORD																										•								
BALLYMONEY																										•								
ST. HELENS BAY	•																							•										

Course descriptions and features

Golf Club/Courses by County	CHARLESLAND	COOLLATTIN	DRUIDS GLEN	EUROPEAN CLUB	GLEN MILL	GLEN OF THE DOWNS	POWERSCOURT	RATHSALLAGH	WICKLOW
COUNTY WICKLOW									
Views	●	●		●	●	●	●	●	●
Streams					●		●		
Lakes					●	●	●	●	
Deep Bunkers				●			●	●	
Large Bunkers				●			●	●	
Ideal for the Elderly			●		●		●		
Tends to Flood									
Drains Well					●		●	●	
Tight									
Short					●				
Medium Length			●				●		
Long				●					●
Open	●						●		
Sheltered					●		●		
Championship	●		●				●	●	
Undulating					●		●		
Cliff Top									
Valley					●				
Hilltop									
Downland									
Breckland									
Moorland									
Heath Land									
Links				●					
Wooded								●	
Parkland	●	●	●			●	●	●	●
Built of Gravel									
Built on Clay									
Built on Soil					●		●		
Built on Sand			●	●				●	
Built on Chalk									
Green Speed Slow									
Green Speed Medium	●	●			●		●		
Green Speed Fast				●	●	●	●	●	

Course descriptions and features

Golf Club/Courses by County

Feature	ALLEN PARK	BALLYCASTLE	BALLYMENA	BELFAST	BENTRA MUNICIPAL	CAIRNDHU	CLIFTONVILLE	CUSHENDALL	DOWN ROYAL PARK: DOWN ROYAL PARK	GALGORM CASTLE	GRACEHILL	GREENACRES GOLF CTRE	KNOCK	LARNE	LISBURN	MOUNT OBER	ORMEAU	PORTRUSH (ROYAL); DUNLUCE	TEMPLE CLUB	WHITEHEAD	TANDRAGEE	ARDGLASS	BANBRIDGE	CARNALEA	CLOVERHILL	DONAGHADEE	DOWN (ROYAL COUNTY): ANNESLEY LINKS	DOWN (ROYAL COUNTY): CHAMPIONSHIP	DOWNPATRICK
NORTHERN IRELAND																													
COUNTY ANTRIM																					**COUNTY ARMAGH**	**COUNTY DOWN**							
Views	●	●	●		●	●	●	●	●	●	●	●		●	●			●	●		●		●	●		●	●		● ●
Streams	●	●			●	●			●					●						●				●			●		●
Lakes	●	●	●					●		●	●	●		●				●		●				●			●		●
Deep Bunkers			●				● ●		●	●	●	● ●															●		●
Large Bunkers			●					●		●																	●		●
Ideal for the Elderly	●	●	●	●	●	●	●		●	●							●		●	●		●		●	● ●		●		● ●
Tends to Flood																													
Drains Well	●	●	●	●	●		●		●	●			● ●	●		●		●	● ●		●		●			●			
Tight	●												●			●		●											
Short		●		●																									
Medium Length									●	●	●	●					●	●		●		●		●	● ●		●		●
Long	●				●	●	●		●			● ●						● ●											
Open			●	●					●	●	●	●					●	●				●		●	● ●		●		
Sheltered	●			●	●	●			●	●	●				●														
Championship					●				●	●																	●		
Undulating		●		●				●	●	●	●	●	●	●	●				●			●		●			●		
Cliff Top		●																	●										
Valley			●		●									●															
Hilltop			●				●																						
Downland																													
Breckland																													
Moorland																													
Heath Land	●	●						●																					
Links													●				●									●	● ●		
Wooded								●																					
Parkland	●	●	●	●	●	●	●		●	●	●	●	●		●	●	●		●		●	●	●	●	●				●
Built of Gravel																													
Built on Clay	●			●		●						●											●						
Built on Soil	●				●	●			●	●	●	●					●				●		●						●
Built on Sand	●	●	●				●	●			●	●				●							●				●		
Built on Chalk		●																											
Green Speed Slow																													
Green Speed Medium	●	●	● ●	●			●		●		● ●								●		●		●	● ●		●			
Green Speed Fast				●						●			● ● ●					●											

Course descriptions and features

Golf Club/Courses by County	HELENS BAY	HOLYWOOD	KILKEEL	KIRKISTOWN CASTLE	MAHEE ISLAND	RINGDUFFERIN: RINGDUFFERIN	SCRABO	WARRENPOINT	ASHWOODS	CASTLE HUME	ENNISKILLEN	BROWN TROUT	DERRY: DUNHUGH	DERRY: PREHEN	FAUGHAN VALLEY	FOYLE: PARKLAND	FOYLE: WOODLANDS PAR 3	PORTSTEWART: STRAND	DUNGANNON	NEWTOWNSTEWART	OMAGH	SPRINGHILL	STRABANE
Views	•	•	•		•	•	•	•	•	•	•		•	•		•	•	•	•		•	•	•
Streams										•	•					•							
Lakes									•	•	•					•	•	•					
Deep Bunkers									•														
Large Bunkers									•														
Ideal for the Elderly			•					•	•	•	•		•	•		•							•
Tends to Flood																							
Drains Well		•	•	•		•	•	•	•	•	•		•	•		•	•				•	•	
Tight	•								•	•	•												•
Short																	•						
Medium Length	•	•	•			•	•		•		•					•					•		
Long								•		•			•	•		•							•
Open		•								•			•	•	•						•		
Sheltered			•			•		•		•	•						•	•					•
Championship			•					•		•	•						•	•					•
Undulating					•	•				•	•		•	•									
Cliff Top																							
Valley										•						•							
Hilltop		•				•				•	•												
Downland																							
Breckland																							
Moorland																							
Heath Land																							
Links				•			•											•					
Wooded									•		•	•											
Parkland	•	•	•		•	•	•	•		•	•		•	•		•	•		•	•			•
Built of Gravel																							
Built on Clay	•												•	•									
Built on Soil	•	•	•				•		•							•	•		•	•			•
Built on Sand	•									•	•					•	•	•					
Built on Chalk									•														
Green Speed Slow																							
Green Speed Medium	•	•				•	•		•	•			•	•	•	•				•	•	•	
Green Speed Fast			•						•	•	•		•	•									

www.hccgolfworld.com

Course descriptions and features

Golf Club/Courses by County

Golf Club/Course	Views	Streams	Lakes	Deep Bunkers	Large Bunkers	Ideal for the Elderly	Tends to Flood	Drains Well	Tight	Short	Medium Length	Long	Open	Sheltered	Championship	Undulating	Cliff Top	Valley	Hilltop	Downland	Breckland	Moorland	Heath Land	Links	Wooded	Parkland	Built of Gravel	Built on Clay	Built on Soil	Built on Sand	Built on Chalk	Green Speed Slow	Green Speed Medium	Green Speed Fast
SCOTLAND																																		
ABERDEEN (CITY OF)																																		
CALEDONIAN																								●						●				
CRAIBSTONE	●					●				●															●	●			●	●				●
DEESIDE: HAUGHTON	●	●			●			●				●	●			●										●			●					
EAST ABERDEENSHIRE												●														●			●					●
HUNTLY	●										●															●								●
MELDRUM HOUSE											●				●											●				●			●	
MURCAR: MURCAR											●														●					●				
MURCAR: STRABATHIE											●						●													●				
NEWMACHAR: HAWKSHILL																										●				●				
PORTLETHEN	●											●				●								●		●			●					
ABERDEENSHIRE																																		
ABOYNE	●		●								●					●										●			●				●	
ALFORD	●																									●								
BALLATER	●	●									●												●											
BANCHORY	●							●																		●				●			●	
BRAEMAR	●																	●																
CRUDEN BAY											●				●									●						●				
DUFF HOUSE ROYAL						●		●	●					●		●		●								●			●					
DUFFTOWN											●			●		●							●	●		●			●				●	
FRASERBURGH: CORBIE HILL																								●						●				
FRASERBURGH: ROSEHILL																								●						●				
INCHMARLO GOLF CTRE: INCHMARLO 18 HOLE	●													●											●	●			●				●	
INSCH	●	●						●																		●			●				●	
INVERURIE	●	●			●	●		●	●		●					●									●	●		●	●				●	
KEMNAY	●					●										●									●	●							●	
KINTORE	●							●	●	●		●												●		●								
NEWBURGH-ON-YTHAN	●												●													●				●				
OLDMELDRUM	●					●		●						●		●										●			●				●	
PETERCULTER	●					●										●										●								
PETERHEAD: NEW	●															●								●		●				●				●
PETERHEAD: OLD	●																							●		●				●				●

Course descriptions and features

Golf Club/Courses by County (legend):

1. STONEHAVEN
2. TARLAIR (ROYAL)
3. TORPHINS
4. TURRIFF

ANGUS

5. ARBROATH
6. BRECHIN GOLF & SQUASH CLUB
7. CARNOUSTIE: BUDDON LINKS
8. CARNOUSTIE: BURNSIDE
9. CARNOUSTIE: CHAMPIONSHIP
10. EDZELL: EDZELL
11. EDZELL: WEST WATER
12. FORFAR
13. KIRRIEMUIR
14. LETHAM GRANGE RESORT: GLENS
15. LETHAM GRANGE RESORT: OLD
16. MONIFIETH GOLF LINKS: ASHLUDIE
17. MONIFIETH GOLF LINKS: MEDAL
18. MONTROSE LINKS TRUST: MEDAL
19. PANMURE
20. PIPERDAM GOLF

ARGYLL AND BUTE

21. CARDROSS
22. CARRADALE
23. COWAL
24. DUNAVERTY
25. GLENCRUITTEN
26. HELENSBURGH
27. INNELLAN
28. LOCH LOMOND
29. MACHRIE
30. MACHRIHANISH: MACHRIHANISH 18 HOLE
31. PORT BANNATYNE

Feature	Courses (●)
Views	1, 2, 3, 4, 6, 7, 8, 9, 10, 11, 12, 13, 14, 15, 19, 20, 21, 22, 23, 24, 25, 28, 30, 31
Streams	5, 6, 9, 12, 19, 20
Lakes	15, 19, 20, 28, 31
Deep Bunkers	6, 7, 12, 15, 19
Large Bunkers	6, 12, 19
Ideal for the Elderly	10, 11, 12, 13, 16, 17, 24, 28
Tends to Flood	1, 6
Drains Well	3, 4, 7, 8, 9, 10, 16, 21, 30, 31
Tight	1, 3, 17
Short	1, 3, 4, 7, 8, 12, 16, 23, 26, 27, 30, 31
Medium Length	5, 9, 16, 19, 20, 25
Long	10, 19
Open	6, 7, 16, 30, 31
Sheltered	6, 11, 12, 19, 21
Championship	9, 18, 19, 25
Undulating	1, 3, 19, 21, 28, 29, 30
Cliff Top	1, 2
Valley	24
Hilltop	27
Downland	
Breckland	
Moorland	12, 26, 27, 30
Heath Land	11, 12
Links	5, 7, 8, 9, 16, 17, 19, 29
Wooded	4, 6, 10, 11, 12, 16, 17, 28
Parkland	1, 2, 3, 4, 6, 10, 11, 12, 14, 21, 24
Built of Gravel	
Built on Clay	1
Built on Soil	3, 4, 6, 10, 11, 12, 18, 30
Built on Sand	2, 5, 7, 8, 9, 19, 21, 24, 29, 30
Built on Chalk	9, 17
Green Speed Slow	8, 30
Green Speed Medium	1, 3, 4, 9, 12, 16, 17, 19, 20, 23, 24, 30, 31
Green Speed Fast	5, 6, 12, 21

Course descriptions and features

Golf Club/Courses by County

The following table records, for each course, the features marked (●) in the GolfWorld Directory matrix. Features are listed down the left of the chart; courses across the bottom, grouped by county.

Feature	Courses marked (●)
Views	BALLOCHMYLE, LOUDOUN, BETH, GLASGOW GAILES, LARGS, MILLPORT, SHISKINE, WEST KILBRIDE, BELLEISLE & SEAFIELD: BELLEISLE, BELLEISLE & SEAFIELD: SEAFIELD, GIRVAN, TROON (ROYAL): OLD, TROON (ROYAL): PAR 3, TROON (ROYAL): PORTLAND, ALLOA, BRAEHEAD, DOLLAR
Streams	BALLOCHMYLE, LOUDOUN, MILLPORT, BRUNSTON CASTLE, DALMILLING, PRESTWICK, ALLOA
Lakes	BETH
Deep Bunkers	GLASGOW GAILES, MILLPORT, DOLLAR
Large Bunkers	MILLPORT, BELLEISLE & SEAFIELD: BELLEISLE, DALMILLING
Ideal for the Elderly	BALLOCHMYLE, ARDEER, GLASGOW GAILES, MILLPORT, WEST KILBRIDE
Tends to Flood	ARDEER, IRVINE
Drains Well	BETH, GLASGOW GAILES, LARGS, MILLPORT, TROON (ROYAL): OLD, BRAEHEAD, DOLLAR, MUCKHART: MUCKHART, MUCKHART: NAEMOOR
Tight	BELLEISLE & SEAFIELD: BELLEISLE, BELLEISLE & SEAFIELD: SEAFIELD
Short	BETH, MILLPORT, TROON (ROYAL): PAR 3
Medium Length	BALLOCHMYLE, ARDEER, LARGS, MILLPORT, RAVENSPARK, ROUTENBURN, SHISKINE, TROON (ROYAL): OLD, ALLOA, BRAEHEAD, DOLLAR
Long	AYRSHIRE (NORTH), BELLEISLE & SEAFIELD: BELLEISLE, GIRVAN, TROON (ROYAL): OLD, MUCKHART: MUCKHART, MUCKHART: NAEMOOR
Open	GLASGOW GAILES, IRVINE, MILLPORT, SHISKINE, WEST KILBRIDE, BELLEISLE & SEAFIELD: BELLEISLE, BELLEISLE & SEAFIELD: SEAFIELD, PRESTWICK, DOLLAR
Sheltered	SHISKINE
Championship	GLASGOW GAILES, IRVINE, WEST KILBRIDE, BELLEISLE & SEAFIELD: BELLEISLE
Undulating	BALLOCHMYLE, BELLEISLE & SEAFIELD: BELLEISLE, BELLEISLE & SEAFIELD: SEAFIELD, PRESTWICK, ALLOA, BRAEHEAD, DOLLAR, MUCKHART: MUCKHART, MUCKHART: NAEMOOR
Cliff Top	
Valley	LOUDOUN, PRESTWICK, PRESTWICK ST CUTHBERT
Hilltop	ARDEER, ROUTENBURN
Downland	
Breckland	
Moorland	BETH
Heath Land	SHISKINE
Links	GLASGOW GAILES, IRVINE, LARGS, SHISKINE, WEST KILBRIDE
Wooded	BALLOCHMYLE, LOUDOUN, RAVENSPARK, BELLEISLE & SEAFIELD: BELLEISLE, BELLEISLE & SEAFIELD: SEAFIELD, BRAEHEAD, MUCKHART: MUCKHART, MUCKHART: NAEMOOR
Parkland	BALLOCHMYLE, LOUDOUN, ARDEER, AUCHENHARVIE, BETH, LARGS, BELLEISLE & SEAFIELD: BELLEISLE, BELLEISLE & SEAFIELD: SEAFIELD, PRESTWICK ST CUTHBERT, BRAEHEAD
Built of Gravel	
Built on Clay	BALLOCHMYLE, ARDEER, RAVENSPARK, ROUTENBURN, SHISKINE, BELLEISLE & SEAFIELD: BELLEISLE, BELLEISLE & SEAFIELD: SEAFIELD, BRAEHEAD
Built on Soil	AUCHENHARVIE, LARGS, ALLOA, MUCKHART: MUCKHART, MUCKHART: NAEMOOR
Built on Sand	AUCHENHARVIE, GLASGOW GAILES, SHISKINE, WEST KILBRIDE, MUCKHART: MUCKHART, MUCKHART: NAEMOOR
Built on Chalk	
Green Speed Slow	RAVENSPARK
Green Speed Medium	BALLOCHMYLE, ARDEER, LARGS, RAVENSPARK, SHISKINE, WEST KILBRIDE, BELLEISLE & SEAFIELD: BELLEISLE, BELLEISLE & SEAFIELD: SEAFIELD, DALMILLING, ALLOA, DOLLAR
Green Speed Fast	LOUDOUN, GLASGOW GAILES, IRVINE, BELLEISLE & SEAFIELD: BELLEISLE, BELLEISLE & SEAFIELD: SEAFIELD, PRESTWICK, BRAEHEAD

County groupings (column headers):

- **AYRSHIRE (EAST):** BALLOCHMYLE, LOUDOUN
- **AYRSHIRE (NORTH):** ARDEER, AUCHENHARVIE, BETH, GLASGOW GAILES, IRVINE, KILBIRNIE PLACE, LARGS, MILLPORT, RAVENSPARK, ROUTENBURN, SHISKINE, WEST KILBRIDE
- **AYRSHIRE (SOUTH):** BELLEISLE & SEAFIELD: BELLEISLE, BELLEISLE & SEAFIELD: SEAFIELD, BRUNSTON CASTLE, DALMILLING, GIRVAN, MAYBOLE MUNICIPAL, PRESTWICK, PRESTWICK ST CUTHBERT, TROON (ROYAL): OLD, TROON (ROYAL): PAR 3, TROON (ROYAL): PORTLAND
- **CLACKMANNANSHIRE:** ALLOA, BRAEHEAD, DOLLAR, MUCKHART: MUCKHART, MUCKHART: NAEMOOR

Course descriptions and features

Golf Club/Courses by County	MUCKHART: NEW 9 HOLE	DUMFRIES AND GALLOWAY	BRIGHOUSE BAY	COLVEND	CRAIGIEKNOWES	CRICHTON	DUMFRIES & COUNTY	GALLOWAY	GATEHOUSE	KIRKCUDBRIGHT	LAGGANMORE	LOCHMABEN	LOCKERBIE	MOFFAT	NEW GALLOWAY	NEWTON STEWART	PARK TONGLAND	PINES	PORTPATRICK - DUNSKEY: DINVIN	PORTPATRICK - DUNSKEY: DUNSKEY	POWFOOT	SOLWAY LINKS	SOUTHERNESS	ST. MEDAN	STRANRAER	THORNHILL	WIGTOWN & BLADNOCH	WIGTOWNSHIRE	EDINBURGH (CITY OF)	BRAID HILLS: BRAIDS NO 1	BRAID HILLS: BRAIDS NO 2	BRUNTSFIELD GOLF CLUB	CRAIGENTINNY	CRAIGMILLAR PARK
Views				●	●	●	●	●		●	●		●	●	●	●	●	●	●	●	●	●	●	●	●	●	●			●	●	●	●	
Streams			●									●	●								●	●		●	●									
Lakes			●							●	●				●						●													
Deep Bunkers			●	●					●				●										●											
Large Bunkers						●																		●										
Ideal for the Elderly	●						●	●		●				●							●	●	●				●							●
Tends to Flood				●	●	●																												●
Drains Well							●	●	●	●	●				●						●	●	●	●										
Tight																●	●	●	●															
Short			●							●					●		●				●													
Medium Length				●	●				●	●	●			●			●				●	●		●		●	●		●				●	
Long	●																																	
Open			●	●							●				●						●	●	●	●		●		◐						
Sheltered			●						●		●					●			●															
Championship																							●											
Undulating			●	●	●		●				●			●			●						●								●	●		
Cliff Top			●																															
Valley																																		
Hilltop				●												●																		
Downland																																		
Breckland				●					●									●					●											
Moorland																●	●																	
Heath Land																●				●	●													
Links																						●	●	●	●			◐						
Wooded	●								●						●																			
Parkland	●			●			●	●	●	●	●	●				●	●										●	●	●				●	●
Built of Gravel																																		
Built on Clay													●																					●
Built on Soil	●		●	●	●	●					●		●				●	●	●	●			●									●		
Built on Sand	●					●	●															●		●				◐						
Built on Chalk																																		
Green Speed Slow																									●									
Green Speed Medium			●	●	●					●	●	●				●	●				●	●						◐		●			●	
Green Speed Fast						●										●						●	●											

Course descriptions and features

www.hcgolfworld.com

Scotland — GolfWorld Directory

The following table lists golf courses by county with a matrix of course descriptions and features. Features (columns): Views, Streams, Lakes, Deep Bunkers, Large Bunkers, Ideal for the Elderly, Tends to Flood, Drains Well, Tight, Short, Medium Length, Long, Open, Sheltered, Championship, Undulating, Cliff Top, Valley, Hilltop, Downland, Breckland, Moorland, Heath Land, Links, Wooded, Parkland, Built of Gravel, Built on Clay, Built on Soil, Built on Sand, Built on Chalk, Green Speed Slow, Green Speed Medium, Green Speed Fast.

Golf Club/Courses by County	Views	Streams	Lakes	Deep Bunkers	Large Bunkers	Ideal for the Elderly	Tends to Flood	Drains Well	Tight	Short	Medium Length	Long	Open	Sheltered	Championship	Undulating	Cliff Top	Valley	Hilltop	Downland	Breckland	Moorland	Heath Land	Links	Wooded	Parkland	Built of Gravel	Built on Clay	Built on Soil	Built on Sand	Built on Chalk	Green Speed Slow	Green Speed Medium	Green Speed Fast
DALMAHOY: EAST												●				●																		
DALMAHOY: WEST									●																								●	
LIBERTON										●									●							●								
LOTHIANBURN	●								●		●		●										●			●							●	
PRESTONFIELD	●																									●								
SILVERKNOWES	●							●																		●								
SWANSTON	●										●		●													●								●
FALKIRK																																		
BONNYBRIDGE				●				●	●														●			●							●	
FALKIRK	●	●						●					●			●										●								
POLMONT																●									●	●								
FIFE																																		
ABERDOUR	●					●		●		●			●					●								●			●				●	
ANSTRUTHER	●					●		●		●			●											●					●	●			●	
AUCHTERDERRAN								●		●			●												●	●		●					●	
BALBIRNIE PARK	●										●														●	●		●					●	
CANMORE								●		●						●										●			●			●	●	
CHARLETON: CHARLETON	●		●		●			●			●		●	●	●			●								●			●					●
CRAIL: BALCOMIE LINKS	●	●			●									●										●						●				●
CRAIL: CRAIGHEAD LINKS COURSE	●			●	●			●			●		●											●					●	●				●
CUPAR	●									●				●												●							●	
DUKES	●											●		●		●									●	●								●
DUNFERMLINE	●			●		●					●		●	●												●								●
DUNNIKIER	●					●		●			●			●		●					●					●		●					●	
ELIE GOLF	●			●	●		●	●				●	●											●						●				●
ELMWOOD	●				●									●											●	●		●						
FALKLAND	●	●									●			●		●										●			●		●		●	
KINGHORN	●				●			●				●												●						●				●
KINGSBARNS GOLF LINKS	●				●			●					●																●	●				
KIRKCALDY	●					●					●			●												●							●	
LADYBANK	●																								●	●			●				●	
LESLIE	●									●												●				●							●	
LEVEN LINKS	●	●	●			●						●	●											●						●				
LEVEN THISTLE	●					●								●										●										●

Course descriptions and features

Golf Club/Courses by County

A feature matrix (● indicates the course has the feature). Courses (columns):
LOCHGELLY, LUNDIN, NEW, PITREAVIE, SALINE, SCOTSCRAIG, SCOTTISH GOLF NATIONAL CTRE, ST. ANDREWS LINKS: BALGOVE, ST. ANDREWS LINKS: EDEN, ST. ANDREWS LINKS: JUBILEE, ST. ANDREWS LINKS: NEW, ST. ANDREWS LINKS: OLD, ST. ANDREWS LINKS: STRATHTYRUM, ST. MICHAELS, THORNTON, GLASGOW (CITY OF), ALEXANDRA, BEARSDEN, BLAIRBETH, CAMPSIE, DOUGLAS PARK, EAST RENFREWSHIRE, EASTWOOD, ESPORTA DOUGALSTON, KIRKHILL, KNIGHTSWOOD, LENZIE, WESTERWOOD, WINDYHILL, HIGHLANDS, ALNESS, BOAT OF GARTEN, BRORA, CARNEGIE

Feature	Courses marked ●
Views	LUNDIN, NEW, PITREAVIE, SALINE, SCOTSCRAIG, BALGOVE, EDEN, JUBILEE, NEW, OLD, STRATHTYRUM, ST. MICHAELS, ALEXANDRA, BEARSDEN, BLAIRBETH, LENZIE, WESTERWOOD, WINDYHILL, ALNESS, BOAT OF GARTEN, BRORA
Streams	LOCHGELLY, LUNDIN, NEW, PITREAVIE, SALINE, SCOTSCRAIG, CARNEGIE
Lakes	EDEN, EASTWOOD, KIRKHILL
Deep Bunkers	LOCHGELLY, LUNDIN, NEW, PITREAVIE, SCOTSCRAIG, THORNTON, BRORA
Large Bunkers	LUNDIN, NEW, SCOTSCRAIG
Ideal for the Elderly	LOCHGELLY, LUNDIN, NEW, PITREAVIE, SALINE, SCOTSCRAIG, ALEXANDRA, KNIGHTSWOOD, ALNESS
Tends to Flood	
Drains Well	LOCHGELLY, LUNDIN, NEW, PITREAVIE, ALEXANDRA, EAST RENFREWSHIRE, EASTWOOD, ESPORTA DOUGALSTON, ALNESS, BRORA, CARNEGIE
Tight	BRORA, CARNEGIE
Short	NEW, JUBILEE, THORNTON, ALEXANDRA
Medium Length	LOCHGELLY, LUNDIN, PITREAVIE, SALINE, BEARSDEN, DOUGLAS PARK, EAST RENFREWSHIRE, KNIGHTSWOOD, BRORA
Long	
Open	LOCHGELLY, LUNDIN, NEW, PITREAVIE, SALINE, ALEXANDRA, DOUGLAS PARK, EAST RENFREWSHIRE, KNIGHTSWOOD
Sheltered	PITREAVIE, SALINE, THORNTON
Championship	LUNDIN, SALINE, NEW, OLD, CARNEGIE
Undulating	LUNDIN, PITREAVIE, SALINE, STRATHTYRUM, ST. MICHAELS, ALEXANDRA, BEARSDEN, DOUGLAS PARK, WINDYHILL, BOAT OF GARTEN, BRORA
Cliff Top	
Valley	LOCHGELLY
Hilltop	NEW, PITREAVIE, SALINE
Downland	
Breckland	LOCHGELLY
Moorland	EASTWOOD, LENZIE, WINDYHILL
Heath Land	SCOTSCRAIG, ALNESS
Links	LUNDIN, NEW, SCOTSCRAIG, EDEN, JUBILEE, NEW, OLD, BRORA, CARNEGIE
Wooded	LOCHGELLY, NEW, THORNTON
Parkland	LOCHGELLY, STRATHTYRUM, ST. MICHAELS, THORNTON, ALEXANDRA, BEARSDEN, BLAIRBETH, DOUGLAS PARK, EASTWOOD, KIRKHILL, KNIGHTSWOOD, LENZIE, ALNESS
Built of Gravel	
Built on Clay	NEW, PITREAVIE, ALEXANDRA, DOUGLAS PARK
Built on Soil	LOCHGELLY, NEW, PITREAVIE, EASTWOOD, KNIGHTSWOOD
Built on Sand	LUNDIN, NEW, EDEN, JUBILEE, NEW, OLD, ALEXANDRA, BRORA, CARNEGIE
Built on Chalk	
Green Speed Slow	EASTWOOD
Green Speed Medium	LOCHGELLY, PITREAVIE, SALINE, THORNTON, DOUGLAS PARK, EAST RENFREWSHIRE, KNIGHTSWOOD, ALNESS
Green Speed Fast	LUNDIN, NEW, SALINE, SCOTSCRAIG, BEARSDEN, BRORA

www.hccgolfworld.com

Course descriptions and features

Golf Club/Courses by County

Feature	CARRBRIDGE	DURNESS	FORTROSE & ROSEMARKIE	GAIRLOCH	GOLSPIE	INVERGORDON	INVERNESS	ISLE OF SKYE	LOCH NESS	MUIR OF ORD	NAIRN: NAIRN	NAIRN: NEWTON	NEWTONMORE	REAY	STRATHPEFFER SPA	TAIN	THURSO	ULLAPOOL	INVERCLYDE	GOUROCK	WHINHILL	ISLE OF ARRAN	LOCHRANZA GOLF	LANARKSHIRE (NORTH)	EASTER MOFFAT	PALACERIGG	LANARKSHIRE (SOUTH)	CARNWATH	KAMES GOLF: KAMES	KAMES GOLF: MOUSE VALLEY	LANARK: OLD	LOTHIAN (EAST)	CASTLE PARK	DUNBAR
Views	●	●	●	●	●	●	●			●		●	●	●	●	●	●		●	●	●		●		●				●	●		●		●
Streams		●					●									●	●		●	●			●		●	●				●	●			
Lakes																														●				
Deep Bunkers		●																												●				
Large Bunkers		●																								●								
Ideal for the Elderly							●	●																										
Tends to Flood																				●														
Drains Well		●					●									●					●						●			●			●	●
Tight		●					●																											
Short		●	●																	●														
Medium Length							●							●													●			●	●	●		
Long																				●									●	●	●			●
Open		●	●		●						●	●	●	●						●									●	●				●
Sheltered								●	●								●												●					●
Championship							●																											●
Undulating		●											●				●	●	●	●										●				●
Cliff Top																																		
Valley																																		
Hilltop														●						●														
Downland																																		
Breckland																																		
Moorland		●							●				●								●													
Heath Land	●		●							●																								
Links		●	●	●							●	●		●			●																	●
Wooded				●	●	●															●	●												
Parkland	●			●	●	●	●		●			●				●	●	●						●		●	●		●					
Built of Gravel																																		
Built on Clay																				●					●									
Built on Soil							●	●													●												●	
Built on Sand		●	●	●	●							●																	●	●	●			●
Built on Chalk																																		
Green Speed Slow																																		
Green Speed Medium		●						●											●	●						●			●	●				
Green Speed Fast						●							●	●				●											●	●		●	●	

Course descriptions and features

Golf Club/Courses by County	GLEN	GULLANE: GULLANE NO. 1	HADDINGTON	LUFFNESS	MUIRFIELD	MUSSELBURGH (ROYAL)	MUSSELBURGH LINKS	NORTH BERWICK	WHITEKIRK	LOTHIAN (MID)	KINGS ACRE	MUSSELBURGH	LOTHIAN (WEST)	BRIDGECASTLE	BRIDGEND	DEER PARK	GREENBURN	LINLITHGOW	WEST LOTHIAN	MORAY	BUCKPOOL	CULLEN	FORRES	GARMOUTH & KINGSTON	GRANTOWN-ON-SPEY	HOPEMAN	KINLOSS: KINLOSS 1	KINLOSS: KINLOSS 2	MORAY: NEW	MORAY: OLD	ROTHES	STRATHLENE	PERTH AND KINROSS	CRAIGIE HILL
Views	●	●						●		●		●		●				●	●		●	●	●		●	●	●	●	●		●			●
Streams										●					●								●	●										
Lakes										●				●																				
Deep Bunkers						●																				●			●	●				
Large Bunkers	●									●																								
Ideal for the Elderly			●	●		●										●		●		●											●			
Tends to Flood			●									●																			●			
Drains Well	●	●		●	●		●	●	●		●					●		●	●						●		●	●	●					
Tight					●									●	●		●																	
Short												●		●			●			●														●
Medium Length	●		●					●		●		●					●		●				●		●	●	●	●	●					
Long		●										●				●																		
Open	●					●	●											●													●			
Sheltered			●	●						●																								
Championship				●		●	●	●	●	●					●											●	●							
Undulating									●				●	●		●										●	●	●						
Cliff Top																										●								
Valley													●																					
Hilltop								●										●													●			
Downland																																		
Breckland																																		
Moorland																	●																	
Heath Land								●							●																			
Links	●	●		●	●		●	●												●	●		●								●			
Wooded										●													●											
Parkland	●		●							●	●		●		●		●		●	●			●		●		●			●				●
Built of Gravel																																		
Built on Clay																																		
Built on Soil															●		●	●							●		●				●			
Built on Sand	●	●				●	●								●					●		●	●	●										
Built on Chalk																																		
Green Speed Slow																																		
Green Speed Medium		●				●		●				●		●	●		●	●	●			●		●	●	●	●							
Green Speed Fast	●	●					●			●																					●			

Course descriptions and features

Feature \ Golf Club/Courses by County	CRIEFF: DORNOCK	CRIEFF: FERNTOWER	DUNKELD	GLENEAGLES: KINGS	GLENEAGLES: PGA CENTENARY	GLENEAGLES: QUEENS	GLENISLA	KENMORE	KILLIN	LYNEDOCH & MURRAYSHALL: LYNEDOCH	LYNEDOCH & MURRAYSHALL: LYNEDOCH & MURRAYSHALL	MILNATHORT	MUTHILL	STRATHMORE GOLF CTRE: LEITFIE LINKS	STRATHMORE GOLF CTRE: RANNALEROCH	TAYMOUTH CASTLE	COCHRANE CASTLE	ELDERSLIE	GLEDDOCH	LOCHWINNOCH	PAISLEY	RALSTON	RANFURLY	CARDRONA	DUNS	EYEMOUTH	GALASHIELS	HAWICK	HIRSEL	INNERLEITHEN	KELSO	LAUDER
Views	•	•	•	•	•	•	•	•	•	•	•		•	•	•	•	•	•	•	•	•	•		•	•	•	•	•	•	•		•
Streams							•							•	•									•	•	•			•			
Lakes					•																			•	•							
Deep Bunkers					•								•									•		•					•			
Large Bunkers					•																											
Ideal for the Elderly							•						•	•										•					•	•		
Tends to Flood																													•			
Drains Well			•									•	•	•	•	•			•			•										
Tight																					•	•										
Short	•	•											•	•																		
Medium Length			•				•									•		•	•					•		•						
Long																			•	•	•			•		•						
Open			•																•	•	•			•								
Sheltered															•	•			•					•					•	•		
Championship				•	•	•																				•				•		
Undulating								•		•	•	•			•	•		•	•	•	•	•	•	•		•						
Cliff Top																																
Valley															•	•													•	•		
Hilltop																		•	•									•	•			
Downland																																•
Breckland																																
Moorland						•																•	•									
Heath Land			•																	•							•					
Links																										•						
Wooded									•	•	•			•		•		•						•								
Parkland	•	•	•			•		•	•	•	•	•			•		•	•	•	•	•			•	•	•	•		•	•	•	•
Built of Gravel																																
Built on Clay																						•							•			
Built on Soil			•				•					•	•	•	•			•			•		•		•	•						
Built on Sand			•																													
Built on Chalk																																
Green Speed Slow																													•			
Green Speed Medium			•				•						•	•		•		•	•	•	•	•	•		•	•			•	•		
Green Speed Fast														•										•	•							

Section headers within columns: RENFREWSHIRE (preceding COCHRANE CASTLE … RANFURLY); SCOTTISH BORDERS (preceding CARDRONA … LAUDER)

Course descriptions and features

Golf Club/Courses by County	MELROSE	MINTO	NEWCASTLETON	PEEBLES	ROXBURGHE	RUTHERFORD CASTLE	SELKIRK	TORWOODLEE	WEST LINTON	STIRLING	ABERFOYLE	BUCHANAN CASTLE	WESTERN ISLES	STORNOWAY
Views	●	●	●	●		●	●	●	●		●			●
Streams				●		●								
Lakes						●						●		
Deep Bunkers					●			●						
Large Bunkers								●						
Ideal for the Elderly									●					
Tends to Flood														
Drains Well				●		●	●	●	●					
Tight														●
Short														●
Medium Length				●		●	●	●	●					
Long					●									
Open						●	●	●	●					
Sheltered				●				●						
Championship			●	●	●									
Undulating				●				●	●					●
Cliff Top														
Valley														
Hilltop		●												
Downland														
Breckland														
Moorland									●					
Heath Land							●							
Links														
Wooded	●				●						●	●		●
Parkland		●		●	●	●		●			●	●		●
Built of Gravel														
Built on Clay														
Built on Soil				●				●						●
Built on Sand									●					
Built on Chalk														
Green Speed Slow														
Green Speed Medium				●			●	●						●
Green Speed Fast					●			●						

Course descriptions and features

Golf Club/Courses by County

Feature	GROVE	CASTELL HEIGHTS: CASTELL HEIGHTS	CASTELL HEIGHTS: MOUNTAIN LAKES	OAKDALE	CARMARTHEN	CILGWYN	DERLLYS COURT	GARNANT PARK	GLYN ABBEY	ABERYSTWYTH	BORTH & YNYSLAS	CAPEL BANGOR	CARDIGAN	CLIFF HOTEL	CWMRHYDNEUADD	PENRHOS: ACADEMY	ABERGELE	BETWS-Y-COED	CONWY	NORTH WALES	OLD COLWYN	PENMAENMAWR	RHOS-ON-SEA	BRYN MORFYDD: DUKES	DENBIGH	KINMEL PARK GOLF	PRESTATYN
Views	●			●	●	●		●	●		●	●	●		●		●	●	●	●		●	●	●	●		
Streams						●		●							●								●				
Lakes	●		●	●		●		●	●						●								●				
Deep Bunkers																											●
Large Bunkers	●							●	●		●	●															
Ideal for the Elderly	●				●		●							●			●							●			●
Tends to Flood																											
Drains Well	●			●	●		●	●			●	●	●	●	●				●	●		●	●				●
Tight											●	●		●					●	●			●				
Short														●							●	●					
Medium Length	●				●	●		●	●		●	●	●	●					●	●			●		●		
Long																											
Open					●			●	●		●	●	●						●			●					
Sheltered				●	●								●	●													
Championship			●										●	●			●	●	●								●
Undulating	●			●						●			●	●											●		
Cliff Top													●	●													
Valley						●																					
Hilltop																											
Downland																											
Breckland																											
Moorland																											
Heath Land					●																						
Links											●		●	●					●	●			●				●
Wooded					●							●					●										
Parkland	●	●		●		●	●					●			●	●	●	●				●		●	●	●	
Built of Gravel																											
Built on Clay				●											●	●	●					●					
Built on Soil							●	●				●				●									●		
Built on Sand				●									●	●	●	●						●					●
Built on Chalk																											
Green Speed Slow						●										●											
Green Speed Medium					●								●			●	●			●					●		
Green Speed Fast	●												●	●	●	●											●

Course descriptions and features

Golf Club/Courses by County

Feature	RHUDDLAN	RHYL	RUTHIN-PWLLGLAS	ST. MELYD	VALE OF LLANGOLLEN	*FLINTSHIRE* ALLT-GYMBYD	HOLYWELL	KINSALE	MOLD	NORTHOP	OLD PADESWOOD	PADESWOOD & BUCKLEY	WEPRE	*GLAMORGAN (VALE OF)* ABERDARE	CASTLECOCH	COTTRELL PARK: BUTTON	COTTRELL PARK: MACKINTOSH	CREIGIAU	MERTHYR TYDFIL	PETERSTONE LAKES	ST. ANDREWS MAJOR	VALE OF GLAMORGAN: HENSOL	VALE OF GLAMORGAN: THE LAKE	WENVOE CASTLE	WHITCHURCH	*GWYNEDD* ABERSOCH	BALA	CAERNARFON (ROYAL TOWN OF)	DOLGELLAU	FAIRBOURNE	HARLECH
Views	●	●	●	●	●	●	●	●	●	●	●	●	●	●	●			●	●	●	●	●	●			●	●	●	●	●	●
Streams	●					●		●			●	●	●									●	●					●			
Lakes	●									●	●	●								●	●		●								
Deep Bunkers	●																														
Large Bunkers	●					●	●													●								●			
Ideal for the Elderly	●			●	●	●					●						●											●		●	
Tends to Flood					●						●																			●	
Drains Well	●	●																													●
Tight																															
Short										●			●						●									●		●	
Medium Length			●	●		●	●				●			●	●									●				●			
Long	●	●				●					●											●									●
Open	●	●				●								●	●	●				●	●		●	●				●			●
Sheltered			●	●		●							●																		
Championship	●			●		●				●	●	●						●				●									
Undulating			●		●	●		●						●														●			
Cliff Top																															
Valley						●		●																							
Hilltop										●	●																				
Downland																															
Breckland				●							●																				
Moorland											●																				
Heath Land																															
Links		●				●	●												●							●				●	●
Wooded	●										●	●																			
Parkland	●		●	●	●	●		●		●	●	●	●	●	●	●	●	●	●	●	●	●		●		●	●	●	●		
Built of Gravel																															
Built on Clay	●			●		●								●			●		●	●								●			
Built on Soil	●		●			●					●	●	●							●					●						
Built on Sand	●											●				●	●			●											●
Built on Chalk																															
Green Speed Slow																														●	
Green Speed Medium	●			●	●	●		●						●	●	●	●											●		●	●
Green Speed Fast		●								●		●			●				●					●							

Wales

www.hccgolfworld.com

Course descriptions and features

Golf Club/Courses by County

Feature	ANGLESEY	BARON HILL	BULL BAY	PRINCE'S	STORWS WEN	ALICE SPRINGS: QUEENS	DEWSTOW: DEWSTOW	MONMOUTH	MONMOUTHSHIRE	PONTYPOOL	RAGLAN PARC	ROLLS OF MONMOUTH	SHIRENEWTON	ST. PIERRE: MATHERN	ST. PIERRE: OLD	WERNDDU	WOODLAKE PARK	EARLSWOOD	LAKESIDE	NEATH	CAERLEON	CELTIC MANOR: COLDRA WOODS	CELTIC MANOR: WENTWOOD HILLS	LLANWERN	TREDEGAR PARK	DAWN 'TIL DUSK	HAVERFORDWEST	HERONS BROOK: KINGS	HERONS BROOK: QUEENS
Views	●	●	●	●	●	●	●	●	●	●	●	●	●	●	●	●	●	●	●	●					●			●	●
Streams	●	●		●	●	●	●				●	●	●			●		●	●		●							●	
Lakes				●	●	●	●				●		●	●	●	●		●	●									●	●
Deep Bunkers							●					●		●					●								●		
Large Bunkers									●	●	●								●					●			●		●
Ideal for the Elderly						●				●			●					●											
Tends to Flood								●	●	●																			
Drains Well						●	●			●	●	●						●	●										
Tight																													
Short																			●					●				●	●
Medium Length				●		●	●	●	●		●					●		●		●			●	●			●		
Long											●														●				
Open						●	●	●		●	●			●	●			●		●					●				
Sheltered						●			●		●			●		●													
Championship													●										●						
Undulating				●		●	●	●	●	●	●	●	●			●	●	●		●					●		●	●	●
Cliff Top								●																					
Valley							●					●																	
Hilltop							●		●		●					●			●										
Downland																													
Breckland																						●							
Moorland																													
Heath Land	●		●														●												
Links	●															●													
Wooded				●			●	●				●			●			●		●							●		
Parkland		●		●	●	●	●	●		●		●	●	●	●		●		●				●		●	●	●	●	●
Built of Gravel																													
Built on Clay							●	●		●	●	●									●						●		
Built on Soil				●		●	●		●		●					●		●	●							●			
Built on Sand							●		●		●					●	●												
Built on Chalk																													
Green Speed Slow																													
Green Speed Medium				●		●	●		●	●	●	●	●	●	●			●					●			●	●	●	
Green Speed Fast			●				●										●	●	●	●				●			●		

Course descriptions and features

Golf Club/Courses by County	NEWPORT	PRISKILLY	SOUTH PEMBROKE	ST. DAVIDS	TENBY	TREFLOYNE	POWYS	BUILTH WELLS	KNIGHTON	LLANDRINDOD WELLS	ST. GILES	WELSH BORDER GOLF COMPLEX	WELSHPOOL	RHONDDA CYNON TAFF	MOUNTAIN ASH	RHONDDA	SWANSEA	ALLT-Y-GRABAN	CLYNE	FAIRWOOD PARK	GOWER	LANGLAND BAY	MORRISTON	PENNARD	TORFAEN	GREEN MEADOW	WREXHAM	CHIRK: CHIRK	CLAYS GOLF CTRE	MOSS VALLEY	PLASSEY
Views	●	●	●	●	●	●		●	●			●	●		●				●	●	●	●	●	●		●	●		●	●	●
Streams						●		●															●						●	●	●
Lakes			●			●														●						●	●		●	●	
Deep Bunkers					●															●						●			●		
Large Bunkers																				●											
Ideal for the Elderly	●		●	●		●		●																							
Tends to Flood												●																			
Drains Well	●	●	●	●										●					●	●		●	●			●	●		●	●	
Tight				●	●											●	●												●	●	
Short									●						●														●		●
Medium Length	●	●	●	●	●	●													●	●		●	●			●			●		
Long																			●	●											
Open			●											●					●	●		●				●			●	●	●
Sheltered		●																		●				●						●	
Championship																				●							●				
Undulating	●	●	●			●								●					●	●				●		●			●		
Cliff Top		●												●															●		
Valley														●																●	
Hilltop														●					●							●					
Downland																															
Breckland																															
Moorland									●					●	●	●			●												
Heath Land	●												●																		
Links			●	●	●				●											●			●								
Wooded					●																								●		
Parkland		●	●			●		●											●	●	●	●	●			●			●	●	●
Built of Gravel																															
Built on Clay		●												●							●					●					
Built on Soil		●		●	●									●					●	●	●					●			●	●	●
Built on Sand	●		●	●														●	●												
Built on Chalk																															
Green Speed Slow														●																	
Green Speed Medium	●	●			●	●													●	●		●							●	●	●
Green Speed Fast		●	●	●															●	●				●		●			●	●	

SECTION 5

This section allows you to search for courses by their designer/designers. Names are listed alphabetically by designer surname.

e.g Jones
Robert Trent Jones

For further information about each club refer to the detailed profile in Section 1, or search for specific details in other sections.

ABERCROMBY

MILL HILL
(Mill Hill), London (Greater), England
Year Built: 1925
Designer: J F Abercromby, Harry Shapland Colt

ADAMS

COWGLEN
(Cowglen), Glasgow (City of), Scotland
Designer: David Adams, James Braid

TOBERMORY
(Tobermory), Argyll and Bute, Scotland
Designer: David Adams

ADAMSON

ALLT-GYMBYD
(Allt-Gwmbyd 9 Hole), Flintshire, Wales
Year Built: 1996
Designer: W Adamson

CARUS GREEN
(Carus Green), Cumbria, England
Year Built: 1995
Designer: W Adamson

CASTERTON
(Casterton), Cumbria, England
Year Built: 1992
Designer: W Adamson

CHERRY BURTON
(Cherry Burton), Yorkshire (East), England
Year Built: 1993
Designer: W Adamson

FARDEW
(Farden), Yorkshire (West), England
Year Built: 1992
Designer: W Adamson

ROBIN HOOD
(Robin Hood), Yorkshire (South), England
Year Built: 1995
Designer: W Adamson

ROMANBY
(Romanby), Yorkshire (North), England
Designer: W Adamson

AINSWORTH

FOYLE
(Parkland), County Londonderry, Northern Ireland
Year Built: 1994
Designer: Frank Ainsworth

FOYLE
(Woodlands Par 3), County Londonderry, Northern Ireland
Year Built: 1993
Designer: Frank Ainsworth

GRACEHILL
(Gracehill), County Antrim, Northern Ireland
Year Built: 1995
Designer: Frank Ainsworth

RADISSON ROE PARK
(Radisson Roe Park), County Londonderry, Northern Ireland
Designer: Frank Ainsworth

RINGDUFFERIN
(Ringdufferin), County Down, Northern Ireland
Year Built: 1993
Designer: Frank Ainsworth

ALISON

BATH
(Bath), Bath & Somerset (North East), England
Designer: Charles Hugh Alison, Harry Shapland Colt

KINGSTHORPE
(Kingsthorpe), Northamptonshire, England
Year Built: 1914
Designer: Charles Hugh Alison

KNOCK
(Knock), County Antrim, Northern Ireland
Year Built: 1921
Designer: Charles Hugh Alison, Harry Shapland Colt, Alistair MacKenzie

THORNDON PARK
(Thorndon Park), Essex, England
Designer: Charles Hugh Alison, Harry Shapland Colt

TRENTHAM
(Trentham), Staffordshire, England
Designer: Charles Hugh Alison, Harry Shapland Colt

TRURO
(Truro), Cornwall, England
Year Built: 1937
Designer: Charles Hugh Alison, Harry Shapland Colt, J S F Morrison

WHITBURN
(Whitburn), Tyne And Wear, England
Designer: Charles Hugh Alison, Harry Shapland Colt, J S F Morrison

YEOVIL
(Newton), Somerset, England
Designer: Charles Hugh Alison, Herbert Fowler

ALLEN

MOORE PLACE
(Moore Place), Surrey, England
Year Built: 1926
Designer: Harry Vardon, David Allen, Nick Gadd

ALLISS

ASTON WOOD
(Aston Wood), Midlands (West), England
Year Built: 1994
Designer: Peter Alliss, Clive Clarke

BELFRY
(Brabazon), Midlands (West), England
Year Built: 1998
Designer: P Alliss, D Thomas

BELFRY
(Derby), Midlands (West), England
Year Built: 1977
Designer: Peter Alliss, David Thomas

BELFRY
(PGA National), Midlands (West), England
Year Built: 1997
Designer: Peter Alliss, D Thomas

BELTON PARK
(Ancaster), Lincolnshire, England
Year Built: 1890
Designer: Peter Alliss, John P Williams

BELTON PARK
(Belmont), Lincolnshire, England
Designer: Peter Alliss, John P Williams

BLAIRGOWRIE
(Lansdowne), Perth And Kinross, Scotland
Designer: Peter Alliss, James Braid, Tom Morris, David Thomas

BLAIRGOWRIE
(Rosemount), Perth And Kinross, Scotland
Designer: Peter Alliss, James Braid, Tom Morris, David Thomas

BLAIRGOWRIE
(Wee), Perth And Kinross, Scotland
Designer: Peter Alliss, James Braid, Tom Morris, David Thomas

BROCKET HALL
(Melbourne), Hertfordshire, England
Year Built: 1992
Designer: Peter Alliss, Clive Clark

BRYN MORFYDD
(Duchess), Denbighshire, Wales
Year Built: 1992
Designer: Peter Alliss, Duncan Muirhead

BRYN MORFYDD
(Dukes), Denbighshire, Wales
Year Built: 1992
Designer: Peter Alliss, Duncan Muirhead

CAMBRIDGE MERIDIAN
(Cambridge Meridian), Cambridgeshire, England
Year Built: 1994
Designer: Peter Alliss, Clive Clark

CAMS HALL ESTATE GOLF CLUB
(Creek), Hampshire, England
Year Built: 1992
Designer: Peter Alliss, Clive Clark

CAMS HALL ESTATE GOLF CLUB
(Park), Hampshire, England
Year Built: 1992
Designer: Peter Alliss, Clive Clark

CHOBHAM
(Chobham), Surrey, England
Year Built: 1993
Designer: Peter Alliss, Clive Clark

COLVEND
(Colvend), Dumfries And Galloway, Scotland
Year Built: 1985
Designer: Peter Alliss, David Thomas

DEER PARK
(Deer Park), Lothian (West), Scotland
Year Built: 1978
Designer: Peter Alliss, David Thomas

DEWSBURY DISTRICT
(Dewsbury District), Yorkshire (West),
England
Designer: Peter Alliss, Tom Morris

DUMMER
(Dummer), Hampshire, England
Designer: Peter Alliss, Clive Clark

HERONS REACH
(Herons Reach), Lancashire, England
Designer: P Alliss, Clive Clark

HESSLE
(Hessle), Yorkshire (East), England
Designer: Peter Alliss, David Thomas

HILL VALLEY
(East), Shropshire, England
Designer: Peter Alliss, David Thomas

HILL VALLEY
(West), Shropshire, England
Designer: Peter Alliss, David Thomas

HURTMORE
(Hurtmore), Surrey, England
Year Built: 1992
Designer: Peter Alliss, Clive Clark

KING'S LYNN
(King's Lynn), Norfolk, England
Year Built: 1972
Designer: Peter Alliss, David Thomas

MANOR HOUSE
(The Manor House at Castle Combe),
Wiltshire, England
Year Built: 1992
Designer: Peter Alliss, Clive Clark

MILFORD GOLF CLUB
(Milford), Surrey, England
Year Built: 1993
Designer: Peter Alliss, Clive Clark

MILL GREEN GOLF CLUB
(Mill Green), Hertfordshire, England
Year Built: 1993
Designer: Peter Alliss, Clive Clark

NEWMACHAR
(Hawkshill), Aberdeen (City of), Scotland
Year Built: 1990
Designer: Peter Alliss, David Thomas

NEWMACHAR
(Swailend), Aberdeen (City of), Scotland
Year Built: 1990
Designer: Peter Alliss, David Thomas

OLD THORNS
(Old Thorns), Hampshire, England
Year Built: 1982
**Designer: Peter Alliss, Commander J
Harris**

PARC
(Parc), Newport, Wales
Designer: T F Hicks, Peter Alliss

PYRFORD GOLF CLUB
(Pyrford), Surrey, England
Year Built: 1993
Designer: Peter Alliss, Clive Clark

SOUTH WINCHESTER
(South Winchester), Hampshire, England

Year Built: 1993
Designer: Peter Alliss, David Thomas

TELFORD
(Telford), Shropshire, England
Year Built: 1975
Designer: Peter Alliss, David Thomas

THORPE WOOD
(Thorpe Wood), Cambridgeshire, England
Year Built: 1975
Designer: Peter Alliss, David Thomas

TREVOSE
(New), Cornwall, England
**Designer: Peter Alliss, T Bennett, P
Gannon**

TYTHERINGTON
(The Tytherington Club), Cheshire, England
Year Built: 1986
Designer: Patrick Dawson, Peter Alliss

WILTSHIRE
(The Wiltshire), Wiltshire, England
Year Built: 1991
Designer: Peter Alliss, Clive Clark

WOBURN
(Marquess), Buckinghamshire, England
Year Built: 2000
Designer: Peter Alliss, Ross McMurry

WOODSPRING
(Avon), Bristol, England
Year Built: 1994
**Designer: Peter Alliss, Clive Clarke,
Donald Steel**

WOODSPRING
(Brunel), Bristol, England
**Designer: Peter Alliss, Clive Clarke,
Donald Steel**

WOODSPRING
(Severn), Bristol, England
**Designer: Peter Alliss, Clive Clarke,
Donald Steel**

AMER

CUCKFIELD
(Cuckfield), Sussex (West), England
Designer: D Amer, A J Pomsford

ANDERSON

CRAIGIE HILL
(Craigie Hill), Perth And Kinross, Scotland
Year Built: 1911
**Designer: Jamie Anderson, William
Fernie**

ST. ANDREWS LINKS
(Old), Fife, Scotland
**Designer: D Anderson, A MacKenzie, Tom
Morris**

ANDREWS

BETHUNE PARK
(Calderfields), London (Greater), England
Year Built: 1930
Designer: Colin Andrews

INSCH
(Insch), Aberdeenshire, Scotland

Year Built: 1980
Designer: Glen Andrews

ARMSTRONG

WHITEHEAD
(Whitehead), County Antrim, Northern
Ireland
Year Built: 1975
Designer: A B Armstrong

ASHTON

EASTBOURNE GOLFING PARK
(Eastbourne Golfing Park), Sussex (East),
England
Year Built: 1991
Designer: David Ashton

ASTBURY

POULTON LE FYLDE
(Poulton Le Fylde), Lancashire, England
Designer: E Astbury

ASTILL

DORSET HEIGHTS
(Dorset Heights), Dorset, England
Designer: David Astill

AUCHTERLONIE

CAMPSIE
(Campsie), Glasgow (City of), Scotland
Year Built: 1897
Designer: William Auchterlonie

LAMLASH
(Lamlash), Isle of Arran, Scotland
Designer: William Auchterlonie

MILNGAVIE
(Milngavie), Glasgow (City of), Scotland
Designer: William Auchterlonie

RANFURLY CASTLE
(Ranfurly Castle), Renfrewshire, Scotland
Designer: W Auchterlomie, A Kirkcaldy

ST. FILLANS
(St Fillans), Perth and Kinross, Scotland
Year Built: 1903
Designer: William Auchterlonie

BACON

DUNGANNON
(Dungannon), County Tyrone, Northern
Ireland
Year Built: 1890
Designer: S Bacon

BADHAM

LIBBATON
(Libbaton), Devon, England
Designer: Badham

BAILEY

POTTERGATE
(Pottergate), Lincolnshire, England
Year Built: 1993
Designer: Mr Bailey

BAILIE

LARNE
(Larne), County Antrim, Northern Ireland

Year Built: 1894
Designer: G L Bailie

BAIN

🏌 **EYEMOUTH**
(Eyemouth), Scottish Borders, Scotland
Year Built: 1997
Designer: J R Bain

BAKER

🏌 **HIMLEY HALL GOLF CTRE**
(Himley Hall Golf Ctre), Midlands (West),
England
Designer: A Baker

BALDOCK

🏌 **HAWKHURST**
(Hawkhurst), Kent, England
Year Built: 1968
Designer: R Baldock

BALDWIN

🏌 **CLEOBURY MORTIMER**
(Deer park), Shropshire, England
Designer: Ray Baldwin

🏌 **CLEOBURY MORTIMER**
(Foxes Run), Shropshire, England
Designer: Ray Baldwin

BALL

🏌 **LEASOWE**
(Leasowe), Merseyside, England
Year Built: 1812
Designer: John Ball

BALLESTEROS

🏌 **WESTERWOOD**
(Westerwood), Glasgow (City of), Scotland
Year Built: 1989
Designer: S Ballesteros, Thomas

BANCROFT

🏌 **MALTON**
(Malton), Hertfordshire, England
Year Built: 1993
Designer: Bruce Critchley, Peter Bancroft

BANKS

🏌 **OAST PARK**
(Oastpark), Kent, England
Designer: J D Banks

BARLOW

🏌 **CAERWYS NINE OF CLUBS**
(Caerwys Nine Of Clubs), Flintshire, Wales
Designer: Eleanor Barlow

BARNES

🏌 **WEST CHILTINGTON**
(West Chiltington), Sussex (West), England
Year Built: 1988
Designer: Brian Barnes, Max Faulkner

BARNETT

🏌 **BURGHILL VALLEY**
(Burghill Valley), Herefordshire, England
Designer: M Barnett

BARRIE

🏌 **STOCKPORT**
(Stockport), Cheshire, England
Designer: P Barrie, A Herd

BARRON

🏌 **STRATHMORE GOLF CTRE**
(Leitfie Links), Perth And Kinross, Scotland
Year Built: 1994
Designer: Jeremy Barron, Daniel Scott

BARROW

🏌 **DALMALLY**
(Dalmally), Argyll and Bute, Scotland
Designer: Barrow, MacFarlane

BEARD

🏌 **HENNERTON**
(Hennerton), Berkshire, England
Year Built: 1992
Designer: D Beard

BENNETT

🏌 **TREVOSE**
(New), Cornwall, England
Designer: Peter Alliss, T Bennett, P Gannon

BENWELL

🏌 **AYLESBURY**
(Aylesbury), Buckinghamshire, England
Year Built: 1991
Designer: T S Benwell

BEVAN

🏌 **AUSTIN LODGE**
(Austin Lodge), Kent, England
Year Built: 1991
Designer: P Bevan, Mike Walsh

BIDWELL

🏌 **HIGH LODGE**
(High Lodge), Suffolk, England
Year Built: 1998
Designer: John Bidwell

BIELENBERG

🏌 **LUTTRELLSTOWN CASTLE**
(Luttrellstown Castle), County Dublin,
Ireland
Designer: N Bielenberg

BILLCLIFFE

🏌 **STOCKS HOTEL**
(Stocks Hotel &), Hertfordshire, England
Designer: Mike Billcliffe

BLAIR

🏌 **ABERDELGHY**
(Aberdelghy), County Antrim, Northern
Ireland
Designer: Alec Blair

BLAKE

🏌 **BISHOPSWOOD**
(Bishopswood), Hampshire, England
Designer: G Blake, M Phillips

🏌 **LEA MARSTON**
(Lea Marston), Midlands (West), England
Designer: J R Blake

🏌 **UPAVON**
(Upavon), Wiltshire, England
Year Built: 1995
Designer: Richard Blake

BLUNDEN

🏌 **RUSPER**
(Rusper), Surrey, England
Year Built: 1992
Designer: Tony Blunden, Hawtree

BODDINGTON

🏌 **WATERHALL**
(Waterhall), Sussex (East), England
Year Built: 1923
Designer: Boddington

BOLT

🏌 **CRICKLADE**
(Cricklade), Wiltshire, England
Designer: Ian Bolt, Colin Smith

BOOT

🏌 **ROUNDWOOD HALL**
(Roundwood Hall), Kent, England
Year Built: 1993
Designer: B Boot

BRADBEER

🏌 **GARSTANG**
(Garstang Country Hotel &), Lancashire,
England
Designer: Richard Bradbeer

BRADFORD BENZ

🏌 **DUKES DENE**
(Dukes Dene), Surrey, England
Designer: Bradford Benz

BRADLEY

🏌 **SOUTH KYME**
(South Kyme), Lincolnshire, England
Year Built: 1990
Designer: G Bradley

BRAID

🏌 **ABERDEEN (ROYAL)**
(Balgownie Links), Aberdeen (City of),
Scotland
Designer: James Braid, Simpson

🏌 **ABERDEEN (ROYAL)**
(Silverburn), Aberdeen (City of), Scotland
Designer: James Braid, Simpson

🏌 **ABERDOVEY**
(Aberdovey), Gwynedd, Wales
Designer: James Braid, Fowler

🏌 **ACCRINGTON & DISTRICT**
(Accrington), Lancashire, England
Year Built: 1893
Designer: James Braid

🏌 **ALLOA**
(Alloa (Shaw Park)), Clackmannanshire,
Scotland

by Course **DESIGNER SURNAME**

Bailie — Braid

Year Built: 1946
Designer: James Braid

🏌 **ALTON**
(Alton), Hampshire, England
Year Built: 1908
Designer: James Braid

🏌 **ALYTH**
(The Alyth 1894), Perth And Kinross,
Scotland
Designer: James Braid

🏌 **ARBROATH**
(Arbroath), Angus, Scotland
Year Built: 1903
Designer: James Braid

🏌 **ARCOT HALL**
(Arcot Hall), Northumberland, England
Designer: James Braid

🏌 **ARKLEY**
(Arkley), Hertfordshire, England
Year Built: 1909
Designer: James Braid

🏌 **BAILDON**
(Baildon), Yorkshire (West), England
Year Built: 1896
Designer: James Braid, Tom Morris

🏌 **BALMORE**
(Balmore), Glasgow (City of), Scotland
Designer: James Braid

🏌 **BANGOR**
(Bangor), County Down, Northern Ireland
Designer: James Braid

🏌 **BANSTEAD DOWNS**
(Banstead Downs), Surrey, England
Year Built: 1890
Designer: James Braid, J H Taylor

🏌 **BARNEHURST**
(Barnehurst Public Pay & Play), Kent,
England
Year Built: 1904
Designer: James Braid

🏌 **BASINGSTOKE**
(Basingstoke), Hampshire, England
Designer: James Braid

🏌 **BELLEISLE & SEAFIELD**
(Belleisle), Ayrshire (South), Scotland
Year Built: 1927
Designer: James Braid

🏌 **BERKHAMSTED**
(Berkhamsted), Hertfordshire, England
Year Built: 1890
Designer: James Braid, Taylor

🏌 **BERWICK**
(Berwick-upon-Tweed (Goswick)),
Northumberland, England
Year Built: 1890
Designer: James Braid

🏌 **BISHOPS STORTFORD**
(Bishop's Stortford), Hertfordshire,
England
Year Built: 1910
Designer: James Braid

🏌 **BLACKHEATH (ROYAL)**
(Royal Blackheath), London (Greater),
England
Designer: James Braid

🏌 **BLAIRGOWRIE**
(Lansdowne), Perth And Kinross, Scotland
**Designer: Peter Alliss, James Braid, Tom
Morris, David Thomas**

🏌 **BLAIRGOWRIE**
(Rosemount), Perth And Kinross, Scotland
**Designer: Peter Alliss, James Braid, Tom
Morris, David Thomas**

🏌 **BLAIRGOWRIE**
(Wee), Perth And Kinross, Scotland
**Designer: Peter Alliss, James Braid, Tom
Morris, David Thomas**

🏌 **BOAT OF GARTEN**
(Boat of Garten), Highlands, Scotland
Designer: James Braid

🏌 **BOGNOR REGIS**
(Bognor Regis), Sussex (West), England
Year Built: 1892
Designer: James Braid

🏌 **BOYCE HILL**
(Boyce Hill), Essex, England
Year Built: 1922
Designer: James Braid

🏌 **BRAMLEY**
(Bramley), Surrey, England
Year Built: 1913
Designer: James Braid

🏌 **BRAMPTON**
(Brampton), Cumbria, England
Year Built: 1900
Designer: James Braid

🏌 **BRANSHAW**
(Branshaw), Yorkshire (West), England
Designer: James Braid

🏌 **BRECHIN GOLF & SQUASH
CLUB**
(Brechin Golf & Squash Club), Angus,
Scotland
Year Built: 1893
Designer: James Braid

🏌 **BRECON**
(Brecon), Powys, Wales
Designer: James Braid

🏌 **BRIDLINGTON**
(Bridlington), Yorkshire (East), England
Year Built: 1905
Designer: James Braid

🏌 **BRIGHTON & HOVE**
(Brighton & Hove), Sussex (East), England
Year Built: 1887
Designer: James Braid

🏌 **BROADWAY**
(Broadway), Worcestershire, England
Designer: James Braid

🏌 **BRORA**
(Brora), Highlands, Scotland
Year Built: 1891
Designer: James Braid

🏌 **BUCHANAN CASTLE**
(Buchanan Castle), Stirling, Scotland
Year Built: 1936
Designer: James Braid

🏌 **BUDOCK VEAN**
(Budock Vean), Cornwall, England
Designer: James Braid

🏌 **CARDROSS**
(Cardross), Argyll and Bute, Scotland
Year Built: 1895
Designer: James Braid

🏌 **CARNOUSTIE**
(Buddon Links), Angus, Scotland
Designer: James Braid

🏌 **CARNOUSTIE**
(Burnside), Angus, Scotland
Designer: James Braid

🏌 **CARNOUSTIE**
(Championship), Angus, Scotland
**Designer: James Braid, Tom Morris,
William Park, A Robertson**

🏌 **CATHKIN BRAES**
(Cathkin Braes), Glasgow (City of),
Scotland
Designer: James Braid

🏌 **CHEVIN**
(Chevin), Derbyshire, England
Year Built: 1894
Designer: James Braid

🏌 **CHILDWALL**
(Chidwall), Merseyside, England
Year Built: 1939
Designer: James Braid

🏌 **CHORLEYWOOD**
(Chorleywood), Hertfordshire, England
Year Built: 1890
Designer: James Braid

🏌 **CHURCH STRETTON**
(Church Stretton), Shropshire, England
Year Built: 1898
Designer: James Braid

🏌 **CINQUE PORTS (ROYAL)**
(Royal Cinque Ports), Kent, England
Designer: James Braid

🏌 **CIRENCESTER**
(Cirencester), Gloucestershire, England
Year Built: 1910
Designer: James Braid

🏌 **CLITHEROE**
(Clitheroe), Lancashire, England
Year Built: 1932
Designer: James Braid

🏌 **COCKERMOUTH**
(Cockermouth), Cumbria, England
Year Built: 1896
Designer: James Braid

🏌 **COLCHESTER**
(Colchester), Essex, England
Year Built: 1907
Designer: James Braid

COLVILLE PARK
(Colville Park), Lanarkshire (North),
Scotland
Designer: James Braid

COPTHORNE
(Copthorne), Sussex (West), England
Designer: James Braid

COWAL
(Cowal), Argyll and Bute, Scotland
Designer: James Braid

COWGLEN
(Cowglen), Glasgow (City of), Scotland
Designer: David Adams, James Braid

CRAIGMILLAR PARK
(Craigmillar Park), Edinburgh (City of),
Scotland
Year Built: 1925
Designer: James Braid

CRIEFF
(Dornock), Perth And Kinross, Scotland
Designer: James Braid

CRIEFF
(Ferntower), Perth And Kinross, Scotland
Designer: James Braid

CROHAM HURST
(Croham Hurst), Surrey, England
Year Built: 1912
Designer: James Braid

CROMER (ROYAL)
(Royal Cromer), Norfolk, England
Year Built: 1888
Designer: James Braid, Tom Morris

CROW WOOD
(Crow Wood), Glasgow (City of), Scotland
Designer: James Braid

DALMAHOY
(East), Edinburgh (City of), Scotland
Year Built: 1927
Designer: James Braid

DALMAHOY
(West), Edinburgh (City of), Scotland
Year Built: 1927
Designer: James Braid

DARTFORD
(Dartford), Kent, England
Designer: James Braid

DEAN WOOD
(Dean Wood), Lancashire, England
Year Built: 1922
Designer: James Braid

DORKING
(Dorking), Surrey, England
Designer: James Braid

DRAYTON PARK
(Drayton Park), Staffordshire, England
Designer: James Braid

DROITWICH
(Droitwich), Worcestershire, England
Designer: James Braid, G Franks

DULLATUR
(Antonine), Glasgow (City of), Scotland
Designer: James Braid

DULLATUR
(Carrickstone), Glasgow (City of), Scotland
Designer: James Braid

DUNSTABLE DOWNS
(Dunstable Downs), Bedfordshire, England
Designer: James Braid

DUNSTANBURGH CASTLE
(Dunstanburgh Castle), Northumberland,
England
Year Built: 1900
Designer: James Braid

EAGLESCLIFFE
(Eaglescliffe), Cleveland, England
Designer: James Braid, Henry Cotton

EAST BRIGHTON
(East Brighton), Sussex (East), England
Year Built: 1893
Designer: James Braid

EAST RENFREWSHIRE
(East Renfrewshire), Glasgow (City of),
Scotland
Year Built: 1922
Designer: James Braid

ELDERSLIE
(Elderslie), Renfrewshire, Scotland
Year Built: 1908
Designer: James Braid

ELLESBOROUGH
(Ellesborough), Buckinghamshire, England
Designer: James Braid

ENFIELD
(Enfield), London (Greater), England
Designer: James Braid

EXETER
(Exeter Golf & Country Club), Devon,
England
Year Built: 1895
Designer: James Braid

FALKIRK
(Carmuirs), Falkirk, Scotland
Year Built: 1922
Designer: James Braid

FILEY
(Filey), Yorkshire (North), England
Designer: James Braid

FINCHLEY
(Finchley), London (Greater), England
Designer: James Braid

FLEMPTON
(Flempton), Suffolk, England
Year Built: 1895
Designer: James Braid

FORRES
(Forres), Moray, Scotland
Year Built: 1889
Designer: James Braid, William Park

FORTROSE & ROSEMARKIE
(Fortrose & Rosemarkie), Highlands,
Scotland
Year Built: 1888
Designer: James Braid

FRASERBURGH
(Corbie Hill), Aberdeenshire, Scotland
Year Built: 1891
Designer: James Braid

FULFORD HEATH
(Fulford Heath), Midlands (West), England
Designer: James Braid, Hawtree

GALASHIELS
(Galashiels), Scottish Borders, Scotland
Year Built: 1884
Designer: James Braid

GANTON
(Ganton Golf Club), Yorkshire (North),
England
Year Built: 1891
**Designer: James Braid, Harry Shapland
Colt, Tom Dunn, Harry Vardon**

GILLINGHAM
(Gillingham), Kent, England
Designer: James Braid

GIRVAN
(Semi-Lynx), Ayrshire (South), Scotland
Year Built: 1800
Designer: James Braid

GLEN
(Glen), Lothian (East), Scotland
Year Built: 1906
Designer: James Braid, Ben Sayers

GLENBERVIE
(Glenbervie Clubhouse), Falkirk, Scotland
Designer: James Braid

GLENCRUITTEN
(Glencruitten), Argyll and Bute, Scotland
Year Built: 1908
Designer: James Braid

GLENEAGLES
(Kings), Perth And Kinross, Scotland
Year Built: 1920
Designer: James Braid

GLENEAGLES
(Queens), Perth And Kinross, Scotland
Year Built: 1924
Designer: James Braid

GOLSPIE
(Golspie), Highlands, Scotland
Year Built: 1889
Designer: James Braid

GOODWOOD
(Goodwood), Sussex (West), England
Year Built: 1892
Designer: James Braid

GOUROCK
(Gourock), Inverclyde, Scotland
Year Built: 1896
Designer: James Braid

GRANGE PARK
(Grange Park), Merseyside, England
Designer: James Braid

GRIMSDYKE
(Grims Dyke), London (Greater), England
Designer: James Braid

by Course **DESIGNER SURNAME**

Braid — Braid

HALIFAX
(Ogden), Yorkshire (West), England
Year Built: 1902
Designer: James Braid, S Herd

HANKLEY COMMON
(Hankley Common), Surrey, England
Designer: James Braid

HAYDOCK PARK
(Haydock Park), Merseyside, England
Year Built: 1877
Designer: James Braid

HAYSTON
(Hayston), Glasgow (City of), Scotland
Designer: James Braid

HELENSBURGH
(Helensburgh), Argyll and Bute, Scotland
Year Built: 1893
Designer: James Braid, Tom Morris

HELSBY
(Helsby), Cheshire, England
Designer: James Braid

HENLEY
(Henley), Oxfordshire, England
Designer: James Braid

HERNE BAY
(Herne Bay), Kent, England
Designer: James Braid

HILTON PARK
(Allander), Glasgow (City of), Scotland
Designer: James Braid

HILTON PARK
(Hilton), Glasgow (City of), Scotland
Designer: James Braid

HOCKLEY
(Hockley), Hampshire, England
Designer: James Braid

HOLYHEAD
(Holyhead), Isle of Anglesey, Wales
Designer: James Braid

HOWTH
(Howth), County Dublin, Ireland
Designer: James Braid

HULL
(Hull), Yorkshire (East), England
Designer: James Braid

HUNSTANTON
(Hunstanton), Norfolk, England
Designer: James Braid

INVERNESS
(Inverness), Highlands, Scotland
Year Built: 1883
Designer: James Braid

IRVINE
(Lynx), Ayrshire (North), Scotland
Year Built: 1887
Designer: James Braid

KEDLESTON PARK
(Kedleston Park), Derbyshire, England
Year Built: 1947
Designer: James Braid

KELSO
(Kelso), Scottish Borders, Scotland
Year Built: 1887
Designer: James Braid

KINGSWOOD
(Kingswood), Surrey, England
Year Built: 1925
Designer: James Braid

KIRKHILL
(Kirkhill), Glasgow (City of), Scotland
Year Built: 1910
Designer: James Braid

KIRKINTILLOCH
(Kirkintilloch), Glasgow (City of), Scotland
Designer: James Braid

KIRKISTOWN CASTLE
(Kirkistown Castle), County Down,
Northern Ireland
Year Built: 1902
Designer: James Braid

KIRRIEMUIR
(Kirriemuir), Angus, Scotland
Year Built: 1908
Designer: James Braid

KNOTT END
(Knott End), Lancashire, England
Year Built: 1911
Designer: James Braid

LA MOYE
(La Moye), Jersey, England
Designer: James Braid

LADYBANK
(Ladybank), Fife, Scotland
Year Built: 1879
Designer: James Braid, Tom Morris

LANCASTER
(Lancaster), Lancashire, England
Year Built: 1932
Designer: James Braid

LEIGH
(Leigh), Cheshire, England
Year Built: 1906
Designer: James Braid

LOCHMABEN
(Lochmaben), Dumfries And Galloway,
Scotland
Year Built: 1927
Designer: James Braid, Committee

LOCKERBIE
(Lockerbie), Dumfries And Galloway,
Scotland
Year Built: 1889
Designer: James Braid

LOTHIANBURN
(Lothianburn), Edinburgh (City of),
Scotland
Year Built: 1893
Designer: James Braid

LUFFENHAM HEATH
(Luffenham Heath), Lincolnshire, England
Year Built: 1911
Designer: James Braid

LUNDIN
(Lundin), Fife, Scotland
Year Built: 1868
Designer: James Braid

MAESTEG
(Maesteg), Bridgend, Wales
Designer: James Braid

MERE
(Mere), Cheshire, England
Year Built: 1934
Designer: James Braid

MILLPORT
(Millport), Ayrshire (North), Scotland
Year Built: 1888
Designer: James Braid

MONMOUTHSHIRE
(Monmouthshire), Monmouthshire, Wales
Year Built: 1892
Designer: James Braid

MORTONHALL
(Mortonhall), Edinburgh (City of), Scotland
Designer: James Braid, Hawtree

MUIR OF ORD
(Muir Of Ord), Highlands, Scotland
Year Built: 1875
Designer: James Braid

MULLINGAR
(Mullingar), County Westmeath, Ireland
Designer: James Braid

MUSSELBURGH
(Musselburgh), Lothian (Mid), Scotland
Year Built: 1938
Designer: James Braid

MUSSELBURGH (ROYAL)
(Royal Musselburgh), Lothian (East),
Scotland
Designer: James Braid

NAIRN
(Nairn), Highlands, Scotland
Year Built: 1887
**Designer: Archie Simpson, Old Tom
Morris, James Braid**

NAIRN
(Newton), Highlands, Scotland
Year Built: 1887
**Designer: Archie Simpson, Old Tom
Morris, James Braid**

NEATH
(Neath), Neath Port Talbot, Wales
Year Built: 1935
Designer: James Braid

NEFYN & DISTRICT
(New), Gwynedd, Wales
Designer: James Braid

NEFYN & DISTRICT
(Old), Gwynedd, Wales
Designer: James Braid

NEW GALLOWAY
(New Galloway), Dumfries And Galloway,
Scotland
Year Built: 1902
Designer: James Braid

NEW NORTH MANCHESTER
(North Manchester), Manchester (Greater),
England
Designer: James Braid

NEWPORT
(Newport (Pemb)), Pembrokeshire, Wales
Year Built: 1925
Designer: James Braid

NORTH CLIFF
(Scarborough North Cliff), Yorkshire
(North), England
Designer: James Braid

NORTH HANTS FLEET
(North Hants Fleet), Hampshire, England
Year Built: 1904
Designer: James Braid

NORTH SHORE
(North Shore Hotel &), Lincolnshire,
England
Year Built: 1910
Designer: James Braid

NORTH WORCESTERSHIRE
(North Worcestershire), Midlands (West),
England
Year Built: 1907
Designer: James Braid

NORWICH (ROYAL)
(Royal Norwich), Norfolk, England
Year Built: 1893
Designer: James Braid

NOTTINGHAM CITY
(Nottingham City), Nottinghamshire,
England
Designer: James Braid

OLD COLWYN
(Old Colwyn), Conwy, Wales
Year Built: 1907
Designer: James Braid

ORSETT
(Orsett), Essex, England
Year Built: 1899
Designer: James Braid

OSWESTRY
(Oswestry), Shropshire, England
Year Built: 1933
Designer: James Braid

PARKSTONE
(Parkstone), Dorset, England
Year Built: 1911
Designer: James Braid, William Park

PEACEHAVEN
(Peacehaven), Sussex (East), England
Year Built: 1923
Designer: James Braid

PENNARD
(Pennard), Swansea, Wales
Year Built: 1896
Designer: James Braid

PERRANPORTH
(Perranporth), Cornwall, England
Year Built: 1927
Designer: James Braid

PETERBOROUGH MILTON
(Peterborough Milton), Cambridgeshire,
England
Year Built: 1938
Designer: James Braid

POLLOK
(Pollok), Glasgow (City of), Scotland
Designer: James Braid

PORTHMADOG
(Porthmadog), Gwynedd, Wales
Designer: James Braid

POTTERS BAR
(Potters Bar), Hertfordshire, England
Designer: James Braid

POWFOOT
(Powfoot), Dumfries And Galloway,
Scotland
Year Built: 1903
Designer: James Braid

PRENTON
(Prenton), Merseyside, England
Year Built: 1905
Designer: James Braid

PRESTON
(Preston (Fulwood)), Lancashire, England
Year Built: 1892
Designer: James Braid

PRESTONFIELD
(Prestonfield), Edinburgh (City of),
Scotland
Year Built: 1920
Designer: James Braid

RALSTON
(Ralston), Renfrewshire, Scotland
Year Built: 1904
Designer: James Braid

RAMSEY
(Ramsey), Isle of Man, England
Designer: James Braid

RATHO PARK
(Ratho Park), Edinburgh (City of), Scotland
Designer: James Braid

RAVELSTON
(Ravelston), Edinburgh (City of), Scotland
Designer: James Braid

REAY
(Reay), Highlands, Scotland
Year Built: 1893
Designer: James Braid

REDHILL & REIGATE
(Redhill & Reigate), Surrey, England
Year Built: 1887
Designer: James Braid

RHYL
(Rhyl), Denbighshire, Wales
Year Built: 1890
Designer: James Braid

RICCARTON
(Hamilton), Lanarkshire (South), Scotland
Designer: James Braid

ROCHFORD HUNDRED
(Rochford Hundred), Essex, England
Designer: James Braid

ROTHERHAM
(Rotherham), Yorkshire (South), England
Designer: James Braid, S Herd

ROTHESAY
(Rothesay), Argyll and Bute, Scotland
Designer: James Braid, Ben Sayers

ROUTENBURN
(Routenburn), Ayrshire (North), Scotland
Year Built: 1897
Designer: James Braid

RYSTON PARK
(Ryston Park), Norfolk, England
Year Built: 1933
Designer: James Braid

SALTBURN
(Saltburn by the Sea), Cleveland, England
Designer: James Braid

SHERBORNE
(Sherborne), Dorset, England
Designer: James Braid

SHERWOOD FOREST
(Sherwood Forest), Nottinghamshire,
England
Year Built: 1895
Designer: James Braid, W S Colt

SHOTTS
(Shotts), Lanarkshire (North), Scotland
Year Built: 1895
Designer: James Braid

SIDCUP
(Sidcup), Kent, England
Designer: James Braid

SKELMORLIE
(Skelmorlie), Ayrshire (North), Scotland
Designer: James Braid

SOUTH SHIELDS
(South Shields), Tyne And Wear, England
**Designer: James Braid, Alistair
MacKenzie**

SOUTHPORT & AINSDALE
(Southport & Ainsdale), Merseyside,
England
Year Built: 1906
Designer: James Braid

SOUTHWOLD
(Southwold), Suffolk, England
Year Built: 1884
Designer: James Braid

ST. AUSTELL
(St Austell), Cornwall, England
Year Built: 1911
Designer: James Braid

ST. DEINIOL
(St Deiniol), Gwynedd, Wales
Designer: James Braid

ST. ENODOC
(Church), Cornwall, England
Designer: James Braid

by Course **DESIGNER SURNAME**

Braid — Braid

🏌 **ST. ENODOC**
(Holywell), Cornwall, England
Designer: James Braid

🏌 **ST. MEDAN**
(St Medan), Dumfries And Galloway,
Scotland
Year Built: 1905
Designer: James Braid

🏌 **STIRLING**
(Stirling), Stirling, Scotland
Designer: James Braid, Henry Cotton

🏌 **STRANRAER**
(Creachmore), Dumfries And Galloway,
Scotland
Year Built: 1952
Designer: James Braid

🏌 **SWINTON PARK**
(Swinton Park), Manchester (Greater),
England
Designer: James Braid

🏌 **TAYMOUTH CASTLE**
(Taymouth Castle), Perth And Kinross,
Scotland
Year Built: 1924
Designer: James Braid

🏌 **TENBY**
(Tenby), Pembrokeshire, Wales
Year Built: 1888
Designer: James Braid

🏌 **THEYDON BOIS**
(Theydon Bois), Essex, England
Designer: James Braid

🏌 **THORNHILL**
(Thornhill), Dumfries And Galloway,
Scotland
Year Built: 1893
Designer: James Braid

🏌 **THORPENESS**
(Thorpeness Hotel &), Suffolk, England
Designer: James Braid

🏌 **TIVERTON**
(Tiverton), Devon, England
Year Built: 1936
Designer: James Braid

🏌 **TULLAMORE**
(Tullamore), County Offaly, Ireland
Designer: James Braid, Paddy Merrigam

🏌 **TURNHOUSE**
(Turnhouse), Edinburgh (City of), Scotland
Designer: James Braid

🏌 **TYRRELLS WOOD**
(Tyrrells Wood), Surrey, England
Designer: James Braid

🏌 **VERULAM**
(Verulam), Hertfordshire, England
Designer: James Braid

🏌 **WALMER & KINGSDOWN**
(Walmer & Kingsdown), Kent, England
Year Built: 1948
Designer: James Braid

🏌 **WANSTEAD**
(Wanstead), London (Greater), England

Year Built: 1893
Designer: James Braid

🏌 **WATERFORD**
(Waterford), County Waterford, Ireland
Designer: William Park, James Braid

🏌 **WELSHPOOL**
(Welshpool), Powys, Wales
Year Built: 1894
Designer: James Braid

🏌 **WEST ESSEX**
(West Essex), London (Greater), England
Year Built: 1900
Designer: James Braid

🏌 **WEST KILBRIDE**
(West Kilbride), Ayrshire (North), Scotland
Year Built: 1893
Designer: James Braid

🏌 **WEYMOUTH**
(Weymouth), Dorset, England
Year Built: 1909
Designer: James Braid

🏌 **WICK**
(Wick), Highlands, Scotland
Designer: James Braid

🏌 **WILLIAMWOOD**
(Williamwood), Glasgow (City of), Scotland
Designer: James Braid

🏌 **WILPSHIRE**
(Wilpshire), Lancashire, England
Designer: James Braid

🏌 **WINDWHISTLE**
(Windwhistle), Somerset, England
Year Built: 1932
Designer: James Braid, Fisher, Taylor

🏌 **WINDYHILL**
(Windyhill), Glasgow (City of), Scotland
Year Built: 1908
Designer: James Braid

🏌 **WISHAW**
(Wishaw), Lanarkshire (North), Scotland
Designer: James Braid

🏌 **WORCESTERSHIRE**
(The Worcestershire (Malvern Wells)),
Worcestershire, England
**Designer: James Braid, Harry Shapland
Colt**

🏌 **WORKINGTON**
(Workington), Cumbria, England
Designer: James Braid

🏌 **WORSLEY**
(Worsley), Manchester (Greater), England
Year Built: 1894
Designer: James Braid

🏌 **WREXHAM**
(Wrexham), Wrexham, Wales
Designer: James Braid

BRAIDE

🏌 **PEEL**
(Peel), Isle of Man, England
Designer: Robert Braide

BRIDGE

🏌 **HEYROSE**
(Heyrose), Cheshire, England
Designer: Bridge

BRODIGAN

🏌 **COCKSFORD**
(Cocksford), Yorkshire (North), England
Year Built: 1992
Designer: Bill Brodigan

BROWN

🏌 **ALDWICKBURY PARK**
(Aldwickbury Park),
Year Built: 1995
Designer: K Brown, Martin Gillett

🏌 **ALDWICKBURY PARK**
(Aldwickbury Park), Hertfordshire, England
Year Built: 1995
Designer: K Brown, Martin Gillett

🏌 **GRANTOWN-ON-SPEY**
(Grantown On Spey), Moray, Scotland
Year Built: 1890
Designer: A C Brown

🏌 **KESWICK**
(Keswick), Cumbria, England
Year Built: 1979
Designer: Eric Brown

🏌 **NEWENT**
(Newent), Gloucestershire, England
Year Built: 1994
Designer: Tom Brown

🏌 **WIMBLEDON PARK**
(Wimbledon Park), London (Greater),
England
Year Built: 1898
Designer: Mr C Brown

BROWNE

🏌 **BEARNA**
(Bearna), County Galway, Ireland
Year Built: 1996
Designer: R Browne

🏌 **BLACK BUSH**
(Course 1), County Meath, Ireland
Designer: R Browne

🏌 **BLACK BUSH**
(Course 2), County Meath, Ireland
Designer: R Browne

🏌 **CASTLE HUME**
(Castle Hume), County Fermanagh,
Northern Ireland
Year Built: 1991
Designer: R Browne

🏌 **CASTLEBLAYNEY**
(Castleblayney), County Monaghan, Ireland
Designer: R Browne

🏌 **FINNSTOWN FAIRWAYS**
(Finnstown Fairways), County Dublin,
Ireland
Designer: R Browne

🏌 **MOATE**
(Moate), County Westmeath, Ireland

Year Built: 1993
Designer: R Browne

BRYSON

STRATHLENE
(Strathlene), Moray, Scotland
Year Built: 1877
Designer: Mr Bryson

BURGESS

GAIRLOCH
(Gairloch), Highlands, Scotland
Year Built: 1898
Designer: Captain Burgess

BURNS

TOP MEADOW
(Top Meadow), Essex, England
Year Built: 1990
Designer: Burns, Stock

BUSH

MERSEY VALLEY
(Mersey Valley), Cheshire, England
Year Built: 1995
Designer: Roger Bush

BUTCHART

WEST BYFLEET
(West Byfleet), Surrey, England
Designer: C S Butchart

WEST HILL
(West Hill), Surrey, England
Designer: C Butchart, William Parke

BYRNE

GLEN MILL
(Glen Mill), County Wicklow, Ireland
Year Built: 1993
Designer: Andrew Byrne

CAIRD

HESSLE
(Hexham), Yorkshire (East), England
Year Built: 1907
Designer: Harry Vardon, James Caird

CAMPBELL

ASHRIDGE
(Ashridge), Hertfordshire, England
Year Built: 1932
Designer: Campbell, C Hutchinson, N Hutchinson

KILLARNEY
(Mahony's Point), County Kerry, Ireland
Designer: Guy Campbell, Henry Longhurst

KILMACOLM
(Kilmacolm), Inverclyde, Scotland
Designer: W Campbell

SEASCALE
(Seascale), Cumbria, England
Year Built: 1893
Designer: W Campbell

WEST SUSSEX
(West Sussex), Sussex (West), England
Year Built: 1930
Designer: Campbell, Hutchinson

CAROLAN

TOWNLEY HALL
(Townley Hall), County Louth, Ireland
Year Built: 1994
Designer: Philip Carolan

CARPENTER

LYNEHAM
(Lyneham), Oxfordshire, England
Year Built: 1990
Designer: D G Carpenter

CARSWELL

SWANSTON
(Swanston), Edinburgh (City of), Scotland
Year Built: 1927
Designer: Margaret Carswell

CARTER

YEOVIL
(Old), Somerset, England
Year Built: 1907
Designer: Charles Carter

CASSIDY

CLONLARA GOLF & LEISURE
(Clonlara Golf & Leisure), County Clare, Ireland
Designer: Noel Cassidy

CASTIGLIA

CAMBRIDGE LAKES
(Cambridge Lakes), Cambridgeshire, England
Year Built: 1995
Designer: Vicenzo Castiglia

CHAMBERS

LIVERPOOL (ROYAL)
(Royal Liverpool), Merseyside, England
Year Built: 1869
Designer: Robert Chambers, Jim Morris

OAST GOLF CTRE
(The Oast Golf Centre), Kent, England
Designer: D Chambers

CHAPMAN

OAKSEY
(Oaksey), Wiltshire, England
Designer: Chapman, Warren

CHEAL

HEWORTH
(Heworth), Yorkshire (North), England
Year Built: 1911
Designer: B Cheal

CHUBB

MOLLINGTON GRANGE
(Mollington Grange), Cheshire, England
Year Built: 1999
Designer: Garry Chubb

CLARK

BRAXTED PARK
(Braxted Park), Essex, England
Year Built: 1953
Designer: A Clark

FOXBRIDGE
(Foxbridge), Sussex (West), England
Year Built: 1991
Designer: P A Clark

HERONS REACH
(Herons Reach), Lancashire, England
Designer: P Alliss, Clive Clark

REGIMENT
(Regiment Way), Essex, England
Year Built: 1994
Designer: R Clark, R Stubbings

CLARKE

ASTON WOOD
(Aston Wood), Midlands (West), England
Year Built: 1994
Designer: Peter Alliss, Clive Clarke

BROCKET HALL
(Melbourne), Hertfordshire, England
Year Built: 1992
Designer: Peter Alliss, Clive Clark

CAMBRIDGE MERIDIAN
(Cambridge Meridian), Cambridgeshire, England
Year Built: 1994
Designer: Peter Alliss, Clive Clark

CAMS HALL ESTATE GOLF CLUB
(Creek), Hampshire, England
Year Built: 1992
Designer: Peter Alliss, Clive Clark

CAMS HALL ESTATE GOLF CLUB
(Park), Hampshire, England
Year Built: 1992
Designer: Peter Alliss, Clive Clark

CHOBHAM
(Chobham), Surrey, England
Year Built: 1993
Designer: Peter Alliss, Clive Clark

DUMMER
(Dummer), Hampshire, England
Designer: Peter Alliss, Clive Clark

HURTMORE
(Hurtmore), Surrey, England
Year Built: 1992
Designer: Peter Alliss, Clive Clark

MANOR HOUSE
(The Manor House at Castle Combe), Wiltshire, England
Year Built: 1992
Designer: Peter Alliss, Clive Clark

MILFORD GOLF CLUB
(Milford), Surrey, England
Year Built: 1993
Designer: Peter Alliss, Clive Clark

MILL GREEN GOLF CLUB
(Mill Green), Hertfordshire, England
Year Built: 1993
Designer: Peter Alliss, Clive Clark

PYRFORD GOLF CLUB
(Pyrford), Surrey, England

by Course **DESIGNER SURNAME**

Browne — Clarke

Year Built: 1993
Designer: Peter Alliss, Clive Clark

🏌 **WILTSHIRE**
(The Wiltshire), Wiltshire, England
Year Built: 1991
Designer: Peter Alliss, Clive Clark

🏌 **WOODSPRING**
(Avon), Bristol, England
Year Built: 1994
Designer: Peter Alliss, Clive Clarke, Donald Steel

🏌 **WOODSPRING**
(Brunel), Bristol, England
Designer: Peter Alliss, Clive Clarke, Donald Steel

🏌 **WOODSPRING**
(Severn), Bristol, England
Designer: Peter Alliss, Clive Clarke, Donald Steel

COLES

🏌 **AUCHMILL**
(Auchmill), Aberdeen (City of), Scotland
Designer: Neil Coles, Brian Huggett

🏌 **BRENT VALLEY PUBLIC**
(Brent Valley Public), London (Greater), England
Year Built: 1938
Designer: Neil Coles

🏌 **CASTLE ROYLE**
(Castle Royle), Berkshire, England
Year Built: 1994
Designer: Neil Coles

🏌 **CHARTHAM PARK**
(Chartham Park), Sussex (West), England
Year Built: 1993
Designer: Neil Coles

🏌 **EPPING FOREST**
(Manor), Essex, England
Year Built: 1994
Designer: Neil Coles

🏌 **HEATHPARK**
(Heathpark), London (Greater), England
Designer: Neil Coles

🏌 **HICKLETON**
(Hickleton), Yorkshire (South), England
Year Built: 1976
Designer: Neil Coles, Brian Huggett

🏌 **LEEDS CASTLE**
(Leeds Castle), Kent, England
Year Built: 1924
Designer: Neil Coles

🏌 **SLALEY HALL GOLF COURSE**
(Priestman), Northumberland, England
Year Built: 1999
Designer: Neil Coles

🏌 **TILGATE FOREST**
(Tilgate Forest), Sussex (West), England
Year Built: 1982
Designer: Neil Coles, Brian Huggett

🏌 **WOODLANDS MANOR**
(Woodlands Manor), Kent, England
Designer: Coles, Lyons

COLLINS

🏌 **PRESTATYN**
(Prestatyn), Denbighshire, Wales
Year Built: 1905
Designer: J Collins

COLT

🏌 **BATH**
(Bath), Bath & Somerset (North East), England
Designer: Charles Hugh Alison, Harry Shapland Colt

🏌 **BOURNEMOUTH & MEYRICK**
(Bournemouth & Meyrick Park), Dorset, England
Designer: Harry Shapland Colt, Tom Dunn

🏌 **BROADSTONE**
(Broadstone), Dorset, England
Designer: Harry Shapland Colt, Tom Dunn

🏌 **CLYNE**
(Clyne), Swansea, Wales
Year Built: 1920
Designer: Harry Shapland Colt, Harris

🏌 **FORMBY**
(Formby), Merseyside, England
Year Built: 1884
Designer: Harry Shapland Colt, William Park, Frank Pennink

🏌 **FORMBY HALL**
(Formby Hall), Merseyside, England
Year Built: 1995
Designer: Harry Shapland Colt, William Park

🏌 **GANTON**
(Ganton Golf Club), Yorkshire (North), England
Year Built: 1891
Designer: James Braid, Harry Shapland Colt, Tom Dunn, Harry Vardon

🏌 **KNOCK**
(Knock), County Antrim, Northern Ireland
Year Built: 1921
Designer: Charles Hugh Alison, Harry Shapland Colt, Alistair MacKenzie

🏌 **MILL HILL**
(Mill Hill), London (Greater), England
Year Built: 1925
Designer: J F Abercromby, Harry Shapland Colt

🏌 **PURLEY DOWNS**
(Purley Downs), Surrey, England
Designer: Harry Shapland Colt, J Taylor

🏌 **SHERWOOD FOREST**
(Sherwood Forest), Nottinghamshire, England
Year Built: 1895
Designer: James Braid, W S Colt

🏌 **SLIGO (COUNTY)**
(Bomore 9 hole), County Sligo, Ireland
Designer: H S Colt

🏌 **SLIGO (COUNTY)**
(Championship), County Sligo, Ireland
Year Built: 1927
Designer: H S Colt

🏌 **THORNDON PARK**
(Thorndon Park), Essex, England
Designer: Charles Hugh Alison, Harry Shapland Colt

🏌 **TRENTHAM**
(Trentham), Staffordshire, England
Designer: Charles Hugh Alison, Harry Shapland Colt

🏌 **TRURO**
(Truro), Cornwall, England
Year Built: 1937
Designer: Charles Hugh Alison, Harry Shapland Colt, J S F Morrison

🏌 **WHITBURN**
(Whitburn), Tyne And Wear, England
Designer: Charles Hugh Alison, Harry Shapland Colt, J S F Morrison

🏌 **WORCESTERSHIRE**
(The Worcestershire (Malvern Wells)), Worcestershire, England
Designer: James Braid, Harry Shapland Colt

CONNAUGHTON

🏌 **CORRSTOWN**
(Orchard), County Dublin, Ireland
Designer: Edward Connaughton

🏌 **CORRSTOWN**
(River), County Dublin, Ireland
Designer: Edward Connaughton

🏌 **PORTUMNA**
(Portumna), County Galway, Ireland
Designer: Edward Connaughton

🏌 **ROSCOMMON**
(Roscommon), County Roscommon, Ireland
Year Built: 1930
Designer: Edward Connaughton

COOKSEY

🏌 **BRIDGNORTH**
(Bridgnorth), Shropshire, England
Year Built: 1925
Designer: M Cooksey

CORBY

🏌 **DELAPRE PARK GOLF COMPLEX**
(Main), Northamptonshire, England
Year Built: 1976
Designer: John Jacobs, John Corby

COTTON

🏌 **ABRIDGE**
(Abridge Golf and Country Club), Essex, England
Designer: Henry Cotton

🏌 **AMPFIELD PAR-THREE**
(Ampfield Par Three), Hampshire, England
Designer: Henry Cotton

🏌 **BASILDON**
(Basildon), Essex, England
Designer: Cotton

🏌 **BEAMISH PARK**
(Beamish Park), County Durham, England

Year Built: 1964
Designer: Henry Cotton

🌑 **BRICKENDON GRANGE**
(Brickendon Grange), Hertfordshire,
England
Year Built: 1965
Designer: Cotton

🌑 **CANONS BROOK**
(Canons Brook), Essex, England
Year Built: 1964
Designer: Henry Cotton

🌑 **CHANNELS**
(Channels), Essex, England
Year Built: 1974
Designer: Henry Cotton

🌑 **EAGLESCLIFFE**
(Eaglescliffe), Cleveland, England
Designer: James Braid, Henry Cotton

🌑 **ELLESMERE PORT**
(Ellesmere Port), Merseyside, England
Designer: Cotton, Lawrie, Pennick

🌑 **ELY CITY**
(Ely), Cambridgeshire, England
Year Built: 1962
Designer: Henry Cotton

🌑 **FARNHAM PARK PAR 3**
(Farnham Park), Surrey, England
Designer: Henry Cotton

🌑 **FELIXSTOWE FERRY**
(Martello), Suffolk, England
Year Built: 1948
Designer: Henry Cotton

🌑 **FOSSEWAY**
(Fosseway Country Club), Bath &
Somerset (North East), England
Year Built: 1970
Designer: Cotton, Pennink

🌑 **FRILFORD HEATH**
(Green), Oxfordshire, England
Year Built: 1908
Designer: D Cotton, J Taylor

🌑 **FRILFORD HEATH**
(Red), Oxfordshire, England
Designer: D Cotton, J Taylor

🌑 **GATTON MANOR**
(Gatton Manor), Surrey, England
Year Built: 1969
Designer: Henry Cotton

🌑 **GLYNNEATH**
(Glynneath), Neath Port Talbot, Wales
**Designer: Cotton Pennick Lawrie &
Partners**

🌑 **GOSFIELD LAKE**
(Lakes), Essex, England
Designer: Henry Cotton, Howard Swan

🌑 **GOSFIELD LAKE**
(Meadows), Essex, England
Designer: Henry Cotton, Howard Swan

🌑 **INGOL**
(Ingol), Lancashire, England
Year Built: 1981
Designer: Henry Cotton

🌑 **LANGLAND BAY**
(Langland Bay), Swansea, Wales
Year Built: 1904
Designer: Henry Cotton

🌑 **LEE PARK**
(Lee Park), Merseyside, England
Year Built: 1954
Designer: Cotton

🌑 **PALACERIGG**
(Palacerigg), Lanarkshire (North), Scotland
Year Built: 1974
Designer: Henry Cotton

🌑 **PHOENIX**
(Phoenix), Yorkshire (South), England
Designer: Cotton

🌑 **SENE VALLEY**
(Sene Valley), Kent, England
Year Built: 1966
Designer: Henry Cotton

🌑 **ST. PIERRE**
(Old), Monmouthshire, Wales
Year Built: 1962
Designer: C K Cotton, J J Frank Pennink

🌑 **STAPLEFORD ABBOTTS GOLF
CLUB**
(Abbotts), Essex, England
Designer: Henry Cotton, Howard Swan

🌑 **STAPLEFORD ABBOTTS GOLF
CLUB**
(Friars), Essex, England
Designer: Henry Cotton, Howard Swan

🌑 **STAPLEFORD ABBOTTS GOLF
CLUB**
(Priors), Essex, England
Designer: Henry Cotton, Howard Swan

🌑 **STIRLING**
(Stirling), Stirling, Scotland
Designer: James Braid, Henry Cotton

🌑 **STOCKSFIELD**
(Stocksfield), Northumberland, England
Year Built: 1913
**Designer: Cotton Pennick Lawrie &
Partners**

🌑 **THREE HAMMERS**
(Three Hammers Short), Midlands (West),
England
Designer: Henry Cotton

🌑 **WATERLOOVILLE**
(Waterlooville), Hampshire, England
Designer: Henry Cotton

🌑 **WINDMILL HILL**
(Windmill Hill), Buckinghamshire, England
Designer: Henry Cotton

COVEY

🌑 **OAKS**
(The Oaks), Yorkshire (North), England
Year Built: 1996
Designer: Julian Covey

COX

🌑 **BENTON HALL**
(Benton Hall), Essex, England

Year Built: 1990
Designer: Charlie Cox, Alan Walker

🌑 **GOAL FARM**
(Goal Farm), Surrey, England
Year Built: 1978
Designer: B Cox

🌑 **SEDGLEY GOLF CTRE**
(Sedgley Golf Ctra), Midlands (West),
England
Designer: W Cox

🌑 **ST. PIERRE**
(Mathern), Monmouthshire, Wales
Year Built: 1962
Designer: B Cox

CRADDOCK

🌑 **BALLYLIFFIN**
(Glashedy Links), County Donegal, Ireland
Year Built: 1995
Designer: Tom Craddock, Pat Ruddy

🌑 **BALLYLIFFIN**
(Old Links), County Donegal, Ireland
Designer: Tom Craddock, Pat Ruddy

🌑 **CLAREMORRIS**
(Claremorris), County Mayo, Ireland
Designer: T Craddock

🌑 **DRUIDS GLEN**
(Druids Glen), County Wicklow, Ireland
Year Built: 1995
Designer: Pat Ruddy, Tom Craddock

🌑 **MEATH (COUNTY)**
(Meath), County Meath, Ireland
Designer: T Craddock, Edward Hackett

🌑 **ST. MARGARETS**
(St Margaret's), County Dublin, Ireland
Designer: Craddock, Ruddy

🌑 **WICKLOW**
(Wicklow), County Wicklow, Ireland
Year Built: 1904
Designer: Craddock, Ruddy

CRAWFORD

🌑 **GREENACRES GOLF CTRE**
(Greenacres), County Antrim, Northern
Ireland
Year Built: 1995
Designer: Stephen Crawford

CRAY

🌑 **SOLWAY LINKS**
(Solway Links), Dumfries And Galloway,
Scotland
Year Built: 1992
Designer: Gordon Cray

CRESSWELL

🌑 **EAST ABERDEENSHIRE**
(East Aberdeenshire Golf Centre), Aberdeen
(City of), Scotland
Year Built: 1999
Designer: Ian Creswell

CRITCHLEY

🌑 **MALTON**
(Malton), Hertfordshire, England

by Course **DESIGNER SURNAME**

Cotton — Critchley

Year Built: 1993
Designer: Bruce Critchley, Peter Bancroft

CROXTON

COLD ASHBY
(Winwick/Ashby), Northamptonshire,
England
Year Built: 1974
Designer: David Croxton

CUNNINGHAM

WIGTOWNSHIRE
(County), Dumfries And Galloway, Scotland
Year Built: 1894
Designer: G Cunningham

CUPP

EAST SUSSEX NATIONAL
(East), Sussex (East), England
Year Built: 1990
Designer: Robert Cupp

EAST SUSSEX NATIONAL
(West), Sussex (East), England
Year Built: 1990
Designer: Robert Cupp

DALEY

BATTLE
(Battle), Sussex (East), England
Year Built: 1994
Designer: John Daley

BEARSDEN
(Bearsden), Glasgow (City of), Scotland
Year Built: 1994
Designer: John Daley

DOWN ROYAL PARK
(Down Royal Park), County Antrim,
Northern Ireland
Year Built: 1844
Designer: Fred Daley

DANCER

SHENDISH MANOR
(Shendish Manor), Hertfordshire, England
Year Built: 1995
Designer: A Dancer, Donald Steel

DARCY

TEST VALLEY
(Test Valley), Hampshire, England
Year Built: 1992
Designer: E Darcy, D Wright

DARWIN

IFIELD
(Ifield), Sussex (West), England
Year Built: 1927
Designer: Bernard Darwin

DAVIES

CHERWELL EDGE
(Cherwell Edge), Oxfordshire, England
Year Built: 1980
Designer: R Davies

CWMRHYDNEUADD
(Cwmrhydneuadd 9 Hole), Ceredigion,
Wales

Year Built: 1991
Designer: Gerwyn Davies

SUTTON GREEN
(Sutton Green), Surrey, England
Year Built: 1994
Designer: L Davies, D Walker

UPTON-BY-CHESTER
(Upton-By-Chester), Cheshire, England
Year Built: 1934
Designer: Bill Davies

DAVIS

MILLTOWN
(Milltown), County Dublin, Ireland
Designer: F Davis

DAWSON

LONG SUTTON
(Long Sutton), Somerset, England
Year Built: 1990
Designer: P Dawson

OAK PARK GOLF CLUB
(Village), Surrey, England
Designer: P Dawson

OAK PARK GOLF CLUB
(Woodland), Surrey, England
Year Built: 1983
Designer: P Dawson

RIDGE GOLF CLUB
(Ridge), Kent, England
Year Built: 1993
Designer: P Dawson

STANDISH COURT
(Standish Court), Lancashire, England
Year Built: 1995
Designer: P Dawson

TYTHERINGTON
(The Tytherington Club), Cheshire, England
Year Built: 1986
Designer: Patrick Dawson, Peter Alliss

DAY

BURGHLEY PARK
(Burghley Park), Lincolnshire, England
Designer: Reverend J Day

CATTERICK
(Catterick), Yorkshire (North), England
Designer: Arthur Day

CHERRY LODGE
(Cherry Lodge), Kent, England
Year Built: 1969
Designer: John Day

DELVIN CASTLE
(Delvin Castle), County Westmeath, Ireland
Designer: John Day

FOREST OF DEAN
(Forest Of Dean), Gloucestershire, England
Year Built: 1971
Designer: John Day

FRODSHAM
(Frodsham), Cheshire, England
Year Built: 1990
Designer: John Day

KILNWICK PERCY
(Kilnwick Percy), Yorkshire (North),
England
Year Built: 1994
Designer: John Day

MANGOTSFIELD
(Mangotsfield), Bristol, England
Designer: John Day

NOTLEYS
(Notleys), Essex, England
Designer: John Day

PRYORS HAYES
(Pryors Hayes), Cheshire, England
Year Built: 1993
Designer: John Day

DEELEY

PRINCES
(Himalayas), Kent, England
Year Built: 1951
Designer: Deeley, Lucas, Mallaby

DEFOY

BRYN MEADOWS
(Bryn Meadows Golf & Country Hotel),
Caerphilly, Wales
Designer: Defoy, Mayo

DELARGY

CUSHENDALL
(Cushendall), County Antrim, Northern
Ireland
Year Built: 1937
Designer: D Delargy

DELVLIN

AUCHTERDERRAN
(Auchterderran), Fife, Scotland
Year Built: 1904
Designer: Reverend Delvlin

DERRY

ST. KEW
(St Kew), Cornwall, England
Designer: David Derry

DOHERTY

CRUIT ISLAND
(Cruit Island), County Donegal, Ireland
Designer: Michael Doherty

DONALDSON

FARTHINGSTONE
(Farthingstone Hotel &), Northamptonshire,
England
Year Built: 1973
Designer: D Donaldson

NIZELS
(Nizels), Kent, England
Designer: D Donaldson, Edwards

DOW

THORNEY
(Fen), Cambridgeshire, England
Year Built: 1991
Designer: Angus Dow

DRAKE

WAVENDON GOLF CTRE
(Wavendon Golf Ctre), Buckinghamshire,
England
Year Built: 1990
Designer: J Drake, N Elmer

DUGGAN

CASTLE BARNA
(Castle Barna), County Offaly, Ireland
Year Built: 1992
Designer: Alan Duggan

HIGHFIELD
(Highfield), County Kildare, Ireland
Year Built: 1991
Designer: Alan Duggan

DUNCAN

DORNOCH (ROYAL)
(Championship), Highlands, Scotland
**Designer: G Duncan, Tom Morris, J
Sutherland**

KILLIN
(Killin), Perth And Kinross, Scotland
Year Built: 1911
Designer: John Duncan

DUNCTON

PETWORTH
(Petworth G.C), Sussex (West), England
Year Built: 1989
Designer: Chris Duncton, Tim Duncton

DUNKLEY

WARWICK GOLF CTRE
(Warwick), Warwickshire, England
Designer: D G Dunkley

DUNN

BOURNEMOUTH & MEYRICK
(Bournemouth & Meyrick Park), Dorset,
England
Designer: Harry Shapland Colt, Tom Dunn

BROADSTONE
(Broadstone), Dorset, England
Designer: Harry Shapland Colt, Tom Dunn

EPSOM
(Epsom), Surrey, England
Year Built: 1889
Designer: W Dunn

GANTON
(Ganton Golf Club), Yorkshire (North),
England
Year Built: 1891
**Designer: James Braid, Harry Shapland
Colt, Tom Dunn, Harry Vardon**

HAMPSTEAD
(Hampstead), London (Greater), England
Year Built: 1893
Designer: Tom Dunn

SURBITON
(Surbiton), Surrey, England
Designer: Tom Dunn

WESTON
(Weston-Super-Mare), Somerset (North),
England
Designer: Tom Dunn, Alistair MacKenzie

WOKING
(Woking), Surrey, England
Designer: Tom Dunn

WOODFORD
(Woodford), Essex, England
Designer: Tom Dunn

DURHAM

BUNSAY DOWNS
(Bunsay Downs), Essex, England
Year Built: 1982
Designer: John Durham

BUNSAY DOWNS
(Par 3), Essex, England
Year Built: 1989
Designer: John Durham

EDMONSON

OWMBY
(Owmby), Lincolnshire, England
Year Built: 1995
Designer: Bud Edmonson

EDMUNDS

ST. ANDREWS MAJOR
(St Andrews Major), Glamorgan (Vale of),
Wales
Year Built: 1993
Designer: Edmunds, Richard Hurd

EDRICH

OLD NENE
(Old Nene), Cambridgeshire, England
Year Built: 1992
Designer: R Edrich

EDWARDS

NIZELS
(Nizels), Kent, England
Designer: D Donaldson, Edwards

ELLIS

MORTEHOE & WOOLACOMBE
(Mortehoe & Woolacombe), Devon,
England
Year Built: 1989
Designer: H T Ellis

ELMER

WAVENDON GOLF CTRE
(Wavendon Golf Ctre), Buckinghamshire,
England
Year Built: 1990
Designer: J Drake, N Elmer

ENNIS

BRIGHT CASTLE
(Bright Castle), County Down, Northern
Ireland
Designer: Mr Ennis

EVANS

CAPEL BANGOR
(Capel Bangor), Ceredigion, Wales

Year Built: 1992
Designer: W Evans

PENRHOS
(Academy), Ceredigion, Wales
Year Built: 1996
Designer: John Evans

FALCONER

WEST MALLING
(Hurricane), Kent, England
Year Built: 1974
Designer: Max Falconer

WEST MALLING
(Spitfire), Kent, England
Year Built: 1974
Designer: Max Falconer

FALDO

CHART HILLS
(Chart Hills), Kent, England
Year Built: 1993
Designer: Nick Faldo

SANDFORD SPRINGS
(Lakes), Hampshire, England
Year Built: 1990
**Designer: Nick Faldo, Bernhard Gallagher,
Hawtree**

SANDFORD SPRINGS
(Parks), Hampshire, England
Year Built: 1988
**Designer: Nick Faldo, Bernhard Gallagher,
Hawtree**

SANDFORD SPRINGS
(Woods), Hampshire, England
Year Built: 1988
**Designer: Nick Faldo, Bernhard Gallagher,
Hawtree**

FAULKNER

WEST CHILTINGTON
(West Chiltington), Sussex (West), England
Year Built: 1988
Designer: Brian Barnes, Max Faulkner

FEARN

ORMONDE FIELDS
(Ormonde), Derbyshire, England
Year Built: 1930
Designer: John Fearn

FENSON

ASHBURY
(Oakwood), Devon, England
Year Built: 1991
Designer: Mr David Fenson

FERGURSON

NEW ZEALAND
(New Zealand), Surrey, England
Designer: Fergurson, Muir, Simpson

FERNIE

ALDEBURGH
(Aldeburgh), Suffolk, England
Designer: William Fernie, Thompson

APPLEBY
(Appleby), Cumbria, England
Designer: William Fernie

CALLANDER
(Callander), Perth and Kinross, Scotland
Designer: William Fernie, George Morris

CRAIGIE HILL
(Craigie Hill), Perth And Kinross, Scotland
Year Built: 1911
Designer: Jamie Anderson, William Fernie

DOUGLAS PARK
(Douglas Park), Glasgow (City of), Scotland
Year Built: 1897
Designer: William Fernie

DRUMPELLIER
(Drumpellier), Lanarkshire (North), Scotland
Designer: William Fernie

DUMFRIES & COUNTY
(Nunfield), Dumfries And Galloway, Scotland
Year Built: 1912
Designer: William Fernie

GALLOWAY
(Dumfries & Galloway), Dumfries And Galloway, Scotland
Designer: William Fernie

GARESFIELD
(Garesfield), Tyne And Wear, England
Designer: Harry Fernie

MACHRIE BAY
(Machrie Bay), Isle of Arran, Scotland
Designer: William Fernie

NEW CUMNOCK
(New Cumnock), Ayrshire (East), Scotland
Designer: William Fernie

PITLOCHRY
(Pitlochry), Perth And Kinross, Scotland
Designer: William Fernie

SEACROFT
(Seacroft), Lincolnshire, England
Year Built: 1895
Designer: William Fernie

SHISKINE
(Shiskine), Ayrshire (North), Scotland
Year Built: 1896
Designer: William Fernie

SOUTHERNDOWN
(Southerndown), Bridgend, Wales
Designer: William Fernie

STRATHAVEN
(Strathaven), Lanarkshire (South), Scotland
Designer: William Fernie, Stutt

TROON (ROYAL)
(Old), Ayrshire (South), Scotland
Year Built: 1878
Designer: William Fernie

WHITSAND BAY
(Whitsand Bay), Cornwall, England

Year Built: 1905
Designer: William Fernie

FINN

BOWENHURST
(Bowenhurst), Surrey, England
Year Built: 1992
Designer: Finn

FISHER

WINDWHISTLE
(Windwhistle), Somerset, England
Year Built: 1932
Designer: James Braid, Fisher, Taylor

FITTON

ELTON FURZE
(Elton Furze), Cambridgeshire, England
Year Built: 1992
Designer: Fitton

ORTON MEADOWS
(Orton Meadows), Cambridgeshire, England
Year Built: 1982
Designer: Fitton

TOFT HOTEL
(Toft Hotel), Lincolnshire, England
Year Built: 1984
Designer: Fitton

FLANAGAN

HOLLYWOOD LAKES
(Hollywood Lakes), County Dublin, Ireland
Year Built: 1994
Designer: M Flanagan

FORBES

FAUGHAN VALLEY
(Faughan Valley), County Londonderry, Northern Ireland
Year Built: 2000
Designer: David Forbes

FORRESTER

FORRESTER PARK
(Forrester Park), Essex, England
Year Built: 1968
Designer: T R Forrester, Muir

FORTUNE

ROOKWOOD
(Rookwood), Sussex (West), England
Year Built: 1992
Designer: John Fortune

SLINFOLD PARK
(Championship), Sussex (West), England
Year Built: 1993
Designer: John Fortune

SLINFOLD PARK
(Short), Sussex (West), England
Designer: John Fortune

FOWLER

ABBEYDALE
(Abbeydale), Yorkshire (South), England
Designer: Fowler

ABERDOVEY
(Aberdovey), Gwynedd, Wales
Designer: James Braid, Fowler

BEAU DESERT
(Beau Desert), Staffordshire, England
Designer: Fowler

BLACKWELL
(The Blackwell), Worcestershire, England
Designer: Herbert Fowler, T Simpson

NORTH FORELAND
(Main), Kent, England
Designer: Fowler, Simpson

WEST SURREY
(West Surrey), Surrey, England
Year Built: 1910
Designer: Fowler

YELVERTON
(Yelverton), Devon, England
Year Built: 1904
Designer: Fowler

YEOVIL
(Newton), Somerset, England
Designer: Charles Hugh Alison, Herbert Fowler

FOX

SAND MARTINS
(Sand Martins), Berkshire, England
Year Built: 1993
Designer: Edward Fox

FRANKS

DROITWICH
(Droitwich), Worcestershire, England
Designer: James Braid, G Franks

FRASER

RAVENSWORTH
(Ravensworth), Tyne And Wear, England
Designer: J W Fraser

FRAYNE

TRETHORNE
(Threthorne), Cornwall, England
Year Built: 1993
Designer: Frank Frayne

GABB

RODWAY HILL
(Rodway Hill), Gloucestershire, England
Year Built: 1991
Designer: John Gabb

SPARKWELL
(Welbeck Manor & Sparkwell), Devon, England
Year Built: 1993
Designer: John Gabb

GADD

MOORE PLACE
(Moore Place), Surrey, England
Year Built: 1926
Designer: Harry Vardon, David Allen, Nick Gadd

GALAVAN

CARRIGLEADE
(Carrigleade), County Kilkenny, Ireland
Year Built: 1995
Designer: Dan Galavan

GALLAGHER

SANDFORD SPRINGS
(Lakes), Hampshire, England
Year Built: 1990
Designer: Nick Faldo, Bernhard Gallagher, Hawtree

SANDFORD SPRINGS
(Parks), Hampshire, England
Year Built: 1988
Designer: Nick Faldo, Bernhard Gallagher, Hawtree

SANDFORD SPRINGS
(Woods), Hampshire, England
Year Built: 1988
Designer: Nick Faldo, Bernhard Gallagher, Hawtree

WENTWORTH CLUB
(Edinburgh), Surrey, England
Designer: Bernhard Gallagher, John Jacobs, Gary Player

GALWAY

SERLBY PARK
(Serlby Park), Yorkshire (South), England
Designer: Galway

GANNON

TREVOSE
(New), Cornwall, England
Designer: Peter Alliss, T Bennett, P Gannon

GARNER

CHILWORTH
(Manor), Hampshire, England
Designer: J Garner

GARRATT

HAGLEY
(Hagley), Midlands (West), England
Designer: Garratt

GAUNT

CHIDDINGFOLD
(Chiddingfold), Surrey, England
Year Built: 1994
Designer: Jonathan Gaunt

LINDEN HALL
(Linden Hall), Northumberland, England
Year Built: 1997
Designer: Jonathan Gaunt

MAGNOLIA PARK
(Magnolia Park), Buckinghamshire, England
Year Built: 1998
Designer: Jonathan Gaunt

OAKLAND PARK
(Oakland Park), Buckinghamshire, England
Designer: Jonathan Gaunt

RAMSIDE
(Bishops), County Durham, England
Designer: Jonathan Gaunt

RAMSIDE
(Cathedral), County Durham, England
Year Built: 1996
Designer: Jonathan Gaunt

RAMSIDE
(Princes), County Durham, England
Year Built: 1996
Designer: Jonathan Gaunt

REDLIBBETS
(Redlibbets), Kent, England
Year Built: 1995
Designer: Jonathan Gaunt

WILLOW VALLEY
(T.P.C.), Yorkshire (West), England
Year Built: 1997
Designer: Jonathan Gaunt

WOKEFIELD PARK
(Wokefield Park), Berkshire, England
Year Built: 1996
Designer: Jonathan Gaunt

GIBSON

LAHINCH
(Old), County Clare, Ireland
Designer: Gibson, Alistair MacKenzie

GIDMAN

BLACKWOOD GOLF CTRE
(Hamilton), County Down, Northern Ireland
Year Built: 1994
Designer: Simon Gidman

BLACKWOOD GOLF CTRE
(Temple), County Down, Northern Ireland
Year Built: 1994
Designer: Simon Gidman

BRAMPTON PARK
(Brampton Park), Cambridgeshire, England
Year Built: 1991
Designer: Simon Gidman

BRICKHAMPTON COURT
(Glevum), Gloucestershire, England
Year Built: 1994
Designer: Simon Gidman

BRICKHAMPTON COURT
(Spa), Gloucestershire, England
Year Built: 1994
Designer: Simon Gidman

BURHILL
(Burhill (New)), Surrey, England
Year Built: 2001
Designer: Simon Gidman

FOREST OF GALTRES
(Forest of Galtres), Yorkshire (North), England
Designer: Simon Gidman

FRILFORD HEATH
(Blue), Oxfordshire, England
Year Built: 1994
Designer: S Gidman

GALGORM CASTLE
(Galgorm Castle Golf & Country Club), County Antrim, Northern Ireland
Year Built: 1997
Designer: Simon Gidman

HILTON PUCKRUP HALL
(Hilton Puckrup Hall), Gloucestershire, England
Designer: Simon Gidman

SALISBURY & SOUTH WILTS
(Bibury), Wiltshire, England
Designer: S Gidman, J H Taylor

SALISBURY & SOUTH WILTS
(Main), Wiltshire, England
Year Built: 1888
Designer: S Gidman, J H Taylor

STUDLEY WOOD
(Studley Wood), Oxfordshire, England
Year Built: 1994
Designer: Simon Gidman

VALE ROYAL ABBEY
(Vale Royal Abbey), Cheshire, England
Year Built: 1998
Designer: Simon Gidman

WITNEY LAKES
(Whitney Lakes), Oxfordshire, England
Year Built: 1994
Designer: Simon Gidman

GILLETT

ALDWICKBURY PARK
(Aldwickbury Park),
Year Built: 1995
Designer: K Brown, Martin Gillett

ALDWICKBURY PARK
(Aldwickbury Park), Hertfordshire, England
Year Built: 1995
Designer: K Brown, Martin Gillett

ASH VALLEY GOLF CLUB
(Ash Valley), Hertfordshire, England
Year Built: 1994
Designer: Martin Gillett

BOARS HEAD
(Boar's Head), Sussex (East), England
Year Built: 1997
Designer: Martin Gillett

CRONDON PARK
(Crondon Park), Essex, England
Year Built: 1989
Designer: Martin Gillett

STOCK BROOK MANOR
(Manor), Essex, England
Designer: Martin Gillett

STOCK BROOK MANOR
(Stock & Brooks), Essex, England
Designer: Martin Gillett

TOOT HILL
(Toot Hill), Essex, England
Designer: Martin Gillett

GILMAN

TREFLOYNE
(Trefloyne), Pembrokeshire, Wales

by Course **DESIGNER SURNAME**

Galavan — Gilman

Year Built: 1996
Designer: F Gilman

GLASSON

🌀 **COLMWORTH & NORTH BEDFORDSHIRE**
(Colmworth & North Bedfordshire), Bedfordshire, England
Year Built: 1992
Designer: John Glasson

GODIN

🌀 **DEWLANDS MANOR**
(Dewlands), Sussex (East), England
Year Built: 1989
Designer: Godin

GOLF DESIGN

🌀 **TRACY PARK**
(Cromwell), Bristol, England
Year Built: 1976
Designer: Golf Design

🌀 **TRACY PARK**
(Crown), Bristol, England
Year Built: 1976
Designer: Golf Design

🌀 **WOODLANDS**
(Woodlands), Bristol, England
Designer: Golf Design

GOODBAN

🌀 **CHULMLEIGH**
(Summer), Devon, England
Designer: John Goodban

🌀 **CHULMLEIGH**
(Winter Short), Devon, England
Year Built: 1975
Designer: John Goodban

GOODENOUGH

🌀 **OAKDALE**
(Oakdale), Caerphilly, Wales
Year Built: 1990
Designer: Ian Goodenough

GOODFELLOW

🌀 **PARLEY**
(Parley), Dorset, England
Year Built: 1992
Designer: P Goodfellow

GORVETT

🌀 **EARLSWOOD**
(Earlswood), Neath Port Talbot, Wales
Designer: Alistair Gorvett

GOUGH

🌀 **MILE END**
(Mile End), Shropshire, England
Year Built: 1992
Designer: Gough, Price

GOW

🌀 **GIRTON**
(Girton), Cambridgeshire, England
Designer: Allan Gow

GRANT

🌀 **WOODBRIDGE**
(Forest), Suffolk, England
Designer: D Grant

🌀 **WOODBRIDGE**
(Woodbridge), Suffolk, England
Year Built: 1893
Designer: D Grant

GRAY

🌀 **CRAIGIEKNOWES**
(Craigieknowes), Dumfries And Galloway, Scotland
Year Built: 1994
Designer: D Gray

🌀 **PINES**
(Pines), Dumfries And Galloway, Scotland
Year Built: 1997
Designer: D Gray

GREEN

🌀 **GANSTEAD PARK**
(Ganstead Park), Yorkshire (East), England
Year Built: 1976
Designer: P Green

🌀 **WHADDON**
(Whaddon), Hertfordshire, England
Year Built: 1989
Designer: Ken Green, Jeff Huggett

GREENS

🌀 **CRAIBSTONE**
(Craibstone), Aberdeen (City of), Scotland
Year Built: 1999
Designer: Greens of Scotland

🌀 **KEMNAY**
(Kemnay), Aberdeenshire, Scotland
Year Built: 1908
Designer: Greens of Scotland

🌀 **KINLOSS**
(Kinloss 1), Moray, Scotland
Year Built: 1996
Designer: Greens of Scotland

🌀 **NEWBURGH-ON-YTHAN**
(Newburgh-on-Ythan), Aberdeenshire, Scotland
Year Built: 1888
Designer: Greens of Scotland

🌀 **PETERCULTER**
(Peterculter), Aberdeenshire, Scotland
Year Built: 1989
Designer: Greens of Scotland

GRIFFIN

🌀 **PORTSTEWART**
(Strand), County Londonderry, Northern Ireland
Designer: Griffin, Harris, Park

GRIFFITH

🌀 **FLINT**
(Flint), Flintshire, Wales
Designer: H G Griffith

GROOME

🌀 **LIPHOOK**
(Liphook), Hampshire, England
Designer: A C Groome

HACKETT

🌀 **ADARE MANOR**
(Adare Manor), County Limerick, Ireland
Designer: Edward Hackett, Ben Sayers

🌀 **ATHENRY**
(Athenry), County Galway, Ireland
Year Built: 1978
Designer: Edward Hackett

🌀 **BALLINA**
(Ballina), County Mayo, Ireland
Year Built: 1924
Designer: Edward Hackett

🌀 **BALLINASCORNEY**
(Ballinascorney), County Dublin, Ireland
Designer: Edward Hackett

🌀 **BALLINROBE**
(Ballinrobe), County Mayo, Ireland
Designer: Edward Hackett

🌀 **BALLYMOTE**
(Ballymote), County Sligo, Ireland
Designer: Edward Hackett

🌀 **BANTRY BAY**
(Bantry Bay), County Cork, Ireland
Year Built: 1975
Designer: Christy O'Connor, Edward Hackett

🌀 **BLACKLION**
(Blacklion), County Cavan, Ireland
Designer: Edward Hackett

🌀 **BOYLE**
(Boyle), County Roscommon, Ireland
Designer: Edward Hackett

🌀 **CAHIR PARK**
(Cahir Park), County Tipperary, Ireland
Designer: Edward Hackett

🌀 **CARNE**
(Carne Golf Links), County Mayo, Ireland
Designer: Edward Hackett

🌀 **CARRICK ON SUIR**
(Carrick-on-Suir), County Tipperary, Ireland
Designer: Edward Hackett

🌀 **CARRICK-ON-SHANNON**
(Carrick-On-Shannon), County Leitrim, Ireland
Designer: Edward Hackett

🌀 **CAVAN (COUNTY)**
(Cavan), County Cavan, Ireland
Designer: Edward Hackett

🌀 **CEANN SIBEAL**
(Ceann Sibeal), County Kerry, Ireland
Designer: Edward Hackett, O'Connor

🌀 **CHARLESLAND**
(Charlesland), County Wicklow, Ireland
Year Built: 1992
Designer: Edward Hackett

● CLONMEL
(Clonmel), County Tipperary, Ireland
Designer: Edward Hackett

● COBH
(Cobh), County Cork, Ireland
Year Built: 1987
Designer: Edward Hackett

● CONNEMARA
(Connemara), County Galway, Ireland
Year Built: 1973
Designer: Edward Hackett

● DONEGAL
(Donegal), County Donegal, Ireland
Designer: Edward Hackett

● DOOKS
(Dooks), County Kerry, Ireland
Year Built: 1889
Designer: Edward Hackett, Donald Steel

● DUNMORE
(Dunmore), County Cork, Ireland
Designer: Edward Hackett

● EAST CORK
(East Cork), County Cork, Ireland
Designer: Edward Hackett

● EDENDERRY
(Edenderry), County Offaly, Ireland
Designer: Edward Hackett, Havers

● ENNISCORTHY
(Enniscorthy), County Wexford, Ireland
Designer: Edward Hackett

● ENNISCRONE
(Enniscrone), County Mayo, Ireland
Designer: Edward Hackett

● FITZPATRICK FITNESS CTRE
(Fitzpatrick Silver Springs), County Cork,
Ireland
Designer: Edward Hackett

● GLEBE
(Glebe), County Meath, Ireland
Year Built: 1993
Designer: Edward Hackett

● ISLAND
(The Island), County Dublin, Ireland
Designer: Edward Hackett, Hawtree

● KENMARE
(Kenmare), County Kerry, Ireland
Designer: Edward Hackett

● KILCOCK
(Kilcock), County Kildare, Ireland
Designer: Edward Hackett

● KILKEE
(Kilkee), County Clare, Ireland
Year Built: 1896
Designer: Edward Hackett

● KILKEEL
(Kilkeel), County Down, Northern Ireland
Year Built: 1949
Designer: Edward Hackett

● KILLARNEY
(Killeen), County Kerry, Ireland
Designer: Edward Hackett, Billy O'Sullivan

● KILLINBEG
(Killinbeg), County Louth, Ireland
Designer: Edward Hackett

● KILLORGLIN
(Killorglin), County Kerry, Ireland
Designer: Edward Hackett

● KILTERNAN
(Kilternan), County Dublin, Ireland
Designer: Edward Hackett

● LETTERKENNY
(Letterkenny), County Donegal, Ireland
Designer: Edward Hackett

● LOUGHREA
(Loughrea), County Galway, Ireland
Designer: Edward Hackett

● LUCAN
(Lucan), County Dublin, Ireland
Designer: Edward Hackett

● MAHON MUNICIPAL
(Mahon Municipal), County Cork, Ireland
Designer: Edward Hackett

● MALAHIDE
(Main), County Dublin, Ireland
Year Built: 1990
Designer: Edward Hackett

● MEATH (COUNTY)
(Meath), County Meath, Ireland
Designer: T Craddock, Edward Hackett

● NENAGH
(Nenagh), County Tipperary, Ireland
Designer: Edward Hackett

● NUREMORE HOTEL
(Nuremore Hotel), County Monaghan,
Ireland
Designer: Edward Hackett

● OLD CONNA
(Old Conna), County Wicklow, Ireland
Designer: Edward Hackett

● PORTARLINGTON
(Portarlington), County Laois, Ireland
Designer: Edward Hackett

● RATHDOWNEY
(Rathdowney), County Laois, Ireland
Designer: Edward Hackett

● RING OF KERRY
(Ring Of Kerry), County Kerry, Ireland
Year Built: 1998
Designer: Edward Hackett

● SOUTH MEATH
(South Meath Course), County Meath,
Ireland
Year Built: 1993
Designer: Edward Hackett

● STRABANE
(Strabane), County Tyrone, Northern
Ireland
Year Built: 1908
Designer: Edward Hackett, P Jones

● TUAM
(Tuam), County Galway, Ireland
Designer: Edward Hackett

● TUBBERCURRY
(Tobercurry), County Sligo, Ireland
Designer: Edward Hackett

● WATERVILLE HOUSE & GOLF
LINKS
(Waterville House), County Kerry, Ireland
Designer: Edward Hackett

● WEST WATERFORD
(West Waterford), County Waterford,
Ireland
Year Built: 1992
Designer: Edward Hackett

HALES

● ALLHALLOWS
(Allhallows), Kent, England
Year Built: 1998
Designer: W B Hales

HALPIN

● CASTLEWARDEN
(Castlewarden), County Kildare, Ireland
Designer: T Halpin

● SWORDS OPEN
(Swords Open), County Dublin, Ireland
Year Built: 1992
Designer: T Halpin

● WOODLANDS
(Woodlands), County Kildare, Ireland
Designer: T Halpin

HAMER

● ARSCOTT
(Arscott), Shropshire, England
Year Built: 1992
Designer: Martin Hamer

HAMILTON

● HIGHBULLEN HOTEL
(Highbullen Hotel), Devon, England
Designer: M Neil, J Hamilton

HANSE

● CRAIL
(Craighead Links Course), Fife, Scotland
Designer: Gil Hanse

HARGREAVES

● MYTTON FOLD
(Mytton Fold), Lancashire, England
Year Built: 1994
Designer: Frank Hargreaves

HARPER

● NORTON
(Norton), Cleveland, England
Year Built: 1992
Designer: T Harper

HARRIS

● CLYNE
(Clyne), Swansea, Wales
Year Built: 1920
Designer: Harry Shapland Colt, Harris

● COURTOWN
(Courtown), County Wexford, Ireland
Designer: Harris

by Course **DESIGNER SURNAME**

Hackett — Harris

HEMSTED FOREST GOLF CLUB
(Executive), Kent, England
Designer: Commander J Harris

OLD THORNS
(Old Thorns), Hampshire, England
Year Built: 1982
Designer: Commander J Harris, Peter Alliss

PORTSTEWART
(Strand), County Londonderry, Northern Ireland
Designer: Griffin, Harris, Park

RENFREW
(Renfrew), Renfrewshire, Scotland
Designer: Commander J Harris

STAVERTON PARK
(Staverton Park), Northamptonshire, England
Year Built: 1977
Designer: Commander J Harris

YOUGHAL
(Youghal), County Cork, Ireland
Designer: Commander J Harris

HARRISON

MARTIN MOOR
(Martin Moor), Lincolnshire, England
Year Built: 1992
Designer: Mr Harrison

HARTLEY

HOLYWELL BAY
(Holywell Bay), Cornwall, England
Designer: Hartley

HASSALL

BROMBOROUGH
(Bromborough), Merseyside, England
Year Built: 1904
Designer: J Hassall

HAVERS

EDENDERRY
(Edenderry), County Offaly, Ireland
Designer: Edward Hackett, Havers

HAWTHORN

HIGH ELMS
(High Elms), Kent, England
Year Built: 1968
Designer: Hawthorn

HAWTREE

ABERGELE
(Abergele), Conwy, Wales
Year Built: 1910
Designer: Hawtree

ADDINGTON COURT GOLF CLUB
(Addington 9 Hole), Surrey, England
Designer: Hawtree

ADDINGTON COURT GOLF CLUB
(Championship), Surrey, England
Year Built: 1930
Designer: Hawtree, Taylor

ADDINGTON COURT GOLF CLUB
(Falconwood), Surrey, England
Designer: Hawtree

ADLINGTON
(Academy), Cheshire, England
Year Built: 1995
Designer: Hawtree

ARKLOW
(Arklow), County Wicklow, Ireland
Designer: Hawtree, Taylor

ATHERSTONE
(Atherstone), Warwickshire, England
Year Built: 1894
Designer: Hawtree

AYLESBURY PARK
(Aylesbury Park), Buckinghamshire, England
Year Built: 1995
Designer: Hawtree

BEARWOOD LAKES
(Bearwood Lakes), Berkshire, England
Year Built: 1996
Designer: Hawtree

BIRKDALE (ROYAL)
(Royal Birkdale), Merseyside, England
Designer: Hawtree, Lowe

BLAINROE
(Blainroe), County Wicklow, Ireland
Designer: Hawtree

BRAINTREE
(Braintree), Essex, England
Year Built: 1971
Designer: Hawtree

BRIDPORT & WEST DORSET
(Bridport & West Dorset), Dorset, England
Year Built: 1891
Designer: Hawtree

BROMSGROVE
(Bromsgrove), Worcestershire, England
Year Built: 1992
Designer: Hawtree

BROOKMANS PARK
(Brookmans Park), Hertfordshire, England
Year Built: 1933
Designer: Hawtree, Taylor

BROOME MANOR
(Broome Manor), Wiltshire, England
Year Built: 1976
Designer: Hawtree

BROOMIEKNOWE
(Broomieknowe), Lothian (Mid), Scotland
Designer: Hawtree, Ben Sayers

BRUNTSFIELD GOLF CLUB
(Bruntsfield), Edinburgh (City of), Scotland
Designer: Hawtree, Alistair MacKenzie, William Park

BURY ST EDMUNDS
(Bury St Edmunds 9 Hole), Suffolk, England
Year Built: 1992
Designer: Hawtree

CANNINGTON
(Cannington), Somerset, England
Year Built: 1993
Designer: Hawtree

CANWICK PARK
(Canwick Park), Lincolnshire, England
Year Built: 1975
Designer: Hawtree

CARDIGAN
(Cardigan), Ceredigion, Wales
Year Built: 1895
Designer: Hawtree

CHIGWELL
(Chigwell), Essex, England
Year Built: 1925
Designer: Hawtree, Taylor

CHINA FLEET
(China Fleet Country Club), Cornwall, England
Designer: Hawtree

CHIPPING SODBURY
(New), Bristol, England
Designer: Hawtree

CHIPPING SODBURY
(Old), Bristol, England
Designer: Hawtree

CLIFF HOTEL
(Cardigan), Ceredigion, Wales
Year Built: 1895
Designer: Hawtree

CORBY PUBLIC
(Corby Public), Northamptonshire, England
Year Built: 1965
Designer: Hawtree

COSBY
(Cosby), Leicestershire, England
Designer: Hawtree

COVENTRY
(Coventry), Midlands (West), England
Designer: Hawtree, Harry Vardon

DIP FARM
(Dip Farm), Suffolk, England
Year Built: 1893
Designer: Hawtree, S Taylor

DOWNPATRICK
(Downpatrick), County Down, Northern Ireland
Year Built: 1930
Designer: Hawtree

DRAYTON PARK
(Drayton Park), Oxfordshire, England
Designer: Hawtree

DUXBURY JUBILEE PARK
(Duxbury Jubilee Park), Lancashire, England
Designer: Hawtree

DYKE
(Dyke), Sussex (East), England
Designer: Hawtree

EASINGWOLD
(Easingwold), Yorkshire (North), England
Designer: Hawtree

EAST DORSET
(Lakeland), Dorset, England
Year Built: 1981
Designer: Hawtree

EAST DORSET
(Woodland), Dorset, England
Year Built: 1981
Designer: Hawtree

EASTHAM LODGE
(Eastham Lodge), Merseyside, England
Year Built: 1973
Designer: Hawtree, D Hemstock

ENMORE PARK
(Enmore), Somerset, England
Year Built: 1932
Designer: Hawtree

EREWASH VALLEY
(Erewash Valley), Derbyshire, England
Designer: Hawtree

FAIRWOOD PARK
(Fairwood Park), Swansea, Wales
Year Built: 1969
Designer: Hawtree

FARNHAM PARK
(Farnham Park), Berkshire, England
Designer: Hawtree

FIVE LAKES HOTEL
(Lakes), Essex, England
Designer: Hawtree, Taylor

FIVE LAKES HOTEL
(Links), Essex, England
Designer: Hawtree, Taylor

FOXHILLS GOLF
(Bernard Hunt), Surrey, England
Year Built: 1975
Designer: Hawtree

FOXHILLS GOLF
(Longcross), Surrey, England
Designer: Hawtree

FOXHILLS GOLF
(Manor), Surrey, England
Designer: Hawtree

FULFORD HEATH
(Fulford Heath), Midlands (West), England
Designer: James Braid, Hawtree

GLYN ABBEY
(Glyn Abbey), Carmarthenshire, Wales
Year Built: 1992
Designer: Hawtree

GLYNHIR
(Glynhir), Carmarthenshire, Wales
Designer: Hawtree

GOG MAGOG
(The Old), Cambridgeshire, England
Year Built: 1901
Designer: Hawtree

GOG MAGOG
(Wandlebury), Cambridgeshire, England
Year Built: 1901
Designer: Hawtree

GRANGE PARK
(Grange Park), Yorkshire (South), England
Designer: Hawtree

GRASSMOOR GOLF CTRE
(Grassmoor Golf Ctre), Derbyshire,
England
Designer: Hawtree

GUILDFORD
(Guildford), Surrey, England
Designer: Hawtree, Taylor

HARPENDEN
(Harpenden), Hertfordshire, England
Designer: Hawtree, Taylor

HATFIELD LONDON
(Hatfield London), Hertfordshire, England
Designer: Hawtree

HIGH POST
(High Post), Wiltshire, England
Year Built: 1922
Designer: Hawtree

HILLSIDE
(Hillside), Merseyside, England
Designer: Hawtree

HILLTOP
(Hilltop Public), Midlands (West), England
Designer: Hawtree

HINTLESHAM HALL
(Hintlesham Hall), Suffolk, England
Year Built: 1989
Designer: Hawtree

HUMBERSTONE HEIGHTS
(Humberstone Heights), Leicestershire,
England
Designer: Hawtree

HURDWICK
(Hurdwick), Devon, England
Designer: Hawtree

IMMINGHAM
(Immingham), Lincolnshire (North East),
England
Year Built: 1974
Designer: Hawtree

INGESTRE PARK
(Ingestre Park), Staffordshire, England
Designer: Hawtree

ISLAND
(The Island), County Dublin, Ireland
Designer: Edward Hackett, Hawtree

KENILWORTH
(Kenilworth), Warwickshire, England
Designer: Hawtree

KINGS NORTON
(Blue), Midlands (West), England
Designer: Hawtree

KINGS NORTON
(Red), Midlands (West), England
Designer: Hawtree

KINGS NORTON
(Yellow), Midlands (West), England
Designer: Hawtree

KNARESBOROUGH
(Knaresborough), Yorkshire (North),
England
Designer: Hawtree

LEICESTER
(The Leicestershire), Leicestershire,
England
Year Built: 1890
Designer: Hawtree

LISBURN
(Lisburn), County Antrim, Northern Ireland
Year Built: 1971
Designer: Hawtree

LITTLE HAY
(Little Hay), Hertfordshire, England
Year Built: 1978
Designer: Hawtree

LLANGEFNI PUBLIC
(Llangefni (Public)), Isle of Anglesey, Wales
Designer: Hawtree

LONG ASHTON
(Long Ashton), Bristol, England
Year Built: 1893
Designer: Hawtree, S Taylor

MACCLESFIELD
(Macclesfield), Cheshire, England
Year Built: 1889
Designer: Hawtree

MALKINS BANK
(Malkins Bank), Cheshire, England
Designer: Hawtree

MASSEREENE
(Massereene), County Antrim, Northern
Ireland
Designer: Hawtree

MINCHINHAMPTON
(Avening), Gloucestershire, England
Year Built: 1975
Designer: Hawtree

MINCHINHAMPTON
(Cherington), Gloucestershire, England
Year Built: 1995
Designer: Hawtree

MOOR HALL
(Moor Hall), Midlands (West), England
Year Built: 1932
**Designer: Frederick George Hawtree, J H
Taylor**

MOORS VALLEY GOLF CTRE
(Moors Valley), Hampshire, England
Designer: Hawtree

MORTONHALL
(Mortonhall), Edinburgh (City of), Scotland
Designer: James Braid, Hawtree

MOWSBURY
(Mowsbury), Bedfordshire, England
Year Built: 1974
Designer: Hawtree

NORMANBY HALL
(Normanby Hall), Lincolnshire (North),
England
Designer: Hawtree

by Course **DESIGNER SURNAME**

Hawtree — Hawtree

OPEN
(Red Nine), County Dublin, Ireland
Designer: Hawtree

PORTHCAWL (ROYAL)
(Royal Porthcawl), Bridgend, Wales
Year Built: 1892
Designer: Hawtree, Hunter, Simpson, Taylor

PORTMORE GOLF PARK
(Barum), Devon, England
Year Built: 1995
Designer: Hawtree

PORTSMOUTH
(Portsmouth), Hampshire, England
Year Built: 1970
Designer: Hawtree

RAMSDALE PARK
(Ramsdale Park Main), Nottinghamshire, England
Year Built: 1992
Designer: Hawtree

RAMSDALE PARK
(The Par 3), Nottinghamshire, England
Year Built: 1992
Designer: Hawtree

RHUDDLAN
(Rhuddlan), Denbighshire, Wales
Year Built: 1930
Designer: Hawtree

RICHMOND PARK
(Dukes), London (Greater), England
Year Built: 1930
Designer: Hawtree

RICHMOND PARK
(Princes), London (Greater), England
Year Built: 1930
Designer: Hawtree

RISEBRIDGE
(Risebridge 18 Hole), Essex, England
Designer: Hawtree

RISEBRIDGE
(Risebridge 9 Hole), Essex, England
Designer: Hawtree

ROSSLARE
(New), County Wexford, Ireland
Designer: Hawtree, Taylor

ROSSLARE
(Old), County Wexford, Ireland
Designer: Hawtree, Taylor

RUDDING PARK
(Rudding Park), Yorkshire (North), England
Year Built: 1995
Designer: Hawtree

RUSPER
(Rusper), Surrey, England
Year Built: 1992
Designer: Tony Blunden, Hawtree

SANDFORD SPRINGS
(Lakes), Hampshire, England
Year Built: 1990
Designer: Nick Faldo, Bernhard Gallagher, Hawtree

SANDFORD SPRINGS
(Parks), Hampshire, England
Year Built: 1988
Designer: Nick Faldo, Bernhard Gallagher, Hawtree

SANDFORD SPRINGS
(Woods), Hampshire, England
Year Built: 1988
Designer: Nick Faldo, Bernhard Gallagher, Hawtree

SEEDY MILL
(Mill), Staffordshire, England
Year Built: 1991
Designer: Hawtree

SELBY
(Selby), Yorkshire (North), England
Designer: Hawtree, Donald Steel, Taylor

SHROPSHIRE
(Blue/Gold), Shropshire, England
Designer: Hawtree

SHROPSHIRE
(Blue/Silver), Shropshire, England
Designer: Hawtree

SHROPSHIRE
(Silver/Gold), Shropshire, England
Designer: Hawtree

SONNING
(Sonning), Berkshire, England
Designer: Hawtree

SOUTHWOOD
(Southwood), Hampshire, England
Designer: Hawtree

STOKE ALBANY
(Stoke Albany), Leicestershire, England
Year Built: 1994
Designer: Hawtree

TAMWORTH MUNICIPAL
(Tamworth Municipal), Staffordshire, England
Designer: Hawtree

TANKERSLEY PARK
(Tankersley Park), Yorkshire (South), England
Year Built: 1907
Designer: Hawtree

THORNBURY GOLF
(High), Bristol, England
Year Built: 1992
Designer: Hawtree

THORNBURY GOLF
(Low), Bristol, England
Year Built: 1992
Designer: Hawtree

THREE RIVERS
(Kings), Essex, England
Year Built: 1971
Designer: Hawtree

WELLINGBOROUGH
(Wellingborough), Northamptonshire, England
Year Built: 1975
Designer: Hawtree

WEST HOVE
(West Hove), Sussex (East), England
Year Built: 1990
Designer: Hawtree

WESTPORT
(Westport), County Mayo, Ireland
Designer: Hawtree

WILDWOOD COUNTRY CLUB
(Wildwood), Surrey, England
Year Built: 1991
Designer: Hawtree

WILLINGCOTT
(Willingcott), Devon, England
Year Built: 1995
Designer: Hawtree

WORLEBURY
(Worlebury), Somerset (North), England
Designer: Hawtree

WRAG BARN
(Wrag Barn), Wiltshire, England
Designer: Hawtree

WYKE GREEN
(Wyke Green), London (Greater), England
Year Built: 1928
Designer: Hawtree

WYNYARD CLUB
(The Wellington), Cleveland, England
Designer: Hawtree

HEADLEY

LAKESIDE LODGE
(Lodge), Cambridgeshire, England
Year Built: 1992
Designer: Alistair Headley

HEADS

HINKSEY HEIGHTS
(Hinksey Heights), Oxfordshire, England
Year Built: 1995
Designer: David Heads

HEALY

RATHBANE
(Rathbone), County Limerick, Ireland
Year Built: 1997
Designer: James Healy

HEANEY

NEWRY
(Newry), County Down, Northern Ireland
Designer: Michael Heaney

HEFFERNAN

THAMESVIEW
(Riverside), London (Greater), England
Designer: Heffernan

HEMSTOCK

ASHBOURNE
(Ashbourne), Derbyshire, England
Year Built: 1998
Designer: D Hemstock

BARLBOROUGH LINKS
(Barlborough Links Golf), Derbyshire, England

Year Built: 1998
Designer: D Hemstock

CHEDINGTON COURT
(Chedington Court), Dorset, England
Year Built: 1991
Designer: D Hemstock

EASTHAM LODGE
(Eastham Lodge), Merseyside, England
Year Built: 1973
Designer: Hawtree, D Hemstock

MANOR
(The Manor), Yorkshire (West), England
Year Built: 1995
Designer: D Hemstock

RUFFORD PARK GOLF CTRE
(Rufford Park), Nottinghamshire, England
Year Built: 1994
Designer: D Hemstock

HENRY

SWALLOW HALL
(Swallow Hall), Yorkshire (North), England
Year Built: 1990
Designer: Brian Henry

HERD

ASPLEY GUISE & WOBURN SANDS
(Aspley Guise & Woburn Sands),
Buckinghamshire, England
Designer: S Herd

CLEVEDON
(Clevedon), Somerset (North), England
Designer: S Herd

HALIFAX
(Ogden), Yorkshire (West), England
Year Built: 1902
Designer: James Braid, S Herd

HARROGATE
(Harrogate), Yorkshire (North), England
Designer: S Herd

HEYSHAM
(Heysham), Lancashire, England
Year Built: 1929
Designer: A Herd

MELTHAM
(Meltham), Yorkshire (West), England
Year Built: 1908
Designer: A Herd

PANNAL
(Pannal), Yorkshire (North), England
Year Built: 1906
Designer: S Herd

ROTHERHAM
(Rotherham), Yorkshire (South), England
Designer: James Braid, S Herd

RUISLIP GOLF CTRE
(Ruislip), London (Greater), England
Designer: S Herd

STAND
(Stand), Manchester (Greater), England
Year Built: 1904
Designer: A Herd, G Lowe

STOCKPORT
(Stockport), Cheshire, England
Designer: P Barrie, A Herd

TURTON
(Turton), Lancashire, England
Year Built: 1908
Designer: A Herd

WAKEFIELD
(Wakefield), Yorkshire (West), England
Year Built: 1912
Designer: Herd, Alistair MacKenzie

HIBBERT

BRIERLEY FOREST
(Davcolm), Nottinghamshire, England
Year Built: 1993
Designer: Hibbert, Walsh

HICKS

PARC
(Parc), Newport, Wales
Designer: T F Hicks, Peter Alliss

HIGGINS

RICHINGS PARK
(Richings Park), Buckinghamshire, England
Designer: Alan Higgins

HIGHFIELD

THORNE
(Thorne), Yorkshire (South), England
Designer: R D Highfield

HILTON

ANGLESEY
(Anglesey), Isle of Anglesey, Wales
Year Built: 1914
Designer: H Hilton

HOARE

STINCHCOMBE HILL
(Stinchcombe Hill), Gloucestershire,
England
Year Built: 1889
Designer: Arthur Hoare

HOCKLEY

SOUTHAMPTON MUNICIPAL
(Southampton Municipal 18 Hole),
Hampshire, England
Year Built: 1935
Designer: Hockley, A P Taylor

HOLCOMBE-INGLEBY

WEST NORFOLK (ROYAL)
(Royal West Norfolk), Norfolk, England
Designer: Holcombe-Ingleby

HOLDSWORTH

STURMINSTER MARSHALL
(Sturminster Marshall), Dorset, England
Designer: David Holdsworth, John Sharkey

HOLMES

BOYSNOPE PARK
(Boysnope Park), Manchester (Greater),
England

Year Built: 1997
Designer: Tony Holmes

STYAL
(Styal), Cheshire, England
Year Built: 1994
Designer: Tony Holmes

HORN

EAGLES
(Eagles), Norfolk, England
Designer: David W Horn

HORSMAN

MANSFIELD WOODHOUSE
(Mansfield Woodhouse), Nottinghamshire,
England
Year Built: 1973
Designer: Horsman

HORTON

WINDLESHAM
(Windlesham), Surrey, England
Year Built: 1994
Designer: Tommy Horton

HOTCHKIN

LINKS
(Links), Suffolk, England
Designer: Colonel Hotchkin

STOKE ROCHFORD
(Stoke Rochford), Lincolnshire, England
Designer: Colonel Hotchkin

WOODHALL SPA
(Hotchkin), Lincolnshire, England
Designer: Colonel Hotchkin

HOWARD

BURNHAM-ON-CROUCH
(Burnham on Crouch), Essex, England
Year Built: 1923
Designer: Howard

HOWES

FOTA ISLAND
(Fota Island), County Cork, Ireland
Designer: Jeff Howes

GLENLO ABBEY
(Glenlo Abbey), County Galway, Ireland
Designer: Jeff Howes

GOWRAN PARK GOLF & LEISURE
(Gowran Park Golf & Leisure), County
Kilkenny, Ireland
Year Built: 2001
Designer: D Howes

HUGGETT

AUCHMILL
(Auchmill), Aberdeen (City of), Scotland
Designer: Neil Coles, Brian Huggett

HAWKSTONE PARK
(Academy), Shropshire, England
Designer: Brian Huggett

HAWKSTONE PARK
(Hawkstone), Shropshire, England
Designer: Brian Huggett

by Course DESIGNER SURNAME

Hemstock — Huggett

🏌 **HAWKSTONE PARK**
(Windmill), Shropshire, England
Designer: Brian Huggett

🏌 **HICKLETON**
(Hickleton), Yorkshire (South), England
Year Built: 1976
Designer: Neil Coles, Brian Huggett

🏌 **ORCHARDLEIGH**
(Orchardleigh), Bath & Somerset (North East), England
Year Built: 1996
Designer: Brian Huggett

🏌 **TILGATE FOREST**
(Tilgate Forest), Sussex (West), England
Year Built: 1982
Designer: Neil Coles, Brian Huggett

🏌 **WHADDON**
(Whaddon), Hertfordshire, England
Year Built: 1989
Designer: Ken Green, Jeff Huggett

HULL

🏌 **BOURN**
(Bourn), Cambridgeshire, England
Year Built: 1991
Designer: J Hull

🏌 **BRAILES**
(Brailes), Oxfordshire, England
Year Built: 1992
Designer: B A Hull

HUNT

🏌 **FERNDOWN FOREST**
(Ferndown Forest), Dorset, England
Year Built: 1993
Designer: Guy Hunt

🏌 **KINGSWOOD**
(Kingswood), Yorkshire (South), England
Year Built: 1994
Designer: John Hunt

🏌 **PRINCES RISBOROUGH**
(Princes Risborough), Buckinghamshire, England
Year Built: 1990
Designer: Guy Hunt

HUNTER

🏌 **COCHRANE CASTLE**
(Cochrane Castle), Renfrewshire, Scotland
Year Built: 1895
Designer: J Hunter

🏌 **PORTHCAWL (ROYAL)**
(Royal Porthcawl), Bridgend, Wales
Year Built: 1892
Designer: Hawtree, Hunter, Simpson, Taylor

🏌 **PORTPATRICK - DUNSKEY**
(Dunskey), Dumfries And Galloway, Scotland
Year Built: 1903
Designer: W M Hunter

🏌 **PRESTWICK ST NICHOLAS**
(Prestwick St Nicholas), Ayrshire (South), Scotland
Designer: Charles Hunter

🏌 **WINDMILL VILLAGE**
(Windmill Village), Midlands (West), England
Designer: Robert Hunter

HURD

🏌 **ST. ANDREWS MAJOR**
(St Andrews Major), Glamorgan (Vale of), Wales
Year Built: 1993
Designer: Edmunds, Richard Hurd

HURST

🏌 **TYDD ST GILES**
(Tydd St Giles), Cambridgeshire, England
Year Built: 1995
Designer: Adrian Hurst

HUTCHINSON

🏌 **ASHRIDGE**
(Ashridge), Hertfordshire, England
Year Built: 1932
Designer: Campbell, C Hutchinson, N Hutchinson

🏌 **KINGTON**
(Kington), Herefordshire, England
Designer: Hutchinson

🏌 **TADMARTON HEATH**
(Tadmarton Heath), Oxfordshire, England
Designer: Colonel Hutchinson

🏌 **WEST SUSSEX**
(West Sussex), Sussex (West), England
Year Built: 1930
Designer: Campbell, Hutchinson

HUTTON

🏌 **HERSHAM VILLAGE**
(Hersham Village), Surrey, England
Year Built: 1995
Designer: Rodney Hutton

🏌 **SUDBROOK MOOR**
(Sudbrook Moor), Lincolnshire, England
Year Built: 1990
Designer: Tim Hutton

JACKLIN

🏌 **ST. PIERRE PARK**
(St Pierre Park), Guernsey, England
Designer: Tony Jacklin

JACKSON

🏌 **BECKSIDE**
(Beckside), Cumbria, England
Year Built: 1990
Designer: Michael Jackson

🏌 **CRETINGHAM**
(Cretingham), Suffolk, England
Year Built: 1983
Designer: Neil Jackson

JACOBS

🏌 **BUCKINGHAMSHIRE**
(Buckinghamshire), London (Greater), England
Designer: John Jacobs

🏌 **CHARTRIDGE PARK**
(Chartridge Park), Buckinghamshire, England
Year Built: 1989
Designer: John Jacobs

🏌 **DELAPRE PARK GOLF COMPLEX**
(Main), Northamptonshire, England
Year Built: 1976
Designer: John Jacobs, John Corby

🏌 **HOEBRIDGE**
(Main), Surrey, England
Year Built: 1982
Designer: John Jacobs

🏌 **NORTHOP**
(Northop), Flintshire, Wales
Year Built: 1994
Designer: John Jacobs

🏌 **PATSHULL PARK**
(Patshull Park Hotel), Midlands (West), England
Designer: John Jacobs

🏌 **RATHFARNHAM**
(Rathfarnham), County Dublin, Ireland
Designer: John Jacobs

🏌 **SANDOWN GOLF CTRE**
(Par 3), Surrey, England
Year Built: 1971
Designer: John Jacobs

🏌 **STEVENAGE**
(Stevenage), Hertfordshire, England
Year Built: 1982
Designer: John Jacobs

🏌 **WENTWORTH CLUB**
(Edinburgh), Surrey, England
Designer: Bernhard Gallagher, John Jacobs, Gary Player

🏌 **WYCOMBE HEIGHTS GOLF CTRE**
(Family), Buckinghamshire, England
Designer: John Jacobs

🏌 **WYCOMBE HEIGHTS GOLF CTRE**
(Main), Buckinghamshire, England
Designer: John Jacobs

JAMES

🏌 **BURGHAM**
(Burgham park), Northumberland, England
Year Built: 1994
Designer: M James, Andrew Mair

JAYES

🏌 **OAKRIDGE**
(Oakridge), Warwickshire, England
Designer: Algy Jayes

JENKINS

🏌 **STAPLEHURST GOLFING PARK**
(Staplehurst), Kent, England
Year Built: 1995
Designer: Jenkins, Sayner

JESSUP

RICHMOND PARK
(Richmond Park), Norfolk, England
Year Built: 1990
Designer: D Jessup, D Scott

JOHNS

WHITCHURCH
(Whitchurch), Glamorgan (Vale of), Wales
Year Built: 1915
Designer: Fred Johns

JOHNSON

BELLINGHAM
(Boogle Hole), Northumberland, England
Year Built: 1893
Designer: E Johnson, I Wilson

DERLLYS COURT
(Derllys Court), Carmarthenshire, Wales
Designer: Peter Johnson

HALESWORTH
(Halesworth), Suffolk, England
Designer: J W Johnson

HALESWORTH
(Halesworth), Suffolk, England
Year Built: 1991
Designer: J W Johnson

JOHNSTON

NORWOOD PARK
(Norwood Park), Nottinghamshire, England
Year Built: 1996
Designer: Clyde B Johnston

JONES

ARDGLASS
(Ardglass), County Down, Northern Ireland
Designer: David Jones

BALLYHEIGUE CASTLE
(Ballyheigue Castle), County Kerry, Ireland
Year Built: 1995
Designer: Roger Jones

CELTIC MANOR
(Coldra Woods), Newport, Wales
Year Built: 1996
Designer: Robert Trent Jones (Jnr)

CELTIC MANOR
(Roman Road), Newport, Wales
Year Built: 1995
Designer: Robert Trent Jones (Jnr)

CELTIC MANOR
(Wentwood Hills), Newport, Wales
Year Built: 1999
Designer: Robert Trent Jones (Jnr)

CLAYS GOLF CTRE
(Clays), Wrexham, Wales
Year Built: 1993
Designer: Roger Jones

DUNMORE EAST
(Dunmore East), County Waterford, Ireland
Year Built: 1993
Designer: W H Jones

GARNANT PARK
(Garnant Park), Carmarthenshire, Wales
Year Built: 1996
Designer: Roger Jones

MITCHELSTOWN
(Mitchelstown), County Cork, Ireland
Designer: David Jones

MOOR ALLERTON
(Blackmoor), Yorkshire (West), England
Designer: Robert Trent Jones

MOOR ALLERTON
(High), Yorkshire (West), England
Designer: Robert Trent Jones

MOOR ALLERTON
(Lakes), Yorkshire (West), England
Designer: Robert Trent Jones

PYPE HAYES
(Pype Hayes), Midlands (West), England
Year Built: 1933
Designer: Bobby Jones

SOUTH LEEDS
(South Leeds), Yorkshire (West), England
Year Built: 1914
Designer: Robert Trent Jones

STOCKLEY PARK
(Stockley Park), London (Greater), England
Year Built: 1993
Designer: Robert Trent Jones

STONEBRIDGE
(Stonebridge), Midlands (West), England
Year Built: 1995
Designer: M Jones

STORWS WEN
(Storws Wen), Isle of Anglesey, Wales
Year Built: 1996
Designer: Ken Jones

STRABANE
(Strabane), County Tyrone, Northern Ireland
Year Built: 1908
Designer: Edward Hackett, P Jones

KAY

ASHFORD
(Ashford), Kent, England
Year Built: 1992
Designer: Kay

BISHOP AUCKLAND
(Bishop Auckland), County Durham, England
Year Built: 1894
Designer: James Kay

KEANE

BRIDGECASTLE
(The Monster), Lothian (West), Scotland
Year Built: 1996
Designer: Kevin Keane, John Slattery

KEITH

DURNESS
(Durness), Highlands, Scotland
Year Built: 1988
Designer: F Keith, Jan Morrison

KENNEALLY

JACK KENNEALLY

KINSALE
(Farrangalway), County Cork, Ireland
Year Built: 1994
Designer: Jack Kenneally

KINSALE
(Ringenane), County Cork, Ireland
Designer: Jack Kenneally

LISSELAN
(Lisselan Estate), County Cork, Ireland
Year Built: 1994
Designer: Jack Kenneally

KIRBY

LONDON
(International), Kent, England
Designer: Ron Kirby

KIRKCALDY

RANFURLY CASTLE
(Ranfurly Castle), Renfrewshire, Scotland
Designer: W Auchterlomie, A Kirkcaldy

KIRKHAM

PANSHANGER GOLF COMPLEX
(Panshanger Golf Complex), Hertfordshire, England
Year Built: 1974
Designer: Peter Kirkham

LAING

LITTLE LAKES
(Gaudet - Luce), Worcestershire, England
Year Built: 1994
Designer: M Laing

LITTLE LAKES
(Little Lakes), Worcestershire, England
Year Built: 1975
Designer: M Laing

LANDER

ALDER ROOT
(Alder Root), Cheshire, England
Year Built: 1993
Designer: Lander, Millington

LANG

HIGHWORTH GOLF CENTRE
(Highworth), Wiltshire, England
Designer: D Lang, B Sandry, T Watt

LANGAN

BALCARRICK
(Balcarrick), County Dublin, Ireland
Designer: Barry Langan

LANGER

PORTMARNOCK HOTEL
(Portmarnock Links), County Dublin, Ireland
Designer: Bernhard Langer

by Course DESIGNER SURNAME

Jessup — Langer

by Course DESIGNER SURNAME

Lathery — Mainland

LATHERY

BALLYREAGH
(Ballyreagh), County Antrim, Northern Ireland
Designer: V Lathery

LAWDON

HOLLANDBUSH
(Holland Bush), Lanarkshire (South), Scotland
Designer: J Lawdon, K Pate

LAWRIE

ELLESMERE PORT
(Ellesmere Port), Merseyside, England
Designer: Cotton, Lawrie, Pennick

GLYNNEATH
(Glynneath), Neath Port Talbot, Wales
Designer: Cotton Pennick Lawrie & Partners

STOCKSFIELD
(Stocksfield), Northumberland, England
Year Built: 1913
Designer: Cotton Pennick Lawrie & Partners

LE BRUN

LES MIELLES
(Les Mielles),
Designer: J Le Brun, R Whitehead

LITTEN

COOKRIDGE HALL GOLF CLUB
(Cookridge Golf Course), Yorkshire (West), England
Designer: Karl Litten

WARWICKSHIRE
(North West), Warwickshire, England
Designer: Karl Litten

LITTLE

COTSWOLD HILLS
(Cotswold Hills), Gloucestershire, England
Year Built: 1976
Designer: Mr M Little

LONGHURST

KILLARNEY
(Mahony's Point), County Kerry, Ireland
Designer: Guy Campbell, Henry Longhurst

LOWE

BIRKDALE (ROYAL)
(Royal Birkdale), Merseyside, England
Designer: Hawtree, Lowe

DUNSCAR
(Dunscar), Lancashire, England
Year Built: 1908
Designer: G Lowe

ENDERBY GOLF CLUB
(Enderby), Leicestershire, England
Designer: David Lowe

HALLOWES
(Hallowes), Derbyshire, England
Year Built: 1892
Designer: G Lowe

ROCHDALE
(Rochdale), Lancashire, England
Designer: G Lowe

ROWANY
(Rowany), Isle of Man, England
Designer: G Lowe

SADDLEWORTH
(Saddleworth), Manchester (Greater), England
Designer: G Lowe, Alistair MacKenzie

ST. ANNES OLD LINKS
(St Annes Old Links), Lancashire, England
Designer: G Lowe

STAND
(Stand), Manchester (Greater), England
Year Built: 1904
Designer: A Herd, G Lowe

THEALE GOLF CTRE
(Theale), Berkshire, England
Year Built: 1996
Designer: Mike Lowe

WINDERMERE
(Windermere), Cumbria, England
Year Built: 1891
Designer: G Lowe

LUCAS

PRINCES
(Himalayas), Kent, England
Year Built: 1951
Designer: Deeley, Lucas, Mallaby

LUMB

CRIMPLE VALLEY
(Crimple Valley), Yorkshire (North), England
Year Built: 1976
Designer: Robin Lumb

LYONS

WOODLANDS MANOR
(Woodlands Manor), Kent, England
Designer: Coles, Lyons

MACAULEY

ALLEN PARK
(Allen Park), County Antrim, Northern Ireland
Year Built: 1995
Designer: J J Macauley

MACE

SHILLINGLEE PARK
(Shillinglee Park), Surrey, England
Year Built: 1980
Designer: Roger Mace

MACFARLANE

DALMALLY
(Dalmally), Argyll and Bute, Scotland
Designer: Barrow, MacFarlane

MACKENZIE

BRUNTSFIELD GOLF CLUB
(Bruntsfield), Edinburgh (City of), Scotland
Designer: Hawtree, Alistair MacKenzie, William Park

CARLISLE
(Carlisle), Cumbria, England
Year Built: 1908
Designer: Alistair MacKenzie, L Ross

CASTLETOWN GOLF LINKS
(Castletown Golf Links), Isle of Man, England
Designer: Alistair MacKenzie, L Ross

DARLINGTON
(Darlington), County Durham, England
Year Built: 1908
Designer: Alistair MacKenzie

A MacKenzie

GUERNSEY (ROYAL)
(Royal Guernsey), Guernsey, England
Designer: A MacKenzie, L Ross

KNOCK
(Knock), County Antrim, Northern Ireland
Year Built: 1921
Designer: Charles Hugh Alison, Harry Shapland Colt, Alistair MacKenzie

LAHINCH
(Old), County Clare, Ireland
Designer: Gibson, Alistair MacKenzie

SADDLEWORTH
(Saddleworth), Manchester (Greater), England
Designer: G Lowe, Alistair MacKenzie

SCARCROFT
(Scarcroft), Yorkshire (West), England
Designer: Charles MacKenzie

SOUTH SHIELDS
(South Shields), Tyne And Wear, England
Designer: James Braid, Alistair MacKenzie

SOUTHERNESS
(Southerness), Dumfries And Galloway, Scotland
Year Built: 1947
Designer: Alistair MacKenzie, L Ross

ST. ANDREWS LINKS
(Old), Fife, Scotland
Designer: D Anderson, A MacKenzie, Tom Morris

TURNBERRY
(Ailsa), Ayrshire (South), Scotland
Designer: Alistair MacKenzie, L Ross

TURNBERRY
(Kintyre), Ayrshire (South), Scotland
Designer: Alistair MacKenzie, L Ross, Donald Steel

WAKEFIELD
(Wakefield), Yorkshire (West), England
Year Built: 1912
Designer: Herd, Alistair MacKenzie

WESTON
(Weston-Super-Mare), Somerset (North), England
Designer: Tom Dunn, Alistair MacKenzie

MAINLAND

CANNOCK PARK
(Cannock Park), Staffordshire, England

Year Built: 1989
Designer: John Mainland

MAIR
🌣 **BURGHAM**
(Burgham park), Northumberland, England
Year Built: 1994
Designer: M James, Andrew Mair

MAKEY
🌣 **RUTLAND WATER**
(Rutland Water), Rutland, England
Year Built: 1990
Designer: Steve Makey

MALLABY
🌣 **PRINCES**
(Himalayas), Kent, England
Year Built: 1951
Designer: Deeley, Lucas, Mallaby

MARNOCH
🌣 **BLUNDELLS HILL**
(Blundell's Hill), Merseyside, England
Year Built: 1994
Designer: Steve Marnoch

🌣 **MID YORKSHIRE**
(Mid Yorkshire), Yorkshire (West), England
Year Built: 1990
Designer: Steve Marnoch

🌣 **MOSSOCK HALL**
(Mossock Hall), Lancashire, England
Year Built: 1996
Designer: Steve Marnoch

🌣 **PIKEFOLD**
(Pikefold), Lancashire, England
Year Built: 1909
Designer: Steve Marnoch

MASON
🌣 **MAPPERLEY**
(Mapperley), Nottinghamshire, England
Designer: John Mason

🌣 **WHITEFIELDS**
(Whitefields), Warwickshire, England
Year Built: 1992
Designer: R Mason

MATHER
🌣 **BODENSTOWN**
(Bodenstown), County Kildare, Ireland
Designer: Richard Mather

🌣 **BODENSTOWN**
(Ladyhill), County Kildare, Ireland
Designer: Richard Mather

MATHIAS
🌣 **MERTHYR CILSANWS**
(Merthyr Cilsanws), Glamorgan (Vale of),
Wales
Designer: R Mathias, V Price

MAYO
🌣 **BRYN MEADOWS**
(Bryn Meadows Golf & Country Hotel),
Caerphilly, Wales
Designer: Defoy, Mayo

MCALLISTER
🌣 **EDMONDSTOWN**
(Edmondstown), County Dublin, Ireland
Designer: McAllister

MCCAMOND
🌣 **LOCHGILPHEAD**
(Lochgilphead), Argyll and Bute, Scotland
Designer: I McCamond

MCCAULEY
🌣 **BALLYCLARE**
(Ballyclare), County Antrim, Northern
Ireland
Designer: T McCauley

🌣 **BIRCHWOOD**
(Birchwood), Cheshire, England
Designer: T McCauley

🌣 **WELCOMBE HOTEL**
(Welcombe Hotel and), Warwickshire,
England
Designer: T McCauley

MCCAUSLAND
🌣 **TRENT LOCK**
(Trent Lock Golf Centre 18 hole),
Nottinghamshire, England
Year Built: 1990
Designer: E McCausland

MCEVOY
🌣 **COOLLATTIN**
(Coollattin), County Wicklow, Ireland
Designer: P McEvoy

🌣 **DOUGLAS**
(Douglas), County Cork, Ireland
Designer: Peter McEvoy, Harry Vardon

🌣 **GLEN OF THE DOWNS**
(Glen Of The Downs), County Wicklow,
Ireland
Year Built: 1998
Designer: P McEvoy

🌣 **HORSLEY LODGE**
(Horsley Lodge), Derbyshire, England
Year Built: 1990
Designer: P McEvoy

🌣 **POWERSCOURT**
(Powerscourt), County Wicklow, Ireland
Year Built: 1996
Designer: P McEvoy

🌣 **RATHSALLAGH**
(Rathsallagh), County Wicklow, Ireland
Year Built: 1994
Designer: P McEvoy, Christy O'Connor

🌣 **WOODBROOK**
(Woodbrook), County Wicklow, Ireland
Designer: P McEvoy

MCGIBBON
🌣 **TRENT PARK GOLF CLUB**
(Trent Park), London (Greater), England
Year Built: 1972
Designer: D McGibbon

MCGUIRK
🌣 **TURVEY**
(Turvey), County Dublin, Ireland
Year Built: 1994
Designer: P McGuirk

MCLEAN
🌣 **ANNANHILL**
(Annanhill), Ayrshire (East), Scotland
Designer: Jack McLean

MCMURRY
🌣 **WOBURN**
(Marquess), Buckinghamshire, England
Year Built: 2000
Designer: Peter Alliss, Ross McMurry

MEADOW
🌣 **HINCKLEY**
(Hinckley), Leicestershire, England
Designer: Meadow

MENZIES
🌣 **KENMORE**
(Kenmore), Perth And Kinross, Scotland
Year Built: 1992
Designer: Robin Menzies

MERRIGAM
🌣 **TULLAMORE**
(Tullamore), County Offaly, Ireland
Designer: James Braid, Paddy Merrigam

MERRIGAN
🌣 **FAITHLEGG**
(Faithlegg), County Waterford, Ireland
Year Built: 1993
Designer: P Merrigan

🌣 **HARBOUR POINT**
(Harbour Point), County Cork, Ireland
Designer: P Merrigan

🌣 **SLIEVE RUSSELL**
(Slieve Russell), County Cavan, Ireland
Designer: P Merrigan

🌣 **TULFARRIS HOUSE**
(Tulfarris House), County Wicklow, Ireland
Designer: P Merrigan

🌣 **WOODENBRIDGE**
(Woodenbridge), County Wicklow, Ireland
Designer: P Merrigan

MIDDLETON
🌣 **BALBIRNIE PARK**
(Balbirnie Park), Fife, Scotland
Year Built: 1983
Designer: Fraser Middleton

🌣 **HOUNSLOW HEATH**
(Hounslow Heath), London (Greater),
England
Designer: Fraser Middleton

🌣 **WEST LOTHIAN**
(West Lothian), Lothian (West), Scotland
Year Built: 1892
Designer: Fraser Middleton

by Course **DESIGNER SURNAME**

Mainland — Middleton

MILLEN

WEALD OF KENT
(Weald of Kent), Kent,
Designer: John Millen

MILLER

COLLINGTREE PARK
(Collingtree Park), Northamptonshire,
England
Year Built: 1990
Designer: J Miller

WEST LINTON
(West Linton), Scottish Borders, Scotland
Year Built: 1890
Designer: Robert Miller

MILLINGTON

ALDER ROOT
(Alder Root), Cheshire, England
Year Built: 1993
Designer: Lander, Millington

MILTON

BROADWATER PARK
(Broadwater Park), Surrey, England
Year Built: 1989
Designer: Kevin Milton

MITCHELL

CHESTFIELD
(Chestfield), Kent, England
Year Built: 1925
Designer: A Mitchell

MONTGOMERY

GREEN HOTEL
(Blue), Perth And Kinross, Scotland
Designer: David Montgomery

GREEN HOTEL
(Red), Perth And Kinross, Scotland
Designer: David Montgomery

MOON

MAYWOOD
(Maywood), Derbyshire, England
Year Built: 1990
Designer: P Moon

MOONE

EASTWOOD
(Eastwood), Glasgow (City of), Scotland
Year Built: 1893
Designer: Theodore Moone

KILMARNOCK
(Kilmarnock), Ayrshire (South), Scotland
Designer: Theodore Moone

KILMARNOCK
(New 9 hole), Ayrshire (South), Scotland
Designer: Theodore Moone

MOORE

AVISFORD PARK
(Avisford park), Sussex (West), England
Designer: R Moore

HALLGARTH
(Hallgarth), County Durham, England
Designer: Brian Moore

PARK TONGLAND
(Park of Tongland), Dumfries And Galloway,
Scotland
Year Built: 1996
Designer: Brian Moore

MORGAN

ALICE SPRINGS
(Kings), Monmouthshire, Wales
Designer: Keith Morgan

ALICE SPRINGS
(Queens), Monmouthshire, Wales
Year Built: 1989
Designer: Keith Morgan

ANSTY GOLF CTRE
(Ansty Golf Ctre), Midlands (West),
England
Designer: David Morgan

FOREST PINES
(Beeches), Lincolnshire (North), England
Designer: John Morgan

FOREST PINES
(Forest), Lincolnshire (North), England
Designer: John Morgan

FOREST PINES
(Pines), Lincolnshire (North), England
Designer: John Morgan

HUNLEY HALL
(Millenium), Cleveland, England
Year Built: 1993
Designer: John Morgan

OMBERSLEY
(Ombersley), Worcestershire, England
Designer: David Morgan

MORLEY

HADDEN HILL
(Hadden Hill), Oxfordshire, England
Year Built: 1990
Designer: M Morley

MORRIS

BAILDON
(Baildon), Yorkshire (West), England
Year Built: 1896
Designer: James Braid, Tom Morris

BLAIR ATHOLL
(Blair Atholl), Perth And Kinross, Scotland
Designer: Morris

BLAIRGOWRIE
(Lansdowne), Perth And Kinross, Scotland
**Designer: Peter Alliss, James Braid, Tom
Morris, David Thomas**

BLAIRGOWRIE
(Rosemount), Perth And Kinross, Scotland
**Designer: Peter Alliss, James Braid, Tom
Morris, David Thomas**

BLAIRGOWRIE
(Wee), Perth And Kinross, Scotland
**Designer: Peter Alliss, James Braid, Tom
Morris, David Thomas**

BUXTON & HIGH PEAK
(Buxton and High Peak), Derbyshire,
England
Year Built: 1887
Designer: J Morris

CALLANDER
(Callander), Perth and Kinross, Scotland
Designer: William Fernie, George Morris

CARNOUSTIE
(Championship), Angus, Scotland
**Designer: James Braid, Tom Morris,
William Park, A Robertson**

CROMER (ROYAL)
(Royal Cromer), Norfolk, England
Year Built: 1888
Designer: James Braid, Tom Morris

CULLEN
(Cullen), Moray, Scotland
Year Built: 1903
Designer: Tom Morris, C Neaves

DEWSBURY DISTRICT
(Dewsbury District), Yorkshire (West),
England
Designer: Peter Alliss, Tom Morris

DORNOCH (ROYAL)
(Championship), Highlands, Scotland
**Designer: G Duncan, Tom Morris, J
Sutherland**

HEDSOR
(Hedsor), Buckinghamshire, England
Year Built: 1999
Designer: Morris

HELENSBURGH
(Helensburgh), Argyll and Bute, Scotland
Year Built: 1893
Designer: James Braid, Tom Morris

HESKETH
(Hesketh), Merseyside, England
Year Built: 1885
Designer: J Morris

LADYBANK
(Ladybank), Fife, Scotland
Year Built: 1879
Designer: James Braid, Tom Morris

LIVERPOOL (ROYAL)
(Royal Liverpool), Merseyside, England
Year Built: 1869
Designer: Robert Chambers, Jim Morris

LOCH LOMOND
(Loch Lomond), Argyll and Bute, Scotland
Designer: J Morris, T Weiskopf

MITCHAM
(Mitcham), Surrey, England
Designer: Tom Morris, T Scott

MONTROSE LINKS TRUST
(Broomfield), Angus, Scotland
Year Built: 1915
Designer: Tom Morris, William Park

MONTROSE LINKS TRUST
(Medal), Angus, Scotland
Year Built: 1915
Designer: Tom Morris, William Park

NAIRN
(Nairn), Highlands, Scotland
Year Built: 1887
Designer: Archie Simpson, Old Tom Morris, James Braid

NAIRN
(Newton), Highlands, Scotland
Year Built: 1887
Designer: Archie Simpson, Old Tom Morris, James Braid

ST. ANDREWS LINKS
(Old), Fife, Scotland
Designer: D Anderson, A MacKenzie, Tom Morris

STRATHPEFFER SPA
(Strathpeffer Spa), Highlands, Scotland
Year Built: 1888
Designer: Tom Morris, William Park

MORRISON

CAIRNDHU
(Cairndhu), County Antrim, Northern Ireland
Year Built: 1958
Designer: Morrison

DURNESS
(Durness), Highlands, Scotland
Year Built: 1988
Designer: F Keith, Jan Morrison

PORT BANNATYNE
(Port Bannatyne), Argyll and Bute, Scotland
Year Built: 1912
Designer: Morrison

TRURO
(Truro), Cornwall, England
Year Built: 1937
Designer: Charles Hugh Alison, Harry Shapland Colt, J S F Morrison

WHITBURN
(Whitburn), Tyne And Wear, England
Designer: Charles Hugh Alison, Harry Shapland Colt, J S F Morrison

MORTRAM

REASEHEATH
(Reaseheath), Cheshire, England
Designer: D Mortram

MOSELEY

WERGS
(Wergs), Midlands (West), England
Year Built: 1990
Designer: C W Moseley

MOWER

SPROWSTON MANOR
(Marriot Sprawston Manor), Norfolk, England
Year Built: 1980
Designer: Tony Mower

MUDDLE

SOUTHWELL
(Southwell), Nottinghamshire, England
Year Built: 1994
Designer: R Muddle

MUIR

FORRESTER PARK
(Forrester Park), Essex, England
Year Built: 1968
Designer: T R Forrester, Muir

NEW ZEALAND
(New Zealand), Surrey, England
Designer: Fergurson, Muir, Simpson

WIGTOWN & BLADNOCH
(Wigtown & Bladnoch), Dumfries And Galloway, Scotland
Year Built: 1960
Designer: Muir

MUIRHEAD

BRYN MORFYDD
(Duchess), Denbighshire, Wales
Year Built: 1992
Designer: Peter Alliss, Duncan Muirhead

BRYN MORFYDD
(Dukes), Denbighshire, Wales
Year Built: 1992
Designer: Peter Alliss, Duncan Muirhead

MURRAY

HAZLEMERE
(Hazlemere), Buckinghamshire, England
Designer: T Murray

ISLE OF WEDMORE
(Isle Of Wedmore), Somerset, England
Year Built: 1992
Designer: T Murray

TALL PINES
(Tall Pines), Bristol, England
Year Built: 1990
Designer: T Murray

NEAVES

CULLEN
(Cullen), Moray, Scotland
Year Built: 1903
Designer: Tom Morris, C Neaves

NEIL

HIGHBULLEN HOTEL
(Highbullen Hotel), Devon, England
Designer: M Neil, J Hamilton

NEWMAN

COTSWOLD EDGE
(Cotswold Edge), Gloucestershire, England
Year Built: 1980
Designer: A J & N Newman

NICHOLSON

BLACKNEST
(Blacknest), Hampshire, England
Year Built: 1992
Designer: Nicholson

HEVER
(Hever), Kent, England
Designer: Nicholson

TEIGN VALLEY
(Teign Valley), Devon, England
Designer: Nicholson

NICKLAUS

GLENEAGLES
(PGA Centenary), Perth And Kinross, Scotland
Year Built: 1993
Designer: Jack Nicklaus

HANBURY MANOR
(Hanbury Manor), Hertfordshire, England
Designer: Jack Nicklaus

HERTFORDSHIRE
(The Hertfordshire), Hertfordshire, England
Year Built: 1993
Designer: Jack Nicklaus

LONDON
(Heritage), Kent, England
Designer: Jack Nicklaus

MOUNT JULIET
(Jack Nicklaus Signature), County Kilkenny, Ireland
Designer: Jack Nicklaus

ST. MELLION INTERNATIONAL
(Nicklaus), Cornwall, England
Year Built: 1988
Designer: Jack Nicklaus

NORMAN

DOONBEG
(Doonbeg), County Clare, Ireland
Designer: Greg Norman

OAKDEN

WYBOSTON
(Wyboston Lakes), Bedfordshire, England
Designer: N Oakden

O'CONNOR

BANTRY BAY
(Bantry Bay), County Cork, Ireland
Year Built: 1975
Designer: Christy O'Connor, Edward Hackett

CEANN SIBEAL
(Ceann Sibeal), County Kerry, Ireland
Designer: Edward Hackett, O'Connor

GALWAY BAY
(Galway Bay Golf & Country Club), County Galway, Ireland
Designer: Christy O'Connor

GORT
(Gort), County Galway, Ireland
Designer: Christy O'Connor

LEE VALLEY
(Lee Valley), County Cork, Ireland
Designer: Christy O'Connor

RATHSALLAGH
(Rathsallagh), County Wicklow, Ireland
Year Built: 1994
Designer: P McEvoy, Christy O'Connor

O'DOLAN

ASHWOODS
(Ashwoods), County Fermanagh, Northern Ireland

Year Built: 1995
Designer: O'Dolan

🏌 **MOUNT TEMPLE**
(Mount Temple), County Westmeath,
Ireland
Designer: O'Dolan

O'GAUNT

🏌 **JOHN O'GAUNT**
(Carthagena), Bedfordshire, England
Year Built: 1980
Designer: John O'Gaunt

🏌 **JOHN O'GAUNT**
(John O'Gaunt), Bedfordshire, England
Designer: John O'Gaunt

O'HARA

🏌 **BROWN TROUT**
(Brown Trout), County Londonderry,
Northern Ireland
Year Built: 1973
Designer: Bill O'Hara

OLIVER

🏌 **KILLIOW PARK**
(Killiow Park), Cornwall, England
Designer: R Oliver

🏌 **MERLIN**
(Merlin), Cornwall, England
Year Built: 1991
Designer: R Oliver

O'SULLIVAN

🏌 **KILLARNEY**
(Killeen), County Kerry, Ireland
Designer: Edward Hackett, Billy O'Sullivan

🏌 **MOUNTAIN VIEW**
(Mountain View), County Kilkenny, Ireland
Designer: Mr John O' Sullivan

PAIN

🏌 **WHEATHILL**
(Wheathill), Somerset, England
Year Built: 1993
Designer: J Pain

PALMER

🏌 **CHALGRAVE MANOR**
(Chalgrave Manor), Bedfordshire, England
Year Built: 1992
Designer: Mike Palmer

🏌 **K CLUB**
(The K Club), County Kildare, Ireland
Designer: Arnold Palmer

🏌 **TRALEE**
(Tralee), County Kerry, Ireland
Designer: Arnold Palmer

PARAMOIR

🏌 **BALBRIGGAN**
(Balbriggan), County Dublin, Ireland
Designer: Paramoir

PARK

🏌 **BABERTON**
(Baberton), Edinburgh (City of), Scotland
Designer: William Park

🏌 **BATHGATE**
(Bathgate), Lothian (West), Scotland
Designer: William Park

🏌 **BIGGAR**
(Biggar), Lanarkshire (South), Scotland
Designer: William Park

🏌 **BRUNTSFIELD GOLF CLUB**
(Bruntsfield), Edinburgh (City of), Scotland
Designer: Hawtree, Alistair MacKenzie, William Park

🏌 **BURHILL**
(Burhill (Old)), Surrey, England
Year Built: 1907
Designer: William Park

🏌 **BURNTISLAND**
(Burntisland), Fife, Scotland
Designer: William Park

🏌 **CARNOUSTIE**
(Championship), Angus, Scotland
Designer: James Braid, Tom Morris, William Park, A Robertson

🏌 **CHISLEHURST**
(Chislehurst), Kent, England
Designer: William Park

🏌 **FORMBY**
(Formby), Merseyside, England
Year Built: 1884
Designer: Harry Shapland Colt, William Park, Frank Pennink

🏌 **FORMBY HALL**
(Formby Hall), Merseyside, England
Year Built: 1995
Designer: Harry Shapland Colt, William Park

🏌 **FORRES**
(Forres), Moray, Scotland
Year Built: 1889
Designer: James Braid, William Park

🏌 **FRINTON**
(Long), Essex, England
Designer: William Park

🏌 **FRINTON**
(Short), Essex, England
Designer: William Park

🏌 **GLASGOW GAILES**
(Glasgow Gailes), Ayrshire (North), Scotland
Year Built: 1892
Designer: William Park

🏌 **GLENCORSE**
(Glencorse), Lothian (Mid), Scotland
Designer: William Park

🏌 **HUNTERCOMBE**
(Huntercombe), Oxfordshire, England
Year Built: 1901
Designer: William Park

🏌 **INNERLEITHEN**
(Innerleithen), Scottish Borders, Scotland
Year Built: 1886
Designer: William Park

🏌 **KNEBWORTH**
(Knebworth), Hertfordshire, England
Designer: William Park

🏌 **MAGDALENE FIELDS**
(Magdalene Fields), Northumberland, England
Year Built: 1903
Designer: William Park

🏌 **MONTROSE LINKS TRUST**
(Broomfield), Angus, Scotland
Year Built: 1915
Designer: Tom Morris, William Park

🏌 **MONTROSE LINKS TRUST**
(Medal), Angus, Scotland
Year Built: 1915
Designer: Tom Morris, William Park

🏌 **NORTH MIDDLESEX**
(North Middlesex), London (Greater), England
Designer: William Park

🏌 **NOTTS**
(Notts), Nottinghamshire, England
Year Built: 1901
Designer: William Park

🏌 **PARKSTONE**
(Parkstone), Dorset, England
Year Built: 1911
Designer: James Braid, William Park

🏌 **PORTSTEWART**
(Strand), County Londonderry, Northern Ireland
Designer: Griffin, Harris, Park

🏌 **RANFURLY**
(The Old, Ranfurly), Renfrewshire, Scotland
Year Built: 1905
Designer: William Park

🏌 **SHOOTERS HILL**
(Shooters Hill), London (Greater), England
Year Built: 1903
Designer: William Park

🏌 **SILLOTH**
(Silloth), Cumbria, England
Year Built: 1892
Designer: William Park

🏌 **ST. BOSWELLS**
(St Boswells), Scottish Borders, Scotland
Designer: William Park

🏌 **STONEHAM**
(Stoneham), Hampshire, England
Designer: William Park

🏌 **STRATHPEFFER SPA**
(Strathpeffer Spa), Highlands, Scotland
Year Built: 1888
Designer: Tom Morris, William Park

🏌 **SUNDRIDGE PARK**
(East), Kent, England
Designer: William Park

🏌 **SUNDRIDGE PARK**
(West), Kent, England
Designer: William Park

🏌 **SUNNINGDALE**
(Old), Surrey, England

Year Built: 1901
Designer: William Park (Jnr)

● **TEMPLE**
(Temple), Berkshire, England
Year Built: 1909
Designer: William Park

● **TORWOODLEE**
(Torwoodlee), Scottish Borders, Scotland
Year Built: 1895
Designer: William Park

● **TYNEMOUTH**
(Tynemouth), Tyne And Wear, England
Designer: William Park

● **WATERFORD**
(Waterford), County Waterford, Ireland
Designer: William Park, James Braid

PARKE

● **WEST HILL**
(West Hill), Surrey, England
Designer: C Butchart, William Parke

PARKER

● **OWSTON PARK**
(Owston Park), Yorkshire (South), England
Designer: M Parker

PATE

● **HOLLANDBUSH**
(Holland Bush), Lanarkshire (South), Scotland
Designer: J Lawdon, K Pate

PATON

● **HEMINGFORD ABBOT**
(Hemingford Abbots), Cambridgeshire, England
Designer: Ray Paton

PATTERSON

● **MOYOLA PARK**
(Moyola Park), County Londonderry, Northern Ireland
Designer: D Patterson

PAXTON

● **EAST BERKSHIRE**
(East Berkshire), Berkshire, England
Designer: P Paxton

PAYN

● **BANBURY GOLF CTRE**
(Blue), Oxfordshire, England
Year Built: 1994
Designer: Jon Payn, Mike Reed

● **BANBURY GOLF CTRE**
(Red), Oxfordshire, England
Year Built: 1994
Designer: Jon Payn, Mike Reed

● **BANBURY GOLF CTRE**
(Yellow), Oxfordshire, England
Year Built: 1994
Designer: Jon Payn, Mike Reed

PAYNE

● **TAUNTON VALE**
(Charlton), Somerset, England
Designer: John Payne

● **TAUNTON VALE**
(Durston), Somerset, England
Designer: John Payne

PEARCE

● **EAST HORTON GOLF CTRE**
(Greenwood), Hampshire, England
Year Built: 1991
Designer: T Pearce, M Scott

● **EAST HORTON GOLF CTRE**
(Parkland), Hampshire, England
Year Built: 1991
Designer: T Pearce, M Scott

PEARSON

● **GATHURST**
(Gathurst), Lancashire, England
Designer: Pearson

● **HOUGHWOOD**
(Houghwood), Merseyside, England
Year Built: 1996
Designer: Pearson

● **MARTON MEADOWS**
(Marton Meadows), Cheshire, England
Year Built: 1998
Designer: Pearson

PEDLAR

● **GERRARDS CROSS**
(Gerrards Cross), Buckinghamshire, England
Designer: Bill Pedlar

PENNICK

● **ELLESMERE PORT**
(Ellesmere Port), Merseyside, England
Designer: Cotton, Lawrie, Pennick

● **GLYNNEATH**
(Glynneath), Neath Port Talbot, Wales
Designer: Cotton Pennick Lawrie & Partners

● **STOCKSFIELD**
(Stocksfield), Northumberland, England
Year Built: 1913
Designer: Cotton Pennick Lawrie & Partners

PENNINK

● **BARNHAM BROOM**
(Hill), Norfolk, England
Designer: Frank Pennink, Donald Steel

● **FORMBY**
(Formby), Merseyside, England
Year Built: 1884
Designer: Harry Shapland Colt, William Park, Frank Pennink

● **FOSSEWAY**
(Fosseway Country Club), Bath & Somerset (North East), England
Year Built: 1970
Designer: Cotton, Pennink

● **LURGAN**
(Lurgan), County Armagh, Northern Ireland
Designer: A Pennink

● **NORTH DOWNS**
(North Downs), Surrey, England
Designer: Mr J J Frank Pennink

● **RADCLIFFE-ON-TRENT**
(Radcliffe-On-Trent), Nottinghamshire, England
Year Built: 1909
Designer: Pennink, Tom Williamson

● **RICHMOND**
(Richmond), Yorkshire (North), England
Designer: Pennink

● **ST. PIERRE**
(Old), Monmouthshire, Wales
Year Built: 1962
Designer: C K Cotton, J J Frank Pennink

PERN

● **DARTMOUTH**
(Championship), Devon, England
Year Built: 1992
Designer: Jeremy Pern

● **DARTMOUTH**
(Club), Devon, England
Designer: Jeremy Pern

PHILLIPS

● **BISHOPSWOOD**
(Bishopswood), Hampshire, England
Designer: G Blake, M Phillips

● **KINGSBARNS GOLF LINKS**
(Kingsbarn), Fife, Scotland
Year Built: 2000
Designer: Kyle Phillips

PICKEMAN

● **PORTMARNOCK**
(Old), County Dublin, Ireland
Year Built: 1894
Designer: W C Pickeman, George Ross

PIERSON

● **BREADSALL PRIORY**
(Moorland), Derbyshire, England
Designer: Brian Pierson

PILE

● **FINGLE GLEN**
(Fingle Glen), Devon, England
Year Built: 1989
Designer: Bill Pile

PILGRIM

● **HAVERHILL**
(Haverhill), Suffolk, England
Year Built: 1973
Designer: Philip Pilgrim

● **UFFORD PARK**
(Ufford Park), Suffolk, England
Year Built: 1991
Designer: Philip Pilgrim

by Course **DESIGNER SURNAME**

Park — Pilgrim

● **WALDRINGFIELD HEATH**
(Waldringfield Heath), Suffolk, England
Designer: Philip Pilgrim

PLAYER

● **WENTWORTH CLUB**
(Edinburgh), Surrey, England
Designer: Bernhard Gallagher, John Jacobs, Gary Player

PLUMBRIDGE

● **ESSEX**
(County), Essex, England
Designer: R Plumbridge

● **ESSEX**
(Garden), Essex, England
Designer: R Plumbridge

● **HYLANDS GOLF COMPLEX**
(Hanbury), Essex, England
Year Built: 1996
Designer: R Plumbridge

● **HYLANDS GOLF COMPLEX**
(Pryors), Essex, England
Year Built: 1996
Designer: R Plumbridge

● **SOUTH ESSEX**
(Hawk (Hawk & Vixon)), Essex, England
Year Built: 1992
Designer: R Plumbridge

● **SOUTH ESSEX**
(Heron (Heron & Hawk)), Essex, England
Year Built: 1992
Designer: R Plumbridge

● **SOUTH ESSEX**
(Vixen (Vixen & Heron)), Essex, England
Year Built: 1992
Designer: R Plumbridge

● **WARLEY PARK**
(Course 1), Essex, England
Year Built: 1975
Designer: R Plumbridge

● **WARLEY PARK**
(Course 2), Essex, England
Year Built: 1975
Designer: R Plumbridge

● **WARLEY PARK**
(Course 3), Essex, England
Year Built: 1975
Designer: R Plumbridge

POMSFORD

● **CUCKFIELD**
(Cuckfield), Sussex (West), England
Designer: D Amer, A J Pomsford

POTT

● **NAUNTON DOWNS**
(Naunton Downs), Gloucestershire, England
Year Built: 1993
Designer: J Pott

POTTAGE

● **BEDFORD**
(The Bedford), Bedfordshire, England

Year Built: 1998
Designer: David Pottage

PRICE

● **MERTHYR CILSANWS**
(Merthyr Cilsanws), Glamorgan (Vale of), Wales
Designer: R Mathias, V Price

● **MILE END**
(Mile End), Shropshire, England
Year Built: 1992
Designer: Gough, Price

● **SPALDING**
(Spalding), Lincolnshire, England
Designer: Price, Spencer, Ward

PURVES

● **LITTLESTONE**
(Littlestone), Kent, England
Year Built: 1888
Designer: L Purves

● **ST. GEORGE'S (ROYAL)**
(Royal St George's), Kent, England
Designer: L Purves

RADCLIFFE

● **ROTHBURY**
(Rothbury), Northumberland, England
Designer: J Radcliffe

RAE

● **INVERGORDON**
(Invergordon), Highlands, Scotland
Year Built: 1893
Designer: A Rae

RAY

● **BURY ST EDMUNDS**
(Bury St Edmunds), Suffolk, England
Year Built: 1924
Designer: Ted Ray

● **SANDIWAY**
(Sandiway), Cheshire, England
Designer: Ted Ray

REED

● **BANBURY GOLF CTRE**
(Blue), Oxfordshire, England
Year Built: 1994
Designer: Jon Payn, Mike Reed

● **BANBURY GOLF CTRE**
(Red), Oxfordshire, England
Year Built: 1994
Designer: Jon Payn, Mike Reed

● **BANBURY GOLF CTRE**
(Yellow), Oxfordshire, England
Year Built: 1994
Designer: Jon Payn, Mike Reed

REID

● **MARDYKE VALLEY GOLF CTRE**
(The Valley), Essex, England
Designer: Mike Reid

RENOUF

● **ALDERLEY EDGE**
(Alderley Edge), Cheshire, England
Year Built: 1907
Designer: Renouf

● **CHEADLE**
(Cheadle), Cheshire, England
Designer: Renouf

● **NORTHENDEN**
(Northenden), Manchester (Greater), England
Designer: Renouf

RICHARDSON

● **GREEN MEADOW**
(Green Meadow), Torfaen, Wales
Year Built: 1979
Designer: P Richardson

● **VICARS CROSS**
(Vicars Cross), Cheshire, England
Designer: J Richardson

ROBERTS

● **GREAT HADHAM**
(Great Hadham), Hertfordshire, England
Designer: Iain Roberts

ROBERTSON

● **CARNOUSTIE**
(Championship), Angus, Scotland
Designer: James Braid, Tom Morris, William Park, A Robertson

● **CUPAR**
(Cupar), Fife, Scotland
Year Built: 1855
Designer: A Robertson

● **LOCHRANZA GOLF**
(Lochranza Golf), Isle of Arran, Scotland
Year Built: 1899
Designer: I Robertson

● **MONIFIETH GOLF LINKS**
(Medal), Angus, Scotland
Year Built: 1858
Designer: A Robertson

ROBINSON

● **CLANDEBOYE**
(Ava), County Down, Northern Ireland
Designer: W Robinson

● **CLANDEBOYE**
(Dufferin), County Down, Northern Ireland
Designer: W Robinson

ROCHESTER

● **BAMBURGH CASTLE**
(Bamburgh Castle), Northumberland, England
Designer: George Rochester

ROGERSON

● **COTTESMORE**
(Griffin), Sussex (West), England
Designer: M Rogerson

COTTESMORE
(Phoenix), Sussex (West), England
Designer: M Rogerson

ROKER
ROKER PARK
(Roker Park), Surrey, England
Designer: W V Roker

ROSS
CARLISLE
(Carlisle), Cumbria, England
Year Built: 1908
Designer: Alistair MacKenzie, L Ross

CASTLETOWN GOLF LINKS
(Castletown Golf Links), Isle of Man, England
Designer: Alistair MacKenzie, L Ross

GUERNSEY (ROYAL)
(Royal Guernsey), Guernsey, England
Designer: A MacKenzie, L Ross

MERCHANTS OF EDINBURGH
(Merchants Of Edinburgh), Edinburgh (City of), Scotland
Designer: Ross

PORTMARNOCK
(Old), County Dublin, Ireland
Year Built: 1894
Designer: W C Pickeman, George Ross

SOUTHERNESS
(Southerness), Dumfries And Galloway, Scotland
Year Built: 1947
Designer: Alistair MacKenzie, L Ross

TURNBERRY
(Ailsa), Ayrshire (South), Scotland
Designer: Alistair MacKenzie, L Ross

TURNBERRY
(Kintyre), Ayrshire (South), Scotland
Designer: Alistair MacKenzie, L Ross, Donald Steel

WHITLEY
(Whitley), Wiltshire, England
Year Built: 1993
Designer: L Ross

ROUSE
PORTAL
(Premier), Cheshire, England
Year Built: 1990
Designer: Tim Rouse

PORTAL PREMIER
(Portal Premier), Cheshire, England
Year Built: 1990
Designer: Tim Rouse

ROWE
LEWES
(Lewes), Sussex (East), England
Year Built: 1896
Designer: Jack Rowe

ROYSTON
SANDHILL
(Sandhill), Yorkshire (South), England

Year Built: 1993
Designer: John Royston

RUDDY
BALLYLIFFIN
(Glashedy Links), County Donegal, Ireland
Year Built: 1995
Designer: Tom Craddock, Pat Ruddy

BALLYLIFFIN
(Old Links), County Donegal, Ireland
Designer: Tom Craddock, Pat Ruddy

DRUIDS GLEN
(Druids Glen), County Wicklow, Ireland
Year Built: 1995
Designer: Pat Ruddy, Tom Craddock

EUROPEAN CLUB
(The European Club), County Wicklow, Ireland
Year Built: 1989
Designer: Pat Ruddy

KILLEEN
(Killeen), County Kildare, Ireland
Designer: Pat Ruddy

ST. MARGARETS
(St Margaret's), County Dublin, Ireland
Designer: Craddock, Ruddy

WICKLOW
(Wicklow), County Wicklow, Ireland
Year Built: 1904
Designer: Craddock, Ruddy

SALVERSON
CHARLETON
(Charleton), Fife, Scotland
Year Built: 1992
Designer: John Salverson

STRATHMORE GOLF CTRE
(Rannaleroch), Perth And Kinross, Scotland
Year Built: 1994
Designer: John Salverson

TRAIGH
(Traigh), Highlands, Scotland
Designer: John Salverson

SANDRY
HIGHWORTH GOLF CENTRE
(Highworth), Wiltshire, England
Designer: D Lang, B Sandry, T Watt

SAUNDERS
ABBOTSLEY
(Abbotsley), Cambridgeshire, England
Designer: V Saunders, D Young

BARKWAY PARK
(Barkway Golf), Hertfordshire, England
Year Built: 1992
Designer: V Saunders

CHICHESTER
(Cathedral), Sussex (West), England
Designer: P Saunders

CHICHESTER
(Chichester), Sussex (West), England

Year Built: 1990
Designer: P Saunders

HAMPTWORTH
(Hamptworth), Wiltshire, England
Year Built: 1992
Designer: P Saunders

SAYERS
ADARE MANOR
(Adare Manor), County Limerick, Ireland
Designer: Edward Hackett, Ben Sayers

BROOMIEKNOWE
(Broomieknowe), Lothian (Mid), Scotland
Designer: Hawtree, Ben Sayers

DOLLAR
(Dollar), Clackmannanshire, Scotland
Year Built: 1907
Designer: Ben Sayers

MOFFAT
(The Moffat), Dumfries And Galloway, Scotland
Year Built: 1905
Designer: Ben Sayers

SPEY BAY
(Spey Bay), Moray, Scotland
Designer: Ben Sayers

SAYNER
STAPLEHURST GOLFING PARK
(Staplehurst), Kent, England
Year Built: 1995
Designer: Jenkins, Sayner

SCOTT
DUNS
(Duns), Scottish Borders, Scotland
Year Built: 1894
Designer: A H Scott

EAST HORTON GOLF CTRE
(Greenwood), Hampshire, England
Year Built: 1991
Designer: T Pearce, M Scott

EAST HORTON GOLF CTRE
(Parkland), Hampshire, England
Year Built: 1991
Designer: T Pearce, M Scott

MIDDLETON HALL
(Middleton Hall), Norfolk, England
Year Built: 1989
Designer: P Scott

MITCHAM
(Mitcham), Surrey, England
Designer: Tom Morris, T Scott

RICHMOND PARK
(Richmond Park), Norfolk, England
Year Built: 1990
Designer: D Jessup, D Scott

STRATHMORE GOLF CTRE
(Leitfie Links), Perth And Kinross, Scotland
Year Built: 1994
Designer: Jeremy Barron, Daniel Scott

by Course **DESIGNER SURNAME** Rogerson — Scott

by Course **DESIGNER SURNAME**

Shade — Smart

SHADE

NEWCASTLETON
(Newcastleton), Scottish Borders, Scotland
Year Built: 1894
Designer: J Shade

SHARER

MANOR OF GROVES
(Manor of Groves), Hertfordshire, England
Year Built: 1990
Designer: Stewart Sharer

SHARKEY

STURMINSTER MARSHALL
(Sturminster Marshall), Dorset, England
Designer: David Holdsworth, John Sharkey

SHATTOCKS

CHANNELS
(Belstead), Essex, England
Year Built: 1995
Designer: Michael Shattocks

WESTHOUGHTON
(Hart Common), Lancashire, England
Year Built: 1995
Designer: Michael Shattocks

SHEPPARD

BRINKWORTH
(Brinkworth), Wiltshire, England
Year Built: 1983
Designer: Julian Sheppard

SHIELS

TOWERLANDS
(Towerlands), Essex, England
Designer: G Shiels

SHUTTLEWORTH

MIDDLESBROUGH MUNICIPAL
(Middlesbrough Municipal), Cleveland, England
Year Built: 1977
Designer: Shuttleworth

SICH

MULLION
(Mullion), Cornwall, England
Year Built: 1895
Designer: W Sich

SIMPSON

ABERDEEN (ROYAL)
(Balgownie Links), Aberdeen (City of), Scotland
Designer: James Braid, Simpson

ABERDEEN (ROYAL)
(Silverburn), Aberdeen (City of), Scotland
Designer: James Braid, Simpson

BLACKWELL
(The Blackwell), Worcestershire, England
Designer: Herbert Fowler, T Simpson

CARLOW
(Carlow), County Carlow, Ireland
Designer: Simpson

CRUDEN BAY
(Cruden Bay), Aberdeenshire, Scotland
Designer: Simpson

EDZELL
(Edzell), Angus, Scotland
Year Built: 1895
Designer: Simpson

LINLITHGOW
(Linlithgow), Lothian (West), Scotland
Year Built: 1913
Designer: R Simpson

LOUTH (COUNTY)
(Louth), County Louth, Ireland
Year Built: 1892
Designer: Simpson

MAIDENHEAD
(Maidenhead), Berkshire, England
Year Built: 1896
Designer: Simpson

MURCAR
(Murcar), Aberdeen (City of), Scotland
Year Built: 1909
Designer: Simpson

NAIRN
(Nairn), Highlands, Scotland
Year Built: 1887
Designer: Archie Simpson, Old Tom Morris, James Braid

NAIRN
(Newton), Highlands, Scotland
Year Built: 1887
Designer: Archie Simpson, Old Tom Morris, James Braid

NEW ZEALAND
(New Zealand), Surrey, England
Designer: Fergurson, Muir, Simpson

NORTH FORELAND
(Main), Kent, England
Designer: Fowler, Simpson

PORTHCAWL (ROYAL)
(Royal Porthcawl), Bridgend, Wales
Year Built: 1892
Designer: Hawtree, Hunter, Simpson, Taylor

RHOS-ON-SEA
(Rhos-On-Sea), Conwy, Wales
Year Built: 1899
Designer: Simpson

STONEHAVEN
(Stonehaven), Aberdeenshire, Scotland
Year Built: 1888
Designer: Simpson

SINCLAIR

BLANKNEY
(Blankney), Lincolnshire, England
Designer: C Sinclair

HUMAX
(Melbourne), London (Greater), England
Year Built: 1996
Designer: C Sinclair

PORTLETHEN
(Portlethen), Aberdeen (City of), Scotland
Year Built: 1989
Designer: C Sinclair

RUTLAND COUNTY
(Rutland County), Lincolnshire, England
Year Built: 1991
Designer: C Sinclair

WHITEKIRK
(Whitekirk), Lothian (East), Scotland
Year Built: 1995
Designer: C Sinclair

WHITTLEBURY PARK
(1905), Northamptonshire, England
Designer: C Sinclair

WHITTLEBURY PARK
(Grand Prix), Northamptonshire, England
Year Built: 1992
Designer: C Sinclair

WHITTLEBURY PARK
(Royal Whittlewood), Northamptonshire, England
Designer: C Sinclair

SITWELL

RENISHAW PARK
(Renishaw Park), Yorkshire (South), England
Designer: George Sitwell

SJOBERG

EPPING
(Epping), Essex, England
Year Built: 1996
Designer: N & P Sjoberg

SKERRITT

BALLAGHADERREEN
(Ballaghaderreen), County Roscommon, Ireland
Designer: P Skerritt

SLATER

AINTREE
(Aintree Golf Centre), Merseyside, England
Year Built: 1994
Designer: Mike Slater

PORTAL
(Arderne), Cheshire, England
Designer: Mike Slater

SLATTERY

BRIDGECASTLE
(The Monster), Lothian (West), Scotland
Year Built: 1996
Designer: Kevin Keane, John Slattery

SLIGHT

OXHEY PARK
(Oxhey Park), Hertfordshire, England
Year Built: 1990
Designer: K Slight

SMART

UPCHURCH RIVER VALLEY
(Upchurch River Valley), Kent, England
Designer: David Smart

SMITH

- **CRICKLADE**
(Cricklade), Wiltshire, England
Designer: Ian Bolt, Colin Smith

- **LETHAM GRANGE RESORT**
(Glens), Angus, Scotland
Year Built: 1987
Designer: G K Smith, Donald Steel

- **LETHAM GRANGE RESORT**
(Old), Angus, Scotland
Year Built: 1987
Designer: G K Smith, Donald Steel

- **LYDD**
(Lydd), Kent, England
Year Built: 1994
Designer: Mike Smith

- **PAULTONS GOLF CENTRE**
(Paultons 18 Hole Master), Hampshire, England
Designer: J Smith

- **PAULTONS GOLF CENTRE**
(Paultons Par 3), Hampshire, England
Designer: J Smith

- **PINE RIDGE GOLF CTRE**
(Pine Ridge), Surrey, England
Year Built: 1992
Designer: Clive Smith

- **WINDLERMERE**
(Windlemere), Surrey, England
Year Built: 1979
Designer: Clive Smith

SMYTH

- **BALLYKISTEEN**
(Ballykisteen), County Tipperary, Ireland
Year Built: 1991
Designer: D Smyth

- **LIMERICK (COUNTY)**
(Limerick County), County Limerick, Ireland
Year Built: 1994
Designer: D Smyth

- **NEW ROSS**
(New Ross), County Wexford, Ireland
Designer: D Smyth

- **ROSSMORE**
(Rossmore), County Monaghan, Ireland
Designer: D Smyth

- **SEAPOINT**
(Seapoint), County Louth, Ireland
Year Built: 1993
Designer: D Smyth

- **WATERFORD CASTLE**
(Waterford Castle), County Waterford, Ireland
Designer: D Smyth

SNAPE

- **WARWICKSHIRE**
(South East), Warwickshire, England
Designer: Colin Snape

SNELL

- **BRAMCOTE WATERS**
(Bramcote Waters), Warwickshire, England
Year Built: 1995
Designer: David Snell

- **BREEDON PRIORY**
(Breedon Priory Golf Centre), Derbyshire, England
Designer: David Snell

- **COLLEGE PINES**
(College Pines), Nottinghamshire, England
Year Built: 1994
Designer: David Snell

- **SILVERSTONE**
(Silverstone), Buckinghamshire, England
Year Built: 1992
Designer: David Snell

SOUTARS

- **ABERFELDY**
(Aberfeldy), Perth And Kinross, Scotland
Designer: Soutars

SOUTER

- **ROTHES**
(Rothes), Moray, Scotland
Year Built: 1990
Designer: John Souter

SPARKS

- **BOUGHTON**
(Boughton 18 Hole), Kent, England
Designer: P Sparks

SPENCER

- **SPALDING**
(Spalding), Lincolnshire, England
Designer: Price, Spencer, Ward

SPRING

- **BALLINAMORE**
(Ballinamore), County Leitrim, Ireland
Designer: A Spring

- **CASTLEGREGORY**
(Castlegregory), County Kerry, Ireland
Designer: A Spring

- **CRADDOCKSTOWN**
(Craddockstown), County Kildare, Ireland
Year Built: 1994
Designer: A Spring

- **KERRIES**
(Kerries), County Kerry, Ireland
Designer: A Spring

- **NEWCASTLE WEST**
(Newcastle West), County Limerick, Ireland
Year Built: 1938
Designer: A Spring

STAGG

- **BICESTER GOLF & COUNRTY CLUB**
(Bicester Golf & Counrty Club), Oxfordshire, England
Designer: R Stagg

- **WEST BERKSHIRE**
(West Berkshire), Berkshire, England
Year Built: 1975
Designer: Robin Stagg

STANTON

- **KNOTTY HILL GOLF CTRE**
(Bishops), Cleveland, England
Year Built: 1998
Designer: C Stanton

- **KNOTTY HILL GOLF CTRE**
(Princes), Cleveland, England
Year Built: 1991
Designer: C Stanton

STEBBINGS

- **KINMEL PARK GOLF**
(Kinmel Park), Denbighshire, Wales
Year Built: 1988
Designer: Peter Stebbings

STEEL

- **ASHTON & LEA**
(Ashton & Lea), Lancashire, England
Year Built: 1913
Designer: J Steel

- **BARNHAM BROOM**
(Hill), Norfolk, England
Designer: Frank Pennink, Donald Steel

- **CARNEGIE**
(Carnegie Club), Highlands, Scotland
Year Built: 1898
Designer: Donald Steel, J Sutherland

- **DOOKS**
(Dooks), County Kerry, Ireland
Year Built: 1889
Designer: Edward Hackett, Donald Steel

- **LETHAM GRANGE RESORT**
(Glens), Angus, Scotland
Year Built: 1987
Designer: G K Smith, Donald Steel

- **LETHAM GRANGE RESORT**
(Old), Angus, Scotland
Year Built: 1987
Designer: G K Smith, Donald Steel

- **SELBY**
(Selby), Yorkshire (North), England
Designer: Hawtree, Donald Steel, Taylor

- **SHENDISH MANOR**
(Shendish Manor), Hertfordshire, England
Year Built: 1995
Designer: A Dancer, Donald Steel

- **TURNBERRY**
(Kintyre), Ayrshire (South), Scotland
Designer: Alistair MacKenzie, L Ross, Donald Steel

- **WOODSPRING**
(Avon), Bristol, England
Year Built: 1994
Designer: Peter Alliss, Clive Clarke, Donald Steel

by Course **DESIGNER SURNAME**

Smith — Steel

● **WOODSPRING**
(Brunel), Bristol, England
Designer: Peter Alliss, Clive Clarke, Donald Steel

● **WOODSPRING**
(Severn), Bristol, England
Designer: Peter Alliss, Clive Clarke, Donald Steel

STEER

● **CHORLEY**
(Chorley), Lancashire, England
Designer: J A Steer

● **FAIRHAVEN**
(Fairhaven), Lancashire, England
Designer: J A Steer

● **FLEETWOOD**
(Fleetwood), Lancashire, England
Year Built: 1932
Designer: J A Steer

STIFF

● **CUMBERWELL**
(Woodlands), Wiltshire, England
Year Built: 1995
Designer: Adrian Stiff

● **DAINTON PARK**
(Dainton Park), Devon, England
Year Built: 1993
Designer: Adrian Stiff

● **ERLESTOKE SANDS**
(Erlestoke Sands), Wiltshire, England
Year Built: 1992
Designer: Adrian Stiff

● **FOREST HILLS**
(Forest Hills), Gloucestershire, England
Year Built: 1992
Designer: Adrian Stiff

● **KENDLESHIRE**
(The Kendleshire), Bristol, England
Year Built: 1997
Designer: Adrian Stiff

● **OAKE MANOR**
(Oake Manor), Somerset, England
Year Built: 1993
Designer: Adrian Stiff

STOCK

● **TOP MEADOW**
(Top Meadow), Essex, England
Year Built: 1990
Designer: Burns, Stock

STOKES

● **BRAMPTON GOLF**
(Brampton Golf), Herefordshire, England
Year Built: 1989
Designer: Stokes & Sons International

STONE

● **TANDRAGEE**
(Tandragee), County Armagh, Northern Ireland
Year Built: 1911
Designer: Stone

STRAND

● **SWEETWOODS PARK**
(Sweetwoods Park), Kent, England
Year Built: 1994
Designer: P Strand

STUART

● **SKEABOST**
(Skeabost), Highlands, Scotland
Designer: John Stuart

STUBBINGS

● **REGIMENT**
(Regiment Way), Essex, England
Year Built: 1994
Designer: R Clark, R Stubbings

STUBBS

● **WOODTHORPE HALL**
(Woodthorpe Hall), Lincolnshire, England
Year Built: 1986
Designer: Charles Stubbs

STUTT

● **ARDEER**
(Ardeer), Ayrshire (North), Scotland
Year Built: 1965
Designer: Stutt

● **DUNFERMLINE**
(Dunfermline), Fife, Scotland
Year Built: 1953
Designer: Stutt

● **GLENROTHES**
(Glenrothes), Fife, Scotland
Designer: Stutt

● **ST. MELLION INTERNATIONAL**
(The Old), Cornwall, England
Year Built: 1976
Designer: Stutt

● **STRATHAVEN**
(Strathaven), Lanarkshire (South), Scotland
Designer: William Fernie, Stutt

SUTCLIFFE

● **TICKENHAM**
(Tickenham), Bristol, England
Year Built: 1994
Designer: Andrew Sutcliffe

SUTHERLAND

● **CARNEGIE**
(Carnegie Club), Highlands, Scotland
Year Built: 1898
Designer: Donald Steel, J Sutherland

● **DORNOCH (ROYAL)**
(Championship), Highlands, Scotland
Designer: G Duncan, Tom Morris, J Sutherland

● **LYSHOTT HEATH**
(Lyshott Heath), Bedfordshire, England
Designer: W Sutherland

SUTTLE

● **BALLYMONEY**
(Ballymoney), County Wexford, Ireland

Year Built: 1993
Designer: P Suttle

● **BLARNEY**
(Blarney), County Cork, Ireland
Year Built: 1996
Designer: P Suttle

● **GLENMALURE**
(Glenmalure), County Wicklow, Ireland
Designer: P Suttle

SWAN

● **BIDFORD GRANGE**
(Bidford Grange), Warwickshire, England
Designer: Howard Swan, Paul Tillman

● **GOSFIELD LAKE**
(Lakes), Essex, England
Designer: Henry Cotton, Howard Swan

● **GOSFIELD LAKE**
(Meadows), Essex, England
Designer: Henry Cotton, Howard Swan

● **STAPLEFORD ABBOTTS GOLF CLUB**
(Abbotts), Essex, England
Designer: Henry Cotton, Howard Swan

● **STAPLEFORD ABBOTTS GOLF CLUB**
(Friars), Essex, England
Designer: Henry Cotton, Howard Swan

● **STAPLEFORD ABBOTTS GOLF CLUB**
(Priors), Essex, England
Designer: Henry Cotton, Howard Swan

SWANN

● **BENTLEY**
(Bentley), Essex, England
Designer: Alec Swann

TAIT

● **BRAEHEAD**
(Braehead), Clackmannanshire, Scotland
Year Built: 1891
Designer: Robert Tait

TALLACK

● **ASHLEY WOOD**
(The Ashley Wood), Dorset, England
Year Built: 1896
Designer: P Tallack

● **BURSTEAD**
(The Burstead), Essex, England
Designer: P Tallack

● **C & L**
(C & L), London (Greater), England
Designer: P Tallack

● **CENTRAL LONDON**
(Central London), London (Greater), England
Year Built: 1992
Designer: P Tallack

● **CHESSINGTON**
(Chessington), Surrey, England
Year Built: 1983
Designer: P Tallack

HORTON PARK GOLF
(Horton Park Country Club), Surrey, England
Year Built: 1987
Designer: P Tallack

KENWICK PARK
(Kenwick), Lincolnshire, England
Year Built: 1992
Designer: P Tallack

PAXHILL PARK
(Paxhill Park), Sussex (West), England
Year Built: 1990
Designer: P Tallack

TAYLOR

ABBEYMOOR
(Abbeymoor), Surrey, England
Year Built: 1991
Designer: David Taylor

ADDINGTON COURT GOLF CLUB
(Championship), Surrey, England
Year Built: 1930
Designer: Hawtree, Taylor

ANDOVER
(Andover), Hampshire, England
Designer: Taylor

ARKLOW
(Arklow), County Wicklow, Ireland
Designer: Hawtree, Taylor

ASCOT (ROYAL)
(Royal Ascot), Berkshire, England
Year Built: 1889
Designer: Taylor

ASHBURNHAM
(Ashburnham), Carmarthenshire, Wales
Designer: Taylor

BANSTEAD DOWNS
(Banstead Downs), Surrey, England
Year Built: 1890
Designer: James Braid, J H Taylor

BERKHAMSTED
(Berkhamsted), Hertfordshire, England
Year Built: 1890
Designer: James Braid, Taylor

BIGBURY
(Bigbury), Devon, England
Designer: Taylor

BOSCOMBE LADIES
(Queens Park), Dorset, England
Year Built: 1900
Designer: Taylor

BROOKMANS PARK
(Brookmans Park), Hertfordshire, England
Year Built: 1933
Designer: Hawtree, Taylor

CAME DOWN
(Came Down), Dorset, England
Year Built: 1896
Designer: Taylor

CARMARTHEN
(Carmarthen), Carmarthenshire, Wales

Year Built: 1910
Designer: Taylor

CHESTER-LE-STREET
(Chester-Le-Street), County Durham, England
Year Built: 1908
Designer: Taylor

CHIGWELL
(Chigwell), Essex, England
Year Built: 1925
Designer: Hawtree, Taylor

DIP FARM
(Dip Farm), Suffolk, England
Year Built: 1893
Designer: Hawtree, S Taylor

EASTBOURNE DOWNS
(Eastbourne Downs), Sussex (East), England
Year Built: 1908
Designer: Taylor

EATON
(Eaton), Norfolk, England
Year Built: 1910
Designer: Taylor

ELFORDLEIGH
(Elfordleigh), Devon, England
Designer: Taylor

FIVE LAKES HOTEL
(Lakes), Essex, England
Designer: Hawtree, Taylor

FIVE LAKES HOTEL
(Links), Essex, England
Designer: Hawtree, Taylor

FRESHWATER BAY
(Freshwater Bay), Isle of Wight, England
Year Built: 1893
Designer: Taylor

FRILFORD HEATH
(Green), Oxfordshire, England
Year Built: 1908
Designer: D Cotton, J Taylor

FRILFORD HEATH
(Red), Oxfordshire, England
Designer: D Cotton, J Taylor

GORLESTON
(Gorleston), Norfolk, England
Designer: Taylor

GUILDFORD
(Guildford), Surrey, England
Designer: Hawtree, Taylor

HAINAULT FOREST
(Top), Essex, England
Year Built: 1909
Designer: Taylor

HARPENDEN
(Harpenden), Hertfordshire, England
Designer: Hawtree, Taylor

HEATON PARK
(Heaton Park Golf Centre), Manchester (Greater), England
Year Built: 1900
Designer: Taylor

HIGHWOODS
(Highwoods), Sussex (East), England
Year Built: 1925
Designer: Taylor

HINDHEAD
(Hindhead), Surrey, England
Year Built: 1904
Designer: Taylor

KAMES GOLF
(Kames), Lanarkshire (South), Scotland
Year Built: 1998
Designer: Graham Taylor

KAMES GOLF
(Mouse Valley), Lanarkshire (South), Scotland
Year Built: 1993
Designer: Graham Taylor

KNOWLE
(Knowle), Bristol, England
Year Built: 1905
Designer: Taylor

LANGLEY PARK
(Langley Park), Kent, England
Designer: Taylor

LOFTHOUSE HILL
(Lofthouse Hill), Yorkshire (West), England
Year Built: 1995
Designer: Taylor

LONG ASHTON
(Long Ashton), Bristol, England
Year Built: 1893
Designer: Hawtree, S Taylor

MID-SURREY (ROYAL)
(Inner), Surrey, England
Designer: Taylor

MID-SURREY (ROYAL)
(Outer), Surrey, England
Year Built: 1894
Designer: Taylor

MOOR HALL
(Moor Hall), Midlands (West), England
Year Built: 1932
Designer: Frederick George Hawtree, J H Taylor

OGBOURNE DOWNS
(Ogbourne Downs), Wiltshire, England
Year Built: 1907
Designer: Taylor

OKEHAMPTON
(Okehampton), Devon, England
Year Built: 1913
Designer: Taylor

OLTON
(Olton), Midlands (West), England
Designer: Taylor

PACHESHAM PARK GOLF CTRE
(Pachesham Park Golf Ctre), Surrey, England
Designer: Taylor

PORTHCAWL (ROYAL)
(Royal Porthcawl), Bridgend, Wales

Tallack — Taylor

Year Built: 1892
Designer: Hawtree, Hunter, Simpson, Taylor

● PURLEY DOWNS
(Purley Downs), Surrey, England
Designer: Harry Shapland Colt, J Taylor

● ROSSLARE
(New), County Wexford, Ireland
Designer: Hawtree, Taylor

● ROSSLARE
(Old), County Wexford, Ireland
Designer: Hawtree, Taylor

● SALISBURY & SOUTH WILTS
(Bibury), Wiltshire, England
Designer: S Gidman, J H Taylor

● SALISBURY & SOUTH WILTS
(Main), Wiltshire, England
Year Built: 1888
Designer: S Gidman, J H Taylor

● SEAFORD
(Blatchington), Sussex (East), England
Year Built: 1907
Designer: Taylor

● SELBY
(Selby), Yorkshire (North), England
Designer: Hawtree, Donald Steel, Taylor

● SELSDON PARK
(Selsdon Park), Surrey, England
Year Built: 1929
Designer: Taylor

● SELSEY
(Selsey), Sussex (West), England
Year Built: 1908
Designer: Taylor

● SIDMOUTH
(Sidmouth), Devon, England
Year Built: 1889
Designer: Taylor

● SOUTHAMPTON MUNICIPAL
(Southampton Municipal 18 Hole),
Hampshire, England
Year Built: 1935
Designer: Hockley, A P Taylor

● STRAWBERRY HILL
(Strawberry Hill), London (Greater),
England
Designer: Taylor

● WATERBRIDGE
(Waterbridge), Devon, England
Designer: Taylor

● WEST WILTS
(West Wilts), Wiltshire, England
Designer: Taylor

● WINDWHISTLE
(Windwhistle), Somerset, England
Year Built: 1932
Designer: James Braid, Fisher, Taylor

● YORK
(York), Yorkshire (North), England
Designer: Taylor

THOMAS

● ALLT-Y-GRABAN
(Allt-y-Graban), Swansea, Wales
Year Built: 1993
Designer: F G Thomas

● BELFRY
(Brabazon), Midlands (West), England
Year Built: 1998
Designer: P Alliss, D Thomas

● BELFRY
(Derby), Midlands (West), England
Year Built: 1977
Designer: Peter Alliss, David Thomas

● BELFRY
(PGA National), Midlands (West), England
Year Built: 1997
Designer: Peter Alliss, D Thomas

● BLAIRGOWRIE
(Lansdowne), Perth And Kinross, Scotland
Designer: Peter Alliss, James Braid, Tom Morris, David Thomas

● BLAIRGOWRIE
(Rosemount), Perth And Kinross, Scotland
Designer: Peter Alliss, James Braid, Tom Morris, David Thomas

● BLAIRGOWRIE
(Wee), Perth And Kinross, Scotland
Designer: Peter Alliss, James Braid, Tom Morris, David Thomas

● COLVEND
(Colvend), Dumfries And Galloway,
Scotland
Year Built: 1985
Designer: Peter Alliss, David Thomas

● DEER PARK
(Deer Park), Lothian (West), Scotland
Year Built: 1978
Designer: Peter Alliss, David Thomas

● HESSLE
(Hessle), Yorkshire (East), England
Designer: Peter Alliss, David Thomas

● HILL VALLEY
(East), Shropshire, England
Designer: Peter Alliss, David Thomas

● HILL VALLEY
(West), Shropshire, England
Designer: Peter Alliss, David Thomas

● KING'S LYNN
(King's Lynn), Norfolk, England
Year Built: 1972
Designer: Peter Alliss, David Thomas

● NEWMACHAR
(Hawkshill), Aberdeen (City of), Scotland
Year Built: 1990
Designer: Peter Alliss, David Thomas

● NEWMACHAR
(Swailend), Aberdeen (City of), Scotland
Year Built: 1990
Designer: Peter Alliss, David Thomas

● SCOTTISH GOLF NATIONAL CTRE
(SNGC Practice Facility), Fife, Scotland

Year Built: 1999
Designer: D Thomas

● SOUTH WINCHESTER
(South Winchester), Hampshire, England
Year Built: 1993
Designer: Peter Alliss, David Thomas

● TELFORD
(Telford), Shropshire, England
Year Built: 1975
Designer: Peter Alliss, David Thomas

● THORPE WOOD
(Thorpe Wood), Cambridgeshire, England
Year Built: 1975
Designer: Peter Alliss, David Thomas

● WESTERWOOD
(Westerwood), Glasgow (City of), Scotland
Year Built: 1989
Designer: S Ballesteros, Thomas

THOMPSON

● ALDEBURGH
(Aldeburgh), Suffolk, England
Designer: William Fernie, Thompson

● MALDON
(Maldon), Essex, England
Designer: Thompson

● OTTER VALLEY GOLF CTRE
(Otter Valley), Devon, England
Year Built: 1997
Designer: Andrew Thompson

● PAVENHAM
(Pavenham Park), Bedfordshire, England
Year Built: 1993
Designer: Zac Thompson, Derek Young

THOMSON

● DUKES
(The Dukes), Fife, Scotland
Year Built: 1995
Designer: Peter Thomson

● FARRINGTON
(Executive), Bristol, England
Year Built: 1900
Designer: Peter Thomson

● FARRINGTON
(Main), Bristol, England
Year Built: 1900
Designer: Peter Thomson

TILLMAN

● BIDFORD GRANGE
(Bidford Grange), Warwickshire, England
Designer: Howard Swan, Paul Tillman

TIPPET

● TRAMORE
(Tramore), County Waterford, Ireland
Designer: Captain Tippet

TODD

● MATTISHALL
(Mattishall), Norfolk, England
Designer: B Todd

WENSUM VALLEY
(Wensum Valley), Norfolk, England
Year Built: 1991
Designer: B Todd

TORY
ETCHINGHILL
(Etchinghill), Kent, England
Year Built: 1995
Designer: P Tory

TRAYNOR
STYAL
(Academy Championship Par 3), Cheshire, England
Year Built: 2000
Designer: Glynn Traynor

TUCKER
BEEDLES LAKE
(Beedles Lake), Leicestershire, England
Year Built: 1993
Designer: David Tucker

LINGDALE
(Lingdale), Leicestershire, England
Year Built: 1967
Designer: David Tucker

TUNNICLIFFE
BROUGHTON HEATH
(Broughton Heath), Derbyshire, England
Year Built: 1998
Designer: Ken Tunnicliffe

TURNER
BURFORD
(Burford), Oxfordshire, England
Designer: John Turner

TUSTIN
BEARWOOD
(Bearwood), Berkshire, England
Designer: Barry Tustin

TYACK
WEST CORNWALL
(West Cornwall), Cornwall, England
Designer: Reverend Tyack

TYRRELL
FYNN VALLEY
(Fynn Valley 18 hole), Suffolk, England
Year Built: 1991
Designer: A Tyrrell

FYNN VALLEY
(Fynn Valley 9 hole), Suffolk, England
Year Built: 1989
Designer: A Tyrrell

VARDON
COVENTRY
(Coventry), Midlands (West), England
Designer: Hawtree, Harry Vardon

DOUGLAS
(Douglas), County Cork, Ireland
Designer: Peter McEvoy, Harry Vardon

GANTON
(Ganton Golf Club), Yorkshire (North), England
Year Built: 1891
Designer: James Braid, Harry Shapland Colt, Tom Dunn, Harry Vardon

HESSLE
(Hexham), Yorkshire (East), England
Year Built: 1907
Designer: Harry Vardon, James Caird

MOORE PLACE
(Moore Place), Surrey, England
Year Built: 1926
Designer: Harry Vardon, David Allen, Nick Gadd

WADE
WEST PARK
(West Park), Essex, England
Designer: Graham Wade

WALKER
BENTON HALL
(Benton Hall), Essex, England
Year Built: 1990
Designer: Charlie Cox, Alan Walker

SUTTON GREEN
(Sutton Green), Surrey, England
Year Built: 1994
Designer: L Davies, D Walker

WALLACE
CASTLEROSSE
(Castlerosse), County Kerry, Ireland
Designer: Harry Wallace

WALSH
AUSTIN LODGE
(Austin Lodge), Kent, England
Year Built: 1991
Designer: P Bevan, Mike Walsh

BRIERLEY FOREST
(Davcolm), Nottinghamshire, England
Year Built: 1993
Designer: Hibbert, Walsh

WALTERS
MID WALES GOLF CTRE
(Mid-Wales Golf Centre), Powys, Wales
Designer: Jim Walters

PENRHOS
(Penrhos), Ceredigion, Wales
Designer: Jim Walters

WALTON
ST. HELENS BAY
(St Helen's Bay), County Wexford, Ireland
Year Built: 1993
Designer: Philip Walton

TIPPERARY (COUNTY)
(Tipperary), County Tipperary, Ireland
Designer: Philip Walton

WARD
SPALDING
(Spalding), Lincolnshire, England
Designer: Price, Spencer, Ward

WARDLE
GLENISLA
(Glenisla), Perth And Kinross, Scotland
Year Built: 1998
Designer: Tony Wardle

WARING
DISTINGTON GOLF
(Distington), Cumbria, England
Year Built: 1993
Designer: Keith Waring

WARREN
OAKSEY
(Oaksey), Wiltshire, England
Designer: Chapman, Warren

WATKINS
WERNDDU
(Wernddu), Monmouthshire, Wales
Year Built: 1994
Designer: G Watkins

WATT
HIGHWORTH GOLF CENTRE
(Highworth), Wiltshire, England
Designer: D Lang, B Sandry, T Watt

WEBSTER
EDZELL
(West Water), Angus, Scotland
Year Built: 2000
Designer: Graeme Webster

INCHMARLO GOLF CTRE
(Inchmarlo 18 hole), Aberdeenshire, Scotland
Year Built: 2001
Designer: Graeme Webster

KINGS ACRE
(Kings Acre), Lothian (Mid), Scotland
Year Built: 1997
Designer: Graeme Webster

MELDRUM HOUSE
(The Knights), Aberdeen (City of), Scotland
Designer: Graeme Webster

WEIR
ILFRACOMBE
(Ilfracombe), Devon, England
Year Built: 1892
Designer: K Weir

WEISKOPF
LOCH LOMOND
(Loch Lomond), Argyll and Bute, Scotland
Designer: J Morris, T Weiskopf

WELBERRY
KIRTON HOLME
(Kirton Holme), Lincolnshire, England
Year Built: 1992
Designer: D Welberry

WHIDBORNE
WORLDHAM PARK
(Worldham Park), Hampshire, England
Designer: F J Whidborne

WHITCOMBE

🏌 **LANSDOWN**
(Lansdown), Bath & Somerset (North East), England
Designer: C A Whitcombe

WHITE

🏌 **COWDRAY PARK**
(Cowdray Park), Sussex (West), England
Designer: Jack White

WHITEHEAD

🏌 **LES MIELLES**
(Les Mielles),
Designer: J Le Brun, R Whitehead

WIGGINGTON

🏌 **DROMOLAND CASTLE ESTATE**
(Dromoland Castle), County Clare, Ireland
Designer: Wiggington

WILLIAMS

🏌 **BELFORD**
(Belford), Northumberland, England
Year Built: 1993
Designer: N Williams

🏌 **BELTON PARK**
(Ancaster), Lincolnshire, England
Year Built: 1890
Designer: Peter Alliss, John P Williams

🏌 **BELTON PARK**
(Belmont), Lincolnshire, England
Designer: Peter Alliss, John P Williams

🏌 **CHAPEL-EN-LE-FRITH**
(Chapel-en-le-Frith), Derbyshire, England
Year Built: 1905
Designer: David Williams

🏌 **DUKES MEADOW**
(Dukes Meadows), London (Greater), England
Year Built: 1995
Designer: David Williams

🏌 **GRETNA**
(Gretna), Dumfries And Galloway, Scotland
Designer: N Williams

🏌 **GROVE**
(Grove), Bridgend, Wales
Year Built: 1996
Designer: J C Williams

🏌 **HAPPY VALLEY**
(Happy Valley), Surrey, England
Designer: David Williams

🏌 **KINGS HILL**
(Kings Hill), Kent, England
Designer: David Williams

🏌 **LAGGANMORE**
(Lagganmore), Dumfries And Galloway, Scotland
Year Built: 1990
Designer: N Williams

🏌 **LEXDEN**
(Lexden Wood), Essex, England
Year Built: 1992
Designer: N Williams

🏌 **MANNINGS HEATH**
(Kingfisher), Sussex (West), England
Year Built: 1905
Designer: David Williams

🏌 **MERRIST WOOD**
(Merrist Wood), Surrey, England
Designer: David Williams

🏌 **MID SUSSEX**
(Mid Sussex), Sussex (East), England
Year Built: 1995
Designer: David Williams

🏌 **PADESWOOD & BUCKLEY**
(Padeswood & Buckley), Flintshire, Wales
Year Built: 1976
Designer: Williams

🏌 **REIGATE HILL**
(Reigate Hill), Surrey, England
Year Built: 1995
Designer: David Williams

🏌 **RUSTINGTON**
(Rustington), Sussex (West), England
Year Built: 1992
Designer: David Williams

🏌 **SLEAFORD**
(Sleaford), Lincolnshire, England
Year Built: 1905
Designer: T Williams

🏌 **WORFIELD**
(Worfield), Shropshire, England
Year Built: 1991
Designer: T Williams

WILLIAMSON

🏌 **BEESTON FIELDS**
(Beeston Fields), Nottinghamshire, England
Designer: Tom Williamson

🏌 **BELTON PARK**
(Brownlow), Lincolnshire, England
Year Built: 1890
Designer: Tom Williamson

🏌 **CHILWELL MANOR**
(Chilwell Manor), Nottinghamshire, England
Year Built: 1906
Designer: Tom Williamson

🏌 **COMRIE**
(Comrie), Perth and Kinross, Scotland
Designer: Colonel Williamson

🏌 **RADCLIFFE-ON-TRENT**
(Radcliffe-On-Trent), Nottinghamshire, England
Year Built: 1909
Designer: Pennink, Tom Williamson

🏌 **RETFORD**
(Retford), Nottinghamshire, England
Year Built: 1920
Designer: Tom Williamson

🏌 **STANTON ON THE WOLDS**
(Stanton On The Wolds), Nottinghamshire, England
Designer: Tom Williamson

🏌 **WORKSOP**
(Worksop), Nottinghamshire, England

Year Built: 1914
Designer: Tom Williamson

WILSON

🏌 **BELLINGHAM**
(Boogle Hole), Northumberland, England
Year Built: 1893
Designer: E Johnson, I Wilson

🏌 **CASTLE HAWK**
(New), Lancashire, England
Designer: T Wilson

🏌 **CASTLE HAWK**
(Old), Lancashire, England
Year Built: 1960
Designer: T Wilson

WILTSHIRE

🏌 **WELLOW**
(Ryedown), Hampshire, England
Designer: W Wiltshire

WINSLAND

🏌 **ASPECT PARK**
(Aspect Park Golf Centre), Oxfordshire, England
Year Built: 1989
Designer: Tim Winsland

WINTER

🏌 **CALDERFIELDS**
(Calderfields), Midlands (West), England
Designer: R Winter

WOOD

🏌 **LOSTWITHIEL**
(Lostwithiel), Cornwall, England
Year Built: 1991
Designer: Stuart Wood

WOOSNAM

🏌 **DALE HILL**
(The Ian Woosnam), Sussex (East), England
Year Built: 1997
Designer: Ian Woosnam

WOOTTON

🏌 **LAKESIDE**
(Lakeside), Neath Port Talbot, Wales
Year Built: 1992
Designer: Matthew Wootton

WRIGHT

🏌 **AYLESBURY VALE**
(Aylesbury Vale), Bedfordshire, England
Year Built: 1991
Designer: D Wright

🏌 **FOUR MARKS**
(Four Marks), Hampshire, England
Year Built: 1983
Designer: D Wright

🏌 **HORNCASTLE**
(Horncastle), Lincolnshire, England
Designer: E C Wright

🏌 **TEST VALLEY**
(Test Valley), Hampshire, England

Year Built: 1992
Designer: E Darcy, D Wright

WUNDKE

● **SUTTON HALL**
(Sutton Hall), Cheshire, England
Year Built: 1994
Designer: Stephen Wundke

YATES

● **OPEN**
(Yellow Nine), County Dublin, Ireland
Designer: R Yates

YOUNG

● **ABBOTSLEY**
(Abbotsley), Cambridgeshire, England
Designer: V Saunders, D Young

● **ALRESFORD**
(Alresford), Hampshire, England
Designer: Scott Webb Young

● **DAWN 'TIL DUSK**
(Dawn 'Til Dusk), Pembrokeshire, Wales
Year Built: 1993
Designer: W R Young

● **MOUNT PLEASANT**
(Mount Pleasant 18 tees), Bedfordshire,
England
Year Built: 1991
Designer: D Young

● **PAVENHAM**
(Pavenham Park), Bedfordshire, England
Year Built: 1993
Designer: Zac Thompson, Derek Young

Wright — Young by Course **DESIGNER SURNAME**

SECTION 6

This section allows you to search for courses by the year in which they were built.

e.g 1884, Brocton Hall, Staffordshire, England.

For further information about each club refer to the detailed profile in Section 1, or search for specific details in other sections.

1567

- MUSSELBURGH LINKS
  (The Old), **Lothian (East)**, Scotland

1800

- GIRVAN
  (Semi-Lynx), **Ayrshire (South)**, Scotland
- KILBIRNIE PLACE
  Ayrshire (North), Scotland

1807

- RAVENSPARK
  Ayrshire (North), Scotland

1812

- LEASOWE
  Merseyside, England

1817

- SCOTSCRAIG
  Fife, Scotland

1832

- NORTH BERWICK
  (West Links), **Lothian (East)**, Scotland

1833

- HAYLING
  Hampshire, England

1841

- PETERHEAD
  (New), **Aberdeenshire**, Scotland
- PETERHEAD
  (Old), **Aberdeenshire**, Scotland

1844

- DOWN ROYAL PARK
  County Antrim, Northern Ireland

1848

- NEW FOREST
  Hampshire, England

1850

- BENTRA MUNICIPAL
  County Antrim, Northern Ireland

1851

- LANARK
  (Old), **Lanarkshire (South)**, Scotland
- LANARK
  (Wee), **Lanarkshire (South)**, Scotland
- PRESTWICK
  Ayrshire (South), Scotland

1855

- CUPAR
  Fife, Scotland

1856

- DUNBAR
  Lothian (East), Scotland

1858

- MONIFIETH GOLF LINKS
  (Medal), **Angus**, Scotland

1864

- NORTH DEVON (ROYAL)
  (Royal North), **Devon**, England

1865

- LONDON SCOTTISH
  London (Greater), England

1867

- LEVEN THISTLE
  (Leven Links), **Fife**, Scotland

1868

- LUNDIN
  Fife, Scotland

1869

- LIVERPOOL (ROYAL)
  (Royal Liverpool), **Merseyside**, England

1871

- FORFAR
  Angus, Scotland

1873

- NEWBURY & CROOKHAM
  Berkshire, England

1875

- MUIR OF ORD
  Highlands, Scotland

1876

- MACHRIHANISH
  Argyll and Bute, Scotland

1877

- HAWICK
  Scottish Borders, Scotland
- HAYDOCK PARK
  Merseyside, England
- STRATHLENE
  Moray, Scotland

1878

- TROON (ROYAL)
  (Old), **Ayrshire (South)**, Scotland

1879

- LADYBANK
  Fife, Scotland

1880

- MELROSE
  Scottish Borders, Scotland
- SOUTHPORT OLD LINKS
  Merseyside, England

1881

- FRASERBURGH
  (Rosehill), **Aberdeenshire**, Scotland
- KINGSDOWN
  Wiltshire, England

1882

- GREAT YARMOUTH & CAISTER
  (Traditional Links), **Norfolk**, England
- GULLANE
  Lothian (East), Scotland

- MANCHESTER
  Manchester (Greater), England
- MINEHEAD & WEST SOMERSET
  Somerset, England

1883

- ABOYNE
  Aberdeenshire, Scotland
- INVERNESS
  Highlands, Scotland
- SELKIRK
  Scottish Borders, Scotland

1884

- BROCTON HALL
  Staffordshire, England
- FORMBY
  Merseyside, England
- GALASHIELS
  Scottish Borders, Scotland
- SOUTHWOLD
  Suffolk, England

1885

- BORTH & YNYSLAS
  Ceredigion, Wales
- HESKETH
  Merseyside, England
- LOCHGELLY
  Fife, Scotland
- OLDMELDRUM
  Aberdeenshire, Scotland

1886

- INNERLEITHEN
  Scottish Borders, Scotland

1887

- BRIGHTON & HOVE
  Sussex (East), England
- BUXTON & HIGH PEAK
  (Buxton and High Peak), **Derbyshire**, England
- CLEVELAND
  Cleveland, England
- IRVINE
  (Lynx), **Ayrshire (North)**, Scotland
- KELSO
  Scottish Borders, Scotland
- NAIRN
  Highlands, Scotland
- NAIRN
  (Newton), **Highlands**, Scotland
- REDHILL & REIGATE

- REDHILL & REIGATE
  Surrey, England

1888

- ASHDOWN FOREST (ROYAL)
  (Old), **Sussex (East)**, England
- CROMER (ROYAL)
  (Royal Cromer), **Norfolk**, England
- FORTROSE & ROSEMARKIE
  Highlands, Scotland
- LITTLESTONE
  Kent, England

COURSES by YEAR BUILT

1567 — 1888

- **MILLPORT**
  Ayrshire (North), Scotland
- **NEWBURGH-ON-YTHAN**
  Aberdeenshire, Scotland
- **PORTRUSH (ROYAL)**
  (Dunluce), **County Antrim,** Northern Ireland
- **SALISBURY & SOUTH WILTS**
  (Main), **Wiltshire,** England
- **STONEHAVEN**
  Aberdeenshire, Scotland
- **STRATHPEFFER SPA**
  Highlands, Scotland
- **TENBY**
  Pembrokeshire, Wales
- **WINCHESTER (ROYAL)**
  (Royal Winchester), **Hampshire,** England

1889

- **ASCOT (ROYAL)**
  (Royal Ascot), **Berkshire,** England
- **DOOKS**
  County Kerry, Ireland
- **DOWN (ROYAL COUNTY)**
  (Championship), **County Down,** Northern Ireland
- **DUNARVERTY**
  Argyll and Bute, Scotland
- **EPSOM**
  Surrey, England
- **FORRES**
  Moray, Scotland
- **GOLSPIE**
  Highlands, Scotland
- **LENZIE**
  Glasgow (City of), Scotland
- **LIMPSFIELD CHART**
  Surrey, England
- **LOCKERBIE**
  Dumfries And Galloway, Scotland
- **LUDLOW**
  Shropshire, England
- **MACCLESFIELD**
  Cheshire, England
- **MORAY**
  (Old), **Moray,** Scotland
- **SIDMOUTH**
  Devon, England
- **STINCHCOMBE HILL**
  Gloucestershire, England
- **TUNBRIDGE WELLS**
  Kent, England

1890

- **ABERFOYLE**
  Stirling, Scotland
- **ANSTRUTHER**
  Fife, Scotland
- **BALLYCASTLE**
  County Antrim, Northern Ireland
- **BANSTEAD DOWNS**
  Surrey, England
- **BELTON PARK**
  (Ancaster), **Lincolnshire,** England
- **BELTON PARK**
  (Brownlow), **Lincolnshire,** England

- **BERKHAMSTED**
  Hertfordshire, England
- **BERWICK**
  Northumberland, England
- **BUSHEY HALL**
  Hertfordshire, England
- **CHARNWOOD FOREST**
  Leicestershire, England
- **CHORLEYWOOD**
  Hertfordshire, England
- **CHURSTON**
  Devon, England
- **CONWY**
  Conwy, Wales
- **DATCHET**
  Berkshire, England
- **DUNGANNON**
  County Tyrone, Northern Ireland
- **GRANTOWN-ON-SPEY**
  (Grantown On Spey), **Moray,** Scotland
- **KINGHORN**
  Fife, Scotland
- **LEICESTER**
  Leicestershire, England
- **PORTER'S PARK**
  Hertfordshire, England
- **RHYL**
  Denbighshire, Wales
- **TAIN**
  Highlands, Scotland
- **TAVISTOCK**
  Devon, England
- **WEST LINTON**
  Scottish Borders, Scotland

1891

- **BRAEHEAD**
  Clackmannanshire, Scotland
- **BRIDPORT & WEST DORSET**
  Dorset, England
- **BRISTOL & CLIFTON**
  (Bristol and Clifton), **Bristol,** England
- **BRORA**
  Highlands, Scotland
- **CRAIGENTINNY**
  Edinburgh (City of), Scotland
- **FRASERBURGH**
  (Corbie Hill), **Aberdeenshire,** Scotland
- **GANTON**
  Yorkshire (North), England
- **HUDDERSFIELD**
  Yorkshire (West), England
- **INNELLAN**
  Argyll and Bute, Scotland
- **KENDAL**
  Cumbria, England
- **LAMBERHURST**
  Kent, England
- **LARGS**
  Ayrshire (North), Scotland
- **LINCOLN**
  Lincolnshire, England
- **LINDRICK**
  Nottinghamshire, England

- **MACHRIE**
  Argyll and Bute, Scotland
- **MUIRFIELD**
  Lothian (East), Scotland
- **NORTHWOOD**
  London (Greater), England
- **PAINSWICK**
  Gloucestershire, England
- **PLEASINGTON**
  Lancashire, England
- **ROCHESTER & COBHAM**
  Kent, England
- **RYTON**
  Tyne And Wear, England
- **SHERINGHAM**
  Norfolk, England
- **WALLASEY**
  Merseyside, England
- **WINDERMERE**
  Cumbria, England

1892

- **ALFRETON**
  Derbyshire, England
- **BALLATER**
  Aberdeenshire, Scotland
- **BOGNOR REGIS**
  Sussex (West), England
- **CLACTON**
  Essex, England
- **GLASGOW GAILES**
  Ayrshire (North), Scotland
- **GOODWOOD**
  Sussex (West), England
- **HALLOWES**
  Derbyshire, England
- **HUNTLY**
  Aberdeen (City of), Scotland
- **ILFRACOMBE**
  Devon, England
- **LOUTH (COUNTY)**
  (Louth), **County Louth,** Ireland
- **MONMOUTHSHIRE**
  Monmouthshire, Wales
- **OLDHAM**
  Manchester (Greater), England
- **PORTHCAWL (ROYAL)**
  (Royal Porthcawl), **Bridgend,** Wales
- **PRESTON**
  Lancashire, England
- **SILLOTH**
  Cumbria, England
- **SOUTH BEDS**
  (Galley Hill), **Bedfordshire,** England
- **SOUTH BEDS**
  (Warden Hill), **Bedfordshire,** England
- **SUTTON COLDFIELD LADIES**
  (Sutton Coldfield), **Midlands (West),** England
- **THAMES DITTON & ESHER**
  Surrey, England
- **WARREN**
  Devon, England

- WEST LOTHIAN
  Lothian (West), Scotland
- WHITBY
  Yorkshire (North), England
- WITHINGTON
  Manchester (Greater), England

1893

- ACCRINGTON & DISTRICT
  (Accrington), Lancashire, England
- BELLINGHAM
  (Boogle Hole), Northumberland, England
- BRAID HILLS
  (Braids No 1), Edinburgh (City of),
  Scotland
- BRAID HILLS
  (Braids No 2), Edinburgh (City of),
  Scotland
- BRECHIN GOLF & SQUASH CLUB
  Angus, Scotland
- DIP FARM
  Suffolk, England
- EAST BRIGHTON
  Sussex (East), England
- EASTWOOD
  Glasgow (City of), Scotland
- FRESHWATER BAY
  Isle of Wight, England
- HAMPSTEAD
  London (Greater), England
- HELENSBURGH
  Argyll and Bute, Scotland
- HOLTYE
  Kent, England
- INVERGORDON
  Highlands, Scotland
- KIRBY MUXLOE
  Leicestershire, England
- KIRKCUDBRIGHT
  Dumfries And Galloway, Scotland
- LONG ASHTON
  Bristol, England
- LOTHIANBURN
  Edinburgh (City of), Scotland
- LYME REGIS
  Dorset, England
- MUSWELL HILL
  London (Greater), England
- NEWTONMORE
  Highlands, Scotland
- NORWICH (ROYAL)
  (Royal Norwich), Norfolk, England
- ORMEAU
  County Antrim, Northern Ireland
- OUNDLE
  Cambridgeshire, England
- REAY
  Highlands, Scotland
- ROBIN HOOD
  Midlands (West), England
- SEASCALE
  Cumbria, England
- SKIPTON
  Yorkshire (North), England

- THORNHILL
  Dumfries And Galloway, Scotland
- THURSO
  Highlands, Scotland
- WANSTEAD
  London (Greater), England
- WARRENPOINT
  County Down, Northern Ireland
- WELLS
  Somerset, England
- WEST KILBRIDE
  Ayrshire (North), Scotland
- WOODBRIDGE
  Suffolk, England
- WORLINGTON & NEWMARKET
  (ROYAL)
  (Royal Worlington & Newmarket), Suffolk,
  England

1894

- ATHERSTONE
  Warwickshire, England
- BALLINASLOE
  County Galway, Ireland
- BISHOP AUCKLAND
  County Durham, England
- BULWELL FOREST
  Nottinghamshire, England
- CHEVIN
  Derbyshire, England
- DUNS
  Scottish Borders, Scotland
- HARLECH
  (Royal St Davids), Gwynedd, Wales
- LARNE
  County Antrim, Northern Ireland
- MELLOR & TOWNSCLIFFE
  (Old), Cheshire, England
- MELLOR & TOWNSCLIFFE
  (Valley), Cheshire, England
- MID-SURREY (ROYAL)
  (Outer), Surrey, England
- MULRANNY
  County Mayo, Ireland
- NEWCASTLETON
  Scottish Borders, Scotland
- NORTH WALES
  Conwy, Wales
- PORTMARNOCK
  (Old), County Dublin, Ireland
- PUTTENHAM
  Surrey, England
- ROMFORD
  Essex, England
- SHORTLANDS
  Kent, England
- WELSHPOOL
  Powys, Wales
- WIGTOWNSHIRE
  (County), Dumfries And Galloway,
  Scotland
- WORSLEY
  Manchester (Greater), England

1895

- BALLINROBE
  County Mayo, Ireland
- BARON HILL
  Isle of Anglesey, Wales
- BEARSTED
  Kent, England
- BUSH HILL PARK
  London (Greater), England
- CARDIGAN
  Ceredigion, Wales
- CARDROSS
  Argyll and Bute, Scotland
- CLIFF HOTEL
  (Cardigan), Ceredigion, Wales
- COCHRANE CASTLE
  Renfrewshire, Scotland
- CROWBOROUGH BEACON
  Sussex (East), England
- DONCASTER TOWN MOOR
  Yorkshire (South), England
- EDZELL
  Angus, Scotland
- EXETER
  Devon, England
- FLEMPTON
  Suffolk, England
- HORWICH
  Lancashire, England
- MULLION
  Cornwall, England
- SEACROFT
  Lincolnshire, England
- SHERWOOD FOREST
  Nottinghamshire, England
- SHOTTS
  Lanarkshire (North), Scotland
- ST. ANDREWS LINKS
  (New), Fife, Scotland
- ST. GILES
  (St Giles), Powys, Wales
- TORWOODLEE
  Scottish Borders, Scotland
- TROON (ROYAL)
  (Portland), Ayrshire (South), Scotland

1896

- ABERDOUR
  Fife, Scotland
- ASHLEY WOOD
  Dorset, England
- BAILDON
  Yorkshire (West), England
- BEITH
  Ayrshire (North), Scotland
- BROOKDALE
  Manchester (Greater), England
- CAME DOWN
  Dorset, England
- COCKERMOUTH
  Cumbria, England
- DUFFTOWN
  Aberdeenshire, Scotland

- FARNHAM
  Surrey, England
- GOUROCK
  Inverclyde, Scotland
- HELENS BAY
  (Helen's Bay), **County Down,** Northern Ireland
- KILKEE
  County Clare, Ireland
- LAUDER
  Scottish Borders, Scotland
- LEEDS
  Yorkshire (West), England
- LEWES
  Sussex (East), England
- MAIDENHEAD
  Berkshire, England
- NEWTON STEWART
  Dumfries And Galloway, Scotland
- PENNARD
  Swansea, Wales
- SEDBURGH
  Cumbria, England
- SHISKINE
  Ayrshire (North), Scotland
- TORPHINS
  Aberdeenshire, Scotland
- TURRIFF
  Aberdeenshire, Scotland

1897

- ASHTON-ON-MERSEY
  (Ashton on Mersey), **Cheshire,** England
- CAMPSIE
  Glasgow (City of), Scotland
- CANMORE
  Fife, Scotland
- DOUGLAS PARK
  Glasgow (City of), Scotland
- LOCHWINNOCH
  Renfrewshire, Scotland
- ROUTENBURN
  Ayrshire (North), Scotland
- SANDWELL PARK
  Midlands (West), England
- SAUNTON
  (East), **Devon,** England
- ST. ANDREWS LINKS
  (Jubilee), **Fife,** Scotland
- THURLESTONE
  Devon, England

1898

- BARNARD CASTLE
  County Durham, England
- BECKENHAM PLACE PARK
  Kent, England
- CARNEGIE
  Highlands, Scotland
- CHURCH STRETTON
  Shropshire, England
- GAIRLOCH
  (Gariloch), **Highlands,** Scotland
- GULLANE
  Lothian (East), Scotland

- HORNSEA
  Yorkshire (East), England
- LESLIE
  Fife, Scotland
- WILLINGDON
  Sussex (East), England
- WIMBLEDON PARK
  London (Greater), England

1899

- CHINGFORD
  London (Greater), England
- LOCHRANZA GOLF
  Isle of Arran, Scotland
- ORSETT
  Essex, England
- PRESTWICK ST CUTHBERT
  Ayrshire (South), Scotland
- RHOS-ON-SEA
  Conwy, Wales
- SICKLEHOLME
  Derbyshire, England
- SOUTH HERTS
  London (Greater), England
- WESTWOOD
  Staffordshire, England

1900

- BOSCOMBE LADIES
  (Queens Park), **Dorset,** England
- BRAMPTON
  Cumbria, England
- CHADWELL SPRINGS
  Hertfordshire, England
- DUNSTANBURGH CASTLE
  Northumberland, England
- ELSHAM
  Lincolnshire (North), England
- FARRINGTON
  (Executive), **Bristol,** England
- FARRINGTON
  (Main), **Bristol,** England
- HEATON PARK
  Manchester (Greater), England
- HOWLEY HALL
  Yorkshire (West), England
- LONGFORD (COUNTY)
  (Longford), **County Longford,** Ireland
- PANMURE
  Angus, Scotland
- ROMSEY
  Hampshire, England
- RUSHMERE
  Suffolk, England
- WEST BRADFORD
  Yorkshire (West), England
- WEST ESSEX
  London (Greater), England
- WRANGATON
  Devon, England

1901

- BIRSTALL
  Leicestershire, England

- CHORLTON-CUM-HARDY
  Manchester (Greater), England
- COLNE
  Lancashire, England
- GOG MAGOG
  (The Old), **Cambridgeshire,** England
- GOG MAGOG
  (Wandlebury), **Cambridgeshire,** England
- HUNTERCOMBE
  Oxfordshire, England
- MUNDESLEY
  Norfolk, England
- NOTTS
  Nottinghamshire, England
- POLMONT
  Falkirk, Scotland
- SANDILANDS & LEISURE
  (Sandilands), **Lincolnshire,** England
- SUNNINGDALE
  (Old), **Surrey,** England

1902

- BRAEMAR
  Aberdeenshire, Scotland
- HALIFAX
  (Ogden), **Yorkshire (West),** England
- KIRKISTOWN CASTLE
  County Down, Northern Ireland
- NELSON
  Lancashire, England
- NEW
  Fife, Scotland
- NEW GALLOWAY
  Dumfries And Galloway, Scotland
- ROWLANDS CASTLE
  Hampshire, England
- SUNNINGDALE LADIES
  Berkshire, England
- WALMLEY
  Midlands (West), England
- WARREN
  Essex, England

1903

- ARBROATH
  Angus, Scotland
- BALLYMENA
  County Antrim, Northern Ireland
- CHESTERFIELD
  Derbyshire, England
- COOMBE WOOD
  London (Greater), England
- CULLEN
  Moray, Scotland
- DEESIDE
  (Haughton), **Aberdeen (City of),** Scotland
- HENDON
  London (Greater), England
- MAGDALENE FIELDS
  Northumberland, England
- PONTYPOOL
  Monmouthshire, Wales
- PORTPATRICK - DUNSKEY
  (Dunskey), **Dumfries And Galloway,** Scotland

- POWFOOT
  Dumfries And Galloway, Scotland
- RUTHIN-PWLLGLAS
  Denbighshire, Wales
- SCARBOROUGH SOUTH CLIFF
  Yorkshire (North), England
- SHEERNESS
- SHEERNESS
  Kent, England
- SHOOTERS HILL
  London (Greater), England
- ST. DAVIDS
  (St David's City), **Pembrokeshire**, Wales
- ST. FILLANS
  (St Fillans), **Perth and Kinross**, Scotland
- ST. MICHAELS
  (St Michaels), **Fife**, Scotland
- WARRINGTON
  Cheshire, England

1904

- ALNESS
  Highlands, Scotland
- AUCHTERDERRAN
  Fife, Scotland
- BARNEHURST
  Kent, England
- BELLEISLE & SEAFIELD
  (Seafield), **Ayrshire (South)**, Scotland
- BLACKPOOL NORTH SHORE
  Lancashire, England
- BROMBOROUGH
  Merseyside, England
- HAVERFORDWEST
  Pembrokeshire, Wales
- HINDHEAD
  Surrey, England
- HOLYWOOD
  County Down, Northern Ireland
- KEIGHLEY
  Yorkshire (West), England
- KIBWORTH
  Leicestershire, England
- KIRKCALDY
  Fife, Scotland
- LANGLAND BAY
  Swansea, Wales
- NORTH HANTS FLEET
  Hampshire, England
- RALSTON
  Renfrewshire, Scotland
- STAND
  Manchester (Greater), England
- WALTON HEATH
  (Old), **Surrey**, England
- WHITELEAF
  Buckinghamshire, England
- WICKLOW
  County Wicklow, Ireland
- WOLSTANTON
  Staffordshire, England
- YELVERTON
  Devon, England

1905

- BANCHORY
  Aberdeenshire, Scotland
- BRIDLINGTON
  Yorkshire (East), England
- BURLEY
  Hampshire, England
- CHAPEL-EN-LE-FRITH
  Derbyshire, England
- CHIPSTEAD
  Surrey, England
- DUNNERHOLME
  Cumbria, England
- HINDLEY HALL
  Lancashire, England
- KNOWLE
  Bristol, England
- LEE ON THE SOLENT
  (Lee-on-Solent), **Hampshire**, England
- LLANDRINDOD WELLS
  Powys, Wales
- LONGCLIFFE
  Leicestershire, England
- MANNINGS HEATH
  (Kingfisher), **Sussex (West)**, England
- MARYPORT
  Cumbria, England
- MOFFAT
  Dumfries And Galloway, Scotland
- MONIFIETH GOLF LINKS
  (Ashludie), **Angus**, Scotland
- NUNEATON
  Warwickshire, England
- PEEBLES
  (The Kirlands), **Scottish Borders**, Scotland
- PRENTON
  Merseyside, England
- PRESTATYN
  Denbighshire, Wales
- RANFURLY
  Renfrewshire, Scotland
- SLEAFORD
- SLEAFORD
  Lincolnshire, England
- ST. MEDAN
  (St Medan), **Dumfries And Galloway**, Scotland
- TENTERDEN
  Kent, England
- WHITSAND BAY
  Cornwall, England
- WOODHALL HILLS
  Yorkshire (West), England
- WORTHING
  (Lower), **Sussex (West)**, England
- WREKIN
  Shropshire, England

1906

- BEREHAVEN
  County Cork, Ireland
- CALDY
  Merseyside, England

- CARHOLME
  Lincolnshire, England
- CARRADALE
  Argyll and Bute, Scotland
- CHILWELL MANOR
  Nottinghamshire, England
- DEANE
  Lancashire, England
- ELGIN
  Moray, Scotland
- GLEN
  Lothian (East), Scotland
- HIGHGATE
  London (Greater), England
- HOLYWELL
  Flintshire, Wales
- LEIGH
  Cheshire, England
- MORPETH
  Northumberland, England
- MUCKHART
  (Naemoor), **Clackmannanshire**, Scotland
- OTLEY
  Yorkshire (West), England
- PANNAL
  Yorkshire (North), England
- SOUTHPORT & AINSDALE
  Merseyside, England
- WALMERSLEY
  Lancashire, England

1907

- ABERSOCH
  Gwynedd, Wales
- ALDERLEY EDGE
  Cheshire, England
- ALNWICK
  Northumberland, England
- ALWOODLEY
  Yorkshire (West), England
- BLACKLEY
  Manchester (Greater), England
- BRADLEY HALL
  Yorkshire (West), England
- BURHILL
  Surrey, England
- CAERNARFON (ROYAL TOWN OF)
  (Royal Town of Caernarfon), **Gwynedd**, Wales
- CARNWATH
  Lanarkshire (South), Scotland
- COLCHESTER
  Essex, England
- DOLLAR
  Clackmannanshire, Scotland
- HEADLEY
  Yorkshire (West), England
- HESSLE
  (Hexham), **Yorkshire (East)**, England
- HORSFORTH
  Yorkshire (West), England
- LIGHTCLIFFE
  Yorkshire (West), England

- **NEWTON GREEN**
  Suffolk, England
- **NORTH WORCESTERSHIRE**
  Midlands (West), England
- **OGBOURNE DOWNS**
  Wiltshire, England
- **OLD COLWYN**
  Conwy, Wales
- **SCRABO**
  County Down, Northern Ireland
- **SEAFORD**
  (Blatchington), Sussex (East), England
- **SHIREHAMPTON PARK**
  Bristol, England
- **ST. AGUSTINES**
  (St Agustines), Kent, England
- **TANKERSLEY PARK**
  Yorkshire (South), England
- **YEOVIL**
  (Old), Somerset, England

1908

- **ALTON**
  Hampshire, England
- **CARLISLE**
  Cumbria, England
- **CHESTER-LE-STREET**
  County Durham, England
- **DARLINGTON**
  County Durham, England
- **DELGANY**
  County Dublin, Ireland
- **DUNSCAR**
  Lancashire, England
- **EASTBOURNE DOWNS**
  Sussex (East), England
- **ELDERSLIE**
  Renfrewshire, Scotland
- **FRILFORD HEATH**
  (Green), Oxfordshire, England
- **GLENCRUITTEN**
  Argyll and Bute, Scotland
- **KEMNAY**
  Aberdeenshire, Scotland
- **KIRRIEMUIR**
  Angus, Scotland
- **LEAMINGTON & COUNTY**
  Warwickshire, England
- **MELTHAM**
  Yorkshire (West), England
- **MENDIP**
  Bath & Somerset (North East), England
- **MOUNTAIN ASH**
  Rhondda Cynon Taff, Wales
- **NEWCASTLE-UNDER-LYME**
  Staffordshire, England
- **SELSEY**
  Sussex (West), England
- **STRABANE**
  County Tyrone, Northern Ireland
- **TIDWORTH GARRISON**
  Wiltshire, England
- **TURTON**
  Lancashire, England

- **TYNEDALE**
  Northumberland, England
- **VALE OF LLANGOLLEN**
  Denbighshire, Wales
- **WERNETH**
  Manchester (Greater), England
- **WIMBLEDON COMMON**
  London (Greater), England
- **WINDYHILL**
  Glasgow (City of), Scotland

1909

- **ARKLEY**
  Hertfordshire, England
- **DENTON**
  Manchester (Greater), England
- **FILTON**
  Bristol, England
- **GREENWAY HALL**
  Staffordshire, England
- **HAINAULT FOREST**
  (Top), Essex, England
- **LOUDOUN**
  Ayrshire (East), Scotland
- **MERTHYR TYDFIL**
  Glamorgan (Vale of), Wales
- **MURCAR**
  Aberdeen (City of), Scotland
- **NORTHAMPTONSHIRE COUNTY**
  Northamptonshire, England
- **PIKEFOLD**
  Lancashire, England
- **RADCLIFFE-ON-TRENT**
  Nottinghamshire, England
- **RINGWAY**
  Cheshire, England
- **RUNCORN**
  Cheshire, England
- **SWINLEY FOREST**
  Berkshire, England
- **TEMPLE**
  Berkshire, England
- **ULVERSTON**
  Cumbria, England
- **WEYMOUTH**
  Dorset, England
- **WITHERNSEA**
  Yorkshire (East), England

1910

- **ABERGELE**
  Conwy, Wales
- **BISHOPS STORTFORD**
  (Bishop's Stortford), Hertfordshire, England
- **BLAIRBETH**
  Glasgow (City of), Scotland
- **CARMARTHEN**
  Carmarthenshire, Wales
- **CIRENCESTER**
  Gloucestershire, England
- **CLIFTONVILLE**
  County Antrim, Northern Ireland
- **DARTMOUTH**
  Midlands (West), England

- **DELAMERE FOREST**
  Cheshire, England
- **DUFF HOUSE ROYAL**
  Aberdeenshire, Scotland
- **EATON**
  Norfolk, England
- **ELLAND**
  Yorkshire (West), England
- **GULLANE**
  Lothian (East), Scotland
- **KIRKHILL**
  Glasgow (City of), Scotland
- **MILNATHORT**
  Perth And Kinross, Scotland
- **NORTH SHORE**
  Lincolnshire, England
- **OMAGH**
  County Tyrone, Northern Ireland
- **PENMAENMAWR**
  Conwy, Wales
- **PORTPATRICK - DUNSKEY**
  (Dinvin), Dumfries And Galloway, Scotland
- **TORQUAY**
  Devon, England
- **WEST SURREY**
  Surrey, England

1911

- **ABERYSTWYTH**
  Ceredigion, Wales
- **CHELMSFORD**
  Essex, England
- **CONSETT & DISTRICT**
  County Durham, England
- **COOMBE HILL**
  London (Greater), England
- **CRAIGIE HILL**
  Perth And Kinross, Scotland
- **HEWORTH**
  Yorkshire (North), England
- **KILLIN**
  Perth And Kinross, Scotland
- **KINTORE**
  Aberdeenshire, Scotland
- **KNOTT END**
  Lancashire, England
- **LONGLEY PARK**
  Yorkshire (West), England
- **LUFFENHAM HEATH**
  Lincolnshire, England
- **PARKSTONE**
  Dorset, England
- **RHONDDA**
  Rhondda Cynon Taff, Wales
- **SEAHAM HARBOUR**
  (Seaham), County Durham, England
- **ST. AUSTELL**
  (St Austell), Cornwall, England
- **TANDRAGEE**
  (Tanragee), County Armagh, Northern Ireland
- **WHINHILL**
  Inverclyde, Scotland

WHITSTABLE & SEASALTER
Kent, England

1912

BANBRIDGE
County Down, Northern Ireland

BEDFORD & COUNTY
Bedfordshire, England

BREIGHTMET
Lancashire, England

CLONTARF
County Dublin, Ireland

COODEN BEACH
Sussex (East), England

CROHAM HURST
Surrey, England

DERRY
(Prehen), **County Londonderry**, Northern Ireland

DOLGELLAU
Gwynedd, Wales

DUMFRIES & COUNTY
(Nunfield), **Dumfries And Galloway**, Scotland

FISHWICK HALL
Lancashire, England

PORT BANNATYNE
Argyll and Bute, Scotland

REDDISH VALE
Cheshire, England

SALINE
Fife, Scotland

THETFORD
Norfolk, England

WAKEFIELD
Yorkshire (West), England

WHALLEY
Lancashire, England

1913

AQUARIUS
London (Greater), England

ASHTON & LEA
Lancashire, England

ASHTON-UNDER-LYNE
Lancashire, England

BIDSTON
Merseyside, England

BLACKMOOR
Hampshire, England

BRAMLEY
Surrey, England

BULL BAY
Isle of Anglesey, Wales

CAMBERLEY HEATH
Surrey, England

CLONES
County Monaghan, Ireland

CROMPTON & ROYTON
Manchester (Greater), England

CROSLAND HEATH
Yorkshire (West), England

ELLESMERE
Manchester (Greater), England

KNIGHTON
Powys, Wales

LINLITHGOW
Lothian (West), Scotland

LYTHAM GREEN
Lancashire, England

OKEHAMPTON
Devon, England

SEAHOUSES
Northumberland, England

SILSDEN
Yorkshire (West), England

SITWELL
Yorkshire (South), England

STOCKSFIELD
Northumberland, England

WALTON HEATH
(New), **Surrey**, England

1914

ANGLESEY
Isle of Anglesey, Wales

KINGSTHORPE
Northamptonshire, England

SOUTH LEEDS
Yorkshire (West), England

ST. ANDREWS LINKS
(Eden), **Fife**, Scotland

SUTTON BRIDGE
Lincolnshire, England

WORKSOP
Nottinghamshire, England

1915

MONTROSE LINKS TRUST
(Broomfield), **Angus**, Scotland

MONTROSE LINKS TRUST
(Medal), **Angus**, Scotland

WHITCHURCH
Glamorgan (Vale of), Wales

1916

WEST KENT
Kent, England

1917

GREAT LEVER & FARNWORTH
Lancashire, England

1919

LIMERICK
County Limerick, Ireland

MORRISTON
Swansea, Wales

1920

ADDINGTON PALACE
Surrey, England

ALLERTON
Merseyside, England

CLYNE
Swansea, Wales

GLENEAGLES
(Kings), **Perth And Kinross**, Scotland

GRANGE-OVER-SANDS
Cumbria, England

GREAT SALTERNS
Hampshire, England

GREENMOUNT
(Old), **Lancashire**, England

HILLSBOROUGH
Yorkshire (South), England

PRESTONFIELD
Edinburgh (City of), Scotland

RETFORD
Nottinghamshire, England

1921

ABERDARE
Glamorgan (Vale of), Wales

BENTHAM
Lancashire, England

BUCKINGHAM
Buckinghamshire, England

CREIGIAU
Glamorgan (Vale of), Wales

GATEHOUSE
Dumfries And Galloway, Scotland

HOPEMAN
Moray, Scotland

KNOCK
County Antrim, Northern Ireland

MARSDEN
Yorkshire (West), England

NORTHCLIFFE
Yorkshire (West), England

SHIPLEY
Yorkshire (West), England

THORNTON
Fife, Scotland

1922

BARROW
Cumbria, England

BOYCE HILL
Essex, England

DEAN WOOD
Lancashire, England

DENBIGH
Denbighshire, Wales

DUNKELD
Perth And Kinross, Scotland

EAST RENFREWSHIRE
Glasgow (City of), Scotland

EASTER MOFFAT
Lanarkshire (North), Scotland

FALKIRK
(Carmuirs), **Falkirk**, Scotland

HADLEY WOOD
Hertfordshire, England

HIGH POST
Wiltshire, England

LILLEY BROOK
Gloucestershire, England

PITREAVIE
Fife, Scotland

ROUNDHAY
Yorkshire (West), England

ST. MELYD
(St Melyd), **Denbighshire**, Wales

COURSES by **YEAR BUILT**

1911 — 1922

- STONE
  Staffordshire, England
- TEHIDY
  Cornwall, England
- WOODSOME HALL
  Yorkshire (West), England

1923

- BUILTH WELLS
  Powys, Wales
- BURNHAM-ON-CROUCH
  (Burnham on Crouch), **Essex,** England
- FERNDOWN
  (The Old Course), **Dorset,** England
- INVERURIE
  Aberdeenshire, Scotland
- LEYLAND
  Lancashire, England
- MARCH
  Cambridgeshire, England
- MONMOUTH
  Monmouthshire, Wales
- RYDE
  Isle of Wight, England
- SOUTH MOOR
  County Durham, England
- SUNNINGDALE
  (New), **Surrey,** England
- WATERHALL
  Sussex (East), England

1924

- BALLINA
  County Mayo, Ireland
- BURY ST EDMUNDS
  Suffolk, England
- GLENEAGLES
  (Queens), **Perth And Kinross,** Scotland
- KNOLE PARK
  Kent, England
- LEEDS CASTLE
  Kent, England
- MAYBOLE MUNICIPAL
  Ayrshire (South), Scotland
- TAYMOUTH CASTLE
  Perth And Kinross, Scotland
- TEIGNMOUTH
  Devon, England
- WENTWORTH
  (East), **Surrey,** England

1925

- ASHFORD
  Kent, England
- BONNYBRIDGE
  Falkirk, Scotland
- BRIDGNORTH
  Shropshire, England
- CHESTFIELD
  Kent, England
- CHIGWELL
  Essex, England
- CRAIGMILLAR PARK
  Edinburgh (City of), Scotland

- HIGHWOODS
  Sussex (East), England
- KINGSWOOD
  Surrey, England
- LEIGHTON BUZZARD
  Bedfordshire, England
- MELTON MOWBRAY
  Leicestershire, England
- MILL HILL
  London (Greater), England
- NEWPORT
  Pembrokeshire, Wales
- SEATON CAREW
  (Old Course), **Cleveland,** England
- SHAW HILL
  Lancashire, England

1926

- CARLYON BAY
  Cornwall, England
- EFFINGHAM
  Surrey, England
- MOORE PLACE
  Surrey, England
- TARLAIR (ROYAL)
  (Royal Tarlair), **Aberdeenshire,** Scotland

1927

- BELLEISLE & SEAFIELD
  (Belleisle), **Ayrshire (South),** Scotland
- CANTERBURY
  Kent, England
- CARNALEA
  County Down, Northern Ireland
- DALMAHOY
  (East), **Edinburgh (City of),** Scotland
- DALMAHOY
  (West), **Edinburgh (City of),** Scotland
- EAST BIERLEY
  Yorkshire (West), England
- HASTE HILL
  London (Greater), England
- IFIELD
  Sussex (West), England
- LLANWERN
  Newport, Wales
- LOCHMABEN
  Dumfries And Galloway, Scotland
- MCDONALD
  Aberdeenshire, Scotland
- PERRANPORTH
  Cornwall, England
- RIDDLESDEN
  Yorkshire (West), England
- SLIGO (COUNTY)
  (Championship), **County Sligo,** Ireland
- SWANSTON
  Edinburgh (City of), Scotland

1928

- GORING AND STREATLEY
  (Goring & Streatley), **Berkshire,** England
- MINTO
  Scottish Borders, Scotland

- SCRAPTOFT
  Leicestershire, England
- VIVARY PARK
  Somerset, England
- WYKE GREEN
  London (Greater), England

1929

- HEYSHAM
  Lancashire, England
- MAHEE ISLAND
  County Down, Northern Ireland
- SELSDON PARK
  Surrey, England

1930

- ADDINGTON COURT GOLF CLUB
  (Championship), **Surrey,** England
- BETHUNE PARK
  (Calderfields), **London (Greater),** England
- BUCKPOOL
  Moray, Scotland
- CALCOT PARK
  Berkshire, England
- DOWNPATRICK
  County Down, Northern Ireland
- HAM MANOR
  Sussex (West), England
- HEBDEN BRIDGE
  Yorkshire (West), England
- HILLBARN
  (Hill Barn Municipal), **Sussex (West),**
  England
- KNIGHTSWOOD
  Glasgow (City of), Scotland
- LOOE
  Cornwall, England
- NEWTON ABBOT
  (Newton Abot (Stover)), **Devon,** England
- ORMONDE FIELDS
  (Ormonde), **Derbyshire,** England
- PRUDHOE
  Northumberland, England
- RHUDDLAN
  Denbighshire, Wales
- RICHMOND PARK
  (Dukes), **London (Greater),** England
- RICHMOND PARK
  (Princes), **London (Greater),** England
- ROSCOMMON
  County Roscommon, Ireland
- TRENTHAM PARK
  Staffordshire, England
- WEST SUSSEX
  Sussex (West), England

1931

- HADDINGTON
  Lothian (East), Scotland
- HARPENDEN COMMON
  Hertfordshire, England
- NARIN/PORTNOO
  (Narin & Portnoo), **County Donegal,** Ireland

1932

- **ASHRIDGE**
  Hertfordshire, England

- **BINGLEY ST IVES**
  Yorkshire (West), England

- **CLITHEROE**
  Lancashire, England

- **ENMORE PARK**
  (Enmore), **Somerset**, England

- **FLEETWOOD**
  Lancashire, England

- **GARMOUTH & KINGSTON**
  Moray, Scotland

- **LANCASTER**
  Lancashire, England

- **MOOR HALL**
  Midlands (West), England

- **TOWNELEY MUNICIPAL**
  Lancashire, England

- **WHITEFIELD**
  Manchester (Greater), England

- **WINDWHISTLE**
  Somerset, England

1933

- **BROOKMANS PARK**
  Hertfordshire, England

- **GLEN GORSE**
  Leicestershire, England

- **OLD PADESWOOD**
  Flintshire, Wales

- **OSWESTRY**
  Shropshire, England

- **PYPE HAYES**
  Midlands (West), England

- **RYSTON PARK**
  Norfolk, England

1934

- **DEREHAM**
  Norfolk, England

- **KILRUSH**
  County Clare, Ireland

- **MERE**
  Cheshire, England

- **UPTON-BY-CHESTER**
  Cheshire, England

1935

- **EDGBASTON**
  Midlands (West), England

- **MUTHILL**
  Perth And Kinross, Scotland

- **NEATH**
  Neath Port Talbot, Wales

- **SOUTHAMPTON MUNICIPAL**
  Hampshire, England

1936

- **ASHBY DECOY**
  Lincolnshire (North), England

- **BOLDMERE**
  Midlands (West), England

- **BUCHANAN CASTLE**
  Stirling, Scotland

- **DAVYHULME PARK**
  Manchester (Greater), England

- **MAYLANDS**
  Essex, England

- **TIVERTON**
  Devon, England

- **WENVOE CASTLE**
  Glamorgan (Vale of), Wales

1937

- **BALLOCHMYLE**
  Ayrshire (East), Scotland

- **CUSHENDALL**
  County Antrim, Northern Ireland

- **HOLSWORTHY**
  Devon, England

- **TORRINGTON**
  Devon, England

- **TRURO**
  Cornwall, England

1938

- **BRENT VALLEY PUBLIC**
  London (Greater), England

- **MUSSELBURGH**
  Lothian (Mid), Scotland

- **NEWCASTLE WEST**
  County Limerick, Ireland

- **PETERBOROUGH MILTON**
  Cambridgeshire, England

1939

- **CHILDWALL**
  (Chidwall), **Merseyside**, England

- **GOLD COAST**
  (Goldcoast), **County Waterford**, Ireland

1940

- **PEWIT**
  Derbyshire, England

1945

- **BACUP**
  Lancashire, England

1946

- **ALLOA**
  Clackmannanshire, Scotland

- **LIVERPOOL MUNICIPAL**
  Merseyside, England

1947

- **KEDLESTON PARK**
  Derbyshire, England

- **LANSIL**
  Lancashire, England

- **SILVERKNOWES**
  Edinburgh (City of), Scotland

- **SOUTHERNESS**
  Dumfries And Galloway, Scotland

1948

- **ALLESTREE**
  Derbyshire, England

- **FELIXSTOWE FERRY**
  (Martello), **Suffolk**, England

- **WALMER & KINGSDOWN**
  Kent, England

1949

- **HIRSEL**
  Scottish Borders, Scotland

- **KILKEEL**
  County Down, Northern Ireland

1950

- **LEE VALLEY**
  London (Greater), England

- **MOTE PARK GOLF HUT**
  (Mote Park 18 hole Putting Green), **Kent**,
  England

- **MOTE PARK GOLF HUT**
  (Mote Park Pitch and Putt Par 3), **Kent**,
  England

- **ST. NEOTS**
  (St Neots), **Cambridgeshire**, England

- **STORNOWAY**
  Western Isles, Scotland

1951

- **PAISLEY**
  Renfrewshire, Scotland

- **PRINCES**
  (Himalayas), **Kent**, England

1952

- **KIRKBYMOORSIDE**
  Yorkshire (North), England

- **STRANRAER**
  (Creachmore), **Dumfries And Galloway**,
  Scotland

1953

- **BRAXTED PARK**
  Essex, England

- **DUNFERMLINE**
  Fife, Scotland

- **GREENBURN**
  Lothian (West), Scotland

1954

- **CLARE PARK LAKE**
  (Clare Park Lane and), **Suffolk**, England

- **LEE PARK**
  Merseyside, England

1955

- **SHIRLEY**
  Midlands (West), England

1958

- **CAIRNDHU**
  County Antrim, Northern Ireland

1960

- **BELFAIRS PARK**
  (Belfair Municipal), **Essex**, England

- **CASTLE HAWK**
  (Old), **Lancashire**, England

- **DALMILLING**
  Ayrshire (South), Scotland

- **WIGTOWN & BLADNOCH**
  Dumfries And Galloway, Scotland

1961

- **BARON & BARONESS**
  (Baron Manhattan), **Bedfordshire**, England

DUNHAM FOREST
Cheshire, England

1962

ELY CITY
(Ely), **Cambridgeshire**, England

ST. PIERRE
(Mathern), **Monmouthshire**, Wales

ST. PIERRE
(Old), **Monmouthshire**, Wales

TORVEAN
Highlands, Scotland

1963

DUNNIKIER
Fife, Scotland

LEOPARDSTOWN
County Dublin, Ireland

1964

BEAMISH PARK
County Durham, England

CANONS BROOK
Essex, England

HUMBERSTON PARK
(Humberston), **Lincolnshire (North East)**,
England

ISLE OF SKYE
Highlands, Scotland

1965

ARDEER
Ayrshire (North), Scotland

BRICKENDON GRANGE
Hertfordshire, England

CORBY PUBLIC
Northamptonshire, England

LOUTH
Lincolnshire, England

RAMSEY CLUB
Cambridgeshire, England

ST. THOMAS' PRIORY
(St Thomas' Priory), **Staffordshire**,
England

1966

MURCAR
(Strabathie), **Aberdeen (City of)**, Scotland

SENE VALLEY
Kent, England

1967

BILLINGHAM
(Boggle Hole), **Cleveland**, England

HALTWHISTLE
Cumbria, England

LEOMINSTER
Herefordshire, England

LINGDALE
Leicestershire, England

SHIRLAND
Derbyshire, England

1968

FORRESTER PARK
Essex, England

HAWKHURST
Kent, England

HIGH ELMS
Kent, England

TEMPLEMORE
County Tipperary, Ireland

1969

ALSTON MOOR
Cumbria, England

CHERRY LODGE
Kent, England

FAIRWOOD PARK
Swansea, Wales

FERNDOWN
(Presidents), **Dorset**, England

GATTON MANOR
Surrey, England

SHIFNAL
Shropshire, England

SUFFOLK GOLF
(The Genevieve), **Suffolk**, England

1970

BIRCH GROVE
Essex, England

BREAN
Somerset, England

CRICHTON
Dumfries And Galloway, Scotland

DUNWOOD MANOR
Hampshire, England

FAKENHAM
Norfolk, England

FOSSEWAY
Bath & Somerset (North East), England

PORTSMOUTH
Hampshire, England

SHREWBURY
Shropshire, England

SOUTH PEMBROKE
Pembrokeshire, Wales

TREVOSE
(Short), **Cornwall**, England

1971

BADGEMORE PARK
Oxfordshire, England

BARON & BARONESS
(Baroness Manhattan), **Bedfordshire**,
England

BRAINTREE
Essex, England

FOREST OF DEAN
Gloucestershire, England

LISBURN
County Antrim, Northern Ireland

MUCKHART
Clackmannanshire, Scotland

REDDITCH
Worcestershire, England

SANDOWN GOLF CTRE
(Par 3), **Surrey**, England

THREE RIVERS
(Jubilee), **Essex**, England

THREE RIVERS
(Kings), **Essex**, England

1972

BALA
Gwynedd, Wales

BELHUS PARK
Essex, England

DEANGATE RIDGE
Kent, England

FAIRTHORNE MANOR
(Fairthorne), **Hampshire**, England

FELTWELL
Norfolk, England

KING'S LYNN
Norfolk, England

SHERDLEY PARK MUNICIPAL
(Sherdley Park), **Merseyside**, England

TRENT PARK GOLF CLUB
(Trent Park), **London (Greater)**, England

UTTOXETER
Staffordshire, England

1973

BROWN TROUT
County Londonderry, Northern Ireland

CONNEMARA
County Galway, Ireland

CREDITON
Devon, England

DALE HILL
(The Old), **Sussex (East)**, England

DARENTH VALLEY
Kent, England

DAVENPORT
Cheshire, England

DURHAM CITY
County Durham, England

EASTHAM LODGE
Merseyside, England

FARTHINGSTONE
Northamptonshire, England

HAVERHILL
Suffolk, England

MANSFIELD WOODHOUSE
Nottinghamshire, England

MOSS VALLEY
Wrexham, Wales

PITCHEROAK
Worcestershire, England

SAUNTON
(West), **Devon**, England

STOCKWOOD PARK
Bedfordshire, England

1974

CHANNELS
Essex, England

CILGWYN
Carmarthenshire, Wales

COLD ASHBY
(Winwick/Ashby), **Northamptonshire**,
England

EAST HERTS
Hertfordshire, England

FALKLAND
Fife, Scotland

GLEDDOCH
Renfrewshire, Scotland

HOMELANDS
(Bettergolf centre), Kent, England

IMMINGHAM
Lincolnshire (North East), England

MOWSBURY
Bedfordshire, England

NEWBOLD COMYN
Warwickshire, England

OADBY
Leicestershire, England

PALACERIGG
Lanarkshire (North), Scotland

PANSHANGER GOLF COMPLEX
Hertfordshire, England

WEST MALLING
(Hurricane), Kent, England

WEST MALLING
(Spitfire), Kent, England

WHIPSNADE PARK
Hertfordshire, England

WOBURN
(Duchess), Buckinghamshire, England

1975

ABBEY HILL
Buckinghamshire, England

BANTRY BAY
County Cork, Ireland

BRANSTON

BRANSTON
Staffordshire, England

CANWICK PARK
Lincolnshire, England

CHULMLEIGH
(Winter Short), Devon, England

DRIFT
Surrey, England

FORT WILLIAM
Highlands, Scotland

FOXHILLS GOLF
(Bernard Hunt), Surrey, England

HURST
Berkshire, England

LAVENDER PARK
Berkshire, England

LITTLE LAKES
Worcestershire, England

MINCHINHAMPTON
(Avening), Gloucestershire, England

OAKMERE PARK
Nottinghamshire, England

TELFORD
Shropshire, England

THORPE WOOD
Cambridgeshire, England

TILSWORTH
Bedfordshire, England

WARLEY PARK
(Course 1), Essex, England

WARLEY PARK
(Course 2), Essex, England

WARLEY PARK
(Course 3), Essex, England

WELLINGBOROUGH
Northamptonshire, England

WEST BERKSHIRE
Berkshire, England

WHITEHEAD
County Antrim, Northern Ireland

WOOLER
Northumberland, England

1976

ALSAGER
Staffordshire, England

BROOME MANOR
Wiltshire, England

COTSWOLD HILLS
Gloucestershire, England

CRIMPLE VALLEY
Yorkshire (North), England

DELAPRE PARK GOLF COMPLEX
(Main), Northamptonshire, England

GANSTEAD PARK
Yorkshire (East), England

GLOUCESTER
Gloucestershire, England

HICKLETON
Yorkshire (South), England

MORAY
(New), Moray, Scotland

OAK LEAF
County Durham, England

PADESWOOD & BUCKLEY
Flintshire, Wales

ST. MELLION INTERNATIONAL
(The Old), Cornwall, England

STRESSHOLME
County Durham, England

TEWKESBURY PARK
Gloucestershire, England

TRACY PARK
(Cromwell), Bristol, England

TRACY PARK
(Crown), Bristol, England

WOBURN
(Dukes), Buckinghamshire, England

1977

BELFRY
(Derby), Midlands (West), England

BETWS-Y-COED
Conwy, Wales

BRADLEY PARK
Yorkshire (West), England

BRANDON WOOD MUNICIPAL
(Brandon Wood), Midlands (West), England

ESPORTA DOUGALSTON
Glasgow (City of), Scotland

MIDDLESBROUGH MUNICIPAL
Cleveland, England

STAVERTON PARK
Northamptonshire, England

1978

ALDWARK MANOR
Yorkshire (North), England

ATHENRY
County Galway, Ireland

BARLASTON
Staffordshire, England

DEER PARK
Lothian (West), Scotland

FOREST OF ARDEN
(Aylesford), Midlands (West), England

FOREST OF ARDEN
(Championship - Arden), Midlands (West), England

GOAL FARM
Surrey, England

LITTLE HAY
Hertfordshire, England

1979

BAWBURGH
(Glen Lodge), Norfolk, England

BUSHEY GOLF COURSE
(Bushey), Hertfordshire, England

GREEN MEADOW
Torfaen, Wales

KESWICK
Cumbria, England

WINDLERMERE
(Windlemere), Surrey, England

1980

BROOME PARK
Kent, England

CALVERLEY
Yorkshire (West), England

CARRBRIDGE
Highlands, Scotland

CHERWELL EDGE
Oxfordshire, England

COTSWOLD EDGE
Gloucestershire, England

EFFINGHAM PARK
Sussex (West), England

INSCH
Aberdeenshire, Scotland

JOHN O'GAUNT
(Carthagena), Bedfordshire, England

PENFOLD PARK
Hertfordshire, England

PORTAL
(Championship), Cheshire, England

SEDLESCOMBE
Sussex (East), England

SHILLINGLEE PARK
Surrey, England

SHRIVENHAM PARK
Wiltshire, England

SPROWSTON MANOR
(Marriot Sprawston Manor), Norfolk, England

WESTRIDGE
Isle of Wight, England

WHETSTONE
Leicestershire, England

COURSES by YEAR BUILT

1974 — 1980

1981

- **AUCHENHARVIE**
  Ayrshire (North), Scotland
- **EAST DORSET**
  (Lakeland), **Dorset**, England
- **EAST DORSET**
  (Woodland), **Dorset**, England
- **EDWALTON MUNICIPAL**
  (Edwalton), **Nottinghamshire**, England
- **INGOL**
  Lancashire, England
- **LYNEDOCH & MURRAYSHALL**
  (Murrayshall), **Perth And Kinross**, Scotland
- **WOODBURY PARK**
  (Acorn), **Devon**, England
- **WOODBURY PARK**
  (Oaks), **Devon**, England
- **WOODHAM**
  County Durham, England

1982

- **ALFORD**
  Aberdeenshire, Scotland
- **BOOTHFERRY PARK**
  Yorkshire (East), England
- **BUNSAY DOWNS**
  Essex, England
- **HAINSWORTH PARK**
  Yorkshire (East), England
- **HOEBRIDGE**
  (Main), **Surrey**, England
- **OLD THORNS**
  Hampshire, England
- **ORTON MEADOWS**
  Cambridgeshire, England
- **ROLLS OF MONMOUTH**
  Monmouthshire, Wales
- **SHERDONS**
  (The Manor), **Gloucestershire**, England
- **STEVENAGE**
  Hertfordshire, England
- **TILGATE FOREST**
  Sussex (West), England
- **TREGENNA CASTLE**
  Cornwall, England

1983

- **BALBIRNIE PARK**
  Fife, Scotland
- **BRINKWORTH**
  Wiltshire, England
- **BRUNSHAW**
  Lancashire, England
- **CHESSINGTON**
  Surrey, England
- **CRETINGHAM**
  Suffolk, England
- **FOUR MARKS**
  Hampshire, England
- **GOLDENHILL**
  (Golden Hill), **Staffordshire**, England
- **HORAM PARK**
  Sussex (East), England

- **IVER**
  Buckinghamshire, England
- **OAK PARK GOLF CLUB**
  (Woodland), **Surrey**, England

1984

- **COBTREE MANOR PARK**
  Kent, England
- **COSTESSEY PARK**
  Norfolk, England
- **ENTRY HILL**
  Bath & Somerset (North East), England
- **TOFT HOTEL**
  Lincolnshire, England

1985

- **BELFAST**
  County Antrim, Northern Ireland
- **COLVEND**
  Dumfries And Galloway, Scotland
- **COMBE GROVE MANOR**
  Bath & Somerset (North East), England
- **HERONS BROOK**
  (Kings), **Pembrokeshire**, Wales
- **HERONS BROOK**
  (Queens), **Pembrokeshire**, Wales
- **MOUNT OBER**
  County Antrim, Northern Ireland

1986

- **CRANLEIGH**
  Surrey, England
- **TYTHERINGTON**
  Cheshire, England
- **WOODTHORPE HALL**
  Lincolnshire, England

1987

- **COBH**
  County Cork, Ireland
- **HELSTON**
  Cornwall, England
- **HORTON PARK GOLF**
  (Horton Park Country Club), **Surrey**, England
- **LETHAM GRANGE RESORT**
  (Glens), **Angus**, Scotland
- **LETHAM GRANGE RESORT**
  (Old), **Angus**, Scotland
- **LINGFIELD PARK**
  Surrey, England

1988

- **BRIGGENS HOUSE**
  (Briggens Park), **Hertfordshire**, England
- **CASTLECOCH**
  Glamorgan (Vale of), Wales
- **DEWSTOW**
  Monmouthshire, Wales
- **DONNINGTON VALLEY**
  Berkshire, England
- **DURNESS**
  Highlands, Scotland
- **GEDNEY HILL**
  Lincolnshire, England

- **HALSTOCK**
  Somerset, England
- **KINMEL PARK GOLF**
  (Kimnel Park), **Denbighshire**, Wales
- **RUDDINGTON GRANGE**
  Nottinghamshire, England
- **SANDFORD SPRINGS**
  (Parks), **Hampshire**, England
- **SANDFORD SPRINGS**
  (Woods), **Hampshire**, England
- **ST. MELLION INTERNATIONAL**
  (Nicklaus), **Cornwall**, England
- **TUDOR PARK**
  Kent, England
- **WEST CHILTINGTON**
  Sussex (West), England

1989

- **ALICE SPRINGS**
  (Queens), **Monmouthshire**, Wales
- **ALVASTON HALL**
  (Alvaston), **Cheshire**, England
- **ASPECT PARK**
  Oxfordshire, England
- **BOTLEY PARK**
  Hampshire, England
- **BRADFORD-ON-AVON**
  (Bradford On Avon), **Wiltshire**, England
- **BRAMPTON GOLF**
  Herefordshire, England
- **BROADWATER PARK**
  Surrey, England
- **BUNSAY DOWNS**
  (Par 3), **Essex**, England
- **CANNOCK PARK**
  Staffordshire, England
- **CASTELL HEIGHTS**
  Caerphilly, Wales
- **CASTELL HEIGHTS**
  (Mountain Lakes), **Caerphilly**, Wales
- **CAVE CASTLE**
  Yorkshire (East), England
- **CHARTRIDGE PARK**
  Buckinghamshire, England
- **CRONDON PARK**
  Essex, England
- **DEWLANDS MANOR**
  (Dewlands), **Sussex (East)**, England
- **DINNATON**
  Devon, England
- **ENNISKILLEN**
  County Fermanagh, Northern Ireland
- **EUROPEAN CLUB**
  County Wicklow, Ireland
- **FARINGDON**
  Oxfordshire, England
- **FINGLE GLEN**
  Devon, England
- **FYNN VALLEY**
  Suffolk, England
- **HINTLESHAM HALL**
  Suffolk, England
- **MIDDLETON HALL**
  Norfolk, England

MORTEHOE & WOOLACOMBE
Devon, England

PETERCULTER
Aberdeenshire, Scotland

PETWORTH
Sussex (West), England

PORTLETHEN
Aberdeen (City of), Scotland

SHRIGLEY HALL
Cheshire, England

VILLA
Kent, England

WESTERWOOD
Glasgow (City of), Scotland

WHADDON
Hertfordshire, England

1990

ASHFIELD
County Down, Northern Ireland

BANK HOUSE
(Pine Lakes), Worcestershire, England

BECKSIDE
Cumbria, England

BENTON HALL
Essex, England

BILLINGBEAR PARK
(The Old), Berkshire, England

CADMORE LODGE
Worcestershire, England

CAMBRIDGE
Cambridgeshire, England

CHICHESTER
Sussex (West), England

CHIRK
Wrexham, Wales

COLLINGTREE PARK
Northamptonshire, England

EAST SUSSEX NATIONAL
(East), Sussex (East), England

EAST SUSSEX NATIONAL
(West), Sussex (East), England

FOREST PARK
Yorkshire (North), England

FRODSHAM
Cheshire, England

GREETHAM VALLEY
(Lakes), Rutland, England

GREETHAM VALLEY
(Valley), Rutland, England

HADDEN HILL
Oxfordshire, England

HORSLEY LODGE
Derbyshire, England

LAGGANMORE
Dumfries And Galloway, Scotland

LONG SUTTON
Somerset, England

LYNEHAM
Oxfordshire, England

MALAHIDE
(Main), County Dublin, Ireland

MANOR OF GROVES
Hertfordshire, England

MAYWOOD
Derbyshire, England

MENDIP SPRING
(Brinsea), Bristol, England

MENDIP SPRING
(Lakeside), Bristol, England

MID YORKSHIRE
Yorkshire (West), England

NEWMACHAR
(Hawkshill), Aberdeen (City of), Scotland

NEWMACHAR
(Swailend), Aberdeen (City of), Scotland

NORTHAMPTON
Northamptonshire, England

OAKDALE
Caerphilly, Wales

OXHEY PARK
Hertfordshire, England

PAXHILL PARK
Sussex (West), England

PERTON PARK
Midlands (West), England

PETERSTONE LAKES
(Peterstone), Glamorgan (Vale of), Wales

PORTAL
(Premier), Cheshire, England

PORTAL PREMIER
Cheshire, England

PRINCES RISBOROUGH
Buckinghamshire, England

RICHMOND PARK
Norfolk, England

ROTHES
Moray, Scotland

RUTLAND WATER
Rutland, England

SANDFORD SPRINGS
(Lakes), Hampshire, England

SLALEY HALL GOLF COURSE
(Hunting), Northumberland, England

SOUTH KYME
Lincolnshire, England

SUDBROOK MOOR
Lincolnshire, England

SWALLOW HALL
Yorkshire (North), England

TALL PINES
Bristol, England

TOP MEADOW
Essex, England

TRENT LOCK
Nottinghamshire, England

WAVENDON GOLF CTRE
Buckinghamshire, England

WAVENDON GOLF CTRE
(Family), Buckinghamshire, England

WERGS
Midlands (West), England

WEST HOVE
Sussex (East), England

YORK GOLF CTRE
Yorkshire (North), England

1991

ABBEYMOOR
Surrey, England

ASHBURY
(Oakwood), Devon, England

AUSTIN LODGE
Kent, England

AYLESBURY
Buckinghamshire, England

AYLESBURY VALE
Bedfordshire, England

BALLYKISTEEN
County Tipperary, Ireland

BELTON WOODS
(The Lakes), Lincolnshire, England

BELTON WOODS
(The Woodside), Lincolnshire, England

BOURN
Cambridgeshire, England

BOWOOD
Cornwall, England

BRAMPTON PARK
Cambridgeshire, England

CASTLE HUME
County Fermanagh, Northern Ireland

CHEDINGTON COURT
Dorset, England

CHESFIELD DOWNS
Hertfordshire, England

COLNE VALLEY
Essex, England

COTGRAVE PLACE
(Masters), Nottinghamshire, England

COTGRAVE PLACE
(Open), Nottinghamshire, England

CRANE VALLEY
(Valley 18 Hole), Dorset, England

CWMRHYDNEUADD
Ceredigion, Wales

EAST HORTON GOLF CTRE
(Greenwood), Hampshire, England

EAST HORTON GOLF CTRE
(Parkland), Hampshire, England

EASTBOURNE GOLFING PARK
Sussex (East), England

EATON
Cheshire, England

EDENBRIDGE
(New), Kent, England

FOXBRIDGE
Sussex (West), England

FYNN VALLEY
Suffolk, England

GRANGE PARK
Lincolnshire (North), England

HALESWORTH
Suffolk, England

HIGHFIELD
County Kildare, Ireland

KIRKBY LONSDALE
Lancashire, England

KNOTTY HILL GOLF CTRE
(Princes), Cleveland, England

COURSES by **YEAR BUILT**

1991 — 1992

🏌 LANGDON HILLS GOLF CTRE
(Bulphan), **Essex**, England

🏌 LANGDON HILLS GOLF CTRE
(Horndon), **Essex**, England

🏌 LANGDON HILLS GOLF CTRE
(Langdon), **Essex**, England

🏌 LOSTWITHIEL
Cornwall, England

🏌 MERLIN
Cornwall, England

🏌 MILL RIDE
Berkshire, England

🏌 MILLERS BARN GOLF PARK
(Millers Barn), **Essex**, England

🏌 MOTTRAM HALL
Cheshire, England

🏌 MOUNT PLEASANT
Bedfordshire, England

🏌 OULTON PARK
(Main), **Yorkshire (West)**, England

🏌 PEOVER
Cheshire, England

🏌 PONTEFRACT
Yorkshire (West), England

🏌 RODWAY HILL
Gloucestershire, England

🏌 ROSSHILL PAR 3
County Galway, Ireland

🏌 RUTLAND COUNTY
Lincolnshire, England

🏌 SEEDY MILL
(Mill), **Staffordshire**, England

🏌 SEEDY MILL
(Spires), **Staffordshire**, England

🏌 SPRINGWATER
Nottinghamshire, England

🏌 STOCKWOOD VALE
Bristol, England

🏌 STONELEIGH DEER PARK
(Tantara), **Midlands (West)**, England

🏌 THORNEY
(Fen), **Cambridgeshire**, England

🏌 TOURNERBURY GOLF CTRE
(Tournerbury), **Hampshire**, England

🏌 UFFORD PARK
Suffolk, England

🏌 WELLSHURST
Sussex (East), England

🏌 WENSUM VALLEY
Norfolk, England

🏌 WILDWOOD COUNTRY CLUB
(Wildwood), **Surrey**, England

🏌 WILTSHIRE
Wiltshire, England

🏌 WORFIELD
Shropshire, England

1992

🏌 ARSCOTT
Shropshire, England

🏌 ASHFORD
Kent, England

🏌 BARKWAY PARK
(Barkway Golf), **Hertfordshire**, England

🏌 BIRCHWOOD PARK
Kent, England

🏌 BLACKNEST
Hampshire, England

🏌 BOLTON
Lancashire, England

🏌 BOWENHURST
Surrey, England

🏌 BOWOOD
Wiltshire, England

🏌 BRAILES
Oxfordshire, England

🏌 BROCKET HALL
(Melbourne), **Hertfordshire**, England

🏌 BROCKINGTON
Herefordshire, England

🏌 BROMSGROVE
Worcestershire, England

🏌 BRUNSTON CASTLE
Ayrshire (South), Scotland

🏌 BRYN MORFYDD
(Duchess), **Denbighshire**, Wales

🏌 BRYN MORFYDD
(Dukes), **Denbighshire**, Wales

🏌 BURY ST EDMUNDS
Suffolk, England

🏌 CAMS HALL ESTATE GOLF CLUB
(Creek), **Hampshire**, England

🏌 CAMS HALL ESTATE GOLF CLUB
(Park), **Hampshire**, England

🏌 CAPEL BANGOR
Ceredigion, Wales

🏌 CASTERTON
Cumbria, England

🏌 CASTLE BARNA
County Offaly, Ireland

🏌 CENTRAL LONDON
London (Greater), England

🏌 CHALGRAVE MANOR
Bedfordshire, England

🏌 CHARLESLAND
County Wicklow, Ireland

🏌 CHARLETON
Fife, Scotland

🏌 COCKSFORD
Yorkshire (North), England

🏌 COLMWORTH & NORTH
BEDFORDSHIRE
Bedfordshire, England

🏌 DARTMOUTH
(Championship), **Devon**, England

🏌 DUNGARVAN
County Waterford, Ireland

🏌 EDEN
Cumbria, England

🏌 ELTON FURZE
Cambridgeshire, England

🏌 ERLESTOKE SANDS
Wiltshire, England

🏌 FARDEW
Yorkshire (West), England

🏌 FOREST HILLS
Gloucestershire, England

🏌 FROME GOLF CLUB
(Frome), **Bath & Somerset (North East)**,
England

🏌 GLYN ABBEY
Carmarthenshire, Wales

🏌 HAMPTWORTH
Wiltshire, England

🏌 HENNERTON
Berkshire, England

🏌 HURTMORE
Surrey, England

🏌 ISLE OF WEDMORE
Somerset, England

🏌 KENMORE
Perth And Kinross, Scotland

🏌 KENWICK PARK
(Kenwick), **Lincolnshire**, England

🏌 KINSALE
Flintshire, Wales

🏌 KIRTON HOLME
Lincolnshire, England

🏌 LAKESIDE
Neath Port Talbot, Wales

🏌 LAKESIDE LODGE
(Lodge), **Cambridgeshire**, England

🏌 LAMBOURNE CLUB
(Lambourne.), **Berkshire**, England

🏌 LEXDEN
Essex, England

🏌 MANOR HOUSE
Wiltshire, England

🏌 MAPLEDURHAM
Berkshire, England

🏌 MARTIN MOOR
Lincolnshire, England

🏌 MENTMORE
(Rosebery), **Bedfordshire**, England

🏌 MENTMORE
(Rothschild), **Bedfordshire**, England

🏌 MILE END
Shropshire, England

🏌 MORLEY HAYES
(Manor), **Derbyshire**, England

🏌 MORLEY HAYES
(Tower), **Derbyshire**, England

🏌 NAZEING
Essex, England

🏌 NORTON
Cleveland, England

🏌 OLD NENE
Cambridgeshire, England

🏌 PADBROOK PARK
Devon, England

🏌 PARLEY
Dorset, England

🏌 PINE RIDGE GOLF CTRE
(Pine Ridge), **Surrey**, England

🏌 PLASSEY
Wrexham, Wales

🏌 POCOCKE
County Kilkenny, Ireland

🏌 PRIORS
Essex, England

PRISKILLY
(Priskilly), **Pembrokeshire**, Wales

RAMSDALE PARK
Nottinghamshire, England

RAMSDALE PARK
(The Par 3), **Nottinghamshire**, England

REDHILL GOLF CTRE
(Redhill), **Surrey**, England

ROMNEY WARREN
Kent, England

ROOKWOOD
Sussex (West), England

RUSHMORE PARK
Wiltshire, England

RUSPER
Surrey, England

RUSTINGTON
Sussex (West), England

SCARTHINGWELL
Yorkshire (North), England

SILVERSTONE
Buckinghamshire, England

SINGING HILLS
(Lake), **Sussex (West)**, England

SOLWAY LINKS
Dumfries And Galloway, Scotland

SOUTH ESSEX
(Hawk (Hawk & Vixon)), **Essex**, England

SOUTH ESSEX
(Heron (Heron & Hawk)), **Essex**, England

SOUTH ESSEX
(Vixen (Vixen & Heron)), **Essex**, England

SPOFFORTH
Yorkshire (North), England

SWORDS OPEN
County Dublin, Ireland

TEST VALLEY
Hampshire, England

THORNBURY GOLF
(High), **Bristol**, England

THORNBURY GOLF
(Low), **Bristol**, England

THOULSTONE PARK
Wiltshire, England

WEST WATERFORD
County Waterford, Ireland

WESTON PARK
(Western Park), **Norfolk**, England

WHITEFIELDS
Warwickshire, England

WHITTLEBURY PARK
(Grand Prix), **Northamptonshire**, England

WIDNEY MANOR
Midlands (West), England

1993

ABBEYFEALE
County Limerick, Ireland

ALDER ROOT
Cheshire, England

ALDERSEY GREEN
Cheshire, England

ALLT-Y-GRABAN
Swansea, Wales

ASHTON
Lancashire, England

BALLYMONEY
County Wexford, Ireland

BEEDLES LAKE
Leicestershire, England

BELFORD
Northumberland, England

BRACKEN GHYLL
Yorkshire (West), England

BRETTVALE
Suffolk, England

BRIERLEY FOREST
(Davcolm), **Nottinghamshire**, England

CANNINGTON
Somerset, England

CARDEN PARK
(The Cheshire), **Cheshire**, England

CHART HILLS
Kent, England

CHARTHAM PARK
Sussex (West), England

CHASE
Staffordshire, England

CHERRY BURTON
Yorkshire (East), England

CHOBHAM
Surrey, England

CLAYS GOLF CTRE
(Clays), **Wrexham**, Wales

DAINTON PARK
Devon, England

DAWN 'TIL DUSK
Pembrokeshire, Wales

DISTINGTON GOLF
(Distington), **Cumbria**, England

DUNMORE EAST
County Waterford, Ireland

FAITHLEGG
County Waterford, Ireland

FERNDOWN FOREST
Dorset, England

FOYLE
(Woodlands Par 3), **County Londonderry**,
Northern Ireland

GLEBE
County Meath, Ireland

GLEN MILL
County Wicklow, Ireland

GLENEAGLES
(PGA Centenary), **Perth And Kinross**,
Scotland

HELE PARK GOLF CTRE
(Hele Park), **Devon**, England

HERTFORDSHIRE
Hertfordshire, England

HIGHFIELD
Lancashire, England

HILDEN EUROPRO
(Hilden Golf Centre), **Kent**, England

HUNLEY HALL
(Millenium), **Cleveland**, England

KAMES GOLF
(Mouse Valley), **Lanarkshire (South)**,
Scotland

LEEDS GOLF CTRE
(Wike Ridge), **Yorkshire (West)**, England

MALTON
Hertfordshire, England

MILFORD GOLF CLUB
(Milford), **Surrey**, England

MILL GREEN GOLF CLUB
(Mill Green), **Hertfordshire**, England

MOATE
County Westmeath, Ireland

MOATLANDS
Kent, England

NAUNTON DOWNS
Gloucestershire, England

OAKE MANOR
Somerset, England

PARASAMPIA
Berkshire, England

PAVENHAM
Bedfordshire, England

PENLANLAS
Ceredigion, Wales

POTTERGATE
Lincolnshire, England

PRYORS HAYES
Cheshire, England

PYRFORD GOLF CLUB
(Pyrford), **Surrey**, England

RIDGE GOLF CLUB
(Ridge), **Kent**, England

RINGDUFFERIN
County Down, Northern Ireland

ROUNDWOOD HALL
Kent, England

RYE HILL
Oxfordshire, England

SAND MARTINS
Berkshire, England

SANDHILL
Yorkshire (South), England

SEAPOINT
County Louth, Ireland

SLINFOLD PARK
(Championship), **Sussex (West)**, England

SOUTH MEATH
County Meath, Ireland

SOUTH WINCHESTER
Hampshire, England

SPARKWELL
Devon, England

ST. ANDREWS LINKS
(Balgove), **Fife**, Scotland

ST. ANDREWS LINKS
(Strathtyrum), **Fife**, Scotland

ST. ANDREWS MAJOR
(St Andrews Major), **Glamorgan (Vale of)**,
Wales

ST. HELENS BAY
(St Helen's Bay), **County Wexford**, Ireland

STOCKLEY PARK
London (Greater), England

STONELEES GOLF CTRE
(Par 3), **Kent**, England

SWARLAND HALL
Northumberland, England

THORNEY PARK
Buckinghamshire, England

TRETHORNE
(Threthorne), **Cornwall**, England

VALE OF GLAMORGAN
(Hensol), **Glamorgan (Vale of)**, Wales

VALE OF GLAMORGAN
(The Lake), **Glamorgan (Vale of)**, Wales

WHEATHILL
Somerset, England

WHITLEY
Wiltshire, England

WOODLAKE PARK
Monmouthshire, Wales

1994

ADDLETHORPE
(Caesars Park), **Lincolnshire**, England

AINTREE
Merseyside, England

ANTROBUS
Cheshire, England

ASH VALLEY GOLF CLUB
(Ash Valley), **Hertfordshire**, England

ASTON WOOD
Midlands (West), England

BANBURY GOLF CTRE
(Blue), **Oxfordshire**, England

BANBURY GOLF CTRE
(Red), **Oxfordshire**, England

BANBURY GOLF CTRE
(Yellow), **Oxfordshire**, England

BATTLE
Sussex (East), England

BEARSDEN
Glasgow (City of), Scotland

BLACKWOOD GOLF CTRE
(Hamilton), **County Down**, Northern Ireland

BLACKWOOD GOLF CTRE
(Temple), **County Down**, Northern Ireland

BLUNDELLS HILL
(Blundell's Hill), **Merseyside**, England

BRAILSFORD
Derbyshire, England

BRICKHAMPTON COURT
(Glevum), **Gloucestershire**, England

BRICKHAMPTON COURT
(Spa), **Gloucestershire**, England

BURGHAM
Northumberland, England

CAMBRIDGE MERIDIAN
Cambridgeshire, England

CANFORD MAGNA
Dorset, England

CARSWELL
Oxfordshire, England

CASTLE PARK
Lothian (East), Scotland

CASTLE ROYLE
Berkshire, England

CHARLETON
Fife, Scotland

CHARNOCK RICHARD
Lancashire, England

CHIDDINGFOLD
Surrey, England

CLOUGHANEELY
County Donegal, Ireland

COLLEGE PINES
Nottinghamshire, England

COUNTY
Hampshire, England

CRADDOCKSTOWN
County Kildare, Ireland

CRAIGIEKNOWES
Dumfries And Galloway, Scotland

DELAPRE PARK GOLF COMPLEX
(Harding Stone), **Northamptonshire**,
England

EPPING FOREST
(Manor), **Essex**, England

FOYLE
(Parkland), **County Londonderry**, Northern
Ireland

FRILFORD HEATH
(Blue), **Oxfordshire**, England

HOLLYWOOD LAKES
County Dublin, Ireland

HORNE PARK
Surrey, England

HORSHAM GOLF
Sussex (West), England

HURLSTON
Lancashire, England

KILNWICK PERCY
Yorkshire (North), England

KINGSWOOD
Yorkshire (South), England

KINSALE
(Farrangalway), **County Cork**, Ireland

LEEDS GOLF CTRE
(The Oaks), **Yorkshire (West)**, England

LIMERICK (COUNTY)
(Limerick County), **County Limerick**,
Ireland

LISSELAN
County Cork, Ireland

LITTLE LAKES
(Gaudet - Luce), **Worcestershire**, England

LYDD
Kent, England

MOUNT MURRAY
Isle of Man, England

MYTTON FOLD
Lancashire, England

NEWENT
Gloucestershire, England

NORTHOP
Flintshire, Wales

OPEN
(Blue Nine), **County Dublin**, Ireland

PARK HILL
Leicestershire, England

RAGLAN PARC
Monmouthshire, Wales

RATHSALLAGH
County Wicklow, Ireland

REGIMENT
Essex, England

ROTHER VALLEY GOLF
(Rother Valley), **Yorkshire (South)**, England

RUFFORD PARK GOLF CTRE
(Rufford Park), **Nottinghamshire**, England

SOUTHWELL
Nottinghamshire, England

STOKE ALBANY
Leicestershire, England

STRATHMORE GOLF CTRE
(Leitfie Links), **Perth And Kinross**,
Scotland

STRATHMORE GOLF CTRE
(Rannaleroch), **Perth And Kinross**,
Scotland

STUDLEY WOOD
Oxfordshire, England

STYAL
Cheshire, England

SUTTON GREEN
Surrey, England

SUTTON HALL
Cheshire, England

SWEETWOODS PARK
Kent, England

TEMPLE CLUB
County Antrim, Northern Ireland

TICKENHAM
Bristol, England

TOWNLEY HALL
County Louth, Ireland

TURVEY
County Dublin, Ireland

WATERSTOCK
Oxfordshire, England

WERNDDU
Monmouthshire, Wales

WICKHAM PARK
Hampshire, England

WINCANTON
Somerset, England

WINDLESHAM
Surrey, England

WITNEY LAKES
(Whitney Lakes), **Oxfordshire**, England

WOODSPRING
(Avon), **Bristol**, England

1995

ADLINGTON
(Academy), **Cheshire**, England

ALDWICKBURY PARK

ALDWICKBURY PARK
Hertfordshire, England

ALLEN PARK
County Antrim, Northern Ireland

ASHWOODS
County Fermanagh, Northern Ireland

AYLESBURY PARK
Buckinghamshire, England

BALLYHEIGUE CASTLE
County Kerry, Ireland

BALLYLIFFIN
(Glashedy Links), **County Donegal**, Ireland

BRAMCOTE WATERS
Warwickshire, England

BRAMPTON HEATH
(Main), **Northamptonshire**, England

BRAMPTON HEATH
(Short), **Northamptonshire**, England

CAMBRIDGE LAKES
Cambridgeshire, England

CARRIGLEADE
County Kilkenny, Ireland

CARUS GREEN
Cumbria, England

CELTIC MANOR
(Roman Road), **Newport**, Wales

CHANNELS
(Belstead), **Essex**, England

CROW NEST PARK
Yorkshire (West), England

CUMBERWELL
(Woodlands), **Wiltshire**, England

DEANWOOD PARK
(Deanwood), **Berkshire**, England

DRUIDS GLEN
County Wicklow, Ireland

DUKES
Fife, Scotland

DUKES MEADOW
London (Greater), England

DUNTON HILLS
Essex, England

DYMOCK GRANGE
Gloucestershire, England

ETCHINGHILL
Kent, England

FAIRBOURNE
Gwynedd, Wales

FORMBY HALL
Merseyside, England

GOWER
Swansea, Wales

GRACEHILL
County Antrim, Northern Ireland

GREENACRES GOLF CTRE
(Greenacres), **County Antrim**, Northern Ireland

HASSOCKS
Sussex (West), England

HERSHAM VILLAGE
Surrey, England

HINKSEY HEIGHTS
Oxfordshire, England

KILKEA CASTLE
County Kildare, Ireland

LOFTHOUSE HILL
Yorkshire (West), England

MANOR
Yorkshire (West), England

MERSEY VALLEY
Cheshire, England

MID SUSSEX
Sussex (East), England

MINCHINHAMPTON
(Cherington), **Gloucestershire**, England

MOBBERLEY
Cheshire, England

ORCHARD
Gloucestershire, England

OWMBY
Lincolnshire, England

PORTMORE GOLF PARK
(Barum), **Devon**, England

REDLIBBETS
Kent, England

REIGATE HILL
Surrey, England

ROBIN HOOD
Yorkshire (South), England

RUDDING PARK
Yorkshire (North), England

SHENDISH MANOR
Hertfordshire, England

SHIPTON
Gloucestershire, England

SHIRENEWTON
Monmouthshire, Wales

STANDISH COURT
Lancashire, England

STAPLEHURST GOLFING PARK
(Staplehurst), **Kent**, England

STONEBRIDGE
Midlands (West), England

TYDD ST GILES
Cambridgeshire, England

UPAVON
Wiltshire, England

WESTHOUGHTON
(Hart Common), **Lancashire**, England

WHITEKIRK
Lothian (East), Scotland

WILLINGCOTT
Devon, England

WYRE FOREST
Worcestershire, England

1996

ALLT-GYMBYD
(Allt-Gwmbyd 9 Hole), **Flintshire**, Wales

BATCHWORTH PARK
Hertfordshire, England

BEARNA
County Galway, Ireland

BEARWOOD LAKES
Berkshire, England

BLACKTHORN WOOD
Leicestershire, England

BLARNEY
County Cork, Ireland

BRIDGECASTLE
(The Monster), **Lothian (West)**, Scotland

BROOKLANDS PARK
(Brooklands), **Sussex (West)**, England

CELBRIDGE ELM HALL
County Kildare, Ireland

CELTIC MANOR
(Coldra Woods), **Newport**, Wales

COTTRELL PARK
(Button), **Glamorgan (Vale of)**, Wales

COTTRELL PARK
(Mackintosh), **Glamorgan (Vale of)**, Wales

EPPING
Essex, England

GARNANT PARK
Carmarthenshire, Wales

GROVE
Bridgend, Wales

HAWKESBURY GOLF CENTRE
(Hawkesbury), **Midlands (West)**, England

HOUGHWOOD
Merseyside, England

HUMAX
(Melbourne), **London (Greater)**, England

HYLANDS GOLF COMPLEX
(Hanbury), **Essex**, England

HYLANDS GOLF COMPLEX
(Pryors), **Essex**, England

KINLOSS
Moray, Scotland

LAMERWOOD COUNTRY CLUB
(Lamerwood), **Hertfordshire**, England

LOCH NESS
Highlands, Scotland

MOSSOCK HALL
Lancashire, England

NORWOOD PARK
Nottinghamshire, England

OAKS
Yorkshire (North), England

ORCHARDLEIGH
Bath & Somerset (North East), England

PARK TONGLAND
(Park of Tongland), **Dumfries And Galloway**, Scotland

PEDHAM PLACE GOLF CTRE
(Red), **Kent**, England

PENRHOS
(Academy), **Ceredigion**, Wales

POWERSCOURT
County Wicklow, Ireland

PRINCE'S
(Princes'), **Isle of Anglesey**, Wales

RAMSIDE
(Cathedral), **County Durham**, England

RAMSIDE
(Princes), **County Durham**, England

SPRINGHILL
County Tyrone, Northern Ireland

STILTON OAKS
Cambridgeshire, England

STORWS WEN
Isle of Anglesey, Wales

THEALE GOLF CTRE
(Theale), **Berkshire**, England

TREFLOYNE
Pembrokeshire, Wales

COURSES by **YEAR BUILT**

1995 — 1996

- WESTERHAM
  Kent, England
- WOKEFIELD PARK
  Berkshire, England

1997

- BELFRY
  (PGA National), **Midlands (West),** England
- BOARS HEAD
  (Boar's Head), **Sussex (East),** England
- BOYSNOPE PARK
  Manchester (Greater), England
- DALE HILL
  (The Ian Woosnam), **Sussex (East),**
  England
- DUNTON HILLS
  (Main), **Essex,** England
- ELMWOOD
  Fife, Scotland
- EYEMOUTH
  Scottish Borders, Scotland
- GALGORM CASTLE
  County Antrim, Northern Ireland
- INCHMARLO GOLF CTRE
  (Inchmarlo 9 hole), **Aberdeenshire,**
  Scotland
- KENDLESHIRE
  Bristol, England
- KINGS ACRE
  Lothian (Mid), Scotland
- LINDEN HALL
  Northumberland, England
- LONDON BEACH
  Kent, England
- LONGHIRST HALL
  (The Old), **Northumberland,** England
- MUCKHART
  (New 9 hole), **Clackmannanshire,**
  Scotland
- OTTER VALLEY GOLF CTRE
  (Otter Valley), **Devon,** England
- PINES
  Dumfries And Galloway, Scotland
- PIPERDAM GOLF
  (Osprey), **Angus,** Scotland
- RATHBANE
  (Rathbone), **County Limerick,** Ireland
- ROSERROW
  Cornwall, England
- SOUTHERN VALLEY
  Kent, England
- SURREY GOLF & FITNESS
  Surrey, England
- ULLAPOOL
  Highlands, Scotland
- WILLOW VALLEY
  (T.P.C), **Yorkshire (West),** England

1998

- ALLHALLOWS
  Kent, England
- ASHBOURNE
  Derbyshire, England
- BARLBOROUGH LINKS
  Derbyshire, England

- BEDFORD
  Bedfordshire, England
- BELFRY
  (Brabazon), **Midlands (West),** England
- BRIDGEND
  (Haughborn), **Lothian (West),** Scotland
- BROUGHTON HEATH
  Derbyshire, England
- CALDECOTT HALL
  Norfolk, England
- CARDRONA
  Scottish Borders, Scotland
- GLEN OF THE DOWNS
  County Wicklow, Ireland
- GLENISLA
  Perth And Kinross, Scotland
- HIGH LODGE
  Suffolk, England
- KAMES GOLF
  (Kames), **Lanarkshire (South),** Scotland
- KNOTTY HILL GOLF CTRE
  (Bishops), **Cleveland,** England
- MAGNOLIA PARK
  Buckinghamshire, England
- MARTON MEADOWS
  Cheshire, England
- RING OF KERRY
  County Kerry, Ireland
- RUTHERFORD CASTLE
  Scottish Borders, Scotland
- VALE ROYAL ABBEY
  Cheshire, England
- WESTHOUGHTON
  (Academy), **Lancashire,** England

1999

- BRIGHOUSE BAY
  Dumfries And Galloway, Scotland
- BROCKET HALL
  (Palmerston), **Hertfordshire,** England
- CARDEN PARK
  (The Nicklaus), **Cheshire,** England
- CELTIC MANOR
  (Wentwood Hills), **Newport,** Wales
- CLOVERHILL
  County Down, Northern Ireland
- CRAIBSTONE
  Aberdeen (City of), Scotland
- EAST ABERDEENSHIRE
  Aberdeen (City of), Scotland
- GREENMOUNT
  (White), **Lancashire,** England
- HEDSOR
  Buckinghamshire, England
- HOLLINS HALL
  Yorkshire (West), England
- LYNEDOCH & MURRAYSHALL
  (Lynedoch), **Perth And Kinross,** Scotland
- MOLLINGTON GRANGE
  Cheshire, England
- SAPEY
  (The Oaks), **Worcestershire,** England
- SAPEY
  (The Rowan), **Worcestershire,** England

- SLALEY HALL GOLF COURSE
  (Priestman), **Northumberland,** England
- STRUTT CLUB
  Derbyshire, England
- TRADITIONS GOLF COURSE
  (Traditions), **Surrey,** England
- TREDEGAR PARK
  Newport, Wales
- WORSLEY PARK
  Manchester (Greater), England

2000

- CAVERSHAM HEATH
  Berkshire, England
- EDZELL
  (West Water), **Angus,** Scotland
- FAUGHAN VALLEY
  County Londonderry, Northern Ireland
- KINGSBARNS GOLF LINKS
  (Kingsbarn), **Fife,** Scotland
- PYTCHLEY GOLF LODGE
  Northamptonshire, England
- STYAL
  (Academy Championship Par 3), **Cheshire,**
  England
- WOBURN
  (Marquess), **Buckinghamshire,** England

2001

- BRANSTON
  (Academy),
- BRANSTON
  (Academy), **Staffordshire,** England
- BURHILL
  Surrey, England
- GOWRAN PARK GOLF & LEISURE
  County Kilkenny, Ireland
- INCHMARLO GOLF CTRE
  (Inchmarlo 18 hole), **Aberdeenshire,**
  Scotland
- KINLOSS
  Moray, Scotland
- LONGHIRST HALL
  (The New), **Northumberland,** England

SECTION 7

This section allows you to search for clubs by facilities available. Clubs are listed by country, then by county.

e.g Caddy Hire, Buggy Hire

For further information about each club refer to the detailed profile in Section 1, or search for specific details in other sections.

GolfWorld Directory

Facilities Available at Golf Courses

Golf Courses by County

ENGLAND

BATH & SOMERSET (NORTH EAST)

Course key:
1. BATH
2. COMBE GROVE MANOR
3. ENTRY HILL
4. FOSSEWAY
5. FROME GOLF CLUB
6. LANSDOWN
7. MENDIP
8. ORCHARDLEIGH

BEDFORDSHIRE
9. AYLESBURY VALE
10. BARON & BARONESS
11. BEDFORD
12. BEDFORD & COUNTY
13. BEDFORDSHIRE
14. CHALGRAVE MANOR
15. COLMWORTH & NORTH BEDFORDSHIRE
16. DUNSTABLE DOWNS
17. GRIFFIN
18. IVINGHOE
19. JOHN O'GAUNT
20. LEIGHTON BUZZARD
21. LYSHOTT HEATH
22. MENTMORE
23. MOUNT PLEASANT
24. MOWSBURY
25. OUSE VALLEY
26. PAVENHAM
27. SOUTH BEDS
28. STOCKWOOD PARK

Facility	2	3	4	5	6	7	8	10	11	12	14	16	19	20	22	23	24	26	27	28
Dress Code Anything																				
Dress Code Casual	●		●	●					●								●		●	●
Dress Code Formal	●																			
Golf Shop takes credit cards		●			●			●	●		●	●			●			●	●	●
Club House takes credit card		●						●	●	●							●	●	●	●
Youth Coaching Scheme								●	●							●	●		●	●
Mobiles allowed in Club House																	●			●
Children allowed in Club House								●	●		●		●				●		●	●
Spectators Allowed	●							●	●	●	●	●				●	●		●	●
Disabled Facilities								●	●		●					●				●
Disabled Toilets								●	●							●				●
Disabled Access								●	●							●				●
Satellite TV	●							●	●						●	●		●		
TV Lounge	●							●	●		●					●	●	●	●	●
Snooker Room								●								●				
Members Only Bar																●				
Gym/Weights	●					●								●						
Massage	●																			
Physiotherapy	●																			
Sauna/Solararium	●					●								●						
Swimming Pool	●		●																	
Health Club	●																			
Accommodation	●		●					●												
Hotel On Site	●							●												
Visitors Car Park		●	●				●	●	●		●	●			●	●	●	●	●	●
Members Car Park		●				●		●							●					●
Practice Putting Green		●	●	●		●		●	●		●				●	●	●	●	●	●
Practice Bunkers		●		●	●				●						●			●	●	●
Practice Course		●																●		●
Driving Range		●		●			●	●	●		●	●				●		●		●
Conference Facility			●		●	●					●		●	●						
Evening Functions	●							●	●		●				●		●	●	●	●
On Course Refreshments																●				
Bar Snacks	●	●		●	●	●	●	●	●	●	●	●	●	●	●	●	●	●	●	●
Restaurant Dinner	●	●						●	●		●				●	●	●	●	●	●
Restaurant Lunch					●	●		●	●		●				●	●	●	●	●	●
Restaurant Breakfast	●				●	●		●	●		●				●		●	●	●	●
Shoe Cleaning Service								●			●					●				●
Bag Drop Service																●				
Guests Changing Rooms	●		●	●		●		●	●	●	●	●	●		●	●	●	●	●	●
Guests Showers		●		●				●	●		●		●			●	●	●	●	●
On Course Drinking Fountains																●				
On Course Yardage Markers		●		●				●	●						●	●	●	●	●	●
Spike Bar											●		●			●	●	●	●	●
Plastic Stud Fitting Service			●		●						●					●		●		
Plastic Studs Compulsory											●									
Visitors Need Handicap Proof					●						●				●				●	
Golf Clubs Hire	●	●	●			●	●	●	●				●	●		●	●	●	●	●
Caddy Hire																				
Shoe Hire																●				
Buggy Hire					●	●	●	●	●	●	●						●	●	●	●
Trolley Hire	●		●	●	●	●	●	●	●	●	●						●	●	●	●
Regripping	●	●		●	●			●	●							●		●	●	●
Club Alterations		●		●	●			●	●							●		●	●	●

www.hccgolfworld.com

Facilities Available at Golf Courses

Facility	TILSWORTH	WYBOSTON	ASCOT (ROYAL)	BEARWOOD	BEARWOOD LAKES	BERKSHIRE	BILLINGBEAR PARK	BIRD HILLS	BLUE MOUNTAIN GOLF CENTRE	BURNHAM BEECHES	CALCOT PARK	CASTLE ROYLE	CAVERSHAM HEATH	DATCHET	DEANWOOD PARK	DONNINGTON VALLEY	DOWNSHIRE	EAST BERKSHIRE	FARNHAM PARK	GORING AND STREATLEY	HENNERTON	HURST	LAMBOURNE CLUB	LAVENDER PARK	MAIDENHEAD	MAPLEDURHAM	MILL RIDE	NEWBURY & CROOKHAM	PARASAMPIA	READING	SAND MARTINS
Dress Code Anything																															
Dress Code Casual				●		●		●			●	●	●		●						●	●		●		●		●	●	●	●
Dress Code Formal			●							●						●							●								
Golf Shop takes credit cards	●			●		●				●	●	●		●		●					●	●	●		●	●		●	●	●	●
Club House takes credit card	●			●		●					●			●		●					●	●						●		●	
Youth Coaching Scheme			●									●				●	●				●	●			●	●		●		●	●
Mobiles allowed in Club House																															
Children allowed in Club House	●		●	●		●		●				●				●					●	●	●		●	●		●	●	●	●
Spectators Allowed			●			●															●				●			●		●	●
Disabled Facilities																●									●					●	
Disabled Toilets				●		●						●				●					●		●		●			●		●	●
Disabled Access			●			●						●				●					●		●		●			●		●	●
Satellite TV																●												●			
TV Lounge	●		●	●								●		●		●					●			●		●		●	●	●	●
Snooker Room																												●		●	
Members Only Bar													●																		
Gym/Weights		●											●													●					
Massage													●																		
Physiotherapy																															
Sauna/Solararium	●											●											●					●		●	
Swimming Pool													●																		
Health Club													●																		
Accommodation	●															●											●			●	
Hotel On Site																●											●			●	
Visitors Car Park					●			●				●										●	●	●	●						
Members Car Park			●	●		●		●			●	●									●	●	●	●							
Practice Putting Green			●	●	●	●		●			●	●				●					●	●	●			●		●	●	●	●
Practice Bunkers			●	●	●	●		●			●					●					●	●	●			●				●	●
Practice Course			●	●				●			●					●					●		●								
Driving Range	●	●			●			●	●			●				●					●		●	●							●
Conference Facility	●	●						●	●							●					●		●							●	
Evening Functions	●			●							●	●				●							●			●		●		●	●
On Course Refreshments	●			●								●			●	●							●								●
Bar Snacks	●	●	●	●	●	●	●	●	●	●	●	●	●	●	●	●					●	●	●	●	●	●	●	●	●	●	●
Restaurant Dinner	●	●		●		●		●			●	●			●	●					●		●		●	●		●		●	●
Restaurant Lunch	●	●	●	●		●		●			●	●	●		●	●	●				●	●	●	●	●	●		●	●	●	●
Restaurant Breakfast											●	●	●		●	●	●				●		●		●			●		●	●
Shoe Cleaning Service				●												●															
Bag Drop Service				●												●															
Guests Changing Rooms	●	●	●	●	●	●		●			●	●			●	●	●				●	●	●		●	●		●		●	●
Guests Showers			●	●		●		●			●	●			●	●	●				●	●	●		●	●		●		●	●
On Course Drinking Fountains			●	●																											
On Course Yardage Markers			●	●		●		●				●				●					●	●	●			●		●		●	●
Spike Bar																															
Plastic Stud Fitting Service			●	●							●	●	●		●	●					●	●	●								
Plastic Studs Compulsory											●	●			●	●							●								
Visitors Need Handicap Proof			●	●		●					●	●				●							●								
Golf Clubs Hire	●	●		●	●	●	●	●	●		●	●		●	●	●	●				●	●	●	●	●	●		●	●	●	●
Caddy Hire																															
Shoe Hire																●															
Buggy Hire	●	●		●		●						●				●	●								●			●		●	●
Trolley Hire	●	●		●		●		●			●	●				●	●						●		●			●		●	●
Regripping	●		●	●		●		●													●	●	●		●	●		●		●	●
Club Alterations	●		●	●							●	●	●	●		●					●	●	●		●	●		●		●	●

Facilities Available at Golf Courses

FACILITIES AVAILABLE

Golf Courses by County

Facility	SONNING	STOKE POGES	SUNNINGDALE LADIES	SWINLEY FOREST	TEMPLE	THEALE GOLF CTRE	WEST BERKSHIRE	WEXHAM PARK	WINTER HILL	WOKEFIELD PARK	BRISTOL	BRISTOL & CLIFTON	CHIPPING SODBURY	FARRINGTON	FILTON	HENBURY	KENDLESHIRE	KNOWLE	LONG ASHTON	MANGOTSFIELD	MENDIP SPRING	SALTFORD	SHIREHAMPTON PARK	STOCKWOOD VALE	TALL PINES	THORNBURY GOLF	TICKENHAM	TRACY PARK	WOODLANDS	WOODSPRING	BUCKINGHAMSHIRE	ABBEY HILL GOLF CENTRE
Dress Code Anything																																
Dress Code Casual		●		●	●	●										●											●					
Dress Code Formal					●	●	●			●									●								●					
Golf Shop takes credit cards					●	●	●	●		●		●				●	●	●									●	●				●
Club House takes credit card					●	●	●	●		●		●				●		●	●								●	●				●
Youth Coaching Scheme										●						●	●	●	●	●	●							●				●
Mobiles allowed in Club House		●														●	●	●														
Children allowed in Club House		●								●						●	●	●	●								●	●				●
Spectators Allowed										●						●	●	●	●								●	●				●
Disabled Facilities					●	●	●									●		●										●				●
Disabled Toilets						●	●									●		●	●									●				●
Disabled Access					●	●	●									●		●	●									●				●
Satellite TV					●	●	●																									
TV Lounge				●	●	●	●									●		●									●	●				
Snooker Room						●										●												●				
Members Only Bar				●												●												●				
Gym/Weights										●																						
Massage										●																						
Physiotherapy										●																						
Sauna/Solararium										●						●					●									●		
Swimming Pool										●						●																
Health Club										●																						
Accommodation		●																								●		●				
Hotel On Site										●																●						
Visitors Car Park				●		●	●	●				●				●	●	●	●								●	●				●
Members Car Park				●		●	●	●				●				●	●	●	●								●	●				●
Practice Putting Green						●	●	●				●				●	●	●	●	●	●						●	●				●
Practice Bunkers						●	●									●	●	●	●									●				●
Practice Course						●	●										●															
Driving Range	●					●	●	●	●							●			●							●				●	●	●
Conference Facility	●	●								●																●				●	●	●
Evening Functions						●	●			●																●					●	●
On Course Refreshments					●					●						●	●									●					●	●
Bar Snacks	●	●	●			●	●			●		●	●	●	●	●	●	●	●							●	●		●	●	●	●
Restaurant Dinner	●	●				●	●			●						●	●	●	●							●	●		●	●		●
Restaurant Lunch	●					●	●			●						●	●	●	●						●	●	●					●
Restaurant Breakfast						●	●									●		●								●	●					●
Shoe Cleaning Service							●									●																
Bag Drop Service																																
Guests Changing Rooms	●	●				●	●			●		●				●	●	●	●	●					●	●	●					●
Guests Showers						●	●									●	●	●	●								●					●
On Course Drinking Fountains					●	●										●			●													
On Course Yardage Markers						●	●									●		●	●													
Spike Bar																●	●		●								●	●				
Plastic Stud Fitting Service						●	●	●								●	●										●					●
Plastic Studs Compulsory																			●													
Visitors Need Handicap Proof	●				●											●	●	●	●													
Golf Clubs Hire		●			●	●	●	●				●				●	●	●	●	●					●	●	●	●				●
Caddy Hire																																
Shoe Hire								●								●												●				
Buggy Hire		●						●								●	●	●	●								●	●	●			●
Trolley Hire	●	●				●	●	●								●	●	●	●					●	●	●	●					●
Regripping						●	●	●								●	●	●	●								●	●				●
Club Alterations						●	●	●		●						●	●	●	●	●							●	●				●

Facilities Available at Golf Courses

Facility / Golf Courses by County	ASPLEY GUISE & WOBURN SANDS	AYLESBURY	AYLESBURY PARK	BEACONSFIELD	BUCKINGHAM	CHARTRIDGE PARK	CHESHAM & LEY HILL	CHILTERN FOREST	ELLESBOROUGH	FLACKWELL HEATH	GERRARDS CROSS	HAREWOOD DOWNS	HAZLEMERE	HEDSOR	IVER	LITTLE CHALFONT	MAGNOLIA PARK	OAKLAND PARK	PRINCES RISBOROUGH	RICHINGS PARK	SILVERSTONE	THORNEY PARK	THREE LOCKS	WAVENDON GOLF CTRE	WESTON TURVILLE	WHITELEAF	WINDMILL HILL	WOBURN	WYCOMBE HEIGHTS GOLF CTRE	CAMBRIDGESHIRE	ABBOTSLEY	BOURN
Dress Code Anything																																
Dress Code Casual	●	●		●		●					●	●		●	●	●		●	●			●			●	●			●		●	●
Dress Code Formal																	●											●				
Golf Shop takes credit cards	●	●		●							●			●	●		●	●	●						●	●					●	●
Club House takes credit card	●	●				●					●			●	●		●	●	●						●	●					●	●
Youth Coaching Scheme	●																															
Mobiles allowed in Club House										●																						
Children allowed in Club House	●	●	●			●					●			●			●	●						●							●	●
Spectators Allowed	●	●																													●	●
Disabled Facilities	●	●															●	●													●	●
Disabled Toilets	●	●									●			●	●	●	●								●	●					●	●
Disabled Access											●			●	●	●	●								●	●					●	●
Satellite TV		●		●	●												●															
TV Lounge		●		●						●							●	●													●	●
Snooker Room				●																												
Members Only Bar																															●	●
Gym/Weights																							●								●	●
Massage																															●	●
Physiotherapy																															●	●
Sauna/Solararium																															●	●
Swimming Pool																												●			●	●
Health Club																															●	●
Accommodation																								●							●	●
Hotel On Site																															●	●
Visitors Car Park	●	●	●								●			●	●	●									●	●			●		●	●
Members Car Park	●	●	●								●			●	●	●									●	●			●		●	●
Practice Putting Green	●	●		●		●					●			●	●			●	●	●					●	●			●		●	●
Practice Bunkers	●			●		●												●	●							●			●		●	●
Practice Course																				●					●				●		●	●
Driving Range	●		●	●											●			●		●			●	●			●		●		●	●
Conference Facility				●	●			●			●						●					●			●			●	●		●	●
Evening Functions																									●			●	●		●	●
On Course Refreshments							●																								●	●
Bar Snacks	●	●	●	●	●	●	●	●	●	●	●	●	●	●	●	●	●	●	●	●	●	●	●	●	●	●	●	●	●		●	●
Restaurant Dinner	●	●	●	●		●			●	●	●		●	●			●	●							●	●		●	●		●	●
Restaurant Lunch	●	●	●	●		●			●	●	●		●	●			●	●							●	●		●	●		●	●
Restaurant Breakfast	●	●															●	●							●	●		●	●		●	●
Shoe Cleaning Service		●		●		●											●								●						●	●
Bag Drop Service																															●	●
Guests Changing Rooms	●	●	●	●	●	●	●		●	●	●	●	●	●	●	●	●	●			●			●	●	●		●	●		●	●
Guests Showers	●	●	●			●					●			●	●			●							●	●			●		●	●
On Course Drinking Fountains								●																								
On Course Yardage Markers	●	●				●																			●				●		●	●
Spike Bar		●													●		●		●									●			●	●
Plastic Stud Fitting Service															●		●		●									●	●		●	●
Plastic Studs Compulsory															●																	
Visitors Need Handicap Proof			●												●																	
Golf Clubs Hire	●	●	●	●						●	●	●	●		●	●			●	●		●	●	●	●	●	●	●	●		●	●
Caddy Hire																																
Shoe Hire			●																			●										
Buggy Hire	●	●	●	●		●								●	●		●		●	●		●	●	●	●		●	●	●		●	●
Trolley Hire	●	●	●	●		●			●	●	●	●	●	●	●	●	●		●	●		●	●	●	●		●	●	●		●	●
Regripping	●	●												●	●		●	●							●	●					●	●
Club Alterations	●	●												●			●	●							●	●					●	●

© HCC Publishing Ltd

Facilities Available at Golf Courses

Facilities (rows):

- Dress Code Anything
- Dress Code Casual
- Dress Code Formal
- Golf Shop takes credit cards
- Club House takes credit card
- Youth Coaching Scheme
- Mobiles allowed in Club House
- Children allowed in Club House
- Spectators Allowed
- Disabled Facilities
- Disabled Toilets
- Disabled Access
- Satellite TV
- TV Lounge
- Snooker Room
- Members Only Bar
- Gym/Weights
- Massage
- Physiotherapy
- Sauna/Solarium
- Swimming Pool
- Health Club
- Accommodation
- Hotel On Site
- Visitors Car Park
- Members Car Park
- Practice Putting Green
- Practice Bunkers
- Practice Course
- Driving Range
- Conference Facility
- Evening Functions
- On Course Refreshments
- Bar Snacks
- Restaurant Dinner
- Restaurant Lunch
- Restaurant Breakfast
- Shoe Cleaning Service
- Bag Drop Service
- Guests Changing Rooms
- Guests Showers
- On Course Drinking Fountains
- On Course Yardage Markers
- Spike Bar
- Plastic Stud Fitting Service
- Plastic Studs Compulsory
- Visitors Need Handicap Proof
- Golf Clubs Hire
- Caddy Hire
- Shoe Hire
- Buggy Hire
- Trolley Hire
- Regripping
- Club Alterations

Golf Courses by County (columns):

- BRAMPTON PARK
- CAMBRIDGE
- CAMBRIDGE LAKES
- CAMBRIDGE MERIDIAN
- CAMBRIDGESHIRE MOAT HOUSE
- ELTON FURZE
- ELY CITY
- GIRTON
- GOG MAGOG
- HEMINGFORD ABBOT
- LAKESIDE LODGE
- MARCH
- OLD NENE
- ORTON MEADOWS
- OUNDLE
- PETERBOROUGH MILTON
- RAMSEY CLUB
- ST. IVES
- ST. NEOTS
- STILTON OAKS
- THORNEY
- THORPE WOOD
- TYDD ST GILES

CHANNEL ISLANDS
- ALDERNEY
- LA GRANDE MARE
- ST. CLEMENT

CHESHIRE
- ADLINGTON
- ALDER ROOT
- ALDERLEY EDGE
- ALDERSEY GREEN

England

FACILITIES AVAILABLE

www.hccgolfworld.com

Facilities Available at Golf Courses

Golf Courses by County	ALTRINCHAM	ALVASTON HALL	ANTROBUS	ASHTON-ON-MERSEY	ASTBURY	AVRO	BIRCHWOOD	BRAMALL PARK	BRAMHALL	CARDEN PARK	CHEADLE	CHESTER	CONGLETON	CREWE	DAVENPORT	DELAMERE FOREST	DISLEY	DUKINFIELD	DUNHAM FOREST	EATON	FRODSHAM	GATLEY	HALE	HAZEL GROVE	HEATON MOOR	HELSBY	HEYROSE	HOULDSWORTH	KNIGHTS GRANGE	KNUTSFORD	LEIGH	LYMM
Dress Code Anything																																
Dress Code Casual		●								●					●					●											●	●
Dress Code Formal																																
Golf Shop takes credit cards		●								●					●				●	●											●	●
Club House takes credit card										●										●												
Youth Coaching Scheme		●								●					●				●	●											●	●
Mobiles allowed in Club House										●																						
Children allowed in Club House		●								●						●	●		●	●											●	●
Spectators Allowed																																●
Disabled Facilities																																
Disabled Toilets		●								●																						
Disabled Access		●								●																						
Satellite TV		●								●																						
TV Lounge		●								●					●	●				●											●	●
Snooker Room		●								●										●												
Members Only Bar																																
Gym/Weights										●																						
Massage										●																						
Physiotherapy																																
Sauna/Solararium				●		●				●																						
Swimming Pool										●																						
Health Club										●																						
Accommodation	●									●																						
Hotel On Site		●								●																						
Visitors Car Park		●																	●	●											●	●
Members Car Park		●								●					●	●			●	●											●	●
Practice Putting Green		●													●	●			●	●											●	●
Practice Bunkers		●																	●	●												
Practice Course																			●	●												
Driving Range	●	●	●							●																	●					
Conference Facility					●					●					●				●		●											
Evening Functions		●													●				●	●												●
On Course Refreshments		●																	●													
Bar Snacks	●	●	●		●	●	●	●	●	●	●	●	●	●	●	●	●	●	●	●	●	●	●	●	●	●	●	●		●	●	●
Restaurant Dinner		●	●				●	●		●					●				●	●	●										●	●
Restaurant Lunch		●	●							●					●				●													●
Restaurant Breakfast		●								●									●	●	●											●
Shoe Cleaning Service																																
Bag Drop Service																																
Guests Changing Rooms	●	●	●		●	●	●	●	●	●	●	●	●	●	●	●	●	●	●	●	●	●	●	●	●	●	●	●	●	●	●	●
Guests Showers		●								●					●				●	●											●	●
On Course Drinking Fountains										●									●	●											●	●
On Course Yardage Markers		●								●									●	●												
Spike Bar										●					●				●													
Plastic Stud Fitting Service										●																						
Plastic Studs Compulsory										●																						
Visitors Need Handicap Proof		●													●																	●
Golf Clubs Hire	●	●								●			●	●				●	●	●					●	●	●			●		
Caddy Hire										●																						
Shoe Hire										●																						
Buggy Hire										●					●				●													
Trolley Hire	●	●	●	●	●		●	●	●	●					●	●		●	●	●	●	●	●	●	●	●	●				●	●
Regripping		●								●									●	●											●	●
Club Alterations		●								●									●	●											●	●

Facilities Available at Golf Courses

Facility	MACCLESFIELD	MALKINS BANK	MARTON MEADOWS	MELLOR & TOWNSCLIFFE	MERE	MERSEY VALLEY	MOBBERLEY	MOLLINGTON GRANGE	MOTTRAM HALL	NEW MILLS	ONNELEY	PEOVER	PORTAL	PORTAL PREMIER	PRESTBURY	PRYORS HAYES	QUEENS PARK	REDDISH VALE	RINGWAY	ROMILEY	RUNCORN	SALE	SANDBACH	SANDIWAY	SHRIGLEY HALL	ST MICHAELS JUBILEE	STAMFORD	STOCKPORT	STYAL	SUTTON HALL	TYTHERINGTON	UPTON-BY-CHESTER
Dress Code Anything																																
Dress Code Casual				●		●	●	●					●		●		●		●			●		●					●	●		●
Dress Code Formal					●				●																							
Golf Shop takes credit cards					●	●	●	●					●				●			●									●	●		●
Club House takes credit card					●		●	●					●				●			●									●	●		●
Youth Coaching Scheme					●		●	●					●				●			●									●			
Mobiles allowed in Club House					●		●	●					●				●												●			●
Children allowed in Club House					●	●	●	●					●				●			●									●			●
Spectators Allowed					●		●	●					●																●			
Disabled Facilities					●		●	●					●																			
Disabled Toilets					●		●	●					●				●												●	●		●
Disabled Access					●		●	●					●				●			●									●	●		●
Satellite TV					●		●	●					●				●			●									●	●		●
TV Lounge					●		●	●					●				●			●								●				●
Snooker Room					●				●		●						●			●												
Members Only Bar					●															●												
Gym/Weights					●					●															●							
Massage					●																											
Physiotherapy																																
Sauna/Solararium					●				●																							
Swimming Pool					●				●																●							
Health Club					●				●																							
Accommodation									●																●							
Hotel On Site									●																							
Visitors Car Park			●		●	●	●	●							●				●										●	●		●
Members Car Park					●	●	●	●							●				●										●	●		●
Practice Putting Green					●		●	●				●			●				●										●	●		●
Practice Bunkers					●			●							●				●										●			●
Practice Course								●							●				●										●			
Driving Range					●		●	●							●				●						●				●	●		●
Conference Facility			●	●		●		●																		●						
Evening Functions				●	●	●	●								●																	
On Course Refreshments																																
Bar Snacks	●	●		●	●	●	●	●	●	●	●	●	●	●	●	●	●	●	●	●	●	●		●			●	●	●	●	●	●
Restaurant Dinner				●	●	●	●	●	●		●		●		●		●		●			●		●					●	●	●	●
Restaurant Lunch	●			●	●	●	●	●					●		●		●		●			●		●				●	●	●	●	●
Restaurant Breakfast				●	●	●	●	●					●				●												●	●	●	●
Shoe Cleaning Service																																
Bag Drop Service																																
Guests Changing Rooms	●	●		●	●	●	●	●				●	●		●		●		●	●	●	●		●			●	●	●	●	●	●
Guests Showers				●	●	●	●				●		●		●		●		●	●									●	●		●
On Course Drinking Fountains																			●										●			
On Course Yardage Markers			●		●	●	●	●					●		●		●		●										●	●		●
Spike Bar					●								●		●		●		●										●			
Plastic Stud Fitting Service								●	●						●																	
Plastic Studs Compulsory													●		●				●										●			
Visitors Need Handicap Proof	●													●					●													
Golf Clubs Hire	●	●		●	●	●	●	●	●		●		●		●		●							●		●		●	●	●		
Caddy Hire																																
Shoe Hire				●																										●		
Buggy Hire	●			●		●	●	●					●		●							●								●		●
Trolley Hire	●	●		●	●	●	●	●					●		●		●		●	●		●		●			●	●	●	●		●
Regripping				●		●	●						●		●		●		●	●									●	●		●
Club Alterations				●		●									●		●			●									●	●		

Facilities Available at Golf Courses

Facility \ Golf Courses by County	VALE ROYAL ABBEY	VICARS CROSS	WALTON HALL	WARRINGTON	WERNETH LOW	WIDNES	WILMSLOW	BILLINGHAM	CASTLE EDEN	CLEVELAND	EAGLESCLIFFE	HARTLEPOOL	HUNLEY HALL	KNOTTY HILL GOLF CTRE	MIDDLESBROUGH	MIDDLESBROUGH MUNICIPAL	NORTON	SALTBURN	SEATON CAREW	TEESSIDE	WILTON	WYNYARD CLUB	BOWOOD	BUDE & NORTH CORNWALL	BUDOCK VEAN	CAPE CORNWALL	CARLYON BAY	CHINA FLEET	FALMOUTH	HELSTON
Dress Code Anything																														●
Dress Code Casual													●	●		●	●		●	●		●					●		●	
Dress Code Formal	●											●																		
Golf Shop takes credit cards	●												●			●			●			●	●	●			●	●		
Club House takes credit card										●				●		●			●			●								
Youth Coaching Scheme													●																	
Mobiles allowed in Club House																														
Children allowed in Club House	●									●				●		●						●					●		●	●
Spectators Allowed										●												●								●
Disabled Facilities	●									●							●					●								●
Disabled Toilets	●												●	●			●					●					●			●
Disabled Access	●									●												●							●	●
Satellite TV	●									●											●						●		●	●
TV Lounge										●												●								●
Snooker Room												●										●						●		
Members Only Bar	●																													
Gym/Weights																											●			
Massage																											●			
Physiotherapy																														
Sauna/Solararium																									●		●	●		
Swimming Pool																									●		●	●		
Health Club																											●			
Accommodation													●	●											●		●	●		
Hotel On Site													●	●														●		
Visitors Car Park	●									●		●					●				●				●		●	●	●	●
Members Car Park	●								●																●		●		●	●
Practice Putting Green	●									●			●	●			●					●			●		●	●	●	●
Practice Bunkers	●												●	●								●			●		●		●	●
Practice Course										●				●													●			●
Driving Range		●											●	●			●					●			●		●			●
Conference Facility			●							●				●								●			●		●	●		
Evening Functions	●													●								●			●		●			●
On Course Refreshments																														
Bar Snacks	●	●	●	●		●		●	●	●	●	●	●	●	●	●	●	●	●	●	●	●	●	●	●	●	●	●	●	●
Restaurant Dinner	●	●	●	●		●			●			●	●	●	●	●			●		●	●		●	●		●	●	●	●
Restaurant Lunch	●												●	●	●	●			●		●	●		●	●		●		●	●
Restaurant Breakfast	●												●	●		●			●			●					●			●
Shoe Cleaning Service	●																					●					●			
Bag Drop Service	●																													
Guests Changing Rooms	●	●	●	●	●	●		●	●	●	●	●	●	●	●	●	●	●	●	●	●	●	●	●	●	●	●	●	●	●
Guests Showers	●									●	●						●					●			●		●			●
On Course Drinking Fountains										●																				
On Course Yardage Markers										●	●		●				●					●			●		●		●	●
Spike Bar	●												●																	
Plastic Stud Fitting Service	●															●														
Plastic Studs Compulsory	●																													
Visitors Need Handicap Proof	●																													
Golf Clubs Hire			●	●			●		●		●	●	●	●	●		●					●	●	●	●	●	●	●	●	●
Caddy Hire																														
Shoe Hire													●		●	○														
Buggy Hire	●								●		●	●	●	●	●							●		●	●	●	●	●		●
Trolley Hire	●	●	●	●		●		●	●		●	●	●	●	●						●			●	●		●	●	●	●
Regripping	●								●		●		●		●							●			●		●			
Club Alterations	●										●			●	●							●			●		●			

Facilities Available at Golf Courses

Facility	HOLYWELL BAY	KILLIOW PARK	LANHYDROCK	LAUNCESTON	LOOE	LOSTWITHIEL	MERLIN	MULLION	NEWQUAY	PERRANPORTH	PORTHPEAN	PRAA SANDS	RADNOR GOLF & SKI CTRE	ROSERROW	ST. AUSTELL	ST. ENODOC	ST. KEW	ST. MELLION INTERNATIONAL	ST. NEWLYN EAST	TEHIDY	TREGENNA CASTLE	TRELOY	TRETHORNE	TREVOSE	TRURO	WEST CORNWALL	WHITSAND BAY	AYCLIFFE	BARNARD CASTLE	BEAMISH PARK	BIRTLEY
Dress Code Anything																															
Dress Code Casual						●									● ●																●
Dress Code Formal																					●									●	●
Golf Shop takes credit cards						● ●			● ●					● ●		●		●	● ●		●				●						
Club House takes credit card						● ●			● ●					● ●		●		●		●			●							●	
Youth Coaching Scheme						●												●													
Mobiles allowed in Club House															● ●																
Children allowed in Club House						●									● ●				●											●	
Spectators Allowed						●																								● ●	
Disabled Facilities																															
Disabled Toilets						●																									
Disabled Access						●																									
Satellite TV						●											●													● ●	
TV Lounge						●																								● ●	
Snooker Room						●															●										
Members Only Bar																															
Gym/Weights						●									●					●				●							
Massage																															
Physiotherapy																															
Sauna/Solararium															●					●				●							
Swimming Pool						●														●				●							
Health Club																															
Accommodation		●								●						●		●			●			●							
Hotel On Site				● ●												●		●			●										
Visitors Car Park						●												●												● ●	
Members Car Park						●												●												● ●	
Practice Putting Green						●								●		●	● ●													● ●	●
Practice Bunkers	●					●																							●	●	●
Practice Course				●																										●	
Driving Range	● ●						●				●			● ●	● ●	● ●		●					●			●			●	●
Conference Facility		● ●		● ●											●					●						●					
Evening Functions																															
On Course Refreshments																															
Bar Snacks	● ● ● ●	● ● ● ●		● ●			●	●		●			● ●		● ●	●		●		● ● ●				● ● ●				● ●	●	●	●
Restaurant Dinner		● ● ●		● ●			●						●		● ●			●		●	●			●				● ●		●	
Restaurant Lunch		● ● ●		● ●									●		● ●			●			●			●				● ●		●	
Restaurant Breakfast				● ●											● ●			●			●							● ●			
Shoe Cleaning Service																															
Bag Drop Service																															
Guests Changing Rooms	● ● ●	● ● ● ●		● ●			●			●			● ●		● ●	●		●		●				● ● ●			●	● ●	●	●	●
Guests Showers			● ●	●											●														●	●	
On Course Drinking Fountains															●														● ●		
On Course Yardage Markers						●									● ●			●											● ●		
Spike Bar																															
Plastic Stud Fitting Service						●									●			●													
Plastic Studs Compulsory																															
Visitors Need Handicap Proof						●										● ●			●					●				●	●		
Golf Clubs Hire	● ● ●	● ● ●		● ●		●		●	●					● ● ●		●			●					●				● ●		●	
Caddy Hire																															
Shoe Hire																●															
Buggy Hire		●	●	●	●					●						●				●			● ●					●		●	
Trolley Hire	● ● ●	● ● ●		● ●			●		●					● ● ●		●			●					● ●		●		● ●		●	
Regripping						●									● ●						●								● ●		●	
Club Alterations						●									● ●						●								● ●		●	

County: Cornwall → County Durham (AYCLIFFE, BARNARD CASTLE, BEAMISH PARK, BIRTLEY)

Facilities Available at Golf Courses

Facilities \ Golf Courses by County	BISHOP AUCKLAND	BLACKWELL GRANGE	BRANCEPETH CASTLE	CHESTER-LE-STREET	CONSETT & DISTRICT	CROOK	DARLINGTON	DINSDALE SPA	DURHAM CITY	HALLGARTH	MOUNT OSWALD MANOR	OAK LEAF	RAMSIDE	ROSEBERRY GRANGE	SEAHAM HARBOUR	SOUTH MOOR	STRESSHOLME	WOODHAM	ALSTON MOOR	APPLEBY	BARROW	BECKSIDE	BRAMPTON	CARLISLE	CARUS GREEN	CASTERTON	COCKERMOUTH	DISTINGTON GOLF	DUNNERHOLME	EDEN	FURNESS
Dress Code Anything																											●				
Dress Code Casual				●								●	●								●		●		●						
Dress Code Formal																															
Golf Shop takes credit cards	●		●	●								●	●	●			●			●		●	●								
Club House takes credit card	●											●	●	●						●		●	●								
Youth Coaching Scheme	●			●								●	●	●						●		●	●								
Mobiles allowed in Club House	●			●				●												●		●									
Children allowed in Club House	●		●	●																											
Spectators Allowed	●		●	●								●	●	●																	
Disabled Facilities			●	●								●	●	●																	
Disabled Toilets			●	●								●	●	●																	
Disabled Access			●	●								●	●	●																	
Satellite TV	●								●				●	●			●			●											
TV Lounge	●		●	●					●				●	●	●		●			●		●	●	●	●	●					
Snooker Room	●		●	●									●	●																	
Members Only Bar													●	●																	
Gym/Weights										●		●																			
Massage																															
Physiotherapy																															
Sauna/Solararium								●				●																			
Swimming Pool												●																			
Health Club																															
Accommodation										●		●																●			
Hotel On Site												●																			
Visitors Car Park	●		●	●				●				●	●	●	●		●			●	●	●	●	●	●		●				
Members Car Park	●		●	●				●				●	●	●			●			●	●	●	●	●	●						
Practice Putting Green	●			●								●	●	●						●										●	
Practice Bunkers	●											●	●	●									●								
Practice Course	●												●																		
Driving Range													●	●				●									●			●	●
Conference Facility				●					●	●		●	●				●					●									
Evening Functions	●			●								●	●	●	●					●											
On Course Refreshments			●		●								●	●																	
Bar Snacks	●	●	●	●	●	●	●	●	●	●	●	●	●	●	●	●	●	●	●	●	●		●	●	●	●				●	●
Restaurant Dinner	●	●		●	●			●				●	●	●						●	●			●	●						●
Restaurant Lunch	●			●	●			●				●	●	●			●			●	●				●						
Restaurant Breakfast				●								●	●	●																	
Shoe Cleaning Service				●																											
Bag Drop Service				●																											
Guests Changing Rooms	●	●	●	●	●	●	●	●	●	●	●	●	●	●	●	●	●	●		●	●		●	●	●	●	●			●	●
Guests Showers	●			●								●	●	●			●			●	●		●	●	●						●
On Course Drinking Fountains	●												●	●						●											
On Course Yardage Markers	●		●	●									●	●						●	●		●	●	●						
Spike Bar															●		●					●	●								
Plastic Stud Fitting Service													●																		
Plastic Studs Compulsory													●																		
Visitors Need Handicap Proof			●	●																●			●		●						
Golf Clubs Hire	●	●	●	●		●				●		●	●	●	●	●	●	●		●		●	●	●	●				●		
Caddy Hire				●	●																										
Shoe Hire				●											●		●				●										
Buggy Hire															●		●				●										
Trolley Hire	●	●	●	●				●	●		●	●		●	●		●			●	●		●	●	●					●	●
Regripping	●			●	●								●	●	●		●			●			●								
Club Alterations	●			●	●								●	●	●		●			●			●		●						

Facilities Available at Golf Courses

Golf Courses by County

Cumbria

Facility	GRANGE FELL	GRANGE-OVER-SANDS	HALTWHISTLE	KENDAL	KESWICK	MARYPORT	PENRITH	SEASCALE	SEDBURGH	SILECROFT	SILLOTH	STONY HOLME	ULVERSTON	WINDERMERE	WORKINGTON
Dress Code Anything															
Dress Code Casual															●
Dress Code Formal															
Golf Shop takes credit cards				●											
Club House takes credit card				●											
Youth Coaching Scheme				●											
Mobiles allowed in Club House				●											
Children allowed in Club House				●											
Spectators Allowed				●											
Disabled Facilities				●											
Disabled Toilets				●											
Disabled Access				●											
Satellite TV				●											
TV Lounge				●											●
Snooker Room															●
Members Only Bar															
Gym/Weights															
Massage															
Physiotherapy															
Sauna/Solararium															
Swimming Pool															
Health Club															
Accommodation															
Hotel On Site															
Visitors Car Park				●											●
Members Car Park				●											●
Practice Putting Green				●			●								
Practice Bunkers							●								
Practice Course				●											●
Driving Range					●	●									
Conference Facility				●		●									
Evening Functions				●											●
On Course Refreshments															
Bar Snacks	●	●	●	●	●	●	●	●	●	●	●	●	●	●	●
Restaurant Dinner		●	●	●	●	●	●	●	●	●	●	●	●	●	
Restaurant Lunch		●	●	●	●		●		●		●		●		
Restaurant Breakfast			●	●								●			
Shoe Cleaning Service				●											
Bag Drop Service															
Guests Changing Rooms	●	●	●	●	●	●	●	●	●	●	●	●	●	●	●
Guests Showers				●											●
On Course Drinking Fountains															●
On Course Yardage Markers				●											
Spike Bar															
Plastic Stud Fitting Service															●
Plastic Studs Compulsory															
Visitors Need Handicap Proof															●
Golf Clubs Hire	●		●	●		●	●	●				●	●	●	
Caddy Hire															
Shoe Hire															
Buggy Hire			●									●			
Trolley Hire	●		●	●		●	●	●			●	●	●	●	
Regripping				●											●
Club Alterations				●											●

Derbyshire

Facility	ALFRETON	ALLESTREE PARK	ASHBOURNE	BAKEWELL	BARLBOROUGH LINKS	BIRCH HALL	BRAILSFORD	BREADSALL PRIORY	BREEDON PRIORY	BROUGHTON HEATH	BUXTON & HIGH PEAK	CAVENDISH	CHAPEL-EN-LE-FRITH	CHESTERFIELD	CHEVIN	EREWASH VALLEY
Dress Code Anything																
Dress Code Casual			●					●						●		●
Dress Code Formal			●		●	●		●						●		●
Golf Shop takes credit cards			●		●	●		●						●		●
Club House takes credit card			●		●			●						●		●
Youth Coaching Scheme			●		●			●						●		●
Mobiles allowed in Club House			●		●			●						●		
Children allowed in Club House			●		●			●						●		
Spectators Allowed			●		●			●						●		
Disabled Facilities			●	●				●						●		●
Disabled Toilets			●	●				●						●		●
Disabled Access			●	●				●						●		●
Satellite TV																●
TV Lounge			●	●				●						●		●
Snooker Room				●				●						●		●
Members Only Bar																
Gym/Weights											●					
Massage																
Physiotherapy																
Sauna/Solararium								●								
Swimming Pool								●								
Health Club								●								
Accommodation								●								
Hotel On Site								●								
Visitors Car Park		●	●		●			●			●	●		●		●
Members Car Park		●	●		●			●			●	●		●		●
Practice Putting Green			●		●			●			●			●		●
Practice Bunkers			●					●						●		●
Practice Course		●	●					●			●					●
Driving Range					●		●	●	●				●			
Conference Facility						●		●						●		
Evening Functions								●						●		●
On Course Refreshments																
Bar Snacks	●	●	●	●	●	●	●	●	●	●	●	●	●	●	●	●
Restaurant Dinner	●		●		●	●		●			●	●		●	●	●
Restaurant Lunch	●		●		●	●		●			●	●		●	●	●
Restaurant Breakfast			●		●			●								●
Shoe Cleaning Service								●								
Bag Drop Service																
Guests Changing Rooms	●	●	●		●	●		●			●	●		●	●	●
Guests Showers		●	●					●				●			●	●
On Course Drinking Fountains								●							●	
On Course Yardage Markers			●	●				●			●		●		●	●
Spike Bar								●							●	
Plastic Stud Fitting Service		●	●					●			●	●			●	●
Plastic Studs Compulsory																
Visitors Need Handicap Proof														●		
Golf Clubs Hire		●	●		●			●		●	●	●	●	●	●	●
Caddy Hire																
Shoe Hire								●								
Buggy Hire			●					●	●	●		●			●	
Trolley Hire		●	●		●			●	●	●	●	●	●	●	●	●
Regripping		●	●					●			●	●			●	●
Club Alterations		●	●					●			●	●			●	●

Facilities Available at Golf Courses

Facility / Golf Courses by County	GLOSSOP & DISTRICT	GRASSMOOR GOLF CTRE	HALLOWES	HORSLEY LODGE	KEDLESTON PARK	MATLOCK	MAYWOOD	MICKLEOVER	MORLEY HAYES	ORMONDE FIELDS	PEWIT	SHIRLAND	SICKLEHOLME	SINFIN	STANEDGE	STRUTT CLUB	TAPTON PARK	ASHBURY	AXE CLIFF	BIGBURY	CENTRAL PARK	CHULMLEIGH	CHURSTON	CREDITON	DAINTON PARK	DARTMOUTH	DINNATON	EAST DEVON	ELFORDLEIGH	EXETER	FINGLE GLEN
Dress Code Anything																															
Dress Code Casual		●	●		●			●	●	●	●		●	●				●					●	●	●	●			●		●
Dress Code Formal																		●													
Golf Shop takes credit cards		●	●		●			●		●	●	●						●					●	●	●	●			●		●
Club House takes credit card			●							●	●													●	●	●					
Youth Coaching Scheme			●		●																			●	●				●		
Mobiles allowed in Club House			●										●																		
Children allowed in Club House		●	●		●			●		●	●							●					●	●	●	●			●		●
Spectators Allowed													●					●													
Disabled Facilities		●	●		●													●						●	●	●			●		
Disabled Toilets		●	●		●													●						●	●				●		
Disabled Access		●	●				●											●						●	●				●		
Satellite TV		●	●										●					●						●	●				●		
TV Lounge		●	●						●		●							●						●	●	●					
Snooker Room		●	●										●					●						●	●						
Members Only Bar			●																												
Gym/Weights																									●	●	●			●	●
Massage																										●					
Physiotherapy																										●					
Sauna/Solararium			●	●																						●					
Swimming Pool																										●					
Health Club																										●	●				
Accommodation			●															●					●			●					
Hotel On Site			●															●													
Visitors Car Park		●	●		●		●	●	●	●	●				●			●						●	●	●					
Members Car Park		●	●		●			●	●	●	●							●						●	●	●					
Practice Putting Green		●	●		●			●	●	●	●							●						●	●	●			●		
Practice Bunkers		●	●		●													●						●	●	●			●		
Practice Course		●	●				●											●						●	●						
Driving Range	●	●	●				●				●						●	●						●	●	●					
Conference Facility			●															●						●	●	●			●		
Evening Functions			●						●		●							●						●	●						
On Course Refreshments			●							●	●													●							
Bar Snacks	●	●	●	●	●	●	●	●	●	●	●	●	●	●	●		●	●	●	●			●	●	●	●			●		●
Restaurant Dinner	●		●					●	●		●							●						●	●	●			●		
Restaurant Lunch			●		●			●	●	●	●							●						●	●	●			●		
Restaurant Breakfast			●		●			●		●	●							●						●	●	●					
Shoe Cleaning Service		●	●																										●		
Bag Drop Service																		●													
Guests Changing Rooms	●	●	●	●	●	●	●	●	●	●	●	●	●	●				●	●	●			●	●	●	●			●		●
Guests Showers		●	●		●			●		●	●		●					●						●		●					
On Course Drinking Fountains			●																												
On Course Yardage Markers		●	●					●	●	●	●		●											●	●						
Spike Bar			●																												
Plastic Stud Fitting Service		●	●		●			●		●	●							●						●					●		●
Plastic Studs Compulsory			●	●																											
Visitors Need Handicap Proof		●	●							●			●					●													
Golf Clubs Hire	●		●	●			●	●		●	●	●		●			●	●	●	●	●	●	●	●	●	●	●	●	●		●
Caddy Hire																															
Shoe Hire		●																●						●	●						
Buggy Hire		●						●										●						●	●	●					
Trolley Hire	●	●	●	●	●	●		●		●	●	●						●			●		●	●	●			●	●	●	
Regripping		●	●		●			●		●	●							●						●	●					●	
Club Alterations		●	●		●			●		●	●							●						●	●				●		

DEVON

Facilities Available at Golf Courses

Golf Courses by County

Facility	HARTLAND FOREST	HELE PARK GOLF CTRE	HIGHBULLEN HOTEL	HOLSWORTHY	HONITON	HURDWICK	ILFRACOMBE	LIBBATON	MANOR HOUSE	MORTEHOE & WOOLACOMBE	NEWTON ABBOT	NORTH DEVON (ROYAL)	OKEHAMPTON	OTTER VALLEY GOLF CTRE	PADBROOK PARK	PORTMORE GOLF PARK
Dress Code Anything																
Dress Code Casual		●		●						●	●	●	●	●		●
Dress Code Formal				●			●					●		●		●
Golf Shop takes credit cards		●		●			●			●	●	●	●	●		
Club House takes credit card														●		
Youth Coaching Scheme		●		●			●					●	●	●		●
Mobiles allowed in Club House										●						●
Children allowed in Club House		●		●						●	●		●			●
Spectators Allowed				●			●					●		●		●
Disabled Facilities				●			●						●			●
Disabled Toilets							●			●			●			●
Disabled Access		●		●			●			●		●	●			●
Satellite TV											●	●				
TV Lounge										●	●	●	●	●		●
Snooker Room												●				
Members Only Bar																
Gym/Weights	●		●					●							●	
Massage																
Physiotherapy																
Sauna/Solararium	●		●													
Swimming Pool	●									●						
Health Club																
Accommodation	●		●					●	●	●				●		
Hotel On Site																
Visitors Car Park		●										●	●	●		●
Members Car Park		●					●			●	●	●	●	●		
Practice Putting Green		●		●			●			●	●	●	●	●		●
Practice Bunkers		●		●			●			●	●	●	●	●		●
Practice Course				●					●		●	●		●		●
Driving Range		●					●	●	●					●		●
Conference Facility									●						●	
Evening Functions		●		●			●			●	●	●	●			●
On Course Refreshments																
Bar Snacks	●	●	●	●	●	●	●		●	●	●	●	●		●	●
Restaurant Dinner	●		●	●	●		●		●	●	●	●	●		●	●
Restaurant Lunch	●	●		●			●			●	●	●	●		●	●
Restaurant Breakfast	●			●			●				●	●	●			●
Shoe Cleaning Service																
Bag Drop Service																
Guests Changing Rooms	●	●	●		●	●	●	●	●	●	●	●	●		●	●
Guests Showers		●					●			●	●	●	●			●
On Course Drinking Fountains																
On Course Yardage Markers		●		●			●			●	●	●	●			●
Spike Bar		●										●				●
Plastic Stud Fitting Service		●		●			●					●				●
Plastic Studs Compulsory																
Visitors Need Handicap Proof							●				●	●				
Golf Clubs Hire	●		●	●	●	●	●	●	●	●		●	●	●	●	●
Caddy Hire				●								●				
Shoe Hire																●
Buggy Hire		●	●			●		●	●							
Trolley Hire		●	●	●	●	●	●	●	●	●	●	●	●	●	●	●
Regripping		●		●			●			●	●	●	●	●		●
Club Alterations		●		●			●				●	●	●	●		●

Facility	SAUNTON	SIDMOUTH	SPARKWELL	STADDON HEIGHTS	TAVISTOCK	TEIGN VALLEY	TEIGNMOUTH	THURLESTONE	TIVERTON	TORQUAY	TORRINGTON	WARREN	WATERBRIDGE	WILLINGCOTT	WOODBURY PARK	WRANGATON
Dress Code Anything																
Dress Code Casual	●	●	●		●	●		●	●	●	●	●		●	●	●
Dress Code Formal								●								
Golf Shop takes credit cards	●		●			●			●	●		●			●	●
Club House takes credit card	●	●	●			●									●	●
Youth Coaching Scheme	●	●			●		●	●	●	●	●			●	●	●
Mobiles allowed in Club House					●						●				●	
Children allowed in Club House	●	●	●		●	●	●		●	●	●	●		●	●	●
Spectators Allowed	●						●		●	●	●	●			●	●
Disabled Facilities			●				●		●	●	●			●	●	
Disabled Toilets			●			●			●	●	●			●	●	
Disabled Access			●			●	●		●	●	●			●	●	●
Satellite TV	●				●		●		●	●	●	●		●	●	
TV Lounge	●		●		●				●	●	●	●		●	●	●
Snooker Room	●				●										●	
Members Only Bar																
Gym/Weights															●	
Massage															●	
Physiotherapy															●	
Sauna/Solararium															●	
Swimming Pool														●	●	
Health Club															●	
Accommodation			●	●										●	●	
Hotel On Site			●												●	
Visitors Car Park	●	●	●		●	●	●		●	●	●	●		●	●	●
Members Car Park	●	●			●	●		●	●	●	●	●		●	●	●
Practice Putting Green	●	●	●		●	●	●	●	●	●	●	●		●	●	●
Practice Bunkers	●	●	●		●	●	●	●	●	●	●				●	●
Practice Course			●		●		●		●	●	●			●	●	●
Driving Range	●				●				●						●	
Conference Facility			●	●						●					●	
Evening Functions	●	●	●		●	●	●		●	●	●	●		●	●	●
On Course Refreshments															●	
Bar Snacks	●	●	●	●	●	●	●	●	●	●	●	●	●	●	●	●
Restaurant Dinner	●	●	●	●	●	●	●	●	●	●	●	●		●	●	●
Restaurant Lunch	●	●	●		●	●	●	●	●	●	●	●		●	●	●
Restaurant Breakfast		●	●		●	●	●	●	●	●	●	●		●	●	●
Shoe Cleaning Service																
Bag Drop Service																
Guests Changing Rooms	●	●	●	●	●		●	●	●	●	●	●		●	●	●
Guests Showers	●	●	●		●		●	●	●	●	●	●		●	●	●
On Course Drinking Fountains		●						●	●	●					●	●
On Course Yardage Markers	●	●	●		●	●	●	●	●	●	●	●		●	●	●
Spike Bar			●													
Plastic Stud Fitting Service			●				●	●	●	●					●	●
Plastic Studs Compulsory																
Visitors Need Handicap Proof	●				●			●	●	●					●	
Golf Clubs Hire	●	●	●	●	●	●		●	●	●	●	●	●	●	●	●
Caddy Hire	●											●				
Shoe Hire										●	●	●			●	
Buggy Hire	●		●		●	●				●					●	●
Trolley Hire	●	●	●	●	●	●	●	●	●	●	●	●	●	●	●	●
Regripping	●	●	●		●	●	●	●	●	●		●			●	●
Club Alterations	●	●	●		●	●	●	●	●	●		●			●	●

www.hccgolfworld.com

Facilities Available at Golf Courses

Golf Courses by County

Facility	YELVERTON	ASHLEY WOOD	BOSCOMBE LADIES	BOURNEMOUTH & MEYRICK	BRIDPORT & WEST DORSET	BROADSTONE	BULBURY	CAME DOWN	CHEDINGTON COURT	CRANE VALLEY	DORSET HEIGHTS	DUDMOOR	DUDSBURY	EAST DORSET	FERNDOWN	FERNDOWN FOREST	HIGHCLIFFE CASTLE	IFORD BRIDGE	ISLE OF PURBECK	KNIGHTON HEATH	LYME REGIS	PARKSTONE	PARLEY	QUEENS PARK	SHERBORNE	STURMINSTER MARSHALL	WAREHAM	WEYMOUTH	ABRIDGE	BALLARDS GORE
Dress Code Anything																														
Dress Code Casual	●		●		●	●		●	●	●			●				●			●										
Dress Code Formal			●							●	●																			
Golf Shop takes credit cards	●		●	●	●	●				●	●		●	●						●	●								●	
Club House takes credit card			●	●	●				●	●	●		●	●															●	
Youth Coaching Scheme	●		●	●	●				●	●	●			●						●	●								●	
Mobiles allowed in Club House																														
Children allowed in Club House	●		●	●	●				●	●	●		●	●						●	●								●	
Spectators Allowed	●		●	●	●				●	●			●							●									●	
Disabled Facilities																						●							●	
Disabled Toilets																						●							●	
Disabled Access																						●							●	
Satellite TV													●	●								●							●	
TV Lounge			●	●						●												●	●						●	
Snooker Room	●																													
Members Only Bar				●						●																				
Gym/Weights				●																										
Massage																														
Physiotherapy																														
Sauna/Solararium																													●	
Swimming Pool				●																									●	
Health Club				●																										
Accommodation								●	●	●				●																
Hotel On Site				●										●																
Visitors Car Park	●		●	●	●				●	●	●											●	●						●	
Members Car Park	●		●	●	●				●	●	●											●	●						●	
Practice Putting Green	●		●	●	●				●	●	●											●	●						●	
Practice Bunkers	●		●	●	●				●	●	●											●	●						●	
Practice Course			●	●	●				●	●	●											●	●						●	
Driving Range				●					●	●			●	●	●	●				●									●	
Conference Facility									●		●			●												●			●	
Evening Functions			●	●					●	●	●		●	●	●							●							●	
On Course Refreshments															●														●	
Bar Snacks	●		●	●	●	●	●	●	●	●	●		●	●	●		●		●	●	●	●	●	●	●	●	●	●	●	●
Restaurant Dinner	●		●	●	●	●	●	●	●	●	●		●	●	●				●			●	●				●		●	●
Restaurant Lunch	●		●	●	●	●	●	●	●	●	●		●	●	●			●	●		●	●	●				●	●	●	●
Restaurant Breakfast	●		●	●	●			●	●	●	●			●															●	
Shoe Cleaning Service																														
Bag Drop Service																													●	
Guests Changing Rooms	●		●	●	●	●			●	●	●		●	●	●				●			●	●						●	●
Guests Showers	●		●	●	●	●			●	●	●		●	●	●				●			●	●						●	●
On Course Drinking Fountains	●		●	●	●				●													●							●	
On Course Yardage Markers	●		●	●	●				●	●												●	●						●	
Spike Bar										●				●			●						●							
Plastic Stud Fitting Service																														
Plastic Studs Compulsory																														
Visitors Need Handicap Proof	●					●		●						●																
Golf Clubs Hire	●								●	●	●	●	●	●	●															
Caddy Hire																														
Shoe Hire												●																		
Buggy Hire		●				●				●	●		●	●					●	●									●	●
Trolley Hire	●	●	●	●	●	●	●				●	●										●	●				●		●	
Regripping	●	●	●	●	●				●	●												●	●						●	
Club Alterations	●	●	●	●	●				●	●				●								●	●						●	

DORSET

ESSEX

Facilities Available at Golf Courses

Facility \ Golf Courses by County	BASILDON	BELFAIRS PARK	BELHUS PARK	BENTLEY	BENTON HALL	BIRCH GROVE	BOYCE HILL	BOYCE HILL	BRAINTREE	BRAXTED PARK	BUNSAY DOWNS	BURNHAM-ON-CROUCH	BURSTEAD	CANONS BROOK	CASTLE POINT	CHANNELS	CHELMSFORD	CHIGWELL	CLACTON	COLCHESTER	COLNE VALLEY	CRONDON PARK	DUNTON HILLS	EPPING	EPPING FOREST	ESSEX	FIVE LAKES HOTEL	FORRESTER PARK	FRINTON	GOSFIELD LAKE	HAINAULT FOREST	HARTSWOOD
Dress Code Anything																																
Dress Code Casual																					●											●
Dress Code Formal											●					●											●	●				
Golf Shop takes credit cards		●		●						●		●	●	●	●		●	●				●	●		●							
Club House takes credit card	●	●		●								●		●	●	●					●	●		●	●							
Youth Coaching Scheme		●			●		●	●					●	●	●	●		●	●													
Mobiles allowed in Club House	●	●		●								●				●								●	●	●	●					
Children allowed in Club House	●	●		●		●		●			●	●				●					●	●		●	●	●						
Spectators Allowed				●												●			●			●	●									
Disabled Facilities		●		●		●						●				●				●		●										
Disabled Toilets	●	●		●		●		●				●				●		●		●		●			●	●		●				
Disabled Access	●	●		●		●		●				●				●		●		●		●		●	●	●		●				●
Satellite TV		●																	●				●			●						
TV Lounge		●		●	●	●	●	●								●					●	●	●									
Snooker Room		●																														
Members Only Bar																																
Gym/Weights		●																									●	●				
Massage																																
Physiotherapy																																
Sauna/Solararium																											●	●		●		
Swimming Pool		●																									●	●				
Health Club																											●	●				
Accommodation																						●					●	●				
Hotel On Site																																
Visitors Car Park	●	●		●		●	●									●				●		●	●		●	●		●				●
Members Car Park	●	●		●	●	●	●									●				●		●	●		●	●		●				
Practice Putting Green	●	●		●	●	●	●					●		●		●			●	●		●	●		●	●		●				
Practice Bunkers	●			●	●	●	●							●					●			●			●	●						
Practice Course	●			●	●	●																			●	●						
Driving Range		●											●	●					●			●			●	●		●	●	●		●
Conference Facility				●			●		●	●												●			●		●	●		●		●
Evening Functions		●		●			●		●													●			●			●				
On Course Refreshments																																
Bar Snacks	●	●	●	●	●	●	●	●	●	●	●	●	●	●	●	●	●	●	●	●	●	●	●	●	●	●	●	●	●	●	●	●
Restaurant Dinner		●		●	●	●	●		●		●					●						●			●	●		●				
Restaurant Lunch		●		●	●	●	●		●		●					●						●			●	●		●				
Restaurant Breakfast		●		●	●	●	●		●		●					●						●			●	●		●				
Shoe Cleaning Service				●																												
Bag Drop Service																																
Guests Changing Rooms	●	●	●	●	●	●	●	●	●	●	●	●		●		●	●	●	●	●	●	●	●		●	●		●	●	●		●
Guests Showers	●	●		●	●	●	●		●			●		●				●				●			●	●						●
On Course Drinking Fountains				●		●										●						●										
On Course Yardage Markers	●	●		●	●	●	●					●				●		●		●		●	●	●						●		●
Spike Bar	●			●	●	●	●					●				●				●		●	●	●		●						
Plastic Stud Fitting Service	●	●		●	●	●	●									●						●	●	●	●							
Plastic Studs Compulsory																																
Visitors Need Handicap Proof					●	●	●								●					●		●										
Golf Clubs Hire	●	●	●															●					●		●	●	●		●	●	●		●	●
Caddy Hire																																
Shoe Hire		●				●																										
Buggy Hire		●		●	●	●							●	●	●	●					●	●	●		●	●		●	●	●		●
Trolley Hire	●	●		●	●	●	●							●		●				●	●	●	●		●	●		●	●	●		●
Regripping	●	●		●	●	●				●			●			●				●	●	●			●	●		●				●
Club Alterations	●	●		●	●	●			●	●			●			●				●	●	●			●			●				●

Facilities Available at Golf Courses

Facilities Available at Golf Courses	HARWICH & DOVERCOURT	HIGH BEECH	HYLANDS GOLF COMPLEX	ILFORD	LANGDON HILLS GOLF CTRE	LEXDEN	LOUGHTON	MALDON	MARDYKE VALLEY GOLF CTRE	MAYLANDS	MILLERS BARN GOLF PARK	NAZEING	NORTH WEALD	NOTLEYS	ORSETT	PRIORS	REGIMENT	RISEBRIDGE	ROCHFORD HUNDRED	ROMFORD	SAFFRON WALDEN	SOUTH ESSEX	STAPLEFORD ABBOTTS GOLF CLUB	STOCK BROOK MANOR	STOKE-BY-NAYLAND	THEYDON BOIS	THORNDON PARK	THORPE HALL	THREE RIVERS	TOOT HILL	TOP MEADOW	TOWERLANDS
Dress Code Anything																																
Dress Code Casual									•	•															•							
Dress Code Formal																																
Golf Shop takes credit cards		•		•				•								•	•						•									•
Club House takes credit card		•		•				•								•	•					•	•									•
Youth Coaching Scheme		•		•				•							•		•		•				•									•
Mobiles allowed in Club House		•		•				•								•	•															•
Children allowed in Club House		•		•				•								•	•															•
Spectators Allowed		•		•													•															•
Disabled Facilities		•		•											•		•		•												•	•
Disabled Toilets		•		•				•		•							•		•												•	•
Disabled Access		•		•				•		•							•		•				•								•	•
Satellite TV		•																														
TV Lounge		•														•	•	•				•										
Snooker Room																	•															
Members Only Bar																							•									
Gym/Weights																																
Massage																																
Physiotherapy																																
Sauna/Solararium																						•	•		•							
Swimming Pool																																
Health Club																																
Accommodation			•																													•
Hotel On Site			•																													•
Visitors Car Park				•				•									•	•			•											•
Members Car Park		•			•											•	•	•			•											•
Practice Putting Green		•			•		•		•							•	•	•			•											•
Practice Bunkers		•			•		•		•								•	•			•											•
Practice Course					•										•	•	•		•													•
Driving Range		•			•			•	•	•	•		•	•			•		•		•				•	•				•	•	
Conference Facility			•									•									•	•	•	•	•			•	•			
Evening Functions					•																											
On Course Refreshments					•																											
Bar Snacks	•	•	•	•	•	•	•	•	•	•	•	•			•	•	•	•	•	•	•	•	•	•	•	•	•	•	•	•	•	•
Restaurant Dinner	•	•	•					•				•													•							•
Restaurant Lunch								•							•										•							•
Restaurant Breakfast					•																•				•							•
Shoe Cleaning Service																																•
Bag Drop Service																																•
Guests Changing Rooms	•		•	•	•	•	•	•	•		•			•		•	•	•	•	•		•			•	•						•
Guests Showers		•														•	•	•														•
On Course Drinking Fountains																																
On Course Yardage Markers					•				•		•					•	•	•														•
Spike Bar		•								•						•	•	•														•
Plastic Stud Fitting Service								•								•	•	•														•
Plastic Studs Compulsory								•																								
Visitors Need Handicap Proof									•	•						•																
Golf Clubs Hire		•	•		•	•	•			•					•		•	•	•	•					•	•		•	•	•	•	•
Caddy Hire																																
Shoe Hire																																
Buggy Hire		•		•	•				•		•		•				•	•	•	•		•		•	•	•		•	•	•		•
Trolley Hire	•	•	•		•	•			•		•		•				•	•	•	•		•		•	•	•		•		•		•
Regripping		•			•				•		•					•	•	•			•											•
Club Alterations		•			•			•	•	•						•	•	•			•											•

Facilities Available at Golf Courses

Golf Courses by County

Facility	WARLEY PARK	WARREN	WEALD PARK GOLF CLUB	WOODFORD	GLOUCESTERSHIRE	BRICKHAMPTON COURT	CIRENCESTER	CLEEVE HILL	COTSWOLD EDGE	COTSWOLD HILLS	DYMOCK GRANGE	FOREST HILLS	FOREST OF DEAN	GLOUCESTER	HILTON PUCKRUP HALL	LILLEY BROOK	LYDNEY	MINCHINHAMPTON	NAUNTON DOWNS	NEWENT	ORCHARD	PAINSWICK	RAMADA HOTEL	RODWAY HILL	SHERDONS	SHIPTON	STINCHCOMBE HILL	TEWKESBURY PARK	GUERNSEY	GUERNSEY (ROYAL)	ST. PIERRE PARK
Dress Code Anything																															
Dress Code Casual		•		•		•			•	•		•	•		•		•		•	•	•	•			•	•				•	•
Dress Code Formal																				•											
Golf Shop takes credit cards		•	•			•			•	•	•				•						•										
Club House takes credit card		•	•			•				•	•	•			•						•										
Youth Coaching Scheme		•								•	•				•						•				•	•					
Mobiles allowed in Club House		•																													
Children allowed in Club House		•				•				•	•	•					•				•				•	•	•				
Spectators Allowed		•																							•	•	•				
Disabled Facilities												•			•											•					
Disabled Toilets						•						•			•					•						•					
Disabled Access																				•					•	•					
Satellite TV	•										•	•			•		•		•		•				•						
TV Lounge	•										•	•			•		•		•		•	•			•						
Snooker Room	•														•																
Members Only Bar																															
Gym/Weights																		•					•								•
Massage																															
Physiotherapy																															
Sauna/Solararium																		•					•								•
Swimming Pool																		•					•								•
Health Club																															
Accommodation																•		•					•								•
Hotel On Site																•		•	•				•								•
Visitors Car Park		•	•			•			•	•	•	•	•		•		•		•		•	•			•	•					
Members Car Park		•	•			•			•	•	•	•	•		•		•		•		•	•			•	•					
Practice Putting Green		•	•			•			•	•	•	•	•		•		•		•		•	•			•	•					
Practice Bunkers		•	•							•	•	•	•		•				•		•				•						
Practice Course		•								•		•	•		•				•		•										
Driving Range	•	•				•	•			•	•	•	•		•		•		•		•				•	•	•	•		•	•
Conference Facility		•								•	•	•			•		•		•		•		•								•
Evening Functions		•							•	•	•	•			•		•		•		•				•						
On Course Refreshments																															
Bar Snacks	•	•	•	•		•	•	•	•	•	•	•	•		•	•	•	•	•	•	•	•	•	•	•	•	•	•		•	•
Restaurant Dinner	•	•	•			•			•	•	•	•			•		•	•	•	•	•	•	•	•	•	•		•		•	•
Restaurant Lunch		•	•			•			•	•	•	•			•		•	•	•	•	•	•	•	•	•	•					
Restaurant Breakfast		•	•							•	•	•			•				•		•										
Shoe Cleaning Service												•			•																
Bag Drop Service																															
Guests Changing Rooms	•	•	•	•		•		•	•	•	•	•	•		•		•	•	•	•	•	•	•	•	•	•	•	•		•	•
Guests Showers		•	•			•			•		•	•			•				•		•				•	•				•	•
On Course Drinking Fountains		•											•																		
On Course Yardage Markers		•	•			•			•		•	•			•				•		•				•	•					
Spike Bar						•			•		•	•			•				•		•										
Plastic Stud Fitting Service	•								•		•	•	•		•				•		•										
Plastic Studs Compulsory																															
Visitors Need Handicap Proof	•	•														•		•												•	•
Golf Clubs Hire		•				•					•	•					•	•		•	•	•	•	•	•	•	•	•		•	•
Caddy Hire																															
Shoe Hire													•	•											•						
Buggy Hire	•	•	•			•			•	•	•	•			•		•	•			•				•	•	•			•	•
Trolley Hire	•	•	•			•			•	•	•	•			•		•	•			•				•	•	•			•	•
Regripping		•	•			•			•	•	•	•	•		•		•	•			•				•						
Club Alterations		•	•			•			•	•	•	•	•		•		•	•			•				•						

Facilities Available at Golf Courses

Golf Courses by County — HAMPSHIRE

Facility	ALRESFORD	ALTON	AMPFIELD PAR-THREE	ANDOVER	ARMY	BARTON-ON-SEA	BASINGSTOKE	BASINGSTOKE	BISHOPSWOOD	BLACKMOOR	BLACKNEST	BOTLEY PARK	BRAMSHAW	BROKENHURST MANOR	BURLEY	CAMS HALL ESTATE GOLF CLUB	CHEWTON GLEN	CHILWORTH	CORHAMPTON	COUNTY	DEAN FARM	DIBDEN GOLF CTRE	DUMMER	DUNWOOD MANOR	EAST HORTON GOLF CTRE	FOUR MARKS	FURZELEY	GOSPORT & STOKES BAY	GREAT SALTERNS	HAMPSHIRE	HARTLEY WINTNEY
Dress Code Anything							●																								
Dress Code Casual		●				●				●		●				●				●				●	●	●	●			●	
Dress Code Formal					●																										
Golf Shop takes credit cards		●			●	●	●			●		●				●				●				●	●	●	●			●	
Club House takes credit card												●				●				●					●	●					
Youth Coaching Scheme		●				●				●						●				●					●	●	●				
Mobiles allowed in Club House																									●	●	●				
Children allowed in Club House		●			●					●										●				●	●	●	●			●	
Spectators Allowed		●					●			●						●				●					●		●			●	
Disabled Facilities		●				●				●		●				●				●					●		●			●	
Disabled Toilets		●			●	●				●		●				●				●					●		●			●	
Disabled Access		●			●	●				●		●				●				●					●	●	●			●	
Satellite TV						●				●		●				●				●					●					●	
TV Lounge						●				●		●				●				●				●						●	
Snooker Room						●						●																			
Members Only Bar																															
Gym/Weights											●	●					●			●					●						
Massage																				●											
Physiotherapy												●								●											
Sauna/Solararium											●	●				●	●			●			●		●						
Swimming Pool												●													●						
Health Club												●								●					●						
Accommodation												●	●				●							●	●				●		
Hotel On Site												●	●																		
Visitors Car Park					●		●			●		●				●				●					●	●	●			●	
Members Car Park					●		●			●		●				●				●				●		●	●			●	
Practice Putting Green		●			●	●				●		●				●				●				●	●	●	●			●	
Practice Bunkers		●			●	●				●		●				●				●				●						●	
Practice Course		●			●	●				●		●				●				●										●	
Driving Range							●		●		●	●				●	●	●	●			●	●		●				●	●	
Conference Facility			●					●		●	●	●				●	●					●	●						●		
Evening Functions					●							●				●				●					●	●				●	
On Course Refreshments					●							●																			
Bar Snacks	●	●	●	●	●	●		●	●	●	●	●	●	●	●	●	●	●	●	●	●	●	●	●	●	●	●	●	●	●	●
Restaurant Dinner	●		●	●	●	●		●	●	●	●	●	●	●		●	●	●	●	●		●	●	●	●		●	●	●	●	
Restaurant Lunch						●				●	●	●				●				●		●		●	●	●	●			●	
Restaurant Breakfast					●	●				●	●	●				●				●		●		●	●		●			●	
Shoe Cleaning Service					●	●				●										●											
Bag Drop Service																															
Guests Changing Rooms	●	●	●	●	●	●		●	●	●	●	●	●	●	●	●			●	●		●	●		●	●	●	●		●	●
Guests Showers		●			●					●		●				●				●					●	●	●			●	
On Course Drinking Fountains					●																			●							
On Course Yardage Markers		●			●	●				●		●				●				●				●	●	●	●			●	
Spike Bar		●																		●							●			●	
Plastic Stud Fitting Service												●																		●	
Plastic Studs Compulsory												●																		●	
Visitors Need Handicap Proof					●	●				●		●												●							
Golf Clubs Hire	●		●		●	●	●	●		●	●	●	●			●	●			●	●	●		●	●	●	●	●	●	●	
Caddy Hire										●		●								●											
Shoe Hire												●				●				●											
Buggy Hire						●		●				●	●			●			●	●			●	●	●		●			●	
Trolley Hire	●	●	●	●	●	●		●		●		●	●	●	●	●		●	●	●		●	●	●	●	●	●	●	●	●	●
Regripping		●			●	●	●			●		●				●				●				●	●	●	●			●	
Club Alterations		●			●	●						●								●				●	●	●	●			●	

Facilities Available at Golf Courses

Golf Courses by County

Facility	HAYLING	HOCKLEY	LECKFORD	LEE ON THE SOLENT	LIPHOOK	MEON VALLEY	MOORS VALLEY GOLF CTRE	NEW FOREST	NORTH HANTS FLEET	OLD THORNS	OTTERBOURNE PARK	PAULTONS GOLF CENTRE	PETERSFIELD	PORTSMOUTH	ROMSEY	ROWLANDS CASTLE	SANDFORD SPRINGS	SOUTH WINCHESTER	SOUTHAMPTON MUNICIPAL	SOUTHWICK PARK	SOUTHWOOD	STONEHAM	TEST VALLEY	TOURNERBURY GOLF CTRE	TYLNEY PARK	WATERLOOVILLE	WELLOW	WEYBROOK PARK	WICKHAM PARK	WINCHESTER (ROYAL)
Dress Code Anything											●																			
Dress Code Casual				●			●			●	●				●			●		● ●					●			●		●
Dress Code Formal																														
Golf Shop takes credit cards				●			●		● ●	●					● ●			● ●							●			●		●
Club House takes credit card							●		● ●	●					● ●			● ●										●		●
Youth Coaching Scheme				●					●	●																				
Mobiles allowed in Club House				●			●		● ●	● ●					●			● ●										●		●
Children allowed in Club House				●			●		● ●	● ●					● ●			●										●		●
Spectators Allowed				●			●		●	●													●							●
Disabled Facilities							●			●					●			●									●	●		
Disabled Toilets							●			●					●			●									●	●		
Disabled Access				●			●			●					●			●									●	●		
Satellite TV				●					● ●						● ●			●												●
TV Lounge				●					●									●											●	●
Snooker Room																												●		
Members Only Bar																														
Gym/Weights				●			●																				●			
Massage				●			●																							
Physiotherapy				●																										
Sauna/Solararium				●			●																							
Swimming Pool				●																										
Health Club				●																										
Accommodation				●																										
Hotel On Site				●																										
Visitors Car Park				●			●	●	●	●					● ●		●	●					●			●		●		
Members Car Park				●			●	●	●	●					● ●		●	●					●			●		●		
Practice Putting Green									●	●					● ●		●	●					●			●		●		
Practice Bunkers							●								● ●		●	●										●	●	●
Practice Course																	●													
Driving Range			●		● ●			●		●		●													● ●					
Conference Facility				●			●			●			●		● ●		●	●										●		●
Evening Functions				●					● ●						● ●		●	●					●					●		●
On Course Refreshments																	●													
Bar Snacks	● ●			● ●		● ●	● ●		● ●			● ● ●		● ●	● ●		● ●	●					● ●			● ●		● ●		● ●
Restaurant Dinner	● ●			●			● ●		● ●			●		● ●	●		● ●	●					●					●		●
Restaurant Lunch							●		●			●		●	●		● ●	●					●					●		●
Restaurant Breakfast				●			●		● ●			●			● ●		● ●	●										●		●
Shoe Cleaning Service																														
Bag Drop Service																														
Guests Changing Rooms	● ●	●	● ●	● ●	●	● ●	● ●		● ●	●		●	●	● ●	● ●	●	● ●	●	●	●		●	● ●	●	●	● ●		● ●		● ●
Guests Showers				●			● ●		● ●						● ● ●		●	●					●			●		●		●
On Course Drinking Fountains																	●													
On Course Yardage Markers				●			● ●		●	●					●			●										●		●
Spike Bar				●			● ●		● ●									● ●										●		
Plastic Stud Fitting Service				●			●		● ●									● ●												
Plastic Studs Compulsory							●																							
Visitors Need Handicap Proof	●			●						●							●									●				●
Golf Clubs Hire	●			● ● ●					● ● ●	● ● ●						●		● ● ● ● ● ●	●									● ●		●
Caddy Hire									● ●																					
Shoe Hire				●					● ●														●							
Buggy Hire	●			●		● ●	●	●	● ●			●	● ●			●		● ●	●				●					●		●
Trolley Hire	● ●			● ●	●	● ●	●	●	● ●			●	● ●	●		● ●	●	● ●	●				● ●			●		●		●
Regripping	●			●			●		●						● ● ●		● ●	●					●					●		● ●
Club Alterations				●			●		●						● ●		●	●					●					●		● ●

© HCC Publishing Ltd

Facilities Available at Golf Courses

Facility	WORLDHAM PARK	BELMONT	BRAMPTON GOLF	BROCKINGTON	BURGHILL VALLEY	GROVE	HEREFORD MUNICIPAL	HEREFORDSHIRE	KINGTON	LEOMINSTER	ROSS-ON-WYE	SUMMERHILL	ABBEY VIEW	ALDENHAM	ALDWICKBURY PARK	ARKLEY	ASH VALLEY GOLF CLUB	ASHRIDGE	BARKWAY PARK	BATCHWOOD	BATCHWORTH PARK	BERKHAMSTED	BISHOPS STORTFORD	BOXMOOR	BRICKENDON GRANGE	BRIGGENS HOUSE	BROCKET HALL	BROOKMANS PARK	BUSHEY GOLF COURSE	BUSHEY HALL
Dress Code Anything																														
Dress Code Casual			•	•		•								•	•	•	•	•			•		•		•			•	•	•
Dress Code Formal																														
Golf Shop takes credit cards			•		•				•						•	•		•	•			•		•			•	•	•
Club House takes credit card					•				•						•	•		•		•		•					•	•	•
Youth Coaching Scheme					•				•						•	•												•	•
Mobiles allowed in Club House			•														•												
Children allowed in Club House			•	•		•			•					•	•	•	•	•			•					•		•	•	•
Spectators Allowed			•											•	•														
Disabled Facilities			•	•		•			•					•	•														
Disabled Toilets			•	•		•			•						•	•		•									•	•	•
Disabled Access			•	•		•			•						•			•									•	•	•
Satellite TV																													
TV Lounge			•						•						•			•									•	•	•
Snooker Room																										•			
Members Only Bar																													
Gym/Weights					•					•							•												
Massage																													
Physiotherapy																													
Sauna/Solararium					•					•							•												
Swimming Pool										•																			
Health Club																													
Accommodation		•	•																								•	•	
Hotel On Site																													
Visitors Car Park			•	•		•				•				•	•	•	•	•									•	•	•
Members Car Park			•	•		•				•				•	•	•	•	•			•	•	•				•	•	•
Practice Putting Green			•			•				•				•	•	•	•	•									•	•	•
Practice Bunkers					•					•					•	•	•	•									•	•	
Practice Course			•												•												•	•	
Driving Range	•				•		•	•	•							•			•								•		
Conference Facility		•					•						•											•				•	•
Evening Functions								•					•	•			•										•	•	•
On Course Refreshments													•																
Bar Snacks	•	•	•	•	•	•	•	•	•	•	•	•	•	•	•	•	•	•	•	•	•	•	•	•	•	•	•	•	•	•
Restaurant Dinner	•			•	•			•					•	•		•							•				•	•	•
Restaurant Lunch			•		•			•					•	•		•							•				•	•	•
Restaurant Breakfast			•	•		•		•					•	•		•							•				•	•	•
Shoe Cleaning Service													•	•									•						•
Bag Drop Service																											•		
Guests Changing Rooms	•		•		•	•	•	•	•				•	•	•	•			•			•		•			•	•	•
Guests Showers					•				•					•	•	•												•	
On Course Drinking Fountains																	•	•					•				•	•	•
On Course Yardage Markers			•						•					•	•		•				•		•				•	•	•
Spike Bar																												•	
Plastic Stud Fitting Service			•		•										•								•					•	•
Plastic Studs Compulsory																													
Visitors Need Handicap Proof																		•				•		•			•		
Golf Clubs Hire	•		•	•		•	•	•	•				•	•		•		•									•	•	•
Caddy Hire																												•	
Shoe Hire					•									•															
Buggy Hire	•				•	•		•	•				•	•		•											•	•	•
Trolley Hire	•		•	•	•	•		•	•	•	•	•	•	•	•	•			•			•		•			•	•	•
Regripping			•	•		•			•					•	•		•						•				•	•	•
Club Alterations			•	•		•			•					•	•		•						•				•	•	•

Facilities Available at Golf Courses

Facilities Available	CHADWELL SPRINGS	CHESFIELD DOWNS	CHESHUNT PARK GOLF COURSE	CHORLEYWOOD	DANESBURY PARK	DYRHAM PARK	EAST HERTS	ELSTREE	GREAT HADHAM	HADLEY WOOD	HANBURY MANOR	HARPENDEN	HARPENDEN COMMON	HARTSBOURNE COUNTRY CLUB	HATFIELD LONDON	HERTFORDSHIRE	KINGSWAY	KNEBWORTH	LAMERWOOD COUNTRY CLUB	LETCHWORTH	LITTLE HAY	MALTON	MANOR OF GROVES	MID-HERTS	MILL GREEN GOLF CLUB	MOOR PARK	OLD FOLD MANOR	OXHEY PARK	PANSHANGER GOLF COMPLEX	PENFOLD PARK	PORTER'S PARK	POTTERS BAR
Dress Code Anything																					●							●				
Dress Code Casual				●							●		●		●	●					●			●	●				●		●	●
Dress Code Formal	●				●		●									●							●				●					
Golf Shop takes credit cards	●					●					●					●					●	●	●			●	●			●	●	●
Club House takes credit card	●										●					●		●			●		●			●	●			●	●	●
Youth Coaching Scheme	●					●										●					●		●			●	●			●	●	●
Mobiles allowed in Club House	●										●					●					●	●	●			●				●	●	●
Children allowed in Club House	●					●										●					●		●			●	●		●	●	●	●
Spectators Allowed											●					●					●					●						
Disabled Facilities			●													●					●		●							●	●	
Disabled Toilets			●													●					●		●								●	
Disabled Access			●													●		●			●		●								●	
Satellite TV	●															●					●	●	●			●						
TV Lounge	●		●		●											●		●			●	●	●			●	●	●	●	●	●	
Snooker Room																●										●				●		
Members Only Bar																																
Gym/Weights										●						●										●						
Massage			●													●																
Physiotherapy			●													●																
Sauna/Solararium										●						●																
Swimming Pool					●					●						●										●						
Health Club																●																
Accommodation										●						●																
Hotel On Site																●																
Visitors Car Park	●		●	●		●					●					●		●			●		●			●			●	●	●	●
Members Car Park	●										●					●		●			●		●			●	●	●	●	●	●	●
Practice Putting Green	●										●					●		●			●		●			●	●		●	●	●	●
Practice Bunkers	●										●					●		●			●		●			●			●		●	●
Practice Course							●									●					●					●						
Driving Range		●						●	●	●				●	●	●	●			●	●		●			●			●		●	
Conference Facility		●			●				●				●	●	●	●					●		●			●			●		●	
Evening Functions		●		●			●									●					●		●			●			●		●	
On Course Refreshments																●										●						
Bar Snacks	●	●		●		●	●	●	●		●	●		●	●	●	●	●	●	●	●	●	●	●	●	●	●	●	●	●	●	●
Restaurant Dinner	●	●	●		●	●			●		●			●		●		●			●		●			●	●		●	●	●	●
Restaurant Lunch	●	●	●		●	●					●			●		●		●			●		●			●	●		●	●	●	●
Restaurant Breakfast	●	●	●								●					●										●				●	●	
Shoe Cleaning Service																●										●						
Bag Drop Service																●										●						
Guests Changing Rooms	●	●	●	●	●	●	●	●			●	●	●	●	●	●	●	●	●	●	●	●	●	●	●	●	●	●	●	●	●	●
Guests Showers		●		●		●					●					●					●		●			●		●	●	●	●	●
On Course Drinking Fountains																												●				
On Course Yardage Markers	●	●	●	●							●					●		●			●		●			●	●		●	●	●	
Spike Bar	●										●					●																
Plastic Stud Fitting Service	●			●							●					●					●		●			●		●			●	
Plastic Studs Compulsory				●																												
Visitors Need Handicap Proof	●				●																							●				
Golf Clubs Hire		●	●		●	●	●	●	●		●		●	●		●	●				●		●			●	●	●	●	●	●	●
Caddy Hire																										●						
Shoe Hire											●					●					●											
Buggy Hire		●								●	●				●	●					●		●			●	●		●	●	●	●
Trolley Hire	●	●		●	●	●	●	●	●	●	●	●	●	●	●	●	●	●			●		●	●		●	●	●	●	●	●	●
Regripping	●		●								●					●					●		●			●		●	●		●	
Club Alterations	●		●		●						●					●					●		●			●		●	●		●	

Facilities Available at Golf Courses

Facility	REDBOURN	RICKMANSWORTH	ROYSTON	SHENDISH MANOR	STEVENAGE	STOCKS HOTEL	VERULAM	WELWYN GARDEN CITY	WEST HERTS	WHADDON	WHIPSNADE PARK	WHITEHILL GOLF CTRE	ISLE OF MAN	CASTLETOWN GOLF LINKS	DOUGLAS	KING EDWARD BAY	MOUNT MURRAY	PEEL	PORT ST MARY	RAMSEY	ROWANY	ISLE OF WIGHT	COWES	FRESHWATER BAY	NEWPORT	OSBORNE	RYDE	SHANKLIN & SANDOWN	VENTNOR	WESTRIDGE	ISLES OF SCILLY	ISLES OF SCILLY
Dress Code Anything	●						●																									
Dress Code Casual		●	●	●		●																							●	●		
Dress Code Formal		●																														
Golf Shop takes credit cards		●	●	●	●	●					●																		●	●		
Club House takes credit card		●	●	●	●	●																								●		
Youth Coaching Scheme		●	●								●	●																	●	●		
Mobiles allowed in Club House		●		●							●	●																	●	●		
Children allowed in Club House	●	●		●							●	●																	●	●		
Spectators Allowed																																
Disabled Facilities				●					●																				●			
Disabled Toilets			●	●																									●	●		
Disabled Access			●	●																									●	●		
Satellite TV		●	●	●																									●			
TV Lounge		●	●	●					●	●																			●	●		
Snooker Room	●																															
Members Only Bar																																
Gym/Weights			●		●											●																
Massage			●																													
Physiotherapy			●																													
Sauna/Solararium			●		●									●		●																
Swimming Pool					●									●		●																
Health Club			●											●																		
Accommodation					●									●		●																
Hotel On Site														●																		
Visitors Car Park	●	●	●	●					●	●													●						●	●		
Members Car Park	●	●	●	●					●	●													●						●	●		
Practice Putting Green	●	●		●						●													●				●		●	●		
Practice Bunkers	●	●								●													●				●		●	●		
Practice Course	●	●	●																											●		
Driving Range	●				●	●				●		●				●														●		
Conference Facility		●		●	●	●	●							●		●																
Evening Functions		●		●					●	●																						
On Course Refreshments				●																										●		
Bar Snacks	●	●	●	●	●	●	●			●	●			●	●	●	●	●	●				●	●	●	●	●	●	●	●		
Restaurant Dinner	●	●	●	●	●	●					●	●		●		●	●		●						●			●	●	●		
Restaurant Lunch	●	●	●	●							●			●													●		●	●		
Restaurant Breakfast			●	●							●			●																●		
Shoe Cleaning Service																																
Bag Drop Service																																
Guests Changing Rooms	●	●	●	●	●	●	●	●	●	●	●	●		●	●	●	●	●	●		●		●	●	●	●	●	●	●	●		●
Guests Showers	●	●	●	●						●																			●			
On Course Drinking Fountains																													●			
On Course Yardage Markers	●	●	●	●					●	●																			●			
Spike Bar	●	●	●						●	●																			●			
Plastic Stud Fitting Service	●	●		●					●	●																						
Plastic Studs Compulsory																																
Visitors Need Handicap Proof		●																											●	●		
Golf Clubs Hire	●	●	●	●	●	●	●			●	●			●	●	●	●				●		●	●	●				●	●		●
Caddy Hire																																
Shoe Hire			●																											●		
Buggy Hire	●	●		●	●	●	●	●		●	●			●		●							●						●	●		
Trolley Hire	●	●		●	●	●	●	●		●	●			●		●		●	●				●						●	●		
Regripping	●	●		●							●	●																	●	●		
Club Alterations		●		●							●																		●	●		

Facilities Available at Golf Courses

FACILITIES AVAILABLE

England

Golf Courses by County	JERSEY	JERSEY (ROYAL)	LA MOYE	KENT	ALLHALLOWS	ASHFORD	ASHFORD	AUSTIN LODGE	BARNEHURST	BEARSTED	BECKENHAM PLACE PARK	BEXLEYHEATH	BIRCHWOOD PARK	BOUGHTON	BROMLEY	BROOME PARK	CANTERBURY	CHART HILLS	CHELSFIELD LAKES GOLF CTRE	CHERRY LODGE	CHESTFIELD	CHISLEHURST	CINQUE PORTS (ROYAL)	COBTREE MANOR PARK	CRAY VALLEY	DARENTH VALLEY	DARTFORD	DEANGATE RIDGE	EDENBRIDGE	ETCHINGHILL	FAVERSHAM	FAWKHAM VALLEY GOLF CLUB
Dress Code Anything																																
Dress Code Casual					●		●			●	●			●		●	●	●		●	●		●	●	●	●		●		●		
Dress Code Formal																							●			●	●					
Golf Shop takes credit cards					●		●			●	●			●		●	●	●		●	●			●	●	●	●	●		●		
Club House takes credit card					●		●				●			●		●		●								●		●		●		
Youth Coaching Scheme							●			●	●			●			●			●				●						●		
Mobiles allowed in Club House					●		●				●			●														●		●		
Children allowed in Club House					●		●			●	●			●		●	●	●		●	●			●	●	●		●		●		
Spectators Allowed					●		●			●	●			●		●	●	●		●				●	●		●	●		●		
Disabled Facilities										●				●			●	●						●		●		●		●		
Disabled Toilets					●		●			●				●			●	●	●					●		●		●		●		
Disabled Access					●		●			●				●		●	●	●	●					●		●		●		●		
Satellite TV										●	●						●	●		●	●					●	●	●		●		
TV Lounge										●	●			●			●	●		●	●			●		●	●	●		●		
Snooker Room		●														●		●														
Members Only Bar																																
Gym/Weights																		●										●	●			
Massage																		●														
Physiotherapy																																
Sauna/Solararium																●		●		●												
Swimming Pool																●																
Health Club																		●														
Accommodation									●																							
Hotel On Site																																
Visitors Car Park					●		●			●	●					●	●	●		●	●			●	●	●	●	●		●		
Members Car Park							●			●	●						●	●		●	●			●				●		●		
Practice Putting Green					●	●				●	●			●	●	●	●	●		●				●	●	●	●	●		●		●
Practice Bunkers		●				●	●			●	●			●		●	●	●		●				●	●	●	●			●		
Practice Course		●								●	●			●		●	●	●		●								●		●		
Driving Range			●				●	●					●	●		●	●	●	●	●			●		●			●	●	●		
Conference Facility									●							●		●	●							●			●	●		
Evening Functions							●			●	●			●		●	●	●	●	●	●			●	●	●		●		●		
On Course Refreshments											●			●		●		●						●		●				●		
Bar Snacks			●			●	●	●	●	●	●		●	●	●	●	●	●	●	●	●	●	●	●	●	●	●	●	●	●	●	
Restaurant Dinner			●				●	●		●	●		●	●		●	●	●	●	●	●	●	●	●	●	●		●	●	●	●	
Restaurant Lunch			●			●	●	●		●	●		●	●		●	●	●	●	●	●		●	●	●	●	●	●	●	●		
Restaurant Breakfast							●	●		●	●			●		●	●	●	●	●	●			●	●	●		●	●	●		
Shoe Cleaning Service																		●		●				●								
Bag Drop Service																		●														
Guests Changing Rooms		●	●			●		●	●	●	●	●	●	●		●	●	●	●	●		●	●	●	●	●	●	●	●	●	●	
Guests Showers										●				●			●	●	●	●				●	●	●	●	●		●		
On Course Drinking Fountains						●					●									●						●						
On Course Yardage Markers					●	●				●				●		●	●	●		●				●	●	●	●	●		●		
Spike Bar							●			●	●			●		●	●	●		●					●		●	●		●		
Plastic Stud Fitting Service						●	●				●			●											●					●		
Plastic Studs Compulsory										●																						
Visitors Need Handicap Proof		●				●				●						●							●				●					
Golf Clubs Hire		●			●		●	●	●		●		●	●	●	●	●	●	●		●	●	●	●	●	●		●	●	●		
Caddy Hire																	●	●					●									
Shoe Hire							●				●			●				●						●	●	●						
Buggy Hire			●			●		●			●		●	●		●		●		●	●		●	●	●			●	●	●	●	
Trolley Hire		●	●		●	●		●	●	●	●		●	●	●	●	●	●	●	●	●	●	●	●	●	●	●	●	●	●	●	
Regripping						●	●			●	●			●		●	●	●		●	●			●	●	●	●	●		●		
Club Alterations						●	●			●	●			●		●	●	●		●	●			●	●	●	●	●		●		

www.hccgolfworld.com

www.hccgolfworld.com

Facilities Available at Golf Courses

Facility	GILLINGHAM	HAWKHURST	HEMSTED FOREST GOLF CLUB	HERNE BAY	HEVER	HIGH ELMS	HILDEN EUROPRO	HOLTYE	HOMELANDS	HYTHE IMPERIAL	KINGS HILL	KNOLE PARK	LAMBERHURST	LANGLEY PARK	LEEDS CASTLE	LITTLESTONE	LONDON	LONDON BEACH	LULLINGSTONE PARK	LYDD	MID KENT	MOATLANDS	MOTE PARK GOLF HUT	NEVILL	NIZELS	NORTH FORELAND	OAST GOLF CTRE	OAST PARK	PARK WOOD	PEDHAM PLACE GOLF CTRE	POULT WOOD GOLF CTRE	PRINCES
Dress Code Anything					●																		●									
Dress Code Casual	●						●	●			●	●	●			●	●			●		●	●						●		●	●
Dress Code Formal																																
Golf Shop takes credit cards	●						●	●	●		●	●	●		●	●		●										●		●	●	●
Club House takes credit card							●	●			●		●		●			●										●				●
Youth Coaching Scheme	●						●		●		●							●														
Mobiles allowed in Club House							●	●	●		●							●										●			●	●
Children allowed in Club House	●						●	●	●		●		●	●				●										●		●		●
Spectators Allowed							●	●	●		●							●			●											●
Disabled Facilities							●	●	●		●							●					●									●
Disabled Toilets							●	●			●			●				●														
Disabled Access							●	●			●		●	●				●			●											
Satellite TV							●	●	●																							●
TV Lounge	●							●						●	●		●	●														●
Snooker Room														●	●		●	●														●
Members Only Bar															●																	
Gym/Weights					●		●			●													●	●								
Massage							●																●									
Physiotherapy																																
Sauna/Solararium					●		●			●													●	●								
Swimming Pool					●		●			●													●	●								
Health Club					●		●																	●								
Accommodation						●			●																							●
Hotel On Site																		●														
Visitors Car Park	●						●	●	●		●	●	●			●		●					●					●		●		●
Members Car Park	●						●	●	●		●	●	●			●		●										●		●		●
Practice Putting Green	●						●	●	●		●	●	●		●	●		●					●					●		●		●
Practice Bunkers							●	●	●		●		●		●	●		●												●		●
Practice Course							●	●	●		●		●			●		●												●		●
Driving Range	●			●		●			●									●	●	●	●	●		●		●		●		●	●	●
Conference Facility			●	●					●			●						●	●						●	●				●	●	●
Evening Functions	●						●				●				●	●		●	●										●			●
On Course Refreshments																																
Bar Snacks	●	●	●	●	●	●	●	●	●	●	●	●	●	●	●	●	●	●	●	●	●	●	●	●	●	●	●	●	●	●	●	●
Restaurant Dinner	●	●	●	●			●	●			●	●	●		●	●		●			●		●						●	●		●
Restaurant Lunch	●						●	●	●		●	●	●		●	●		●			●		●						●	●		●
Restaurant Breakfast	●						●	●	●		●	●	●		●	●		●			●								●	●		●
Shoe Cleaning Service							●																									
Bag Drop Service							●										●															
Guests Changing Rooms	●	●	●	●	●	●	●	●	●		●	●	●		●	●		●			●							●		●	●	●
Guests Showers	●						●	●			●	●	●		●	●		●			●							●		●		●
On Course Drinking Fountains	●						●	●			●	●	●		●			●			●							●				
On Course Yardage Markers	●						●	●			●	●	●		●		●	●		●								●		●		●
Spike Bar	●						●	●			●		●	●	●			●												●		
Plastic Stud Fitting Service																																
Plastic Studs Compulsory																														●		
Visitors Need Handicap Proof	●												●	●																●		
Golf Clubs Hire	●	●		●	●	●	●	●	●	●							●	●		●	●	●	●	●	●	●				●	●	●
Caddy Hire																																
Shoe Hire					●		●																									
Buggy Hire													●				●	●			●			●		●						●
Trolley Hire	●	●	●	●	●	●			●			●	●		●	●		●			●			●		●					●	●
Regripping	●						●	●			●		●	●				●											●		●	●
Club Alterations	●						●	●			●		●	●				●											●		●	●

Golf Courses by County

Facilities Available at Golf Courses

Golf Courses by County	REDLIBBETS	RIDGE GOLF CLUB	ROCHESTER & COBHAM	ROMNEY WARREN	ROUNDWOOD HALL	RUXLEY PARK	SENE VALLEY	SHEERNESS	SHORTLANDS	SIDCUP	SITTINGBOURNE & MILTON REGIS	SOUTHERN VALLEY	ST. AGUSTINES	ST. GEORGE'S (ROYAL)	STAPLEHURST GOLFING PARK	STONELEES GOLF CTRE	SUNDRIDGE PARK	SWEETWOODS PARK	TENTERDEN	TUDOR PARK	TUNBRIDGE WELLS	UPCHURCH RIVER VALLEY	VILLA	WALMER & KINGSDOWN	WEST KENT	WEST MALLING	WESTERHAM	WESTGATE & BIRCHINGTON	WHITSTABLE & SEASALTER	WOODLANDS MANOR	WROTHAM HEATH
Dress Code Anything																															
Dress Code Casual	●	●		●	●	●	●	●	●			●	●		●	●		●		●		●	●	●		●			●		
Dress Code Formal														●								●									
Golf Shop takes credit cards	●	●	●	●		●	●	●	●			●	●	●	●	●		●	●	●		●		●		●	●				
Club House takes credit card	●	●		●					●			●			●	●		●	●	●		●		●		●	●				
Youth Coaching Scheme	●		●	●	●		●	●				●	●		●	●			●			●		●		●					
Mobiles allowed in Club House	●					●		●	●			●	●		●			●		●		●									
Children allowed in Club House	●	●	●	●		●	●		●			●	●		●	●		●	●	●		●		●		●	●		●		
Spectators Allowed	●	●	●		●	●			●							●		●	●	●						●					
Disabled Facilities	●	●	●	●				●	●			●			●	●		●		●		●	●				●				
Disabled Toilets	●	●	●					●	●			●			●	●		●		●		●	●				●				
Disabled Access	●	●	●	●				●	●			●			●	●		●		●		●	●				●				
Satellite TV		●							●					●					●	●		●				●	●				
TV Lounge	●	●	●					●	●					●				●	●	●		●				●	●		●		
Snooker Room							●																			●					
Members Only Bar																															
Gym/Weights		●																		●											
Massage																				●											
Physiotherapy																															
Sauna/Solararium		●																		●											
Swimming Pool																				●		●									
Health Club																				●											
Accommodation														●						●											
Hotel On Site																															
Visitors Car Park	●	●	●	●	●	●	●	●	●			●	●		●			●	●	●			●	●		●	●		●		
Members Car Park		●	●	●			●	●	●				●					●	●	●			●	●		●			●		
Practice Putting Green	●	●	●	●	●		●	●	●			●	●		●	●		●	●	●		●		●		●	●		●		
Practice Bunkers	●	●	●	●	●		●	●	●				●		●	●		●	●	●		●		●		●	●				
Practice Course		●	●					●				●	●			●			●				●	●							
Driving Range	●	●	●	●		●	●							●		●				●		●				●	●			●	
Conference Facility		●																		●						●				●	
Evening Functions	●	●	●						●			●	●						●	●		●		●		●	●				
On Course Refreshments	●	●										●														●	●				
Bar Snacks	●	●	●	●			●	●	●	●	●	●	●	●	●	●	●	●	●	●	●	●		●	●	●	●	●	●	●	●
Restaurant Dinner	●	●	●	●		●	●		●	●	●	●	●	●		●	●	●	●	●	●	●		●	●	●	●			●	●
Restaurant Lunch	●	●	●	●		●	●	●	●			●	●	●		●		●	●	●	●	●		●	●	●	●				
Restaurant Breakfast	●	●	●	●		●						●	●	●		●		●	●	●				●			●				
Shoe Cleaning Service															●	●				●											
Bag Drop Service																															
Guests Changing Rooms	●	●	●	●		●	●	●	●	●	●	●	●	●	●		●	●	●	●	●	●		●	●	●	●	●	●	●	●
Guests Showers	●	●	●	●		●	●	●	●			●	●	●	●			●	●	●		●		●		●	●		●		
On Course Drinking Fountains			●	●				●	●				●		●				●					●		●					
On Course Yardage Markers	●	●	●	●	●	●	●	●	●			●	●			●		●	●	●		●	●	●		●	●				
Spike Bar	●	●	●	●		●		●	●			●			●					●				●		●	●				
Plastic Stud Fitting Service	●	●	●			●	●		●			●	●						●	●			●	●		●					
Plastic Studs Compulsory			●		●							●	●					●		●		●				●					
Visitors Need Handicap Proof			●				●		●					●					●					●							
Golf Clubs Hire	●	●	●	●	●	●			●					●	●	●		●	●	●	●		●	●						●	
Caddy Hire														●										●							
Shoe Hire	●													●				●		●		●		●							
Buggy Hire	●	●	●			●	●	●			●	●	●	●	●	●		●	●	●		●		●		●	●			●	
Trolley Hire	●	●	●	●	●	●	●	●	●		●	●	●	●	●	●	●	●	●	●	●	●	●	●	●	●	●	●		●	●
Regripping	●	●	●	●		●	●	●	●			●	●	●	●	●		●	●	●		●	●	●		●	●		●		
Club Alterations	●	●	●	●		●	●	●	●			●	●		●	●		●	●	●		●	●	●		●	●		●		

www.hccgolfworld.com

Facilities Available at Golf Courses

Golf Courses by County

Facility	ACCRINGTON & DISTRICT	ASHTON	ASHTON & LEA	ASHTON IN MAKERFIELD	ASHTON-UNDER-LYNE	BACUP	BAXENDEN & DISTRICT	BEACON PARK	BENTHAM	BLACKBURN	BLACKPOOL NORTH SHORE	BLACKPOOL PARK	BOLTON	BOLTON	BREIGHTMET	BRUNSHAW	BURNLEY	BURY	CASTLE HAWK	CHARNOCK RICHARD	CHORLEY	CLITHEROE	COLNE	DARWEN	DEAN WOOD	DEANE	DUNSCAR	DUXBURY JUBILEE PARK	FAIRHAVEN	FISHWICK HALL	FLEETWOOD
Dress Code Anything																															
Dress Code Casual	●	●	●		●	●		●		●		●			●	●		●		●	●		●	●		●					●
Dress Code Formal																												●			
Golf Shop takes credit cards	●	●	●		●					●		●						●						●	●			●	●		●
Club House takes credit card		●			●							●						●											●		
Youth Coaching Scheme	●	●	●		●	●		●		●		●						●			●			●	●						●
Mobiles allowed in Club House	●	●			●			●																							
Children allowed in Club House	●	●	●		●			●		●		●			●	●		●			●		●	●		●		●	●		●
Spectators Allowed	●									●								●													
Disabled Facilities		●	●		●					●		●			●						●										
Disabled Toilets		●	●		●					●		●			●						●										
Disabled Access		●	●		●					●		●			●						●		●	●		●					
Satellite TV	●				●					●		●																			●
TV Lounge	●	●	●		●	●		●		●		●			●						●		●	●		●					●
Snooker Room	●		●		●	●		●		●								●						●		●					●
Members Only Bar			●		●																●										
Gym/Weights																															
Massage																															
Physiotherapy																															
Sauna/Solararium																															
Swimming Pool																															
Health Club																															
Accommodation																															
Hotel On Site																															
Visitors Car Park	●	●	●		●	●		●		●		●		●	●			●			●		●	●		●					●
Members Car Park	●	●	●		●	●		●		●		●		●	●			●			●		●	●		●					●
Practice Putting Green	●	●	●		●	●		●		●		●		●	●	●		●			●		●	●		●					●
Practice Bunkers	●	●			●					●		●		●							●		●	●		●					●
Practice Course	●				●			●		●											●		●	●		●					●
Driving Range		●						●						●				●					●		●			●			
Conference Facility			●																	●					●					●	
Evening Functions	●	●	●		●	●				●		●			●			●			●		●	●							
On Course Refreshments																		●													
Bar Snacks	●	●	●	●	●	●	●	●	●	●	●	●	●	●	●	●	●	●	●	●	●	●	●	●	●	●	●	●	●	●	●
Restaurant Dinner	●	●	●		●					●		●			●			●			●			●						●	●
Restaurant Lunch	●	●	●		●					●		●			●			●			●		●	●						●	●
Restaurant Breakfast	●	●	●		●					●		●						●			●		●	●							
Shoe Cleaning Service																															
Bag Drop Service																															
Guests Changing Rooms	●	●	●	●	●	●	●	●	●	●	●	●	●	●	●	●	●	●	●	●	●	●	●	●	●	●	●	●	●	●	●
Guests Showers	●	●	●		●	●		●		●		●		●	●			●			●		●	●		●					●
On Course Drinking Fountains	●				●					●		●						●			●					●					
On Course Yardage Markers	●	●	●		●	●		●		●		●			●			●			●		●	●		●					●
Spike Bar					●												●			●					●					●	
Plastic Stud Fitting Service																				●											
Plastic Studs Compulsory																				●											
Visitors Need Handicap Proof	●				●	●				●								●						●				●			
Golf Clubs Hire	●			●			●			●	●	●			●						●	●		●	●		●				
Caddy Hire												●																			
Shoe Hire	●																														
Buggy Hire	●				●			●						●	●	●															
Trolley Hire	●	●	●	●	●			●		●	●	●	●		●		●	●	●	●	●		●	●		●			●	●	●
Regripping	●	●	●		●			●		●	●										●			●	●		●				●
Club Alterations	●		●		●					●		●			●						●			●	●		●				●

Facilities Available at Golf Courses

Golf Courses by County	GARSTANG	GATHURST	GHYLL	GREAT HARWOOD	GREAT LEVER & FARNWORTH	GREEN HAWORTH	GREENMOUNT	HAIGH HALL	HARWOOD	HERONS REACH	HEYSHAM	HIGHFIELD	HINDLEY HALL	HORWICH	HURLSTON	INGOL	KIRKBY LONSDALE	KNOTT END	LANCASTER	LANSIL	LEYLAND	LOBDEN	LONGRIDGE	LOWES PARK	LYTHAM & ST ANNES (ROYAL)	LYTHAM GREEN	MANOR	MARLAND	MARSDEN PARK PUBLIC	MORECAMBE	MOSSOCK HALL	MYTTON FOLD
Dress Code Anything																																
Dress Code Casual							●						●	●	●	●	●	●						●			●		●	●		●
Dress Code Formal																	●								●							
Golf Shop takes credit cards														●		●	●	●						●			●		●			
Club House takes credit card														●		●	●	●						●			●		●			
Youth Coaching Scheme							●							●	●	●	●	●						●			●		●			●
Mobiles allowed in Club House						●	●										●															
Children allowed in Club House						●	● ●							●	●	●	●	●						●			●		●			●
Spectators Allowed														●		●																
Disabled Facilities														●		●	●							●			●					
Disabled Toilets														●	●	●	●							●			●					
Disabled Access														●	●	●	●							●			●					
Satellite TV														●	●		●							●			●					
TV Lounge												●	●		●	●		●									●	●			●	●
Snooker Room							●							●		●		●						●			●					
Members Only Bar																●								●			●					
Gym/Weights										●																						
Massage																																
Physiotherapy																																
Sauna/Solararium										●																						
Swimming Pool										●																						
Health Club																																
Accommodation	●									●										●							●					●
Hotel On Site																																●
Visitors Car Park										●		●	●	●	●	●	●	●								●	●	●				●
Members Car Park								●		●		●	●	●	●	●	●	●								●	●	●				●
Practice Putting Green						●	●							●	●	●	●	●								●	●	●				●
Practice Bunkers						●	●								●	●		●								●	●	●				●
Practice Course													●	●	●	●	●	●								●	●	●				●
Driving Range	●									●																						
Conference Facility	●			●			●			●									●												●	
Evening Functions												●		●	●	●	●									●	●				●	
On Course Refreshments														●		●																
Bar Snacks	●	●	●	●	●	●	●	●	●	●	●	●	●	●	●	●	●	●	●	●	●	●	●	●	●	●	●	●		●	●	●
Restaurant Dinner	●	●					●			●						●	●								●		●	●		●		●
Restaurant Lunch				●												●	●								●		●	●				
Restaurant Breakfast															●	●	●								●		●	●				
Shoe Cleaning Service																●																
Bag Drop Service																●																
Guests Changing Rooms	●	●	●	●	●					●	●	●	●	●	●	●	●	●	●	●	●	●	●	●	●	●	●	●		●	●	●
Guests Showers						●																			●		●	●			●	
On Course Drinking Fountains						●				●					●												●					
On Course Yardage Markers						●							●	●	●	●	●	●									●				●	
Spike Bar						●																					●				●	
Plastic Stud Fitting Service						●							●	●	●										●			●			●	
Plastic Studs Compulsory						●																										
Visitors Need Handicap Proof														●	●	●	●	●								●	●			●		
Golf Clubs Hire	●								●		●					●	●	●										●	●	●	●	●
Caddy Hire																									●							
Shoe Hire																																
Buggy Hire										●						●																
Trolley Hire	●	●			●			●		●	●		●	●	●	●	●	●			●								●	●	●	●
Regripping					●									●	●	●	●										●	●			●	
Club Alterations					●										●	●	●										●	●			●	

Facilities Available at Golf Courses

Golf Courses by County	NELSON	OLD LINKS	ORMSKIRK	PENNINGTON	PENWORTHAM	PIKEFOLD	PLEASINGTON	POULTON LE FYLDE	PRESTON	REGENT PARK	RISHTON	ROCHDALE	ROSENDALE GOLF CLUB	SHAW HILL	SILVERDALE	ST. ANNES OLD LINKS	STANDISH COURT	TOWNELEY MUNICIPAL	TUNSHILL	TURTON	WALMERSLEY	WESTHOUGHTON	WESTHOUGHTON	WHALLEY	WHITTAKER	WIGAN	WILPSHIRE	LEICESTERSHIRE	BEEDLES LAKE	BIRSTALL	BLACKTHORN WOOD	CHARNWOOD FOREST
Dress Code Anything																																
Dress Code Casual						●	●		●									●		●				●		●			●		●	●
Dress Code Formal																								●								
Golf Shop takes credit cards						●			●									●					●	●					●		●	
Club House takes credit card																	●	●													●	
Youth Coaching Scheme						●	●		●									●					●	●					●		●	
Mobiles allowed in Club House																		●													●	
Children allowed in Club House						●	●											●					●	●		●					●	●
Spectators Allowed							●											●					●	●					●		●	
Disabled Facilities						●	●																●								●	●
Disabled Toilets						●	●																●						●		●	●
Disabled Access						●	●																●									●
Satellite TV						●	●										●	●											●		●	
TV Lounge						●	●		●									●		●			●	●		●			●		●	●
Snooker Room						●	●		●									●						●							●	
Members Only Bar							●																									
Gym/Weights														●																		
Massage																																
Physiotherapy																																
Sauna/Solararium														●																		
Swimming Pool								●						●																		
Health Club														●																		
Accommodation														●																		
Hotel On Site														●																		
Visitors Car Park						●	●		●									●		●			●	●							●	●
Members Car Park						●	●		●									●		●				●							●	●
Practice Putting Green						●	●		●											●			●	●		●			●		●	●
Practice Bunkers						●			●											●			●	●					●		●	●
Practice Course						●	●		●											●			●			●						●
Driving Range								●	●								●						●						●		●	
Conference Facility							●	●	●				●	●																		
Evening Functions						●	●		●									●						●		●					●	●
On Course Refreshments							●													●												
Bar Snacks	●	●			●	●	●	●	●	●	●	●	●	●	●	●	●	●		●	●		●	●		●	●		●	●	●	●
Restaurant Dinner	●	●			●	●	●		●	●	●	●	●	●		●	●	●		●	●		●	●		●	●		●	●		●
Restaurant Lunch	●					●	●		●					●			●	●		●	●		●	●		●			●			●
Restaurant Breakfast						●	●		●					●			●	●		●			●			●			●			●
Shoe Cleaning Service																																
Bag Drop Service																																
Guests Changing Rooms	●	●	●		●	●	●	●	●	●	●	●	●	●	●	●	●	●	●	●	●	●	●	●	●	●	●			●	●	●
Guests Showers						●	●		●									●		●			●	●		●					●	●
On Course Drinking Fountains							●		●																							
On Course Yardage Markers						●	●											●		●			●	●								●
Spike Bar																															●	
Plastic Stud Fitting Service						●			●																				●		●	
Plastic Studs Compulsory																																
Visitors Need Handicap Proof							●																									
Golf Clubs Hire				●		●		●	●	●		●		●			●	●									●		●		●	
Caddy Hire																																
Shoe Hire						●																										
Buggy Hire						●								●													●					
Trolley Hire	●	●	●		●	●	●	●	●	●		●	●	●		●	●	●						●			●		●	●	●	●
Regripping						●	●		●									●						●					●		●	
Club Alterations						●	●		●									●						●					●		●	

Facilities Available at Golf Courses

Golf Courses by County	COSBY	ENDERBY GOLF CLUB	FOREST HILL	GLEN GORSE	HINCKLEY	HUMBERSTONE HEIGHTS	KIBWORTH	KILWORTH SPRINGS	KIRBY MUXLOE	LEICESTER	LINGDALE	LONGCLIFFE	LUTTERWORTH	MARKET HARBOROUGH	MELTON MOWBRAY	OADBY	PARK HILL	ROTHLEY PARK	RUSHCLIFFE	SCRAPTOFT	STOKE ALBANY	ULLESTHORPE	WESTERN	WHETSTONE	WILLESLEY PARK	LINCOLNSHIRE	ADDLETHORPE	BELTON PARK	BELTON WOODS	BLANKNEY	BOSTON	BURGHLEY PARK
Dress Code Anything																●											●					
Dress Code Casual					●		●		●	●	●	●					●				●			●			●	●			●	
Dress Code Formal																	●															
Golf Shop takes credit cards					●		●		●	●	●	●				●					●			●				●			●	
Club House takes credit card					●											●					●			●								
Youth Coaching Scheme					●		●		●	●		●				●					●			●				●			●	
Mobiles allowed in Club House																●											●					
Children allowed in Club House					●				●	●	●					●					●			●			●				●	
Spectators Allowed					●				●			●				●											●					
Disabled Facilities											●					●					●											
Disabled Toilets																●					●						●					
Disabled Access					●		●				●					●					●											
Satellite TV					●		●		●	●						●					●											
TV Lounge					●				●	●		●				●					●			●			●				●	
Snooker Room					●		●		●							●																
Members Only Bar																●																
Gym/Weights		●																				●							●			
Massage																																
Physiotherapy																																
Sauna/Solararium		●																				●							●			
Swimming Pool		●																				●							●			
Health Club																																
Accommodation																						●							●	●		
Hotel On Site																																
Visitors Car Park					●		●		●	●	●	●				●					●			●			●				●	
Members Car Park					●		●		●	●	●	●									●			●			●	●			●	
Practice Putting Green					●		●		●	●	●	●				●					●			●				●			●	
Practice Bunkers					●		●		●	●	●	●				●					●							●			●	
Practice Course					●				●	●		●				●											●				●	
Driving Range			●			●	●		●				●								●			●			●		●			
Conference Facility	●																●					●							●			
Evening Functions					●		●		●	●		●				●					●			●				●				
On Course Refreshments					●				●												●											
Bar Snacks	●	●	●	●	●	●	●		●	●	●	●	●	●	●	●	●	●	●		●	●	●	●	●		●	●	●	●	●	●
Restaurant Dinner	●		●	●	●	●	●		●	●	●	●	●	●	●	●	●	●	●	●		●	●	●	●			●	●	●	●	●
Restaurant Lunch					●		●		●	●	●	●			●	●	●			●	●			●				●			●	
Restaurant Breakfast					●				●	●		●				●	●				●			●							●	
Shoe Cleaning Service																																
Bag Drop Service																																
Guests Changing Rooms	●	●	●	●	●	●	●	●	●	●	●	●	●	●	●	●	●	●		●	●	●	●	●	●		●	●	●	●	●	●
Guests Showers					●		●		●	●	●	●				●					●			●			●	●			●	
On Course Drinking Fountains					●		●		●	●		●												●				●				
On Course Yardage Markers					●		●		●	●	●	●				●								●			●					
Spike Bar										●											●											
Plastic Stud Fitting Service					●					●	●	●												●			●					
Plastic Studs Compulsory																																
Visitors Need Handicap Proof					●		●		●	●		●																				
Golf Clubs Hire	●	●	●			●	●		●		●	●	●		●	●		●		●			●				●	●	●	●	●	●
Caddy Hire																																
Shoe Hire																																
Buggy Hire					●	●							●				●					●		●	●			●	●	●	●	●
Trolley Hire	●	●	●	●	●	●	●		●	●	●	●	●	●	●	●	●	●	●		●	●	●	●	●		●	●	●	●	●	●
Regripping					●		●		●	●	●	●				●	●							●			●	●			●	
Club Alterations					●		●		●	●	●	●				●	●							●				●			●	

England

FACILITIES AVAILABLE

www.hccgolfworld.com

www.hccgolfworld.com

FACILITIES AVAILABLE

Facilities Available at Golf Courses

Below: Facilities available listed by golf course (by county).

Facility	CANWICK PARK	CARHOLME	GAINSBOROUGH	GEDNEY HILL	HORNCASTLE	KENWICK PARK	KIRTON HOLME	LINCOLN	LOUTH	LUFFENHAM HEATH	MARKET RASEN & DISTRICT	MARTIN MOOR	MILLFIELD GOLF	NORTH SHORE	OWMBY	POTTERGATE	RUTLAND COUNTY	SANDILANDS & LEISURE	SEACROFT	SLEAFORD	SOUTH KYME	SPALDING	STOKE ROCHFORD	SUDBROOK MOOR	SUTTON BRIDGE	TOFT HOTEL	WOODHALL SPA	WOODTHORPE HALL	CLEETHORPES	GRIMSBY	HUMBERSTON PARK
Dress Code Anything																															
Dress Code Casual					●	●	●		●						●			●	●	●					●	●	●	●			●
Dress Code Formal					●													●	●												
Golf Shop takes credit cards					●	●		●										●							●	●	●				
Club House takes credit card																	●									●	●	●			
Youth Coaching Scheme					●	●	●		●						●				●	●					●						
Mobiles allowed in Club House									●																						
Children allowed in Club House					●	●	●		●						●			●	●						●						
Spectators Allowed					●	●	●		●						●			●							●	●					
Disabled Facilities						●									●																
Disabled Toilets					●	●									●										●	●	●				
Disabled Access						●									●										●	●	●				
Satellite TV															●								●								
TV Lounge					●	●	●		●						●				●						●		●				●
Snooker Room																															
Members Only Bar																															
Gym/Weights						●																									
Massage						●																									
Physiotherapy						●																									
Sauna/Solararium						●																									
Swimming Pool						●																									
Health Club						●																									
Accommodation						●				●	●						●										●	●			
Hotel On Site						●																									
Visitors Car Park				●	●	●		●						●	●		●	●	●					●		●	●	●			●
Members Car Park				●	●	●		●						●	●		●	●	●					●	●	●	●	●			●
Practice Putting Green					●	●		●						●	●		●	●	●				●	●	●	●	●				●
Practice Bunkers					●	●		●					●				●	●	●					●		●	●				●
Practice Course					●	●		●									●	●	●				●	●	●	●	●				●
Driving Range		●	●	●	●										●	●															
Conference Facility		●		●				●			●					●		●					●								
Evening Functions					●	●												●	●	●											
On Course Refreshments															●																
Bar Snacks	●	●	●	●	●	●	●	●	●	●	●			●	●	●	●	●	●	●		●	●	●	●		●	●	●	●	●
Restaurant Dinner		●		●	●	●		●							●		●		●					●	●	●	●				
Restaurant Lunch				●	●	●									●				●					●	●	●	●				
Restaurant Breakfast				●	●	●									●				●					●	●	●	●				
Shoe Cleaning Service																															
Bag Drop Service																															
Guests Changing Rooms	●	●	●	●	●	●		●	●	●	●			●	●		●	●	●					●	●	●	●		●	●	●
Guests Showers					●	●		●							●					●				●	●	●	●				
On Course Drinking Fountains					●			●																	●						
On Course Yardage Markers					●	●		●							●		●		●						●	●	●				
Spike Bar						●	●																								●
Plastic Stud Fitting Service												●						●								●	●	●			
Plastic Studs Compulsory													●					●													
Visitors Need Handicap Proof	●																	●	●						●						
Golf Clubs Hire	●	●	●	●	●	●		●			●		●	●		●	●		●		●			●		●					
Caddy Hire																															
Shoe Hire				●															●							●					
Buggy Hire	●		●			●												●	●	●	●			●	●	●	●				●
Trolley Hire	●	●	●	●	●	●	●				●		●				●		●	●									●	●	●
Regripping					●	●		●									●	●	●					●	●	●	●				
Club Alterations					●	●		●		●			●			●		●	●					●	●	●	●				

Section divider: LINCOLNSHIRE (NORTH EAST) precedes CLEETHORPES, GRIMSBY and HUMBERSTON PARK.

Facilities Available at Golf Courses

The row labels are the facility types; the columns are golf courses grouped by county. Columns 1–9 are under LINCOLNSHIRE (NORTH) and the first listed courses; columns 10 onward are under LONDON (GREATER). The course names (left to right) are:

1. IMMINGHAM
2. MANOR
3. ASHBY DECOY
4. ELSHAM
5. FOREST PINES
6. GRANGE PARK
7. HOLME HALL
8. KINGSWAY
9. NORMANBY HALL
10. AIRLINKS
11. AQUARIUS
12. BETHUNE PARK
13. BLACKHEATH (ROYAL)
14. BRENT VALLEY
15. BRENT VALLEY PUBLIC
16. BUCKINGHAMSHIRE
17. BUSH HILL PARK
18. C & L
19. CENTRAL LONDON
20. CHINGFORD
21. COOMBE HILL
22. COOMBE WOOD
23. CREWS HILL
24. DENHAM
25. DUKES MEADOW
26. DULWICH & SYDENHAM HILL
27. EALING
28. ELTHAM WARREN
29. ENFIELD
30. EPPING FOREST (ROYAL)

Facility	1	2	3	4	5	6	7	8	9	10	11	12	13	14	15	16	17	18	19	20	21	22	23	24	25	26	27	28	29	30
Dress Code Anything													•																	
Dress Code Casual	•					•										•	•			•		•	•	•		•				
Dress Code Formal																•					•	•								
Golf Shop takes credit cards	•		•			•										•	•		•	•		•	•	•	•				•	
Club House takes credit card																•			•	•			•	•						
Youth Coaching Scheme	•															•	•			•		•	•	•		•				
Mobiles allowed in Club House			•													•				•			•	•						
Children allowed in Club House			•													•	•			•		•	•	•	•		•			
Spectators Allowed																•								•						
Disabled Facilities																														
Disabled Toilets																														
Disabled Access																														
Satellite TV																														
TV Lounge			•																	•		•	•	•						
Snooker Room			•																	•			•	•						
Members Only Bar																				•		•	•	•						
Gym/Weights					•																•									
Massage					•																									
Physiotherapy																														
Sauna/Solararium		•			•																•		•		•					
Swimming Pool					•																		•							
Health Club																														
Accommodation					•																									
Hotel On Site					•																									
Visitors Car Park	•		•										•			•			•	•	•	•	•		•					
Members Car Park			•													•			•				•							
Practice Putting Green	•		•										•			•			•	•		•	•							
Practice Bunkers			•													•				•			•							
Practice Course	•		•													•				•			•							
Driving Range		•	•		•	•													•	•			•					•		
Conference Facility			•	•													•		•	•		•	•							
Evening Functions	•		•													•	•			•		•	•	•						
On Course Refreshments			•																•											
Bar Snacks	•	•	•	•		•		•	•		•		•	•	•	•	•	•	•	•	•	•	•	•	•	•	•	•	•	•
Restaurant Dinner	•		•	•	•		•		•				•			•			•	•		•	•	•	•		•			
Restaurant Lunch			•													•			•	•		•	•	•						
Restaurant Breakfast			•													•			•	•		•	•							
Shoe Cleaning Service																							•							
Bag Drop Service																							•							
Guests Changing Rooms	•	•	•		•	•		•	•		•	•	•			•	•	•	•	•	•	•	•	•	•	•	•	•	•	•
Guests Showers			•										•			•			•	•		•	•	•						
On Course Drinking Fountains			•																			•	•							
On Course Yardage Markers	•		•										•			•			•	•		•	•	•						
Spike Bar																					•		•							
Plastic Stud Fitting Service			•																•			•	•	•			•			
Plastic Studs Compulsory																														
Visitors Need Handicap Proof			•										•									•								
Golf Clubs Hire	•				•	•	•	•	•		•		•	•		•			•	•	•			•		•		•		•
Caddy Hire																														
Shoe Hire																														
Buggy Hire	•		•	•	•														•	•		•	•	•		•				
Trolley Hire	•	•	•	•	•		•	•	•				•	•		•			•	•		•	•	•	•	•	•	•	•	•
Regripping	•		•		•														•	•		•	•		•					
Club Alterations	•		•										•				•		•	•		•	•	•		•				

GolfWorld Directory

Facilities Available at Golf Courses

Golf Courses by County

The facilities listed (rows, top to bottom) are:

- Dress Code Anything
- Dress Code Casual
- Dress Code Formal
- Golf Shop takes credit cards
- Club House takes credit card
- Youth Coaching Scheme
- Mobiles allowed in Club House
- Children allowed in Club House
- Spectators Allowed
- Disabled Facilities
- Disabled Toilets
- Disabled Access
- Satellite TV
- TV Lounge
- Snooker Room
- Members Only Bar
- Gym/Weights
- Massage
- Physiotherapy
- Sauna/Solararium
- Swimming Pool
- Health Club
- Accommodation
- Hotel On Site
- Visitors Car Park
- Members Car Park
- Practice Putting Green
- Practice Bunkers
- Practice Course
- Driving Range
- Conference Facility
- Evening Functions
- On Course Refreshments
- Bar Snacks
- Restaurant Dinner
- Restaurant Lunch
- Restaurant Breakfast
- Shoe Cleaning Service
- Bag Drop Service
- Guests Changing Rooms
- Guests Showers
- On Course Drinking Fountains
- On Course Yardage Markers
- Spike Bar
- Plastic Stud Fitting Service
- Plastic Studs Compulsory
- Visitors Need Handicap Proof
- Golf Clubs Hire
- Caddy Hire
- Shoe Hire
- Buggy Hire
- Trolley Hire
- Regripping
- Club Alterations

The golf courses listed (columns, left to right) are:

FINCHLEY, FULWELL, GRIMSDYKE, HAMPSTEAD, HAMPTON COURT PALACE GOLF CLUB, HASTE HILL, HEATHPARK, HENDON, HIGHGATE, HILLINGDON, HORSENDEN HILL, HOUNSLOW HEATH, HUMAX, LEE VALLEY, LIME TREES PARK, LONDON SCOTTISH, MILL HILL, MUSWELL HILL, NORTH MIDDLESEX, NORTHWOOD, PERIVALE PARK, RICHMOND PARK, RUISLIP GOLF CTRE, SANDY LODGE, SHOOTERS HILL, SOUTH HERTS, STANMORE, STOCKLEY PARK, STRAWBERRY HILL, SUDBURY, THAMESVIEW, TRENT PARK GOLF CLUB

Facilities Available at Golf Courses

England

FACILITIES AVAILABLE

Golf Courses by County	TWICKENHAM PARK	UXBRIDGE	WANSTEAD	WEST ESSEX	WEST MIDDLESEX	WHITEWEBBS	WIMBLEDON (ROYAL)	WIMBLEDON COMMON	WIMBLEDON PARK	WYKE GREEN	BLACKLEY	BOYSNOPE PARK	BROOKDALE	CHORLTON-CUM-HARDY	CROMPTON & ROYTON	DAVYHULME PARK	DENTON	DIDSBURY	ELLESMERE	FAIRFIELD GOLF & SAILING CLUB	FLIXTON	HEATON PARK	MANCHESTER	NEW NORTH MANCHESTER	NORTHENDEN	OLDHAM	PRESTWICH	SADDLEWORTH	STAND	SWINTON PARK	WERNETH
Dress Code Anything																										●					
Dress Code Casual			●	●				●	●		●	●	●	●	●				●		●						●		●	●	
Dress Code Formal										●					●																
Golf Shop takes credit cards			●	●				●	●	●	●	●	●	●					●		●		●	●						●	●
Club House takes credit card																								●	●						
Youth Coaching Scheme			●					●			●	●	●	●		●			●		●					●			●		
Mobiles allowed in Club House													●																		
Children allowed in Club House			●	●				●	●		●	●	●	●	●	●			●		●		●	●				●		●	●
Spectators Allowed			●					●																		●					
Disabled Facilities									●																						
Disabled Toilets																		●			●			●						●	●
Disabled Access			●					●																							
Satellite TV		●						●	●	●			●	●	●			●			●					●	●			●	●
TV Lounge								●	●				●	●	●			●			●					●				●	●
Snooker Room								●	●	●											●					●				●	●
Members Only Bar									●					●							●										
Gym/Weights																															
Massage																															
Physiotherapy																															
Sauna/Solararium																															
Swimming Pool																															
Health Club																															
Accommodation																															
Hotel On Site																															
Visitors Car Park			●	●				●			●	●	●	●	●	●		●	●		●		●			●		●			●
Members Car Park			●	●				●			●	●	●	●		●		●	●		●		●			●		●			●
Practice Putting Green			●	●				●	●		●	●	●			●		●	●		●		●			●				●	●
Practice Bunkers				●				●	●		●	●	●						●											●	●
Practice Course								●	●		●	●	●			●			●												●
Driving Range	●	●		●								●	●									●	●			●					
Conference Facility	●	●	●															●					●								
Evening Functions			●					●			●	●	●			●		●	●				●			●		●			
On Course Refreshments								●													●										
Bar Snacks	●	●	●	●	●	●		●	●	●	●	●	●	●	●	●	●	●	●	●	●	●	●	●	●	●	●	●	●	●	●
Restaurant Dinner	●		●	●				●	●		●	●	●	●	●	●	●	●	●	●	●		●			●		●		●	●
Restaurant Lunch			●	●				●	●		●	●	●	●	●	●	●	●	●	●	●		●			●		●		●	●
Restaurant Breakfast			●	●				●			●	●							●		●		●					●		●	●
Shoe Cleaning Service								●										●													
Bag Drop Service								●																							
Guests Changing Rooms	●	●	●	●	●	●		●	●	●	●	●	●	●	●	●	●	●	●	●	●	●	●	●	●	●	●	●	●	●	●
Guests Showers			●	●				●	●		●	●	●	●	●	●		●	●	●	●		●			●		●			●
On Course Drinking Fountains			●	●				●	●																						
On Course Yardage Markers			●	●				●	●		●	●	●	●	●	●		●	●		●		●			●				●	●
Spike Bar			●					●			●		●										●								
Plastic Stud Fitting Service								●																							
Plastic Studs Compulsory																															
Visitors Need Handicap Proof			●	●				●			●	●						●			●										
Golf Clubs Hire	●	●	●			●	●		●		●	●	●						●				●			●		●	●	●	
Caddy Hire							●					●																			
Shoe Hire													●																		
Buggy Hire	●		●	●									●									●									●
Trolley Hire	●	●	●					●			●	●	●	●	●	●			●	●			●			●				●	●
Regripping			●	●				●	●		●	●	●					●	●				●			●				●	●
Club Alterations			●	●				●	●		●	●	●	●	●	●		●	●				●			●				●	●

Facilities Available at Golf Courses

Facility	WHITEFIELD	WILLIAM WROE	WITHINGTON	WORSLEY	WORSLEY PARK	AINTREE	ALLERTON	ARROWE PARK	BIDSTON	BIRKDALE (ROYAL)	BLUNDELLS HILL	BOOTLE	BOWRING PARK	BRACKENWOOD	BROMBOROUGH	CALDY	CHILDWALL	EASTHAM LODGE	ELLESMERE PORT	FORMBY	FORMBY HALL	FORMBY LADIES	GRANGE PARK	HAYDOCK PARK	HESKETH	HESWALL	HILLSIDE	HOUGHWOOD	HUYTON & PRESCOT	LEASOWE	LEE PARK
Dress Code Anything																															
Dress Code Casual			●			●		●	●	●	●	●				●		●				●			●		●		●		● ●
Dress Code Formal											●		●			●	●			●					● ●						
Golf Shop takes credit cards										● ●		● ●				● ●	●			●							●		●		● ●
Club House takes credit card											●	●				●				●					●		●		● ●		● ●
Youth Coaching Scheme				●								●				●	●						●								
Mobiles allowed in Club House						●	●																								
Children allowed in Club House				●		●	●	●	●		●					●				●			●	● ●							
Spectators Allowed				●												●															
Disabled Facilities								●	●							●															●
Disabled Toilets								●	●							● ●															
Disabled Access								●	●							● ●				●											
Satellite TV				●						●																					
TV Lounge			●								●		●			● ●				● ●											● ●
Snooker Room			●								●		●			● ●				●						●					● ●
Members Only Bar																															
Gym/Weights				●																											
Massage																															
Physiotherapy																															
Sauna/Solararium				●																											
Swimming Pool				●																											
Health Club				●																											
Accommodation				●															●												
Hotel On Site				●																											●
Visitors Car Park				● ●		●	●	●			●	●				● ●	●			●					●	● ●			●		● ●
Members Car Park			●								●					● ●															
Practice Putting Green			●			●	●	●	●							● ●	●			●					●	● ●			●		● ●
Practice Bunkers			●													● ●	●			●					●	● ●			●		● ●
Practice Course									●	●		●				●	●			●					●						
Driving Range						●				●						●											●				
Conference Facility																●								●							
Evening Functions			●								●		●			●				●				●		●					● ●
On Course Refreshments										●																					
Bar Snacks	●	●	● ●			●		●	●	●	●	●	●	●	●	● ●	●	●	●	●	●	●	●	●	●	● ●	●	●	●	●	● ●
Restaurant Dinner	●		● ●					●	●		●	●				● ●	●			●					●	● ●			●		● ●
Restaurant Lunch			● ●					●	●		●					● ●	●			●					●	● ●			●		● ●
Restaurant Breakfast			● ●					●	●							● ●				●						●					
Shoe Cleaning Service																									●						
Bag Drop Service																															
Guests Changing Rooms	●	●	● ●					●	●		●	●				● ●	●			●					●	● ●			●		● ●
Guests Showers			●					●	●		●					●				●						●			●		● ●
On Course Drinking Fountains																				●											
On Course Yardage Markers								●	●	●		●				●	●			●						● ●					● ●
Spike Bar									●		●					●									●						
Plastic Stud Fitting Service									●	●						● ●	●									●			●		●
Plastic Studs Compulsory																●															
Visitors Need Handicap Proof			●							●	●	●								●				●		● ●					
Golf Clubs Hire		●	●			●	●	●	●	●		●			●		●		●			●		●		●		●	● ●		
Caddy Hire																															
Shoe Hire						●																									
Buggy Hire	●												●	●		●										●	●				
Trolley Hire	●		● ●			●	●						●	●		●	●	●							●	● ●			●		
Regripping			●			●	●	●	●		●					●	●									● ●			●		●
Club Alterations			●			●	●	●	●		●					●	●									● ●			●		●

Facilities Available at Golf Courses

FACILITIES AVAILABLE

England

Golf Courses by County

Facility	LIVERPOOL (ROYAL)	LIVERPOOL MUNICIPAL	PARK	PRENTON	SHERDLEY PARK MUNICIPAL	SOUTHPORT & AINSDALE	SOUTHPORT MUNICIPAL	SOUTHPORT OLD LINKS	WALLASEY	WARREN	WEST DERBY	WEST LANCASHIRE	WIRRAL LADIES	WOOLTON
Dress Code Anything							●							
Dress Code Casual		●		●	●	●		●	●			●		
Dress Code Formal						●						●		
Golf Shop takes credit cards				●		●	●		●					
Club House takes credit card				●		●								
Youth Coaching Scheme				●	●			●						
Mobiles allowed in Club House		●			●		●							
Children allowed in Club House	●	●		●	●		●	●						
Spectators Allowed	●			●			●	●						
Disabled Facilities		●		●			●	●						
Disabled Toilets		●		●			●	●						
Disabled Access		●		●			●	●						
Satellite TV		●			●	●	●	●						
TV Lounge		●		●	●		●	●	●					
Snooker Room	●			●	●	●		●	●					
Members Only Bar														
Gym/Weights														
Massage														
Physiotherapy														
Sauna/Solararium														
Swimming Pool														
Health Club														
Accommodation														
Hotel On Site														
Visitors Car Park	●	●		●	●		●	●	●			●		
Members Car Park	●	●		●	●		●	●	●			●		
Practice Putting Green	●	●		●	●	●	●	●	●					
Practice Bunkers		●		●		●								
Practice Course		●		●										
Driving Range					●	●								
Conference Facility														
Evening Functions				●	●		●	●						
On Course Refreshments														
Bar Snacks	●	●	●	●	●	●	●	●	●	●	●	●	●	●
Restaurant Dinner		●	●	●	●	●	●	●			●	●		
Restaurant Lunch		●		●	●	●	●	●	●			●		
Restaurant Breakfast		●		●	●	●	●	●	●					
Shoe Cleaning Service														
Bag Drop Service														
Guests Changing Rooms	●	●		●	●	●	●	●	●		●	●	●	●
Guests Showers	●	●		●	●			●	●					
On Course Drinking Fountains						●								
On Course Yardage Markers		●		●	●	●	●	●	●					
Spike Bar							●		●					
Plastic Stud Fitting Service		●		●	●		●							
Plastic Studs Compulsory		●												
Visitors Need Handicap Proof	●			●		●		●	●					
Golf Clubs Hire	●	●	●	●	●	●	●		●	●				
Caddy Hire	●					●								
Shoe Hire														
Buggy Hire		●					●							●
Trolley Hire	●	●		●	●	●	●	●	●	●	●	●	●	
Regripping		●		●	●	●	●	●	●					
Club Alterations	●	●		●	●	●	●	●	●					

MIDLANDS (WEST)

Facility	ANSTY GOLF CTRE	ASTON WOOD	BELFRY	BLOXWICH	BOLDMERE	BRANDHALL	BRANDON WOOD MUNICIPAL	CALDERFIELDS	COCKS MOORS WOODS	COPT HEATH	CORNGREAVES	COVENTRY	DARTMOUTH	DRUIDS HEATH	DUDLEY	EDGBASTON	ENVILLE
Dress Code Anything			●				●										
Dress Code Casual		●	●		●												
Dress Code Formal			●														
Golf Shop takes credit cards		●			●		●									●	
Club House takes credit card		●															
Youth Coaching Scheme		●														●	
Mobiles allowed in Club House		●					●										
Children allowed in Club House		●			●												
Spectators Allowed		●															
Disabled Facilities		●															
Disabled Toilets		●															
Disabled Access		●															
Satellite TV		●															
TV Lounge		●					●										
Snooker Room		●														●	
Members Only Bar		●														●	
Gym/Weights			●						●								
Massage																	
Physiotherapy																	
Sauna/Solararium			●						●								
Swimming Pool			●						●								
Health Club																	
Accommodation		●	●														
Hotel On Site																	
Visitors Car Park		●	●		●		●									●	
Members Car Park		●	●													●	
Practice Putting Green		●			●		●									●	
Practice Bunkers		●					●									●	
Practice Course																	
Driving Range	●	●	●				●	●		●							
Conference Facility	●		●						●		●					●	
Evening Functions		●														●	
On Course Refreshments		●															
Bar Snacks	●	●	●	●	●	●	●	●	●	●	●	●	●	●	●	●	●
Restaurant Dinner		●	●	●				●		●		●	●	●	●	●	●
Restaurant Lunch		●			●		●						●			●	
Restaurant Breakfast		●			●												
Shoe Cleaning Service																●	
Bag Drop Service																	
Guests Changing Rooms	●	●	●	●	●		●	●	●	●		●	●	●	●	●	●
Guests Showers		●					●									●	
On Course Drinking Fountains																	
On Course Yardage Markers		●			●		●									●	
Spike Bar		●														●	
Plastic Stud Fitting Service		●															
Plastic Studs Compulsory		●															
Visitors Need Handicap Proof																●	
Golf Clubs Hire	●	●	●		●	●	●	●	●		●					●	
Caddy Hire		●														●	
Shoe Hire		●														●	
Buggy Hire	●	●	●			●	●	●		●						●	●
Trolley Hire	●	●	●	●	●	●	●	●	●	●	●	●		●	●	●	●
Regripping		●			●		●									●	
Club Alterations		●			●		●									●	

www.hccgolfworld.com

Facilities Available at Golf Courses

Golf Courses by County	FOREST OF ARDEN	FULFORD HEATH	GAY HILL	GREAT BARR	HAGLEY	HALESOWEN	HANDSWORTH	HARBORNE	HARBORNE CHURCH FARM	HATCHFORD BROOK	HAWKESBURY GOLF CENTRE	HEARSALL	HILLTOP	HIMLEY HALL GOLF CTRE	KINGS NORTON	LADBROOK PARK	LEA MARSTON	LICKEY HILLS	LITTLE ASTON	MAXSTOKE PARK	MOOR HALL	MOSELEY	NORTH WARWICKSHIRE	NORTH WORCESTERSHIRE	OLTON	OXLEY PARK	PATSHULL PARK	PENN	PERTON PARK	PYPE HAYES	ROBIN HOOD	SANDWELL PARK
Dress Code Anything																																
Dress Code Casual	●																							●							●	●
Dress Code Formal	●																		●													
Golf Shop takes credit cards																								●								●
Club House takes credit card	●																															
Youth Coaching Scheme																																
Mobiles allowed in Club House																																
Children allowed in Club House											●													●							●	●
Spectators Allowed																																
Disabled Facilities																																
Disabled Toilets																																●
Disabled Access																																●
Satellite TV																								●							●	●
TV Lounge																								●							●	●
Snooker Room																								●								
Members Only Bar																																
Gym/Weights	●																●										●					
Massage																																
Physiotherapy																																
Sauna/Solararium	●																●										●					
Swimming Pool	●																●										●					
Health Club	●																															
Accommodation	●																●															
Hotel On Site	●																															
Visitors Car Park	●																							●								
Members Car Park																															●	●
Practice Putting Green											●													●							●	●
Practice Bunkers																															●	●
Practice Course																																●
Driving Range	●				●						●																		●			●
Conference Facility	●			●													●	●									●					●
Evening Functions																						●										
On Course Refreshments																																
Bar Snacks	●	●	●	●	●	●	●	●		●	●	●	●	●	●	●	●		●	●	●		●	●	●	●	●	●	●	●	●	●
Restaurant Dinner	●		●	●	●	●	●			●	●	●				●	●		●					●			●		●		●	●
Restaurant Lunch	●																		●					●				●			●	●
Restaurant Breakfast	●																							●								
Shoe Cleaning Service																								●								
Bag Drop Service																																
Guests Changing Rooms	●	●	●	●	●	●	●			●	●	●			●		●		●		●		●	●	●	●	●	●	●		●	●
Guests Showers																								●							●	●
On Course Drinking Fountains																								●							●	●
On Course Yardage Markers																								●							●	●
Spike Bar																																
Plastic Stud Fitting Service																								●								
Plastic Studs Compulsory																																
Visitors Need Handicap Proof																															●	●
Golf Clubs Hire	●		●		●		●	●	●	●		●		●	●	●	●		●	●				●		●	●	●	●			
Caddy Hire																																
Shoe Hire																																
Buggy Hire	●		●	●	●																											
Trolley Hire	●	●	●	●	●	●	●	●			●	●		●			●							●			●	●	●			
Regripping										●														●							●	●
Club Alterations										●														●							●	●

Facilities Available at Golf Courses

Golf Courses by County	SEDGLEY GOLF CTRE	SHIRLEY	SOUTH STAFFORDSHIRE	STONEBRIDGE	STONELEIGH DEER PARK	STOURBRIDGE	SUTTON COLDFIELD	SUTTON COLDFIELD LADIES	SWINDON	THREE HAMMERS	WALMLEY	WALSALL	WARLEY	WERGS	WIDNEY MANOR	WINDMILL VILLAGE	BARNHAM BROOM	BAWBURGH	CALDECOTT HALL	COSTESSEY PARK	CROMER (ROYAL)	DEREHAM	DISS	EAGLES	EATON	FAKENHAM	FELTWELL	GORLESTON	GREAT YARMOUTH & CAISTER	HUNSTANTON	KING'S LYNN
Dress Code Anything																															
Dress Code Casual		●			●			●			● ●						● ● ● ● ●		● ● ● ●												
Dress Code Formal																				●											
Golf Shop takes credit cards		●						●			● ●						● ● ● ●		● ● ● ●											●
Club House takes credit card		●						●			● ●						● ● ●		● ● ● ●											●
Youth Coaching Scheme		●			●			●									● ● ● ●		● ●											
Mobiles allowed in Club House		●									●						● ● ●													
Children allowed in Club House								●			●						●		● ●											●
Spectators Allowed				●				●									● ●		●												
Disabled Facilities		●						●			● ●						● ● ●		●											●
Disabled Toilets		●						●			● ●						● ● ●		●											●
Disabled Access		●						●			● ●						● ● ●		● ●											●
Satellite TV		●															●														●
TV Lounge		●						●			● ●						● ● ● ●		● ●											●
Snooker Room																			●												
Members Only Bar								●																							
Gym/Weights													●	●																	
Massage																															
Physiotherapy																															
Sauna/Solararium													●	●																	
Swimming Pool													●																		
Health Club																															
Accommodation																															
Hotel On Site																	●														
Visitors Car Park		●						●			● ●						● ● ● ●		● ● ● ●											●
Members Car Park		●			●			●			● ●						● ● ● ● ●		● ● ● ● ●											●
Practice Putting Green		●			●			●			● ●						● ● ● ●		● ● ● ●											●
Practice Bunkers		●			●			●									● ● ●		● ●											●
Practice Course								●									●		● ●											
Driving Range	●	●				● ●											● ●														
Conference Facility		●						●			●						●		● ● ●											●
Evening Functions		●						●									● ● ● ●		● ●											●
On Course Refreshments		●						●									●														
Bar Snacks	●	● ● ● ● ● ● ● ● ● ● ● ● ● ● ●														● ● ● ● ●		● ● ● ●											●
Restaurant Dinner		● ● ● ● ●														● ● ● ● ●		● ●											●
Restaurant Lunch		●						●			● ●						● ● ● ●		● ●											●
Restaurant Breakfast		●						●			● ●						● ● ●		●											●
Shoe Cleaning Service								●																							
Bag Drop Service								●																							
Guests Changing Rooms		● ● ● ● ● ● ● ● ● ● ● ● ● ●	●											● ● ● ● ●		● ● ● ● ●											●
Guests Showers		●			●			●			● ●						● ● ● ●		● ● ● ●											●
On Course Drinking Fountains					●			●																							
On Course Yardage Markers		●			●			●									● ● ● ●		● ● ● ●											●
Spike Bar		●						●			● ●																				●
Plastic Stud Fitting Service		●						●									● ●		● ●							● ●				
Plastic Studs Compulsory																															
Visitors Need Handicap Proof							●		●									●		●				●						●
Golf Clubs Hire		● ●						● ●		●		●			●					●			●			●		●	●
Caddy Hire																															
Shoe Hire		●																							●						
Buggy Hire	●	● ● ●				●								● ●		● ● ● ●		● ●										● ●	● ●
Trolley Hire	●	● ● ● ● ● ● ●		●						● ●		● ● ● ●		● ● ● ●		●		● ● ● ● ●		●	● ●	● ●
Regripping		●			●			●			●						● ● ●		● ● ●										●
Club Alterations		●			●			●									● ● ●		● ● ●										●

NORFOLK

Facilities Available at Golf Courses

Facility	MATTISHALL	MIDDLETON HALL	MUNDESLEY	NORFOLK	NORWICH (ROYAL)	RICHMOND PARK	RYSTON PARK	SHERINGHAM	SPROWSTON MANOR	SWAFFHAM	THETFORD	WENSUM VALLEY	WEST NORFOLK (ROYAL)	WESTON PARK	BRAMPTON HEATH	COLD ASHBY	COLLINGTREE PARK	CORBY PUBLIC	DAVENTRY & DISTRICT	DELAPRE PARK GOLF COMPLEX	FARTHINGSTONE	KETTERING	KINGSTHORPE	NORTHAMPTON	NORTHAMPTONSHIRE COUNTY	OVERSTONE PARK	PYTCHLEY GOLF LODGE	RUSHDEN	STAVERTON PARK	WELLINGBOROUGH	WHITTLEBURY PARK
Dress Code Anything																															
Dress Code Casual	●	●		●					●	●		●			●	●	●	●		●				●	●	●			●		●
Dress Code Formal							●																						●		
Golf Shop takes credit cards	●			●					●			●	●		●	●	●	●		●				●	●			●			●
Club House takes credit card	●	●							●			●	●		●	●	●	●		●				●	●						●
Youth Coaching Scheme		●					●					●			●	●								●	●	●					●
Mobiles allowed in Club House									●			●																			●
Children allowed in Club House	●			●		●			●			●			●	●								●	●	●	●				●
Spectators Allowed					●		●					●			●	●															
Disabled Facilities		●										●				●										●					
Disabled Toilets	●	●										●				●										●		●			
Disabled Access												●				●										●					●
Satellite TV									●			●		●	●	●			●							●					●
TV Lounge	●	●				●			●			●	●	●	●	●		●						●	●						
Snooker Room												●				●															
Members Only Bar																															
Gym/Weights						●						●														●			●		
Massage												●														●					
Physiotherapy												●		●																	
Sauna/Solarium												●														●			●		
Swimming Pool												●														●			●		
Health Club												●														●					
Accommodation						●						●									●					●					
Hotel On Site									●			●																			
Visitors Car Park	●	●					●					●			●	●	●	●		●				●	●	●		●	●		●
Members Car Park	●	●					●					●			●	●	●	●		●				●	●	●		●	●	●	
Practice Putting Green	●	●		●		●						●	●		●	●	●	●		●				●	●				●		●
Practice Bunkers	●	●		●								●			●	●	●			●								●	●		●
Practice Course				●		●		●				●	●		●	●	●			●						●				●	●
Driving Range	●	●							●			●	●		●	●	●			●				●					●		●
Conference Facility			●		●	●			●			●		●	●		●			●				●						●	●
Evening Functions			●		●			●				●		●	●		●			●				●						●	●
On Course Refreshments															●					●											
Bar Snacks	●	●	●	●	●	●	●	●	●	●	●	●	●	●	●	●	●	●	●	●	●	●	●	●	●				●	●	●
Restaurant Dinner	●	●		●		●			●			●	●		●	●	●	●		●				●	●				●	●	●
Restaurant Lunch	●	●		●	●	●			●			●	●		●	●	●	●		●				●	●				●	●	●
Restaurant Breakfast	●	●		●	●	●			●			●	●		●	●				●				●					●	●	●
Shoe Cleaning Service									●							●													●		
Bag Drop Service																				●											
Guests Changing Rooms	●	●	●	●	●	●	●	●	●	●		●	●		●	●	●	●		●		●		●	●	●		●	●	●	●
Guests Showers	●	●				●			●			●			●	●		●							●			●	●		●
On Course Drinking Fountains																			●										●		●
On Course Yardage Markers	●			●					●			●	●		●	●	●	●		●				●				●	●		●
Spike Bar	●			●					●			●			●										●	●			●		
Plastic Stud Fitting Service	●	●		●			●		●			●			●										●	●	●				
Plastic Studs Compulsory																															
Visitors Need Handicap Proof		●			●				●			●													●	●					
Golf Clubs Hire	●				●	●			●	●	●	●			●	●	●			●		●		●	●			●	●		●
Caddy Hire																															
Shoe Hire																										●					●
Buggy Hire			●	●					●			●					●			●						●				●	●
Trolley Hire	●	●	●	●	●		●		●		●	●	●		●	●	●			●			●	●			●	●	●		●
Regripping	●	●		●					●			●			●	●	●	●		●				●					●		●
Club Alterations	●	●		●					●			●			●	●	●			●				●					●		●

Facilities Available at Golf Courses

Golf Courses by County

NORTHUMBERLAND: ALLENDALE, ALNMOUTH, ALNMOUTH VILLAGE, ALNWICK, ARCOT HALL, BAMBURGH CASTLE, BEDLINGTONSHIRE, BELFORD, BELLINGHAM, BERWICK, BLYTH, BURGHAM, DUNSTANBURGH CASTLE, HAGGERSTON CASTLE, HEXHAM, LINDEN HALL, LONGHIRST HALL, MAGDALENE FIELDS, MORPETH, NEWBIGGIN, PRUDHOE, ROTHBURY, SEAHOUSES, SLALEY HALL GOLF COURSE, STOCKSFIELD, SWARLAND HALL, TYNEDALE, WARKWORTH, WOOLER

NOTTINGHAMSHIRE: BEESTON FIELDS

Facility	ALLENDALE	ALNMOUTH	ALNMOUTH VILLAGE	ALNWICK	ARCOT HALL	BAMBURGH CASTLE	BEDLINGTONSHIRE	BELFORD	BELLINGHAM	BERWICK	BLYTH	BURGHAM	DUNSTANBURGH CASTLE	HAGGERSTON CASTLE	HEXHAM	LINDEN HALL	LONGHIRST HALL	MAGDALENE FIELDS	MORPETH	NEWBIGGIN	PRUDHOE	ROTHBURY	SEAHOUSES	SLALEY HALL	STOCKSFIELD	SWARLAND HALL	TYNEDALE	WARKWORTH	WOOLER	BEESTON FIELDS
Dress Code Anything																														
Dress Code Casual									●	●	●		●		●	●		●	●						○			●	●	
Dress Code Formal													●												○			●	●	
Golf Shop takes credit cards										●			●			●			●					● ●						
Club House takes credit card													●			●			●											
Youth Coaching Scheme									●				●			●			●									●	●	
Mobiles allowed in Club House													●			●			●											
Children allowed in Club House									●	●	●		●			●			●						○			●	● ●	
Spectators Allowed															●													●	●	
Disabled Facilities																			●										●	
Disabled Toilets																			●										●	
Disabled Access																			●										●	
Satellite TV									●				●			●			●						○				●	
TV Lounge									●	●	●														○			●	● ●	
Snooker Room															●			●							○					
Members Only Bar																														
Gym/Weights																●								●						
Massage																●														
Physiotherapy																●														
Sauna/Solararium																●														
Swimming Pool													●			●														
Health Club																●								●						
Accommodation	●																	●						●						
Hotel On Site																●	●							●						
Visitors Car Park									●	●	●		●			●		●	●					●			●	● ●		
Members Car Park									●	●	●		●			●		●	●					●			●	● ●		
Practice Putting Green									●	●			●			●	●	●	●					●			●	● ●		
Practice Bunkers																●		●	●					●			●	●		
Practice Course																●			●					●						
Driving Range									●	●			●			●			●					●						
Conference Facility																						●								
Evening Functions											●					●			●									●		
On Course Refreshments													●		●															
Bar Snacks	●	●	●	●	●	●	●	●	●	●	●	●	●		●	●	●	●	●	●	●	●	●	●	●	●	●	●	●	●
Restaurant Dinner	●	●	●								●				●	●			●					●						●
Restaurant Lunch			●								●					●			●					●						
Restaurant Breakfast									●	●			●			●			●					●	●		●			
Shoe Cleaning Service																														
Bag Drop Service																														
Guests Changing Rooms	●	●	●	●	●	●	●	●	●	●	●	●	●		●	●	●	●	●	●	●	●	●	●	●	●	●	●	●	●
Guests Showers									●	●			●			●		●	●				●				●	●		
On Course Drinking Fountains									●				●															●		
On Course Yardage Markers									●				●			●		●	●					●				●	●	
Spike Bar															●															
Plastic Stud Fitting Service																														
Plastic Studs Compulsory																														
Visitors Need Handicap Proof																														
Golf Clubs Hire		●			●		●	●	●			●	●	●	●	●						●			●	○	●	●	●	●
Caddy Hire															●															
Shoe Hire															●															
Buggy Hire		●					●		●	●		●	●	●	●									●	○				●	
Trolley Hire		●			●		●	●	●	●		●	●	●										●	○	●		●		●
Regripping									●	●			●		●	●		●							●		●			
Club Alterations										●			●		●				●								●			

Facilities Available at Golf Courses

Golf Courses by County

Facility	BONDHAY GOLF & FISHING CLUB	BRAMCOTE HILLS	BRIERLEY FOREST	BULWELL FOREST	CHILWELL MANOR	COLLEGE PINES	COTGRAVE PLACE	COXMOOR	EDWALTON MUNICIPAL	KILTON FOREST	LINDRICK	MANSFIELD WOODHOUSE	MAPPERLEY	NEWARK	NORWOOD PARK	NOTTINGHAM CITY
Dress Code Anything																
Dress Code Casual		●	●	●	●	●	●		●	●		●			●	
Dress Code Formal											●					
Golf Shop takes credit cards				●	●		●		●	●	●				●	
Club House takes credit card							●		●			●				
Youth Coaching Scheme				●	●				●	●	●				●	
Mobiles allowed in Club House			●			●	●			●		●			●	
Children allowed in Club House			●	●	●		●		●	●	●	●			●	
Spectators Allowed			●						●	●						
Disabled Facilities			●	●					●	●		●				
Disabled Toilets			●			●	●		●	●	●	●				
Disabled Access			●			●	●		●	●		●				
Satellite TV							●			●		●				
TV Lounge			●	●	●		●		●	●	●	●				
Snooker Room											●					
Members Only Bar																
Gym/Weights																
Massage																
Physiotherapy																
Sauna/Solararium																
Swimming Pool																
Health Club																
Accommodation																
Hotel On Site																
Visitors Car Park		●	●	●	●	●	●		●	●	●	●			●	
Members Car Park			●	●	●	●	●		●	●	●	●			●	
Practice Putting Green				●	●	●	●		●	●	●				●	
Practice Bunkers					●	●			●	●	●				●	
Practice Course			●		●				●	●	●				●	
Driving Range	●					●	●		●						●	
Conference Facility	●						●									
Evening Functions				●	●		●		●	●		●				
On Course Refreshments							●									
Bar Snacks	●	●	●	●	●	●		●	●	●	●	●	●	●	●	●
Restaurant Dinner	●			●	●	●	●	●	●	●	●	●	●	●		●
Restaurant Lunch				●	●	●	●		●	●	●	●				
Restaurant Breakfast				●	●	●	●		●	●	●	●				
Shoe Cleaning Service			●													
Bag Drop Service																
Guests Changing Rooms	●		●	●	●	●	●	●	●	●	●		●	●	●	●
Guests Showers					●	●	●		●		●				●	
On Course Drinking Fountains											●					
On Course Yardage Markers			●	●	●	●	●		●		●				●	
Spike Bar			●			●	●					●				
Plastic Stud Fitting Service				●	●				●	●		●				
Plastic Studs Compulsory																
Visitors Need Handicap Proof					●						●					
Golf Clubs Hire	●	●	●	●		●			●	●	●	●	●		●	●
Caddy Hire											●					
Shoe Hire																
Buggy Hire	●					●	●		●	●	●		●		●	
Trolley Hire	●			●	●	●	●	●	●	●	●	●	●	●	●	●
Regripping				●	●	●	●		●	●	●	●			●	
Club Alterations				●	●	●	●		●	●	●	●			●	

Facility	NOTTS	OAKMERE PARK	RADCLIFFE-ON-TRENT	RAMSDALE PARK	RETFORD	RIVERSIDE	RUDDINGTON GRANGE	RUFFORD PARK GOLF CTRE	SHERWOOD FOREST	SOUTHWELL	SPRINGWATER	STANTON ON THE WOLDS	TRENT LOCK	WOLLATON PARK	WORKSOP
Dress Code Anything															
Dress Code Casual	●	●	●	●	●	●		●	●	●	●	●	●		
Dress Code Formal			●	●		●								●	●
Golf Shop takes credit cards	●	●	●	●	●	●		●	●	●	●	●	●	●	●
Club House takes credit card		●		●		●		●			●				
Youth Coaching Scheme	●	●	●	●	●	●		●	●	●		●	●	●	●
Mobiles allowed in Club House						●									
Children allowed in Club House		●	●	●	●	●		●	●	●	●	●	●	●	●
Spectators Allowed	●	●		●		●		●			●	●	●		
Disabled Facilities					●	●		●			●	●	●	●	
Disabled Toilets				●	●	●		●			●	●	●	●	
Disabled Access				●	●	●		●			●	●	●	●	
Satellite TV	●	●	●			●		●	●			●		●	
TV Lounge		●	●	●	●	●		●	●	●	●	●	●	●	●
Snooker Room									●	●		●			●
Members Only Bar															
Gym/Weights															
Massage															
Physiotherapy															
Sauna/Solararium															
Swimming Pool															
Health Club															
Accommodation										●					
Hotel On Site															
Visitors Car Park	●	●	●	●	●	●		●		●	●	●	●		●
Members Car Park	●	●	●		●	●		●		●	●	●	●	●	●
Practice Putting Green	●	●	●	●	●	●		●	●	●	●	●	●	●	●
Practice Bunkers	●		●	●	●	●		●	●	●	●	●	●	●	●
Practice Course			●		●	●		●	●			●		●	●
Driving Range	●	●		●		●		●			●		●		
Conference Facility		●		●			●		●				●		
Evening Functions	●	●	●	●	●	●		●	●	●	●	●	●	●	●
On Course Refreshments	●										●	●			
Bar Snacks	●	●	●	●	●	●	●	●	●	●	●	●	●	●	●
Restaurant Dinner	●	●	●	●	●	●	●	●	●	●	●	●	●	●	●
Restaurant Lunch	●	●	●	●	●	●	●	●	●	●	●	●	●	●	●
Restaurant Breakfast	●	●	●	●	●	●		●	●	●	●	●	●	●	●
Shoe Cleaning Service		●													
Bag Drop Service															
Guests Changing Rooms	●	●	●	●	●	●	●	●		●	●	●	●	●	●
Guests Showers	●	●	●	●	●	●		●		●	●	●	●	●	●
On Course Drinking Fountains	●							●				●			
On Course Yardage Markers	●	●		●	●			●	●	●	●	●	●	●	●
Spike Bar	●	●		●		●		●			●	●			
Plastic Stud Fitting Service	●	●	●	●	●	●		●	●	●	●	●	●	●	●
Plastic Studs Compulsory						●									
Visitors Need Handicap Proof	●		●									●			●
Golf Clubs Hire	●	●		●	●	●		●		●	●	●		●	
Caddy Hire	●					●									
Shoe Hire		●				●		●							
Buggy Hire	●	●		●	●			●			●	●	●		
Trolley Hire	●	●	●	●	●	●	●	●	●	●	●	●	●	●	●
Regripping	●	●	●	●	●	●		●	●	●	●	●	●	●	●
Club Alterations	●	●	●	●	●	●		●	●	●	●	●	●	●	●

Facilities Available at Golf Courses

Golf Courses by County

Columns (left to right):
1. ASPECT PARK
2. BADGEMORE PARK
3. BANBURY GOLF C'TRE
4. BICESTER GOLF & COUNTRY CLUB
5. BRAILES
6. BURFORD
7. CARSWELL
8. CHERWELL EDGE
9. CHIPPING NORTON
10. DRAYTON PARK
11. FARINGDON
12. FRILFORD HEATH
13. HADDEN HILL
14. HENLEY
15. HINKSEY HEIGHTS
16. HUNTERCOMBE
17. LYNEHAM
18. NORTH OXFORD
19. OXFORDSHIRE
20. RYE HILL
21. SOUTHFIELD
22. STUDLEY WOOD
23. TADMARTON HEATH
24. WATERSTOCK
25. WITNEY LAKES
26. GREETHAM VALLEY
27. RUTLAND WATER
28. ARSCOTT
29. BRIDGNORTH

County groupings: OXFORDSHIRE (columns 1–25), RUTLAND (columns 26–27), SHROPSHIRE (columns 28–29)

Facility	1	2	3	4	5	6	7	8	9	10	11	12	13	14	15	16	17	18	19	20	21	22	23	24	25	26	27	28	29
Dress Code Anything																											•		
Dress Code Casual			•					•	•			•	•	•		•	•	•			•		•		•		•		•
Dress Code Formal																•													
Golf Shop takes credit cards			•					•	•				•	•			•	•			•		•		•		•		•
Club House takes credit card			•					•	•				•	•			•	•			•		•		•		•	•	•
Youth Coaching Scheme			•					•	•			•					•	•			•		•		•		•	•	
Mobiles allowed in Club House			•					•	•		•														•		•		
Children allowed in Club House			•					•	•			•	•	•			•	•			•		•		•		•		•
Spectators Allowed			•					•	•			•	•	•											•				•
Disabled Facilities												•													•		•		
Disabled Toilets												•													•		•		
Disabled Access												•													•		•		
Satellite TV			•						•							•	•				•				•		•		
TV Lounge									•							•	•								•		•		
Snooker Room																									•				•
Members Only Bar																									•				
Gym/Weights								•																	•				
Massage								•																	•				
Physiotherapy								•																	•				
Sauna/Solararium								•																	•				
Swimming Pool								•																	•				
Health Club								•																	•				
Accommodation		•						•																	•				
Hotel On Site								•																	•				
Visitors Car Park	•							•	•			•	•	•		•	•	•			•		•		•		•		•
Members Car Park	•		•					•	•			•	•	•		•	•	•			•		•		•		•	•	•
Practice Putting Green	•		•									•	•	•		•	•	•			•		•	•	•		•	•	•
Practice Bunkers	•											•	•	•		•	•	•			•		•				•		•
Practice Course								•				•															•		
Driving Range	•							•	•		•					•					•	•	•	•	•		•		
Conference Facility	•	•		•			•	•		•		•			•		•			•	•	•	• •				•		
Evening Functions		•						•	•			•			•		•				•		•				•		•
On Course Refreshments		•										•	•						•				•				•		
Bar Snacks	•	•	•	•	•			•	•		•	•	•	•	•	•	•	•	•	•	•	•	•	•	•		•	•	•
Restaurant Dinner	•	•						•	•			•	•	•		•	•	•			•		•		•		•		•
Restaurant Lunch	•	•						•	•			•	•	•		•	•	•			•		•		•		•		•
Restaurant Breakfast	•	•						•	•			•	•			•	•	•					•		• •				•
Shoe Cleaning Service																													
Bag Drop Service																													
Guests Changing Rooms	•	•		•	•	•	•	•	•	•		•	•		•	•	•		•	•	•		•	• •		•		•
Guests Showers								•	•			•	•			•		•			•		•		•		•		•
On Course Drinking Fountains												•																	
On Course Yardage Markers			•					•				•				•		•			•		•		•		•		
Spike Bar			•					•				•									•				•		•		
Plastic Stud Fitting Service			•					•								•		•			•		•		•		•		
Plastic Studs Compulsory								•																					
Visitors Need Handicap Proof												•				•									•				
Golf Clubs Hire	•	•	•			•	•		•	•			•	•		•	•	•	•	•	•	•	•	•	•		•		•
Caddy Hire																													
Shoe Hire								•																					
Buggy Hire	•	•	•					•			•	•	•			•			•		•		•		•		•		•
Trolley Hire	•	•	•	•	•			•	•		•	•	•	•		•	•	•	•	•	•		•	•	•		•		•
Regripping		•						•	•			•	•	•		•	•	•			•		•		•		•		•
Club Alterations		•						•	•			•	•	•		•	•	•			•		•		•		•		•

Facilities Available at Golf Courses

Golf Courses by County	Dress Code Anything	Dress Code Casual	Dress Code Formal	Golf Shop takes credit cards	Club House takes credit card	Youth Coaching Scheme	Mobiles allowed in Club House	Children allowed in Club House	Spectators Allowed	Disabled Facilities	Disabled Toilets	Disabled Access	Satellite TV	TV Lounge	Snooker Room	Members Only Bar	Gym/Weights	Massage	Physiotherapy	Sauna/Solararium	Swimming Pool	Health Club	Accommodation	Hotel On Site	Visitors Car Park	Members Car Park	Practice Putting Green	Practice Bunkers	Practice Course	Driving Range	Conference Facility	Evening Functions	On Course Refreshments	Bar Snacks	Restaurant Dinner	Restaurant Lunch	Restaurant Breakfast	Shoe Cleaning Service	Bag Drop Service	Guests Changing Rooms	Guests Showers	On Course Drinking Fountains	On Course Yardage Markers	Spike Bar	Plastic Stud Fitting Service	Plastic Studs Compulsory	Visitors Need Handicap Proof	Golf Clubs Hire	Caddy Hire	Shoe Hire	Buggy Hire	Trolley Hire	Regripping	Club Alterations
BROW		●					●	●		●	●	●													●		●	●				●		●	●	●	●			●	●		●					●		●			●	●
CHURCH STRETTON		●		●	●	●				●	●	●		●	●										●	●	●	●					●	●	●	●	●			●	●	●	●	●	●			●		●	●	●	●	●
CLEOBURY MORTIMER																							●							●	●			●	●	●				●								●			●	●		
HAWKSTONE PARK																	●			●			●							●	●			●		●				●								●			●	●		
HILL VALLEY																							●											●		●				●												●		
LILLESHALL HALL																																		●						●								●				●		
LLANYMYNECH																																		●	●					●												●		
LUDLOW																																		●		●				●							●					●		
MARKET DRAYTON																																		●	●	●				●												●		
MEOLE BRACE																																		●	●					●												●		
MILE END																																		●	●	●				●												●		
OSWESTRY		●		●			●	●						●	●										●	●	●	●				●		●	●	●				●								●		●		●	●	●
SEVEN MEADOWS		●		●		●	●	●						●	●										●	●	●	●		●		●	●	●	●	●				●			●					●			●	●	●	●
SHIFNAL																									●	●	●			●				●	●					●			●	●	●	●		●		●	●	●		
SHREWSBURY		●		●				●						●	●										●	●	●	●		●	●	●		●	●	●	●			●			●				●	●		●	●	●	●	●
SHROPSHIRE																											●	●		●	●			●						●							●	●			●	●		
TELFORD		●						●															●		●		●	●		●	●	●		●						●			●				●	●			●	●		
WELSH BORDER GOLF COMPLEX																									●		●	●												●								●			●	●		
WORFIELD																											●							●						●											●	●		
WREKIN		●		●						●	●	●	●	●	●	●				●	●		●				●	●			●	●		●	●	●	●			●			●										●	●
SOMERSET																																																						
BREAN		●		●	●		●	●		●	●	●			●										●	●	●	●	●	●	●	●		●	●	●	●			●	●							●		●	●	●	●	●
BURNHAM & BERROW		●							●														●				●	●						●						●	●							●		●		●		
CANNINGTON		●		●	●	●	●	●	●	●	●	●		●	●								●				●	●	●	●				●	●	●				●			●					●		●		●	●	●
ENMORE PARK																											●	●	●					●						●								●				●		
HALSTOCK		●						●	●	●	●	●		●											●		●	●	●			●		●						●			●					●		●		●	●	
ISLE OF WEDMORE																											●	●						●						●								●				●		
LONG SUTTON		●																									●	●	●	●		●		●						●								●		●	●	●		
MINEHEAD & WEST SOMERSET																									●		●	●						●						●	●							●			●	●		
OAKE MANOR																											●	●		●				●						●			●		●			●			●	●		
TAUNTON & PICKERIDGE				●			●	●		●	●	●		●													●	●		●				●		●				●			●					●			●	●	●	●
TAUNTON VALE		●	●	●				●		●	●	●	●														●	●		●		●		●	●		●							●				●		●	●	●		

Facilities Available at Golf Courses

Facility	VIVARY PARK	WELLS	WHEATHILL	WINCANTON	WINDWHISTLE	YEOVIL	SOMERSET (NORTH)	CLEVEDON	WESTON	WORLEBURY	STAFFORDSHIRE	ALSAGER	BARLASTON	BEAU DESERT	BRANSTON	BROCTON HALL	BURSLEM	BURTON ON TRENT	CANNOCK PARK	CHASE	CRAYTHORNE	DRAYTON PARK	GOLDENHILL	GREENWAY HALL	INGESTRE PARK	IZAAK WALTON	KEELE MUNICIPAL	LEEK	NEWCASTLE-UNDER-LYME	SEEDY MILL	ST. THOMAS PRIORY	STAFFORD CASTLE
Dress Code Anything		●																														
Dress Code Casual	●			●	●	●			●							●	●			●												
Dress Code Formal					●	●																										
Golf Shop takes credit cards	●	●		●	●	●			●							●	●			●	●											●
Club House takes credit card		●		●	●	●										●	●			●	●											●
Youth Coaching Scheme					●	●										●	●															
Mobiles allowed in Club House	●	●		●												●																
Children allowed in Club House	●	●														●	●						●									
Spectators Allowed				●	●				●							●	●						●									
Disabled Facilities	●															●				●	●	●										
Disabled Toilets	●															●				●	●	●										●
Disabled Access	●															●				●	●	●										●
Satellite TV	●	●				●			●							●				●												
TV Lounge	●	●		●	●	●			●							●	●			●	●											
Snooker Room	●				●											●																
Members Only Bar																																
Gym/Weights																●				●									●			
Massage																●																
Physiotherapy																																
Sauna/Solararium																●				●										●		
Swimming Pool																●				●										●		
Health Club																●														●		
Accommodation																																
Hotel On Site																																
Visitors Car Park	●	●		●	●				●							●				●	●											
Members Car Park	●	●		●	●				●							●				●	●											
Practice Putting Green	●	●		●	●	●			●				●			●				●	●		●									
Practice Bunkers	●	●		●	●											●				●												
Practice Course				●	●				●							●																
Driving Range		●			●	●										●							●	●				●		●		
Conference Facility									●					●		●							●	●								
Evening Functions	●	●														●																
On Course Refreshments	●															●																
Bar Snacks	●	●	●			●		●	●	●		●	●	●	●	●	●	●	●	●	●	●	●	●	●	●	●	●	●	●	●	●
Restaurant Dinner	●	●	●		●			●	●				●	●	●	●	●	●	●	●	●		●		●				●		●	●
Restaurant Lunch	●	●	●		●					●			●	●		●				●	●							●				●
Restaurant Breakfast	●	●														●	●			●								●				
Shoe Cleaning Service																																
Bag Drop Service																																
Guests Changing Rooms	●	●	●		●	●			●			●			●	●	●	●	●	●	●		●		●			●	●	●	●	●
Guests Showers	●	●		●	●				●							●	●	●		●	●		●									
On Course Drinking Fountains				●					●							●																
On Course Yardage Markers				●	●	●										●				●			●									
Spike Bar	●		●		●											●				●												
Plastic Stud Fitting Service					●											●				●												
Plastic Studs Compulsory									●							●				●												
Visitors Need Handicap Proof						●								●	●																	●
Golf Clubs Hire	●	●	●	●	●	●		●				●	●		●	●		●	●	●	●						●			●	●	●
Caddy Hire																																
Shoe Hire																●																
Buggy Hire	●	●	●					●	●							●							●						●	●		●
Trolley Hire	●	●	●	●	●			●	●							●	●		●	●	●		●					●	●	●		●
Regripping	●	●		●	●											●	●			●	●											●
Club Alterations	●	●		●	●											●	●			●	●											

Golf Courses by County

www.hccgolfworld.com

Facilities Available at Golf Courses

Facility \ Golf Courses by County	STONE	TAMWORTH MUNICIPAL	TRENTHAM	TRENTHAM PARK	UTTOXETER	WESTWOOD	WHISTON HALL	WHITTINGTON HEATH	WOLSTANTON	SUFFOLK	ALDEBURGH	ALNESBOURNE PRIORY	BECCLES	BRETTVALE	BUNGAY & WAVENEY VALLEY	BURY ST EDMUNDS	CLARE PARK LAKE	CRETINGHAM	DIP FARM	FELIXSTOWE FERRY	FLEMPTON	FYNN VALLEY	HALESWORTH	HAVERHILL	HIGH LODGE	HINTLESHAM HALL	IPSWICH	LINKS	NEWTON GREEN	ROOKERY PARK	RUSHMERE	SECKFORD
Dress Code Anything															•		•							•								
Dress Code Casual				•	•	•								•		•			•	•	•	•	•						•			
Dress Code Formal											•							•				•				•				•		•
Golf Shop takes credit cards						•	•							•		•		•		•		•	•			•	•					
Club House takes credit card	•													•		•				•		•			•	•		•				•
Youth Coaching Scheme					•									•		•		•		•		•	•			•						
Mobiles allowed in Club House														•								•				•						
Children allowed in Club House				•	•	•					•			•		•		•		•	•	•	•			•	•			•		•
Spectators Allowed											•									•		•				•						•
Disabled Facilities						•					•					•				•		•		•	•	•						
Disabled Toilets						•												• •		•				•		•						
Disabled Access						•														•		•				•						
Satellite TV	•													•					•			•				•						•
TV Lounge	•			•		•					•					•		•				•				• •						•
Snooker Room	•		•													•		•				•				•						
Members Only Bar																																
Gym/Weights																										•						•
Massage																										•						
Physiotherapy																										•						
Sauna/Solararium																										•						•
Swimming Pool													•					•				•				•						
Health Club																										•						
Accommodation													•			•		•				•				•						
Hotel On Site																						•				•						
Visitors Car Park				•	•						•					•		•		•	•	•	•	•	•	•	•			•	•	•
Members Car Park				•	•	•	•				•					•		•		•	•	•	•	•	•	•	•			•	•	•
Practice Putting Green				•	•	•	•				•					•		•		•	•	•	•	•	•	•	•		•	•	•	•
Practice Bunkers				•	•						•					•		•		•		•			•	•						•
Practice Course					•						•					•		•				•			•	•						
Driving Range		•														•		•				• •				•						•
Conference Facility	•			•							•					•		•				• •		•		•						
Evening Functions				•	•	•					•					•		•		•		• •	•			•				•		•
On Course Refreshments																						•										
Bar Snacks	•	•	•	•	•	•	•	•	•		•	•	•	•		•	•	•		•	•	•	•	•	•	•	•	•	•	•	•	•
Restaurant Dinner	•	•	•		•	•					•	•				•		•		•		• •		•		•		•		•	•	•
Restaurant Lunch	•		•		•	•		•			•					•		•		•		• •		•		•		•		•	•	•
Restaurant Breakfast	•			•		•					•					•		•				•		•		•		•		•	•	•
Shoe Cleaning Service																																
Bag Drop Service																										•						
Guests Changing Rooms	•	•	•	•	•	•	•	•	•		•	•	•	•		•	•	•		•	•	•	•	•	•	•	•	•	•	•	•	•
Guests Showers				•	•	•					•					•		•		•	•	•	•	•		•				•	•	•
On Course Drinking Fountains				•	•	•					•					•		•		•		•	•	•		•		•		•	•	•
On Course Yardage Markers				•	•	•					•					•		•		•	•	•	•	•		•	•	•		•	•	•
Spike Bar																		•				•			•		•					
Plastic Stud Fitting Service				•	•													•				•			•		•					
Plastic Studs Compulsory					•													•														
Visitors Need Handicap Proof				•		•					•									•	•				•	•						
Golf Clubs Hire		•	•			•	•				•	•	•	•		•	•	•		•		•						•	•	•		•
Caddy Hire																																
Shoe Hire																																
Buggy Hire		•	•											•		•																
Trolley Hire	•	•	•	•	•	•	•				•	•	•			•	•	•		•		• •	•			•	•	•		•	•	•
Regripping				•	•	•										•		•				• •				•		•		•	•	•
Club Alterations				•	•	•										•		•		•		• •				•		•		•	•	•

Facilities Available at Golf Courses

Golf Courses by County	SOUTHWOLD	STOWMARKET	SUFFOLK GOLF	THORPENESS	UFFORD PARK	WALDRINGFIELD HEATH	WOODBRIDGE	WORLINGTON & NEWMARKET (ROYAL)	SURREY	ABBEYMOOR	ADDINGTON	ADDINGTON COURT GOLF CLUB	ADDINGTON PALACE	ASHFORD MANOR	BANSTEAD DOWNS	BETCHWORTH PARK	BOWENHURST	BRAMLEY	BROADWATER PARK	BURHILL	CAMBERLEY HEATH	CHESSINGTON	CHIDDINGFOLD	CHIPSTEAD	CHOBHAM	CLANDON REGIS	COULSDON MANOR	CRANLEIGH	CROHAM HURST	CUDDINGTON	DORKING
Dress Code Anything																									●						
Dress Code Casual	●					●								●	●		●		●	●	●								●		
Dress Code Formal												●	●		●			●		●	●	●								●	
Golf Shop takes credit cards	●	●				●	●				●	●		●		●	●	●	●	●	●							●		
Club House takes credit card		●				●	●					●			●	●	●	●	●	●							●			
Youth Coaching Scheme	●	●									●				●	●	●	●										●		
Mobiles allowed in Club House		●										●			●	●	●													
Children allowed in Club House	●	●					●				●	●		●	●	●	●											●		
Spectators Allowed											●	●		●	●															
Disabled Facilities	●	●									●	●		●	●	●												●		
Disabled Toilets	●	●									●	●		●	●	●														
Disabled Access	●	●									●	●		●	●	●												●		
Satellite TV		●										●	●															●	●	
TV Lounge	●	●									●	●		●	●	●		●	●	●								●	●	
Snooker Room											●	●		●																
Members Only Bar																														
Gym/Weights		●	●																								●	●		
Massage		●																												
Physiotherapy		●																												
Sauna/Solararium		●	●																							●	●	●		
Swimming Pool		●																										●		
Health Club		●																												
Accommodation		●	●	●																								●		
Hotel On Site		●																												
Visitors Car Park	●					●	●				●	●		●	●	●	●	●										●		
Members Car Park		●					●				●	●		●	●	●	●	●	●									●		
Practice Putting Green	●	●					●					●		●	●	●	●	●										●		
Practice Bunkers	●	●					●						●			●	●											●		
Practice Course	●																											●		
Driving Range		●	●	●			●			●			●		●	●	●	●	●											
Conference Facility			●	●							●					●	●	●		●	●	●								
Evening Functions	●	●											●	●			●	●										●		
On Course Refreshments																														
Bar Snacks	●	●	●	●	●	●	●			●	●	●	●	●	●	●	●	●	●	●	●			●				●	●	●
Restaurant Dinner	●	●	●	●		●					●	●	●	●	●	●	●				●							●	●	●
Restaurant Lunch	●	●		●							●	●	●	●	●	●	●											●	●	●
Restaurant Breakfast	●	●				●					●	●		●														●	●	
Shoe Cleaning Service											●	●				●												●		
Bag Drop Service												●																		
Guests Changing Rooms	●	●	●	●	●	●				●	●	●	●	●	●	●	●	●			●			●				●	●	●
Guests Showers		●				●	●				●	●																●		
On Course Drinking Fountains																												●		
On Course Yardage Markers		●				●					●	●		●	●	●	●											●		
Spike Bar		●										●					●											●		
Plastic Stud Fitting Service		●									●	●		●	●	●												●		
Plastic Studs Compulsory																														
Visitors Need Handicap Proof		●				●	●				●	●		●														●		
Golf Clubs Hire	●	●			●				●	●					●	●	●											●	●	●
Caddy Hire																														
Shoe Hire	●																												●	
Buggy Hire		●	●	●	●																								●	
Trolley Hire	●	●								●	●	●		●	●	●	●							●			●	●	●	
Regripping	●	●				●	●					●	●		●	●	●											●	●	
Club Alterations	●	●				●	●				●	●	●	●	●	●	●											●	●	

GolfWorld Directory

Facilities Available at Golf Courses

Golf Courses by County	DRIFT	DUKES DENE	EFFINGHAM	EPSOM	FARNHAM	FARNHAM PARK PAR 3	FOXHILLS GOLF	GATTON MANOR	GOAL FARM	GUILDFORD	HANKLEY COMMON	HERSHAM VILLAGE	HINDHEAD	HOEBRIDGE	HORNE PARK	HORTON PARK GOLF	HURTMORE	KINGSWOOD	LALEHAM	LEATHERHEAD	LIMPSFIELD CHART	LINGFIELD PARK	MALDEN	MID-SURREY (ROYAL)	MILFORD GOLF CLUB	MITCHAM	MOORE PLACE	NEW ZEALAND	NORTH DOWNS	OAK PARK GOLF CLUB	OAKS SPORTS CTRE	PACHESHAM PARK GOLF CTRE
Dress Code Anything																•																
Dress Code Casual	•		•	•	•		•		•			•	•		•	•	•					•		•			•		•	•		
Dress Code Formal																																
Golf Shop takes credit cards			•	•	•		•					•	•		•	•	•	•												•		
Club House takes credit card	•		•	•								•	•		•	•	•	•									•			•		
Youth Coaching Scheme	•		•	•									•		•	•																
Mobiles allowed in Club House									•				•			•	•													•		
Children allowed in Club House	•		•	•								•	•		•	•	•	•									•			•		
Spectators Allowed	•															•																
Disabled Facilities			•																													
Disabled Toilets			•	•	•																											
Disabled Access			•	•	•				•				•			•	•										•			•		
Satellite TV	•															•														•		
TV Lounge	•		•	•			•		•				•			•	•	•									•			•		
Snooker Room			•	•												•																
Members Only Bar																•																
Gym/Weights							•																									
Massage							•																									
Physiotherapy							•																									
Sauna/Solararium							•																									
Swimming Pool							•																									
Health Club							•																						•			
Accommodation							•																									
Hotel On Site							•																									
Visitors Car Park	•		•	•								•	•		•	•	•	•				•					•			•		
Members Car Park	•		•	•								•	•		•	•	•	•												•		
Practice Putting Green	•	•	•										•		•		•									•	•			•		
Practice Bunkers	•	•	•									•				•		•													•	
Practice Course														•																		
Driving Range	•		•		•		•			•		•		•		•		•								•				•	•	•
Conference Facility	•	•		•			•		•							•	•									•				•	•	
Evening Functions	•			•													•									•				•		
On Course Refreshments																																
Bar Snacks	•	•	•	•	•	•	•	•	•	•	•	•	•	•	•	•	•	•	•	•	•	•	•	•	•	•	•	•	•	•	•	•
Restaurant Dinner	•		•	•	•		•					•	•		•	•	•	•									•			•		
Restaurant Lunch	•		•	•	•		•					•	•		•	•	•	•									•			•		
Restaurant Breakfast	•		•	•	•		•					•	•		•	•	•	•									•			•		
Shoe Cleaning Service			•													•																
Bag Drop Service																																
Guests Changing Rooms	•	•	•	•	•	•	•	•	•	•	•	•	•	•	•	•	•	•			•	•		•	•	•	•	•	•	•	•	
Guests Showers	•		•	•								•	•		•	•														•		
On Course Drinking Fountains	•		•	•																												
On Course Yardage Markers	•		•		•							•	•		•	•									•					•		
Spike Bar	•		•	•					•							•	•	•									•					
Plastic Stud Fitting Service	•															•	•	•									•					
Plastic Studs Compulsory	•																															
Visitors Need Handicap Proof			•					•								•					•						•					
Golf Clubs Hire	•	•	•	•		•	•	•		•				•	•			•				•		•			•			•	•	•
Caddy Hire																																
Shoe Hire	•												•			•	•										•					
Buggy Hire	•	•	•				•			•			•	•	•	•	•	•				•	•		•		•		•	•		
Trolley Hire	•	•	•	•		•	•			•			•	•	•	•	•	•	•				•		•		•		•	•		
Regripping	•		•	•	•										•	•							•				•			•		
Club Alterations	•		•	•	•										•	•							•				•					

Facilities Available at Golf Courses

Golf Courses by County

Columns (Golf Courses):
PENNYHILL PARK · PURLEY DOWNS · PUTTENHAM · PYRFORD GOLF CLUB · REDHILL & REIGATE · REDHILL GOLF CTRE · REIGATE HEATH · REIGATE HILL · RICHMOND · ROKER PARK · RUSPER · SANDOWN GOLF CTRE · SELSDON PARK · SHILLINGLEE PARK · SHIRLEY PARK · SILVERMERE GOLF COMPLEX · ST. GEORGES HILL · SUNBURY · SUNNINGDALE · SURBITON · SURREY GOLF & FITNESS · SUTTON GREEN · TANDRIDGE · THAMES DITTON & ESHER · TRADITIONS GOLF COURSE · TYRRELLS WOOD · WALTON HEATH · WENTWORTH CLUB · WEST BYFLEET · WEST HILL · WEST SURREY · WILDWOOD COUNTRY CLUB

Facilities (rows):
- Dress Code Anything
- Dress Code Casual
- Dress Code Formal
- Golf Shop takes credit cards
- Club House takes credit card
- Youth Coaching Scheme
- Mobiles allowed in Club House
- Children allowed in Club House
- Spectators Allowed
- Disabled Facilities
- Disabled Toilets
- Disabled Access
- Satellite TV
- TV Lounge
- Snooker Room
- Members Only Bar
- Gym/Weights
- Massage
- Physiotherapy
- Sauna/Solararium
- Swimming Pool
- Health Club
- Accommodation
- Hotel On Site
- Visitors Car Park
- Members Car Park
- Practice Putting Green
- Practice Bunkers
- Practice Course
- Driving Range
- Conference Facility
- Evening Functions
- On Course Refreshments
- Bar Snacks
- Restaurant Dinner
- Restaurant Lunch
- Restaurant Breakfast
- Shoe Cleaning Service
- Bag Drop Service
- Guests Changing Rooms
- Guests Showers
- On Course Drinking Fountains
- On Course Yardage Markers
- Spike Bar
- Plastic Stud Fitting Service
- Plastic Studs Compulsory
- Visitors Need Handicap Proof
- Golf Clubs Hire
- Caddy Hire
- Shoe Hire
- Buggy Hire
- Trolley Hire
- Regripping
- Club Alterations

FACILITIES AVAILABLE

Facilities Available at Golf Courses

Facilities (rows):

- Dress Code Anything
- Dress Code Casual
- Dress Code Formal
- Golf Shop takes credit cards
- Club House takes credit card
- Youth Coaching Scheme
- Mobiles allowed in Club House
- Children allowed in Club House
- Spectators Allowed
- Disabled Facilities
- Disabled Toilets
- Disabled Access
- Satellite TV
- TV Lounge
- Snooker Room
- Members Only Bar
- Gym/Weights
- Massage
- Physiotherapy
- Sauna/Solararium
- Swimming Pool
- Health Club
- Accommodation
- Hotel On Site
- Visitors Car Park
- Members Car Park
- Practice Putting Green
- Practice Bunkers
- Practice Course
- Driving Range
- Conference Facility
- Evening Functions
- On Course Refreshments
- Bar Snacks
- Restaurant Dinner
- Restaurant Lunch
- Restaurant Breakfast
- Shoe Cleaning Service
- Bag Drop Service
- Guests Changing Rooms
- Guests Showers
- On Course Drinking Fountains
- On Course Yardage Markers
- Spike Bar
- Plastic Stud Fitting Service
- Plastic Studs Compulsory
- Visitors Need Handicap Proof
- Golf Clubs Hire
- Caddy Hire
- Shoe Hire
- Buggy Hire
- Trolley Hire
- Regripping
- Club Alterations

Golf Courses by County (columns):

- WINDLERMERE
- WINDLESHAM
- WISLEY
- WOKING
- WOODCOTE PARK
- WORPLESDON
- SUSSEX (EAST)
- ASHDOWN FOREST
- ASHDOWN FOREST (ROYAL)
- BATTLE
- BOARS HEAD
- BRIGHTON & HOVE
- COODEN BEACH
- CROWBOROUGH BEACON
- DALE HILL
- DEWLANDS MANOR
- DYKE
- EAST BRIGHTON
- EAST SUSSEX NATIONAL
- EASTBOURNE (ROYAL)
- EASTBOURNE DOWNS
- EASTBOURNE GOLFING PARK
- HASTINGS
- HIGHWOODS
- HOLLINGBURY PARK
- HORAM PARK
- LEWES
- MID SUSSEX
- PEACEHAVEN
- PILTDOWN
- PYECOMBE
- RYE

Facilities Available at Golf Courses

England

FACILITIES AVAILABLE

The following table lists facilities available at golf courses in Sussex (East and West), listed alphabetically by course.

Facility	SEAFORD	SEAFORD HEAD	SEDLESCOMBE	WATERHALL	WELLSHURST	WEST HOVE	WILLINGDON	AVISFORD PARK	BOGNOR REGIS	BROOKLANDS PARK	BURGESS HILL	CHARTHAM PARK	CHICHESTER	COPTHORNE	COTTESMORE	COWDRAY PARK	CUCKFIELD	EFFINGHAM PARK	FOXBRIDGE	GOODWOOD	HAM MANOR	HASSOCKS	HAYWARDS HEATH	HILL BARN	HORSHAM GOLF	IFIELD	LITTLEHAMPTON GOLF	MANNINGS HEATH	PAXHILL PARK	PETWORTH	ROOKWOOD
Dress Code Anything											•													•	•					•	
Dress Code Casual	•		•	•	•	•	•	•	•			•	•					•	•	•	•	•								•	•
Dress Code Formal	•												•																		
Golf Shop takes credit cards	•		•		•	•	•	•	•		•	•					•	•	•	•	•		•	•		•			•	•	•
Club House takes credit card	•		•	•	•				•			•					•			•			•	•					•	•	•
Youth Coaching Scheme	•		•	•	•			•										•	•			•								•	
Mobiles allowed in Club House			•	•	•						•								•												
Children allowed in Club House			•	•	•	•	•	•	•			•						•	•	•		•	•						•	•	•
Spectators Allowed				•	•	•			•			•										•								•	•
Disabled Facilities	•		•		•	•			•			•						•	•	•		•	•							•	•
Disabled Toilets	•		•	•	•	•		•	•			•						•	•	•		•	•						•	•	•
Disabled Access	•		•		•	•		•	•			•						•	•	•		•	•						•	•	•
Satellite TV	•		•		•	•	•	•	•			•										•									•
TV Lounge	•		•	•	•	•		•	•			•										•							•	•	•
Snooker Room	•			•		•		•				•									•	•						•			
Members Only Bar												•																			
Gym/Weights			•		•											•					•							•			
Massage					•																•										
Physiotherapy					•																•										
Sauna/Solararium			•		•											•					•							•			
Swimming Pool					•																•										
Health Club			•		•																•										
Accommodation	•		•		•			•													•										•
Hotel On Site	•	•						•																							
Visitors Car Park	•	•	•	•	•	•	•	•	•		•	•					•	•	•	•	•	•	•		•		•	•	•	•	•
Members Car Park	•	•	•	•	•	•	•	•	•		•	•				•	•	•	•	•	•	•	•		•		•	•	•	•	•
Practice Putting Green	•			•	•	•	•	•	•			•					•	•	•	•	•	•			•		•	•	•	•	•
Practice Bunkers			•	•	•	•	•	•	•			•					•	•		•	•	•						•	•	•	•
Practice Course			•		•			•				•				•				•		•						•	•	•	•
Driving Range	•		•		•	•						•	•	•		•				•	•	•						•	•	•	•
Conference Facility	•		•		•							•			•	•			•	•											•
Evening Functions	•		•		•	•			•			•						•	•	•		•							•	•	•
On Course Refreshments	•		•		•				•			•						•				•							•	•	•
Bar Snacks	•		•	•	•	•	•	•	•		•	•			•	•	•	•	•	•	•	•	•		•		•	•	•	•	•
Restaurant Dinner	•		•		•	•		•	•			•			•	•	•	•	•	•	•	•			•		•	•	•	•	•
Restaurant Lunch	•		•	•	•	•	•	•	•		•	•			•	•	•	•	•	•	•	•			•		•	•	•	•	•
Restaurant Breakfast	•		•	•		•			•			•					•	•	•	•	•	•			•		•	•	•	•	•
Shoe Cleaning Service						•						•										•									
Bag Drop Service																•															
Guests Changing Rooms	•	•	•	•	•	•	•	•	•		•	•				•	•	•	•	•	•	•			•		•	•	•	•	•
Guests Showers	•		•	•	•	•	•	•	•		•	•				•	•	•	•	•	•	•			•		•	•	•	•	•
On Course Drinking Fountains	•		•	•	•	•			•			•						•	•	•		•						•		•	•
On Course Yardage Markers	•		•	•	•	•	•	•	•			•					•	•	•	•	•	•			•		•	•	•	•	•
Spike Bar			•	•	•	•	•	•				•					•	•		•	•							•			•
Plastic Stud Fitting Service	•		•		•	•			•			•						•	•			•							•		•
Plastic Studs Compulsory																															
Visitors Need Handicap Proof	•																	•		•		•							•		
Golf Clubs Hire	•		•	•	•	•	•	•	•		•	•					•	•	•		•	•			•		•	•	•	•	•
Caddy Hire				•																•											
Shoe Hire																				•		•									
Buggy Hire	•		•	•	•	•			•			•		•	•	•		•			•							•		•	•
Trolley Hire	•		•	•	•	•	•	•	•			•					•	•	•		•	•			•		•	•	•	•	•
Regripping	•		•	•	•	•	•	•	•			•					•	•		•	•	•			•		•	•	•	•	•
Club Alterations	•		•	•	•	•	•	•	•			•					•	•		•	•	•			•		•	•	•	•	•

Golf Courses by County

SUSSEX (WEST)

Facilities Available at Golf Courses

Facility	RUSTINGTON	SELSEY	SINGING HILLS	SLINFOLD PARK	TILGATE FOREST	WEST CHILTINGTON	WEST SUSSEX	WORTHING	BACKWORTH	BOLDON	ELEMORE	GARESFIELD	GEORGE WASHINGTON	GOSFORTH	HEWORTH	HOBSON	HOUGHTON LE SPRING	NEWCASTLE	NEWCASTLE UNITED	NORTHUMBERLAND	PARKLANDS	PONTELAND	RAVENSWORTH	RYHOPE	RYTON	SOUTH SHIELDS	TYNEMOUTH	TYNESIDE	WALLSEND	WEARSIDE	WESTERHOPE
Dress Code Anything																															
Dress Code Casual	●	●			●	●		●																							
Dress Code Formal			●				●																								
Golf Shop takes credit cards	●		●		●	●	●	●																							
Club House takes credit card					●	●																									
Youth Coaching Scheme		●			●	●																									
Mobiles allowed in Club House	●				●																										
Children allowed in Club House	●	●	●		●	●	●	●																							
Spectators Allowed	●		●		●																										
Disabled Facilities			●			●																									
Disabled Toilets	●		●			●																									
Disabled Access			●			●																									
Satellite TV		●	●			●																									
TV Lounge			●		●	●		●																							
Snooker Room																															
Members Only Bar						●																									
Gym/Weights													●																		
Massage																															
Physiotherapy																															
Sauna/Solararium													●																		
Swimming Pool	●												●																		
Health Club																															
Accommodation													●																		
Hotel On Site																															
Visitors Car Park	●	●	●		●	●		●																							
Members Car Park	●	●	●		●	●		●																							
Practice Putting Green	●	●	●		●	●	●	●																							
Practice Bunkers	●	●	●		●	●																									
Practice Course	●	●	●																												
Driving Range	●			●	●	●	●	●	●				●									●									●
Conference Facility			●	●					●				●																		
Evening Functions	●	●			●	●																									
On Course Refreshments					●	●																									
Bar Snacks		●	●	●	●	●	●	●	●	●	●	●	●	●		●	●	●	●	●	●	●	●			●	●		●	●	●
Restaurant Dinner		●	●	●	●	●	●	●				●	●													●	●				●
Restaurant Lunch		●	●	●	●	●	●	●																	●						
Restaurant Breakfast		●	●	●	●	●	●	●																							
Shoe Cleaning Service																															
Bag Drop Service																															
Guests Changing Rooms		●	●	●	●	●	●	●	●	●	●	●	●	●		●	●	●	●	●	●	●	●			●	●		●	●	●
Guests Showers		●	●		●	●		●																							
On Course Drinking Fountains		●	●					●																							
On Course Yardage Markers	●	●	●			●		●																							
Spike Bar		●	●		●		●																								
Plastic Stud Fitting Service	●							●																							
Plastic Studs Compulsory																															
Visitors Need Handicap Proof							●	●																							
Golf Clubs Hire	●	●	●	●	●	●						●	●	●		●			●						●	●	●				
Caddy Hire																															
Shoe Hire																															
Buggy Hire	●	●								●		●														●	●				●
Trolley Hire	●	●	●					●		●	●	●	●			●			●	●	●					●	●	●	●	●	●
Regripping	●	●	●		●	●	●	●																							
Club Alterations	●	●	●		●	●	●	●																							

Golf Courses by County

TYNE AND WEAR

FACILITIES AVAILABLE

Facilities Available at Golf Courses

Golf Courses by County

Facility	WHICKHAM	WHITBURN	WHITLEY BAY	ATHERSTONE	BIDFORD GRANGE	BRAMCOTE WATERS	KENILWORTH	LEAMINGTON & COUNTY	NEWBOLD COMYN	NUNEATON	OAKRIDGE	PURLEY CHASE	RUGBY	STRATFORD OAKS	STRATFORD ON AVON	WARWICK GOLF CTRE	WARWICKSHIRE	WELCOMBE HOTEL	WHITEFIELDS	BOWOOD	BRADFORD ON AVON	BRINKWORTH	BROOME MANOR	CHIPPENHAM	CRICKLADE	CUMBERWELL	ERLESTOKE SANDS	HAMPTWORTH	HIGH POST	HIGHWORTH GOLF CENTRE
Dress Code Anything						•																								
Dress Code Casual				•																	•	•	•			•	•	•	•	
Dress Code Formal																														
Golf Shop takes credit cards								•	•																	•	•	•	•	
Club House takes credit card				•				•	•																	•	•	•	•	
Youth Coaching Scheme								•	•																	•	•	•	•	
Mobiles allowed in Club House				•				•	•																			•	•	
Children allowed in Club House				•				•	•																	•		•	•	
Spectators Allowed				•				•	•											•								•	•	
Disabled Facilities																										•		•	•	
Disabled Toilets																										•		•	•	
Disabled Access							•																			•		•	•	
Satellite TV				•																										
TV Lounge				•					•	•																•		•	•	
Snooker Room																									•					
Members Only Bar																														
Gym/Weights									•									•										•	•	
Massage																														
Physiotherapy																														
Sauna/Solararium									•																			•		
Swimming Pool									•																			•		
Health Club									•																					
Accommodation					•													•	•	•							•			
Hotel On Site																		•												
Visitors Car Park				•				•	•							•	•	•		•						•		•	•	•
Members Car Park				•				•	•									•								•		•	•	•
Practice Putting Green				•				•	•									•								•		•	•	•
Practice Bunkers								•	•									•								•			•	•
Practice Course				•				•	•									•								•			•	•
Driving Range													•	•		•	•	•	•	•						•			•	
Conference Facility				•				•	•									•	•	•						•		•		
Evening Functions				•				•	•									•								•		•	•	•
On Course Refreshments																														
Bar Snacks	•	•	•	•	•	•	•	•	•	•						•	•	•	•	•	•		•	•		•	•	•	•	•
Restaurant Dinner	•	•	•	•	•	•	•	•	•	•				•	•	•	•	•	•	•	•		•	•		•	•	•	•	•
Restaurant Lunch				•				•	•	•																•		•	•	
Restaurant Breakfast				•				•	•																	•		•	•	
Shoe Cleaning Service																										•				
Bag Drop Service																														
Guests Changing Rooms	•	•	•	•			•	•	•	•	•		•	•	•	•	•	•	•	•	•		•	•		•	•	•	•	•
Guests Showers				•				•	•												•					•		•	•	•
On Course Drinking Fountains																														
On Course Yardage Markers				•				•	•											•	•					•		•	•	•
Spike Bar					•															•	•							•	•	•
Plastic Stud Fitting Service																				•	•							•	•	•
Plastic Studs Compulsory																														
Visitors Need Handicap Proof									•																					
Golf Clubs Hire	•			•	•		•	•		•				•	•	•	•	•	•	•		•	•	•		•	•	•	•	•
Caddy Hire																														
Shoe Hire																										•				
Buggy Hire				•	•			•	•							•	•			•	•		•	•		•	•	•	•	
Trolley Hire	•	•		•	•			•	•					•	•	•				•	•		•	•		•	•	•	•	
Regripping				•	•			•	•												•	•				•	•	•	•	
Club Alterations				•	•			•	•												•	•				•	•	•	•	

Facilities Available at Golf Courses

Facility	KINGSDOWN	MANOR HOUSE	MARLBOROUGH	NORTH WILTS	OAKSEY	OGBOURNE DOWNS	RUSHMORE PARK	SALISBURY & SOUTH WILTS	SHRIVENHAM PARK	THOULSTONE PARK	TIDWORTH GARRISON	UPAVON	WEST WILTS	WHITLEY	WILTSHIRE	WRAG BARN	WORCESTERSHIRE	ABBEY HOTEL	BANK HOUSE	BLACKWELL	BROADWAY	BROMSGROVE	CADMORE LODGE	CHURCHILL & BLAKEDOWN	DROITWICH	EVESHAM	HABBERLEY	KIDDERMINSTER	LITTLE LAKES	LITTLE LAKES	OMBERSLEY	PERDISWELL PARK GOLF COURSE
Dress Code Anything															•																	
Dress Code Casual	•			•		•	•	•		•	•							•			•			•					•			•
Dress Code Formal																•																
Golf Shop takes credit cards	•				•	•	•		•	•								•		•	•								•		•	•
Club House takes credit card				•		•	•	•										•														•
Youth Coaching Scheme	•				•	•	•		•	•																			•			•
Mobiles allowed in Club House				•		•																										
Children allowed in Club House	•			•		•	•		•	•	•		•			•		•		•	•								•			•
Spectators Allowed						•	•	•	•	•																						
Disabled Facilities						•	•							•																		
Disabled Toilets						•	•	•						•																		
Disabled Access						•	•							•																		
Satellite TV	•				•		•	•												•				•								
TV Lounge	•			•			•	•	•			•		•							•											•
Snooker Room								•																•								
Members Only Bar																								•								
Gym/Weights																		•	•					•								•
Massage																																
Physiotherapy																																
Sauna/Solararium		•																•	•					•								
Swimming Pool	•																	•						•						•		
Health Club																		•														
Accommodation	•			•														•	•					•								
Hotel On Site	•																	•														
Visitors Car Park	•			•		•	•	•		•	•		•					•		•	•			•								•
Members Car Park	•			•		•	•	•		•	•							•		•	•			•								
Practice Putting Green	•					•	•	•		•								•		•	•			•								
Practice Bunkers	•						•	•		•								•						•								
Practice Course						•		•										•														
Driving Range	•	•			•	•	•		•		•							•	•							•			•	•	•	•
Conference Facility		•	•		•			•	•						•	•		•	•						•			•		•	•	•
Evening Functions	•						•	•		•						•								•								•
On Course Refreshments																		•														
Bar Snacks	•	•	•	•	•	•	•	•	•	•	•	•	•	•	•	•		•	•	•	•	•	•	•	•	•	•	•	•	•	•	•
Restaurant Dinner	•	•		•		•	•	•	•	•	•				•	•		•		•	•			•					•		•	•
Restaurant Lunch	•	•		•		•	•	•		•	•				•	•		•		•	•			•					•		•	•
Restaurant Breakfast	•	•				•	•	•							•	•		•		•	•								•			•
Shoe Cleaning Service	•								•																							
Bag Drop Service																																
Guests Changing Rooms	•	•	•	•	•	•	•	•	•	•	•	•	•		•	•		•	•	•	•	•	•	•	•	•	•	•	•	•	•	•
Guests Showers	•						•	•	•					•		•								•								
On Course Drinking Fountains	•																															
On Course Yardage Markers	•					•	•	•		•				•		•				•				•								•
Spike Bar							•	•		•				•																		
Plastic Stud Fitting Service	•					•	•	•		•				•				•			•			•								•
Plastic Studs Compulsory														•																		
Visitors Need Handicap Proof	•						•	•		•				•										•								
Golf Clubs Hire	•	•		•		•	•	•	•	•	•	•	•	•				•	•	•				•			•				•	•
Caddy Hire																																
Shoe Hire																																
Buggy Hire		•	•	•			•	•					•			•		•	•	•	•		•	•					•	•	•	•
Trolley Hire	•	•	•	•			•	•			•		•			•		•		•			•	•					•	•	•	•
Regripping	•					•	•	•		•				•				•					•	•								•
Club Alterations	•					•	•	•		•	•			•				•			•		•	•					•			•

Facilities Available at Golf Courses

Golf Courses by County	PITCHEROAK	RAVENMEADOW	REDDITCH	SAPEY	TOLLADINE	VALE	WHARTON PARK	WORCESTER	WORCESTERSHIRE	WYRE FOREST	BEVERLEY & EAST RIDING	BOOTHFERRY PARK	BRIDLINGTON	BRIDLINGTON	BROUGH	CAVE CASTLE	CHERRY BURTON	DRIFFIELD	FLAMBOROUGH HEAD	GANSTEAD PARK	HAINSWORTH PARK	HESSLE	HORNSEA	HULL	SPRINGHEAD PARK MUNICIPAL	SUTTON PARK	WITHERNSEA	ALDWARK MANOR	BEDALE	CATTERICK
Dress Code Anything																														
Dress Code Casual	●		●			●		●		●				●			●	●				●	●				●	●		
Dress Code Formal																●														
Golf Shop takes credit cards	●		●			●			●				●			●		●	●			●	●					●		
Club House takes credit card						●			●				●			●			●									●		
Youth Coaching Scheme	●					●			●							●			●									●		
Mobiles allowed in Club House	●		●			●			●							●			●									●		
Children allowed in Club House	●					●			●							●			●			●						●		
Spectators Allowed	●		●			●			●							●											●	●		
Disabled Facilities																●			●	●			●				●	●		
Disabled Toilets										●																				
Disabled Access			●													●												●		
Satellite TV			●																									●		
TV Lounge	●		●			●										●	●	●			●							●		
Snooker Room			●				●									●												●		
Members Only Bar																												●		
Gym/Weights																●												●		
Massage																●												●		
Physiotherapy																●												●		
Sauna/Solararium																●												●		
Swimming Pool																●												●		
Health Club																●												●		
Accommodation																●												●		
Hotel On Site																●						●						●		
Visitors Car Park	●		●			●							●	●		●			●			●	●				●	●		
Members Car Park	●												●	●					●			●						●		
Practice Putting Green	●	●	●						●				●	●		●	●					●						●		
Practice Bunkers			●			●							●	●		●						●						●		
Practice Course	●	●				●							●			●						●						●		
Driving Range		●		●		●	●			●						●			●											
Conference Facility				●	●											●														
Evening Functions	●		●			●										●											●			
On Course Refreshments																●														
Bar Snacks	●		●	●		●	●	●	●	●	●	●	●	●	●	●	●	●	●	●	●	●	●	●	●		●	●	●	●
Restaurant Dinner	●		●	●		●	●	●	●	●	●	●	●	●	●	●	●	●	●	●	●	●	●	●	●		●	●	●	●
Restaurant Lunch	●		●			●			●		●					●						●						●		●
Restaurant Breakfast	●					●				●		●	●			●												●		
Shoe Cleaning Service																●														
Bag Drop Service																														
Guests Changing Rooms	●		●	●	●	●	●	●	●	●		●	●	●	●	●	●	●	●	●	●	●	●	●		●	●	●	●	●
Guests Showers	●		●			●						●	●		●	●						●					●	●	●	●
On Course Drinking Fountains			●			●							●			●														
On Course Yardage Markers	●		●			●			●				●			●						●					●	●		
Spike Bar	●					●										●												●		
Plastic Stud Fitting Service						●			●																					
Plastic Studs Compulsory			●																											
Visitors Need Handicap Proof			●																											
Golf Clubs Hire	●		●	●					●		●	●	●	●	●	●	●			●	●			●	●			●		●
Caddy Hire																														
Shoe Hire																●														
Buggy Hire			●	●		●	●		●	●		●	●	●		●			●			●						●	●	
Trolley Hire	●	●				●	●		●	●		●	●	●	●	●			●			●	●		●		●	●	●	●
Regripping		●				●			●			●	●			●			●			●	●				●			
Club Alterations	●					●			●			●	●			●			●			●	●							

Facilities Available at Golf Courses

Facility	COCKSFORD	CRIMPLE VALLEY	EASINGWOLD	FILEY	FOREST OF GALTRES	FOREST PARK	FULFORD	GANTON	HARROGATE	HEWORTH	KILNWICK PERCY	KIRKBYMOORSIDE	KNARESBOROUGH	MALTON & NORTON	MASHAM	NORTH CLIFF	OAKDALE	OAKS	PANNAL	RAVEN HALL	RICHMOND	RIPON CITY	ROMANBY	RUDDING PARK	SCARBOROUGH SOUTH CLIFF	SCARTHINGWELL	SELBY	SETTLE	SKIPTON	SPOFFORTH	SWALLOW HALL	THIRSK & NORTHALLERTON
Dress Code Anything		●																													●	
Dress Code Casual	●					●		●		●	●						●	●					●		●	●			●			
Dress Code Formal							●																									
Golf Shop takes credit cards	●	●				●		●		●							●	●					●		●							
Club House takes credit card	●	●				●											●															
Youth Coaching Scheme									●	●							●															
Mobiles allowed in Club House	●	●															●								●	●					●	
Children allowed in Club House	●	●				●		●		●	●						●	●					●		●						●	
Spectators Allowed	●																															
Disabled Facilities								●																								
Disabled Toilets								●		●	●												●		●						●	
Disabled Access								●		●	●						●						●		●						●	
Satellite TV																	●														●	
TV Lounge		●				●		●									●								●							
Snooker Room		●																														
Members Only Bar																	●						●									
Gym/Weights																																
Massage																																
Physiotherapy																																
Sauna/Solararium																●																
Swimming Pool																																
Health Club																																
Accommodation	●																●	●					●								●	
Hotel On Site																									●							
Visitors Car Park	●	●				●		●		●	●						●						●		●						●	●
Members Car Park	●	●				●		●		●	●						●	●					●		●						●	●
Practice Putting Green						●		●		●				● ●			●	●					●		●						●	●
Practice Bunkers						●		●		●	●						●	●					●									●
Practice Course																	●									●						
Driving Range					●	●	●										●	●				●	●			●					●	●
Conference Facility	●							●									●							●	●						●	
Evening Functions	●	●								●							●								●							
On Course Refreshments																																
Bar Snacks	●	●	●	●	●	●	●	●	●	●	●	●	●	●	●	●	●	●	●	●	●	●	●	●	●	●	●	●	●	●	●	●
Restaurant Dinner	●	●	●	●	●	●		●		●	●		●				●	●					●	●	●	●					●	●
Restaurant Lunch	●	●				●		●		●							●						●		●							
Restaurant Breakfast	●	●						●									●	●					●		●							
Shoe Cleaning Service								●																								
Bag Drop Service																																
Guests Changing Rooms	●	●	●	●	●	●	●	●	●	●	●	●	●	●	●	●	●	●	●	●	●	●	●	●	●	●	●	●	●	●	●	●
Guests Showers	●					●		●		●							●	●					●		●							●
On Course Drinking Fountains								●									●															
On Course Yardage Markers	●	●				●		●		●							●	●					●		●						●	●
Spike Bar					●			●									●								●						●	
Plastic Stud Fitting Service									●								●											●				
Plastic Studs Compulsory																																
Visitors Need Handicap Proof								●									●															
Golf Clubs Hire	●	●		●		●		● ●		●	●		●		●		●	●	●	●	●	●	●						●		●	●
Caddy Hire								●																								
Shoe Hire	●																															
Buggy Hire	●	●					●	●									●	●	●				●	●	●							●
Trolley Hire	●	●	●	●	●	●	●	●		●	●						●	●					●	●	●	●		●			●	●
Regripping	●	●						●		●	●						●	●							●	●		●				●
Club Alterations	●	●						●		●	●						●	●							●	●						●

Facilities Available at Golf Courses

Golf Courses by County — YORKSHIRE (SOUTH)

Facility	WHITBY	YORK	YORK GOLF CTRE	ABBEYDALE	AUSTERFIELD	BARNSLEY	BEAUCHIEF MUNICIPAL	BIRLEY WOOD	CONCORD GOLF CTRE	CROOKHILL PARK MUNICIPAL	DONCASTER TOWN MOOR	DORE & TOTLEY	GRANGE PARK	HALLAMSHIRE	HICKLETON	HILLSBOROUGH	KINGSWOOD	LEES HALL	OWSTON PARK	PHOENIX	RENISHAW PARK	ROBIN HOOD	ROTHER VALLEY GOLF	ROTHERHAM	SANDHILL	SERLBY PARK	SILKSTONE	SITWELL	STOCKSBRIDGE	TANKERSLEY PARK	THORNE
Dress Code Anything																	●														
Dress Code Casual		●																				●	●								
Dress Code Formal																															
Golf Shop takes credit cards		●														●	●					●	●								
Club House takes credit card		●															●					●	●								
Youth Coaching Scheme																●	●					●	●								
Mobiles allowed in Club House		●														●	●					●	●								
Children allowed in Club House		●															●					●	●								
Spectators Allowed																	●					●									
Disabled Facilities																	●					●									
Disabled Toilets																	●					●	●								
Disabled Access																	●					●	●								
Satellite TV																															
TV Lounge																	●					●									
Snooker Room																	●					●									
Members Only Bar																															
Gym/Weights								●													●										
Massage																															
Physiotherapy																															
Sauna/Solararium								●														●									
Swimming Pool								●																							
Health Club																						●									
Accommodation																															
Hotel On Site																						●									
Visitors Car Park		●														●	●					●	●								
Members Car Park		●														●	●					●	●								
Practice Putting Green																	●					●	●								
Practice Bunkers																	●					●									
Practice Course																															
Driving Range						●							●			●	●		●		●			●							
Conference Facility																	●				●										
Evening Functions																	●					●	●								
On Course Refreshments																															
Bar Snacks	●	●		●	●	●	●	●	●	●	●	●	●	●			●					●	●	●	●	●	●	●	●	●	●
Restaurant Dinner		●		●	●	●							●				●					●	●								
Restaurant Lunch																	●					●	●		●		●				
Restaurant Breakfast																	●					●	●								
Shoe Cleaning Service																	●														
Bag Drop Service																															
Guests Changing Rooms	●	●		●	●	●	●	●	●	●	●	●	●	●			●					●	●	●	●	●	●	●	●	●	●
Guests Showers																	●					●	●								
On Course Drinking Fountains																															
On Course Yardage Markers																●	●					●									
Spike Bar																	●					●									
Plastic Stud Fitting Service		●														●	●					●									
Plastic Studs Compulsory																															
Visitors Need Handicap Proof																	●														
Golf Clubs Hire	●		●			●	●	●	●					●		●	●			●		●		●				●		●	●
Caddy Hire																															
Shoe Hire																	●					●	●								
Buggy Hire				●				●								●	●				●	●					●	●			
Trolley Hire	●	●	●	●	●	●	●						●	●		●	●	●		●		●	●							●	●
Regripping		●														●	●					●	●								
Club Alterations		●														●	●					●	●								

Facilities Available at Golf Courses

Golf Courses by County	TINSLEY PARK	WATH	WHEATLEY	WORTLEY	YORKSHIRE (WEST)	ALWOODLEY	BAGDEN HALL	BAILDON	BEN RHYDDING	BINGLEY ST IVES	BRACKEN GHYLL	BRADFORD	BRADFORD MOOR	BRADLEY HALL	BRADLEY PARK	BRANDON	BRANSHAW	CALVERLEY	CLAYTON	CLECKHEATON & DISTRICT	COOKRIDGE HALL GOLF CLUB	CROSLAND HEATH	CROW NEST PARK	DEWSBURY DISTRICT	EAST BIERLEY	ELLAND	FARDEW	FULNECK	GARFORTH	HALIFAX	HANGING HEATON	HEADINGLEY
Dress Code Anything																						●										
Dress Code Casual						●		●			●			●							● ●		●							●		
Dress Code Formal																									●	●						
Golf Shop takes credit cards						●		●			●			● ●							● ●		●							●		
Club House takes credit card						●															●											
Youth Coaching Scheme						●		●						● ●							●		●									
Mobiles allowed in Club House																					●											
Children allowed in Club House						●		●		●				●							● ●									●		●
Spectators Allowed						●								● ●							●		●									●
Disabled Facilities						●															●											
Disabled Toilets						●								●							●		●									●
Disabled Access						●					●										● ●									● ●		●
Satellite TV								●			●										●									● ●		
TV Lounge						●		●						● ●				●												● ●		●
Snooker Room						●		●						●																		
Members Only Bar																																
Gym/Weights																																
Massage																																
Physiotherapy																																
Sauna/Solararium																																
Swimming Pool																																
Health Club																																
Accommodation							●																									
Hotel On Site							●																									
Visitors Car Park						●		●						●			●				●		● ● ●						●		
Members Car Park						●		●						●							● ●		● ●							●		
Practice Putting Green						●		●			●			● ●							● ●		●							● ●		●
Practice Bunkers						●		●						●							● ●									●		
Practice Course						●		●						● ●							● ●		●							● ●		●
Driving Range											●										●											
Conference Facility	●						●		●												● ●			●								
Evening Functions						●		●						●					●		●		●	●						●		●
On Course Refreshments						●															●											
Bar Snacks	● ●		●			● ●		● ●		●	● ●	●	●	● ●	● ●	●	●	●	●	●	● ●	●	● ●	●	●	●	●	●	●	●	●	● ●
Restaurant Dinner	● ●		●			● ●		●						● ●							● ●		●							●		●
Restaurant Lunch						● ●								● ●							● ●		●							●		●
Restaurant Breakfast														●							● ●		●							●		●
Shoe Cleaning Service																																
Bag Drop Service																																
Guests Changing Rooms	● ●	●	●	●		● ●		● ●		●	● ●	●	●	●	●	●	●	●	●	●	●	●	●	●	●	●	●	●	●	●	●	●
Guests Showers						●		●						●							● ●		● ●							●		●
On Course Drinking Fountains						●															●											
On Course Yardage Markers						●		●			●			● ●									●							●		●
Spike Bar						●								●							●											
Plastic Stud Fitting Service								●																								
Plastic Studs Compulsory																																
Visitors Need Handicap Proof						●																										
Golf Clubs Hire	●			●		● ●		● ●						● ●	●		●		●		●		●			●			● ●		● ●		●
Caddy Hire						●																										
Shoe Hire						●																										
Buggy Hire										●																						
Trolley Hire	● ●		●			● ●		● ●		●	●	●	●	● ●	●	●	●				●											
Regripping						●		●						● ●							● ●									● ●		
Club Alterations						●		●						●					●		● ●		●							● ●		

© HCC Publishing Ltd

Facilities Available at Golf Courses

Golf Courses by County

Facilities (rows):

- Dress Code Anything
- Dress Code Casual
- Dress Code Formal
- Golf Shop takes credit cards
- Club House takes credit card
- Youth Coaching Scheme
- Mobiles allowed in Club House
- Children allowed in Club House
- Spectators Allowed
- Disabled Facilities
- Disabled Toilets
- Disabled Access
- Satellite TV
- TV Lounge
- Snooker Room
- Members Only Bar
- Gym/Weights
- Massage
- Physiotherapy
- Sauna/Solararium
- Swimming Pool
- Health Club
- Accommodation
- Hotel On Site
- Visitors Car Park
- Members Car Park
- Practice Putting Green
- Practice Bunkers
- Practice Course
- Driving Range
- Conference Facility
- Evening Functions
- On Course Refreshments
- Bar Snacks
- Restaurant Dinner
- Restaurant Lunch
- Restaurant Breakfast
- Shoe Cleaning Service
- Bag Drop Service
- Guests Changing Rooms
- Guests Showers
- On Course Drinking Fountains
- On Course Yardage Markers
- Spike Bar
- Plastic Stud Fitting Service
- Plastic Studs Compulsory
- Visitors Need Handicap Proof
- Golf Clubs Hire
- Caddy Hire
- Shoe Hire
- Buggy Hire
- Trolley Hire
- Regripping
- Club Alterations

Golf Courses (columns):

HEADLEY · HEBDEN BRIDGE · HOLLINS HALL · HORSFORTH · HOWLEY HALL · HUDDERSFIELD · ILKLEY · KEIGHLEY · LEEDS · LEEDS GOLF CTRE · LIGHTCLIFFE · LOFTHOUSE HILL · LONGLEY PARK · LOW LAITHES · MANOR · MARSDEN · MELTHAM · MID YORKSHIRE · MIDDLETON PARK MUNICIPAL · MOOR ALLERTON · MOORTOWN · NORTHCLIFFE · OTLEY · OULTON PARK · OUTLANE · PAINTHORPE HOUSE · PONTEFRACT · PONTEFRACT & DISTRICT · QUEENSBURY · RAWDON · RIDDLESDEN · ROUNDHAY

Facilities Available at Golf Courses

Facility	RYBURN	SAND MOOR	SCARCROFT	SHIPLEY	SILSDEN	SOUTH BRADFORD	SOUTH LEEDS	TEMPLE NEWSAM	TODMORDEN	WAKEFIELD	WAKEFIELD	WATERTON PARK	WEST BOWLING	WEST BRADFORD	WEST END	WETHERBY	WILLOW VALLEY	WOODHALL HILLS	WOODSOME HALL
Dress Code Anything																			●
Dress Code Casual		●			●			●									●		
Dress Code Formal																			
Golf Shop takes credit cards		●			●												●	●	●
Club House takes credit card																	●		
Youth Coaching Scheme		●						●									●	●	●
Mobiles allowed in Club House		●																	
Children allowed in Club House		●			●			●									●	●	●
Spectators Allowed		●															●		
Disabled Facilities		●																●	●
Disabled Toilets		●																	●
Disabled Access		●															●	●	●
Satellite TV					●			●									●	●	
TV Lounge		●			●			●									●	●	●
Snooker Room		●			●			●										●	●
Members Only Bar																			
Gym/Weights																			
Massage																			
Physiotherapy																			
Sauna/Solararium																			
Swimming Pool																			
Health Club																			
Accommodation																			
Hotel On Site																			
Visitors Car Park		●			●			●									●	●	●
Members Car Park		●			●			●									●	●	●
Practice Putting Green		●			●			●									●	●	●
Practice Bunkers		●						●									●	●	●
Practice Course					●			●											●
Driving Range																	●	●	
Conference Facility																	●		
Evening Functions		●			●			●									●		
On Course Refreshments		●															●		●
Bar Snacks	●	●	●	●	●	●	●	●	●	●			●	●	●	●	●	●	●
Restaurant Dinner	●	●	●	●	●	●	●	●	●	●						●	●	●	●
Restaurant Lunch		●			●			●									●	●	●
Restaurant Breakfast		●			●			●									●	●	●
Shoe Cleaning Service																			
Bag Drop Service																			
Guests Changing Rooms	●	●	●	●	●	●	●	●	●	●			●	●	●	●	●	●	●
Guests Showers		●			●			●										●	●
On Course Drinking Fountains		●						●											●
On Course Yardage Markers		●			●			●									●	●	
Spike Bar																	●	●	
Plastic Stud Fitting Service																	●		
Plastic Studs Compulsory																			
Visitors Need Handicap Proof					●			●											
Golf Clubs Hire		●	●				●			●	●				●	●			
Caddy Hire																			
Shoe Hire							●												
Buggy Hire																	●		
Trolley Hire	●	●	●		●	●		●		●	●		●	●	●	●			
Regripping		●			●			●									●	●	●
Club Alterations		●			●			●									●	●	●

Facilities Available at Golf Courses

Golf Courses by County	COUNTY CARLOW	BORRIS	CARLOW	MOUNT WOLSELEY HOTEL	COUNTY CAVAN	BELTURBET	BLACKLION	CAVAN (COUNTY)	SLIEVE RUSSELL	VIRGINIA	COUNTY CLARE	CLONLARA GOLF & LEISURE	DOONBEG	DROMOLAND CASTLE ESTATE	EAST CLARE	ENNIS	KILKEE	KILRUSH	LAHINCH	SHANNON	SPANISH POINT	COUNTY CORK	BANDON	BANTRY BAY	BEREHAVEN	BLARNEY	CHARLEVILLE	COBH	CORK	DONERAILE
Dress Code Anything																														
Dress Code Casual													●				●											●	●	
Dress Code Formal													●	●														●	●	
Golf Shop takes credit cards													●	●														●		
Club House takes credit card													●	●														●		
Youth Coaching Scheme																													●	
Mobiles allowed in Club House																												●	●	
Children allowed in Club House														●														●	●	
Spectators Allowed																													●	
Disabled Facilities																														
Disabled Toilets																														
Disabled Access																														
Satellite TV																												●	●	
TV Lounge														●														●	●	
Snooker Room																														
Members Only Bar																														
Gym/Weights									●					●																
Massage																														
Physiotherapy																														
Sauna/Solararium									●			●		●												●				
Swimming Pool									●																					
Health Club																														
Accommodation									●	●			●	●																
Hotel On Site																														
Visitors Car Park													●	●														●	●	
Members Car Park													●																●	
Practice Putting Green													●															●	●	
Practice Bunkers																													●	
Practice Course																														
Driving Range									●				●	●						●								●	●	
Conference Facility									●				●	●										●					●	
Evening Functions																													●	
On Course Refreshments													●																	
Bar Snacks		●	●			●	●	●	●				●	●	●	●	●	●	●	●	●		●	●	●	●	●	●	●	●
Restaurant Dinner			●					●	●				●	●	●		●							●	●				●	
Restaurant Lunch													●	●			●							●	●				●	
Restaurant Breakfast														●											●					
Shoe Cleaning Service																														
Bag Drop Service													●																	
Guests Changing Rooms		●	●			●	●	●	●			●	●	●	●	●	●	●	●	●	●		●	●	●	●		●	●	●
Guests Showers									●				●	●												●			●	
On Course Drinking Fountains																													●	
On Course Yardage Markers													●	●															●	
Spike Bar																														
Plastic Stud Fitting Service																														
Plastic Studs Compulsory													●																	
Visitors Need Handicap Proof													●															●		
Golf Clubs Hire			●						●			●	●	●	●	●	●	●	●	●	●		●	●	●	●			●	
Caddy Hire													●																	
Shoe Hire																														
Buggy Hire				●				●	●								●	●		●	●		●			●				
Trolley Hire		●	●	●			●	●	●			●	●	●		●	●	●	●	●	●		●	●	●	●			●	
Regripping																														
Club Alterations																														

Facilities Available at Golf Courses

County Cork courses

Facility	DOUGLAS	DUNMORE	EAST CORK	FERMOY	FERNHILL	FITZPATRICK FITNESS CTRE	FOTA ISLAND	GLENGARRIFF	HARBOUR POINT	KINSALE	LEE VALLEY	MAHON MUNICIPAL	MAHON MUNICIPAL	MALLOW	MITCHELSTOWN	MONKSTOWN	MUSKERRY	SKIBBEREEN & WEST CARBERY	WATER ROCK	YOUGHAL
Dress Code Anything																				
Dress Code Casual										•										
Dress Code Formal																				
Golf Shop takes credit cards										•										
Club House takes credit card										•										
Youth Coaching Scheme										•										
Mobiles allowed in Club House										•										
Children allowed in Club House										•										
Spectators Allowed										•										
Disabled Facilities										•										
Disabled Toilets										•										
Disabled Access										•										
Satellite TV										•										
TV Lounge										•										
Snooker Room																				
Members Only Bar																				
Gym/Weights					•	•														
Massage																				
Physiotherapy																				
Sauna/Solararium					•	•									•					
Swimming Pool					•	•														
Health Club																				
Accommodation	•				•	•														
Hotel On Site																				
Visitors Car Park										•									•	
Members Car Park										•									•	
Practice Putting Green										•									•	
Practice Bunkers																				
Practice Course										•										
Driving Range		•						•	•	•	•									
Conference Facility		•		•		•	•		•	•	•									
Evening Functions										•										
On Course Refreshments																				
Bar Snacks			•	•	•	•	•	•	•	•	•	•	•	•	•	•	•	•	•	•
Restaurant Dinner	•	•	•	•	•	•	•	•	•	•	•	•	•	•	•	•	•	•	•	•
Restaurant Lunch										•										
Restaurant Breakfast																				
Shoe Cleaning Service																				
Bag Drop Service																				
Guests Changing Rooms	•	•	•	•	•	•	•	•	•	•	•	•	•	•	•	•	•	•	•	•
Guests Showers										•									•	
On Course Drinking Fountains																				
On Course Yardage Markers										•										
Spike Bar																				
Plastic Stud Fitting Service										•										
Plastic Studs Compulsory																				
Visitors Need Handicap Proof																				
Golf Clubs Hire	•	•	•	•	•	•	•	•	•	•						•	•	•		
Caddy Hire										•										
Shoe Hire										•										
Buggy Hire				•	•	•	•		•	•										
Trolley Hire	•	•	•	•	•	•	•	•	•	•				•	•	•	•			•
Regripping										•										
Club Alterations										•										

County Donegal courses

Facility	BALLYBOFEY & STRANORLAR	BALLYLIFFIN	BUNCRANA	BUNDORAN	CLOUGHANEELY	CRUIT ISLAND	DONEGAL	DUNFANAGHY	GREENCASTLE	GWEEDORE	LETTERKENNY
Dress Code Casual					•						
Youth Coaching Scheme					•						
Mobiles allowed in Club House					•						
Children allowed in Club House					•						
Members Only Bar					•						
Visitors Car Park					•						
Practice Putting Green					•						
Conference Facility					•						•
Evening Functions					•						
Bar Snacks					•	•	•			•	•
Restaurant Dinner					•			•		•	•
Guests Changing Rooms	•	•		•	•		•				
Guests Showers			•								
On Course Yardage Markers					•						
Visitors Need Handicap Proof					•						
Golf Clubs Hire				•	•		•	•			•
Buggy Hire					•	•		•			
Trolley Hire	•		•		•	•		•		•	•

Facilities Available at Golf Courses

Facility	NARIN/PORTNOO	NORTH WEST	OTWAY	PORTSALON	REDCASTLE	ROSAPENNA	COUNTY DUBLIN	BALBRIGGAN	BALCARRICK	BALLINASCORNEY	BEAVERSTOWN	BEECH PARK	CARRICKMINES	CASTLE	CLONTARF	CORBALLIS PUBLIC LINKS	CORRSTOWN	DEER PARK HOTEL	DELGANY	DONABATE	DUBLIN (ROYAL)	DUN LAOGHAIRE	EDMONDSTOWN	ELM PARK GOLF & SPORTS CLUB	FINNSTOWN FAIRWAYS	FORREST LITTLE	FOXROCK	HERMITAGE	HOLLYWOOD LAKES	HOWTH	ISLAND	KILCOOLE
Dress Code Anything																																
Dress Code Casual	●																							●								
Dress Code Formal																								●								
Golf Shop takes credit cards																								●								
Club House takes credit card																								●								
Youth Coaching Scheme	●														●									●								
Mobiles allowed in Club House	●														●																	
Children allowed in Club House	●														●																	
Spectators Allowed	●														●																	
Disabled Facilities															●									●								
Disabled Toilets															●																	
Disabled Access															●																	
Satellite TV	●														●									●								
TV Lounge	●														●									●								
Snooker Room															●									●								
Members Only Bar																								●								
Gym/Weights				●																									●			
Massage																																
Physiotherapy																																
Sauna/Solararium				●																									●			
Swimming Pool				●																									●			
Health Club																																
Accommodation					●	●													●										●			
Hotel On Site																																
Visitors Car Park																								●								
Members Car Park															●									●								
Practice Putting Green															●									●								
Practice Bunkers															●																	
Practice Course															●																	
Driving Range				●											●																	
Conference Facility															●									●	●							●
Evening Functions															●																	
On Course Refreshments																																
Bar Snacks	●	●		●	●	●		●	●	●			●	●	●		●		●	●	●	●	●	●					●	●	●	●
Restaurant Dinner		●			●	●									●			●										●				●
Restaurant Lunch	●																							●								●
Restaurant Breakfast	●																															●
Shoe Cleaning Service																																
Bag Drop Service																																
Guests Changing Rooms	●	●	●	●		●		●	●	●	●		●	●	●	●			●	●	●	●		●					●	●	●	●
Guests Showers	●														●									●								
On Course Drinking Fountains	●														●																	
On Course Yardage Markers	●														●																	
Spike Bar																																
Plastic Stud Fitting Service															●									●								
Plastic Studs Compulsory																																
Visitors Need Handicap Proof	●														●																	
Golf Clubs Hire				●	●								●		●	●	●	●	●	●	●	●		●	●	●	●	●		●		●
Caddy Hire																																
Shoe Hire																																
Buggy Hire	●	●												●	●		●		●				●						●		●	●
Trolley Hire	●	●		●	●				●		●			●	●		●		●	●	●	●	●						●	●	●	●
Regripping															●																	
Club Alterations															●																	

Facilities Available at Golf Courses

Golf Courses by County	KILLINEY	KILTERNAN	LEOPARDSTOWN	LUCAN	LUTTRELLSTOWN CASTLE	MALAHIDE	MILLTOWN	NEWLANDS	OPEN	PORTMARNOCK	PORTMARNOCK HOTEL	RATHFARNHAM	RUSH	SKERRIES	SLADE VALLEY	ST. ANNES	ST. MARGARETS	STACKSTOWN	SWORDS OPEN	TURVEY	ATHENRY	BALLINASLOE	BEARNA	CONNEMARA	GALWAY	GALWAY BAY	GLENLO ABBEY	GORT	LOUGHREA	OUGHTERARD	PORTUMNA
Dress Code Anything									●																						
Dress Code Casual		●		●					●	●								●	●		●	●									
Dress Code Formal										●	●																				
Golf Shop takes credit cards		●		●					●	●	●										●	●									
Club House takes credit card		●		●					●	●	●										●	●									
Youth Coaching Scheme		●		●					●												●										
Mobiles allowed in Club House									●										●	●	●										
Children allowed in Club House		●							●												●	●									
Spectators Allowed																				●											
Disabled Facilities																				●											
Disabled Toilets																				●											
Disabled Access																				●											
Satellite TV				●					●	●										●											
TV Lounge																				●	●										
Snooker Room				●																						●					
Members Only Bar				●																●											
Gym/Weights	●																														
Massage																															
Physiotherapy																															
Sauna/Solararium	●		●															●						●							
Swimming Pool	●		●																												
Health Club																															
Accommodation	●							●			●											●	●								
Hotel On Site									●																						
Visitors Car Park		●		●			●		●	●									●	●	●	●									
Members Car Park		●		●			●		●	●									●	●	●										
Practice Putting Green		●		●			●		●	●									●		●										
Practice Bunkers				●			●		●												●										
Practice Course		●		●			●		●	●											●										
Driving Range		●		●					●					●							●			●	●		●				
Conference Facility	●			●	●	●			●		●										●				●	●	●	●			
Evening Functions				●																●	●										
On Course Refreshments																		●													
Bar Snacks	●	●	●	●	●		●		●	●	●		●	●		●	●			●	●	●	●	●	●	●	●	●	●	●	●
Restaurant Dinner	●	●		●	●		●		●	●	●			●						●	●	●	●	●	●	●	●			●	●
Restaurant Lunch		●		●			●		●	●										●	●						●				
Restaurant Breakfast		●		●			●		●	●	●									●	●						●				
Shoe Cleaning Service																															
Bag Drop Service																															
Guests Changing Rooms	●	●	●	●	●	●	●	●	●	●	●	●	●	●	●	●	●	●	●	●	●	●	●	●	●	●	●	●	●	●	●
Guests Showers		●		●					●	●	●									●	●										
On Course Drinking Fountains																				●											
On Course Yardage Markers								●											●		●	●									
Spike Bar																							●								
Plastic Stud Fitting Service		●																			●										
Plastic Studs Compulsory																															
Visitors Need Handicap Proof																															
Golf Clubs Hire	●	●	●		●	●	●	●	●	●				●		●		●		●	●		●	●	●	●				●	●
Caddy Hire										●									●												
Shoe Hire																					●										
Buggy Hire	●	●					●								●		●			●	●	●	●	●		●	●		●	●	●
Trolley Hire	●	●	●	●	●	●	●	●	●	●			●	●		●	●	●		●	●	●	●	●	●	●	●	●	●	●	●
Regripping		●		●			●														●		●								
Club Alterations		●		●			●														●		●								

Facilities Available at Golf Courses

Ireland

FACILITIES AVAILABLE

Facility	RENVYLE HOUSE	TUAM	BALLYBUNION	BALLYHEIGUE CASTLE	BEAUFORT	CASTLEGREGORY	CASTLEROSSE	CEANN SIBEAL	DOOKS	KENMARE	KERRIES	KILLARNEY	KILLORGLIN	PARKNASILLA	RING OF KERRY	TRALEE	WATERVILLE HOUSE & GOLF LINKS	ATHY	BODENSTOWN	CASTLEWARDEN	CELBRIDGE ELM HALL	CILL DARA	CRADDOCKSTOWN	CURRAGH	HIGHFIELD	K CLUB	KILCOCK	KILKEA CASTLE	KILLEEN	KNOCKANALLY
Dress Code Anything												●																		
Dress Code Casual			●			●	●									●					●		●	●						
Dress Code Formal			●																		●									
Golf Shop takes credit cards					●	●	●					●												●						
Club House takes credit card					●	●	●					●									●									
Youth Coaching Scheme																								●						
Mobiles allowed in Club House			●																											
Children allowed in Club House			●				●	●				●									●									
Spectators Allowed			●					●															●							
Disabled Facilities																								●						
Disabled Toilets																								●						
Disabled Access																								●						
Satellite TV																●					●									
TV Lounge																●														
Snooker Room																														
Members Only Bar																														
Gym/Weights					●					●																			●	●
Massage					●																									
Physiotherapy																														
Sauna/Solararium				●								●		●	●														●	●
Swimming Pool	●				●										●	●													●	●
Health Club					●																									
Accommodation	●				●									●	●		●											●	●	●
Hotel On Site					●																									
Visitors Car Park			●			●	●					●										●		●	●					
Members Car Park			●			●	●					●										●		●	●					
Practice Putting Green						●	●					●										●		●	●					
Practice Bunkers																														
Practice Course																														
Driving Range												●				●								●	●					
Conference Facility	●																								●	●		●	●	
Evening Functions															●							●								
On Course Refreshments															●															
Bar Snacks	●	●	●		●		●	●	●	●	●	●			●	●	●	●	●	●	●	●	●	●	●	●		●	●	●
Restaurant Dinner	●		●		●		●	●	●	●	●	●	●		●	●	●	●	●	●	◐	●	●	◐	●	●	●	●	●	●
Restaurant Lunch							●									●					◐			◐						
Restaurant Breakfast																●					●			◐						
Shoe Cleaning Service				●																										
Bag Drop Service																●														
Guests Changing Rooms		●	●	●	●	●	●	●		●		●			●	●					●	●	●	◐	●	●	●	●	●	●
Guests Showers			●			●		●			●					●					●		●	◐						
On Course Drinking Fountains			●				●		●							●														
On Course Yardage Markers			●			●		●								●					●		●							
Spike Bar																●														
Plastic Stud Fitting Service																●														
Plastic Studs Compulsory			●			●										●														
Visitors Need Handicap Proof			●																			●								
Golf Clubs Hire	●	●	●	●	●	●	●		●		●	●	●			●	●		●	●			●		●	●	●	●	●	●
Caddy Hire			●													●							●							
Shoe Hire																							●							
Buggy Hire			●		●	●																	●							
Trolley Hire	●	●	●	●	●	●	●		●		●	●	●	●	●	●	●		●	●			●		●	●	●	●	●	●
Regripping																●							●							
Club Alterations																							●							

Golf Courses by County

© HCC Publishing Ltd

Facilities Available at Golf Courses

www.hccgolfworld.com

Facility / Golf Courses by County	NAAS	WOODLANDS	COUNTY KILKENNY	CALLAN	CARRIGLEADE	CASTLECOMER	GOWRAN PARK GOLF & LEISURE	KILKENNY	MOUNT JULIET	MOUNTAIN VIEW	POCOCKE	COUNTY LAOIS	ABBEYLEIX	HEATH	MOUNTRATH	PORTARLINGTON	RATHDOWNEY	COUNTY LEITRIM	BALLINAMORE	CARRICK-ON-SHANNON	COUNTY LIMERICK	ABBEYFEALE GOLF CTRE	ADARE MANOR	CASTLETROY	KILLELINE GOLF	LIMERICK	LIMERICK (COUNTY)	NEWCASTLE WEST	RATHBANE	COUNTY LONGFORD	LONGFORD (COUNTY)
Dress Code Anything																															
Dress Code Casual				●		●		●	●	●																		●			●
Dress Code Formal				●																											
Golf Shop takes credit cards									●																			●			
Club House takes credit card						●			●	●																		●			
Youth Coaching Scheme																															
Mobiles allowed in Club House				●						●	●																	●			
Children allowed in Club House				●						●	●																	●			●
Spectators Allowed						●			●																						
Disabled Facilities																															
Disabled Toilets						●			●																			●			
Disabled Access						●			●													●						●			
Satellite TV						●				●																					
TV Lounge						●			●	●																		●			
Snooker Room						●																						●			
Members Only Bar																															
Gym/Weights						●																									
Massage																															
Physiotherapy																															
Sauna/Solararium						●																									
Swimming Pool						●																									
Health Club																															
Accommodation						●																	●								
Hotel On Site						●																									
Visitors Car Park				●		●		●	●	●												●						●			
Members Car Park						●		●		●												●									
Practice Putting Green				●		●			●													●						●			
Practice Bunkers						●																									
Practice Course						●																●									
Driving Range								●	●							●						●						●	●		
Conference Facility					●			●	●															●	●		●	●			
Evening Functions								●																							
On Course Refreshments					●																	●									
Bar Snacks	●	●		●				●	●	●				●	●	●			●	●		●	●	●	●	●	●	●	●		●
Restaurant Dinner				●				●						●	●									●		●	●	●	●		
Restaurant Lunch						●																						●			
Restaurant Breakfast						●																						●			
Shoe Cleaning Service																															
Bag Drop Service																															
Guests Changing Rooms	●	●		●	●	●		●	●	●			●	●	●	●	●			●			●	●	●	●	●	●	●		●
Guests Showers						●		●	●																			●			
On Course Drinking Fountains																												●			
On Course Yardage Markers					●		●			●	●											●									
Spike Bar								●																							
Plastic Stud Fitting Service								●																				●			
Plastic Studs Compulsory																													●		
Visitors Need Handicap Proof				●					●																						
Golf Clubs Hire				●	●		●	●	●	●				●						●		●	●	●	●	●	●	●	●		●
Caddy Hire						●			●																						
Shoe Hire																						●									
Buggy Hire			●	●			●	●																●	●		●	●			●
Trolley Hire	●	●		●	●		●	●	●				●	●	●	●	●					●		●	●	●	●	●	●		●
Regripping				●						●												●		●							
Club Alterations																						●		●							

Facilities Available at Golf Courses

FACILITIES AVAILABLE

Facility / Golf Courses by County	COUNTY LOUTH	BALLYMASCANLON HOUSE	DUNDALK	GREENORE	KILLIN PARK	KILLINBEG	LOUTH (COUNTY)	SEAPOINT	TOWNLEY HALL	COUNTY MAYO	ACHILL ISLAND	BALLINA	BALLINROBE	BALLYHAUNIS	CARNE	CASTLEBAR	CLAREMORRIS	ENNISCRONE	MULRANNY	SWINFORD	WESTPORT	COUNTY MEATH	BLACK BUSH	GLEBE	HEADFORT	LAYTOWN & BETTYSTOWN	MEATH (COUNTY)	SOUTH MEATH	TARA (ROYAL)	COUNTY MONAGHAN	CASTLEBLAYNEY	CLONES
Dress Code Anything																																
Dress Code Casual					●			●	●		●								●						●							●
Dress Code Formal																																
Golf Shop takes credit cards								●																								
Club House takes credit card								●			●																					●
Youth Coaching Scheme																																●
Mobiles allowed in Club House									●			●							●													●
Children allowed in Club House								●	●			●							●													●
Spectators Allowed									●										●													
Disabled Facilities																																
Disabled Toilets								●																								
Disabled Access								●																								
Satellite TV																																●
TV Lounge								●				●							●												●	●
Snooker Room								●																								
Members Only Bar								●																								
Gym/Weights		●																														
Massage																																
Physiotherapy																																
Sauna/Solararium		●	●																													
Swimming Pool		●																														
Health Club																																
Accommodation		●						●											●													
Hotel On Site																																
Visitors Car Park					●	●	●	●	●			●							●								●					●
Members Car Park					●	●	●	●	●			●							●								●					●
Practice Putting Green								●	●												●											●
Practice Bunkers								●																								
Practice Course								●				●																				●
Driving Range							●	●								●					●		●									●
Conference Facility		●																					●								●	
Evening Functions																																
On Course Refreshments																																
Bar Snacks		●		●	●	●	●	●			●	●	●	●	●	●	●	●		●	●		●	●	●	●					●	●
Restaurant Dinner		●		●		●	●	●				●				●	●	●		●	●		●	●	●	●					●	●
Restaurant Lunch								●	●																							●
Restaurant Breakfast								●																								●
Shoe Cleaning Service																																
Bag Drop Service																																
Guests Changing Rooms		●	●	●				●				●	●	●	●	●	●	●	●	●	●		●	●	●	●	●		●			●
Guests Showers								●	●			●							●				●									●
On Course Drinking Fountains																																
On Course Yardage Markers						●		●	●										●					●								
Spike Bar																			●													
Plastic Stud Fitting Service																																
Plastic Studs Compulsory									●																							
Visitors Need Handicap Proof								●																								
Golf Clubs Hire				●	●	●	●				●	●	●		●	●		●			●		●	●	●	●	●		●			
Caddy Hire																																
Shoe Hire																																
Buggy Hire					●	●					●	●	●		●			●	●				●									
Trolley Hire		●		●	●	●	●	●			●	●	●	●	●			●	●		●		●	●	●	●		●				●
Regripping								●	●																							
Club Alterations								●	●																							

www.hccgolfworld.com

© HCC Publishing Ltd

FACILITIES AVAILABLE — Ireland

www.hccgolfworld.com

Facilities Available at Golf Courses

Golf Courses by County

Facility	MANNAN CASTLE	NUREMORE HOTEL	ROSSMORE	COUNTY OFFALY	BIRR	CASTLE BARNA	EDENDERRY	TULLAMORE	COUNTY ROSCOMMON	ATHLONE	BALLAGHADERREEN	BOYLE	CASTLEREA	ROSCOMMON	STROKESTOWN	COUNTY SLIGO	BALLYMOTE	SLIGO (COUNTY)	STRANDHILL	TUBBERCURRY	COUNTY TIPPERARY	BALLYKISTEEN	CAHIR PARK	CARRICK ON SUIR	CLONMEL	NENAGH	ROSCREA	TEMPLEMORE	THURLES	TIPPERARY	TIPPERARY (COUNTY)
Dress Code Anything																															
Dress Code Casual						●								●				●				●							●		
Dress Code Formal																															
Golf Shop takes credit cards						●												●				●									
Club House takes credit card						●												●				●									
Youth Coaching Scheme														●				●				●									
Mobiles allowed in Club House														●				●													
Children allowed in Club House						●								●				●													
Spectators Allowed						●								●				●													
Disabled Facilities						●								●																	
Disabled Toilets						●								●																	
Disabled Access						●								●																	
Satellite TV						●								●															●		
TV Lounge						●												●				●							●		
Snooker Room																															
Members Only Bar																		●													
Gym/Weights	●																													●	
Massage																															
Physiotherapy																															
Sauna/Solararium	●																													●	
Swimming Pool	●																														
Health Club																															
Accommodation	●																														●
Hotel On Site																															
Visitors Car Park						●								●				●				●							●		
Members Car Park						●								●				●				●									
Practice Putting Green						●								●																	
Practice Bunkers																															
Practice Course														●																	
Driving Range			●		●									●				●	●			●				●		●		●	●
Conference Facility	●																					●									●
Evening Functions														●				●				●							●		
On Course Refreshments																															
Bar Snacks	●	●	●		●	●	●	●		●	●	●	●	●			●	●	●	●		●	●	●	●		●	●	●	●	●
Restaurant Dinner		●				●						●		●				●	●			●						●			
Restaurant Lunch						●								●				●				●							●		
Restaurant Breakfast						●												●				●									
Shoe Cleaning Service																															
Bag Drop Service																															
Guests Changing Rooms	●	●	●		●	●	●	●		●	●	●	●	●			●	●	●	●		●	●	●	●		●	●	●	●	●
Guests Showers						●								●				●				●							●		
On Course Drinking Fountains														●				●				●									
On Course Yardage Markers						●								●				●				●							●		
Spike Bar						●												●				●									
Plastic Stud Fitting Service														●				●				●									
Plastic Studs Compulsory																		●				●									
Visitors Need Handicap Proof														●																	
Golf Clubs Hire		●				●	●		●			●		●	●			●				●				●	●	●	●	●	●
Caddy Hire						●																									
Shoe Hire																															
Buggy Hire		●	●			●	●	●				●			●			●	●	●		●	●	●						●	●
Trolley Hire		●	●		●	●	●	●		●	●			●	●			●	●	●		●	●	●					●	●	●
Regripping														●				●				●									
Club Alterations														●				●				●									

Facilities Available at Golf Courses

Golf Courses by County

Facility	COUNTY WATERFORD	DUNGARVAN	DUNMORE EAST	FAITHLEGG	GOLD COAST	LISMORE	TRAMORE	WATERFORD	WATERFORD CASTLE	WEST WATERFORD	COUNTY WESTMEATH	DELVIN CASTLE	GLASSON	MOATE	MOUNT TEMPLE	MULLINGAR	COUNTY WEXFORD	BALLYMONEY	COURTOWN	ENNISCORTHY	NEW ROSS	ROSSLARE	SCARKE	ST. HELENS BAY	WEXFORD	COUNTY WICKLOW	ARKLOW	BALTINGLASS	BLAINROE	BRAY	CHARLESLAND	COOLLATTIN
Dress Code Anything																																
Dress Code Casual				●				●										●														●
Dress Code Formal			●																													
Golf Shop takes credit cards		●		●	●			●	●																							●
Club House takes credit card		●		●	●			●	●																							●
Youth Coaching Scheme		●		●	●			●																								●
Mobiles allowed in Club House		●		●	●			●																								
Children allowed in Club House		●		●	●			●	●																							
Spectators Allowed		●		●	●							●	●																			
Disabled Facilities		●																														
Disabled Toilets		●																														
Disabled Access		●		●	●													●														
Satellite TV		●		●	●					●																						
TV Lounge		●		●	●							●																				
Snooker Room		●		●																												
Members Only Bar					●																											
Gym/Weights				●	●																											
Massage				●	●																											
Physiotherapy				●																												
Sauna/Solararium				●	●																										●	
Swimming Pool				●	●																											
Health Club				●	●																											
Accommodation				●	●							●												●							●	
Hotel On Site				●	●							●																				
Visitors Car Park		●		●	●							●						●														●
Members Car Park		●		●	●							●																				●
Practice Putting Green		●		●	●				●	●		●						●														●
Practice Bunkers		●		●	●							●																				●
Practice Course		●		●	●							●																				
Driving Range		●							●			●				●			●	●							●				●	●
Conference Facility												●																			●	●
Evening Functions		●		●								●																				
On Course Refreshments		●																														
Bar Snacks		●	●	●	●	●	●	●	●	●		●	●	●	●	●		●	●	●	●						●	●	●	●	●	●
Restaurant Dinner		●	●	●	●		●	●		●		●	●	●	●	●			●	●	●						●				●	●
Restaurant Lunch		●	●	●	●					●		●	●			●			●												●	●
Restaurant Breakfast		●	●	●	●					●			●	●					●													●
Shoe Cleaning Service				●																												
Bag Drop Service				●																												
Guests Changing Rooms		●	●	●	●	●	●	●	●	●		●	●	●	●	●		●	●	●	●	●		●	●		●	●	●	●	●	●
Guests Showers		●		●	●				●			●																				●
On Course Drinking Fountains																																
On Course Yardage Markers		●		●	●							●																				●
Spike Bar												●																				
Plastic Stud Fitting Service		●		●								●																				●
Plastic Studs Compulsory												●																				●
Visitors Need Handicap Proof																																
Golf Clubs Hire		●	●	●			●	●	●	●		●	●		●	●			●	●							●		●	●	●	●
Caddy Hire				●					●																							
Shoe Hire																																
Buggy Hire		●		●	●		●	●	●	●		●	●	●				●	●	●	●	●		●			●			●		
Trolley Hire		●		●	●	●	●	●	●	●		●	●	●	●	●		●	●	●	●	●		●			●		●	●		
Regripping		●		●																											●	●
Club Alterations		●		●																											●	●

Facilities Available at Golf Courses

Facility \ Golf Courses by County	DRUIDS GLEN	EUROPEAN CLUB	GLEN MILL	GLEN OF THE DOWNS	GLENMALURE	GREYSTONES	OLD CONNA	POWERSCOURT	RATHSALLAGH	TULFARRIS HOUSE	WICKLOW	WOODBROOK	WOODENBRIDGE
Dress Code Anything													
Dress Code Casual		●	●	●				●	●				
Dress Code Formal	●												
Golf Shop takes credit cards		●	●	●				●	●				
Club House takes credit card	●	●	●	●				●	●				
Youth Coaching Scheme								●					
Mobiles allowed in Club House													
Children allowed in Club House				●									
Spectators Allowed								●					
Disabled Facilities	●		●					●					
Disabled Toilets	●		●					●	●				
Disabled Access	●		●					●	●				
Satellite TV	●							●					
TV Lounge	●		●					●					
Snooker Room								●					
Members Only Bar								●					
Gym/Weights										●			
Massage								●					
Physiotherapy													
Sauna/Solararium								●	●				
Swimming Pool								●	●				
Health Club													
Accommodation						●		●	●	●			
Hotel On Site								●					
Visitors Car Park	●	●	●	●				●	●				
Members Car Park	●	●	●	●				●	●				
Practice Putting Green	●	●	●	●				●	●				
Practice Bunkers	●	●		●				●	●				
Practice Course	●		●					●	●				
Driving Range	●							●	●	●			
Conference Facility								●	●	●			
Evening Functions	●		●					●	●				
On Course Refreshments													
Bar Snacks	●	●	●	●	●	●	●	●	●			●	●
Restaurant Dinner	●	●	●			●		●	●			●	●
Restaurant Lunch	●		●					●	●				
Restaurant Breakfast	●	●	●					●	●				
Shoe Cleaning Service								●					
Bag Drop Service								●					
Guests Changing Rooms	●	●	●	●	●	●	●	●	●	●	●	●	●
Guests Showers	●	●	●	●				●	●				
On Course Drinking Fountains													
On Course Yardage Markers	●	●						●	●				
Spike Bar	●		●					●	●				
Plastic Stud Fitting Service			●					●	●				
Plastic Studs Compulsory			●					●	●				
Visitors Need Handicap Proof													
Golf Clubs Hire			●	●	●	●	●	●	●		●		
Caddy Hire	●		●					●	●				
Shoe Hire								●					
Buggy Hire	●	●	●	●			●	●	●				●
Trolley Hire	●	●	●	●	●	●		●	●		●	●	●
Regripping								●	●				
Club Alterations								●	●				

Facilities Available at Golf Courses

Golf Courses by County

NORTHERN IRELAND
COUNTY ANTRIM

Northern Ireland

FACILITIES AVAILABLE

Facility	ABERDELGHY	ALLEN PARK	BALLYCASTLE	BALLYCLARE	BALLYMENA	BALLYREAGH	BALMORAL	BELFAST	BELVOIR PARK	BENTRA MUNICIPAL	BUSHFOOT	CAIRNDHU	CARRICKFERGUS	CLIFTONVILLE	CUSHENDALL	DOWN ROYAL PARK	DUNMURRY	FORT WILLIAM	GALGORM CASTLE	GRACEHILL	GREENACRES GOLF CTRE	GREENISLAND	KNOCK	LARNE	LISBURN	MALONE	MASSEREENE	MOUNT OBER	ORMEAU
Dress Code Anything																													
Dress Code Casual																													
Dress Code Formal																													
Golf Shop takes credit cards				•																	•	•			•				
Club House takes credit card			•	•								•					•				•	•	•		•				
Youth Coaching Scheme				•		•							•				•				•	•		•	•				
Mobiles allowed in Club House			•	•		•		•					•				•				•	•		•	•				•
Children allowed in Club House			•	•	•	•							•				•				•	•		•	•				•
Spectators Allowed		•	•	•									•				•				•	•		•	•				•
Disabled Facilities		•	•	•									•				•				•	•		•	•				•
Disabled Toilets		•	•										•				•				•	•		•	•				•
Disabled Access		•	•														•				•	•		•	•				•
Satellite TV		•	•																		•	•		•	•				•
TV Lounge		•	•	•													•				•	•		•	•				•
Snooker Room		•	•	•													•				•			•	•				•
Members Only Bar																					•			•	•				
Gym/Weights					•																								
Massage																													
Physiotherapy																													
Sauna/Solararium																													
Swimming Pool																													
Health Club																													
Accommodation																	•		•										
Hotel On Site																	•		•										
Visitors Car Park		•	•	•			•						•				•				•	•	•		•				•
Members Car Park		•	•	•			•						•				•				•	•	•	•	•				•
Practice Putting Green		•	•	•									•				•				•	•	•	•	•				•
Practice Bunkers		•	•										•				•				•	•	•	•	•				
Practice Course				•									•								•	•	•	•					
Driving Range	•												•				•				•								
Conference Facility						•			•			•					•		•	•	•			•			•		
Evening Functions		•	•										•				•				•	•		•	•				
On Course Refreshments											•						•												
Bar Snacks	•	•	•		•		•		•	•	•	•	•	•	•	•	•		•	•	•	•	•	•	•	•	•	•	•
Restaurant Dinner			•	•			•		•	•	•		•	•	•	•	•		•	•	•	•	•	•	•	•	•	•	•
Restaurant Lunch		•	•	•			•		•	•	•		•	•	•	•	•				•	•	•	•	•	•	•	•	•
Restaurant Breakfast		•	•				•		•				•				•				•	•		•	•				
Shoe Cleaning Service													•			•													
Bag Drop Service			•														•												
Guests Changing Rooms	•	•	•	•	•	•	•	•	•	•	•	•	•	•	•	•	•	•	•	•	•	•	•	•	•	•	•	•	•
Guests Showers		•	•	•									•				•				•	•		•	•				
On Course Drinking Fountains		•	•	•									•				•				•	•		•	•				
On Course Yardage Markers		•	•	•			•		•				•				•				•	•		•	•				•
Spike Bar		•	•										•				•					•			•				
Plastic Stud Fitting Service		•	•						•			•				•					•				•				
Plastic Studs Compulsory																													
Visitors Need Handicap Proof																													
Golf Clubs Hire	•	•	•									•	•	•					•	•		•		•	•	•	•	•	•
Caddy Hire	•																		•										
Shoe Hire																			•										
Buggy Hire			•	•															•										
Trolley Hire	•	•	•	•		•	•		•				•		•		•		•				•	•	•	•	•		•
Regripping		•	•	•					•			•					•				•	•		•	•				•
Club Alterations		•	•	•					•			•				•	•		•		•			•	•				•

FACILITIES AVAILABLE

www.hccgolfworld.com

Facilities Available at Golf Courses

Facilities Available by County	ORMEAU	PORTRUSH (ROYAL)	SHANDON PARK	TARA GLEN	TEMPLE CLUB	WHITEHEAD	ARMAGH (COUNTY)	CRAIGAVON	EDENMORE	LURGAN	PORTADOWN	TANDRAGEE	ARDGLASS	BANBRIDGE	BANGOR	BELFAST (ROYAL)	BLACKWOOD GOLF CTRE	BRIGHT CASTLE	CARNALEA	CLANDEBOYE	CLOVERHILL	DONAGHADEE	DOWN (ROYAL COUNTY)	DOWNPATRICK	HELENS BAY	HOLYWOOD	KILKEEL	KIRKISTOWN CASTLE	MAHEE ISLAND	NEWRY
Dress Code Anything																														
Dress Code Casual												●	●									●		●		●	●	●	●	
Dress Code Formal																														
Golf Shop takes credit cards					●							●	●										●	●		●				
Club House takes credit card					●							●	●										●	●						
Youth Coaching Scheme	●				●	●						●	●		●	●						●	●	●	●	●	●			
Mobiles allowed in Club House	●				●	●						●	●		●							●		●						
Children allowed in Club House	●				●	●						●	●		●	●						●	●	●	●	●	●			
Spectators Allowed	●											●	●									●	●	●	●	●	●			
Disabled Facilities	●											●	●											●	●					
Disabled Toilets	●											●	●									●		●	●		●			
Disabled Access	●											●	●									●		●	●	●	●			
Satellite TV	●				●	●						●	●		●							●	●	●	●	●	●			
TV Lounge	●				●	●						●	●		●							●	●	●	●	●	●	●		
Snooker Room					●	●						●	●										●		●			●		
Members Only Bar						●																								
Gym/Weights									●			●																		
Massage																														
Physiotherapy																														
Sauna/Solararium												●																		
Swimming Pool																														
Health Club																														
Accommodation																														
Hotel On Site																														
Visitors Car Park	●				●	●						●	●									●		●	●	●	●	●		
Members Car Park	●				●	●						●	●									●	●	●	●	●	●	●	●	
Practice Putting Green					●	●						●	●									●	●	●	●					
Practice Bunkers						●						●	●									●	●	●						
Practice Course						●						●	●									●	●	●						
Driving Range							●	●				●										●								
Conference Facility										●		●	●	●		●		●								●				●
Evening Functions	●				●	●						●	●																	
On Course Refreshments																														
Bar Snacks	●	●	●	●	●		●	●	●	●		●	●	●	●	●	●		●	●	●	●	●	●	●	●	●	●	●	●
Restaurant Dinner	●	●	●				●		●			●	●								●		●			●				
Restaurant Lunch	●				●	●		●		●		●	●							●		●				●				
Restaurant Breakfast									●			●	●									●								
Shoe Cleaning Service					●																									
Bag Drop Service																														
Guests Changing Rooms	●	●	●				●	●	●	●	●	●	●	●	●	●	●	●	●	●	●	●	●	●	●	●	●	●	●	●
Guests Showers					●	●						●	●											●		●				
On Course Drinking Fountains												●												●						
On Course Yardage Markers	●				●	●						●	●									●	●	●	●		●	●		
Spike Bar						●						●	●									●								
Plastic Stud Fitting Service					●	●						●	●										●							
Plastic Studs Compulsory												●	●																	
Visitors Need Handicap Proof		●																				●	●		●					
Golf Clubs Hire	●	●	●		●				●	●		●	●		●	●	●			●	●	●	●				●		●	
Caddy Hire	●											●	●																	
Shoe Hire	●											●	●																	
Buggy Hire		●	●									●	●		●			●	●			●								●
Trolley Hire	●	●	●		●	●		●	●	●		●	●		●	●	●		●	●	●	●	●		●		●	●		●
Regripping					●	●						●	●									●	●	●	●		●			
Club Alterations	●				●	●						●	●									●								

COUNTY ARMAGH spans the columns ARMAGH (COUNTY) through TANDRAGEE. *COUNTY DOWN* spans the columns ARDGLASS through NEWRY.

Facilities Available at Golf Courses

Facility	RINGDUFFERIN	ROCKMOUNT	SCRABO	SPA	WARRENPOINT	ASHWOODS	CASTLE HUME	ENNISKILLEN	BENONE	BROWN TROUT	CASTLEROCK	DERRY	FAUGHAN VALLEY	FOYLE	KILREA	MOYOLA PARK	PORTSTEWART	RADISSON ROE PARK	DUNGANNON	FINTONA	KILLYMOON	NEWTOWNSTEWART	OMAGH	SPRINGHILL	STRABANE
Dress Code Anything																									
Dress Code Casual	•	•		•									•	•			•						•	•	•
Dress Code Formal																									
Golf Shop takes credit cards			•		•	•							•	•	•		•								
Club House takes credit card						•	•						•	•			•								
Youth Coaching Scheme	•			•			•																		•
Mobiles allowed in Club House			•	•		•	•	•					•												•
Children allowed in Club House	•		•	•		•	•	•					•	•									•	•	•
Spectators Allowed	•					•	•	•					•	•									•	•	•
Disabled Facilities			•					•					•	•	•								•	•	
Disabled Toilets			•	•									•	•	•								•	•	•
Disabled Access			•	•		•							•	•	•									•	•
Satellite TV			•	•									•	•									•	•	•
TV Lounge			•	•		•	•						•	•			•						•	•	•
Snooker Room			•	•									•	•									•	•	•
Members Only Bar				•																					
Gym/Weights												•						•							
Massage																									
Physiotherapy																									
Sauna/Solararium																		•							
Swimming Pool												•						•							
Health Club																									
Accommodation	•											•						•							
Hotel On Site																									
Visitors Car Park	•	•	•			•	•						•	•	•								•		
Members Car Park	•	•	•			•	•						•	•	•								•		
Practice Putting Green	•	•	•			•	•						•										•	•	•
Practice Bunkers	•		•			•	•						•											•	•
Practice Course			•			•							•												
Driving Range			•				•						•				•								
Conference Facility				•								•					•	•		•		•	•		
Evening Functions	•			•		•	•	•					•												
On Course Refreshments																									
Bar Snacks	•	•	•	•	•	•	•	•		•	•	•	•			•	•	•	•	•	•	•	•	•	•
Restaurant Dinner	•	•	•	•	•	•				•			•				•	•	•						
Restaurant Lunch	•	•	•			•							•				•	•	•						
Restaurant Breakfast	•	•				•	•											•							
Shoe Cleaning Service				•																		•	•		
Bag Drop Service																									
Guests Changing Rooms		•	•	•		•	•	•	•	•	•	•	•	•	•	•	•	•	•	•	•	•			
Guests Showers			•	•		•	•						•										•	•	•
On Course Drinking Fountains																									
On Course Yardage Markers	•	•				•	•						•	•			•						•		
Spike Bar				•																					
Plastic Stud Fitting Service				•		•	•																		
Plastic Studs Compulsory				•																					
Visitors Need Handicap Proof				•									•												
Golf Clubs Hire	•		•	•		•	•		•	•	•	•	•			•	•	•				•		•	•
Caddy Hire																									
Shoe Hire				•																					
Buggy Hire			•	•									•	•			•	•				•			•
Trolley Hire	•		•	•						•	•		•	•			•	•		•		•	•		•
Regripping	•	•	•	•		•	•						•	•	•		•						•		
Club Alterations	•	•		•		•	•						•	•	•		•								

Facilities Available at Golf Courses

GolfWorld Directory

FACILITIES AVAILABLE — Scotland

Facilities (rows):

- Dress Code Anything
- Dress Code Casual
- Dress Code Formal
- Golf Shop takes credit cards
- Club House takes credit card
- Youth Coaching Scheme
- Mobiles allowed in Club House
- Children allowed in Club House
- Spectators Allowed
- Disabled Facilities
- Disabled Toilets
- Disabled Access
- Satellite TV
- TV Lounge
- Snooker Room
- Members Only Bar
- Gym/Weights
- Massage
- Physiotherapy
- Sauna/Solararium
- Swimming Pool
- Health Club
- Accommodation
- Hotel On Site
- Visitors Car Park
- Members Car Park
- Practice Putting Green
- Practice Bunkers
- Practice Course
- Driving Range
- Conference Facility
- Evening Functions
- On Course Refreshments
- Bar Snacks
- Restaurant Dinner
- Restaurant Lunch
- Restaurant Breakfast
- Shoe Cleaning Service
- Bag Drop Service
- Guests Changing Rooms
- Guests Showers
- On Course Drinking Fountains
- On Course Yardage Markers
- Spike Bar
- Plastic Stud Fitting Service
- Plastic Studs Compulsory
- Visitors Need Handicap Proof
- Golf Clubs Hire
- Caddy Hire
- Shoe Hire
- Buggy Hire
- Trolley Hire
- Regripping
- Club Alterations

Golf Courses by County (columns):

SCOTLAND

ABERDEEN (CITY OF)
- ABERDEEN (ROYAL)
- AUCHMILL
- BALNAGASK
- CALEDONIAN
- CRAIBSTONE
- DEESIDE
- EAST ABERDEENSHIRE
- HAZLEHEAD
- HUNTLY
- KINGS LINKS GOLF CTRE
- MELDRUM HOUSE
- MURCAR
- NEWMACHAR
- NORTHERN
- PORTLETHEN

ABERDEENSHIRE
- ABOYNE
- ALFORD
- AUCHENBLAE
- BALLATER
- BANCHORY
- BRAEMAR
- CRUDEN BAY
- DUFF HOUSE ROYAL
- DUFFTOWN
- FRASERBURGH
- INCHMARLO GOLF CTRE
- INSCH
- INVERALLOCHY

Facilities Available at Golf Courses

Facility	INVERURIE	KEMNAY	KINTORE	MCDONALD	NEWBURGH-ON-YTHAN	OLDMELDRUM	PETERCULTER	PETERHEAD	STONEHAVEN	TARLAIR (ROYAL)	TARLAND	TORPHINS	TURRIFF	WESTHILL	ARBROATH	BRECHIN GOLF & SQUASH CLUB	CAIRD PARK	CAMPERDOWN	CARNOUSTIE	DOWNFIELD	EDZELL	FORFAR	KIRRIEMUIR	LETHAM GRANGE RESORT	MONIFIETH GOLF LINKS	MONTROSE LINKS TRUST	PANMURE	PIPERDAM GOLF	BUTE	CARDROSS
Dress Code Anything																														
Dress Code Casual	●	●	●	●	●	●		●	●			●	●		●	●			●		●	●	●				●	●		●
Dress Code Formal																				●						●				
Golf Shop takes credit cards	●	●			●			●		●				●	●	●				●	●	●		●			●	●		●
Club House takes credit card		●			●			●												●	●	●	●				●	●		
Youth Coaching Scheme								●	●				●		●	●				●	●	●					●	●		●
Mobiles allowed in Club House	●							●					●		●	●					●									
Children allowed in Club House	●	●	●	●	●			●	●			●	●		●	●				●	●						●		●	●
Spectators Allowed								●				●			●	●				●	●	●								
Disabled Facilities		●	●	●	●			●				●			●													●		●
Disabled Toilets		●	●	●	●	●		●				●			●					●								●		●
Disabled Access		●	●	●	●	●		●				●			●					●								●		●
Satellite TV	●	●				●									●	●				●										●
TV Lounge	●	●								●	●				●	●				●							●	●		●
Snooker Room				●						●	●					●														
Members Only Bar															●								●							
Gym/Weights																				●										
Massage																														
Physiotherapy																														
Sauna/Solararium															●															
Swimming Pool															●															
Health Club															●															
Accommodation																								●			●			
Hotel On Site																								●			●			
Visitors Car Park	●		●	●	●	●			●			●	●		●	●				●	●	●				●	●			●
Members Car Park	●				●			●	●	●		●	●		●	●				●	●	●				●	●			●
Practice Putting Green	●	●			●			●	●	●		●	●		●	●				●	●	●		●			●	●		●
Practice Bunkers	●	●						●	●	●					●	●				●										
Practice Course	●	●	●	●	●	●			●				●		●	●				●	●	●		●			●	●		●
Driving Range								●							●	●				●		●								
Conference Facility	●																			●				●		●				
Evening Functions	●					●			●						●	●					●	●	●	●		●				
On Course Refreshments																														
Bar Snacks	●	●	●	●	●	●	●	●	●	●	●	●	●	●	●	●	●		●	●	●	●	●	●	●	●	●	●	●	●
Restaurant Dinner	●	●		●	●	●		●	●				●		●	●				●	●	●	●	●			●	●		●
Restaurant Lunch	●	●		●	●	●		●	●				●		●	●				●	●	●	●	●		●	●	●		●
Restaurant Breakfast	●			●	●	●	●		●				●		●					●	●	●		●			●	●		●
Shoe Cleaning Service															●															
Bag Drop Service															●															
Guests Changing Rooms	●	●	●		●	●	●	●	●	●	●	●	●	●	●	●	●	●	●	●	●	●	●	●	●	●	●	●	●	●
Guests Showers	●	●	●		●	●	●	●	●	●	●	●	●	●	●	●		●		●	●	●	●	●	●	●	●	●	●	●
On Course Drinking Fountains	●	●													●					●	●	●					●	●		●
On Course Yardage Markers	●	●					●			●	●				●					●	●	●				●	●	●		●
Spike Bar									●						●					●										
Plastic Stud Fitting Service	●														●					●	●							●		
Plastic Studs Compulsory																														
Visitors Need Handicap Proof								●	●						●					●	●									
Golf Clubs Hire	●	●		●	●	●	●	●	●			●	●		●	●	●			●	●	●		●	●	●	●	●		●
Caddy Hire							●		●						●															
Shoe Hire			●												●											●				
Buggy Hire	●		●	●	●			●	●						●	●	●			●	●	●		●	●		●	●		●
Trolley Hire	●	●	●	●	●	●		●	●	●	●	●	●		●	●	●			●	●	●		●	●	●	●	●		●
Regripping	●				●										●					●	●	●			●	●				●
Club Alterations	●			●									●		●					●	●	●				●	●			●

www.hccgolfworld.com

Facilities Available at Golf Courses

Golf Courses by County

The following facilities are listed (rows) against each golf course (columns). A ● indicates the facility is available.

Facility	CARRADALE	CLYDEBANK & DISTRICT	COLONSAY	COWAL	CRAIGNURE	DALMALLY	DALMUIR MUNICIPAL	DUMBARTON	DUNARVERTY	GIGHA	GLENCRUITTEN	HELENSBURGH	INNELLAN	INVERARAY	KYLES OF BUTE	LOCH LOMOND	LOCHGILPHEAD	MACHRIE	MACHRIHANISH	PORT BANNATYNE	ROTHESAY	TOBERMORY	VALE OF LEVEN	ANNANHILL	BALLOCHMYLE	CAPRINGTON	LOUDOUN	NEW CUMNOCK	ARDEER	AUCHENHARVIE
Dress Code Anything																														
Dress Code Casual				●					●							●			●					●					●	●
Dress Code Formal																														
Golf Shop takes credit cards																●								●					●	●
Club House takes credit card																●														
Youth Coaching Scheme									●										●											
Mobiles allowed in Club House									●										●	●									●	
Children allowed in Club House			●						●							●			●	●				●					●	
Spectators Allowed				●												●														●
Disabled Facilities				●												●														
Disabled Toilets				●												●				●										
Disabled Access				●												●														
Satellite TV				●																										
TV Lounge																●			●					●					●	
Snooker Room				●														●	●					●					●	
Members Only Bar				●												●			●											
Gym/Weights																●														
Massage																														
Physiotherapy																														
Sauna/Solararium																														
Swimming Pool																														●
Health Club																														
Accommodation								●										●										●		
Hotel On Site																●		●												
Visitors Car Park				●					●							●			●	●				●					●	●
Members Car Park				●												●			●	●									●	●
Practice Putting Green				●												●								●					●	●
Practice Bunkers				●												●														
Practice Course									●						●	●			●					●					●	
Driving Range																●		●										●	●	
Conference Facility																●														
Evening Functions																●			●										●	
On Course Refreshments																													●	
Bar Snacks	●	●		●		●	●	●	●	●						●	●	●	●	●	●			●	●		●	●	●	●
Restaurant Dinner	●	●		●		●	●	●	●							●		●	●										●	
Restaurant Lunch				●												●			●							●			●	
Restaurant Breakfast				●												●		●	●										●	
Shoe Cleaning Service																														
Bag Drop Service									●																					
Guests Changing Rooms	●	●		●	●	●	●	●	●		●					●	●	●	●	●	●	●		●	●	●	●		●	
Guests Showers				●												●			●										●	●
On Course Drinking Fountains																														●
On Course Yardage Markers				●												●													●	
Spike Bar											●					●		●											●	
Plastic Stud Fitting Service																													●	
Plastic Studs Compulsory																														
Visitors Need Handicap Proof									●																					
Golf Clubs Hire		●	●	●	●	●	●				●					●			●			●	●						●	●
Caddy Hire																●		●	●											
Shoe Hire																●													●	
Buggy Hire																●			●										●	
Trolley Hire	●		●	●		●		●		●	●					●	●	●	●		●			●	●	●			●	●
Regripping		●		●								●				●								●					●	●
Club Alterations				●								●				●													●	●

Facilities Available at Golf Courses

Golf Courses by County

Facility	BEITH	BRODICK	CORRIE	GLASGOW GAILES	IRVINE	KILBIRNIE PLACE	LARGS	MILLPORT	RAVENSPARK	ROUTENBURN	SHISKINE	SKELMORLIE	WEST KILBRIDE	WESTERN GAILES	WHITING BAY	BELLEISLE & SEAFIELD	BRUNSTON CASTLE	DALMILLING	DOON VALLEY	GIRVAN	KILMARNOCK	MAYBOLE MUNICIPAL	PRESTWICK	PRESTWICK ST CUTHBERT	PRESTWICK ST NICHOLAS	ROODLEA	TROON (ROYAL)	TROON MUNICIPAL	TURNBERRY	ALLOA
Dress Code Anything													●													●				
Dress Code Casual				●	●		●	●			●			●		●	●	●		●							●			●
Dress Code Formal	●			●	●								●			●	●		●							●			●	
Golf Shop takes credit cards				●	●			●		●						●	●	●	●							●				●
Club House takes credit card				●												●	●	●	●							●				●
Youth Coaching Scheme				●									●			●										●				●
Mobiles allowed in Club House	●			●	●			●		●			●																	●
Children allowed in Club House	●			●	●		●	●	●	●	●					●														●
Spectators Allowed							●						●			●						●								●
Disabled Facilities				●									●			●	●													●
Disabled Toilets				●							●					●	●					●								●
Disabled Access				●									●			●	●													●
Satellite TV								●	●	●			●			●	●													●
TV Lounge	●			●	●			●		●			●			●	●		●											●
Snooker Room				●	●																									●
Members Only Bar									●																					
Gym/Weights																●													●	
Massage																														
Physiotherapy																														
Sauna/Solararium																●													●	●
Swimming Pool																●								●						●
Health Club																●														
Accommodation																●	●												●	●
Hotel On Site																														
Visitors Car Park	●			●	●	●	●	●	●	●						●	●	●												●
Members Car Park	●			●	●	●	●	●	●	●	●	●	●			●	●	●												●
Practice Putting Green				●					●	●	●	●	●	●		●									●	●			●	●
Practice Bunkers				●												●											●			●
Practice Course				●									●			●			●											●
Driving Range				●									●			●											●		●	●
Conference Facility																●	●												●	
Evening Functions				●	●	●	●		●		●		●			●	●													●
On Course Refreshments				●																										
Bar Snacks	●	●	●	●	●		●	●	●	●	●	●	●	●	●	●	●	●		●	●		●	●	●	●	●			●
Restaurant Dinner	●		●	●	●		●	●		●		●	●	●	●	●	●	●			●									●
Restaurant Lunch	●			●	●		●	●			●	●	●	●		●	●	●			●			●						●
Restaurant Breakfast	●						●	●	●	●						●	●													●
Shoe Cleaning Service				●																										
Bag Drop Service				●														●												
Guests Changing Rooms	●	●		●	●	●	●	●	●	●	●	●	●	●	●	●	●	●		●	●		●	●	●	●	●	●		●
Guests Showers	●			●	●			●	●		●	●	●			●	●	●			●			●						●
On Course Drinking Fountains	●			●				●		●			●																	●
On Course Yardage Markers	●			●				●			●					●														●
Spike Bar			●							●			●			●	●													●
Plastic Stud Fitting Service				●				●	●	●						●		●												
Plastic Studs Compulsory																														
Visitors Need Handicap Proof				●							●																			
Golf Clubs Hire		●	●	●		●			●	●	●	●		●		●	●				●	●		●	●	●		●		●
Caddy Hire		●	●																									●		
Shoe Hire		●	●																											
Buggy Hire		●	●			●			●					●							●			●				●		●
Trolley Hire	●	●	●			●	●	●	●	●		●	●	●		●	●				●	●		●	●	●		●		●
Regripping		●	●		●	●		●	●	●			●			●	●													●
Club Alterations			●	●			●	●		●			●			●	●	●												●

Facilities Available at Golf Courses

GolfWorld Directory

Facilities Available by County	ALVA	BRAEHEAD	BRIDGE OF ALLAN	DOLLAR	MUCKHART	TILLICOULTRY	TULLIALLAN	BRIGHOUSE BAY	CASTLE DOUGLAS	COLVEND	CRAIGIEKNOWES	CRICHTON	DUMFRIES & COUNTY	GALLOWAY	GATEHOUSE	GRETNA	KIRKCUDBRIGHT	LAGGANMORE	LANGHOLM	LOCHMABEN	LOCKERBIE	MOFFAT	NEW GALLOWAY	NEWTON STEWART	PARK TONGLAND	PINES	PORTPATRICK - DUNSKEY	POWFOOT	SANQUHAR	SOLWAY LINKS	SOUTHERNESS
Dress Code Anything																						•									
Dress Code Casual	•		•									•	•	•	•	•			•		•	•		•	•	•	•	•		•	•
Dress Code Formal				•																											
Golf Shop takes credit cards	•			•									•													•	•				•
Club House takes credit card	•			•											•											•					
Youth Coaching Scheme				•									•					•													
Mobiles allowed in Club House	•			•							•	•	•			•	•		•	•		•		•	•					•	•
Children allowed in Club House	•			•							•	•	•		•	•	•		•	•		•		•	•					•	•
Spectators Allowed											•	•	•			•	•			•											
Disabled Facilities				•							•	•	•			•				•	•										•
Disabled Toilets	•			•							•	•	•			•				•	•									•	•
Disabled Access	•			•							•	•	•			•				•	•									•	•
Satellite TV	•			•																											
TV Lounge	•			•							•			•					•	•				•	•					•	•
Snooker Room			•	•												•							•								
Members Only Bar																															
Gym/Weights								•																							
Massage																															
Physiotherapy																															
Sauna/Solararium																															
Swimming Pool								•																							
Health Club																															
Accommodation								•																							
Hotel On Site																									•						
Visitors Car Park	•			•							•		•	•	•		•		•	•		•		•	•	•	•	•		•	•
Members Car Park				•							•		•		•	•			•	•		•		•	•		•	•		•	•
Practice Putting Green				•							•		•	•	•		•			•		•		•	•		•	•		•	•
Practice Bunkers	•			•									•							•		•					•	•			
Practice Course				•				•				•	•	•			•					•									•
Driving Range								•													•							•			
Conference Facility				•																											
Evening Functions				•							•					•					•				•						
On Course Refreshments																															
Bar Snacks	•	•	•	•	•			•	•	•	•	•	•	•			•	•	•	•	•	•	•	•	•	•	•	•		•	•
Restaurant Dinner	•		•	•									•				•			•		•			•		•	•		•	•
Restaurant Lunch	•		•	•								•	•				•			•		•		•	•		•	•		•	•
Restaurant Breakfast	•											•										•		•	•		•	•		•	•
Shoe Cleaning Service																						•									
Bag Drop Service																															
Guests Changing Rooms	•	•	•	•	•	•		•	•	•	•	•	•	•	•		•		•	•	•	•		•	•	•	•	•		•	•
Guests Showers	•			•	•						•		•		•	•	•			•		•		•	•		•	•		•	•
On Course Drinking Fountains				•									•			•												•			
On Course Yardage Markers	•			•							•		•	•	•					•				•	•		•			•	•
Spike Bar													•									•						•			•
Plastic Stud Fitting Service	•			•									•											•	•			•			
Plastic Studs Compulsory													•																		
Visitors Need Handicap Proof				•																						•		•			•
Golf Clubs Hire	•		•	•			•		•	•	•		•	•		•	•				•	•	•	•	•	•	•	•		•	•
Caddy Hire																															•
Shoe Hire																						•									
Buggy Hire	•									•		•										•	•				•				•
Trolley Hire	•	•	•	•	•			•	•	•		•	•	•		•	•			•		•		•	•	•	•	•		•	•
Regripping	•			•									•	•		•								•	•	•	•				
Club Alterations	•			•									•	•										•	•	•	•				

Golf Courses by County

ALVA · BRAEHEAD · BRIDGE OF ALLAN · DOLLAR · MUCKHART · TILLICOULTRY · TULLIALLAN · DUMFRIES AND GALLOWAY · BRIGHOUSE BAY · CASTLE DOUGLAS · COLVEND · CRAIGIEKNOWES · CRICHTON · DUMFRIES & COUNTY · GALLOWAY · GATEHOUSE · GRETNA · KIRKCUDBRIGHT · LAGGANMORE · LANGHOLM · LOCHMABEN · LOCKERBIE · MOFFAT · NEW GALLOWAY · NEWTON STEWART · PARK TONGLAND · PINES · PORTPATRICK - DUNSKEY · POWFOOT · SANQUHAR · SOLWAY LINKS · SOUTHERNESS

Facilities Available at Golf Courses

Golf Courses by County	ST. MEDAN	STRANRAER	THORNHILL	WIGTOWN & BLADNOCH	WIGTOWNSHIRE	EDINBURGH (CITY OF)	BABERTON	BRAID HILLS	BRUNTSFIELD GOLF CLUB	BURGESS (ROYAL)	CARRICK KNOWE	CRAIGENTINNY	CRAIGMILLAR PARK	DALMAHOY	DUDDINGSTON	KINGSKNOWE	LIBERTON	LOTHIANBURN	MERCHANTS OF EDINBURGH	MORTONHALL	MURRAYFIELD	PORTOBELLO	PRESTONFIELD	RATHO PARK	RAVELSTON	SILVERKNOWES	SWANSTON	TORPHIN HILL	TURNHOUSE	FALKIRK	BONNYBRIDGE	FALKIRK
Dress Code Anything																																
Dress Code Casual	•	•		•									•														•				•	•
Dress Code Formal																																
Golf Shop takes credit cards	•	•											•														•					
Club House takes credit card	•																															•
Youth Coaching Scheme	•	•								•																	•				•	
Mobiles allowed in Club House	•	•								•																	•					
Children allowed in Club House	•	•					•			•																	•				•	•
Spectators Allowed	•	•					•			•																						•
Disabled Facilities	•	•																														
Disabled Toilets	•	•																														
Disabled Access	•	•																														
Satellite TV													•																			
TV Lounge	•	•		•						•																	•				•	•
Snooker Room										•			•																		•	
Members Only Bar										•																					•	
Gym/Weights													•																			
Massage																																
Physiotherapy																																
Sauna/Solararium													•																			
Swimming Pool													•																			
Health Club													•																			
Accommodation									•				•																			
Hotel On Site													•																			
Visitors Car Park	•	•		•			•			•								•									•				•	•
Members Car Park	•	•		•			•			•																	•				•	•
Practice Putting Green	•	•		•			•			•								•									•				•	•
Practice Bunkers	•	•					•			•																	•				•	•
Practice Course		•		•			•			•																					•	•
Driving Range								•	•																						•	•
Conference Facility																								•								
Evening Functions	•	•						•		•																	•					
On Course Refreshments							•																									
Bar Snacks	•	•	•	•	•		•		•	•			•	•	•	•			•	•	•	•		•		•	•	•		•	•	•
Restaurant Dinner	•	•	•	•				•	•	•			•	•	•		•		•	•	•		•	•		•	•	•		•	•	•
Restaurant Lunch	•	•	•	•				•	•	•			•	•			•		•				•			•		•		•	•	•
Restaurant Breakfast	•	•		•									•	•																	•	
Shoe Cleaning Service																																
Bag Drop Service																																
Guests Changing Rooms	•	•	•	•	•		•	•	•	•			•	•	•	•		•	•	•	•	•		•	•	•	•	•		•	•	•
Guests Showers	•	•	•							•			•																			
On Course Drinking Fountains	•	•								•																						
On Course Yardage Markers	•	•		•						•																	•					•
Spike Bar																																
Plastic Stud Fitting Service	•	•								•																						
Plastic Studs Compulsory		•																														
Visitors Need Handicap Proof										•																					•	
Golf Clubs Hire	•	•	•				•	•	•	•	•	•	•	•				•	•	•	•			•		•	•		•			
Caddy Hire	•																															
Shoe Hire	•									•																						
Buggy Hire	•	•						•	•	•	•			•													•					
Trolley Hire	•	•		•			•			•		•	•	•				•	•	•	•		•	•					•			
Regripping		•		•				•		•																	•				•	•
Club Alterations		•		•				•		•																	•				•	•

www.hccgolfworld.com

Facilities Available at Golf Courses

Golf Courses by County

Facility	FALKIRK TRYST	GLENBERVIE	GRANGEMOUTH	POLMONT	FIFE	ABERDOUR	ANSTRUTHER	AUCHTERDERRAN	BALBIRNIE PARK	BURNTISLAND	CANMORE	CHARLETON	COWDENBEATH	CRAIL
Dress Code Anything														
Dress Code Casual				●		●	●	●	●		●	●		●
Dress Code Formal														
Golf Shop takes credit cards						●			●		●	●		●
Club House takes credit card									●			●		●
Youth Coaching Scheme				●		●		●	●		●	●		●
Mobiles allowed in Club House				●					●					
Children allowed in Club House				●		●	●	●	●		●	●		●
Spectators Allowed						●		●	●		●	●		●
Disabled Facilities								●	●					●
Disabled Toilets								●	●			●		●
Disabled Access								●	●			●		●
Satellite TV						●		●	●		●			
TV Lounge				●		●		●	●		●	●		●
Snooker Room				●										●
Members Only Bar						●								
Gym/Weights														
Massage														
Physiotherapy														
Sauna/Solararium														
Swimming Pool														
Health Club														
Accommodation									●					
Hotel On Site									●					
Visitors Car Park				●			●	●	●		●	●		●
Members Car Park				●		●	●		●		●			●
Practice Putting Green				●		●		●	●		●	●		●
Practice Bunkers								●	●		●	●	●	●
Practice Course						●		●	●		●	●	●	●
Driving Range										●		●		
Conference Facility									●					
Evening Functions				●		●			●		●			
On Course Refreshments									●					
Bar Snacks	●	●	●	●		●	●	●	●	●	●	●	●	●
Restaurant Dinner	●	●	●	●		●	●		●	●	●	●		●
Restaurant Lunch				●		●	●		●		●	●		●
Restaurant Breakfast				●		●			●		●	●		●
Shoe Cleaning Service														
Bag Drop Service														
Guests Changing Rooms		●	●	●		●	●	●	●	●	●	●		●
Guests Showers				●		●	●	●	●		●	●		●
On Course Drinking Fountains														
On Course Yardage Markers				●		●	●		●		●	●		●
Spike Bar														
Plastic Stud Fitting Service						●			●		●			●
Plastic Studs Compulsory														
Visitors Need Handicap Proof														
Golf Clubs Hire	●					●			●	●		●		●
Caddy Hire									●					●
Shoe Hire									●					
Buggy Hire						●			●			●		●
Trolley Hire	●		●			●	●		●	●	●	●	●	●
Regripping						●			●		●			●
Club Alterations						●			●		●			●

Facility	CUPAR	DUKES	DUNFERMLINE	DUNNIKIER	ELIE GOLF	ELMWOOD	FALKLAND	GLENROTHES	KINGHORN	KINGSBARNS GOLF LINKS	KIRKCALDY	LADYBANK	LESLIE	LEVEN LINKS	LEVEN THISTLE	LOCHGELLY	LOCHORE MEADOWS	LUNDIN
Dress Code Anything									●									
Dress Code Casual	●	●	●	●	●	●	●		●	●		●	●		●			●
Dress Code Formal					●													
Golf Shop takes credit cards		●	●	●	●					●		●				●		●
Club House takes credit card		●		●		●	●			●		●						
Youth Coaching Scheme	●		●		●		●		●			●			●	●		●
Mobiles allowed in Club House			●	●		●	●		●				●			●		
Children allowed in Club House	●	●	●	●	●	●	●		●			●	●		●	●		
Spectators Allowed	●	●	●	●	●		●						●		●	●		
Disabled Facilities	●					●	●			●		●	●			●		
Disabled Toilets	●	●				●	●			●		●	●			●		
Disabled Access	●	●				●	●					●	●			●		
Satellite TV		●	●	●								●			●			●
TV Lounge	●		●	●								●	●			●		●
Snooker Room			●												●	●		
Members Only Bar			●															
Gym/Weights																		
Massage																		
Physiotherapy																		
Sauna/Solararium																		
Swimming Pool																		
Health Club																		
Accommodation																		
Hotel On Site																		
Visitors Car Park	●	●		●	●	●				●		●	●		●	●		●
Members Car Park		●		●	●							●			●	●		●
Practice Putting Green	●	●	●	●	●	●	●			●		●				●		●
Practice Bunkers		●	●	●	●	●				●		●						●
Practice Course				●	●	●						●						
Driving Range		●			●					●						●		
Conference Facility											●						●	
Evening Functions	●	●	●	●			●					●	●					
On Course Refreshments		●								●								
Bar Snacks	●	●	●	●	●	●	●	●	●	●	●	●	●	●	●	●	●	●
Restaurant Dinner		●	●	●	●	●	●	●	●		●	●		●	●	●		●
Restaurant Lunch	●	●	●	●	●	●	●				●	●			●	●		●
Restaurant Breakfast	●	●	●	●	●	●	●					●			●	●		
Shoe Cleaning Service																		
Bag Drop Service		●								●								
Guests Changing Rooms	●	●	●	●	●	●	●	●	●	●	●	●	●	●	●	●	●	●
Guests Showers	●	●	●	●	●	●	●			●		●			●	●		●
On Course Drinking Fountains			●							●		●				●		●
On Course Yardage Markers	●	●	●			●	●			●					●	●		
Spike Bar		●		●						●						●		●
Plastic Stud Fitting Service			●	●								●						●
Plastic Studs Compulsory			●													●		
Visitors Need Handicap Proof					●					●		●						
Golf Clubs Hire	●	●	●	●	●		●			●	●	●		●		●		●
Caddy Hire				●	●					●		●						●
Shoe Hire		●								●						●		
Buggy Hire		●				●					●	●						
Trolley Hire	●	●	●	●	●	●	●			●	●	●		●	●	●		●
Regripping		●	●	●	●							●				●		●
Club Alterations		●	●	●	●							●				●		●

Facilities Available at Golf Courses

Golf Courses by County

Facility	LUNDIN LADIES	NEW	PITREAVIE	SALINE	SCOONIE	SCOTSCRAIG	SCOTTISH GOLF NATIONAL CTRE	ST. ANDREWS LINKS	ST. MICHAELS	THORNTON
Dress Code Anything							●			
Dress Code Casual		●	●	●		●				●
Dress Code Formal										
Golf Shop takes credit cards			●			●	●	●		
Club House takes credit card		●				●	●			
Youth Coaching Scheme		●	●			●	●			●
Mobiles allowed in Club House				●		●	●			●
Children allowed in Club House		●	●	●		●	●			●
Spectators Allowed			●			●	●	●		●
Disabled Facilities			●	●		●	●			●
Disabled Toilets			●	●			●			●
Disabled Access			●	●		●	●	●		●
Satellite TV		●	●	●		●	●			
TV Lounge		●	●	●		●				●
Snooker Room		●								
Members Only Bar		●								●
Gym/Weights							●			
Massage							●			
Physiotherapy							●			
Sauna/Solararium										
Swimming Pool										
Health Club										
Accommodation			●				●			
Hotel On Site			●				●			
Visitors Car Park			●	●			●	●		●
Members Car Park			●				●			●
Practice Putting Green			●	●		●	●	●		●
Practice Bunkers			●			●	●	●		●
Practice Course			●			●	●	●		●
Driving Range				●		●	●	●		
Conference Facility										
Evening Functions		●	●	●						●
On Course Refreshments			●							
Bar Snacks	●		●	●		●	●	●	●	●
Restaurant Dinner		●	●	●		●		●	●	●
Restaurant Lunch		●	●	●		●	●	●	●	●
Restaurant Breakfast			●	●		●	●	●		●
Shoe Cleaning Service										
Bag Drop Service										
Guests Changing Rooms			●	●	●	●	●	●	●	●
Guests Showers			●	●		●	●	●		●
On Course Drinking Fountains						●				
On Course Yardage Markers			●			●				●
Spike Bar			●			●				
Plastic Stud Fitting Service			●							
Plastic Studs Compulsory										
Visitors Need Handicap Proof										
Golf Clubs Hire			●	●	●	●		●		
Caddy Hire								●		
Shoe Hire			●					●		
Buggy Hire						●		●		
Trolley Hire	●		●			●		●	●	●
Regripping			●				●			
Club Alterations			●			●	●			

Facility	GLASGOW (CITY OF)	ALEXANDRA	BALMORE	BEARSDEN	BISHOPBRIGGS	BLAIRBETH	BONNYTON	BOTHWELL CASTLE	CALDERBRAES	CALDWELL	CAMPSIE	CATHCART CASTLE	CATHKIN BRAES	CAWDER	CLOBER	COWGLEN	CROW WOOD	DOUGLAS PARK	DULLATUR	EAST KILBRIDE	EAST RENFREWSHIRE	EASTWOOD
Dress Code Anything																						
Dress Code Casual																						
Dress Code Formal																						
Golf Shop takes credit cards												●						●			●	
Club House takes credit card																						
Youth Coaching Scheme																		●			●	
Mobiles allowed in Club House				●																		
Children allowed in Club House												●						●			●	
Spectators Allowed				●								●									●	
Disabled Facilities												●										
Disabled Toilets												●										
Disabled Access												●										
Satellite TV				●														●			●	
TV Lounge				●														●			●	
Snooker Room												●										
Members Only Bar												●										
Gym/Weights																			●			
Massage																						
Physiotherapy																						
Sauna/Solararium																			●			
Swimming Pool																						
Health Club																						
Accommodation																						
Hotel On Site																						
Visitors Car Park		●		●								●						●			●	●
Members Car Park		●		●								●						●			●	●
Practice Putting Green																					●	●
Practice Bunkers																					●	●
Practice Course		●																			●	●
Driving Range																●						
Conference Facility		●																	●			
Evening Functions				●								●						●				●
On Course Refreshments																						
Bar Snacks			●	●		●	●	●	●	●	●	●	●		●	●		●	●	●	●	●
Restaurant Dinner			●	●		●	●	●	●	●	●	●	●		●	●		●	●	●	●	●
Restaurant Lunch				●								●						●			●	●
Restaurant Breakfast				●								●									●	●
Shoe Cleaning Service																						
Bag Drop Service																						
Guests Changing Rooms		●	●	●	●	●	●	●	●	●	●	●	●	●	●	●	●	●	●	●	●	●
Guests Showers				●								●						●			●	●
On Course Drinking Fountains												●										
On Course Yardage Markers		●		●								●						●			●	●
Spike Bar				●								●										●
Plastic Stud Fitting Service																						
Plastic Studs Compulsory																						
Visitors Need Handicap Proof																						
Golf Clubs Hire							●	●				●		●					●	●	●	●
Caddy Hire												●										
Shoe Hire												●										
Buggy Hire							●	●										●	●			
Trolley Hire							●	●		●		●	●		●		●	●	●	●	●	●
Regripping				●								●						●			●	●
Club Alterations				●								●						●			●	●

Scotland

FACILITIES AVAILABLE

Facilities Available at Golf Courses

Facility	ESPORTA-DOUGALSTON	FERENEZE	HAGGS CASTLE	HAYSTON	HILTON PARK	KILSYTH LENNOX	KIRKHILL	KIRKINTILLOCH	KNIGHTSWOOD	LENZIE	LETHAMHILL	LINN PARK	LITTLEHILL	MILNGAVIE	MOUNT ELLEN	POLLOK	TORRANCE HOUSE	WESTERWOOD	WHITECRAIGS	WILLIAMWOOD	WINDYHILL	ABERNETHY	AIGAS	AIGAS	ALNESS	BOAT OF GARTEN	BONAR BRIDGE/ARDGAY	BRORA	CARNEGIE	CARRBRIDGE	DORNOCH (ROYAL)
Dress Code Anything																															
Dress Code Casual									•																	•	•				•
Dress Code Formal																												•			
Golf Shop takes credit cards							•																					•			
Club House takes credit card																												•			
Youth Coaching Scheme																												•			
Mobiles allowed in Club House									•																			•			
Children allowed in Club House							•																					•			
Spectators Allowed							•																								
Disabled Facilities							•																								
Disabled Toilets							•																		•			•	•		
Disabled Access							•																					•	•		
Satellite TV							•																			•		•			
TV Lounge							•																			•		•			
Snooker Room							•																								
Members Only Bar																															
Gym/Weights																		•										•			
Massage																															
Physiotherapy																															
Sauna/Solararium																		•										•			
Swimming Pool																		•										•			
Health Club																															
Accommodation																		•													
Hotel On Site																		•													
Visitors Car Park							•																			•		•	•		
Members Car Park							•																					•			
Practice Putting Green							•			•																•	•	•			
Practice Bunkers							•																					•			
Practice Course							•																					•			
Driving Range																		•										•			
Conference Facility										•								•			•							•	•		
Evening Functions																															
On Course Refreshments																															
Bar Snacks		•	•	•	•	•	•		•			•	•	•		•	•	•	•	•	•	•			•	•	•	•	•	•	•
Restaurant Dinner	•	•	•	•	•		•							•	•	•	•	•	•	•	•	•				•	•	•	•		•
Restaurant Lunch	•						•											•										•	•		•
Restaurant Breakfast							•											•													
Shoe Cleaning Service																															
Bag Drop Service																															
Guests Changing Rooms		•	•	•	•	•	•	•	•	•	•	•	•	•	•	•	•	•	•	•	•	•			•	•	•	•	•	•	•
Guests Showers							•																			•		•	•		
On Course Drinking Fountains							•																					•			
On Course Yardage Markers							•																					•			
Spike Bar																															
Plastic Stud Fitting Service																															
Plastic Studs Compulsory																															
Visitors Need Handicap Proof																												•			
Golf Clubs Hire		•	•		•												•	•	•		•	•			•	•	•	•		•	•
Caddy Hire										•																		•			
Shoe Hire																															
Buggy Hire			•	•		•	•							•				•								•		•	•		•
Trolley Hire			•	•	•	•				•							•	•			•	•			•	•	•	•	•	•	•
Regripping							•																					•			
Club Alterations							•																					•			

Facilities Available at Golf Courses

Golf Courses by County

Facility	DURNESS	FORT AUGUSTUS	FORT WILLIAM	FORTROSE & ROSEMARKIE	GAIRLOCH	GOLSPIE	HELMSDALE	INVERGORDON	INVERNESS	ISLE OF SKYE	KINGUSSIE	LOCH NESS	LOCHCARRON	LYBSTER	MUIR OF ORD	NAIRN	NAIRN DUNBAR	NEWTONMORE	REAY	SKEABOST	STRATHPEFFER SPA	TAIN	TARBAT	THURSO	TORVEAN	TRAIGH	ULLAPOOL	WICK	INVERCLYDE	GOUROCK	KILMACOLM	WHINHILL
Dress Code Anything																																
Dress Code Casual									●	●									●	●										●		●
Dress Code Formal																●														●		●
Golf Shop takes credit cards									●							●														●		
Club House takes credit card																●														●		
Youth Coaching Scheme									●	●								●												●		
Mobiles allowed in Club House									●	●														●	●					●	●	●
Children allowed in Club House									●	●									●	●				●						●	●	●
Spectators Allowed									●	●								●														●
Disabled Facilities									●	●								●														
Disabled Toilets									●	●									●	●												
Disabled Access									●	●									●	●												
Satellite TV																								●						●		●
TV Lounge									●																	●				●		●
Snooker Room																																
Members Only Bar																																
Gym/Weights																																
Massage																																
Physiotherapy																																
Sauna/Solararium																																
Swimming Pool																																
Health Club																																
Accommodation																				●												
Hotel On Site																																
Visitors Car Park									●	●									●	●						●				●		●
Members Car Park									●	●																●				●		
Practice Putting Green									●							●											●			●		●
Practice Bunkers									●							●											●					
Practice Course									●							●																
Driving Range														●		●																
Conference Facility																				●												
Evening Functions									●									●														●
On Course Refreshments																																
Bar Snacks	●		●	●	●	●	●	●	●	●					●	●	●	●	●	●		●	●	●	●			●		●	●	●
Restaurant Dinner			●	●					●	●						●	●	●		●										●		●
Restaurant Lunch			●			●			●	●						●	●		●	●										●		●
Restaurant Breakfast									●																					●		
Shoe Cleaning Service																																
Bag Drop Service																																
Guests Changing Rooms	●	●	●	●	●	●	●	●	●	●					●	●	●	●	●	●		●	●	●	●	●	●	●		●	●	●
Guests Showers									●	●																				●		●
On Course Drinking Fountains																																
On Course Yardage Markers									●								●	●									●					
Spike Bar																																
Plastic Stud Fitting Service									●																					●		
Plastic Studs Compulsory																																
Visitors Need Handicap Proof									●							●														●		
Golf Clubs Hire	●	●	●	●	●				●	●	●				●	●	●	●	●	●					●	●	●	●		●		●
Caddy Hire																																
Shoe Hire																																
Buggy Hire		●	●																													
Trolley Hire	●	●	●	●	●				●	●					●	●	●	●	●					●	●		●	●		●		●
Regripping									●																					●		
Club Alterations									●																					●		

Facilities Available at Golf Courses

Facility	LAMLASH	LOCHRANZA GOLF	MACHRIE BAY	AIRDRIE	BELLSHILL	COLVILLE PARK	DALZIEL	DRUMPELLIER	EASTER MOFFAT	PALACERIGG	SHOTTS	WISHAW	BIGGAR	CARLUKE	CARNWATH	DOUGLAS WATER	HOLLANDBUSH	KAMES GOLF	LANARK	RICCARTON	STRATHAVEN	STRATHCLYDE PARK	CASTLE PARK	DUNBAR	GIFFORD	GLEN	GULLANE	HADDINGTON
Dress Code Anything																												
Dress Code Casual									•									•	•				•	•			•	•
Dress Code Formal																												
Golf Shop takes credit cards																		•	•				•	•			•	•
Club House takes credit card																			•					•		•		
Youth Coaching Scheme									•										•							•		
Mobiles allowed in Club House									•										•									
Children allowed in Club House									•									•	•				•	•				
Spectators Allowed																											•	
Disabled Facilities																												
Disabled Toilets																		•	•							•		
Disabled Access																		•	•							•		
Satellite TV																												
TV Lounge									•										•							•	•	
Snooker Room									•																			
Members Only Bar									•																			
Gym/Weights																												
Massage																												
Physiotherapy																												
Sauna/Solararium																												
Swimming Pool																												
Health Club																												
Accommodation	•																											
Hotel On Site	•																											
Visitors Car Park									•								•		•				•	•		•	•	•
Members Car Park																	•	•										
Practice Putting Green									•									•	•				•	•		•	•	•
Practice Bunkers																		•	•				•	•			•	
Practice Course																											•	
Driving Range						•																•					•	
Conference Facility							•																					
Evening Functions									•										•				•				•	•
On Course Refreshments																												
Bar Snacks	•	•	•		•	•	•	•	•	•	•		•	•	•		•	•	•	•	•	•	•	•		•	•	•
Restaurant Dinner	•	•			•	•			•									•	•					•		•	•	
Restaurant Lunch								•	•									•						•			•	
Restaurant Breakfast																		•	•					•				
Shoe Cleaning Service																								•				
Bag Drop Service																												
Guests Changing Rooms	•	•	•		•	•	•	•	•	•	•	•	•	•			•	•	•	•	•	•	•	•		•	•	•
Guests Showers									•										•				•	•		•	•	
On Course Drinking Fountains																		•	•								•	
On Course Yardage Markers																		•	•				•	•		•		
Spike Bar																							•	•			•	•
Plastic Stud Fitting Service																											•	
Plastic Studs Compulsory																											•	
Visitors Need Handicap Proof																											•	
Golf Clubs Hire		•					•											•	•				•	•		•	•	•
Caddy Hire																								•			•	
Shoe Hire																		•						•			•	
Buggy Hire	•	•									•	•	•				•	•	•				•	•			•	•
Trolley Hire	•	•						•			•	•	•	•			•	•	•	•			•	•		•	•	•
Regripping										•									•				•	•			•	•
Club Alterations																						•	•	•			•	•

FACILITIES AVAILABLE

Facilities Available at Golf Courses

Facility	KILSPINDIE	LONGNIDDRY	LUFFNESS	MUIRFIELD	MUSSELBURGH (ROYAL)	MUSSELBURGH LINKS	NORTH BERWICK	WHITEKIRK	WINTERFIELD	BROOMIEKNOWE	DUNDAS PARKS	GLENCORSE	KINGS ACRE	MUSSELBURGH	NEWBATTLE	VOGRIE	BATHGATE	BRIDGECASTLE	BRIDGEND	DEER PARK	GREENBURN	HARBURN	LINLITHGOW	NIDDRY CASTLE	POLKEMMET	PUMPHERSTON	UPHALL	WEST LOTHIAN	BUCKPOOL
Dress Code Anything								●																					
Dress Code Casual							●	●	●					●	●			●			●		●				●		●
Dress Code Formal																													
Golf Shop takes credit cards							●	●						●	●											●		●	
Club House takes credit card								●							●													●	
Youth Coaching Scheme														●														●	
Mobiles allowed in Club House								●						●	●						●								
Children allowed in Club House								●						●	●			●		●	●		●				●		●
Spectators Allowed							●	●	●					●				●			●								
Disabled Facilities		●						●	●					●	●													●	●
Disabled Toilets		●						●	●					●	●													●	●
Disabled Access		●						●	●					●	●													●	●
Satellite TV								●						●														●	
TV Lounge								●						●	●			●		●								●	
Snooker Room																				●									●
Members Only Bar		●																											
Gym/Weights								●													●								
Massage								●																					
Physiotherapy								●																					
Sauna/Solararium								●													●								
Swimming Pool								●													●								
Health Club								●													●								
Accommodation														●															
Hotel On Site																													
Visitors Car Park		●			●		●	●						●	●			●	●		●							●	
Members Car Park		●			●		●							●	●														
Practice Putting Green		●					●							●	●						●		●				●	●	
Practice Bunkers		●					●							●									●				●		
Practice Course		●			●	●								●													●	●	●
Driving Range								●			●	●		●									●		●			●	
Conference Facility																	●												
Evening Functions		●					●	●						●				●		●	●		●				●		
On Course Refreshments																													
Bar Snacks	●	●	●		●			●		●			●	●	●	●		●	●	●	●	●	●	●		●	●	●	●
Restaurant Dinner		●	●	●		●		●		●			●	●	●	●		●	●	●	●	●	●	●		●	●	●	●
Restaurant Lunch			●	●				●						●	●					●	●	●	●	●			●	●	●
Restaurant Breakfast				●				●						●	●					●	●	●	●					●	●
Shoe Cleaning Service																													
Bag Drop Service																													
Guests Changing Rooms	●	●	●		●	●	●	●	●	●			●	●	●	●		●		●	●	●	●	●		●	●	●	●
Guests Showers		●				●		●						●	●					●		●	●			●		●	●
On Course Drinking Fountains		●																											
On Course Yardage Markers								●						●				●								●		●	●
Spike Bar								●						●															
Plastic Stud Fitting Service																													
Plastic Studs Compulsory																													
Visitors Need Handicap Proof			●	●			●							●														●	●
Golf Clubs Hire	●	●			●	●	●	●	●	●			●	●			●			●	●						●	●	
Caddy Hire				●										●															
Shoe Hire														●															
Buggy Hire				●				●	●					●	●			●			●						●	●	
Trolley Hire	●	●	●	●	●			●	●		●		●	●	●		●	●	●	●	●	●	●		●		●	●	●
Regripping								●	●					●	●				●			●	●				●		
Club Alterations								●	●					●	●				●				●				●		

LOTHIAN (MID)

LOTHIAN (WEST)

MORAY

Golf Courses by County

Facilities Available at Golf Courses

Facilities / Golf Courses by County	CULLEN	ELGIN	FORRES	GARMOUTH & KINGSTON	GRANTOWN-ON-SPEY	HOPEMAN	KEITH	KINLOSS	MORAY	ROTHES	SPEY BAY	STRATHLENE	ORKNEY	STROMNESS	WESTRAY	ABERFELDY	ALYTH	AUCHTERARDER	BLAIR ATHOLL	BLAIRGOWRIE	CALLANDER	COMRIE	CRAIGIE HILL	CRIEFF	DALMUNZIE	DUNBLANE NEW	DUNKELD	DUNNING	GLENEAGLES	GLENISLA
Dress Code Anything	●																													
Dress Code Casual		●		●	●		●					●																●		●
Dress Code Formal																														
Golf Shop takes credit cards		●		●				●																						●
Club House takes credit card								●				●																		●
Youth Coaching Scheme		●		●	●							●																		
Mobiles allowed in Club House								●																						
Children allowed in Club House	●	●		●	●			●																				●		●
Spectators Allowed	●	●										●																	●	●
Disabled Facilities	●																												●	●
Disabled Toilets	●			●	●							●																	●	●
Disabled Access	●											●																		●
Satellite TV	●																													
TV Lounge	●	●						●																						
Snooker Room																														
Members Only Bar																														
Gym/Weights																													●	
Massage																														
Physiotherapy																														
Sauna/Solararium																													●	
Swimming Pool																													●	
Health Club																														
Accommodation												●											●						●	
Hotel On Site																													●	
Visitors Car Park				●	●	●	●																				●		●	●
Members Car Park				●	●		●																				●		●	●
Practice Putting Green	●			●	●		●					●																	●	●
Practice Bunkers				●								●																	●	
Practice Course																													●	
Driving Range	●								●			●					●							●			●		●	●
Conference Facility									●		●	●					●										●		●	●
Evening Functions		●																											●	
On Course Refreshments																													●	
Bar Snacks	●	●	●	●				●	●	●	●	●		●			●	●	●	●	●	●	●	●	●	●	●	●	●	●
Restaurant Dinner	●	●	●	●				●	●		●	●					●									●			●	●
Restaurant Lunch	●		●	●	●			●				●																	●	●
Restaurant Breakfast	●		●	●								●																	●	●
Shoe Cleaning Service																														
Bag Drop Service																														
Guests Changing Rooms	●	●	●	●	●	●	●	●	●	●		●	●	●			●	●	●	●	●	●		●		●		●	●	●
Guests Showers	●		●	●		●						●																	●	●
On Course Drinking Fountains			●	●																										
On Course Yardage Markers	●			●			●					●																		●
Spike Bar																														
Plastic Stud Fitting Service																														
Plastic Studs Compulsory																														
Visitors Need Handicap Proof																									●					
Golf Clubs Hire		●	●		●			●	●			●	●	●	●		●	●	●	●	●	●	●	●	●	●	●		●	●
Caddy Hire																													●	
Shoe Hire		●																											●	
Buggy Hire	●	●		●	●		●										●	●						●					●	●
Trolley Hire	●	●	●	●	●	●	●	●			●	●		●			●	●		●				●					●	●
Regripping		●																												
Club Alterations		●																												

Facilities Available at Golf Courses

Golf Courses by County	GREEN HOTEL	KENMORE	KILLIN	KING JAMES VI	KINROSS	LYNEDOCH & MURRAYSHALL	MILNATHORT	MUTHILL	NORTH INCH MUNICIPAL	PITLOCHRY	ST. FILLANS	STRATHMORE GOLF CTRE	TAYMOUTH CASTLE	BARSHAW	COCHRANE CASTLE	ELDERSLIE	ERSKINE	GLEDDOCH	LOCHWINNOCH	PAISLEY	PORT GLASGOW	RALSTON	RANFURLY	RANFURLY CASTLE	RENFREW	CARDRONA	DUNS	EYEMOUTH	GALASHIELS	HAWICK
Dress Code Anything																														
Dress Code Casual							●					●			●			●		●			●	●		●	●	●		
Dress Code Formal																		●												
Golf Shop takes credit cards												●	●					●		●		●							●	
Club House takes credit card												●						●		●		●								
Youth Coaching Scheme												●						●				●					●	●		
Mobiles allowed in Club House																										●				
Children allowed in Club House							●						●		●			●		●		●					●	●		
Spectators Allowed															●			●		●		●					●	●		
Disabled Facilities															●			●												
Disabled Toilets							●								●			●		●		●					●			
Disabled Access													●		●			●		●		●					●			
Satellite TV															●			●		●		●						●		
TV Lounge															●			●		●		●					●	●		
Snooker Room															●			●												
Members Only Bar																		●												
Gym/Weights						●			●																					
Massage																														
Physiotherapy																														
Sauna/Solararium	●					●																								
Swimming Pool	●																													
Health Club																														
Accommodation	●	●										●																		
Hotel On Site																										●				
Visitors Car Park												●	●			●		●		●		●	●			●	●	●		
Members Car Park						●						●			●		●	●		●		●	●			●	●	●		
Practice Putting Green						●						●	●		●		●	●		●		●	●			●	●	●		
Practice Bunkers						●						●						●		●						●				
Practice Course						●						●						●												
Driving Range						●						●			●															
Conference Facility	●	●				●			●									●			●									
Evening Functions												●				●		●		●		●								
On Course Refreshments																														
Bar Snacks	●	●	●	●		●	●	●	●		●	●			●	●	●	●	●	●	●	●	●	●	●		●	●	●	●
Restaurant Dinner	●	●				●		●		●	●	●	●				●	●		●		●			●		●	●	●	
Restaurant Lunch		●	●			●						●	●					●				●					●	●		
Restaurant Breakfast			●			●						●	●					●				●					●	●		
Shoe Cleaning Service																														
Bag Drop Service																														
Guests Changing Rooms	●	●	●	●	●	●	●				●	●	●		●	●	●	●	●	●	●	●	●		●		●	●	●	●
Guests Showers						●						●	●					●									●			
On Course Drinking Fountains																														
On Course Yardage Markers						●												●		●		●					●	●		
Spike Bar																		●		●			●	●						
Plastic Stud Fitting Service												●						●		●		●								
Plastic Studs Compulsory																		●												
Visitors Need Handicap Proof																		●				●								
Golf Clubs Hire	●	●	●	●	●	●			●	●	●		●				●	●	●			●			●			●		
Caddy Hire																														
Shoe Hire																														
Buggy Hire	●	●	●	●							●	●	●			●	●	●	●					●		●		●		
Trolley Hire	●	●	●	●		●			●	●	●	●		●	●	●	●	●	●	●			●	●	●		●	●	●	●
Regripping												●						●		●		●	●							
Club Alterations												●						●		●		●	●							

RENFREWSHIRE

SCOTTISH BORDERS

Facilities Available at Golf Courses

www.hccgolfworld.com

Facility	HIRSEL	INNERLEITHEN	JEDBURGH	KELSO	LAUDER	MELROSE	MINTO	NEWCASTLETON	PEEBLES	ROXBURGHE	RUTHERFORD CASTLE	SELKIRK	ST. BOSWELLS	TORWOODLEE	WEST LINTON	SHETLAND	WHALSAY	ABERFOYLE	BUCHANAN CASTLE	STIRLING	ASKERNISH	STORNOWAY
Dress Code Anything																						
Dress Code Casual	●	●							●			●	●	●	●							
Dress Code Formal																						
Golf Shop takes credit cards	●								●					●								
Club House takes credit card	●								●						●							
Youth Coaching Scheme	●	●										●		●	●							
Mobiles allowed in Club House	●											●	●	●	●							
Children allowed in Club House	●								●			●	●	●	●							
Spectators Allowed	●													●	●							●
Disabled Facilities	●													●	●							
Disabled Toilets	●								●			●		●	●							●
Disabled Access	●								●			●		●	●							
Satellite TV		●																				●
TV Lounge	●	●										●		●	●							
Snooker Room		●																				
Members Only Bar																						
Gym/Weights																						
Massage																						
Physiotherapy																						
Sauna/Solararium																						
Swimming Pool																						
Health Club																						
Accommodation									●													
Hotel On Site									●													
Visitors Car Park	●								●		●	●										
Members Car Park	●										●	●	●									●
Practice Putting Green	●	●							●			●		●	●							●
Practice Bunkers	●								●					●	●							●
Practice Course	●	●												●	●							
Driving Range				●					●										●	●		
Conference Facility									●													
Evening Functions	●	●										●		●	●							●
On Course Refreshments														●								
Bar Snacks	●	●	●	●		●	●		●	●		●	●	●	●	●	●	●	●	●	●	●
Restaurant Dinner	●		●			●			●			●	●	●	●			●	●	●		
Restaurant Lunch	●					●			●			●		●	●							
Restaurant Breakfast	●								●					●								
Shoe Cleaning Service																						
Bag Drop Service																						
Guests Changing Rooms	●	●	●	●	●	●	●	●	●	●		●	●	●	●	●	●	●	●	●		●
Guests Showers									●			●		●	●							
On Course Drinking Fountains	●														●							
On Course Yardage Markers	●	●							●			●			●							●
Spike Bar											●	●										
Plastic Stud Fitting Service	●													●								
Plastic Studs Compulsory																						
Visitors Need Handicap Proof																						
Golf Clubs Hire	●			●				●	●			●		●	●	●			●	●	●	●
Caddy Hire	●																					
Shoe Hire																						
Buggy Hire	●								●					●	●							●
Trolley Hire			●			●		●	●	●	●	●							●	●	●	
Regripping	●								●						●							●
Club Alterations	●								●					●	●							●

Golf Courses by County

Facilities Available at Golf Courses

FACILITIES AVAILABLE

Wales

Golf Courses by County	WALES	BLAENAU GWENT	TREDEGAR & RHYMNEY	WEST MONMOUTHSHIRE	BRIDGEND	COED Y MWSTWR	GROVE	MAESTEG	PORTHCAWL (ROYAL)	PYLE & KENFIG	SOUTHERNDOWN	ST. MARYS HOTEL	CAERPHILLY	BARGOED	BLACKWOOD	BRYN MEADOWS	CAERPHILLY	CASTELL HEIGHTS	OAKDALE	VIRGINIA PARK	CARMARTHENSHIRE	ASHBURNHAM	CARMARTHEN	CILGWYN	DERLLYS COURT	GARNANT PARK	GLYN ABBEY	GLYNHIR	LLANSTEFFAN	SARON	CEREDIGION
Dress Code Anything																			●												
Dress Code Casual							●																		●	●	●				
Dress Code Formal																															
Golf Shop takes credit cards							●																●		●	●					
Club House takes credit card							●																●		●	●					
Youth Coaching Scheme							●																●	●		●	●				
Mobiles allowed in Club House							●												●				●	●	●	●	●				
Children allowed in Club House							●												●				●	●	●	●	●				
Spectators Allowed							●																●	●		●	●				
Disabled Facilities							●												●						●		●				
Disabled Toilets							●												●						●	●	●				
Disabled Access							●												●						●	●	●				
Satellite TV							●																			●	●				
TV Lounge																			●					●		●	●				
Snooker Room																			●												
Members Only Bar																															
Gym/Weights																●											●				
Massage																															
Physiotherapy																															
Sauna/Solararium																●											●				
Swimming Pool																●															
Health Club																											●				
Accommodation									●			●				●								●			●	●			
Hotel On Site																											●				
Visitors Car Park							●												●					●	●	●	●				
Members Car Park							●												●					●		●	●				
Practice Putting Green							●																●	●		●	●				
Practice Bunkers							●																●			●	●				
Practice Course							●		●														●	●			●				
Driving Range									●	●	●	●						●	●	●						●	●				
Conference Facility									●			●				●		●													
Evening Functions							●												●				●	●	●	●	●				
On Course Refreshments																															
Bar Snacks						●	●	●	●	●	●	●		●			●	●	●	●		●	●	●	●	●	●	●			
Restaurant Dinner						●	●	●	●	●	●	●		●				●				●	●	●		●	●	●			
Restaurant Lunch							●											●					●	●	●	●	●				
Restaurant Breakfast							●											●					●	●	●	●	●				
Shoe Cleaning Service																															
Bag Drop Service																															
Guests Changing Rooms			●	●		●	●	●	●	●	●	●		●	●	●	●	●	●	●		●		●	●	●	●	●			
Guests Showers																								●	●	●	●				
On Course Drinking Fountains																							●								
On Course Yardage Markers							●												●				●	●		●	●				
Spike Bar																			●							●	●				
Plastic Stud Fitting Service							●																●				●				
Plastic Studs Compulsory																															
Visitors Need Handicap Proof									●																						
Golf Clubs Hire								●	●	●		●				●		●	●	●		●	●	●	●	●	●	●	●	●	
Caddy Hire																															
Shoe Hire																															
Buggy Hire							●		●	●	●	●		●		●		●								●	●				
Trolley Hire				●		●	●	●	●	●	●	●		●		●	●	●	●	●		●	●	●	●	●	●	●	●	●	
Regripping							●												●				●		●		●				
Club Alterations							●												●				●		●		●				

FACILITIES AVAILABLE

Facilities Available at Golf Courses

Facilities listed:

- Dress Code Anything
- Dress Code Casual
- Dress Code Formal
- Golf Shop takes credit cards
- Club House takes credit card
- Youth Coaching Scheme
- Mobiles allowed in Club House
- Children allowed in Club House
- Spectators Allowed
- Disabled Facilities
- Disabled Toilets
- Disabled Access
- Satellite TV
- TV Lounge
- Snooker Room
- Members Only Bar
- Gym/Weights
- Massage
- Physiotherapy
- Sauna/Solararium
- Swimming Pool
- Health Club
- Accommodation
- Hotel On Site
- Visitors Car Park
- Members Car Park
- Practice Putting Green
- Practice Bunkers
- Practice Course
- Driving Range
- Conference Facility
- Evening Functions
- On Course Refreshments
- Bar Snacks
- Restaurant Dinner
- Restaurant Lunch
- Restaurant Breakfast
- Shoe Cleaning Service
- Bag Drop Service
- Guests Changing Rooms
- Guests Showers
- On Course Drinking Fountains
- On Course Yardage Markers
- Spike Bar
- Plastic Stud Fitting Service
- Plastic Studs Compulsory
- Visitors Need Handicap Proof
- Golf Clubs Hire
- Caddy Hire
- Shoe Hire
- Buggy Hire
- Trolley Hire
- Regripping
- Club Alterations

Golf Courses by County:

- ABERYSTWYTH
- BORTH & YNYSLAS
- CAPEL BANGOR
- CARDIGAN
- CLIFF HOTEL
- CWMRHYDNEUADD
- PENLLANLAS
- PENRHOS
- CONWY
- ABERGELE
- BETWS-Y-COED
- CONWY
- MAESDU
- NORTH WALES
- OLD COLWYN
- PENMAENMAWR
- RHOS-ON-SEA
- DENBIGHSHIRE
- BRYN MORFYDD
- DENBIGH
- KINMEL PARK GOLF
- PRESTATYN
- RHUDDLAN
- RHYL
- RUTHIN-PWLLGLAS
- ST. MELYD
- VALE OF LLANGOLLEN
- FLINTSHIRE
- ALLT-GYMBYD
- CAERWYS NINE OF CLUBS
- FLINT
- HAWARDEN

Facilities Available at Golf Courses

Golf Courses by County

	Club Alterations	Regripping	Trolley Hire	Buggy Hire	Shoe Hire	Caddy Hire	Golf Clubs Hire	Visitors Need Handicap Proof	Plastic Studs Compulsory	Plastic Stud Fitting Service	On Course Yardage Markers	Spike Bar	On Course Drinking Fountains	Guests Changing Rooms	Guests Showers	Bag Drop Service	Shoe Cleaning Service	Restaurant Breakfast	Restaurant Lunch	Restaurant Dinner	Bar Snacks	On Course Refreshments	Evening Functions	Conference Facility	Driving Range	Practice Course	Practice Bunkers	Practice Putting Green	Members Car Park	Visitors Car Park	Hotel On Site	Accommodation	Health Club	Swimming Pool	Sauna/Solarium	Physiotherapy	Massage	Gym/Weights	Members Only Bar	Snooker Room	TV Lounge	Satellite TV	Disabled Access	Disabled Toilets	Disabled Facilities	Spectators Allowed	Children allowed in Club House	Mobiles allowed in Club House	Youth Coaching Scheme	Club House takes credit cards	Golf Shop takes credit cards	Dress Code Formal	Dress Code Casual	Dress Code Anything
HOLYWELL			•											•						• •																																		
KINSALE	• •		•			•								•				• •		• •		• •	•		• •		•	•		• •													• •		•							•
MOLD	• •	•	• •		•					• •	• •	• •		•				•	• •	•			• •	• •	• •	• •				•		•									• •			• •	•	• •		• •		• •	• •	
NORTHOP	• •	•	• •		•					• •	• •	• •	• •	•				• •	•	•			• •	• •	• •	• •	•	•	•	•		•									• •			• •	• •	• •		• •		• •	• •	
OLD PADESWOOD	• •	•	• •		•					• •	• •	•		•				• •	•	•			• •	• •	• •	• •	•	•	• •	•		•			•						•			• •	• •	• •		• •		• •	•	
PADESWOOD & BUCKLEY	•					• •												• •	•	•			• •	•			•			•														• •	• •	• •		• •		• •		
WEPRE						•																							•																								

ABERDARE			•											•						• •																																		
BRYNHILL			•											•						• •																																		
CARDIFF			•											•						• •																																		
CASTLECOCH						•								•						• •							• •	•																										
COTTRELL PARK	• •	•	• •		•						•	•		•				• •	•	• •			•				•	• •	•												•			• •	• •	•	• •	• •		•		
CREIGIAU	• •	•	•											•						• •			•																														
DINAS POWYS			•											•						• •																																		
GLAMORGANSHIRE		•	•				•							•						• •			•																															
LLANISHEN			•											•						• •																																		
MORLAIS CASTLE																				• •																																		
PETERSTONE LAKES	• •	•	•				• •				•			•						• •			•																			•			•		• •	•			• •		•
RADYR			•											•						• •					•																													
RAF ST ATHAN																																																						
ST. ANDREWS MAJOR		•	•		•		•					•		•					•	• •			•					•	• •	•															•		• •	•			• •		•
ST. MELLONS		•	• •				•					•		•						• •			•					•																	•		• •	• •			•		•
VALE OF GLAMORGAN			•											•					•	• •			•								•	•																					
WENVOE CASTLE			•											•						• •																																		
WHITCHURCH	• •	•	•				• •				•		•	• •						• •		•							• •	•															• •	• •	•	• •	•		•	•	
WHITEHALL																																																							

ABERDOVEY			• •																																																			
ABERSOCH			• •											•						• •																																		
BALA														•						• •																																		
CAERNARFON (ROYAL TOWN OF)	• •		• •		•		•				•	• •	•	•						•			•				•	• •	•														• •	•	•		• •	•		• •		

FACILITIES AVAILABLE Wales

Facilities Available at Golf Courses

Facility	CRICCIETH	DOLGELLAU	FAIRBOURNE	FFESTINIOG	HARLECH	LLANFAIRFECHAN	NEFYN & DISTRICT	PORTHMADOG	PWLLHELI	ST. DEINIOL	ANGLESEY	BARON HILL	BULL BAY	HOLYHEAD	LLANGEFNI PUBLIC	PRINCE'S	STORWS WEN	ALICE SPRINGS	DEWSTOW	MONMOUTH	MONMOUTHSHIRE	PONTYPOOL	RAGLAN PARC	ROLLS OF MONMOUTH	SHIRENEWTON	ST. PIERRE	WERNDDU	WOODLAKE PARK	BRITISH STEEL PORT TALBOT
County											*ISLE OF ANGLESEY*							*MONMOUTHSHIRE*											*NEATH PORT TALBOT*
Dress Code Anything		●																											
Dress Code Casual			●														●	●	●	●	●	●		●	●	●	●	●	
Dress Code Formal																													
Golf Shop takes credit cards			●														●	●	●	●	●	●		●	●	●	●	●	
Club House takes credit card																		●	●	●	●	●			●	●	●	●	
Youth Coaching Scheme		●	●														●	●	●	●	●	●	●			●	●		
Mobiles allowed in Club House		●	●															●	●	●	●					●	●		
Children allowed in Club House		●	●															●	●	●	●					●	●		
Spectators Allowed			●														●	●	●	●	●					●			
Disabled Facilities																	●	●	●	●	●					●			
Disabled Toilets																	●	●	●	●	●					●			
Disabled Access		●															●	●	●	●	●					●			
Satellite TV			●														●	●	●	●						●	●		
TV Lounge																	●	●	●	●				●		●		●	
Snooker Room																	●	●		●						●			
Members Only Bar																		●				●				●			
Gym/Weights																										●			
Massage																										●			
Physiotherapy																										●			
Sauna/Solararium																										●			
Swimming Pool																										●			
Health Club																										●			
Accommodation	●															●	●									●			
Hotel On Site																										●			
Visitors Car Park		●	●															●	●	●	●			●	●	●	●	●	
Members Car Park		●	●														●	●	●	●	●			●	●	●	●	●	
Practice Putting Green		●	●														●	●	●	●	●	●		●	●	●	●	●	
Practice Bunkers			●														●	●	●	●						●	●	●	
Practice Course																●	●	●	●	●	●	●				●			
Driving Range	●		●													●		●	●	●	●	●				●	●	●	
Conference Facility				●	●												●	●	●							●	●		●
Evening Functions			●														●	●	●	●						●	●	●	
On Course Refreshments																●										●			
Bar Snacks	●	●	●				●	●	●	●	●	●	●				●	●	●	●	●	●	●	●	●	●	●	●	●
Restaurant Dinner	●		●				●	●	●			●					●	●	●	●	●	●		●	●	●	●	●	
Restaurant Lunch			●										●	●			●	●	●	●	●			●	●	●	●	●	
Restaurant Breakfast			●														●	●	●	●				●	●	●	●	●	
Shoe Cleaning Service																										●			
Bag Drop Service																										●			
Guests Changing Rooms	●	●	●	●	●	●	●				●	●	●	●			●	●	●	●	●	●	●	●	●	●	●	●	●
Guests Showers			●														●	●	●	●	●	●		●	●	●	●	●	
On Course Drinking Fountains			●																							●			
On Course Yardage Markers		●	●														●	●	●	●				●	●	●	●	●	
Spike Bar																●		●	●							●			
Plastic Stud Fitting Service			●													●	●	●	●							●			
Plastic Studs Compulsory																													
Visitors Need Handicap Proof			●																							●			
Golf Clubs Hire		●			●				●			●	●	●				●	●	●	●	●		●	●	●	●	●	
Caddy Hire																			●							●			
Shoe Hire																										●			
Buggy Hire			●													●	●	●	●	●				●	●	●	●	●	
Trolley Hire	●		●	●			●	●	●	●	●	●	●			●	●	●	●	●	●	●		●	●	●	●	●	
Regripping		●	●														●	●	●	●				●		●			
Club Alterations																	●	●	●	●						●			

Facilities Available at Golf Courses

FACILITIES AVAILABLE — Wales

Golf Courses by County

Facility	EARLSWOOD	GLYNNEATH	LAKESIDE	NEATH	SWANSEA BAY GOLF SHOP	CAERLEON	CELTIC MANOR	LLANWERN	NEWPORT GOLF	PARC	TREDEGAR PARK	DAWN 'TIL DUSK	HAVERFORDWEST	HERONS BROOK	MILFORD HAVEN	NEWPORT	PRISKILLY	SOUTH PEMBROKE	ST. DAVIDS	TENBY	TREFLOYNE	BRECON	BUILTH WELLS	CRADOC	KNIGHTON	LLANDRINDOD WELLS	MACHYNLLETH	MID WALES GOLF CTRE	OLD RECTORY
Dress Code Anything																	●												
Dress Code Casual	●		●	●		●	●	●												●			●						
Dress Code Formal										●																			
Golf Shop takes credit cards			●	●		●	●			●			●	●		●	●		●	●									
Club House takes credit card			●	●		●	●			●						●	●		●										
Youth Coaching Scheme			●	●		●	●			●	●		●	●	●	●	●	●	●	●		●							
Mobiles allowed in Club House			●	●		●	●			●	●		●	●		●	●	●	●	●		●							
Children allowed in Club House			●	●		●	●	●		●	●		●	●		●	●	●	●	●		●							
Spectators Allowed						●	●	●		●	●			●		●	●	●	●	●									
Disabled Facilities			●			●	●			●						●	●	●	●										
Disabled Toilets			●	●		●	●			●						●	●	●	●			●							
Disabled Access			●	●		●	●			●						●	●	●	●										
Satellite TV			●	●		●	●																						
TV Lounge			●	●		●	●						●	●		●			●		●	●							
Snooker Room	●		●	●				●												●		●							
Members Only Bar						●																							
Gym/Weights						●																							
Massage						●																							
Physiotherapy						●																							
Sauna/Solararium						●																							
Swimming Pool						●																							●
Health Club						●																							
Accommodation						●										●	●												●
Hotel On Site						●										●	●												
Visitors Car Park	●		●	●				●		●	●	●	●	●		●	●			●	●		●						
Members Car Park			●	●		●				●	●	●	●	●		●	●		●	●									
Practice Putting Green	●		●	●			●	●		●		●	●	●		●	●			●	●		●						
Practice Bunkers			●	●		●	●			●			●	●		●	●		●	●									
Practice Course			●	●				●		●			●	●		●	●		●	●									
Driving Range			●			●	●		●																			●	
Conference Facility							●		●																				●
Evening Functions			●	●			●							●			●			●									
On Course Refreshments						●											●												
Bar Snacks	●	●	●	●	●	●	●	●	●	●	●		●	●	●	●		●	●	●		●	●	●		●	●	●	●
Restaurant Dinner			●	●		●	●			●				●		●	●		●										
Restaurant Lunch			●			●	●							●	●	●	●		●					●		●			
Restaurant Breakfast			●	●		●								●	●	●	●												
Shoe Cleaning Service						●																							
Bag Drop Service						●																							
Guests Changing Rooms	●	●	●	●		●	●	●	●	●	●		●	●	●	●		●	●	●		●	●	●	●	●	●	●	●
Guests Showers			●	●		●	●																						
On Course Drinking Fountains																													
On Course Yardage Markers	●		●	●				●					●	●				●	●	●			●						
Spike Bar			●			●														●			●						
Plastic Stud Fitting Service			●													●		●		●									
Plastic Studs Compulsory																													
Visitors Need Handicap Proof							●			●									●				●						
Golf Clubs Hire	●		●	●	●		●	●	●			●	●	●		●	●		●	●			●	●		●		●	●
Caddy Hire																													
Shoe Hire						●									●	●	●												
Buggy Hire		●														●											●		
Trolley Hire	●	●	●	●	●	●	●		●	●	●		●	●		●	●		●	●			●	●		●	●	●	
Regripping			●	●		●	●	●						●		●	●		●	●		●	●						
Club Alterations			●	●		●	●	●		●				●		●	●		●	●			●						

County groupings: **NEWPORT** (CAERLEON, CELTIC MANOR, LLANWERN, NEWPORT GOLF, PARC, TREDEGAR PARK); **PEMBROKESHIRE** (DAWN 'TIL DUSK, HAVERFORDWEST, HERONS BROOK, MILFORD HAVEN, NEWPORT, PRISKILLY, SOUTH PEMBROKE, ST. DAVIDS, TENBY, TREFLOYNE); **POWYS** (BRECON, BUILTH WELLS, CRADOC, KNIGHTON, LLANDRINDOD WELLS, MACHYNLLETH, MID WALES GOLF CTRE, OLD RECTORY)

Facilities Available at Golf Courses

Facility	RHOSGOCH GOLF	ST. GILES	ST. IDLOES	WELSH BORDER GOLF COMPLEX	WELSHPOOL	RHONDDA CYNON TAFF	LLANTRISANT & PONTYCLUN	MOUNTAIN ASH	PONTYPRIDD	RHONDDA	SWANSEA	ALLT-Y-GRABAN	CLYNE	FAIRWOOD PARK	GOWER	LANGLAND BAY	MORRISTON	PALLEG	PENNARD	PONTARDAWE	TORFAEN	GREEN MEADOW	PONTNEWYDD	WREXHAM	CHIRK	CLAYS GOLF CTRE	MOSS VALLEY	PLASSEY	WREXHAM
Dress Code Anything																													
Dress Code Casual			●		●			●					●	●	●	●	●		●			●				●	●	●	
Dress Code Formal																													
Golf Shop takes credit cards					●								●	●	●	●	●		●			●				●			
Club House takes credit card														●	●				●			●				●			
Youth Coaching Scheme													●	●	●	●	●					●				●	●		
Mobiles allowed in Club House															●				●			●					●	●	
Children allowed in Club House					●								●	●	●		●		●			●				●	●	●	
Spectators Allowed								●														●				●	●		
Disabled Facilities														●					●										
Disabled Toilets														●					●										
Disabled Access					●									●					●										
Satellite TV					●								●	●					●							●	●		
TV Lounge								●					●	●	●		●		●			●				●	●		
Snooker Room													●				●		●										
Members Only Bar																													
Gym/Weights																													
Massage																													
Physiotherapy																													
Sauna/Solararium																												●	
Swimming Pool																												●	
Health Club																													
Accommodation																●													
Hotel On Site																													
Visitors Car Park				●									●	●	●	●	●		●			●				●	●		
Members Car Park				●					●				●	●	●	●	●		●			●				●	●		
Practice Putting Green				●				●					●	●	●	●	●		●			●				●	●		
Practice Bunkers													●	●	●		●		●			●							
Practice Course															●	●	●		●										
Driving Range			●							●			●									●			●	●			
Conference Facility	●							●					●									●							
Evening Functions								●					●	●	●	●	●		●			●				●			
On Course Refreshments																													
Bar Snacks	●	●		●			●	●	●	●			●	●	●	●	●		●	●		●	●		●	●	●	●	●
Restaurant Dinner	●	●		●			●	●	●				●	●	●	●	●		●	●		●	●		●	●	●	●	●
Restaurant Lunch	●		●	●				●		●			●	●	●	●	●		●	●		●	●		●	●	●	●	●
Restaurant Breakfast													●	●	●	●	●		●			●							
Shoe Cleaning Service																													
Bag Drop Service																													
Guests Changing Rooms	●	●	●	●	●		●	●	●	●		●	●	●	●	●	●	●	●	●		●	●		●	●	●	●	●
Guests Showers													●	●	●	●	●		●			●				●	●	●	
On Course Drinking Fountains																													
On Course Yardage Markers			●										●	●	●	●	●		●			●				●	●	●	
Spike Bar			●											●					●			●							
Plastic Stud Fitting Service													●		●	●			●			●				●	●		
Plastic Studs Compulsory																													
Visitors Need Handicap Proof								●					●		●				●			●							
Golf Clubs Hire	●	●	●	●						●			●		●	●						●			●	●	●	●	
Caddy Hire																													
Shoe Hire																													
Buggy Hire								●	●	●												●				●	●	●	
Trolley Hire	●	●	●	●			●	●	●				●	●	●	●	●		●	●		●	●		●	●	●	●	
Regripping			●										●	●	●	●	●		●			●				●	●		
Club Alterations													●	●	●	●	●		●			●				●			

Golf Courses by County

SECTION 8

This section allows you to search for courses by the green fees charged on weekdays, without a member.

e.g Ireland, **Under £20, County Cork, Lisselan,** £10.00

Once you have located a club using this section you can then refer to the detailed profile of the club in Section 1, or search for specific details in other sections.

UNDER £10

BATH & SOMERSET (NORTH EAST)
- COMBE GROVE MANOR £4.00
- ENTRY HILL £6.50

BEDFORDSHIRE
- MOUNT PLEASANT £7.50
- SOUTH BEDS
  Warden Hill £9.00
- STOCKWOOD PARK £8.95

BERKSHIRE
- BILLINGBEAR PARK
  The New £5.00
- BILLINGBEAR PARK
  The Old £8.00
- DEANWOOD PARK £8.50
- HURST £6.50

BUCKINGHAMSHIRE
- HEDSOR £8.00
- THORNEY PARK £8.00

CAMBRIDGESHIRE
- CAMBRIDGE LAKES £5.00
- THORNEY
  Fen £7.00

CHESHIRE
- ADLINGTON £4.50
- MARTON MEADOWS £6.00

CORNWALL
- HELSTON £4.50
- TRELOY £7.50

COUNTY DURHAM
- OAK LEAF £9.50

CUMBRIA
- BECKSIDE £7.00
- DISTINGTON GOLF £5.00

DERBYSHIRE
- BARLBOROUGH LINKS £6.00
- BROUGHTON HEATH £7.50
- PEWIT £6.90

DEVON
- CENTRAL PARK £2.50
- FINGLE GLEN £8.00
- OTTER VALLEY GOLF CTRE £6.00

DORSET
- PARLEY £5.00

ESSEX
- BELHUS PARK £9.00
- BRAXTED PARK £9.00
- DUNTON HILLS
  Dunton Hills 18 Hole Par 3 £6.00
- EPPING £7.00
- MILLERS BARN GOLF PARK £7.50
- PRIORS £8.00
- REGIMENT £8.00

GLOUCESTERSHIRE
- BRICKHAMPTON COURT
  Glevum £6.50
- SHIPTON £6.00

HAMPSHIRE
- BASINGSTOKE £2.70
- FOUR MARKS £9.90
- OTTERBOURNE £4.00
- PARK £6.75
- SOUTHAMPTON MUNICIPAL
  Southampton Municipal 18 Hole £9.90
- SOUTHAMPTON MUNICIPAL
  Southampton Municipal 9 hole £4.50
- TOURNERBURY GOLF CTRE £7.00

HEREFORDSHIRE
- BRAMPTON GOLF £4.50
- BROCKINGTON £5.00
- GROVE £6.00
- LEOMINSTER £8.00
- SOUTH HEREFORDSHIRE
  South Herefordshire 9 Hole Course £4.00

HERTFORDSHIRE
- ASH VALLEY GOLF CLUB £9.00
- OXHEY PARK £7.00
- PENFOLD PARK £4.40
- WHADDON £3.00

ISLE OF WIGHT
- WESTRIDGE £8.50

KENT
- ASHFORD £3.80
- BROMLEY £5.60
- HILDEN EUROPRO £6.00
- MOTE PARK GOLF HUT
  Mote Park 18 hole Putting Green £3.00
- MOTE PARK GOLF HUT
  Mote Park Pitch and Put Par 3 £3.00
- NORTH FORELAND
  Par 3 £6.00
- PEDHAM PLACE GOLF CTRE
  Red £5.50
- ROUNDWOOD HALL £5.00
- STAPLEHURST GOLFING PARK £9.00
- SWEETWOODS PARK £3.00
- UPCHURCH RIVER VALLEY
  River Valley 9 hole £6.75
- VILLA £8.00

LANCASHIRE
- ASHTON £6.00
- CASTLE HAWK
  Old £6.00
- HIGHFIELD £5.00
- TOWNELEY MUNICIPAL £9.00

LEICESTERSHIRE
- BLACKTHORN WOOD £6.50

LINCOLNSHIRE
- ADDLETHORPE £9.00
- KIRTON HOLME £5.00

- MARTIN MOOR £5.50
- OWMBY £7.00
- POTTERGATE £7.50
- SUDBROOK MOOR £7.00

LINCOLNSHIRE (NORTH)
- GRANGE PARK £6.00

LONDON (GREATER)
- BETHUNE PARK £3.30
- CENTRAL LONDON £8.50
- DUKES MEADOW £8.50
- LEE VALLEY £3.30
- THAMESVIEW £6.50

MERSEYSIDE
- AINTREE £6.00
- ALLERTON
  Allerton 18 Hole £7.10
- ALLERTON
  Allerton 9 Hole £4.20
- ARROWE PARK
  Long £7.50
- LIVERPOOL MUNICIPAL £7.10
- SHERDLEY PARK MUNICIPAL £8.50
- SOUTHPORT MUNICIPAL £6.70

MIDLANDS (WEST)
- BOLDMERE £9.50
- HAWKESBURY GOLF CENTRE £8.50
- PYPE HAYES £9.50
- WIDNEY MANOR £9.95

NORTHAMPTONSHIRE
- DELAPRE PARK GOLF COMPLEX
  Harding Stone £7.00

NORTHUMBERLAND
- HAGGERSTON CASTLE £5.00

NOTTINGHAMSHIRE
- BRAMCOTE HILLS £6.30
- EDWALTON MUNICIPAL £5.00
- KILTON FOREST £9.00
- MANSFIELD WOODHOUSE £5.20

OXFORDSHIRE
- FARINGDON £5.00

RUTLAND
- RUTLAND WATER £5.00

SOMERSET
- VIVARY PARK £8.90
- WINCANTON £6.00

STAFFORDSHIRE
- BRANSTON
  Academy £6.00

SUFFOLK
- CLARE PARK LAKE £5.00
- HIGH LODGE £9.00

SURREY
- ABBEYMOOR £8.50
- BROADWATER PARK £7.50

GREEN FEE Without Member in England — Weekdays (Mon - Fri)

Under £10 — Under £10

- CHESSINGTON £7.50
- GOAL FARM £8.50
- HERSHAM VILLAGE £9.50
- HORNE PARK £9.50
- REDHILL GOLF CTRE £5.50
- SURREY GOLF & FITNESS £5.00

SUSSEX (EAST)

- BOARS HEAD £8.00
- EASTBOURNE GOLFING PARK £9.00

SUSSEX (WEST)

- BROOKLANDS PARK £4.20
- EFFINGHAM PARK £9.00
- CUCKFIELD £7.50

WARWICKSHIRE

- BRAMCOTE WATERS £7.00
- NEWBOLD COMYN £9.00

WILTSHIRE

- WHITLEY £9.00

YORKSHIRE (NORTH)

- CRIMPLE VALLEY £5.00
- YORK GOLF CTRE £9.00
- SWALLOW HALL £9.00

YORKSHIRE (SOUTH)

- KINGSWOOD £7.00

YORKSHIRE (WEST)

- OULTON PARK
  Main £9.90
- PONTEFRACT £6.00
- ROUNDHAY £7.75

UNDER £20

BATH & SOMERSET (NORTH EAST)

- FROME GOLF CLUB £13.50

BEDFORDSHIRE

- BARON & BARONESS
  Baron Manhattan £10.00
- BARON & BARONESS
  Baroness Manhattan £12.00
- CHALGRAVE MANOR £15.00
- COLMWORTH & NORTH BEDFORDSHIRE £12.00
- MOWSBURY £10.00

BERKSHIRE

- DATCHET £18.00
- HENNERTON £15.00
- MAPLEDURHAM £17.00
- THEALE GOLF CTRE £16.00

BUCKINGHAMSHIRE

- AYLESBURY £10.00
- AYLESBURY PARK £14.00
- ABBEY HILL GOLF CENTRE
  Abbey Hill £10.45
- IVER £12.00
- PRINCES RISBOROUGH £14.00
- SILVERSTONE £14.00
- WHITELEAF £18.00

- WINDMILL HILL £11.00

CAMBRIDGESHIRE

- ABBOTSLEY
  Abbotsley £19.00
- ABBOTSLEY
  Cromwell £10.00
- BOURN £16.00
- CAMBRIDGE £10.00
- LAKESIDE LODGE
  Lodge £12.00
- MARCH £16.50
- ORTON MEADOWS £11.20
- STILTON OAKS £10.00
- THORNEY
  Lakes £11.50
- THORPE WOOD £11.20
- TYDD ST GILES £10.50

CHANNEL ISLANDS

- ALDERNEY £10.00
- ST. CLEMENT £10.00

CHESHIRE

- ALDER ROOT £14.00
- ALDERSEY GREEN £15.00
- MERSEY VALLEY £18.00
- MOBBERLEY £14.50
- MOLLINGTON GRANGE £18.00
- STYAL
  Academy Championship Par 3 £12.00
- STYAL
  Styal £18.00
- SUTTON HALL £18.00

CLEVELAND

- NORTON £10.00
- KNOTTY HILL GOLF CTRE
  Bishops £13.00

CORNWALL

- PORTHPEAN £13.00
- PRAA SANDS £14.50
- WHITSAND BAY £17.50

COUNTY DURHAM

- BEAMISH PARK £16.00
- CONSETT & DISTRICT £18.00
- STRESSHOLME £11.00

CUMBRIA

- CARUS GREEN £12.00
- CASTERTON £10.00
- COCKERMOUTH £15.00

DERBYSHIRE

- ALLESTREE PARK £11.20
- BRAILSFORD £13.50
- MAYWOOD £15.00
- ORMONDE FIELDS £17.50
- SHIRLAND £17.00
- STANEDGE £10.00

DEVON

- ASHBURY
  Oakwood £10.45

- DAINTON PARK £18.00
- ELFORDLEIGH £15.00
- TORRINGTON £12.00
- PORTMORE GOLF PARK
  Barum £12.00
- SPARKWELL £18.00
- TEIGN VALLEY £17.00
- WILLINGCOTT £15.00

DORSET

- BOSCOMBE LADIES £16.50
- CHEDINGTON COURT £16.00
- FERNDOWN FOREST £12.00

ESSEX

- SOUTH ESSEX
  Hawk (Hawk & Vixon) £16.00
- SOUTH ESSEX
  Heron (Heron & Hawk) £16.00
- SOUTH ESSEX
  Vixen (Vixen & Heron) £16.00
- BELFAIRS PARK £15.00
- BIRCH GROVE £12.00
- BUNSAY DOWNS
  Bunsay Downs £11.00
- CHANNELS
  Belstead £18.00
- DUNTON HILLS
  Main £10.00
- HAINAULT FOREST
  Top £15.00
- LEXDEN £18.00
- MARDYKE VALLEY GOLF CTRE
  The Valley £10.00
- TOP MEADOW £12.00

GLOUCESTERSHIRE

- BRICKHAMPTON COURT
  Spa £19.00
- COTSWOLD EDGE £15.00
- DYMOCK GRANGE £12.00
- FOREST HILLS £17.00
- FOREST OF DEAN £15.00
- PAINSWICK £15.00
- SHERDONS £11.00

HAMPSHIRE

- ALTON £15.00
- COUNTY £13.00
- EAST HORTON GOLF CTRE
  Greenwood £13.00
- EAST HORTON GOLF CTRE
  Parkland £13.00
- FURZELEY £10.70
- MEON VALLEY
  Valley £10.00
- PORTSMOUTH £10.50
- WELLOW
  Embley £16.00
- WICKHAM PARK £12.00

HERTFORDSHIRE

- MILL GREEN GOLF CLUB £19.00
- BARKWAY PARK £10.00

- BUSHEY GOLF COURSE £16.00
- CHADWELL SPRINGS £15.00
- CHORLEYWOOD £16.00
- DANESBURY PARK £12.50
- LITTLE HAY £12.00
- MALTON £10.00
- PANSHANGER GOLF COMPLEX £12.90
- RICKMANSWORTH £10.00
- SHENDISH MANOR £15.00
- STEVENAGE £11.80

ISLE OF WIGHT

- RYDE £15.00

KENT

- CRAY VALLEY
  Cray Valley 18 holes £16.75
- RUXLEY PARK
  Ruxley Park 18 Hole £16.75
- BECKENHAM PLACE PARK £10.00
- BOUGHTON £17.00
- COBTREE MANOR PARK £15.00
- DARENTH VALLEY £16.50
- DEANGATE RIDGE
  Deangate Ridge £11.00
- ETCHINGHILL £18.00
- HAWKHURST £18.00
- HOLTYE £16.00
- HOMELANDS £11.00
- LULLINGSTONE PARK
  Lullingstone Park 18 hole £11.00
- PEDHAM PLACE GOLF CTRE
  Yellow £15.00
- ROMNEY WARREN £15.00
- SOUTHERN VALLEY £15.50
- ST. AGUSTINES £15.00
- UPCHURCH RIVER VALLEY
  Upchurch River Valley £11.45
- WHITSTABLE & SEASALTER £15.00

LANCASHIRE

- BACUP £14.00
- BENTHAM £15.00
- BOLTON £10.00
- BREIGHTMET £15.00
- COLNE £16.00
- GREENMOUNT
  Old £15.00
- GREENMOUNT
  White £15.00
- STANDISH COURT £10.00
- WESTHOUGHTON
  Hart Common £12.00
- WHALLEY £16.00

LEICESTERSHIRE

- BEEDLES LAKE £10.00
- STOKE ALBANY £15.00
- WHETSTONE £15.00

LINCOLNSHIRE

- SANDILANDS & LEISURE £15.00

- SLEAFORD £18.00
- SUTTON BRIDGE £18.00
- WOODTHORPE HALL £10.00

LINCOLNSHIRE (NORTH EAST)

- IMMINGHAM £12.00

LONDON (GREATER)

- TRENT PARK GOLF CLUB £13.00
- BRENT VALLEY PUBLIC £10.00
- CHINGFORD £11.00
- HASTE HILL £12.50
- LONDON SCOTTISH £10.00
- RICHMOND PARK
  Dukes £15.00
- RICHMOND PARK
  Princes £15.00
- EPPING FOREST (ROYAL) £11.00
- WIMBLEDON COMMON £15.00

MANCHESTER (GREATER)

- BOYSNOPE PARK £11.00
- HEATON PARK £10.00
- OLDHAM £18.00
- WERNETH £18.50

MERSEYSIDE

- HOUGHWOOD £17.50

MIDLANDS (WEST)

- WERGS £15.00

NORFOLK

- DEREHAM £17.50
- EAGLES £15.00
- FAKENHAM £18.00
- FELTWELL £15.00
- WENSUM VALLEY £18.00

NORTHAMPTONSHIRE

- BRAMPTON HEATH
  Main £13.00
- COLD ASHBY £15.00
- CORBY PUBLIC £10.60
- DELAPRE PARK GOLF COMPLEX
  Main £10.00

NORTHUMBERLAND

- BELFORD £14.00
- BURGHAM £18.00
- MAGDALENE FIELDS £17.00
- TYNEDALE £12.00
- WARKWORTH £12.00

NOTTINGHAMSHIRE

- COTGRAVE PLACE
  Open £16.00
- BRIERLEY FOREST £10.00
- BULWELL FOREST £11.00
- COLLEGE PINES £12.00
- NORWOOD PARK £14.00
- OAKMERE PARK £18.00
- RAMSDALE PARK
  Ramsdale Park Main £15.00

- RUFFORD PARK GOLF CTRE £15.00
- SOUTHWELL £15.00
- SPRINGWATER £15.00
- TRENT LOCK
  Trent Lock Golf Centre 18 hole £12.50

OXFORDSHIRE

- CARSWELL £16.00
- CHERWELL EDGE £16.00
- HADDEN HILL £15.00
- HINKSEY HEIGHTS £15.00
- RYE HILL £15.00
- WITNEY LAKES £16.00

SHROPSHIRE

- ARSCOTT £16.00

SOMERSET

- BREAN £15.00
- BURNHAM & BERROW
  Channel £12.00
- CANNINGTON £13.00
- LONG SUTTON £16.00
- WINDWHISTLE £18.00

STAFFORDSHIRE

- CHASE £14.50
- STONE £15.00
- WESTWOOD £18.00

SUFFOLK

- CRETINGHAM £16.00
- HALESWORTH
  Halesworth £15.00
- NEWTON GREEN £18.00
- SOUTHWOLD £18.00

SURREY

- ADDINGTON COURT GOLF CLUB
  Championship £15.35
- ADDINGTON COURT GOLF CLUB
  Falconwood £15.35
- BOWENHURST £11.00
- CHIDDINGFOLD £16.00
- HORTON PARK GOLF £16.00
- HURTMORE £12.00
- LIMPSFIELD CHART £18.00
- MOORE PLACE £10.00
- RUSPER £11.50
- SANDOWN GOLF CTRE
  Par 3 £13.50
- THAMES DITTON & ESHER £14.00
- WINDLERMERE £16.00

SUSSEX (EAST)

- BATTLE £15.00
- SEDLESCOMBE £16.00
- WATERHALL £12.50
- WELLSHURST £18.00
- WILLINGDON £18.00

SUSSEX (WEST)

- AVISFORD PARK £12.00
- FOXBRIDGE £18.00

GREEN FEE Without Member in England   Weekdays (Mon - Fri)

Under £20 — Under £20

- HASSOCKS £14.25
- HILLBARN £14.00
- HORSHAM GOLF £18.00
- PAXHILL PARK £18.00
- PETWORTH £10.00
- RUSTINGTON £16.50
- SELSEY £12.00
- TILGATE FOREST £13.00
- WEST CHILTINGTON £15.00

WILTSHIRE
- BRADFORD ON AVON £10.00
- BRINKWORTH £10.00
- BROOME MANOR £12.50
- OAKSEY £12.00
- RUSHMORE PARK £14.00
- SHRIVENHAM PARK £12.00

WORCESTERSHIRE
- BROMSGROVE £14.50
- LITTLE LAKES £15.00
- WYRE FOREST £10.50

YORKSHIRE (EAST)
- CAVE CASTLE £15.00
- WITHERNSEA £10.00

YORKSHIRE (NORTH)
- COCKSFORD £18.00
- FOREST PARK £18.00
- HEWORTH £14.00
- KILNWICK PERCY £15.00
- SCARTHINGWELL £16.00
- SPOFFORTH £10.00

YORKSHIRE (SOUTH)
- ROBIN HOOD £12.00
- ROTHER VALLEY GOLF
  Rother Valley £12.00

YORKSHIRE (WEST)
- BAILDON £16.00
- BRACKEN GHYLL £18.00
- BRADLEY HALL £18.00
- BRADLEY PARK £12.00
- CALVERLEY £15.00
- CROW NEST PARK £10.00
- EAST BIERLEY £12.00
- ELLAND £15.00
- FARDEW £10.00
- HEADLEY £15.00
- HEBDEN BRIDGE £12.00
- LEEDS GOLF CTRE
  Wike Ridge £14.50
- LOFTHOUSE HILL £14.00
- MANOR £15.00
- MARSDEN £10.00
- MID YORKSHIRE £15.00
- OUTLANE £18.00
- SILSDEN £15.00
- SOUTH LEEDS £18.00

UNDER £30
BATH & SOMERSET (NORTH EAST)
- MENDIP £21.00

BEDFORDSHIRE
- BEDFORD £25.00
- PAVENHAM £20.00

BERKSHIRE
- CAVERSHAM HEATH £28.00
- GORING AND STREATLEY £28.00
- MAIDENHEAD £27.00
- SUNNINGDALE LADIES £22.00
- WOKEFIELD PARK £29.00

BRISTOL
- FARRINGTON
  Executive £20.00
- FILTON £27.00
- HENBURY £25.00
- KENDLESHIRE £25.00
- KNOWLE £22.00
- MENDIP SPRING
  Brinsea £23.00

BUCKINGHAMSHIRE
- BUCKINGHAM £28.00
- CHILTERN FOREST £25.00
- OAKLAND PARK £25.00
- RICHINGS PARK £22.00

CAMBRIDGESHIRE
- ELTON FURZE £22.00
- OUNDLE £25.50
- RAMSEY CLUB £25.00
- ST. NEOTS £25.00

CHESHIRE
- ANTROBUS £20.00
- LYMM £22.00
- MACCLESFIELD £25.00
- PEOVER £20.00
- PRYORS HAYES £20.00
- REDDISH VALE £25.00
- VALE ROYAL ABBEY £25.00

CLEVELAND
- BILLINGHAM £25.00
- CASTLE EDEN £25.00
- HUNLEY HALL £20.00

CORNWALL
- BUDE & NORTH CORNWALL £25.00
- LOOE £20.00
- LOSTWITHIEL £25.00
- NEWQUAY £20.00
- ROSERROW £25.00
- ST. AUSTELL £20.00
- TEHIDY £25.00
- TRETHORNE £22.00

COUNTY DURHAM
- BARNARD CASTLE £20.00

- BISHOP AUCKLAND £22.00
- DURHAM CITY £24.00
- RAMSIDE
  Princes £27.00

CUMBRIA
- BARROW £20.00
- BRAMPTON £22.00
- CARLISLE £25.00
- EDEN £22.00
- KENDAL £22.00
- SEASCALE £24.00
- SILLOTH £28.00

DERBYSHIRE
- ASHBOURNE £20.00
- BUXTON & HIGH PEAK £29.00
- CHAPEL-EN-LE-FRITH £22.00
- CHESTERFIELD £26.00
- CHEVIN £27.00
- SICKLEHOLME £28.00

DEVON
- DARTMOUTH
  Championship £27.00
- CREDITON £22.00
- HOLSWORTHY £20.00
- ILFRACOMBE £20.00
- NEWTON ABBOT £25.00
- OKEHAMPTON £20.00
- SIDMOUTH £20.00
- TAVISTOCK £24.00
- TEIGNMOUTH £25.00
- TIVERTON £20.00
- TORQUAY £25.00
- WARREN £21.50
- WRANGATON £20.00

DORSET
- ASHLEY WOOD £20.00
- CAME DOWN £24.00
- CRANE VALLEY
  Valley 18 Hole £25.00

ESSEX
- BENTON HALL £20.00
- BOYCE HILL £25.00
- BURNHAM-ON-CROUCH £26.00
- CANONS BROOK £23.00
- CHANNELS
  Channels £28.00
- COLCHESTER £27.50
- COLNE VALLEY £25.00
- CRONDON PARK
  Crondon Park £20.00
- EPPING FOREST £27.50
- WARREN £25.00

GLOUCESTERSHIRE
- CIRENCESTER £25.00
- COTSWOLD HILLS £26.00
- LILLEY BROOK £25.00

- MINCHINHAMPTON
Avening **£26.00**

HAMPSHIRE
- CAMS HALL ESTATE GOLF CLUB
Creek **£20.00**
- CAMS HALL ESTATE GOLF CLUB
Park **£20.00**
- ARMY **£25.00**
- DUNWOOD MANOR **£24.00**
- ROMSEY **£23.00**
- SOUTH WINCHESTER **£25.00**

HERTFORDSHIRE
- ALDWICKBURY PARK **£22.00**
- HERTFORDSHIRE **£25.00**
- ARKLEY **£22.00**
- BISHOPS STORTFORD **£28.00**
- BUSHEY HALL **£20.00**
- MANOR OF GROVES **£20.00**
- OLD FOLD MANOR **£27.00**
- ROYSTON **£25.00**
- WHIPSNADE PARK **£26.00**

ISLE OF WIGHT
- SHANKLIN & SANDOWN **£25.00**

KENT
- RIDGE GOLF CLUB **£20.00**
- ASHFORD **£28.00**
- CHESTFIELD **£22.00**
- DARTFORD **£21.00**
- FAWKHAM VALLEY GOLF CLUB **£20.00**
- LAMBERHURST **£25.00**
- LONDON BEACH **£20.00**
- SENE VALLEY **£25.00**
- TENTERDEN **£22.00**
- WALMER & KINGSDOWN **£25.00**
- WEST MALLING
Spitfire **£25.00**

LANCASHIRE
- ACCRINGTON & DISTRICT **£22.00**
- ASHTON & LEA **£23.00**
- ASHTON-UNDER-LYNE **£25.00**
- CHARNOCK RICHARD **£20.00**
- DEANE **£20.00**
- DUNSCAR **£20.00**
- HINDLEY HALL **£20.00**
- HURLSTON **£28.00**
- INGOL **£20.00**
- KIRKBY LONSDALE **£25.00**
- KNOTT END **£22.00**
- LEYLAND **£25.00**
- PIKEFOLD **£20.00**
- PRESTON **£27.00**
- TURTON **£20.00**

LEICESTERSHIRE
- CHARNWOOD FOREST **£20.00**
- HINCKLEY **£25.00**
- KIRBY MUXLOE **£25.00**
- LEICESTER **£27.00**
- LINGDALE **£23.00**
- LONGCLIFFE **£29.00**

LINCOLNSHIRE
- BELTON PARK
Brownlow **£27.00**
- KENWICK PARK **£25.00**
- LINCOLN **£26.00**
- TOFT HOTEL **£20.00**

LONDON (GREATER)
- BUSH HILL PARK **£27.00**
- COOMBE WOOD **£25.00**
- CREWS HILL **£25.00**
- DULWICH & SYDENHAM HILL **£25.00**
- ELTHAM WARREN **£25.00**
- FINCHLEY **£25.00**
- HENDON **£28.00**
- HUMAX **£25.00**
- NORTH MIDDLESEX **£23.00**
- SHOOTERS HILL **£27.00**
- WEST ESSEX **£28.00**
- WYKE GREEN **£25.00**

MANCHESTER (GREATER)
- BLACKLEY **£24.00**
- BROOKDALE **£22.00**
- CHORLTON-CUM-HARDY **£25.00**
- DENTON **£25.00**
- ELLESMERE **£22.00**
- SWINTON PARK **£25.00**

MERSEYSIDE
- BIDSTON **£22.00**
- BLUNDELLS HILL **£20.00**
- BROMBOROUGH **£28.00**
- CHILDWALL **£26.00**
- HAYDOCK PARK **£27.00**
- LEASOWE **£25.00**
- LEE PARK **£20.00**
- SOUTHPORT OLD LINKS **£22.00**

MIDLANDS (WEST)
- ASTON WOOD **£22.00**
- NORTH WORCESTERSHIRE **£25.00**
- SHIRLEY **£25.00**
- SUTTON COLDFIELD LADIES **£25.00**

NORFOLK
- CALDECOTT HALL **£20.00**
- COSTESSEY PARK **£20.00**
- BAWBURGH **£22.00**
- SPROWSTON MANOR **£21.00**
- MUNDESLEY **£20.00**
- RYSTON PARK **£25.00**
- WESTON PARK **£28.50**

NORTHAMPTONSHIRE
- COLLINGTREE PARK **£20.00**
- KINGSTHORPE **£25.00**

NORTHUMBERLAND
- BELLINGHAM **£20.00**
- LINDEN HALL **£20.00**
- MORPETH **£22.00**
- STOCKSFIELD **£25.00**

NOTTINGHAMSHIRE
- CHILWELL MANOR **£20.00**
- RADCLIFFE-ON-TRENT **£23.00**
- RETFORD **£20.00**
- STANTON ON THE WOLDS **£22.00**
- WOLLATON PARK **£27.50**

OXFORDSHIRE
- HUNTERCOMBE **£28.00**
- LYNEHAM **£20.00**

RUTLAND
- GREETHAM VALLEY
Lakes **£28.00**
- GREETHAM VALLEY
Valley **£28.00**

SHROPSHIRE
- BRIDGNORTH **£24.00**
- CLEOBURY MORTIMER
Deer park **£20.00**
- CLEOBURY MORTIMER
Foxes Run **£20.00**

SOMERSET
- ENMORE PARK **£20.00**
- MINEHEAD & WEST SOMERSET **£24.50**
- WELLS **£20.00**
- YEOVIL
Old **£25.00**

SOMERSET (NORTH)
- WESTON **£24.00**

STAFFORDSHIRE
- BRANSTON
Branston **£28.00**
- CRAYTHORNE **£22.00**
- ST. THOMAS' PRIORY **£20.00**
- UTTOXETER **£20.00**

SUFFOLK
- BRETTVALE **£20.00**
- BURY ST EDMUNDS
Bury St Edmunds **£25.00**
- FYNN VALLEY
Fynn Valley 18 hole **£22.00**
- HAVERHILL **£22.00**
- RUSHMERE **£25.00**
- SUFFOLK GOLF **£25.00**

SURREY
- TRADITIONS GOLF COURSE **£20.00**
- OAK PARK GOLF CLUB
Woodland **£20.00**

Weekdays (Mon - Fri)   GREEN FEE Without Member in England   Under £30 — Under £30

- BRAMLEY £28.00
- CRANLEIGH £23.00
- EPSOM £26.00
- PINE RIDGE GOLF CTRE £22.00
- PUTTENHAM £25.00
- REIGATE HILL £25.00
- WEST SURREY £27.00
- WINDLESHAM £25.00

SUSSEX (EAST)
- CROWBOROUGH BEACON £27.50
- HIGHWOODS £28.00
- MID SUSSEX £25.00
- SEAFORD £27.00
- WEST HOVE £25.00

SUSSEX (WEST)
- BOGNOR REGIS £25.00
- CHARTHAM PARK £25.00
- CHICHESTER
  Chichester £21.00
- ROOKWOOD £25.00
- SINGING HILLS
  Lake £20.00

WILTSHIRE
- CUMBERWELL
  Woodlands £22.00
- ERLESTOKE SANDS £20.00
- HAMPTWORTH £25.00
- HIGH POST £28.00
- KINGSDOWN £26.00
- SALISBURY & SOUTH WILTS
  Main £25.00
- TIDWORTH GARRISON £27.50
- UPAVON £22.00
- WRAG BARN £27.00

WORCESTERSHIRE
- BANK HOUSE £20.00
- CHURCHILL & BLAKEDOWN £20.00
- REDDITCH £28.00

YORKSHIRE (EAST)
- HAINSWORTH PARK £20.00
- HORNSEA £22.00

YORKSHIRE (NORTH)
- ALDWARK MANOR £25.00
- OAKS £22.00
- RUDDING PARK £22.50

YORKSHIRE (WEST)
- HALIFAX £20.00
- HOWLEY HALL £27.50
- MELTHAM £22.00
- NORTHCLIFFE £20.00
- OTLEY £29.00
- SHIPLEY £26.00
- WILLOW VALLEY
  T.P.C £22.00
- WOODHALL HILLS £20.50

£30 AND ABOVE
BEDFORDSHIRE
- JOHN O'GAUNT
  Carthagena £45.00

BERKSHIRE
- BERKSHIRE
  Blue £60.00
- CALCOT PARK £40.00
- LAMBOURNE CLUB £40.00
- MILL RIDE £60.00
- NEWBURY & CROOKHAM £30.00
- PARASAMPIA £30.00
- READING £33.00
- TEMPLE £36.00
- WEST BERKSHIRE £35.00

BRISTOL
- BRISTOL & CLIFTON £32.00
- LONG ASHTON £30.00
- TRACY PARK
  Cromwell £30.00
- TRACY PARK
  Crown £30.00

BUCKINGHAMSHIRE
- MAGNOLIA PARK £35.00
- WOBURN
  Duchess £50.00
- WOBURN
  Marquess £100.00

CAMBRIDGESHIRE
- ELY CITY £30.00
- GOG MAGOG
  The Old £35.00

CHESHIRE
- CARDEN PARK
  The Cheshire £40.00
- CARDEN PARK
  The Nicklaus £60.00
- DAVENPORT £30.00
- DUNHAM FOREST £40.00
- EATON £30.00
- LEIGH £30.00
- MERE £70.00
- PORTAL PREMIER £30.00
- RINGWAY £35.00
- UPTON-BY-CHESTER £30.00

CLEVELAND
- SEATON CAREW
  Old Course £34.00
- WYNYARD CLUB £50.00

CORNWALL
- BOWOOD £30.00
- CARLYON BAY £37.00

DERBYSHIRE
- HALLOWES £30.00
- HORSLEY LODGE £30.00
- BREADSALL PRIORY
  Priory £40.00

DEVON
- CHURSTON £30.00
- NORTH DEVON (ROYAL) £32.00
- SAUNTON
  East £45.00
- SAUNTON
  West £45.00
- WOODBURY PARK
  Oaks £40.00
- YELVERTON £30.00

DORSET
- BROADSTONE £35.00
- EAST DORSET
  Lakeland £30.00
- FERNDOWN
  The Old Course £45.00
- ISLE OF PURBECK
  Purbeck £35.00
- PARKSTONE £35.00

ESSEX
- ABRIDGE £33.00
- CHELMSFORD £36.00
- CHIGWELL £35.00
- ORSETT £35.00
- ROMFORD £37.50

GUERNSEY
- GUERNSEY (ROYAL) £38.00

HAMPSHIRE
- BLACKMOOR £35.00
- BOTLEY PARK £30.00
- HAYLING £31.00
- LEE ON THE SOLENT £30.00
- LIPHOOK £35.00
- MEON VALLEY
  Meon £36.00
- NORTH HANTS FLEET £32.00
- OLD THORNS £35.00
- ROWLANDS CASTLE £30.00
- WINCHESTER (ROYAL) £33.00
- WATERLOOVILLE £30.00

HERTFORDSHIRE
- BERKHAMSTED £30.00
- BROOKMANS PARK £32.00
- EAST HERTS £38.00

ISLE OF MAN
- CASTLETOWN GOLF LINKS £45.00

JERSEY
- LA MOYE £45.00
- JERSEY (ROYAL) £45.00

KENT
- BEARSTED £30.00
- BROOME PARK £30.00
- CANTERBURY £30.00
- CHART HILLS £55.00
- CHERRY LODGE £30.00
- KINGS HILL £30.00

KNOLE PARK £35.00

LANGLEY PARK £35.00

LITTLESTONE £36.00

TUDOR PARK £35.00

PRINCES
Himalayas £55.00

REDLIBBETS £30.00

ROCHESTER & COBHAM £30.00

CINQUE PORTS (ROYAL) £60.00

LANCASHIRE

BLACKPOOL NORTH SHORE £30.00

CLITHEROE £33.00

DEAN WOOD £30.00

FLEETWOOD £30.00

LYTHAM GREEN £30.00

MOSSOCK HALL £30.00

PLEASINGTON £36.00

LYTHAM & ST ANNES (ROYAL) £100.00

LINCOLNSHIRE

LUFFENHAM HEATH £35.00

SEACROFT £30.00

WOODHALL SPA
Bracken £40.00

WOODHALL SPA
Hotchkin £55.00

LONDON (GREATER)

COOMBE HILL £60.00

HAMPSTEAD £30.00

HIGHGATE £30.00

MUSWELL HILL £30.00

BLACKHEATH (ROYAL) £40.00

SOUTH HERTS £30.00

WANSTEAD £30.00

WIMBLEDON PARK £40.00

MANCHESTER (GREATER)

MANCHESTER £30.00

WORSLEY £30.00

MERSEYSIDE

CALDY £42.00

FORMBY HALL £35.00

HESKETH £40.00

HESWALL £35.00

HILLSIDE £45.00

PRENTON £30.00

LIVERPOOL (ROYAL) £95.00

SOUTHPORT & AINSDALE £45.00

WALLASEY £45.00

WEST LANCASHIRE £50.00

MIDLANDS (WEST)

BELFRY
Brabazon £120.00

EDGBASTON £35.00

LITTLE ASTON £50.00

ROBIN HOOD £30.00

SANDWELL PARK £35.00

WALMLEY £30.00

NORFOLK

EATON £30.00

HUNSTANTON £55.00

KING'S LYNN £40.00

MIDDLETON HALL £30.00

CROMER (ROYAL) £37.00

NORWICH (ROYAL) £36.00

WEST NORFOLK (ROYAL) £60.00

THETFORD £34.00

NORTHAMPTONSHIRE

NORTHAMPTON £32.00

NORTHAMPTONSHIRE COUNTY £45.00

WELLINGBOROUGH £30.00

NORTHUMBERLAND

HEXHAM £30.00

SLALEY HALL GOLF COURSE
Hunting £60.00

SLALEY HALL GOLF COURSE
Priestman £40.00

NOTTINGHAMSHIRE

LINDRICK £48.00

NOTTS £50.00

SHERWOOD FOREST £40.00

WORKSOP £32.00

OXFORDSHIRE

FRILFORD HEATH
Green £50.00

STUDLEY WOOD £30.00

SOMERSET

BURNHAM & BERROW
Championship £40.00

SUFFOLK

ALDEBURGH
Aldeburgh £45.00

DIP FARM £30.00

FELIXSTOWE FERRY £30.00

FLEMPTON £30.00

HINTLESHAM HALL £30.00

WORLINGTON & NEWMARKET (ROYAL) £48.00

WOODBRIDGE
Woodbridge £33.00

SURREY

ADDINGTON £50.00

ADDINGTON PALACE £35.00

PYRFORD GOLF CLUB £38.00

ASHFORD MANOR £30.00

BANSTEAD DOWNS £35.00

BURHILL
Burhill (New) £60.00

BURHILL
Burhill (Old) £60.00

CAMBERLEY HEATH £48.00

CROHAM HURST £37.00

EFFINGHAM £35.00

FARNHAM £35.00

FOXHILLS GOLF
Bernard Hunt £60.00

HANKLEY COMMON £50.00

HINDHEAD £47.00

KINGSWOOD £36.00

NEW ZEALAND £42.00

MID-SURREY (ROYAL)
Outer £68.00

SUNNINGDALE
New £85.00

SUNNINGDALE
Old £120.00

SUTTON GREEN £40.00

WALTON HEATH
Old £77.00

WILDWOOD COUNTRY CLUB £30.00

WORPLESDON £46.00

SUSSEX (EAST)

COODEN BEACH £32.00

DALE HILL
The Ian Woosnam £50.00

EAST SUSSEX NATIONAL
East £40.00

ASHDOWN FOREST (ROYAL) £55.00

SUSSEX (WEST)

MANNINGS HEATH
Kingfisher £42.00

GOODWOOD £32.00

HAM MANOR £30.00

WEST SUSSEX £47.50

WORTHING
Lower £40.00

WARWICKSHIRE

LEAMINGTON & COUNTY £32.00

WORCESTERSHIRE

BROADWAY £30.00

YORKSHIRE (EAST)

HESSLE
Hexham £30.00

YORKSHIRE (NORTH)

GANTON £60.00

YORKSHIRE (SOUTH)

HILLSBOROUGH £30.00

YORKSHIRE (WEST)

ALWOODLEY £55.00

HUDDERSFIELD £37.00

MOORTOWN £55.00

WAKEFIELD £32.00

WOODSOME HALL £30.00

GREEN FEE Without Member in England — Weekdays (Mon - Fri)

£30 and Above — £30 and Above

Weekdays (Mon - Fri)

GREEN FEE Without Member in Ireland

Under £10 — £30 and Above

UNDER £10

COUNTY DUBLIN

- OPEN
  Blue Nine **£6.00**

COUNTY KILKENNY

- CARRIGLEADE **£4.30**
- POCOCKE **£8.00**

COUNTY LIMERICK

- ABBEYFEALE GOLF CTRE **£6.00**

COUNTY LOUTH

- TOWNLEY HALL **£7.00**

COUNTY MEATH

- GLEBE **£6.50**
- SOUTH MEATH **£8.00**
- SUMMERHILL **£8.00**

COUNTY WICKLOW

- GLEN MILL **£6.00**

UNDER £20

COUNTY CORK

- BLARNEY **£14.00**
- COBH **£12.00**
- KINSALE
  Ringenane **£12.00**
- LISSELAN **£10.00**
- WATER ROCK **£12.00**

COUNTY DUBLIN

- OPEN
  Red Nine **£11.00**

COUNTY KERRY

- BALLYHEIGUE CASTLE **£10.00**
- CASTLEROSSE **£12.00**
- KERRIES **£18.00**

COUNTY KILDARE

- CELBRIDGE ELM HALL **£15.00**
- CRADDOCKSTOWN **£16.00**
- HIGHFIELD **£14.00**

COUNTY KILKENNY

- MOUNTAIN VIEW **£12.00**

COUNTY LIMERICK

- RATHBANE **£15.00**

COUNTY LOUTH

- KILLIN PARK **£12.00**

COUNTY MAYO

- BALLINA **£16.00**
- MULRANNY **£10.00**

COUNTY OFFALY

- CASTLE BARNA **£15.00**

COUNTY ROSCOMMON

- ROSCOMMON **£15.00**

COUNTY TIPPERARY

- BALLYKISTEEN **£18.00**
- TEMPLEMORE **£10.00**

COUNTY WEXFORD

- BALLYMONEY **£13.00**

UNDER £30

COUNTY CLARE

- KILKEE **£20.00**

COUNTY CORK

- KINSALE
  Farrangalway **£20.00**

COUNTY DONEGAL

- NARIN/PORTNOO **£20.00**

COUNTY DUBLIN

- CLONTARF **£26.00**
- TURVEY **£20.00**

COUNTY GALWAY

- ATHENRY **£20.00**
- BEARNA **£25.00**
- CONNEMARA
  Connemara **£29.00**

COUNTY KILKENNY

- GOWRAN PARK GOLF & LEISURE
  £25.00

COUNTY WATERFORD

- DUNGARVAN **£20.00**
- FAITHLEGG **£22.00**
- GOLD COAST **£22.00**
- WEST WATERFORD **£20.00**

£30 AND ABOVE

COUNTY CLARE

- DOONBEG **£114.02**
- LAHINCH
  Old **£75.00**

COUNTY DUBLIN

- MALAHIDE **£35.00**
- PORTMARNOCK HOTEL **£62.50**

COUNTY KERRY

- DOOKS **£40.00**
- RING OF KERRY **£45.00**
- WATERVILLE HOUSE & GOLF
  LINKS **£75.00**

COUNTY LOUTH

- LOUTH (COUNTY) **£55.00**

COUNTY SLIGO

- SLIGO (COUNTY)
  Championship **£31.67**

COUNTY WICKLOW

- DRUIDS GLEN **£85.00**
- EUROPEAN CLUB **£63.20**
- GLEN OF THE DOWNS **£40.00**
- POWERSCOURT **£75.00**
- RATHSALLAGH **£45.00**

UNDER £10

COUNTY ANTRIM

🌤 BENTRA MUNICIPAL £8.00

🌤 BELFAST £6.80

🌤 TEMPLE CLUB £6.00

COUNTY DOWN

🌤 RINGDUFFERIN
Ringdufferin £9.00

COUNTY FERMANAGH

🌤 ASHWOODS £6.00

COUNTY LONDONDERRY

🌤 FAUGHAN VALLEY £8.00

COUNTY TYRONE

🌤 SPRINGHILL £7.00

UNDER £20

COUNTY ANTRIM

🌤 ALLEN PARK £13.00

🌤 BALLYMENA £17.00

🌤 CLIFTONVILLE £12.00

🌤 DOWN ROYAL PARK
Down Royal Park £17.00

🌤 GRACEHILL £15.00

🌤 GREENACRES GOLF CTRE £12.00

🌤 LARNE £10.00

🌤 ORMEAU £14.00

🌤 WHITEHEAD £16.00

COUNTY ARMAGH

🌤 TANDRAGEE £15.00

COUNTY DOWN

🌤 BANBRIDGE £15.00

🌤 CARNALEA £16.00

🌤 CLOVERHILL £10.00

🌤 DOWNPATRICK £15.00

🌤 HOLYWOOD £16.00

🌤 KILKEEL £18.00

🌤 KIRKISTOWN CASTLE £18.75

🌤 SCRABO £15.00

COUNTY FERMANAGH

🌤 CASTLE HUME £15.00

🌤 ENNISKILLEN £15.00

COUNTY LONDONDERRY

🌤 FOYLE
Parkland £12.00

COUNTY TYRONE

🌤 NEWTOWNSTEWART £12.00

🌤 OMAGH £12.00

🌤 STRABANE £15.00

UNDER £30

COUNTY ANTRIM

🌤 BALLYCASTLE £20.00

🌤 CAIRNDHU £20.00

🌤 GALGORM CASTLE £20.00

🌤 KNOCK £20.00

🌤 LISBURN £25.00

COUNTY DOWN

🌤 ARDGLASS £20.00

🌤 DONAGHADEE £22.00

🌤 WARRENPOINT £20.00

COUNTY LONDONDERRY

🌤 DERRY
Prehen £20.00

£30 AND ABOVE

COUNTY ANTRIM

🌤 PORTRUSH (ROYAL)
Dunluce £80.00

🌤 PORTRUSH (ROYAL)
Valley £30.00

GREEN FEE Without Member in N.Ireland   Weekdays (Mon - Fri)

Under £10 — £30 and Above

GREEN FEE Without Member in **Scotland** Weekdays (Mon - Fri)

Under £10 — Under £30

UNDER £10

AYRSHIRE (NORTH)
- AUCHENHARVIE £5.00

AYRSHIRE (SOUTH)
- MAYBOLE MUNICIPAL £6.00

DUMFRIES AND GALLOWAY
- CRAIGIEKNOWES £9.00
- PARK TONGLAND £4.50

FALKIRK
- POLMONT £8.00

FIFE
- CHARLETON
  Charleton 9 hole £5.00
- FALKLAND £8.00

GLASGOW (CITY OF)
- ALEXANDRA £3.30
- KNIGHTSWOOD £7.20

INVERCLYDE
- WHINHILL £7.00

LANARKSHIRE (NORTH)
- PALACERIGG £8.00

LOTHIAN (EAST)
- MUSSELBURGH LINKS £8.00

LOTHIAN (WEST)
- BRIDGEND £8.00

PERTH AND KINROSS
- STRATHMORE GOLF CTRE
  Leitfie Links £8.00

UNDER £20

ABERDEEN (CITY OF)
- CRAIBSTONE £16.00
- EAST ABERDEENSHIRE £15.00
- HUNTLY £12.00
- PORTLETHEN £15.00

ABERDEENSHIRE
- ABOYNE £19.00
- BALLATER £18.00
- DUFF HOUSE ROYAL £18.00
- DUFFTOWN £12.00
- FRASERBURGH
  Corbie Hill £15.00
- FRASERBURGH
  Rosehill £10.00
- INVERURIE £14.00
- KEMNAY £18.00
- KINTORE £13.00
- NEWBURGH-ON-YTHAN £16.00
- OLDMELDRUM £14.00
- PETERHEAD
  New £18.00
- TARLAIR (ROYAL) £10.00
- STONEHAVEN £18.00
- TORPHINS £12.00
- TURRIFF £18.00

ANGUS
- ARBROATH £18.00
- EDZELL
  West Water £10.00
- MONIFIETH GOLF LINKS
  Ashludie £17.00
- MONTROSE LINKS TRUST
  Broomfield £12.00

ARGYLL AND BUTE
- DUNAVERTY £14.00
- PORT BANNATYNE £10.00

AYRSHIRE (NORTH)
- ARDEER £18.00
- BEITH £15.00
- KILBIRNIE PLACE £12.00
- RAVENSPARK £10.50
- ROUTENBURN £10.00

AYRSHIRE (SOUTH)
- BELLEISLE & SEAFIELD
  Belleisle £18.00
- BELLEISLE & SEAFIELD
  Seafield £12.00
- DALMILLING £12.00
- GIRVAN £12.00

CLACKMANNANSHIRE
- BRAEHEAD £18.50
- DOLLAR £13.50
- MUCKHART
  Muckhart £17.00

DUMFRIES AND GALLOWAY
- CRICHTON £12.00
- GATEHOUSE £10.00
- LAGGANMORE £12.00
- LOCHMABEN £18.00
- LOCKERBIE £16.00
- NEW GALLOWAY £13.00
- PINES £14.00
- SOLWAY LINKS £13.00

EDINBURGH (CITY OF)
- SWANSTON £10.00

FALKIRK
- BONNYBRIDGE £16.00
- FALKIRK £15.00

FIFE
- ABERDOUR £17.00
- ANSTRUTHER £12.00
- CANMORE £15.00
- CHARLETON
  Charleton £18.00
- CUPAR £15.00
- ELMWOOD £18.00
- KINGHORN £14.00
- LESLIE £12.00
- LOCHGELLY £14.00
- PITREAVIE £19.50
- SALINE £10.00

ST. ANDREWS LINKS
- ST. ANDREWS LINKS
  Balgove £10.00
- ST. ANDREWS LINKS
  Strathtyrum £18.00
- THORNTON £17.00

GLASGOW (CITY OF)
- BEARSDEN £15.00

HIGHLANDS
- ABERNETHY £13.00
- ISLE OF SKYE £15.00
- ULLAPOOL £15.00

LANARKSHIRE (SOUTH)
- CARNWATH £16.00
- KAMES GOLF
  Mouse Valley £14.00

LOTHIAN (EAST)
- CASTLE PARK £12.00
- HADDINGTON £18.00

LOTHIAN (MID)
- KINGS ACRE £17.00

LOTHIAN (WEST)
- BRIDGECASTLE £12.50
- GREENBURN £17.00
- WEST LOTHIAN £10.00

MORAY
- BUCKPOOL £15.00
- CULLEN £12.00
- HOPEMAN £13.00
- STRATHLENE £15.00

PERTH AND KINROSS
- DUNKELD £18.00
- MILNATHORT £12.00

RENFREWSHIRE
- PAISLEY £18.00
- RALSTON £18.00

SCOTTISH BORDERS
- DUNS £16.00
- INNERLEITHEN £11.00
- RUTHERFORD CASTLE £15.00
- SELKIRK £16.00

UNDER £30

ABERDEENSHIRE
- BANCHORY £20.00

ANGUS
- BRECHIN GOLF & SQUASH CLUB
  £25.00
- CARNOUSTIE
  Buddon Links £20.00
- CARNOUSTIE
  Burnside £25.00
- EDZELL
  Edzell £24.00
- FORFAR £20.00
- KIRRIEMUIR £20.00
- MONTROSE LINKS TRUST
  Medal £28.00

- PIPERDAM GOLF £20.00

ARGYLL AND BUTE
- COWAL £23.00

AYRSHIRE (NORTH)
- MILLPORT £25.00
- SHISKINE £20.00
- WEST KILBRIDE £27.00

AYRSHIRE (SOUTH)
- BRUNSTON CASTLE £26.00

CLACKMANNANSHIRE
- ALLOA £24.00

DUMFRIES AND GALLOWAY
- COLVEND £20.00
- GALLOWAY £26.00
- KIRKCUDBRIGHT £23.00
- NEWTON STEWART £21.00
- PORTPATRICK - DUNSKEY
  Dunskey £22.00
- POWFOOT £24.00
- STRANRAER £22.00
- WIGTOWNSHIRE £20.00

EDINBURGH (CITY OF)
- LIBERTON £20.00

FIFE
- BALBIRNIE PARK £25.00
- ST. ANDREWS LINKS
  Eden £28.00

GLASGOW (CITY OF)
- DOUGLAS PARK £22.00

HIGHLANDS
- BOAT OF GARTEN £23.00
- BRORA £25.00
- INVERNESS £29.00
- REAY £20.00

INVERCLYDE
- GOUROCK £22.00

LANARKSHIRE (NORTH)
- EASTER MOFFAT £20.00

LANARKSHIRE (SOUTH)
- LANARK
  Old £26.00

LOTHIAN (EAST)
- GLEN £20.00
- WHITEKIRK £20.00

LOTHIAN (WEST)
- LINLITHGOW £20.00

MORAY
- FORRES £24.00
- GRANTOWN-ON-SPEY £20.00

PERTH AND KINROSS
- GLENISLA £22.00
- STRATHMORE GOLF CTRE
  Rannaleroch £20.00
- TAYMOUTH CASTLE £22.00

RENFREWSHIRE
- ELDERSLIE £24.00

SCOTTISH BORDERS
- CARDRONA £20.00
- EYEMOUTH £20.00
- HIRSEL £20.00
- PEEBLES £20.00
- TORWOODLEE £20.00
- WEST LINTON £20.00

WESTERN ISLES
- STORNOWAY £20.00

£30 AND ABOVE

ABERDEEN (CITY OF)
- MURCAR
  Murcar £40.00
- NEWMACHAR
  Hawkshill £30.00
- ABERDEEN (ROYAL)
  Balgownie Links £65.00

ABERDEENSHIRE
- CRUDEN BAY £50.00
- INCHMARLO GOLF CTRE
  Inchmarlo 18 hole £35.00

ANGUS
- CARNOUSTIE
  Championship £75.00
- MONIFIETH GOLF LINKS
  Medal £33.00
- PANMURE £35.00

ARGYLL AND BUTE
- MACHRIHANISH
  Machrihanish 18 Hole £50.00

AYRSHIRE (EAST)
- BALLOCHMYLE £30.00

AYRSHIRE (NORTH)
- GLASGOW GAILES £45.00
- IRVINE £45.00

AYRSHIRE (SOUTH)
- PRESTWICK £85.00

DUMFRIES AND GALLOWAY
- DUMFRIES & COUNTY £30.00
- SOUTHERNESS £35.00

EDINBURGH (CITY OF)
- BRUNTSFIELD GOLF CLUB £40.00

FIFE
- CRAIL
  Balcomie Links £30.00
- CRAIL
  Craighead Links Course £30.00
- DUKES £65.00
- ELIE GOLF £38.00
- KINGSBARNS GOLF LINKS £125.00
- LADYBANK £35.00
- LUNDIN £35.00
- SCOTSCRAIG £35.00
- ST. ANDREWS LINKS
  Jubilee £37.00

- ST. ANDREWS LINKS
  New £42.00
- ST. ANDREWS LINKS
  Old £85.00

HIGHLANDS
- CARNEGIE £130.00
- FORTROSE & ROSEMARKIE £32.00

LOTHIAN (EAST)
- DUNBAR £32.00
- LUFFNESS £37.00
- NORTH BERWICK £42.00

RENFREWSHIRE
- GLEDDOCH £30.00
- RANFURLY £30.00

SCOTTISH BORDERS
- ROXBURGHE £50.00

GREEN FEE Without Member in Scotland Weekdays (Mon - Fri)

Under £30 — £30 and Above

GREEN FEE Without Member in Wales   Weekdays (Mon - Fri)

Under £10 — £30 and Above

UNDER £10

CAERPHILLY
- OAKDALE £5.00

CARMARTHENSHIRE
- DERLLYS COURT £6.00

CEREDIGION
- CAPEL BANGOR £5.00
- CWMRHYDNEUADD £7.00

DENBIGHSHIRE
- KINMEL PARK GOLF £4.00

FLINTSHIRE
- ALLT-GYMBYD £8.00

GLAMORGAN (VALE OF)
- CASTLECOCH £5.00

GWYNEDD
- FAIRBOURNE £3.00

NEATH PORT TALBOT
- EARLSWOOD £8.00
- LAKESIDE £9.50

NEWPORT
- CAERLEON £4.15

PEMBROKESHIRE
- HERONS BROOK
  Kings £3.50
- HERONS BROOK
  Queens £2.00
- PRISKILLY £8.00

WREXHAM
- MOSS VALLEY £9.00

UNDER £20

BRIDGEND
- GROVE £15.00

CARMARTHENSHIRE
- CILGWYN £10.00
- GARNANT PARK £11.00
- GLYN ABBEY £12.00

CEREDIGION
- PENRHOS
  Academy £18.00

CONWY
- BETWS-Y-COED £15.00

DENBIGHSHIRE
- RHYL £15.00
- ST. MELYD £18.00

FLINTSHIRE
- KINSALE £11.00
- MOLD £17.00

GLAMORGAN (VALE OF)
- PETERSTONE LAKES £16.50
- ST. ANDREWS MAJOR £16.00

GWYNEDD
- CAERNARFON (ROYAL TOWN OF) £15.00

ISLE OF ANGLESEY
- PRINCE'S £18.00
- STORWS WEN £15.00

MONMOUTHSHIRE
- ALICE SPRINGS
  Queens £15.00
- DEWSTOW
  Dewstow £12.00
- MONMOUTH £15.00
- RAGLAN PARC £15.00
- SHIRENEWTON £12.00
- WERNDDU £15.00

NEWPORT
- TREDEGAR PARK £15.00

PEMBROKESHIRE
- HAVERFORDWEST £19.00
- NEWPORT £12.00
- SOUTH PEMBROKE £15.00
- ST. DAVIDS £15.00

POWYS
- BUILTH WELLS £16.00
- WELSH BORDER GOLF COMPLEX £10.00

RHONDDA CYNON TAFF
- MOUNTAIN ASH £15.00

SWANSEA
- GOWER £15.00
- MORRISTON £18.00

TORFAEN
- GREEN MEADOW £10.00

WREXHAM
- CLAYS GOLF CTRE £15.00
- PLASSEY £10.00

UNDER £30

CARMARTHENSHIRE
- CARMARTHEN £20.00

CEREDIGION
- BORTH & YNYSLAS £28.00
- CARDIGAN £20.00
- CLIFF HOTEL £20.00

CONWY
- NORTH WALES £26.00
- RHOS-ON-SEA £20.00

DENBIGHSHIRE
- DENBIGH £24.50
- PRESTATYN £25.00
- RHUDDLAN £20.00
- VALE OF LLANGOLLEN £20.00

FLINTSHIRE
- OLD PADESWOOD £20.00
- PADESWOOD & BUCKLEY £20.00

GLAMORGAN (VALE OF)
- COTTRELL PARK
  Button £25.00

- COTTRELL PARK
  Mackintosh £25.00

MONMOUTHSHIRE
- PONTYPOOL £20.00
- WOODLAKE PARK £20.00

NEATH PORT TALBOT
- NEATH £20.00

NEWPORT
- LLANWERN £20.00

PEMBROKESHIRE
- TENBY £26.00
- TREFLOYNE £20.00

SWANSEA
- CLYNE £25.00
- FAIRWOOD PARK £25.00
- LANGLAND BAY £28.00
- PENNARD £27.00

£30 AND ABOVE

BRIDGEND
- PORTHCAWL (ROYAL) £45.00

FLINTSHIRE
- NORTHOP £30.00

GLAMORGAN (VALE OF)
- CREIGIAU £30.00
- WHITCHURCH £35.00

GWYNEDD
- HARLECH £30.00

MONMOUTHSHIRE
- ST. PIERRE
  Mathern £35.00
- ST. PIERRE
  Old £55.00
- MONMOUTHSHIRE £30.00
- ROLLS OF MONMOUTH £34.00

**Green Fees - Without Member
WEEKENDS**

SECTION 9

*This section allows you
to search for courses by the
green fees charged
at weekends, without a
member.*

e.g Scotland, **Under £10, Fife,
Charleton**, £6.00

Once you have located a club
using this section you can then
refer to the detailed profile of the
club in Section 1, or search for
specific details in other sections.

UNDER £10

BATH & SOMERSET (NORTH EAST)
- COMBE GROVE MANOR £4.00

BERKSHIRE
- BILLINGBEAR PARK
  The New £6.00
- HURST £8.00

BUCKINGHAMSHIRE
- THORNEY PARK £9.50

CAMBRIDGESHIRE
- CAMBRIDGE LAKES £6.00
- THORNEY
  Fen £9.00

CHESHIRE
- MARTON MEADOWS £8.00

CORNWALL
- HELSTON £4.50

CUMBRIA
- BECKSIDE £7.00
- DISTINGTON GOLF £5.00

DERBYSHIRE
- BARLBOROUGH LINKS £7.50
- BROUGHTON HEATH £9.00
- PEWIT £6.90

DEVON
- CENTRAL PARK £2.50
- OTTER VALLEY GOLF CTRE £6.00

DORSET
- PARLEY £8.00

ESSEX
- DUNTON HILLS
  Dunton Hills 18 Hole Par 3 £6.00
- MILLERS BARN GOLF PARK £8.00
- REGIMENT £9.00

GLOUCESTERSHIRE
- BRICKHAMPTON COURT
  Glevum £8.00
- SHIPTON £8.00

HAMPSHIRE
- BASINGSTOKE £3.20
- OTTERBOURNE £5.00
- PARK £9.75
- SOUTHAMPTON MUNICIPAL
  Southampton Municipal 9 hole £6.50
- TOURNERBURY GOLF CTRE £8.30

HEREFORDSHIRE
- BRAMPTON GOLF £4.50
- BROCKINGTON £6.00
- GROVE £7.00
- SOUTH HEREFORDSHIRE
  South Herefordshire 9 Hole Course £4.00

HERTFORDSHIRE
- OXHEY PARK £9.00
- PENFOLD PARK £5.50

- WHADDON £3.50

ISLE OF WIGHT
- WESTRIDGE £9.50

KENT
- ASHFORD £3.80
- BROMLEY £7.35
- MOTE PARK GOLF HUT
  Mote Park 18 hole Putting Green £3.00
- MOTE PARK GOLF HUT
  Mote Park Pitch and Put Par 3 £3.00
- NORTH FORELAND
  Par 3 £7.50
- PEDHAM PLACE GOLF CTRE
  Red £6.75
- ROUNDWOOD HALL £6.00
- UPCHURCH RIVER VALLEY
  River Valley 9 hole £7.75

LANCASHIRE
- ASHTON £9.00
- CASTLE HAWK
  Old £8.00
- HIGHFIELD £5.00

LEICESTERSHIRE
- BLACKTHORN WOOD £7.50

LINCOLNSHIRE
- ADDLETHORPE £9.00
- KIRTON HOLME £6.00
- MARTIN MOOR £6.50
- OWMBY £8.00
- SUDBROOK MOOR £9.00

LINCOLNSHIRE (NORTH)
- GRANGE PARK £8.00

LONDON (GREATER)
- BETHUNE PARK £3.90
- LEE VALLEY £3.80
- THAMESVIEW £8.50

MERSEYSIDE
- AINTREE £7.00
- ALLERTON
  Allerton 18 Hole £8.10
- ALLERTON
  Allerton 9 Hole £4.85
- ARROWE PARK
  Long £7.50
- LIVERPOOL MUNICIPAL £8.10
- SOUTHPORT MUNICIPAL £8.70

NORTHAMPTONSHIRE
- DELAPRE PARK GOLF COMPLEX
  Harding Stone £9.00

NORTHUMBERLAND
- HAGGERSTON CASTLE £5.00

NOTTINGHAMSHIRE
- BRAMCOTE HILLS £6.80
- EDWALTON MUNICIPAL £5.50
- MANSFIELD WOODHOUSE £5.20

OXFORDSHIRE
- FARINGDON £6.00

RUTLAND
- RUTLAND WATER £5.50

SOMERSET
- VIVARY PARK £8.90
- WINCANTON £8.00

STAFFORDSHIRE
- BRANSTON
  Academy £8.00

SUFFOLK
- CLARE PARK LAKE £6.00

SURREY
- BROADWATER PARK £9.25
- CHESSINGTON £9.00
- GOAL FARM £9.50
- REDHILL GOLF CTRE £6.50
- SURREY GOLF & FITNESS £6.00

SUSSEX (EAST)
- EASTBOURNE GOLFING PARK
  £9.00

SUSSEX (WEST)
- BROOKLANDS PARK £4.20
- CUCKFIELD £8.50

WARWICKSHIRE
- BRAMCOTE WATERS £8.00

WILTSHIRE
- WHITLEY £9.00

YORKSHIRE (NORTH)
- CRIMPLE VALLEY £6.00

YORKSHIRE (SOUTH)
- KINGSWOOD £8.00

YORKSHIRE (WEST)
- FARDEW £8.00
- ROUNDHAY £9.25

UNDER £20

BATH & SOMERSET (NORTH EAST)
- FROME GOLF CLUB £15.50

BEDFORDSHIRE
- BARON & BARONESS
  Baron Manhattan £15.00
- BARON & BARONESS
  Baroness Manhattan £18.00
- COLMWORTH & NORTH
  BEDFORDSHIRE £18.00
- MOUNT PLEASANT £10.00
- MOWSBURY £13.50
- SOUTH BEDS
  Warden Hill £12.00
- STOCKWOOD PARK £11.90

BERKSHIRE
- BILLINGBEAR PARK
  The Old £10.00
- DEANWOOD PARK £10.50
- HENNERTON £18.00

GREEN FEE Without Member in England Weekends Under £10 — Under £20

BUCKINGHAMSHIRE
- AYLESBURY £14.00
- ABBEY HILL GOLF CENTRE
  Abbey Hill £15.95
- HEDSOR £10.00
- IVER £15.50
- PRINCES RISBOROUGH £18.00
- SILVERSTONE £18.00
- WINDMILL HILL £15.00

CAMBRIDGESHIRE
- ABBOTSLEY
  Cromwell £17.00
- CAMBRIDGE £13.00
- LAKESIDE LODGE
  Lodge £19.00
- MARCH £16.50
- ORTON MEADOWS £14.75
- STILTON OAKS £12.00
- THORNEY
  Lakes £18.50
- THORPE WOOD £14.75
- TYDD ST GILES £11.50

CHANNEL ISLANDS
- ST. CLEMENT £10.00

CHESHIRE
- ALDER ROOT £18.00
- MOBBERLEY £18.00
- STYAL
  Academy Championship Par 3 £12.00

CLEVELAND
- NORTON £12.00
- KNOTTY HILL GOLF CTRE
  Bishops £13.00

COUNTY DURHAM
- OAK LEAF £11.00
- STRESSHOLME £13.00

CUMBRIA
- CARUS GREEN £15.00
- CASTERTON £14.00

DERBYSHIRE
- ALLESTREE PARK £11.20
- BRAILSFORD £16.00

DEVON
- ASHBURY
  Oakwood £15.95
- FINGLE GLEN £10.00
- TORRINGTON £12.00
- PORTMORE GOLF PARK
  Barum £12.00
- SPARKWELL £12.00
- WILLINGCOTT £18.00

DORSET
- BOSCOMBE LADIES £18.00
- FERNDOWN FOREST £14.00

ESSEX
- BELFAIRS PARK £18.00
- BELHUS PARK £15.00
- BIRCH GROVE £12.00
- BRAXTED PARK £12.00
- DUNTON HILLS
  Main £12.50
- EPPING £10.00
- HAINAULT FOREST
  Top £19.00
- MARDYKE VALLEY GOLF CTRE
  The Valley £12.00
- PRIORS £17.00

GLOUCESTERSHIRE
- DYMOCK GRANGE £15.00
- SHERDONS £14.00

HAMPSHIRE
- ALTON £18.00
- COUNTY £14.50
- EAST HORTON GOLF CTRE
  Greenwood £16.00
- EAST HORTON GOLF CTRE
  Parkland £16.00
- FOUR MARKS £10.90
- FURZELEY £12.00
- MEON VALLEY
  Valley £12.00
- PORTSMOUTH £13.50
- SOUTHAMPTON MUNICIPAL
  Southampton Municipal 18 Hole £14.00
- WICKHAM PARK £15.00

HERTFORDSHIRE
- BARKWAY PARK £15.00
- BUSHEY GOLF COURSE £19.00
- CHADWELL SPRINGS £17.00
- DANESBURY PARK £15.00
- LITTLE HAY £16.30
- MALTON £16.00
- ASH VALLEY GOLF CLUB £12.00
- PANSHANGER GOLF COMPLEX
  £18.00
- RICKMANSWORTH £14.20
- STEVENAGE £15.50

KENT
- BECKENHAM PLACE PARK £15.00
- COBTREE MANOR PARK £18.50
- DEANGATE RIDGE
  Deangate Ridge £14.50
- HILDEN EUROPRO £10.00
- HOMELANDS £14.00
- LULLINGSTONE PARK
  Lullingstone Park 18 hole £15.00
- SOUTHERN VALLEY £18.50
- ST. AGUSTINES £16.50
- STAPLEHURST GOLFING PARK
  £10.00
- UPCHURCH RIVER VALLEY
  Upchurch River Valley £14.45
- VILLA £10.00
- WHITSTABLE & SEASALTER £15.00

LANCASHIRE
- BACUP £18.00
- BENTHAM £15.00
- BOLTON £12.00
- BREIGHTMET £18.00
- STANDISH COURT £15.00
- TOWNELEY MUNICIPAL £10.00
- WESTHOUGHTON
  Hart Common £15.00

LEICESTERSHIRE
- BEEDLES LAKE £13.00
- STOKE ALBANY £18.00
- WHETSTONE £16.00

LINCOLNSHIRE
- POTTERGATE £10.00
- SANDILANDS & LEISURE £18.00
- WOODTHORPE HALL £10.00

LINCOLNSHIRE (NORTH EAST)
- IMMINGHAM £18.00

LONDON (GREATER)
- TRENT PARK GOLF CLUB £16.50
- BRENT VALLEY PUBLIC £14.50
- CENTRAL LONDON £10.50
- CHINGFORD £15.25
- DUKES MEADOW £10.00
- HASTE HILL £18.50
- LONDON SCOTTISH £18.00
- RICHMOND PARK
  Dukes £18.00
- RICHMOND PARK
  Princes £18.00
- EPPING FOREST (ROYAL) £15.25

MANCHESTER (GREATER)
- BOYSNOPE PARK £12.00
- HEATON PARK £12.50

MERSEYSIDE
- SHERDLEY PARK MUNICIPAL
  £10.00

MIDLANDS (WEST)
- BOLDMERE £11.00
- BRANDON WOOD MUNICIPAL
  £10.20
- HAWKESBURY GOLF CENTRE
  £10.00
- PYPE HAYES £11.00
- WIDNEY MANOR £14.95

NORFOLK
- EAGLES £17.00
- WENSUM VALLEY £18.00

NORTHAMPTONSHIRE
- BRAMPTON HEATH
  Main £17.00
- COLD ASHBY £18.00
- CORBY PUBLIC £13.70
- DELAPRE PARK GOLF COMPLEX
  Main £14.00

NORTHUMBERLAND
- BELFORD £17.00
- MAGDALENE FIELDS £19.00

NOTTINGHAMSHIRE
- BRIERLEY FOREST £11.50
- BULWELL FOREST £11.00
- COLLEGE PINES £18.00
- KILTON FOREST £12.00
- NORWOOD PARK £17.50
- RAMSDALE PARK
  Ramsdale Park Main £18.50
- SOUTHWELL £18.00
- TRENT LOCK
  Trent Lock Golf Centre 18 hole £15.00

SOMERSET
- BURNHAM & BERROW
  Channel £12.00
- CANNINGTON £16.50

STAFFORDSHIRE
- CHASE £17.50

SUFFOLK
- CRETINGHAM £18.00
- HALESWORTH
  Halesworth £15.00
- HIGH LODGE £10.00

SURREY
- ABBEYMOOR £10.00
- ADDINGTON COURT GOLF CLUB
  Championship £18.60
- ADDINGTON COURT GOLF CLUB
  Falconwood £18.60
- BOWENHURST £14.00
- HERSHAM VILLAGE £11.50
- HORNE PARK £10.50
- HORTON PARK GOLF £18.00
- HURTMORE £16.00
- RUSPER £15.50
- SANDOWN GOLF CTRE
  Par 3 £13.50
- THAMES DITTON & ESHER £14.00
- WINDLERMERE £18.00

SUSSEX (EAST)
- BATTLE £15.00
- BOARS HEAD £10.00
- WATERHALL £16.50

SUSSEX (WEST)
- AVISFORD PARK £15.00
- EFFINGHAM PARK £10.00
- HASSOCKS £17.50
- HILLBARN £16.00
- HORSHAM GOLF £11.00
- PETWORTH £11.00
- RUSTINGTON £16.50
- SELSEY £15.00
- TILGATE FOREST £18.00
- WEST CHILTINGTON £17.50

WARWICKSHIRE
- BIDFORD GRANGE £18.00
- NEWBOLD COMYN £12.00

WILTSHIRE
- BRADFORD ON AVON £10.00
- BRINKWORTH £12.00
- BROOME MANOR £12.50
- OAKSEY £15.00
- RUSHMORE PARK £17.00
- SHRIVENHAM PARK £15.00

WORCESTERSHIRE
- BROMSGROVE £19.00
- LITTLE LAKES £18.00
- WYRE FOREST £15.50

YORKSHIRE (EAST)
- WITHERNSEA £10.00

YORKSHIRE (NORTH)
- HEWORTH £18.00
- KILNWICK PERCY £18.00
- SCARTHINGWELL £18.00
- YORK GOLF CTRE £10.00
- SPOFFORTH £12.00
- SWALLOW HALL £10.00

YORKSHIRE (SOUTH)
- ROBIN HOOD £15.00
- ROTHER VALLEY GOLF
  Rother Valley £16.00

YORKSHIRE (WEST)
- BRADLEY PARK £15.00
- CROW NEST PARK £10.00
- EAST BIERLEY £15.00
- HEBDEN BRIDGE £15.00
- LEEDS GOLF CTRE
  Wike Ridge £16.50
- LOFTHOUSE HILL £17.50
- MANOR £19.00
- OULTON PARK
  Main £12.90
- PONTEFRACT £10.00

UNDER £30

BEDFORDSHIRE
- CHALGRAVE MANOR £20.00
- PAVENHAM £28.00

BERKSHIRE
- GORING AND STREATLEY £28.00
- MAPLEDURHAM £22.00
- SUNNINGDALE LADIES £25.00
- THEALE GOLF CTRE £20.00

BRISTOL
- FARRINGTON
  Executive £25.00
- FILTON £22.00
- KNOWLE £27.00
- MENDIP SPRING
  Brinsea £26.00

BUCKINGHAMSHIRE
- AYLESBURY PARK £20.00

CAMBRIDGESHIRE
- BOURN £22.00

CHANNEL ISLANDS
- ALDERNEY £20.00

CHESHIRE
- ALDERSEY GREEN £20.00
- ANTROBUS £24.00
- MERSEY VALLEY £20.00
- MOLLINGTON GRANGE £25.00
- PEOVER £25.00
- PRYORS HAYES £25.00
- STYAL
  Styal £22.00
- SUTTON HALL £22.00

CORNWALL
- LOSTWITHIEL £29.00
- NEWQUAY £25.00
- ROSERROW £25.00
- ST. AUSTELL £22.00
- TRETHORNE £28.00
- WHITSAND BAY £20.00

COUNTY DURHAM
- BARNARD CASTLE £27.00
- BEAMISH PARK £24.00
- BISHOP AUCKLAND £28.00
- CONSETT & DISTRICT £26.00

CUMBRIA
- BARROW £20.00
- CARLISLE £25.00
- COCKERMOUTH £20.00
- EDEN £27.00
- KENDAL £27.50
- SEASCALE £27.00

DERBYSHIRE
- MAYWOOD £20.00
- ORMONDE FIELDS £22.50
- SHIRLAND £22.00

DEVON
- DAINTON PARK £20.00
- CREDITON £25.00
- ELFORDLEIGH £20.00
- HOLSWORTHY £20.00
- ILFRACOMBE £25.00
- NEWTON ABBOT £28.00
- OKEHAMPTON £25.00
- SIDMOUTH £20.00
- TEIGN VALLEY £20.00
- TEIGNMOUTH £27.50
- WARREN £24.50
- WRANGATON £20.00

DORSET
- CAME DOWN £28.00

Weekends — GREEN FEE Without Member in England — Under £20 — Under £30

ESSEX
- SOUTH ESSEX
  Hawk (Hawk & Vixon) **£21.00**
- SOUTH ESSEX
  Heron (Heron & Hawk) **£21.00**
- SOUTH ESSEX
  Vixen (Vixen & Heron) **£21.00**
- BENTON HALL **£25.00**
- BOYCE HILL **£25.00**
- CHANNELS
  Belstead **£20.00**
- LEXDEN **£20.00**
- ROMFORD **£27.50**

GLOUCESTERSHIRE
- BRICKHAMPTON COURT
  Spa **£25.00**
- COTSWOLD EDGE **£20.00**
- FOREST HILLS **£22.00**
- FOREST OF DEAN **£25.00**
- PAINSWICK **£20.00**

HAMPSHIRE
- CAMS HALL ESTATE GOLF CLUB
  Creek **£27.50**
- CAMS HALL ESTATE GOLF CLUB
  Park **£27.50**
- WELLOW
  Embley **£20.00**

HEREFORDSHIRE
- LEOMINSTER **£22.00**

HERTFORDSHIRE
- ALDWICKBURY PARK **£25.00**
- MILL GREEN GOLF CLUB **£25.00**
- CHORLEYWOOD **£20.00**
- MANOR OF GROVES **£25.00**
- SHENDISH MANOR **£20.00**

ISLE OF WIGHT
- RYDE **£20.00**

KENT
- CRAY VALLEY
  Cray Valley 18 holes **£22.00**
- RUXLEY PARK
  Ruxley Park 18 Hole **£22.00**
- BOUGHTON **£23.00**
- CHESTFIELD **£25.00**
- DARENTH VALLEY **£22.50**
- ETCHINGHILL **£24.00**
- FAWKHAM VALLEY GOLF CLUB **£27.50**
- HAWKHURST **£20.00**
- LONDON BEACH **£25.00**
- PEDHAM PLACE GOLF CTRE
  Yellow **£20.00**
- ROMNEY WARREN **£20.00**

LANCASHIRE
- ACCRINGTON & DISTRICT **£28.00**
- ASHTON & LEA **£25.00**
- ASHTON-UNDER-LYNE **£25.00**
- COLNE **£20.00**
- DEANE **£25.00**
- HINDLEY HALL **£27.00**
- INGOL **£25.00**
- PIKEFOLD **£25.00**
- TURTON **£25.00**
- WHALLEY **£20.00**

LEICESTERSHIRE
- CHARNWOOD FOREST **£25.00**
- LINGDALE **£28.00**

LINCOLNSHIRE
- SLEAFORD **£25.00**
- TOFT HOTEL **£25.00**

LONDON (GREATER)
- NORTH MIDDLESEX **£29.00**

MANCHESTER (GREATER)
- BLACKLEY **£24.00**
- ELLESMERE **£28.00**
- OLDHAM **£24.00**

MERSEYSIDE
- BIDSTON **£25.00**
- HOUGHWOOD **£25.50**
- LEE PARK **£28.00**

MIDLANDS (WEST)
- WERGS **£20.00**

NORFOLK
- CALDECOTT HALL **£25.00**
- COSTESSEY PARK **£25.00**
- FAKENHAM **£24.00**
- FELTWELL **£24.00**
- BAWBURGH **£25.00**
- SPROWSTON MANOR **£27.00**
- MUNDESLEY **£25.00**

NORTHAMPTONSHIRE
- COLLINGTREE PARK **£25.00**

NORTHUMBERLAND
- BELLINGHAM **£25.00**
- BURGHAM **£22.00**
- LINDEN HALL **£25.00**
- MORPETH **£27.00**
- WARKWORTH **£20.00**

NOTTINGHAMSHIRE
- COTGRAVE PLACE
  Open **£25.00**
- CHILWELL MANOR **£20.00**
- OAKMERE PARK **£24.00**
- RADCLIFFE-ON-TRENT **£28.00**
- RETFORD **£25.00**
- RUFFORD PARK GOLF CTRE **£20.00**
- SPRINGWATER **£20.00**

OXFORDSHIRE
- CARSWELL **£25.00**
- CHERWELL EDGE **£20.00**
- HADDEN HILL **£20.00**
- HINKSEY HEIGHTS **£20.00**
- LYNEHAM **£24.00**
- RYE HILL **£20.00**
- WITNEY LAKES **£22.00**

SHROPSHIRE
- ARSCOTT **£20.00**
- CLEOBURY MORTIMER
  Deer park **£24.00**
- CLEOBURY MORTIMER
  Foxes Run **£24.00**

SOMERSET
- BREAN **£20.00**
- LONG SUTTON **£20.00**
- MINEHEAD & WEST SOMERSET **£27.50**
- WELLS **£25.00**
- WINDWHISTLE **£22.00**

STAFFORDSHIRE
- CRAYTHORNE **£28.00**
- ST. THOMAS' PRIORY **£25.00**
- WESTWOOD **£20.00**

SUFFOLK
- BRETTVALE **£25.00**
- FYNN VALLEY
  Fynn Valley 18 hole **£25.00**
- HAVERHILL **£28.00**
- RUSHMERE **£25.00**
- SOUTHWOLD **£20.00**

SURREY
- TRADITIONS GOLF COURSE **£25.00**
- CHIDDINGFOLD **£22.00**
- CRANLEIGH **£25.00**
- PINE RIDGE GOLF CTRE **£28.00**

SUSSEX (EAST)
- MID SUSSEX **£25.00**
- SEAFORD **£27.00**
- SEDLESCOMBE **£20.00**
- WELLSHURST **£22.00**
- WILLINGDON **£20.00**

SUSSEX (WEST)
- CHICHESTER
  Chichester **£29.00**
- FOXBRIDGE **£25.00**
- PAXHILL PARK **£22.00**
- SINGING HILLS
  Lake **£28.00**

WARWICKSHIRE
- ATHERSTONE **£20.00**

WILTSHIRE
- CUMBERWELL
  Woodlands **£28.00**
- ERLESTOKE SANDS **£25.00**
- UPAVON **£25.00**

WORCESTERSHIRE
- BANK HOUSE **£25.00**

YORKSHIRE (EAST)
- BRIDLINGTON £28.00
- CAVE CASTLE £20.00
- HAINSWORTH PARK £25.00

YORKSHIRE (NORTH)
- COCKSFORD £24.00
- FOREST PARK £23.00
- RUDDING PARK £27.50

YORKSHIRE (WEST)
- BAILDON £20.00
- BRACKEN GHYLL £20.00
- BRADLEY HALL £28.00
- CALVERLEY £20.00
- ELLAND £25.00
- HALIFAX £25.00
- MELTHAM £27.00
- MID YORKSHIRE £20.00
- NORTHCLIFFE £25.00
- OUTLANE £28.00
- SHIPLEY £29.00
- SILSDEN £20.00
- SOUTH LEEDS £26.00
- WILLOW VALLEY
  T.P.C £26.00
- WOODHALL HILLS £25.50

£30 AND ABOVE

BATH & SOMERSET (NORTH EAST)
- MENDIP £31.00

BEDFORDSHIRE
- BEDFORD £50.00
- JOHN O'GAUNT
  Carthagena £50.00

BERKSHIRE
- CAVERSHAM HEATH £38.00
- MAIDENHEAD £35.00
- MILL RIDE £40.00
- PARASAMPIA £35.00
- TEMPLE £44.00
- WEST BERKSHIRE £35.00
- WOKEFIELD PARK £36.00

BRISTOL
- BRISTOL & CLIFTON £35.00
- KENDLESHIRE £40.00
- TRACY PARK
  Cromwell £36.00
- TRACY PARK
  Crown £36.00

BUCKINGHAMSHIRE
- MAGNOLIA PARK £50.00
- RICHINGS PARK £30.00

CAMBRIDGESHIRE
- ABBOTSLEY
  Abbotsley £30.00
- ELTON FURZE £32.00
- ELY CITY £36.00
- OUNDLE £35.50

CHESHIRE
- CARDEN PARK
  The Cheshire £40.00
- CARDEN PARK
  The Nicklaus £60.00
- DAVENPORT £40.00
- DUNHAM FOREST £45.00
- EATON £30.00
- LEIGH £40.00
- MACCLESFIELD £30.00
- PORTAL PREMIER £35.00
- RINGWAY £45.00
- UPTON-BY-CHESTER £30.00

CLEVELAND
- BILLINGHAM £40.00
- CASTLE EDEN £35.00
- HUNLEY HALL £30.00
- SEATON CAREW
  Old Course £44.00

CORNWALL
- BOWOOD £30.00
- BUDE & NORTH CORNWALL £30.00
- CARLYON BAY £37.00
- TEHIDY £30.00

COUNTY DURHAM
- DURHAM CITY £30.00
- RAMSIDE
  Princes £33.00

CUMBRIA
- BRAMPTON £30.00
- SILLOTH £37.00

DERBYSHIRE
- ASHBOURNE £30.00
- BUXTON & HIGH PEAK £34.00
- CHAPEL-EN-LE-FRITH £30.00
- HALLOWES £30.00
- HORSLEY LODGE £30.00
- BREADSALL PRIORY
  Priory £40.00
- SICKLEHOLME £32.00

DEVON
- CHURSTON £30.00
- DARTMOUTH
  Championship £30.00
- NORTH DEVON (ROYAL) £38.00
- SAUNTON
  East £45.00
- SAUNTON
  West £45.00
- TAVISTOCK £30.00
- TIVERTON £30.00
- TORQUAY £30.00
- WOODBURY PARK
  Oaks £50.00
- YELVERTON £40.00

DORSET
- BROADSTONE £45.00
- CRANE VALLEY
  Valley 18 Hole £25.00
- EAST DORSET
  Lakeland £35.00
- FERNDOWN
  The Old Course £50.00
- ISLE OF PURBECK
  Purbeck £40.00
- PARKSTONE £45.00

ESSEX
- ABRIDGE £35.00
- CANONS BROOK £30.00
- COLCHESTER £37.50
- COLNE VALLEY £35.00
- CRONDON PARK
  Crondon Park £30.00
- EPPING FOREST £35.00

GLOUCESTERSHIRE
- CIRENCESTER £30.00
- COTSWOLD HILLS £32.00
- LILLEY BROOK £30.00
- MINCHINHAMPTON
  Avening £30.00

GUERNSEY
- GUERNSEY (ROYAL) £38.00

HAMPSHIRE
- DUNWOOD MANOR £30.00
- HAYLING £40.00
- LEE ON THE SOLENT £35.00
- MEON VALLEY
  Meon £40.00
- NORTH HANTS FLEET £44.00
- OLD THORNS £45.00
- WINCHESTER (ROYAL) £40.00
- SOUTH WINCHESTER £40.00

HERTFORDSHIRE
- HERTFORDSHIRE £30.00
- BERKHAMSTED £40.00
- BUSHEY HALL £30.00

ISLE OF MAN
- CASTLETOWN GOLF LINKS £50.00

ISLE OF WIGHT
- SHANKLIN & SANDOWN £30.00

JERSEY
- LA MOYE £50.00
- JERSEY (ROYAL) £45.00

KENT
- ASHFORD £35.00
- BROOME PARK £35.00
- CANTERBURY £36.00
- CHART HILLS £65.00
- LAMBERHURST £40.00
- LITTLESTONE £45.00
- TUDOR PARK £40.00

Weekends

GREEN FEE Without Member in England

Under £30 — £30 and Above

- PRINCES
  Himalayas **£60.00**
- CINQUE PORTS (ROYAL) **£60.00**
- SENE VALLEY **£30.00**
- SWEETWOODS PARK **£32.00**
- WALMER & KINGSDOWN **£30.00**
- WEST MALLING
  Spitfire **£35.00**

LANCASHIRE
- BLACKPOOL NORTH SHORE
  £35.00
- CHARNOCK RICHARD **£30.00**
- CLITHEROE **£39.00**
- DEAN WOOD **£33.00**
- DUNSCAR **£30.00**
- FLEETWOOD **£40.00**
- HURLSTON **£34.00**
- KIRKBY LONSDALE **£30.00**
- KNOTT END **£30.00**
- LYTHAM GREEN **£38.00**
- MOSSOCK HALL **£35.00**

LEICESTERSHIRE
- KIRBY MUXLOE **£30.00**
- LEICESTER **£33.00**
- LONGCLIFFE **£39.00**

LINCOLNSHIRE
- BELTON PARK
  Brownlow **£33.00**
- KENWICK PARK **£35.00**
- LUFFENHAM HEATH **£35.00**
- SEACROFT **£35.00**
- WOODHALL SPA
  Bracken **£40.00**
- WOODHALL SPA
  Hotchkin **£55.00**

LONDON (GREATER)
- COOMBE WOOD **£33.00**
- DULWICH & SYDENHAM HILL
  £35.00
- FINCHLEY **£34.00**
- HAMPSTEAD **£35.00**
- HENDON **£35.00**
- HUMAX **£30.00**
- MUSWELL HILL **£35.00**

MANCHESTER (GREATER)
- CHORLTON-CUM-HARDY **£30.00**
- DENTON **£30.00**
- MANCHESTER **£45.00**
- WORSLEY **£35.00**

MERSEYSIDE
- BLUNDELLS HILL **£30.00**
- BROMBOROUGH **£30.00**
- CHILDWALL **£35.00**
- FORMBY HALL **£40.00**
- HESKETH **£50.00**
- HESWALL **£40.00**

- HILLSIDE **£60.00**
- LEASOWE **£30.00**
- PRENTON **£35.00**
- SOUTHPORT & AINSDALE **£60.00**
- SOUTHPORT OLD LINKS **£30.00**
- WALLASEY **£70.00**
- WEST LANCASHIRE **£70.00**

MIDLANDS (WEST)
- EDGBASTON **£50.00**
- SUTTON COLDFIELD LADIES
  £35.00

NORFOLK
- EATON **£40.00**
- HUNSTANTON **£65.00**
- KING'S LYNN **£50.00**
- MIDDLETON HALL **£35.00**
- CROMER (ROYAL) **£42.00**
- NORWICH (ROYAL) **£44.00**
- WEST NORFOLK (ROYAL) **£70.00**
- WESTON PARK **£32.00**

NORTHAMPTONSHIRE
- NORTHAMPTONSHIRE COUNTY
  £45.00

NORTHUMBERLAND
- HEXHAM **£40.00**
- STOCKSFIELD **£30.00**

NOTTINGHAMSHIRE
- LINDRICK **£48.00**
- WOLLATON PARK **£32.50**
- WORKSOP **£40.00**

OXFORDSHIRE
- FRILFORD HEATH
  Green **£65.00**
- HUNTERCOMBE **£40.00**
- STUDLEY WOOD **£40.00**

RUTLAND
- GREETHAM VALLEY
  Lakes **£32.00**
- GREETHAM VALLEY
  Valley **£32.00**

SHROPSHIRE
- BRIDGNORTH **£30.00**

SOMERSET
- BURNHAM & BERROW
  Championship **£60.00**
- ENMORE PARK **£30.00**
- YEOVIL
  Old **£30.00**

SOMERSET (NORTH)
- WESTON **£35.00**

STAFFORDSHIRE
- BRANSTON
  Branston **£40.00**
- UTTOXETER **£30.00**

SUFFOLK
- ALDEBURGH
  Aldeburgh **£60.00**
- FLEMPTON **£30.00**
- HINTLESHAM HALL **£38.00**
- SUFFOLK GOLF **£30.00**

SURREY
- ADDINGTON **£75.00**
- PYRFORD GOLF CLUB **£52.00**
- OAK PARK GOLF CLUB
  Woodland **£30.00**
- CROHAM HURST **£46.00**
- EPSOM **£30.00**
- FOXHILLS GOLF
  Bernard Hunt **£70.00**
- HINDHEAD **£57.00**
- KINGSWOOD **£50.00**
- NEW ZEALAND **£62.00**
- REIGATE HILL **£35.00**
- SUTTON GREEN **£50.00**
- WALTON HEATH
  Old **£86.00**
- WEST SURREY **£36.00**
- WILDWOOD COUNTRY CLUB
  £45.00
- WINDLESHAM **£35.00**

SUSSEX (EAST)
- COODEN BEACH **£35.00**
- CROWBOROUGH BEACON **£32.50**
- DALE HILL
  The Ian Woosnam **£60.00**
- EAST SUSSEX NATIONAL
  East **£45.00**
- HIGHWOODS **£33.00**
- ASHDOWN FOREST (ROYAL)
  £60.00
- WEST HOVE **£30.00**

SUSSEX (WEST)
- BOGNOR REGIS **£30.00**
- CHARTHAM PARK **£35.00**
- MANNINGS HEATH
  Kingfisher **£56.00**
- GOODWOOD **£42.00**
- HAM MANOR **£40.00**
- ROOKWOOD **£30.00**
- WEST SUSSEX **£52.50**
- WORTHING
  Lower **£50.00**

WARWICKSHIRE
- LEAMINGTON & COUNTY **£80.00**

WILTSHIRE
- HAMPTWORTH **£30.00**
- HIGH POST **£35.00**
- SALISBURY & SOUTH WILTS
  Main **£40.00**
- TIDWORTH GARRISON **£35.00**
- WRAG BARN **£32.00**

Weekends

GREEN FEE Without Member in England

£30 and Above — £30 and Above

WORCESTERSHIRE

- **BROADWAY £37.00**

YORKSHIRE (EAST)

- **HESSLE**
  Hexham **£40.00**
- **HORNSEA £30.00**

YORKSHIRE (NORTH)

- **ALDWARK MANOR £30.00**
- **GANTON £70.00**

YORKSHIRE (SOUTH)

- **HILLSBOROUGH £35.00**

YORKSHIRE (WEST)

- **ALWOODLEY £75.00**
- **HOWLEY HALL £38.00**
- **HUDDERSFIELD £47.00**
- **MOORTOWN £65.00**
- **OTLEY £36.00**
- **WAKEFIELD £40.00**
- **WOODSOME HALL £40.00**

GREEN FEE Without Member in Ireland   **Weekends**

Under £10 — £30 and Above

UNDER £10

COUNTY KILKENNY
- CARRIGLEADE £4.95
- POCOCKE £8.00

COUNTY LIMERICK
- ABBEYFEALE GOLF CTRE £8.00

COUNTY LOUTH
- TOWNLEY HALL £9.00

COUNTY MEATH
- GLEBE £7.50

COUNTY WICKLOW
- GLEN MILL £8.00

UNDER £20

COUNTY CORK
- BLARNEY £18.00
- KINSALE
  Ringenane £12.00
- LISSELAN £10.00
- WATER ROCK £15.00

COUNTY DUBLIN
- OPEN
  Blue Nine £10.00
- OPEN
  Red Nine £17.00

COUNTY KERRY
- BALLYHEIGUE CASTLE £10.00
- CASTLEROSSE £12.00
- KERRIES £18.00

COUNTY KILDARE
- CELBRIDGE ELM HALL £18.00
- HIGHFIELD £18.00

COUNTY KILKENNY
- MOUNTAIN VIEW £15.00

COUNTY LIMERICK
- RATHBANE £17.00

COUNTY LOUTH
- KILLIN PARK £16.00

COUNTY MAYO
- MULRANNY £15.00

COUNTY MEATH
- SOUTH MEATH £10.00
- SUMMERHILL £10.00

COUNTY ROSCOMMON
- ROSCOMMON £15.00

COUNTY TIPPERARY
- BALLYKISTEEN £19.00
- TEMPLEMORE £15.00

COUNTY WEXFORD
- BALLYMONEY £15.00

UNDER £30

COUNTY CLARE
- KILKEE £20.00

COUNTY CORK
- KINSALE
  Farrangalway £25.00

COUNTY DONEGAL
- NARIN/PORTNOO £25.00

COUNTY DUBLIN
- TURVEY £24.00

COUNTY GALWAY
- ATHENRY £25.00

COUNTY KILDARE
- CRADDOCKSTOWN £20.00

COUNTY MAYO
- BALLINA £20.00

COUNTY OFFALY
- CASTLE BARNA £20.00

COUNTY WATERFORD
- DUNGARVAN £25.00
- GOLD COAST £27.00
- WEST WATERFORD £25.00

£30 AND ABOVE

COUNTY CLARE
- DOONBEG £114.02

COUNTY DUBLIN
- CLONTARF £35.00
- MALAHIDE £50.00
- PORTMARNOCK HOTEL £62.50

COUNTY GALWAY
- BEARNA £32.00
- CONNEMARA
  Connemara £32.00

COUNTY KERRY
- DOOKS £40.00
- RING OF KERRY £45.00
- WATERVILLE HOUSE & GOLF LINKS £75.00

COUNTY KILKENNY
- GOWRAN PARK GOLF & LEISURE £30.00

COUNTY LOUTH
- LOUTH (COUNTY) £70.00

COUNTY SLIGO
- SLIGO (COUNTY)
  Championship £39.58

COUNTY WATERFORD
- FAITHLEGG £32.00

COUNTY WICKLOW
- EUROPEAN CLUB £63.20
- GLEN OF THE DOWNS £50.00
- POWERSCOURT £75.00
- RATHSALLAGH £55.00

UNDER £10

COUNTY ANTRIM
- BELFAST £9.40

COUNTY TYRONE
- SPRINGHILL £7.00

UNDER £20

COUNTY ANTRIM
- ALLEN PARK £16.00
- BENTRA MUNICIPAL £11.00
- CLIFTONVILLE £17.00
- GREENACRES GOLF CTRE £18.00
- LARNE £18.00
- ORMEAU £16.50
- TEMPLE CLUB £10.00

COUNTY DOWN
- CLOVERHILL £10.00
- HELENS BAY £17.50
- RINGDUFFERIN
  Ringdufferin £10.00

COUNTY FERMANAGH
- ENNISKILLEN £18.00

COUNTY LONDONDERRY
- FAUGHAN VALLEY £11.00
- FOYLE
  Parkland £15.00

COUNTY TYRONE
- NEWTOWNSTEWART £17.00
- OMAGH £18.00
- STRABANE £17.00

UNDER £30

COUNTY ANTRIM
- BALLYMENA £22.00
- CAIRNDHU £25.00
- DOWN ROYAL PARK
  Down Royal Park £20.00
- GALGORM CASTLE £25.00
- GRACEHILL £20.00
- KNOCK £25.00
- WHITEHEAD £20.00

COUNTY ARMAGH
- TANDRAGEE £20.00

COUNTY DOWN
- ARDGLASS £26.00
- BANBRIDGE £20.00
- CARNALEA £20.00
- DONAGHADEE £25.00
- DOWNPATRICK £25.00
- HOLYWOOD £21.00
- KILKEEL £22.00
- KIRKISTOWN CASTLE £25.75
- WARRENPOINT £27.00

COUNTY FERMANAGH
- CASTLE HUME £20.00

COUNTY LONDONDERRY
- DERRY
  Prehen £25.00

£30 AND ABOVE

COUNTY ANTRIM
- BALLYCASTLE £30.00
- LISBURN £30.00
- PORTRUSH (ROYAL)
  Dunluce £90.00
- PORTRUSH (ROYAL)
  Valley £35.00

GREEN FEE Without Member in N.Ireland Weekends
Under £10 — £30 and Above

UNDER £10

AYRSHIRE (NORTH)
- AUCHENHARVIE £6.80

AYRSHIRE (SOUTH)
- MAYBOLE MUNICIPAL £8.00

DUMFRIES AND GALLOWAY
- CRAIGIEKNOWES £9.00
- PARK TONGLAND £4.50

FIFE
- CHARLETON
  Charleton 9 hole £6.00

GLASGOW (CITY OF)
- ALEXANDRA £3.30
- KNIGHTSWOOD £7.20

INVERCLYDE
- WHINHILL £7.00

LOTHIAN (EAST)
- MUSSELBURGH LINKS £8.00

LOTHIAN (WEST)
- BRIDGEND £5.00

UNDER £20

ABERDEEN (CITY OF)
- HUNTLY £18.00

ABERDEENSHIRE
- DUFFTOWN £12.00
- FRASERBURGH
  Rosehill £12.00
- INVERURIE £18.00
- KINTORE £19.00
- TARLAIR (ROYAL) £15.00
- TORPHINS £14.00

ANGUS
- EDZELL
  West Water £10.00

ARGYLL AND BUTE
- DUNARVERTY £16.00
- PORT BANNATYNE £15.00

AYRSHIRE (NORTH)
- RAVENSPARK £13.50
- ROUTENBURN £13.00

AYRSHIRE (SOUTH)
- BELLEISLE & SEAFIELD
  Seafield £16.00
- DALMILLING £16.00
- GIRVAN £16.00

DUMFRIES AND GALLOWAY
- CRICHTON £12.00
- GATEHOUSE £10.00
- LAGGANMORE £15.00
- NEW GALLOWAY £13.00
- PINES £14.00
- SOLWAY LINKS £13.00

EDINBURGH (CITY OF)
- SWANSTON £15.00

FALKIRK
- BONNYBRIDGE £16.00
- POLMONT £15.00

FIFE
- CUPAR £15.00
- FALKLAND £10.00
- KINGHORN £18.00
- LESLIE £12.00
- SALINE £13.00

GLASGOW (CITY OF)
- BEARSDEN £15.00

HIGHLANDS
- ABERNETHY £16.00
- ISLE OF SKYE £15.00
- ULLAPOOL £15.00

LANARKSHIRE (NORTH)
- PALACERIGG £12.00

LANARKSHIRE (SOUTH)
- KAMES GOLF
  Mouse Valley £16.50

LOTHIAN (EAST)
- CASTLE PARK £14.00

LOTHIAN (WEST)
- BRIDGECASTLE £15.00
- WEST LOTHIAN £15.00

MORAY
- CULLEN £16.00
- HOPEMAN £18.00
- STRATHLENE £15.00

PERTH AND KINROSS
- MILNATHORT £14.00
- STRATHMORE GOLF CTRE
  Leitfie Links £10.00

SCOTTISH BORDERS
- DUNS £19.00
- INNERLEITHEN £15.00
- SELKIRK £16.00

UNDER £30

ABERDEEN (CITY OF)
- CRAIBSTONE £20.00
- EAST ABERDEENSHIRE £20.00
- PORTLETHEN £22.00

ABERDEENSHIRE
- ABOYNE £23.00
- BALLATER £21.00
- BANCHORY £23.00
- DUFF HOUSE ROYAL £25.00
- FRASERBURGH
  Corbie Hill £20.00
- KEMNAY £22.00
- NEWBURGH-ON-YTHAN £21.00
- OLDMELDRUM £20.00

- PETERHEAD
  New £22.00
- STONEHAVEN £25.00
- TURRIFF £22.00

ANGUS
- ARBROATH £24.00
- FORFAR £25.00
- KIRRIEMUIR £25.00
- MONIFIETH GOLF LINKS
  Ashludie £20.00
- PIPERDAM GOLF £24.00

AYRSHIRE (NORTH)
- ARDEER £25.00
- BEITH £20.00
- KILBIRNIE PLACE £20.00
- SHISKINE £24.00

AYRSHIRE (SOUTH)
- BELLEISLE & SEAFIELD
  Belleisle £25.00

CLACKMANNANSHIRE
- ALLOA £28.00
- BRAEHEAD £24.50
- DOLLAR £22.00
- MUCKHART
  Muckhart £25.00

DUMFRIES AND GALLOWAY
- COLVEND £20.00
- KIRKCUDBRIGHT £23.00
- LOCHMABEN £22.00
- LOCKERBIE £20.00
- NEWTON STEWART £23.00
- PORTPATRICK - DUNSKEY
  Dunskey £27.00
- POWFOOT £26.00
- STRANRAER £27.00
- WIGTOWNSHIRE £22.00

FIFE
- CANMORE £20.00
- CHARLETON
  Charleton £22.00
- ELMWOOD £22.00
- LOCHGELLY £20.00
- PITREAVIE £24.50
- THORNTON £25.00

HIGHLANDS
- BOAT OF GARTEN £28.00
- INVERNESS £29.00
- REAY £20.00

LANARKSHIRE (SOUTH)
- CARNWATH £22.00

LOTHIAN (EAST)
- GLEN £27.00
- HADDINGTON £23.00
- WHITEKIRK £28.00

LOTHIAN (MID)
- KINGS ACRE £24.00

LOTHIAN (WEST)
- GREENBURN £25.00
- LINLITHGOW £25.00

MORAY
- BUCKPOOL £20.00
- FORRES £24.00
- GRANTOWN-ON-SPEY £25.00

PERTH AND KINROSS
- DUNKELD £21.00
- GLENISLA £26.00
- STRATHMORE GOLF CTRE
  Rannaleroch £25.00
- TAYMOUTH CASTLE £26.00

SCOTTISH BORDERS
- CARDRONA £25.00
- EYEMOUTH £25.00
- HIRSEL £27.00
- PEEBLES £25.00
- RUTHERFORD CASTLE £25.00
- TORWOODLEE £25.00

WESTERN ISLES
- STORNOWAY £20.00

£30 AND ABOVE

ABERDEEN (CITY OF)
- MURCAR
  Murcar £50.00
- ABERDEEN (ROYAL)
  Balgownie Links £70.00

ABERDEENSHIRE
- CRUDEN BAY £60.00
- INCHMARLO GOLF CTRE
  Inchmarlo 18 hole £45.00

ANGUS
- BRECHIN GOLF & SQUASH CLUB
  £30.00
- EDZELL
  Edzell £30.00
- MONIFIETH GOLF LINKS
  Medal £42.00
- MONTROSE LINKS TRUST
  Medal £32.00
- PANMURE £35.00

ARGYLL AND BUTE
- COWAL £33.00
- MACHRIHANISH
  Machrihanish 18 Hole £60.00

AYRSHIRE (EAST)
- BALLOCHMYLE £35.00

AYRSHIRE (NORTH)
- GLASGOW GAILES £58.00
- IRVINE £45.00
- MILLPORT £31.00

AYRSHIRE (SOUTH)
- BRUNSTON CASTLE £30.00

DUMFRIES AND GALLOWAY
- DUMFRIES & COUNTY £30.00

- GALLOWAY £32.00
- SOUTHERNESS £45.00

EDINBURGH (CITY OF)
- BRUNTSFIELD GOLF CLUB £45.00
- LIBERTON £30.00

FIFE
- ABERDOUR £35.00
- BALBIRNIE PARK £30.00
- CRAIL
  Balcomie Links £35.00
- CRAIL
  Craighead Links Course £35.00
- DUKES £75.00
- ELIE GOLF £48.00
- KINGSBARNS GOLF LINKS £125.00
- LADYBANK £40.00
- LUNDIN £45.00
- SCOTSCRAIG £40.00

HIGHLANDS
- BRORA £30.00
- FORTROSE & ROSEMARKIE £37.00

INVERCLYDE
- GOUROCK £30.00

LOTHIAN (EAST)
- DUNBAR £37.00
- NORTH BERWICK £65.00

RENFREWSHIRE
- GLEDDOCH £40.00

SCOTTISH BORDERS
- ROXBURGHE £50.00
- WEST LINTON £30.00

Weekends

GREEN FEE Without Member in Scotland

Under £30 — £30 and Above

GREEN FEE Without Member in Wales — Weekends

Under £10 — £30 and Above

UNDER £10

CAERPHILLY
- OAKDALE £5.00

CARMARTHENSHIRE
- DERLLYS COURT £7.00

CEREDIGION
- CAPEL BANGOR £6.00

DENBIGHSHIRE
- KINMEL PARK GOLF £5.00

GLAMORGAN (VALE OF)
- CASTLECOCH £5.00

GWYNEDD
- FAIRBOURNE £3.00

NEATH PORT TALBOT
- EARLSWOOD £8.00
- LAKESIDE £9.50

NEWPORT
- CAERLEON £5.20

PEMBROKESHIRE
- HERONS BROOK
  Kings £3.50
- HERONS BROOK
  Queens £2.00

UNDER £20

BRIDGEND
- GROVE £18.00

CARMARTHENSHIRE
- CILGWYN £15.00
- GARNANT PARK £15.00
- GLYN ABBEY £15.00

CEREDIGION
- CWMRHYDNEUADD £18.00

FLINTSHIRE
- ALLT-GYMBYD £14.00
- KINSALE £11.00

GLAMORGAN (VALE OF)
- ST. ANDREWS MAJOR £16.00

MONMOUTHSHIRE
- ALICE SPRINGS
  Queens £15.00
- DEWSTOW
  Dewstow £16.00
- SHIRENEWTON £15.00
- WERNDDU £15.00

PEMBROKESHIRE
- NEWPORT £16.00
- PRISKILLY £10.00
- ST. DAVIDS £15.00

POWYS
- WELSH BORDER GOLF COMPLEX
  £10.00

RHONDDA CYNON TAFF
- MOUNTAIN ASH £18.00

TORFAEN
- GREEN MEADOW £15.00

WREXHAM
- CLAYS GOLF CTRE £18.50
- MOSS VALLEY £12.00
- PLASSEY £12.00

UNDER £30

CARMARTHENSHIRE
- CARMARTHEN £25.00

CEREDIGION
- CARDIGAN £25.00
- CLIFF HOTEL £25.00
- PENRHOS
  Academy £24.00

CONWY
- BETWS-Y-COED £20.00
- RHOS-ON-SEA £28.00

DENBIGHSHIRE
- RHYL £20.00
- ST. MELYD £22.00

FLINTSHIRE
- OLD PADESWOOD £25.00
- PADESWOOD & BUCKLEY £25.00

GLAMORGAN (VALE OF)
- PETERSTONE LAKES £22.50

GWYNEDD
- CAERNARFON (ROYAL TOWN OF)
  £20.00

ISLE OF ANGLESEY
- PRINCE'S £22.00
- STORWS WEN £20.00

MONMOUTHSHIRE
- MONMOUTH £20.00
- PONTYPOOL £24.00
- RAGLAN PARC £20.00
- WOODLAKE PARK £25.00

NEWPORT
- LLANWERN £25.00
- TREDEGAR PARK £20.00

PEMBROKESHIRE
- HAVERFORDWEST £22.00
- SOUTH PEMBROKE £20.00
- TREFLOYNE £25.00

POWYS
- BUILTH WELLS £22.00

SWANSEA
- GOWER £20.00

£30 AND ABOVE

BRIDGEND
- PORTHCAWL (ROYAL) £60.00

CEREDIGION
- BORTH & YNYSLAS £35.00

CONWY
- NORTH WALES £36.00

DENBIGHSHIRE
- DENBIGH £30.50
- PRESTATYN £30.00
- RHUDDLAN £30.00
- VALE OF LLANGOLLEN £30.00

FLINTSHIRE
- MOLD £31.00
- NORTHOP £35.00

GLAMORGAN (VALE OF)
- COTTRELL PARK
  Button £35.00
- COTTRELL PARK
  Mackintosh £35.00
- CREIGIAU £30.00
- WHITCHURCH £40.00

GWYNEDD
- HARLECH £35.00

MONMOUTHSHIRE
- ST. PIERRE
  Mathern £35.00
- ST. PIERRE
  Old £65.00
- MONMOUTHSHIRE £35.00
- ROLLS OF MONMOUTH £38.00

PEMBROKESHIRE
- TENBY £32.00

SWANSEA
- CLYNE £30.00
- FAIRWOOD PARK £30.00
- LANGLAND BAY £30.00
- MORRISTON £30.00
- PENNARD £35.00

Green Fees - With Member WEEKDAYS

SECTION 10

This section allows you to search for courses by the green fees charged on weekdays, with a member.

e.g England, **Under £10, Hertfordshire, Oxhey Park,** £7.00

Once you have located a club using this section you can then refer to the detailed profile of the club in Section 1, or search for specific details in other sections.

UNDER £10

BEDFORDSHIRE
- MOUNT PLEASANT £5.00
- MOWSBURY £8.50
- SOUTH BEDS
  Warden Hill £7.00

BERKSHIRE
- DEANWOOD PARK £8.50

BRISTOL
- TICKENHAM £6.00

CAMBRIDGESHIRE
- ABBOTSLEY
  Cromwell £8.00
- MARCH £8.50
- THORNEY
  Fen £7.00
- THORNEY
  Lakes £8.00

CHESHIRE
- ALDER ROOT £8.00
- LYMM £8.50
- STYAL
  Styal £8.00

CORNWALL
- HELSTON £4.50

COUNTY DURHAM
- OAK LEAF £9.50

DERBYSHIRE
- BARLBOROUGH LINKS £5.00
- BRAILSFORD £9.00
- BROUGHTON HEATH £5.00

DEVON
- ASHBURY
  Oakwood £7.50
- TORRINGTON £6.00
- OTTER VALLEY GOLF CTRE £6.00
- PORTMORE GOLF PARK
  Landkey £7.00
- WILLINGCOTT £8.00

DORSET
- FERNDOWN FOREST £9.00

ESSEX
- BRAXTED PARK £7.00
- EPPING £7.00
- MARDYKE VALLEY GOLF CTRE
  The Valley £8.00
- TOP MEADOW £6.00
- WEST PARK £4.05

GLOUCESTERSHIRE
- SHERDONS £6.50

HAMPSHIRE
- DIBDEN GOLF CTRE
  Dibden 9 Hole £5.20
- MEON VALLEY
  Valley £5.00

HEREFORDSHIRE
- LEOMINSTER £8.00

HERTFORDSHIRE
- BARKWAY PARK £7.00
- CHORLEYWOOD £8.00
- OXHEY PARK £7.00
- WHADDON £3.00

ISLE OF WIGHT
- RYDE £7.50
- WESTRIDGE £5.00

KENT
- HOMELANDS £9.00
- NORTH FORELAND
  Par 3 £3.50
- STAPLEHURST GOLFING PARK
  £8.00

LANCASHIRE
- BACUP £9.00
- BENTHAM £7.80
- BOLTON £7.00
- CHARNOCK RICHARD £8.00
- COLNE £8.00
- HINDLEY HALL £8.00
- HORWICH £9.00
- STANDISH COURT £7.50
- TOWNELEY MUNICIPAL £9.00
- WHALLEY £8.00

LEICESTERSHIRE
- BEEDLES LAKE £7.00
- BLACKTHORN WOOD £5.50
- WHETSTONE £7.50

LINCOLNSHIRE
- ADDLETHORPE £9.00
- OWMBY £5.00
- POTTERGATE £5.50

LONDON (GREATER)
- DUKES MEADOW £8.50
- LONDON SCOTTISH £8.00
- WIMBLEDON COMMON £8.00

MANCHESTER (GREATER)
- BOYSNOPE PARK £7.00
- ELLESMERE £9.00

MERSEYSIDE
- AINTREE £6.00
- HAYDOCK PARK £9.00

MIDLANDS (WEST)
- BOLDMERE £9.50
- HAWKESBURY GOLF CENTRE
  £8.50
- WIDNEY MANOR £9.95

NORFOLK
- EAGLES £9.00
- FAKENHAM £9.00
- FELTWELL £7.50

NORTHAMPTONSHIRE
- PYTCHLEY GOLF LODGE £7.00

NORTHUMBERLAND
- BELFORD £4.00
- HAGGERSTON CASTLE £5.00
- MAGDALENE FIELDS £6.00
- WARKWORTH £8.00

NOTTINGHAMSHIRE
- BRIERLEY FOREST £8.00
- COLLEGE PINES £8.00
- EDWALTON MUNICIPAL £5.00
- KILTON FOREST £9.00
- MANSFIELD WOODHOUSE £5.20

RUTLAND
- RUTLAND WATER £5.00

SHROPSHIRE
- ARSCOTT £9.00

SOMERSET
- BURNHAM & BERROW
  Channel £6.00
- VIVARY PARK £8.90
- WINCANTON £6.00

STAFFORDSHIRE
- BRANSTON
  Academy £4.00
- CANNOCK PARK £9.00
- GOLDENHILL £7.50
- ST. THOMAS' PRIORY £8.00
- STONE £7.00

SUFFOLK
- CLARE PARK LAKE £5.00
- HIGH LODGE £6.00
- SOUTHWOLD £9.00

SURREY
- ABBEYMOOR £7.00
- BROADWATER PARK £7.50
- GOAL FARM £8.50
- HERSHAM VILLAGE £7.00
- LIMPSFIELD CHART £9.00
- REDHILL GOLF CTRE £5.50
- RUSPER £9.50
- SURREY GOLF & FITNESS £5.00

SUSSEX (EAST)
- BOARS HEAD £8.00

SUSSEX (WEST)
- EFFINGHAM PARK £8.00
- HORSHAM GOLF £7.00
- RUSTINGTON £7.50
- SELSEY £6.00
- WEST CHILTINGTON £8.00

WARWICKSHIRE
- NEWBOLD COMYN £9.00

WILTSHIRE
- SHRIVENHAM PARK £8.00

GREEN FEE With Member in England   Weekdays (Mon - Fri)

Under £10 — Under £10

- WHITLEY £9.00

WORCESTERSHIRE
- CHURCHILL & BLAKEDOWN £7.50

YORKSHIRE (EAST)
- WITHERNSEA £8.00

YORKSHIRE (NORTH)
- SCARTHINGWELL £9.00
- SWALLOW HALL £5.00

YORKSHIRE (SOUTH)
- ROTHER VALLEY GOLF
  Rother Valley £9.00

YORKSHIRE (WEST)
- BAILDON £8.00
- CROW NEST PARK £6.00
- EAST BIERLEY £6.00
- ELLAND £7.00
- FARDEW £9.00
- HEBDEN BRIDGE £6.00
- MARSDEN £5.00
- OUTLANE £9.00
- PONTEFRACT £4.00
- ROUNDHAY £7.75
- SOUTH LEEDS £9.00

UNDER £20

BATH & SOMERSET (NORTH EAST)
- FROME GOLF CLUB £12.50
- MENDIP £12.50

BEDFORDSHIRE
- BEDFORD £10.00
- COLMWORTH & NORTH BEDFORDSHIRE £12.00
- LEIGHTON BUZZARD £16.00
- PAVENHAM £10.00

BERKSHIRE
- CAVERSHAM HEATH £18.00
- DATCHET £18.00
- GORING AND STREATLEY £15.00
- HENNERTON £10.00
- MAIDENHEAD £15.00
- MAPLEDURHAM £12.00
- NEWBURY & CROOKHAM £15.00
- READING £17.50
- ASCOT (ROYAL) £15.00
- SWINLEY FOREST £16.00
- TEMPLE £18.00
- THEALE GOLF CTRE £16.00
- WEST BERKSHIRE £12.00
- WOKEFIELD PARK £10.00

BRISTOL
- BRISTOL & CLIFTON £16.00
- FARRINGTON
  Executive £10.00
- FILTON £12.00
- HENBURY £15.00

- KENDLESHIRE £16.00
- KNOWLE £12.00
- LONG ASHTON £16.00
- MENDIP SPRING
  Brinsea £15.00
- TRACY PARK
  Cromwell £18.00
- TRACY PARK
  Crown £18.00

BUCKINGHAMSHIRE
- AYLESBURY PARK £14.00
- BUCKINGHAM £14.00
- OAKLAND PARK £18.00
- PRINCES RISBOROUGH £12.00
- WHITELEAF £10.00
- WYCOMBE HEIGHTS GOLF CTRE
  Main £10.95

CAMBRIDGESHIRE
- ABBOTSLEY
  Abbotsley £15.00
- BOURN £12.00
- CAMBRIDGE £10.00
- ELTON FURZE £13.00
- ELY CITY £15.00
- GOG MAGOG
  The Old £17.50
- LAKESIDE LODGE
  Lodge £12.00
- ORTON MEADOWS £11.20
- OUNDLE £10.50
- RAMSEY CLUB £12.50
- ST. NEOTS £10.00
- THORPE WOOD £11.20
- TYDD ST GILES £10.50

CHESHIRE
- ALDERSEY GREEN £10.00
- ANTROBUS £11.00
- DAVENPORT £12.50
- EATON £10.00
- LEIGH £13.00
- MERE £17.50
- MERSEY VALLEY £14.00
- MOBBERLEY £11.50
- MOLLINGTON GRANGE £12.00
- PEOVER £12.00
- PORTAL PREMIER £12.50
- PRYORS HAYES £10.00
- REDDISH VALE £10.00
- RINGWAY £11.00
- SUTTON HALL £12.00
- UPTON-BY-CHESTER £10.00
- VALE ROYAL ABBEY £15.00

CLEVELAND
- BILLINGHAM £15.00
- CASTLE EDEN £12.00
- HUNLEY HALL £10.00

- KNOTTY HILL GOLF CTRE
  Bishops £13.00
- SEATON CAREW
  Old Course £17.00

CORNWALL
- BUDE & NORTH CORNWALL £12.50
- CARLYON BAY £15.00
- LOSTWITHIEL £15.00
- ST. AUSTELL £12.00
- ST. ENODOC
  Holywell £15.00
- TEHIDY £15.00
- TRETHORNE £12.00

COUNTY DURHAM
- BARNARD CASTLE £14.00
- BEAMISH PARK £10.00
- BISHOP AUCKLAND £11.00
- CONSETT & DISTRICT £10.00
- DURHAM CITY £12.00
- RAMSIDE
  Princes £17.00
- ROSEBERRY GRANGE £11.50
- STRESSHOLME £11.00

CUMBRIA
- BARROW £10.00
- BRAMPTON £11.00
- CARLISLE £12.50
- CARUS GREEN £10.00
- CASTERTON £10.00
- KENDAL £11.00

DERBYSHIRE
- ALLESTREE PARK £11.20
- ASHBOURNE £10.00
- BUXTON & HIGH PEAK £15.00
- CHAPEL-EN-LE-FRITH £10.00
- CHESTERFIELD £13.00
- CHEVIN £14.00
- HALLOWES £15.00
- HORSLEY LODGE £15.00
- MAYWOOD £10.00
- ORMONDE FIELDS £12.50
- SHIRLAND £12.00
- SICKLEHOLME £14.00
- STANEDGE £10.00

DEVON
- CHURSTON £15.50
- DAINTON PARK £10.00
- DARTMOUTH
  Championship £17.00
- CREDITON £12.00
- ELFORDLEIGH £10.00
- HOLSWORTHY £10.00
- ILFRACOMBE £10.00
- MORTEHOE & WOOLACOMBE £12.00
- NEWTON ABBOT £13.00

- OKEHAMPTON £10.00
- PORTMORE GOLF PARK
  Barum £10.00
- NORTH DEVON (ROYAL) £16.00
- SIDMOUTH £10.00
- SPARKWELL £10.00
- TAVISTOCK £12.00
- TEIGN VALLEY £10.00
- TEIGNMOUTH £12.50
- TIVERTON £10.00
- TORQUAY £12.00
- WARREN £11.50
- WRANGATON £12.00
- YELVERTON £15.00

DORSET

- ASHLEY WOOD £10.00
- BOSCOMBE LADIES £16.50
- BOURNEMOUTH & MEYRICK £14.60
- BROADSTONE £15.00
- CAME DOWN £12.00
- CHEDINGTON COURT £12.00
- CRANE VALLEY
  Valley 18 Hole £13.00
- EAST DORSET
  Lakeland £15.00
- FERNDOWN
  Presidents £18.00
- ISLE OF PURBECK
  Dene £13.00

ESSEX

- SOUTH ESSEX
  Hawk (Hawk & Vixon) £14.00
- SOUTH ESSEX
  Heron (Heron & Hawk) £14.00
- SOUTH ESSEX
  Vixen (Vixen & Heron) £14.00
- BIRCH GROVE £10.00
- BOYCE HILL £12.00
- BURNHAM-ON-CROUCH £14.00
- CANONS BROOK £17.00
- CHANNELS
  Belstead £10.00
- CHANNELS
  Channels £15.00
- CHELMSFORD £18.00
- CHIGWELL £15.00
- COLCHESTER £12.00
- COLNE VALLEY £15.00
- CRONDON PARK
  Crondon Park £17.00
- LEXDEN £14.00
- NOTLEYS £11.00
- WARREN £12.50

GLOUCESTERSHIRE

- BRICKHAMPTON COURT
  Spa £12.35
- CIRENCESTER £15.00
- COTSWOLD EDGE £10.00

- COTSWOLD HILLS £13.00
- DYMOCK GRANGE £10.00
- FOREST HILLS £13.00
- FOREST OF DEAN £10.00
- LILLEY BROOK £15.00
- MINCHINHAMPTON
  Avening £13.00
- ORCHARD £11.00
- PAINSWICK £10.00

GUERNSEY

- ST. PIERRE PARK £12.00

HAMPSHIRE

- ALTON £10.00
- CAMS HALL ESTATE GOLF CLUB
  Creek £15.00
- CAMS HALL ESTATE GOLF CLUB
  Park £15.00
- ARMY £15.00
- DIBDEN GOLF CTRE
  Dibden 18 Hole £11.80
- DUNWOOD MANOR £13.00
- LEE ON THE SOLENT £15.00
- OLD THORNS £17.50
- ROMSEY £15.00
- ROWLANDS CASTLE £15.00
- SOUTH WINCHESTER £17.00
- WELLOW
  Embley £11.00
- WICKHAM PARK £12.00

HERTFORDSHIRE

- ALDWICKBURY PARK £16.00
- MILL GREEN GOLF CLUB £15.00
- ARKLEY £12.00
- BERKHAMSTED £15.00
- BISHOPS STORTFORD £16.00
- BROOKMANS PARK £17.00
- BUSHEY GOLF COURSE £11.00
- CHADWELL SPRINGS £10.00
- EAST HERTS £15.00
- LITTLE HAY £12.00
- MANOR OF GROVES £15.00
- OLD FOLD MANOR £15.00
- PANSHANGER GOLF COMPLEX £12.90
- RICKMANSWORTH £10.00
- ROYSTON £12.50
- SHENDISH MANOR £15.00
- STEVENAGE £11.80
- WHIPSNADE PARK £16.00

ISLE OF WIGHT

- SHANKLIN & SANDOWN £12.50

JERSEY

- LA MOYE £15.00

KENT

- RIDGE GOLF CLUB £15.00

- RUXLEY PARK
  Ruxley Park 18 Hole £16.75
- ASHFORD £15.00
- BEARSTED £15.00
- BROOME PARK £15.00
- CANTERBURY £15.00
- CHERRY LODGE £15.00
- CHESTFIELD £12.00
- DARTFORD £12.50
- ETCHINGHILL £15.00
- FAWKHAM VALLEY GOLF CLUB £12.50
- HAWKHURST £12.00
- HOLTYE £11.00
- KINGS HILL £15.00
- KNOLE PARK £15.00
- LITTLESTONE £15.00
- LONDON BEACH £18.00
- TUDOR PARK £15.00
- REDLIBBETS £15.00
- ROCHESTER & COBHAM £15.00
- ROMNEY WARREN £12.00
- SENE VALLEY £15.00
- SHORTLANDS £10.00
- ST. AGUSTINES £11.50
- SWEETWOODS PARK £18.00
- TENTERDEN £14.00
- WALMER & KINGSDOWN £12.50
- WEST MALLING
  Spitfire £15.00
- WHITSTABLE & SEASALTER £10.50

LANCASHIRE

- ACCRINGTON & DISTRICT £11.00
- ASHTON & LEA £11.00
- ASHTON-UNDER-LYNE £10.00
- BLACKPOOL NORTH SHORE £11.00
- BREIGHTMET £10.00
- CLITHEROE £12.00
- DEAN WOOD £10.00
- DEANE £10.00
- DUNSCAR £10.00
- FLEETWOOD £12.00
- GREENMOUNT
  Old £10.00
- GREENMOUNT
  White £10.00
- HURLSTON £15.00
- INGOL £12.00
- KIRKBY LONSDALE £13.00
- KNOTT END £11.00
- LEYLAND £13.00
- LYTHAM GREEN £12.00
- MOSSOCK HALL £12.50
- MYTTON FOLD £14.00
- PIKEFOLD £12.00
- PLEASINGTON £13.00

GREEN FEE With Member in England Weekdays (Mon - Fri)

Under £20 — Under £20

- PRESTON £10.00
- TURTON £10.00
- WESTHOUGHTON
  Hart Common £10.00

LEICESTERSHIRE

- CHARNWOOD FOREST £10.00
- HINCKLEY £14.00
- KIRBY MUXLOE £10.00
- LEICESTER £14.00
- LINGDALE £18.00
- LONGCLIFFE £12.00
- STOKE ALBANY £13.00

LINCOLNSHIRE

- BELTON PARK
  Brownlow £13.50
- LINCOLN £13.00
- LUFFENHAM HEATH £18.00
- SANDILANDS & LEISURE £10.00
- SEACROFT £16.00
- SLEAFORD £12.00
- SUTTON BRIDGE £10.00
- TOFT HOTEL £14.00

LINCOLNSHIRE (NORTH EAST)

- IMMINGHAM £10.00

LONDON (GREATER)

- AQUARIUS £10.00
- BETHUNE PARK £13.00
- BRENT VALLEY PUBLIC £10.00
- BUSH HILL PARK £16.00
- CHINGFORD £11.00
- COOMBE WOOD £16.00
- CREWS HILL £15.00
- ELTHAM WARREN £10.00
- FINCHLEY £14.00
- HAMPSTEAD £10.00
- HENDON £10.00
- HIGHGATE £13.00
- MUSWELL HILL £10.00
- NORTH MIDDLESEX £15.00
- SHOOTERS HILL £15.00
- SOUTH HERTS £15.00
- WANSTEAD £15.00
- WEST ESSEX £14.00
- WIMBLEDON PARK £10.00
- WYKE GREEN £15.00

MANCHESTER (GREATER)

- BLACKLEY £12.00
- BROOKDALE £12.00
- CHORLTON-CUM-HARDY £12.50
- DENTON £12.00
- MANCHESTER £12.00
- OLDHAM £10.00
- SWINTON PARK £12.00
- WERNETH £10.50
- WORSLEY £12.00

MERSEYSIDE

- BIDSTON £11.00
- BLUNDELLS HILL £12.00
- BROMBOROUGH £11.00
- CALDY £14.00
- CHILDWALL £10.00
- HESKETH £10.00
- HESWALL £12.50
- HOUGHWOOD £10.00
- LEASOWE £12.50
- LEE PARK £10.00
- PRENTON £12.00
- SOUTHPORT & AINSDALE £10.00
- SOUTHPORT OLD LINKS £10.00

MIDLANDS (WEST)

- ASTON WOOD £13.00
- BRANDON WOOD MUNICIPAL £10.20
- EDGBASTON £10.00
- NORTH WORCESTERSHIRE £10.00
- ROBIN HOOD £13.00
- SANDWELL PARK £12.00
- SHIRLEY £12.00
- SUTTON COLDFIELD LADIES £12.00
- WALMLEY £10.00
- WERGS £12.50

NORFOLK

- CALDECOTT HALL £10.00
- COSTESSEY PARK £10.00
- DEREHAM £12.00
- EATON £15.00
- BAWBURGH £13.00
- SPROWSTON MANOR £15.00
- MIDDLETON HALL £15.00
- MUNDESLEY £10.00
- CROMER (ROYAL) £18.50
- NORWICH (ROYAL) £18.00
- RYSTON PARK £12.00
- THETFORD £17.00
- WENSUM VALLEY £12.00
- WESTON PARK £14.00

NORTHAMPTONSHIRE

- BRAMPTON HEATH
  Main £10.00
- COLD ASHBY £10.00
- COLLINGTREE PARK £13.00
- KINGSTHORPE £12.00
- NORTHAMPTONSHIRE COUNTY £15.00
- WELLINGBOROUGH £15.00

NORTHUMBERLAND

- BELLINGHAM £10.00
- LINDEN HALL £10.00
- LONGHIRST HALL
  The Old £12.00

- MORPETH £12.00
- STOCKSFIELD £10.00

NOTTINGHAMSHIRE

- COTGRAVE PLACE
  Open £12.00
- BULWELL FOREST £11.00
- CHILWELL MANOR £18.00
- LINDRICK £10.00
- NORWOOD PARK £12.00
- NOTTS £12.00
- OAKMERE PARK £12.00
- RADCLIFFE-ON-TRENT £10.00
- RAMSDALE PARK
  Ramsdale Park Main £15.00
- RETFORD £12.00
- RUFFORD PARK GOLF CTRE £12.00
- SHERWOOD FOREST £15.00
- SOUTHWELL £10.00
- SPRINGWATER £12.00
- STANTON ON THE WOLDS £12.00
- TRENT LOCK
  Trent Lock Golf Centre 18 hole £10.00
- WOLLATON PARK £13.75

OXFORDSHIRE

- CARSWELL £12.80
- HINKSEY HEIGHTS £12.00
- LYNEHAM £12.00
- RYE HILL £12.00
- STUDLEY WOOD £17.00
- WITNEY LAKES £12.00

RUTLAND

- GREETHAM VALLEY
  Lakes £14.00
- GREETHAM VALLEY
  Valley £14.00

SHROPSHIRE

- BRIDGNORTH £12.00
- CLEOBURY MORTIMER
  Deer park £10.00
- CLEOBURY MORTIMER
  Foxes Run £10.00
- SHREWSBURY £19.00

SOMERSET

- BREAN £10.00
- BURNHAM & BERROW
  Championship £10.00
- CANNINGTON £10.00
- ENMORE PARK £10.00
- LONG SUTTON £12.00
- MINEHEAD & WEST SOMERSET £12.00
- WELLS £12.00
- YEOVIL
  Old £12.50

SOMERSET (NORTH)

- WESTON £12.00

STAFFORDSHIRE
- BRANSTON
  Branston **£12.00**
- CRAYTHORNE **£11.00**
- UTTOXETER **£10.00**

SUFFOLK
- BRETTVALE **£15.00**
- BURY ST EDMUNDS
  Bury St Edmunds **£15.00**
- CRETINGHAM **£14.00**
- DIP FARM **£15.00**
- FELIXSTOWE FERRY **£15.00**
- FLEMPTON **£15.00**
- FYNN VALLEY
  Fynn Valley 18 hole **£14.00**
- HALESWORTH
  Halesworth **£10.00**
- HAVERHILL **£11.00**
- HINTLESHAM HALL **£15.00**
- NEWTON GREEN **£12.50**
- WORLINGTON & NEWMARKET
  (ROYAL) **£12.00**
- RUSHMERE **£12.50**
- SUFFOLK GOLF **£10.00**

SURREY
- ADDINGTON PALACE **£15.00**
- PYRFORD GOLF CLUB **£18.00**
- OAK PARK GOLF CLUB
  Woodland **£16.00**
- BANSTEAD DOWNS **£12.50**
- BOWENHURST **£11.00**
- BRAMLEY **£16.00**
- CHIDDINGFOLD **£12.00**
- CRANLEIGH **£13.00**
- CROHAM HURST **£18.00**
- EFFINGHAM **£14.00**
- EPSOM **£13.00**
- FARNHAM **£15.00**
- HINDHEAD **£14.00**
- HORTON PARK GOLF **£13.00**
- HURTMORE **£12.00**
- KINGSWOOD **£18.00**
- PUTTENHAM **£14.00**
- REIGATE HILL **£15.00**
- MID-SURREY (ROYAL)
  Outer **£18.50**
- SANDOWN GOLF CTRE
  Par 3 **£13.50**
- SUTTON GREEN **£17.50**
- THAMES DITTON & ESHER **£10.00**
- WEST SURREY **£14.00**
- WILDWOOD COUNTRY CLUB
  £15.00

SUSSEX (EAST)
- BATTLE **£15.00**
- COODEN BEACH **£12.00**
- CROWBOROUGH BEACON **£15.00**
- HIGHWOODS **£15.00**
- HORAM PARK **£10.50**
- MID SUSSEX **£15.00**
- ASHDOWN FOREST (ROYAL)
  £15.00
- SEAFORD **£15.00**
- SEDLESCOMBE **£16.00**
- WELLSHURST **£12.00**
- WEST HOVE **£15.00**
- WILLINGDON **£14.00**

SUSSEX (WEST)
- AVISFORD PARK **£10.00**
- BOGNOR REGIS **£12.50**
- CHARTHAM PARK **£15.00**
- CHICHESTER
  Chichester **£16.00**
- FOXBRIDGE **£16.00**
- HAM MANOR **£13.00**
- HASSOCKS **£11.25**
- PAXHILL PARK **£15.00**
- PETWORTH **£10.00**
- ROOKWOOD **£12.50**
- SINGING HILLS
  Lake **£12.00**
- WEST SUSSEX **£18.00**
- WORTHING
  Lower **£17.50**

WARWICKSHIRE
- ATHERSTONE **£10.00**
- LEAMINGTON & COUNTY **£13.00**

WILTSHIRE
- BRINKWORTH **£10.00**
- BROOME MANOR **£12.50**
- CUMBERWELL
  Woodlands **£14.00**
- ERLESTOKE SANDS **£15.00**
- HAMPTWORTH **£15.00**
- HIGH POST **£10.00**
- KINGSDOWN **£14.00**
- OAKSEY **£12.00**
- RUSHMORE PARK **£10.00**
- SALISBURY & SOUTH WILTS
  Main **£15.00**
- TIDWORTH GARRISON **£12.00**
- UPAVON **£12.00**
- WRAG BARN **£12.00**

WORCESTERSHIRE
- BANK HOUSE **£12.00**
- BROMSGROVE **£11.50**
- LITTLE LAKES **£10.00**

YORKSHIRE (EAST)
- HAINSWORTH PARK **£10.00**
- HESSLE
  Hexham **£10.00**
- HORNSEA **£11.00**

YORKSHIRE (NORTH)
- ALDWARK MANOR **£12.50**
- COCKSFORD **£12.00**
- FOREST PARK **£12.00**
- HEWORTH **£10.00**
- KILNWICK PERCY **£13.00**
- OAKS **£15.00**

YORKSHIRE (SOUTH)
- HILLSBOROUGH **£14.50**
- ROBIN HOOD **£10.00**

YORKSHIRE (WEST)
- ALWOODLEY **£15.00**
- BRADLEY HALL **£10.00**
- CALVERLEY **£10.00**
- HALIFAX **£12.00**
- HEADLEY **£10.00**
- HOWLEY HALL **£14.00**
- HUDDERSFIELD **£13.00**
- LEEDS GOLF CTRE
  Wike Ridge **£12.50**
- LOFTHOUSE HILL **£10.00**
- MANOR **£11.00**
- MELTHAM **£10.00**
- NORTHCLIFFE **£10.00**
- OTLEY **£14.50**
- SHIPLEY **£15.00**
- SILSDEN **£10.00**
- WAKEFIELD **£12.00**
- WILLOW VALLEY
  T.P.C **£11.00**
- WOODHALL HILLS **£12.00**
- WOODSOME HALL **£12.00**

UNDER £30

BEDFORDSHIRE
- JOHN O'GAUNT
  Carthagena **£20.00**

BERKSHIRE
- CALCOT PARK **£20.00**
- LAMBOURNE CLUB **£20.00**
- PARASAMPIA **£20.00**

BUCKINGHAMSHIRE
- MAGNOLIA PARK **£20.00**

CHESHIRE
- CARDEN PARK
  The Cheshire **£20.00**

CLEVELAND
- CLEVELAND **£22.00**
- WYNYARD CLUB **£25.00**

COUNTY DURHAM
- CHESTER-LE-STREET **£20.00**

DEVON
- SAUNTON
  East **£22.50**
- WOODBURY PARK
  Oaks **£20.00**

GREEN FEE With Member in England   Weekdays (Mon - Fri)

Under £20 — Under £30

Weekdays (Mon - Fri)

GREEN FEE With Member in England

Under £30 — £30 and Above

DORSET

- FERNDOWN
  The Old Course **£22.50**
- PARKSTONE **£20.00**

ESSEX

- ABRIDGE **£22.00**
- CLACTON **£20.00**
- EPPING FOREST **£22.50**
- ORSETT **£20.00**

HAMPSHIRE

- BOTLEY PARK **£20.00**
- MEON VALLEY
  Meon **£20.00**

HERTFORDSHIRE

- HERTFORDSHIRE **£20.00**
- BATCHWORTH PARK **£23.00**

JERSEY

- JERSEY (ROYAL) **£20.00**

KENT

- PRINCES
  Himalayas **£27.50**

LINCOLNSHIRE

- KENWICK PARK **£20.00**

LONDON (GREATER)

- COOMBE HILL **£20.00**
- HUMAX **£20.00**
- MILL HILL **£25.00**

MERSEYSIDE

- FORMBY HALL **£20.00**

NORFOLK

- KING'S LYNN **£20.00**

NORTHUMBERLAND

- BERWICK **£25.00**
- DUNSTANBURGH CASTLE **£20.00**

OXFORDSHIRE

- FRILFORD HEATH
  Green **£28.00**

SHROPSHIRE

- SHIFNAL **£25.00**
- WREKIN **£22.00**

STAFFORDSHIRE

- BARLASTON **£20.00**

SURREY

- ASHFORD MANOR **£20.00**
- CAMBERLEY HEATH **£22.00**
- PINE RIDGE GOLF CTRE **£22.00**
- WINDLESHAM **£20.00**

SUSSEX (EAST)

- EAST SUSSEX NATIONAL
  East **£25.00**

SUSSEX (WEST)

- MANNINGS HEATH
  Kingfisher **£21.00**

YORKSHIRE (NORTH)

- KIRKBYMOORSIDE **£20.00**

£30 AND ABOVE

BERKSHIRE

- BEARWOOD LAKES **£45.00**
- MILL RIDE **£35.00**

BUCKINGHAMSHIRE

- WOBURN
  Duchess **£35.00**
- WOBURN
  Marquess **£50.00**

CORNWALL

- ST. ENODOC
  Church **£35.00**

HERTFORDSHIRE

- BROCKET HALL
  Melbourne **£35.00**

KENT

- ST. GEORGE'S (ROYAL) **£100.00**

LINCOLNSHIRE

- WOODHALL SPA
  Bracken **£30.00**
- WOODHALL SPA
  Hotchkin **£40.00**

STAFFORDSHIRE

- BROCTON HALL **£33.00**

SURREY

- BURHILL
  Burhill (New) **£40.00**
- BURHILL
  Burhill (Old) **£40.00**
- FOXHILLS GOLF
  Bernard Hunt **£40.00**
- WOKING **£58.00**

SUSSEX (EAST)

- DALE HILL
  The Ian Woosnam **£35.00**

YORKSHIRE (NORTH)

- GANTON **£60.00**

YORKSHIRE (WEST)

- HOLLINS HALL **£30.00**

UNDER £10

COUNTY CORK
- COBH £6.00
- KINSALE
Farrangalway £9.00

COUNTY DONEGAL
- CLOUGHANEELY £8.00

COUNTY DUBLIN
- OPEN
Blue Nine £5.00

COUNTY KERRY
- BALLYHEIGUE CASTLE £7.00

COUNTY KILDARE
- CRADDOCKSTOWN £8.00

COUNTY LIMERICK
- ABBEYFEALE GOLF CTRE £6.00

COUNTY LOUTH
- TOWNLEY HALL £6.00

COUNTY MEATH
- SOUTH MEATH £7.00

COUNTY TIPPERARY
- TEMPLEMORE £5.00

COUNTY WICKLOW
- GLEN MILL £5.00

UNDER £20

COUNTY CLARE
- KILKEE £15.00

COUNTY CORK
- KINSALE
Ringenane £10.00

COUNTY DUBLIN
- LEOPARDSTOWN £12.00
- MALAHIDE £10.00
- OPEN
Red Nine £11.00
- STEPASIDE £10.00
- TURVEY £10.00

COUNTY GALWAY
- ATHENRY £10.00

COUNTY KERRY
- KERRIES £14.00

COUNTY KILDARE
- CELBRIDGE ELM HALL £12.00
- HIGHFIELD £10.00

COUNTY KILKENNY
- GOWRAN PARK GOLF & LEISURE £15.00
- MOUNTAIN VIEW £10.00

COUNTY LIMERICK
- RATHBANE £15.00

COUNTY LOUTH
- KILLIN PARK £10.00

COUNTY MAYO
- BALLINA £10.00
- MULRANNY £10.00

COUNTY MONAGHAN
- CLONES £10.00

COUNTY OFFALY
- CASTLE BARNA £15.00

COUNTY TIPPERARY
- BALLYKISTEEN £16.00

COUNTY WATERFORD
- DUNGARVAN £12.00
- FAITHLEGG £10.00
- GOLD COAST £17.00
- WEST WATERFORD £11.00

COUNTY WICKLOW
- RATHSALLAGH £18.00

UNDER £30

COUNTY DONEGAL
- BALLYLIFFIN
Old Links £24.00

COUNTY GALWAY
- BEARNA £20.00

COUNTY WICKLOW
- GLEN OF THE DOWNS £20.00

£30 AND ABOVE

COUNTY CLARE
- DOONBEG £70.88
- WOODSTOCK £30.00

COUNTY DONEGAL
- BALLYLIFFIN
Glashedy Links £35.00

COUNTY KERRY
- BALLYBUNION
Cashen £46.22
- BALLYBUNION
Old £67.50
- RING OF KERRY £30.00

COUNTY WICKLOW
- POWERSCOURT £37.50

Weekdays (Mon - Fri)

GREEN FEE With Member in Ireland

Under £10 — £30 and Above

GREEN FEE With Member in N.Ireland   Weekdays (Mon - Fri)
Under £10 — £30 and Above

UNDER £10

COUNTY ANTRIM
- BENTRA MUNICIPAL £8.00
- GREENACRES GOLF CTRE £8.00
- LARNE £5.00
- ORMEAU £8.00
- TEMPLE CLUB £5.00
- WHITEHEAD £9.00

COUNTY ARMAGH
- TANDRAGEE £8.00

COUNTY DOWN
- BANBRIDGE £8.00
- CLOVERHILL £8.00
- DOWNPATRICK £8.00
- RINGDUFFERIN
  Ringdufferin £8.00
- SCRABO £8.00

COUNTY FERMANAGH
- ASHWOODS £8.00
- ENNISKILLEN £7.50

COUNTY LONDONDERRY
- FAUGHAN VALLEY £6.00

COUNTY TYRONE
- NEWTOWNSTEWART £9.00
- SPRINGHILL £7.00

UNDER £20

COUNTY ANTRIM
- ALLEN PARK £10.00
- BALLYMENA £12.00
- CAIRNDHU £10.00
- CLIFTONVILLE £10.00
- DOWN ROYAL PARK
  Down Royal Park £12.00
- GALGORM CASTLE £15.00
- GRACEHILL £12.00
- KNOCK £10.00
- LISBURN £10.00

COUNTY DOWN
- ARDGLASS £12.50
- CARNALEA £12.00
- DONAGHADEE £15.00
- HOLYWOOD £12.00
- KILKEEL £10.00
- KIRKISTOWN CASTLE £10.75
- DOWN (ROYAL COUNTY)
  Annesley Links £17.00
- WARRENPOINT £10.00

COUNTY FERMANAGH
- CASTLE HUME £12.00

COUNTY LONDONDERRY
- DERRY
  Prehen £15.00
- FOYLE
  Parkland £10.00

COUNTY TYRONE
- OMAGH £10.00
- STRABANE £12.00

UNDER £30

COUNTY ANTRIM
- BALLYCASTLE £20.00

£30 AND ABOVE

COUNTY DOWN
- DOWN (ROYAL COUNTY)
  Championship £80.00

UNDER £10

ABERDEEN (CITY OF)
- CRAIBSTONE £8.00
- EAST ABERDEENSHIRE £8.00
- MURCAR
  Strabathie £7.00

ABERDEENSHIRE
- BANCHORY £8.00
- DUFF HOUSE ROYAL £7.00
- INVERURIE £7.00
- OLDMELDRUM £7.00
- STONEHAVEN £5.00
- TORPHINS £6.00

ANGUS
- EDZELL
  Edzell £6.00
- EDZELL
  West Water £3.00
- FORFAR £8.00
- KIRRIEMUIR £6.00
- PANMURE £5.00

ARGYLL AND BUTE
- DUNAVERTY £6.00
- PORT BANNATYNE £6.00

AYRSHIRE (NORTH)
- BEITH £2.00
- SHISKINE £5.00
- WEST KILBRIDE £4.00

AYRSHIRE (SOUTH)
- BELLEISLE & SEAFIELD
  Seafield £6.00

CLACKMANNANSHIRE
- ALLOA £5.00
- BRAEHEAD £5.00
- MUCKHART
  Muckhart £5.00

DUMFRIES AND GALLOWAY
- COLVEND £6.00
- CRICHTON £6.00
- DUMFRIES & COUNTY £8.00
- GALLOWAY £6.00
- GATEHOUSE £5.00
- LOCHMABEN £6.00
- LOCKERBIE £5.00
- NEW GALLOWAY £5.00
- NEWTON STEWART £6.00
- PINES £7.00
- PORTPATRICK - DUNSKEY
  Dinvin £9.00
- SOUTHERNESS £8.00
- STRANRAER £5.00
- WIGTOWNSHIRE £4.00

EDINBURGH (CITY OF)
- BRUNTSFIELD GOLF CLUB £7.00
- LIBERTON £6.00
- SWANSTON £7.00

FALKIRK
- BONNYBRIDGE £6.00
- FALKIRK £5.00
- POLMONT £4.00

FIFE
- ABERDOUR £5.00
- ANSTRUTHER £6.00
- BALBIRNIE PARK £7.00
- CANMORE £6.00
- CHARLETON
  Charleton £7.00
- CUPAR £5.00
- DUNFERMLINE £8.00
- ELIE GOLF £7.50
- LESLIE £6.00
- LOCHGELLY £6.00
- LUNDIN £8.00
- PITREAVIE £5.50
- SALINE £4.50
- SCOTSCRAIG £8.00
- THORNTON £6.00

GLASGOW (CITY OF)
- KNIGHTSWOOD £7.20

HIGHLANDS
- INVERNESS £7.50
- ISLE OF SKYE £7.50
- NAIRN
  Nairn £5.00
- NAIRN
  Newton £3.00

INVERCLYDE
- GOUROCK £2.00

ISLE OF ARRAN
- LOCHRANZA GOLF £8.50

LANARKSHIRE (NORTH)
- PALACERIGG £8.00

LANARKSHIRE (SOUTH)
- LANARK
  Old £5.00

LOTHIAN (EAST)
- CASTLE PARK £5.00
- HADDINGTON £5.00
- MUSSELBURGH LINKS £4.50
- NORTH BERWICK £5.00
- WHITEKIRK £5.00

LOTHIAN (WEST)
- BRIDGECASTLE £5.50
- BRIDGEND £4.00
- GREENBURN £5.00
- LINLITHGOW £5.00

MORAY
- GRANTOWN-ON-SPEY £8.00
- HOPEMAN £6.50

PERTH AND KINROSS
- KENMORE £9.00
- MILNATHORT £4.00
- ST. FILLANS £9.00
- STRATHMORE GOLF CTRE
  Leitfie Links £6.00

RENFREWSHIRE
- ELDERSLIE £4.00
- GLEDDOCH £6.00
- PAISLEY £5.00
- RALSTON £3.00

SCOTTISH BORDERS
- DUNS £5.00
- EYEMOUTH £5.00
- HIRSEL £5.00
- INNERLEITHEN £5.00
- RUTHERFORD CASTLE £5.00

UNDER £20

ABERDEEN (CITY OF)
- CALEDONIAN £11.25
- DEESIDE
  Haughton £10.00
- NEWMACHAR
  Swailend £15.00

ABERDEENSHIRE
- INCHMARLO GOLF CTRE
  Inchmarlo 18 hole £17.50

ANGUS
- ARBROATH £10.00
- BRECHIN GOLF & SQUASH CLUB
  £17.00
- MONIFIETH GOLF LINKS
  Medal £10.00
- PIPERDAM GOLF £10.00

AYRSHIRE (EAST)
- BALLOCHMYLE £10.00

AYRSHIRE (NORTH)
- ARDEER £18.00
- KILBIRNIE PLACE £12.00
- RAVENSPARK £10.50

AYRSHIRE (SOUTH)
- BELLEISLE & SEAFIELD
  Belleisle £12.00
- DALMILLING £12.00
- GIRVAN £12.00

DUMFRIES AND GALLOWAY
- KIRKCUDBRIGHT £11.50
- LAGGANMORE £12.00
- POWFOOT £10.00

EDINBURGH (CITY OF)
- CRAIGMILLAR PARK £18.00

FIFE
- KINGHORN £14.00

GLASGOW (CITY OF)
- BEARSDEN £15.00

GREEN FEE With Member in Scotland   Weekdays (Mon - Fri)   Under £10 — Under £20

GREEN FEE With Member in Scotland — Weekdays (Mon - Fri)

Under £20 — £30 and Above

HIGHLANDS
- BRORA £10.00
- MUIR OF ORD £16.00
- REAY £10.00
- STRATHPEFFER SPA £15.00
- ULLAPOOL £15.00

LOTHIAN (EAST)
- GULLANE
  Gullane No. 3 £17.00

LOTHIAN (MID)
- KINGS ACRE £12.00

MORAY
- FORRES £10.00

PERTH AND KINROSS
- GLENISLA £11.00
- KILLIN £12.00
- STRATHMORE GOLF CTRE
  Rannaleroch £10.00
- TAYMOUTH CASTLE £11.00

WESTERN ISLES
- STORNOWAY £10.00

UNDER £30

AYRSHIRE (SOUTH)
- BRUNSTON CASTLE £26.00

GLASGOW (CITY OF)
- EASTWOOD £24.00
- KIRKHILL £20.00

HIGHLANDS
- GOLSPIE £25.00

LOTHIAN (EAST)
- GULLANE
  Gullane No. 2 £29.00

LOTHIAN (MID)
- MUSSELBURGH £20.00

SCOTTISH BORDERS
- ROXBURGHE £20.00

STIRLING
- ABERFOYLE £20.00

£30 AND ABOVE

ABERDEEN (CITY OF)
- MELDRUM HOUSE £41.00

ARGYLL AND BUTE
- MACHRIE £32.50
- MACHRIHANISH
  Machrihanish 18 Hole £30.00

GLASGOW (CITY OF)
- EAST RENFREWSHIRE £30.00

LOTHIAN (EAST)
- GULLANE
  Gullane No. 1 £65.00

PERTH AND KINROSS
- GLENEAGLES
  Kings £110.00

RENFREWSHIRE
- RANFURLY £30.00

UNDER £10

CAERPHILLY
- OAKDALE £5.00

CARMARTHENSHIRE
- CILGWYN £6.00

CONWY
- BETWS-Y-COED £7.00

DENBIGHSHIRE
- RHYL £7.50
- ST. MELYD £9.00

FLINTSHIRE
- ALLT-GYMBYD £5.00
- KINSALE £7.50
- MOLD £8.50

ISLE OF ANGLESEY
- PRINCE'S £9.00
- STORWS WEN £5.00

MONMOUTHSHIRE
- DEWSTOW
  Dewstow £8.00
- WERNDDU £8.00

NEATH PORT TALBOT
- LAKESIDE £9.50

NEWPORT
- CAERLEON £4.15

PEMBROKESHIRE
- DAWN 'TIL DUSK £8.00
- HERONS BROOK
  Kings £2.50
- HERONS BROOK
  Queens £1.50
- NEWPORT £9.00
- PRISKILLY £6.00
- ST. DAVIDS £7.50

POWYS
- WELSH BORDER GOLF COMPLEX
  £5.00

TORFAEN
- GREEN MEADOW £8.00

WREXHAM
- PLASSEY £8.00

UNDER £20

BRIDGEND
- GROVE £12.00

CARMARTHENSHIRE
- CARMARTHEN £10.00
- GARNANT PARK £11.00
- GLYN ABBEY £10.00

CEREDIGION
- BORTH & YNYSLAS £14.00
- CARDIGAN £10.00
- CLIFF HOTEL £10.00
- CWMRHYDNEUADD £14.00

- PENRHOS
  Academy £12.00

CONWY
- RHOS-ON-SEA £10.00

DENBIGHSHIRE
- DENBIGH £12.50
- PRESTATYN £10.00
- RHUDDLAN £10.00
- VALE OF LLANGOLLEN £10.00

FLINTSHIRE
- NORTHOP £15.00
- PADESWOOD & BUCKLEY £10.00

GLAMORGAN (VALE OF)
- COTTRELL PARK
  Button £12.50
- COTTRELL PARK
  Mackintosh £12.50
- CREIGIAU £14.00
- PETERSTONE LAKES £12.50
- ST. ANDREWS MAJOR £16.00
- WHITCHURCH £15.00

GWYNEDD
- HARLECH £15.00

MONMOUTHSHIRE
- ALICE SPRINGS
  Queens £12.00
- MONMOUTH £10.00
- MONMOUTHSHIRE £15.00
- PONTYPOOL £14.00
- ROLLS OF MONMOUTH £17.00
- SHIRENEWTON £10.00
- WOODLAKE PARK £15.00

NEATH PORT TALBOT
- NEATH £13.00

NEWPORT
- LLANWERN £10.00
- TREDEGAR PARK £11.00

PEMBROKESHIRE
- HAVERFORDWEST £10.00
- SOUTH PEMBROKE £10.00
- TREFLOYNE £12.00

POWYS
- BUILTH WELLS £10.00

RHONDDA CYNON TAFF
- MOUNTAIN ASH £10.00

SWANSEA
- CLYNE £12.50
- GOWER £12.00
- LANGLAND BAY £14.00
- MORRISTON £12.00
- PENNARD £15.00

WREXHAM
- CLAYS GOLF CTRE £10.00

UNDER £30

GWYNEDD
- ABERDOVEY £29.00

SWANSEA
- FAIRWOOD PARK £20.00

GREEN FEE With Member in **Wales** Weekdays (Mon - Fri)

Under £10 — Under £30

SECTION 11

This section allows you to search for courses by the green fees charged at weekends, with a member.

e.g Under £10, Leicestershire, Beedles Lake, £9.50

Once you have located a club using this section you can then refer to the detailed profile of the club in Section 1, or search for specific details in other sections.

UNDER £10

BEDFORDSHIRE
- MOUNT PLEASANT £7.00
- SOUTH BEDS
  Warden Hill £6.00

BERKSHIRE
- READING £9.00

BRISTOL
- TICKENHAM £8.00

CAMBRIDGESHIRE
- MARCH £8.50
- THORNEY
  Fen £9.00

CHESHIRE
- ALDER ROOT £9.00
- STYAL
  Academy Championship Par 3 £8.00

CORNWALL
- HELSTON £4.50

DERBYSHIRE
- BARLBOROUGH LINKS £6.00
- BROUGHTON HEATH £6.00

DEVON
- TORRINGTON £6.00
- OTTER VALLEY GOLF CTRE £6.00
- PORTMORE GOLF PARK
  Landkey £7.00
- SPARKWELL £7.00

ESSEX
- WEST PARK £4.05

GLOUCESTERSHIRE
- SHERDONS £7.50

HAMPSHIRE
- DIBDEN GOLF CTRE
  Dibden 9 Hole £6.30
- MEON VALLEY
  Valley £6.00

HERTFORDSHIRE
- OXHEY PARK £9.00
- WHADDON £3.50

ISLE OF WIGHT
- WESTRIDGE £5.00

KENT
- NORTH FORELAND
  Par 3 £4.00
- STAPLEHURST GOLFING PARK
  £9.00

LANCASHIRE
- BACUP £9.00
- BENTHAM £7.80
- BOLTON £9.00
- HINDLEY HALL £8.00
- HORWICH £9.00

LEICESTERSHIRE
- BEEDLES LAKE £9.50

- BLACKTHORN WOOD £6.50
- WHETSTONE £8.00

LINCOLNSHIRE
- ADDLETHORPE £9.00
- OWMBY £8.00
- POTTERGATE £6.50

MANCHESTER (GREATER)
- BOYSNOPE PARK £8.00

MERSEYSIDE
- AINTREE £7.00
- HAYDOCK PARK £9.00

NORTHAMPTONSHIRE
- PYTCHLEY GOLF LODGE £9.00

NORTHUMBERLAND
- BELFORD £4.00
- HAGGERSTON CASTLE £5.00
- MAGDALENE FIELDS £6.00

NOTTINGHAMSHIRE
- BRIERLEY FOREST £8.00
- EDWALTON MUNICIPAL £5.50
- MANSFIELD WOODHOUSE £5.20

RUTLAND
- RUTLAND WATER £5.50

SHROPSHIRE
- ARSCOTT £9.00

SOMERSET
- BURNHAM & BERROW
  Channel £6.00
- VIVARY PARK £8.90
- WINCANTON £8.00

STAFFORDSHIRE
- BRANSTON
  Academy £6.00
- GOLDENHILL £9.00
- STONE £7.00

SUFFOLK
- CLARE PARK LAKE £6.00
- HIGH LODGE £6.00

SURREY
- ABBEYMOOR £8.00
- BROADWATER PARK £9.25
- GOAL FARM £9.50
- HERSHAM VILLAGE £9.00
- LIMPSFIELD CHART £9.00
- REDHILL GOLF CTRE £6.50
- SURREY GOLF & FITNESS £6.00

SUSSEX (WEST)
- EFFINGHAM PARK £9.00
- HORSHAM GOLF £8.00
- SELSEY £7.50

WILTSHIRE
- WHITLEY £9.00

YORKSHIRE (NORTH)
- SWALLOW HALL £5.00

YORKSHIRE (SOUTH)
- ROTHER VALLEY GOLF
  Rother Valley £9.00

YORKSHIRE (WEST)
- CROW NEST PARK £7.00
- EAST BIERLEY £7.50
- HEBDEN BRIDGE £7.50
- OUTLANE £9.00
- PONTEFRACT £7.50
- ROUNDHAY £9.25

UNDER £20

BATH & SOMERSET (NORTH EAST)
- FROME GOLF CLUB £14.50
- MENDIP £12.50

BEDFORDSHIRE
- BEDFORD £15.00
- COLMWORTH & NORTH
  BEDFORDSHIRE £15.00
- LEIGHTON BUZZARD £16.00
- MOWSBURY £11.00
- PAVENHAM £15.00

BERKSHIRE
- DEANWOOD PARK £10.50
- GORING AND STREATLEY £15.00
- HENNERTON £15.00
- MAIDENHEAD £18.00
- MAPLEDURHAM £17.00
- NEWBURY & CROOKHAM £15.00
- ASCOT (ROYAL) £18.50
- SWINLEY FOREST £16.00
- WEST BERKSHIRE £16.00
- WOKEFIELD PARK £15.00

BRISTOL
- FARRINGTON
  Executive £12.50
- FILTON £12.00
- HENBURY £15.00
- KNOWLE £14.00
- MENDIP SPRING
  Brinsea £15.00

BUCKINGHAMSHIRE
- PRINCES RISBOROUGH £14.00
- WHITELEAF £10.00
- WYCOMBE HEIGHTS GOLF CTRE
  Main £16.95

CAMBRIDGESHIRE
- ABBOTSLEY
  Abbotsley £19.00
- ABBOTSLEY
  Cromwell £12.50
- BOURN £15.00
- CAMBRIDGE £13.00
- ELTON FURZE £15.00
- ELY CITY £18.00

Weekends

GREEN FEE With Member in England

Under £10 — Under £20

GOG MAGOG
The Old **£17.50**

LAKESIDE LODGE
Lodge **£19.00**

ORTON MEADOWS **£14.75**

OUNDLE **£15.50**

RAMSEY CLUB **£15.00**

ST. NEOTS **£10.00**

THORNEY
Lakes **£10.00**

THORPE WOOD **£14.75**

TYDD ST GILES **£11.50**

CHESHIRE

ALDERSEY GREEN **£12.00**

ANTROBUS **£13.00**

DAVENPORT **£15.00**

EATON **£10.00**

LEIGH **£13.00**

LYMM **£10.50**

MERSEY VALLEY **£16.00**

MOBBERLEY **£18.00**

MOLLINGTON GRANGE **£15.00**

PEOVER **£15.00**

PORTAL PREMIER **£15.00**

PRYORS HAYES **£15.00**

RINGWAY **£11.00**

STYAL
Styal **£12.00**

SUTTON HALL **£15.00**

UPTON-BY-CHESTER **£10.00**

CLEVELAND

CASTLE EDEN **£12.00**

HUNLEY HALL **£15.00**

KNOTTY HILL GOLF CTRE
Bishops **£13.00**

CORNWALL

BUDE & NORTH CORNWALL
£15.00

CARLYON BAY **£15.00**

LOSTWITHIEL **£19.00**

ST. AUSTELL **£12.00**

TEHIDY **£19.00**

TRETHORNE **£12.00**

COUNTY DURHAM

BARNARD CASTLE **£16.00**

BEAMISH PARK **£14.00**

BISHOP AUCKLAND **£13.00**

CONSETT & DISTRICT **£15.00**

DURHAM CITY **£15.00**

OAK LEAF **£11.00**

ROSEBERRY GRANGE **£15.00**

STRESSHOLME **£13.00**

CUMBRIA

BARROW **£10.00**

BRAMPTON **£15.00**

CARLISLE **£12.50**

CARUS GREEN **£12.00**

CASTERTON **£14.00**

KENDAL **£13.75**

DERBYSHIRE

ALLESTREE PARK **£11.20**

ASHBOURNE **£15.00**

BRAILSFORD **£11.00**

BUXTON & HIGH PEAK **£18.00**

CHAPEL-EN-LE-FRITH **£12.00**

CHESTERFIELD **£13.00**

CHEVIN **£14.00**

HALLOWES **£15.00**

HORSLEY LODGE **£15.00**

MAYWOOD **£15.00**

ORMONDE FIELDS **£17.50**

SHIRLAND **£17.00**

SICKLEHOLME **£16.00**

STANEDGE **£15.00**

DEVON

ASHBURY
Oakwood **£10.00**

CHURSTON **£18.50**

DAINTON PARK **£10.00**

DARTMOUTH
Championship **£17.00**

CREDITON **£14.00**

ELFORDLEIGH **£12.50**

HOLSWORTHY **£10.00**

ILFRACOMBE **£12.00**

NEWTON ABBOT **£14.00**

OKEHAMPTON **£12.50**

PORTMORE GOLF PARK
Barum **£10.00**

NORTH DEVON (ROYAL) **£19.00**

SIDMOUTH **£10.00**

TAVISTOCK **£15.00**

TEIGN VALLEY **£13.00**

TIVERTON **£15.00**

TORQUAY **£17.00**

WARREN **£13.00**

WILLINGCOTT **£10.00**

WRANGATON **£12.00**

DORSET

ASHLEY WOOD **£11.50**

BOSCOMBE LADIES **£18.00**

BOURNEMOUTH & MEYRICK
£15.40

BROADSTONE **£15.00**

CHEDINGTON COURT **£15.00**

CRANE VALLEY
Valley 18 Hole **£16.00**

EAST DORSET
Lakeland **£17.50**

FERNDOWN FOREST **£11.00**

ISLE OF PURBECK
Dene **£13.00**

ESSEX

BIRCH GROVE **£12.00**

BOYCE HILL **£12.00**

BRAXTED PARK **£10.00**

BURNHAM-ON-CROUCH **£16.00**

CHANNELS
Belstead **£12.00**

CHANNELS
Channels **£15.00**

CHIGWELL **£18.00**

COLCHESTER **£15.00**

COLNE VALLEY **£18.00**

EPPING **£10.00**

LEXDEN **£16.00**

MARDYKE VALLEY GOLF CTRE
The Valley **£10.00**

NOTLEYS **£15.00**

GLOUCESTERSHIRE

BRICKHAMPTON COURT
Spa **£16.25**

COTSWOLD EDGE **£15.00**

COTSWOLD HILLS **£16.00**

DYMOCK GRANGE **£10.00**

FOREST HILLS **£18.00**

FOREST OF DEAN **£15.00**

LILLEY BROOK **£15.00**

MINCHINHAMPTON
Avening **£15.00**

ORCHARD **£13.00**

GUERNSEY

ST. PIERRE PARK **£14.00**

HAMPSHIRE

ALTON **£14.00**

CAMS HALL ESTATE GOLF CLUB
Creek **£18.00**

CAMS HALL ESTATE GOLF CLUB
Park **£18.00**

ARMY **£17.00**

DIBDEN GOLF CTRE
Dibden 18 Hole **£13.80**

DUNWOOD MANOR **£18.00**

ROWLANDS CASTLE **£16.00**

WELLOW
Embley **£15.00**

WICKHAM PARK **£15.00**

HEREFORDSHIRE

LEOMINSTER **£11.00**

HERTFORDSHIRE

MILL GREEN GOLF CLUB **£18.00**

ARKLEY **£12.00**

BARKWAY PARK **£11.00**

BERKHAMSTED **£15.00**

BROOKMANS PARK **£17.00**

BUSHEY GOLF COURSE **£12.00**

CHADWELL SPRINGS **£10.00**

CHORLEYWOOD **£10.00**

EAST HERTS **£15.00**

- LITTLE HAY £16.30
- OLD FOLD MANOR £12.00
- PANSHANGER GOLF COMPLEX £18.00
- RICKMANSWORTH £14.20
- ROYSTON £15.00
- STEVENAGE £15.50

ISLE OF WIGHT
- RYDE £10.00
- SHANKLIN & SANDOWN £15.00

JERSEY
- LA MOYE £15.00

KENT
- ASHFORD £15.00
- CHERRY LODGE £15.00
- CHESTFIELD £15.00
- DARTFORD £12.50
- FAWKHAM VALLEY GOLF CLUB £17.50
- HAWKHURST £12.00
- HOLTYE £13.00
- HOMELANDS £12.00
- KNOLE PARK £15.00
- LITTLESTONE £18.00
- ROMNEY WARREN £15.00
- SENE VALLEY £15.00
- SHORTLANDS £10.00
- ST. AGUSTINES £11.50
- TENTERDEN £16.00
- WALMER & KINGSDOWN £15.00
- WEST MALLING
  Spitfire £15.00
- WHITSTABLE & SEASALTER £10.50

LANCASHIRE
- ACCRINGTON & DISTRICT £14.00
- ASHTON & LEA £12.50
- ASHTON-UNDER-LYNE £10.00
- BLACKPOOL NORTH SHORE £12.00
- BREIGHTMET £10.00
- CHARNOCK RICHARD £10.00
- CLITHEROE £12.00
- COLNE £10.00
- DEAN WOOD £10.00
- DEANE £10.00
- DUNSCAR £10.00
- FLEETWOOD £14.00
- GREENMOUNT
  Old £10.00
- GREENMOUNT
  White £10.00
- HURLSTON £15.00
- INGOL £15.00
- KIRKBY LONSDALE £15.00
- KNOTT END £12.00
- LEYLAND £15.00

- MOSSOCK HALL £15.00
- MYTTON FOLD £16.00
- PIKEFOLD £12.00
- PLEASINGTON £13.00
- PRESTON £10.00
- STANDISH COURT £10.00
- TOWNELEY MUNICIPAL £10.00
- TURTON £12.00
- WESTHOUGHTON
  Hart Common £12.00
- WHALLEY £10.00

LEICESTERSHIRE
- CHARNWOOD FOREST £15.00
- HINCKLEY £14.00
- KIRBY MUXLOE £10.00
- LEICESTER £18.00
- LONGCLIFFE £12.00
- STOKE ALBANY £16.00

LINCOLNSHIRE
- BELTON PARK
  Brownlow £16.50
- LUFFENHAM HEATH £18.00
- SANDILANDS & LEISURE £13.00
- SEACROFT £16.00
- SLEAFORD £16.00
- TOFT HOTEL £16.00

LINCOLNSHIRE (NORTH EAST)
- IMMINGHAM £12.00

LONDON (GREATER)
- AQUARIUS £10.00
- BETHUNE PARK £13.00
- BRENT VALLEY PUBLIC £12.00
- CHINGFORD £15.25
- CREWS HILL £15.00
- DUKES MEADOW £10.00
- ELTHAM WARREN £10.00
- FINCHLEY £17.00
- HENDON £15.00
- HUMAX £15.00
- LONDON SCOTTISH £12.00
- MUSWELL HILL £10.00
- NORTH MIDDLESEX £15.00
- SHOOTERS HILL £15.00
- WEST ESSEX £14.00
- WIMBLEDON COMMON £10.00
- WIMBLEDON PARK £15.00

MANCHESTER (GREATER)
- BLACKLEY £12.00
- BROOKDALE £12.00
- CHORLTON-CUM-HARDY £15.00
- ELLESMERE £10.50
- MANCHESTER £12.00
- OLDHAM £13.00
- WERNETH £18.50
- WORSLEY £15.00

MERSEYSIDE
- BIDSTON £12.50
- BLUNDELLS HILL £15.00
- BROMBOROUGH £11.00
- CALDY £14.00
- CHILDWALL £15.00
- HESKETH £15.00
- HESWALL £12.50
- HOUGHWOOD £13.00
- LEASOWE £12.50
- LEE PARK £15.00
- PRENTON £12.00
- SOUTHPORT & AINSDALE £10.00
- SOUTHPORT OLD LINKS £10.00

MIDLANDS (WEST)
- ASTON WOOD £15.00
- BOLDMERE £11.00
- BRANDON WOOD MUNICIPAL £13.55
- EDGBASTON £10.00
- HAWKESBURY GOLF CENTRE £10.50
- NORTH WORCESTERSHIRE £15.00
- SANDWELL PARK £12.00
- SHIRLEY £12.00
- SUTTON COLDFIELD LADIES £12.00
- WALMLEY £10.00
- WERGS £17.50
- WIDNEY MANOR £14.95

NORFOLK
- CALDECOTT HALL £12.00
- COSTESSEY PARK £10.00
- DEREHAM £12.50
- EAGLES £10.00
- FAKENHAM £12.00
- FELTWELL £12.00
- BAWBURGH £14.00
- MIDDLETON HALL £15.00
- MUNDESLEY £12.00
- RYSTON PARK £12.00
- THETFORD £17.00
- WENSUM VALLEY £12.00
- WESTON PARK £16.50

NORTHAMPTONSHIRE
- COLD ASHBY £10.00
- KINGSTHORPE £12.00
- NORTHAMPTONSHIRE COUNTY £15.00
- WELLINGBOROUGH £15.00

NORTHUMBERLAND
- BELLINGHAM £10.00
- LINDEN HALL £12.50
- LONGHIRST HALL
  The Old £12.00
- STOCKSFIELD £12.00

Weekends

GREEN FEE With Member in England

Under £20 — Under £20

WARWORTH £12.00

NOTTINGHAMSHIRE

COTGRAVE PLACE
Open £15.00

BULWELL FOREST £11.00

CHILWELL MANOR £18.00

COLLEGE PINES £10.00

KILTON FOREST £12.00

LINDRICK £10.00

NORWOOD PARK £14.00

NOTTS £12.00

OAKMERE PARK £15.00

RADCLIFFE-ON-TRENT £12.00

RAMSDALE PARK
Ramsdale Park Main £18.50

RETFORD £12.00

RUFFORD PARK GOLF CTRE
£15.00

SOUTHWELL £10.00

SPRINGWATER £14.00

STANTON ON THE WOLDS £14.00

TRENT LOCK
Trent Lock Golf Centre 18 hole £12.00

WOLLATON PARK £16.25

OXFORDSHIRE

HINKSEY HEIGHTS £15.00

LYNEHAM £15.00

RYE HILL £15.00

WITNEY LAKES £18.00

RUTLAND

GREETHAM VALLEY
Lakes £16.00

GREETHAM VALLEY
Valley £16.00

SHROPSHIRE

BRIDGNORTH £15.00

CLEOBURY MORTIMER
Deer park £14.00

CLEOBURY MORTIMER
Foxes Run £14.00

SOMERSET

BREAN £13.00

CANNINGTON £12.50

ENMORE PARK £15.00

LONG SUTTON £15.00

MINEHEAD & WEST SOMERSET
£14.00

WELLS £18.00

YEOVIL
Old £12.50

SOMERSET (NORTH)

WESTON £17.50

STAFFORDSHIRE

BRANSTON
Branston £15.00

CANNOCK PARK £11.00

CRAYTHORNE £14.00

ST. THOMAS' PRIORY £12.00

UTTOXETER £15.00

SUFFOLK

BURY ST EDMUNDS
Bury St Edmunds £17.50

CRETINGHAM £13.00

FLEMPTON £15.00

FYNN VALLEY
Fynn Valley 18 hole £17.00

HALESWORTH
Halesworth £10.00

HAVERHILL £14.00

HINTLESHAM HALL £15.00

NEWTON GREEN £12.50

WORLINGTON & NEWMARKET
(ROYAL) £14.00

RUSHMERE £12.50

SOUTHWOLD £10.00

SUFFOLK GOLF £15.00

SURREY

ADDINGTON PALACE £15.00

BANSTEAD DOWNS £12.50

BOWENHURST £14.00

BRAMLEY £16.00

CHIDDINGFOLD £17.00

CRANLEIGH £13.00

EFFINGHAM £17.00

EPSOM £15.00

FARNHAM £15.00

HORTON PARK GOLF £15.00

HURTMORE £16.00

PUTTENHAM £14.00

RUSPER £13.50

SANDOWN GOLF CTRE
Par 3 £13.50

THAMES DITTON & ESHER £11.00

WEST SURREY £16.00

SUSSEX (EAST)

BATTLE £15.00

BOARS HEAD £10.00

COODEN BEACH £15.00

HIGHWOODS £15.00

HORAM PARK £11.00

MID SUSSEX £17.50

ASHDOWN FOREST (ROYAL)
£15.00

SEAFORD £15.00

WILLINGDON £18.00

SUSSEX (WEST)

AVISFORD PARK £10.00

BOGNOR REGIS £15.00

HASSOCKS £14.50

PAXHILL PARK £18.00

PETWORTH £11.00

ROOKWOOD £15.00

RUSTINGTON £10.50

SINGING HILLS
Lake £14.50

WEST CHILTINGTON £10.00

WARWICKSHIRE

LEAMINGTON & COUNTY £13.00

NEWBOLD COMYN £12.00

WILTSHIRE

BRINKWORTH £12.00

BROOME MANOR £12.50

CUMBERWELL
Woodlands £18.00

ERLESTOKE SANDS £18.00

HAMPTWORTH £15.00

HIGH POST £12.50

KINGSDOWN £14.00

OAKSEY £15.00

RUSHMORE PARK £13.00

SHRIVENHAM PARK £10.00

TIDWORTH GARRISON £12.00

UPAVON £14.00

WRAG BARN £15.00

WORCESTERSHIRE

BANK HOUSE £16.00

BROMSGROVE £14.00

CHURCHILL & BLAKEDOWN
£10.00

LITTLE LAKES £13.00

YORKSHIRE (EAST)

HAINSWORTH PARK £10.00

HESSLE
Hexham £10.00

HORNSEA £15.00

WITHERNSEA £10.00

YORKSHIRE (NORTH)

ALDWARK MANOR £15.00

COCKSFORD £14.00

FOREST PARK £17.00

HEWORTH £10.00

KILNWICK PERCY £16.00

OAKS £18.00

SCARTHINGWELL £12.00

YORKSHIRE (SOUTH)

HILLSBOROUGH £18.50

ROBIN HOOD £10.00

YORKSHIRE (WEST)

ALWOODLEY £15.00

BAILDON £10.00

BRADLEY HALL £14.00

CALVERLEY £12.00

ELLAND £10.00

FARDEW £10.00

HALIFAX £12.00

HOWLEY HALL £19.00

LEEDS GOLF CTRE
Wike Ridge £14.50

LOFTHOUSE HILL £10.00

MANOR £15.00

- MELTHAM £10.00
- NORTHCLIFFE £12.00
- OTLEY £18.00
- SHIPLEY £15.00
- SILSDEN £10.00
- SOUTH LEEDS £13.00
- WILLOW VALLEY
  T.P.C £13.00
- WOODSOME HALL £12.00

UNDER £30

BEDFORDSHIRE

- JOHN O'GAUNT
  Carthagena £25.00

BERKSHIRE

- CALCOT PARK £20.00
- CAVERSHAM HEATH £25.00
- PARASAMPIA £25.00
- TEMPLE £22.00
- THEALE GOLF CTRE £20.00

BRISTOL

- KENDLESHIRE £20.00
- TRACY PARK
  Cromwell £22.00
- TRACY PARK
  Crown £22.00

BUCKINGHAMSHIRE

- AYLESBURY PARK £20.00
- MAGNOLIA PARK £25.00
- OAKLAND PARK £20.00

CHESHIRE

- CARDEN PARK
  The Cheshire £20.00
- MERE £22.50
- REDDISH VALE £25.00
- VALE ROYAL ABBEY £20.00

CLEVELAND

- BILLINGHAM £20.00
- CLEVELAND £20.00
- SEATON CAREW
  Old Course £22.00

COUNTY DURHAM

- CHESTER-LE-STREET £25.00
- RAMSIDE
  Princes £23.00

DEVON

- SAUNTON
  East £22.50
- WOODBURY PARK
  Oaks £20.00
- YELVERTON £20.00

DORSET

- CAME DOWN £24.00
- FERNDOWN
  Presidents £20.00
- FERNDOWN
  The Old Course £25.00
- PARKSTONE £20.00

ESSEX

- ABRIDGE £28.00
- SOUTH ESSEX
  Hawk (Hawk & Vixon) £20.00
- SOUTH ESSEX
  Heron (Heron & Hawk) £20.00
- SOUTH ESSEX
  Vixen (Vixen & Heron) £20.00
- CANONS BROOK £22.00
- CLACTON £25.00
- CRONDON PARK
  Crondon Park £25.00

GLOUCESTERSHIRE

- CIRENCESTER £20.00

HAMPSHIRE

- BOTLEY PARK £20.00
- MEON VALLEY
  Meon £20.00
- OLD THORNS £22.50
- SOUTH WINCHESTER £25.00

HERTFORDSHIRE

- ALDWICKBURY PARK £20.00
- HERTFORDSHIRE £25.00
- BATCHWORTH PARK £28.00
- BISHOPS STORTFORD £20.00
- MANOR OF GROVES £20.00
- SHENDISH MANOR £20.00
- WHIPSNADE PARK £22.00

JERSEY

- JERSEY (ROYAL) £20.00

KENT

- RUXLEY PARK
  Ruxley Park 18 Hole £22.00
- BROOME PARK £20.00
- CANTERBURY £20.00
- ETCHINGHILL £20.00
- KINGS HILL £20.00
- LONDON BEACH £22.00
- TUDOR PARK £25.00
- REDLIBBETS £25.00
- SWEETWOODS PARK £24.00

LEICESTERSHIRE

- LINGDALE £22.00

LINCOLNSHIRE

- KENWICK PARK £20.00

LONDON (GREATER)

- COOMBE WOOD £25.00
- HAMPSTEAD £20.00
- WYKE GREEN £22.00

MERSEYSIDE

- FORMBY HALL £20.00

NORFOLK

- EATON £20.00
- KING'S LYNN £25.00
- SPROWSTON MANOR £20.00

CROMER (ROYAL) £21.00
- NORWICH (ROYAL) £22.00

NORTHUMBERLAND

- DUNSTANBURGH CASTLE £26.00

NOTTINGHAMSHIRE

- SHERWOOD FOREST £20.00

OXFORDSHIRE

- CARSWELL £20.00
- FRILFORD HEATH
  Green £28.00
- STUDLEY WOOD £21.00

SHROPSHIRE

- SHREWSBURY £23.00

SUFFOLK

- BRETTVALE £20.00

SURREY

- PYRFORD GOLF CLUB £26.00
- OAK PARK GOLF CLUB
  Woodland £26.00
- ASHFORD MANOR £23.00
- CAMBERLEY HEATH £25.00
- CROHAM HURST £23.00
- HINDHEAD £20.00
- KINGSWOOD £22.00
- PINE RIDGE GOLF CTRE £28.00
- REIGATE HILL £20.00
- MID-SURREY (ROYAL)
  Outer £23.50
- SUTTON GREEN £22.50
- WILDWOOD COUNTRY CLUB
  £22.50
- WINDLESHAM £25.00

SUSSEX (EAST)

- CROWBOROUGH BEACON £20.00
- SEDLESCOMBE £20.00
- WEST HOVE £20.00

SUSSEX (WEST)

- CHARTHAM PARK £20.00
- CHICHESTER
  Chichester £20.00
- MANNINGS HEATH
  Kingfisher £28.00
- FOXBRIDGE £20.00
- GOODWOOD £21.00
- HAM MANOR £20.00
- WEST SUSSEX £20.00
- WORTHING
  Lower £20.00

WILTSHIRE

- SALISBURY & SOUTH WILTS
  Main £20.00

YORKSHIRE (NORTH)

- KIRKBYMOORSIDE £27.00

YORKSHIRE (WEST)

- HUDDERSFIELD £20.00
- WAKEFIELD £20.00

GREEN FEE With Member in England   Weekends   Under £20 — Under £30

£30 AND ABOVE

BERKSHIRE
- BEARWOOD LAKES £55.00
- LAMBOURNE CLUB £30.00
- MILL RIDE £35.00

BUCKINGHAMSHIRE
- WOBURN
  Duchess £35.00
- WOBURN
  Marquess £50.00

CORNWALL
- ST. ENODOC
  Church £40.00

ESSEX
- EPPING FOREST £30.00
- ORSETT £30.00

HERTFORDSHIRE
- BROCKET HALL
  Melbourne £45.00

KENT
- BEARSTED £35.00
- PRINCES
  Himalayas £30.00
- ST. GEORGE'S (ROYAL) £100.00

LINCOLNSHIRE
- WOODHALL SPA
  Bracken £30.00
- WOODHALL SPA
  Hotchkin £40.00

LONDON (GREATER)
- COOMBE HILL £30.00
- MILL HILL £30.00

NORTHUMBERLAND
- BERWICK £30.00

SHROPSHIRE
- WREKIN £30.00

SOMERSET
- BURNHAM & BERROW
  Championship £30.00

STAFFORDSHIRE
- BARLASTON £30.00
- BROCTON HALL £40.00

SURREY
- BURHILL
  Burhill (New) £55.00
- BURHILL
  Burhill (Old) £55.00
- FOXHILLS GOLF
  Bernard Hunt £45.00
- WOKING £58.00

SUSSEX (EAST)
- DALE HILL
  The Ian Woosnam £45.00
- EAST SUSSEX NATIONAL
  East £30.00

YORKSHIRE (NORTH)
- GANTON £70.00

YORKSHIRE (WEST)
- HOLLINS HALL £50.00

UNDER £10

COUNTY CORK
- KINSALE
  Farrangalway **£9.00**

COUNTY DUBLIN
- OPEN
  Blue Nine **£7.00**

COUNTY KERRY
- BALLYHEIGUE CASTLE **£7.00**

COUNTY KILDARE
- CRADDOCKSTOWN **£8.00**

COUNTY LIMERICK
- ABBEYFEALE GOLF CTRE **£8.00**

COUNTY LOUTH
- TOWNLEY HALL **£8.00**

COUNTY MEATH
- SOUTH MEATH **£9.00**

COUNTY TIPPERARY
- TEMPLEMORE **£5.00**

COUNTY WICKLOW
- GLEN MILL **£7.00**

UNDER £20

COUNTY CLARE
- KILKEE **£15.00**

COUNTY CORK
- KINSALE
  Ringenane **£10.00**

COUNTY DONEGAL
- CLOUGHANEELY **£10.00**

COUNTY DUBLIN
- LEOPARDSTOWN **£15.00**
- MALAHIDE **£10.00**
- OPEN
  Red Nine **£17.00**
- TURVEY **£12.00**

COUNTY GALWAY
- ATHENRY **£10.00**

COUNTY KERRY
- KERRIES **£14.00**

COUNTY KILDARE
- CELBRIDGE ELM HALL **£14.00**
- HIGHFIELD **£12.00**

COUNTY KILKENNY
- GOWRAN PARK GOLF & LEISURE **£15.00**
- MOUNTAIN VIEW **£12.00**

COUNTY LIMERICK
- RATHBANE **£17.00**

COUNTY LOUTH
- KILLIN PARK **£12.00**

COUNTY MAYO
- BALLINA **£10.00**
- MULRANNY **£15.00**

COUNTY MONAGHAN
- CLONES **£12.00**

COUNTY TIPPERARY
- BALLYKISTEEN **£18.00**

COUNTY WATERFORD
- DUNGARVAN **£15.00**
- FAITHLEGG **£10.00**
- WEST WATERFORD **£16.00**

COUNTY WICKLOW
- RATHSALLAGH **£18.00**

UNDER £30

COUNTY CLARE
- WOODSTOCK **£25.00**

COUNTY DONEGAL
- BALLYLIFFIN
  Old Links **£27.00**

COUNTY GALWAY
- BEARNA **£25.00**

COUNTY OFFALY
- CASTLE BARNA **£20.00**

COUNTY WATERFORD
- GOLD COAST **£22.00**

COUNTY WICKLOW
- GLEN OF THE DOWNS **£25.00**

£30 AND ABOVE

COUNTY CLARE
- DOONBEG **£70.88**

COUNTY DONEGAL
- BALLYLIFFIN
  Glashedy Links **£40.00**

COUNTY KERRY
- BALLYBUNION
  Cashen **£46.22**
- BALLYBUNION
  Old **£67.50**
- RING OF KERRY **£30.00**

COUNTY WICKLOW
- POWERSCOURT **£37.50**

GREEN FEE With Member in Ireland

Weekends

Under £10 — £30 and Above

Under £10 — £30 and Above | **GREEN FEE With Member in N.Ireland** | **Weekends**

UNDER £10

COUNTY ANTRIM

- LARNE **£9.00**
- TEMPLE CLUB **£7.00**

COUNTY DOWN

- CLOVERHILL **£8.00**
- RINGDUFFERIN
  Ringdufferin **£9.00**

COUNTY FERMANAGH

- ENNISKILLEN **£9.00**

COUNTY LONDONDERRY

- FAUGHAN VALLEY **£8.00**

COUNTY TYRONE

- SPRINGHILL **£7.00**

UNDER £20

COUNTY ANTRIM

- ALLEN PARK **£13.00**
- BALLYCASTLE **£15.00**
- BALLYMENA **£15.00**
- CAIRNDHU **£16.00**
- CLIFTONVILLE **£14.00**
- DOWN ROYAL PARK
  Down Royal Park **£12.00**
- GRACEHILL **£15.00**
- GREENACRES GOLF CTRE **£12.00**
- KNOCK **£12.00**
- ORMEAU **£10.00**
- WHITEHEAD **£15.00**

COUNTY ARMAGH

- TANDRAGEE **£10.00**

COUNTY DOWN

- ARDGLASS **£16.00**
- BANBRIDGE **£10.00**
- CARNALEA **£14.00**
- DONAGHADEE **£15.00**
- DOWNPATRICK **£12.00**
- HOLYWOOD **£15.00**
- KILKEEL **£12.00**
- KIRKISTOWN CASTLE **£13.75**
- WARRENPOINT **£13.50**

COUNTY FERMANAGH

- CASTLE HUME **£18.00**

COUNTY LONDONDERRY

- FOYLE
  Parkland **£13.00**

COUNTY TYRONE

- NEWTOWNSTEWART **£14.00**
- OMAGH **£13.00**
- STRABANE **£15.00**

UNDER £30

COUNTY ANTRIM

- GALGORM CASTLE **£20.00**

COUNTY DOWN

- DOWN (ROYAL COUNTY)
  Annesley Links **£25.00**

COUNTY LONDONDERRY

- DERRY
  Prehen **£20.00**

£30 AND ABOVE

COUNTY DOWN

- DOWN (ROYAL COUNTY)
  Championship **£90.00**

© HCC Publishing Ltd

UNDER £10

ABERDEENSHIRE

- BANCHORY £8.00
- DUFF HOUSE ROYAL £7.00
- INVERURIE £9.00
- STONEHAVEN £7.00
- TORPHINS £7.00

ANGUS

- EDZELL
  Edzell £8.00
- EDZELL
  West Water £3.00
- FORFAR £8.00
- KIRRIEMUIR £6.00
- PANMURE £5.00

ARGYLL AND BUTE

- DUNAVERTY £6.00

AYRSHIRE (NORTH)

- BEITH £2.00
- SHISKINE £5.00
- WEST KILBRIDE £4.00

CLACKMANNANSHIRE

- ALLOA £5.00
- BRAEHEAD £5.00
- MUCKHART
  Muckhart £7.50

DUMFRIES AND GALLOWAY

- COLVEND £6.00
- CRICHTON £6.00
- DUMFRIES & COUNTY £8.00
- GALLOWAY £6.00
- GATEHOUSE £5.00
- LOCHMABEN £6.00
- LOCKERBIE £5.00
- NEW GALLOWAY £5.00
- NEWTON STEWART £6.00
- PINES £7.00
- PORTPATRICK - DUNSKEY
  Dinvin £9.00
- SOUTHERNESS £8.00
- STRANRAER £5.00
- WIGTOWNSHIRE £4.00

EDINBURGH (CITY OF)

- BRUNTSFIELD GOLF CLUB £7.00
- LIBERTON £7.00
- SWANSTON £7.00

FALKIRK

- BONNYBRIDGE £6.00
- FALKIRK £5.00
- POLMONT £4.00

FIFE

- ABERDOUR £5.00
- ANSTRUTHER £6.00
- BALBIRNIE PARK £7.00
- CANMORE £6.00

- CHARLETON
  Charleton £7.00
- CUPAR £5.00
- DUNFERMLINE £8.00
- ELIE GOLF £7.50
- LESLIE £6.00
- LOCHGELLY £6.00
- LUNDIN £8.00
- PITREAVIE £5.50
- SALINE £4.50
- SCOTSCRAIG £8.00
- THORNTON £6.00

GLASGOW (CITY OF)

- KNIGHTSWOOD £7.20

HIGHLANDS

- INVERNESS £7.50
- ISLE OF SKYE £7.50
- NAIRN
  Nairn £5.00
- NAIRN
  Newton £3.00

INVERCLYDE

- GOUROCK £2.00

LOTHIAN (EAST)

- CASTLE PARK £5.00
- HADDINGTON £5.00
- MUSSELBURGH LINKS £4.50
- NORTH BERWICK £5.00
- WHITEKIRK £5.00

LOTHIAN (WEST)

- BRIDGECASTLE £5.50
- GREENBURN £5.00
- LINLITHGOW £5.00

MORAY

- GRANTOWN-ON-SPEY £8.00
- HOPEMAN £9.00

PERTH AND KINROSS

- MILNATHORT £4.00
- STRATHMORE GOLF CTRE
  Leitfie Links £8.00

RENFREWSHIRE

- ELDERSLIE £5.00
- GLEDDOCH £8.50
- RANFURLY £6.00
- PAISLEY £5.00
- RALSTON £4.00

SCOTTISH BORDERS

- DUNS £5.00
- EYEMOUTH £5.00
- HIRSEL £5.00
- INNERLEITHEN £5.00
- RUTHERFORD CASTLE £7.00

UNDER £20

ABERDEEN (CITY OF)

- CALEDONIAN £13.25

- CRAIBSTONE £10.00
- DEESIDE
  Haughton £12.00
- EAST ABERDEENSHIRE £10.00
- MURCAR
  Strabathie £10.00

ABERDEENSHIRE

- OLDMELDRUM £10.00

ANGUS

- ARBROATH £10.00
- MONIFIETH GOLF LINKS
  Medal £13.00
- PIPERDAM GOLF £12.00

ARGYLL AND BUTE

- PORT BANNATYNE £11.00

AYRSHIRE (EAST)

- BALLOCHMYLE £10.00

AYRSHIRE (NORTH)

- IRVINE £12.00
- RAVENSPARK £13.50

AYRSHIRE (SOUTH)

- BELLEISLE & SEAFIELD
  Seafield £12.00
- DALMILLING £16.00
- GIRVAN £16.00

DUMFRIES AND GALLOWAY

- KIRKCUDBRIGHT £11.50
- LAGGANMORE £15.00
- POWFOOT £10.00

FIFE

- KINGHORN £18.00

GLASGOW (CITY OF)

- BEARSDEN £15.00

HIGHLANDS

- BRORA £10.00
- REAY £10.00
- STRATHPEFFER SPA £15.00
- ULLAPOOL £15.00

LANARKSHIRE (NORTH)

- PALACERIGG £12.00

LOTHIAN (MID)

- KINGS ACRE £18.00

LOTHIAN (WEST)

- BRIDGEND £10.00

MORAY

- FORRES £10.00

PERTH AND KINROSS

- GLENISLA £13.00
- KENMORE £10.00
- KILLIN £13.50
- ST. FILLANS £10.00
- STRATHMORE GOLF CTRE
  Rannaleroch £12.00
- TAYMOUTH CASTLE £13.00

GREEN FEE With Member in Scotland   **Weekends**

Under £10 — Under £20

WESTERN ISLES

🏌 STORNOWAY £10.00

UNDER £30

ABERDEEN (CITY OF)

🏌 NEWMACHAR
Swailend £20.00

ABERDEENSHIRE

🏌 INCHMARLO GOLF CTRE
Inchmarlo 18 hole £22.50

ANGUS

🏌 BRECHIN GOLF & SQUASH CLUB
£22.00

AYRSHIRE (NORTH)

🏌 ARDEER £25.00

🏌 KILBIRNIE PLACE £20.00

AYRSHIRE (SOUTH)

🏌 BELLEISLE & SEAFIELD
Belleisle £25.00

EDINBURGH (CITY OF)

🏌 CRAIGMILLAR PARK £26.00

HIGHLANDS

🏌 GOLSPIE £25.00

🏌 MUIR OF ORD £20.00

LOTHIAN (EAST)

🏌 GULLANE
Gullane No. 3 £24.00

LOTHIAN (MID)

🏌 MUSSELBURGH £25.00

SCOTTISH BORDERS

🏌 ROXBURGHE £20.00

£30 AND ABOVE

ABERDEEN (CITY OF)

🏌 MELDRUM HOUSE £47.00

ARGYLL AND BUTE

🏌 MACHRIE £32.50

🏌 MACHRIHANISH
Machrihanish 18 Hole £40.00

AYRSHIRE (SOUTH)

🏌 BRUNSTON CASTLE £30.00

GLASGOW (CITY OF)

🏌 EAST RENFREWSHIRE £40.00

LOTHIAN (EAST)

🏌 GULLANE
Gullane No. 1 £80.00

🏌 GULLANE
Gullane No. 2 £35.00

PERTH AND KINROSS

🏌 GLENEAGLES
Kings £110.00

UNDER £10

CAERPHILLY
- OAKDALE £5.00

FLINTSHIRE
- KINSALE £7.50

ISLE OF ANGLESEY
- STORWS WEN £5.00

MONMOUTHSHIRE
- DEWSTOW
  Dewstow £8.00
- WERNDDU £8.00

NEATH PORT TALBOT
- LAKESIDE £9.50

NEWPORT
- CAERLEON £5.20

PEMBROKESHIRE
- DAWN 'TIL DUSK £8.00
- HERONS BROOK
  Kings £2.50
- HERONS BROOK
  Queens £1.50
- PRISKILLY £8.00
- ST. DAVIDS £7.50

POWYS
- WELSH BORDER GOLF COMPLEX £5.00

UNDER £20

BRIDGEND
- GROVE £15.00

CARMARTHENSHIRE
- CARMARTHEN £12.50
- CILGWYN £10.00
- GARNANT PARK £15.00
- GLYN ABBEY £12.00

CEREDIGION
- BORTH & YNYSLAS £17.50
- CARDIGAN £12.50
- CLIFF HOTEL £12.50
- CWMRHYDNEUADD £14.00
- PENRHOS
  Academy £12.00

CONWY
- BETWS-Y-COED £10.00
- RHOS-ON-SEA £14.00

DENBIGHSHIRE
- DENBIGH £15.50
- PRESTATYN £12.00
- RHUDDLAN £10.00
- RHYL £10.00
- ST. MELYD £11.00
- VALE OF LLANGOLLEN £15.00

FLINTSHIRE
- ALLT-GYMBYD £14.00
- MOLD £15.00
- NORTHOP £17.50
- PADESWOOD & BUCKLEY £12.00

GLAMORGAN (VALE OF)
- COTTRELL PARK
  Button £17.50
- COTTRELL PARK
  Mackintosh £17.50
- CREIGIAU £14.00
- PETERSTONE LAKES £15.50
- ST. ANDREWS MAJOR £16.00
- WHITCHURCH £15.00

GWYNEDD
- HARLECH £17.50

ISLE OF ANGLESEY
- PRINCE'S £11.00

MONMOUTHSHIRE
- ALICE SPRINGS
  Queens £17.00
- MONMOUTH £10.00
- MONMOUTHSHIRE £17.50
- PONTYPOOL £18.00
- ROLLS OF MONMOUTH £18.00
- SHIRENEWTON £10.00
- WOODLAKE PARK £18.00

NEATH PORT TALBOT
- NEATH £13.00

NEWPORT
- LLANWERN £15.00
- TREDEGAR PARK £15.00

PEMBROKESHIRE
- HAVERFORDWEST £15.00
- NEWPORT £12.00
- SOUTH PEMBROKE £15.00
- TREFLOYNE £16.00

POWYS
- BUILTH WELLS £13.00

RHONDDA CYNON TAFF
- MOUNTAIN ASH £18.00

SWANSEA
- CLYNE £15.00
- GOWER £12.00
- LANGLAND BAY £15.00

TORFAEN
- GREEN MEADOW £13.00

WREXHAM
- CLAYS GOLF CTRE £10.00
- PLASSEY £10.00

UNDER £30

SWANSEA
- FAIRWOOD PARK £25.00
- MORRISTON £20.00
- PENNARD £20.00

£30 AND ABOVE

GWYNEDD
- ABERDOVEY £35.00

GREEN FEE With Member in **Wales**   Weekends

Under £10 — £30 and Above

SECTION 12a

This section allows you to select golf professionals at courses by county and where applicable will give details of lesson prices.

e.g Berkshire, Geary, Steve
(Club Professional)
Maidenhead, £30.00 for 45 minutes

If you prefer, you can also search for professionals in the following section 12b, by the professionals' surname.

Once you have located a club using this section you can then refer to the detailed profile of the club in Section 1, or search for specific details in other sections.

BATH & SOMERSET (NORTH EAST)

HENDERSON, Nigel
(Club Professional)
Entry Hill

MARSH, Adrian
(Club Professional)
Mendip

MCEWAN, Murdoch
(Club Professional)
Frome Golf Club

TAPLEY, Tim
(Professional)
Entry Hill

BEDFORDSHIRE

BUNYAN, Terry
(Club Professional)
Chalgrave Manor
£15.00 for 45 minutes

CAMPBELL, Maurice
(Club Professional)
Leighton Buzzard
£30.00 for 45 minutes

CHOLTON, Darren
(Professional)
Tilsworth
£13.00 for 60 minutes

COGLE, Eddie
(Professional)
South Beds
£18.00 for 60 minutes.

DAVIES, Rob
(Club Professional)
Mentmore

DIXON, Geraint
(Club Professional)
Lyshott Heath

GOBLE, Guy
(Club Professional)
Aylesbury Vale

MCCARTHY, Glynn
(Club Professional)
Stockwood Park
£28.00 for 60 minutes

NICHOLAS, Kevin
(Club Professional)
Pavenham
£34.00 for 60 minutes

PAYNE, Warwick
(Professional)
Tilsworth
£13.00 for 60 minutes

POULTER, Ian
(Touring Professional)
Leighton Buzzard
£30.00 for 45 minutes

RICHARDSON, Gerry
(Club Professional)
Mowsbury
£22.50 for 60 minutes

ROBERTS, Mike
(Club Professional)
Mount Pleasant
£18.00 for 60 minutes

SHORT, James
(Professional)
Stockwood Park
£28.00 for 60 minutes

SUMMERS, Malcolm
(Professional)

Mowsbury
£22.50 for 60 minutes

SWAIN, Geoff
(Club Professional)
Baron & Baroness
£25.00 for 60 minutes

TATTERSALL, Roger
(Club Professional)
Bedford & County

THOMPSON, Zac
(Club Professional)
Bedford
£34.00 for 60 minutes

WEBB, Nick
(Professional)
Tilsworth
£13.00 for 60 minutes

WELDON, Michael
(Club Professional)
Dunstable Downs

WHITE, Alex
(Professional)
Tilsworth
£13.00 for 60 minutes

WILLIAMS, Greg
(Professional)
Pavenham
£34.00 for 60 minutes

WILLIAMS, Paul
(Professional)
Mount Pleasant
£18.00 for 60 minutes

BERKSHIRE

ANDERSON, P
(Professional)
Berkshire

BALFOUR, Martin
(Club Professional)
Donnington Valley

BLAINEY, M
(Club Professional)
Billingbear Park

BOLTON, R
(Club Professional)
Burnham Beeches

BOWEN, Jason
(Professional)
Wokefield Park
£40.00 - £54.00 for 60 minutes

BRANT, Jason
(Club Professional)
Castle Royle
£18-20 for 30 minutes

BURTON, Douglas
(Club Professional)
Mapledurham
£18.00 for 30 minutes

CAMPBELL, Ian
(Club Professional)
Calcot Park

EVANS, Gary
(Touring Professional)
Mill Ride
£30.00 for 60 minutes

FARROW, William
(Club Professional)
Hennerton
£20 for 30 minutes

FOTHERINGHAM, Scott

(Club Professional)
Reading
£40.00 for 60 minutes

GEARY, Steve
(Club Professional)
Maidenhead
£30.00 for 45 minutes

GODLEMAN, Ian
(Club Professional)
Datchet

HACKER, Danny
(Professional)
Wokefield Park
£40.00 - £54.00 for 60 minutes

HADLAND, Jason
(Club Professional)
Goring and Streatley
£28.00 for 60 minutes

HALL, Andrew
(Club Professional)
Sand Martins

HARRIS, David
(Club Professional)
Newbury & Crookham

HART, David
(Club Professional)
Lambourne Club
£19-23 for 40 minutes

HENNERSY, Justin
(Club Professional)
Hurst
£16.00 for 30 minutes

HILL, Stuart
(Club Professional)
Swinley Forest

INGUS, Euan
(Professional)
Bearwood Lakes
£40.00 for 60 minutes

JOHNSON, David
(Head Professional)
Lavender Park
£16-00 - £20.00 for 30 minutes

JOHNSON, Glen
(Professional)
Hennerton
£20 for 30 minutes

KENNEDY, John
(Club Professional)
Wexham Park

LOOMS, Ian
(Club Professional)
Blue Mountain Golf Centre

MANNION, Mike
(Professional)
Woodcray Manor

MCDOUGALL, R
(Club Professional)
Sonning

MITCHELL, Nick
(Professional)
Newbury Racecourse

NEIL, Russell
(Professional)
Mill Ride
£30.00 for 60 minutes

NEWMAN, Lee
(Club Professional)
Theale Golf Ctre
£12.50 for 30 minutes

PURTON, James
(Club Professional)
Deanwood Park
£16.00 for 60 minutes

RAJ, Michael
(Professional)
Reading
£40.00 for 60 minutes

ROE, Arthur
(Club Professional)
East Berkshire

RUTHERFORD, Carl
(Professional)
Caversham Heath
£30.00 for 60 minutes

SIMPSON, Paul
(Club Professional)
West Berkshire

SMITH, Gary
(Club Professional)
Wokefield Park
£40.00 - £54.00 for 60 minutes

WATTS, Robert
(Professional)
Lambourne Club
£19-23 for 40 minutes

WHITE, Alistair
(Club Professional)
Ascot (Royal)
£15.00 for 30 minutes

WHITELEY, J
(Club Professional)
Temple

WILD, Terry
(Club Professional)
Mill Ride
£30.00 for 60 minutes

WILLIAMS, G
(Professional)
Parasampia
£20.00 for 60 minutes

BRISTOL

BARRINGTON, Paul
(Club Professional)
Kendleshire

BEER, Nigel
(Club Professional)
Woodspring

BLACKBURN, J
(Club Professional)
Mendip Spring

BLANNIN, Ryan
(Professional)
Farrington
£17.50 for 60 minutes

BRAND, G M
(Professional)
Knowle
£25.00 for 60 minutes

BROOKS, Mark
(Professional)
Kendleshire

COWGILL, Jon
(Club Professional)
Farrington
£17.50 for 60 minutes

ELLIS, Brent
(Club Professional)
Shirehampton Park

HART, Mike
(Club Professional)
Long Ashton

HUBBARD, Simon
(Club Professional)
Thornbury Golf

JARRETT, Sarah
(Club Professional)
Tickenham
£14.00 for 30 minutes

MANSON, Peter
(Club Professional)
Bristol & Clifton

MITCHELL, Paul
(Professional)
Bristol & Clifton

MOSS, R
(Club Professional)
Mendip Spring

MURRAY, Alex
(Club Professional)
Tall Pines

RICHARDS, John
(Club Professional)
Stockwood Vale

RILEY, Nick
(Club Professional)
Henbury

ROBINSON, Darren
(Club Professional)
Filton
£25.00 for 60 minutes

SMITH, Adrian
(Professional)
Tickenham
£14.00 for 30 minutes

THOMPSON-GREEN, Tim
(Professional)
Tracy Park
£20.00 for 60 minutes

BUCKINGHAMSHIRE

BARR, Matthew
(Professional)
Gerrards Cross

BLACKLOCK, Luther
(Club Professional)
Woburn

BOND, Keith
(Professional)
Abbey Hill
£18.00 for 30 minutes

CANNON, S
(Club Professional)
Hedsor
£26.00 for 60 minutes

CLINGAN, Colin
(Club Professional)
Windmill Hill
£15.00 for 30 minutes

DAVIES, Jon
(Professional)
Woburn

FLYNN, Patrick
(Professional)
Woburn

GIBBINS, Peter
(Club Professional)
Chartridge Park

IRON, Greg
(Club Professional)
Wavendon Golf Ctre

JACKSON, Lee
(Club Professional)
Harleyford

KILLING, Andrew
(Club Professional)
Thorney Park
£30.00 for 60 minutes

LAMB, Jonathan
(Professional)
Woburn

LENAGHAN, Gary
(Professional)
Woburn

LOWRY, Simon
(Club Professional)
Princes Risborough

MORRIS, G C
(Club Professional)
Harewood Downs

SAARY, Alex
(Club Professional)
Aylesbury
£25.00 for 60 minutes

TESCHNEL, Karl
(Club Professional)
Iver
£16.00 for 30 minutes

TESCHNEL, Karl
(Touring Professional)
Iver
£16.00 for 30 minutes

THATCHER, Alistair
(Club Professional)
Oakland Park
£35.00 for 60 minutes

WARD, Ken
(Club Professional)
Whiteleaf
£12.00 for 30 minutes. £24.00 for 60 minutes

WATSON, Paul
(Club Professional)
Flackwell Heath

CAMBRIDGESHIRE

BAMBOROUGH, Ian
(Club Professional)
Gog Magog
£18.50 for 30 minutes

BROWN, Stewart
(Club Professional)
March
£12.50 for 30 minutes

CASEY, Gary
(PGA Professional)
Thorpe Wood

CLEMONS, Michael
(Club Professional)
Cambridge Meridian

CONNOLLY, Steve
(Club Professional)
Abbotsley
£16.00 for 30 minutes

CURRIE, Alisdair
(Club Professional)
Brampton Park

ENGELMAN, Adrienne

(Club Professional)
Cambridge
£15.00 for 30 minutes

🏌 **FITTON**, Dennis
(PGA Professional)
Thorpe Wood

🏌 **GALLAGHER**, Mike
(Club Professional)
Peterborough Milton

🏌 **GEORGE**, Andrew
(Club Professional)
Ely City

🏌 **HOWARD**, Ashley
(Professional)
Orton Meadows
£15.00 for 30 minutes

🏌 **HUGGETT**, Geoff
(Club Professional)
Cambridge
£15.00 for 30 minutes

🏌 **KEYS**, Richard
(Club Professional)
Oundle
£10.00 for 30 minutes

🏌 **KIDDIE**, Frank
(Club Professional)
Elton Furze

🏌 **MITCHELL**, Jason
(Club Professional)
Orton Meadows
£15.00 for 30 minutes

🏌 **PERKINS**, Martin
(Club Professional)
Tydd St Giles
£25.00 for 60 minutes

🏌 **ROUND**, Peter
(Club Professional)
St. Neots
£15.00 for 50 minutes

🏌 **SCOTT**, Stewart
(Club Professional)
Ramsey Club
£13.50 for 30 minutes

🏌 **TEMPLEMAN**, Mark
(Club Professional)
Thorney
£12.00 for 30 minutes

🏌 **THOMSON**, Scott
(Club Professional)
Girton

🏌 **VAUGHN**, Lee
(Professional)
Thorpe Wood

🏌 **WATERMAN**, Scott
(Club Professional)
Lakeside Lodge
£13.00 for 30 minutes

🏌 **WATSON**, Craig
(Club Professional)
Bourn
£12.50 for 30 minutes

CHESHIRE

🏌 **BAGULEY**, Andrew
(Club Professional)
Leigh
£12.50 for 30 minutes

🏌 **BOWRING**, Peter
(Club Professional)
Alderley Edge
£14.00 for 60 minutes

🏌 **BRADBURY**, Steven
(Club Professional)
Aldersey Green
£12.00 for 30 minutes

🏌 **BRADLEY**, Gary
(Club Professional)
Mellor & Townscliffe

🏌 **BRUNTON**, D
(Touring Professional)
Ringway
£17.00 for 30 minutes

🏌 **CORCORAN**, Lee
(Professional)
Mollington Grange
£11.00 for 30 minutes

🏌 **CROSS**, Carl P
(Club Professional)
New Mills

🏌 **DENNIS**, Paul
(Professional)
Dunham Forest
£17.00 for 30 minutes

🏌 **DEWHURST**, Stephen
(Club Professional)
Mobberley
£15.00 for 40 minutes

🏌 **DUNROE**, Neil
(Club Professional)
Eaton

🏌 **EYRE**, Peter
(Club Professional)
Mere
£30.00 for 60 minutes

🏌 **FARRANCE**, Paul
(Club Professional)
Antrobus
£14.00 for 30 minutes

🏌 **FRANKLIN**, A
(Club Professional)
Runcorn

🏌 **FREEMAN**, Bob
(Club Professional)
Reddish Vale

🏌 **GARDNER**, Peter
(Club Professional)
Upton-By-Chester

🏌 **HOPLEY**, J
(Club Professional)
Gatley

🏌 **IDDON**, Colin
(Professional)
Heyrose

🏌 **JONES**, Ellis B
(Club Professional)
Delamere Forest

🏌 **MACKAY**, Reay
(Club Professional)
Warrington

🏌 **MARSH**, Simon
(Professional)
Heaton Moor

🏌 **MCCARTHY**, Stephen
(Club Professional)
Lymm

🏌 **MCLEOD**, Gordon
(Club Professional)
Tytherington

🏌 **MYERS**, D
(Professional)
Marple

🏌 **NAYLOR**, David
(Club Professional)
Houldsworth

🏌 **NORCOTT**, Gary
(Club Professional)
Davenport

🏌 **O'CONNER**, Sean
(Professional)
Pryors Hayes
£30.00 for 60 minutes

🏌 **RASTALL**, Tim
(Professional)
Mottram Hall

🏌 **RYAN**, N
(Club Professional)
Ringway
£17.00 for 30 minutes

🏌 **SMITH**, Ian
(Club Professional)
Sutton Hall
£13.50 for 60 minutes

🏌 **SPROSTON**, Anthony
(Club Professional)
High Legh Park

🏌 **STATHAM**, Judy
(Club Professional)
Portal Premier
£25.00 for 60 minutes

🏌 **STEVENSON**, Andy
(Club Professional)
Mersey Valley
£14.00 for 60 minutes

🏌 **STEWART**, M
(Club Professional)
Sale

🏌 **STOCKDALE**, Richard
(Club Professional)
Vale Royal Abbey
£30.00 for 60 minutes

🏌 **TAYLOR**, Tony
(Club Professional)
Macclesfield

🏌 **TONGE**, Graham
(Professional)
Frodsham

🏌 **TURNER**, D
(Professional)
Ringway
£17.00 for 30 minutes

🏌 **VALENTINE**, Kevin
(Professional)
Alvaston Hall

🏌 **WHEELER**, David
(Club Professional)
Malkins Bank

🏌 **WILLIAMS**, Michael
(Professional)
Ashton-on-Mersey

🏌 **WRIGLEY**, Ian
(Club Professional)
Dunham Forest
£17.00 for 30 minutes

🏌 **YOUNG**, Bobby
(Club Professional)
Peover
£14.00 for 60 minutes or £35.00 for a 9 hole lesson.

Cambridgeshire — Cheshire

Professionals by COUNTY in England

CLEVELAND

BROOK, Andrew S
(Club Professional)
Hunley Hall
£25.00 for 60 minutes

DONALDSON, Craig
(Club Professional)
Cleveland

HECTOR, W
(Professional)
Seaton Carew

HOPE, Alan
(Club Professional)
Middlesbrough Municipal
£24.00 for 60 minutes

JACKSON, Peter
(Club Professional)
Castle Eden
£28.00 for 60 minutes

OLIPHANT, Andrew
(Club Professional)
Wynyard Club
£50.00 for 60 minutes

URE, Michael
(Club Professional)
Billingham
£15.00 for 30 minutes

CORNWALL

ALLISS, Gary
(Club Professional)
Trevose

BICKNELL, Nigel
(Club Professional)
Truro

BLUNDELL, Phil
(Club Professional)
Mullion

BOUNDY, Mark
(Club Professional)
Trethorne
£20.00 for 60 minutes

CULLEN, A J
(Club Professional)
Newquay

CULLEN, Andrew
(Club Professional)
Roserrow
£14.00 for 60 minutes

DUMBRECK, James
(Club Professional)
Tehidy
£20.00 for 60 minutes

KAMINSKI, Chris
(Professional)
Lostwithiel
£25.00 for 60 minutes

MACDONALD, Alastair
(Club Professional)
Looe

MICHELL, D
(Club Professional)
Perranporth

MOON, David
(Club Professional)
St. Mellion International

NASH, Tony
(Club Professional)
Lostwithiel
£25.00 for 60 minutes

PAGE, Rob
(Professional)
Bowood

PITTS, T
(Club Professional)
St. Austell

POOLE, D
(Club Professional)
Whitsand Bay

ROWE, Mark
(Club Professional)
Carlyon Bay
£25.00 for 60 minutes

TOZER, J
(Club Professional)
Launceston

WILLIAMS, Nick
(Club Professional)
St. Enodoc

YEO, John
(Club Professional)
Bude & North Cornwall

COUNTY DURHAM

COLE, Chris
(Club Professional)
Beamish Park

CORBALLY, Steve
(Club Professional)
Durham City

COWELL, Sean
(Club Professional)
South Moor

DILLEY, Craig
(Club Professional)
Darlington

FLETCHER, David
(Club Professional)
Chester-Le-Street

GIVENS, Ralph
(Club Professional)
Stressholme
£24.00 for 60 minutes

HARTLEY, Alan
(Club Professional)
Roseberry Grange
£10.00 - £12.50 for 30 minutes

ORD, Jack
(Club Professional)
Consett & District
£7.50 for 60 minutes

PEARCE, Darren
(Club Professional)
Barnard Castle
£15.00 for 60 minutes

SKIFFINGTON, David
(Club Professional)
Bishop Auckland

WHITE, Andrew
(Club Professional)
Oak Leaf
£12.00 for 30 minutes

WILSON, Ernie
(Club Professional)
Woodham

CUMBRIA

GRAHAM, J
(Club Professional)
Silloth

HARRISON, Steve
(Professional)
Eden

HEGGIE, Martin
(Club Professional)
Carlisle
£14.00 for 30 minutes

KEY, Gary
(Club Professional)
Appleby
£10.00 for 40 minutes

PICKERING, A J
(Club Professional)
Grange-Over-Sands

ROOKE, W S M
(Club Professional)
Windermere

RUDD, Sean
(Club Professional)
Seascale

SCOTT, Peter
(Club Professional)
Kendal
£15.00 for 30 minutes

SMITH, Mike
(Club Professional)
Ulverston

TURNER, D
(Club Professional)
Carus Green

WAREING, Keith
(Club Professional)
Distington Golf
£15.00 for 60 minutes

WHITEHALL, A
(Club Professional)
Barrow

WILKINSON, Stewart
(Club Professional)
Brampton
£17.00 for 45 minutes

WILLIAMSON, Roy
(Club Professional)
Casterton
£20.00 for 60 minutes

DERBYSHIRE

ADAMS, David
(Professional)
Hallowes
£15.00 for 45 minutes

BIRD, Willie
(Club Professional)
Chevin
£15.00 - £17.00 for 30 minutes

BROWN, Gary
(Club Professional)
Buxton & High Peak

CARNALL, J
(Club Professional)
Barlborough Links
£15.00 for 30 minutes

COXON, Tim
(PGA Professional)
Mickleover

CULLEN, David
(Club Professional)
Chapel-en-le-Frith
£24.00 for 60 minutes

DOTT, Gavin

(Professional)
Hallowes
£15.00 for 45 minutes

DUNN, Philip
(Club Professional)
Hallowes
£15.00 for 45 minutes

HALLAM, Neville
(Club Professional)
Shirland
£15.00 for 30 minutes

HYLAND, Andy
(PGA Professional)
Broughton Heath
£10.00 for 30 minutes

LYLE, Graham
(Club Professional)
Horsley Lodge
£13.00 for 30 minutes

MCARTHY, D
(Club Professional)
Brailsford
£10.00 - £13.00 for 30 minutes

MCLEAN, Mike
(Club Professional)
Chesterfield

SHERRATT, Simon
(Club Professional)
Maywood
£12.00 for 30 minutes

SMITH, Andrew
(Club Professional)
Ashbourne
£15.00 for 45 minutes

STEELS, Damon
(Club Professional)
Breadsall Priory

STIFF, Sean
(Club Professional)
Broughton Heath
£10.00 for 30 minutes

TAYLOR, P
(Club Professional)
Sickleholme
£15.00 for 40 minutes

WALKER, Graham
(Club Professional)
Barlborough Links
£15.00 for 30 minutes

WESSELINGH, Paul
(Club Professional)
Kedleston Park

DEVON

ADWICK, Stewart
(Club Professional)
Padbrook Park

AMIET, Scott
(Club Professional)
Teign Valley
£20.00 for 60 minutes

CADE, Reg
(Club Professional)
Ashbury
£18.00 for 30 minutes

CRAIG, Malcolm
(Club Professional)
Newton Abbot

DAVIES, Mark
(Professional)
Ilfracombe

£12.00 for 60 minutes

DISNEY, Stuart
(Professional)
Torquay
£26.00 for 60 minutes

DOUGAN, Steven
(Club Professional)
Dartmouth
£26.00 for 60 minutes

EVERETT, Darren
(Club Professional)
Portmore Golf Park
£16.50 for 60 minutes

FINCH, Howard
(Club Professional)
Crediton
£30.00 for 60 minutes

GILL, Chris
(Professional)
Crediton
£30.00 for 60 minutes

GOULD, Steve
(Club Professional)
Fingle Glen

GOULDS, Steven
(Club Professional)
Portmore Golf Park
£16.50 for 60 minutes

HAWTON, Michael
(Club Professional)
Tiverton

HERRING, Richard
(Club Professional)
North Devon (Royal)
£24.00 for 60 minutes

HOLMAN, Neil
(Club Professional)
Churston
£12.00 for 60 minutes

JEFFERIES, Simon
(Club Professional)
Okehampton
£25.00 for 60 minutes

KEMP, Mervyn
(Club Professional)
Fingle Glen

LANGMEAD, James
(Club Professional)
Hele Park Golf Ctre
£30.00 for 60 minutes. £15.00 for 30 minutes

LAUGHER, Peter
(Club Professional)
Thurlestone

LEWIS, R
(Professional)
Manor House

MACKENZIE, Albert
(Club Professional)
Saunton
£18.00 for 45 minutes.

MACKENZIE, Albert
(Professional)
Saunton
£18.00 for 45 minutes.

MCASKELL, Scott
(Club Professional)
Elfordleigh
£20.00 for 60 minutes

MCGHEE, Jimmy

(Club Professional)
Willingcott
£20.00 for 60 minutes

MCSHERRY, Tim
(Club Professional)
Yelverton

PROWSE, Darren
(Club Professional)
Warren
£20.00 for 60 minutes

REHAAG, Domonic
(Club Professional)
Tavistock
£24.00 for 60 minutes

RICHARDS, Alan
(Club Professional)
Woodbury Park
£18.00 for 30 minutes.

RICHARDS, Glenn
(Club Professional)
Wrangaton

RIDYARD, David
(Professional)
Dinnaton

ROWETT, Mike
(Club Professional)
Exeter

RUTH, Martin
(Club Professional)
Torquay
£26.00 for 60 minutes

TAPPER, Gaele
(Club Professional)
Sidmouth
£24.00 for 60 minutes

THOMSON, Andrew
(Club Professional)
Otter Valley Golf Ctre
£15.00 for 60 minutes

TROAKE, Russ
(Club Professional)
Elfordleigh
£20.00 for 60 minutes

TYSON, Martin
(Club Professional)
Dainton Park

UNDERWOOD, Trevor
(Club Professional)
East Devon

WARD, Peter
(Club Professional)
Teignmouth

WEBB, Graham
(Club Professional)
Holsworthy
£12.00 for 60 minutes

WHITLEY, Neville
(Club Professional)
Sparkwell
£20.00 for 60 minutes

DORSET

BLACK, Andrew
(Club Professional)
Lyme Regis

BROOK, Chris
(Professional)
Parley
£13.50 for 30 minutes

CONGDON, Damian

(Professional)
Dudsbury

🏌 **DODD,** Mike
(Club Professional)
Ferndown Forest
£30.00 for 60 minutes

🏌 **EMERSON,** Gary
(Touring Professional)
Broadstone

🏌 **GILLESPY,** Ken
(Professional)
Parley
£13.50 for 30 minutes

🏌 **HILL,** Richard
(Club Professional)
Boscombe Ladies

🏌 **HONAN,** Derwin
(Club Professional)
East Dorset
£14.50 for 30 minutes

🏌 **HUNT,** Tony
(Professional)
Crane Valley
£14.00 for 60 minutes

🏌 **LOCHRIE,** Des
(Club Professional)
Weymouth

🏌 **MILES,** David
(Club Professional)
Bournemouth & Meyrick
£15.00 for 30 minutes

🏌 **MILES,** Jane
(Professional)
Parley
£13.50 for 30 minutes

🏌 **PARKER,** Iain
(Club Professional)
Ferndown
£30.00 for 60 minutes

🏌 **PARSONS,** David
(Club Professional)
Bridport & West Dorset

🏌 **RANSON,** D
(Club Professional)
Crane Valley
£14.00 for 60 minutes

🏌 **ROGERS,** Nick
(Club Professional)
Came Down

🏌 **STATHAM,** N
(Club Professional)
Wessex Golf Ctre

🏌 **STUPPLE,** Mike
(Professional)
Parley
£13.50 for 30 minutes

🏌 **THOMAS,** Mark
(Club Professional)
Dudsbury

🏌 **THOMPSON,** Martyn
(Club Professional)
Parkstone

🏌 **THOMPSON,** Peter
(Professional)
Parley
£13.50 for 30 minutes

🏌 **TOKELY,** Nigel
(Club Professional)
Broadstone

🏌 **TUDDENHAM,** Roger
(Club Professional)
Canford Magna

ESSEX

🏌 **ANGEL,** Mark
(Club Professional)
Colchester
£25.00 for 60 minutes

🏌 **BAKER,** C
(Professional)
High Beech

🏌 **BARHAM,** P
(Club Professional)
Crondon Park

🏌 **BERRY,** P
(Club Professional)
Millers Barn Golf Park
£14.00 for 30 minutes

🏌 **BLACKBURN,** A
(Professional)
Hanover

🏌 **BOARD,** Ray
(Club Professional)
Chigwell

🏌 **BROOKES,** David
(Professional)
Warren
£20 for 60 minutes

🏌 **BUGG,** D
(Club Professional)
West Park

🏌 **BURROWS,** Graham
(Club Professional)
Boyce Hill
£15.00 for 30 minutes

🏌 **CARDY,** Steven
(Club Professional)
Burnham-on-Crouch

🏌 **CLAYTON,** Richard
(Club Professional)
Loughton

🏌 **COCKER,** Lee
(Professional)
Essex

🏌 **COLE,** S
(Golf Professional)
Hartswood

🏌 **CURRY,** Andrew
(Club Professional)
Hobbs Cross

🏌 **DAVIS,** Philip
(Professional)
Saffron Walden

🏌 **DICKS,** Wendy
(Touring Professional)
Regiment
£14.00 for 30 minutes

🏌 **DUFFIN,** Andrew
(Professional)
Clacton

🏌 **EADY,** P
(Club Professional)
Epping Forest
£15.00 for 30 minutes

🏌 **FAIRWEATHER,** Colin
(Club Professional)
Benton Hall

🏌 **GATHERCOLE,** James

(Professional)
Essex

🏌 **GLENN,** Danny
(Professional)
Epping

🏌 **GODDARD,** Chris
(Professional)
Romford
£15.00 for 30 minutes

🏌 **GREEN,** Phil
(Club Professional)
Three Rivers

🏌 **GREEN,** Robert
(Club Professional)
Nazeing

🏌 **GRICE,** Phil
(Club Professional)
Lexden
£16.50 for 60 minutes

🏌 **GROAT,** Jason
(Club Professional)
Warley Park

🏌 **HALL,** Alan
(Club Professional)
Priors
£15.00 for 30 minutes

🏌 **HALL,** Alan
(Professional/Pro Shop)
Stapleford Abbotts Golf Club

🏌 **HOPKIN,** John
(Club Professional)
Maylands

🏌 **HUDSON,** John
(Club Professional)
Braxted Park

🏌 **JENNINGS,** Paul
(Head Professional)
Risebridge

🏌 **JOINER,** Paul
(Professional)
Orsett

🏌 **LAITT,** C
(Club Professional)
Birch Grove

🏌 **LEVERMORE,** Stuart
(Club Professional)
Clacton

🏌 **LEYTON,** Stuart
(Club Professional)
Abridge
£25.00 for 60 minutes

🏌 **LOWE,** Jamie
(Club Professional)
Lexden
£16.50 for 60 minutes

🏌 **MARCH,** Dave
(PGA Professional)
Regiment
£14.00 for 30 minutes

🏌 **MARCH,** Dave
(Touring Professional)
Regiment
£14.00 for 30 minutes

🏌 **MCBRIDE,** Pete
(Professional)
Lexden
£16.50 for 60 minutes

🏌 **MCCOLL,** Bill
(Professional)

Thorpe Hall

MCGINN, Alan
(Club Professional)
Canons Brook
£22.00 for 45 minutes

MONCUR, Terry
(Club Professional)
Langdon Hills Golf Ctre

PARCELL, Tony
(Club Professional)
Braintree

PIKE, Gary
(Club Professional)
Forrester Park

PORTER, Lee
(Club Professional)
Hylands Golf Complex
£15.00 for 30 minutes

PORTER, Roy
(Club Professional)
Top Meadow
£10.00 for 30 minutes

REID, Matt
(Club Professional)
Mardyke Valley Golf Ctre
£15.00 for 40 minutes

ROBLIN, Henry
(Club Professional)
Bunsay Downs
£15.00 for 30 minutes

SINCLAIR, Ian
(Club Professional)
Channels

STEWART, Gary
(Club Professional)
South Essex
£20.00 for 60 minutes

TAYLOR, Robert
(Club Professional)
Colne Valley
£35.00 for 60 minutes

TINGY, David
(Professional)
Hylands Golf Complex
£15.00 for 30 minutes

UTTERIDGE, M
(Club Professional)
Castle Point

WALKER (OBE), Nicky
(Club Professional)
Warren
£20 for 60 minutes

WARN, Ian
(Club Professional)
Regiment
£14.00 for 30 minutes

WARN, Ian
(Professional)
Regiment
£14.00 for 30 minutes

WELCH, Mark
(Club Professional)
Chelmsford

GLOUCESTERSHIRE

ALLEN, Norman
(Club Professional)
Cotswold Hills
£25.00 for 60 minutes

BALLARD, R

(Club Professional)
Forest Hills
£11.50 for 30 minutes

BOAST, Charlie
(Club Professional)
Tewkesbury Park

BOLAND, N
(Club Professional)
Shipton
£25.00 for 60 minutes

BROWN, Ian
(Club Professional)
Newent

BUSHELL, Paul
(Club Professional)
Stinchcombe Hill

CAMERON, A
(Club Professional)
Orchard
£12.00 for 30 minutes

CLARK, Philip
(Club Professional)
Sherdons
£15.00 for 30 minutes

ELLIS, Nick
(Club Professional)
Naunton Downs

GARRATT, Peter
(Club Professional)
Cirencester

GILLICK, Chris
(Club Professional)
Gloucester

GOSLING, David
(Club Professional)
Cotswold Edge
£10.00 - £12.00 for 30 minutes

GREY, Andy
(Club Professional)
Forest Of Dean
£10.00 for 30 minutes

GRUBB, Tony
(Club Professional)
Rodway Hill

HADDON, F
(Club Professional)
Lilley Brook
£15.00 for 40 minutes

LATHAM, James
(Professional)
Cotswold Hills
£25.00 for 60 minutes

PARKER, John
(Professional)
Sherdons
£15.00 for 30 minutes

PICKETT, Kevin
(Club Professional)
Hilton Puckrup Hall

STEELE, C
(Club Professional)
Minchinhampton
£20.00 for 30 minutes

WATTS, Ian
(Club Professional)
Cannons Court

WHIDDON, John
(Club Professional)
Gloucester

WOOD, Keith
(Assistant Professional)
Ramada Hotel

HAMPSHIRE

ADAMS, Richard
(Club Professional)
South Winchester
£15.00 for 60 minutes

BALFOUR, Martin
(Professional)
Winchester (Royal)
£14.00 for 30 minutes

BANTING, Jason
(Club Professional)
Portsmouth
£30.00 for 60 minutes

BARTER, Tim
(Club Professional)
Botley Park

BENFLEET, Ben
(Club Professional)
Southampton Municipal

BENSON, Ian
(Club Professional)
Blacknest

BRATLEY, Neil
(Club Professional)
Wellow
£24.00 for 60 minutes

BRIGGS, Alastair
(Club Professional)
Test Valley

BROWN, Derek
(Club Professional)
Furzeley
£13.50 for 30 minutes

BROWN, Paul
(Club Professional)
Alton
£30.00 for 60 minutes

BROWN, Robert
(Club Professional)
Tournerbury Golf Ctre
£25.00 for 60 minutes

BRYDEN, Phillip
(Professional)
Tournerbury Golf Ctre
£25.00 for 60 minutes

CAMERON, Rod
(Club Professional)
Meon Valley
£30.00 for 60 minutes

CHAPMAN, Peter
(Club Professional)
Four Marks
£18.00 for 40 minutes

CLAY, Stephen
(Club Professional)
Blackmoor
£19.00 for 45 minutes

CONLEY, G
(Club Professional)
Army

CRONIN, Stewart
(Club Professional)
Hampshire
£35.00 for 60 minutes. £17.50 for 30 minutes

DAWSON, Peter
(Touring Professional)

Essex — Hampshire

Professionals by **COUNTY** in **England**

Hampshire — Hertfordshire

Professionals by COUNTY in England

South Winchester
£15.00 for 60 minutes

DE BRUIN, Chris
(Professional)
Tylney Park

EDWARDS, Scott
(Club Professional)
Wickham Park
£24.00 for 60 minutes

FANNON, Andrew
(Professional)
Dummer

GADD, Ray
(Club Professional)
Hayling

HARRIS, Danny
(Club Professional)
New Forest

HEALY, Terry
(Club Professional)
Great Salterns

HENRY, Kieron Stevenson
(Club Professional)
Old Thorns
£20.00 for 30 minutes

HUDSON, C
(Touring Professional)
Army

HUNTER, Steven
(Club Professional)
Winchester (Royal)
£14.00 for 30 minutes

KLEPACZ, P
(Club Professional)
Rowlands Castle
£20.00 for 60 minutes

LEE, Geoffrey
(Professional)
Liphook

NEVE, Jason
(Club Professional)
Cams Hall Estate Golf Club
£10.00 - £15.00 for 30 minutes

PEARCE, Trevor
(Professional)
East Horton Golf Ctre
£26.00 for 60 minutes

PORTER, George
(Professional)
North Hants Fleet
£18.00 for 30 minutes

PORTER, Steve
(Club Professional)
North Hants Fleet
£18.00 for 30 minutes

RICHARDSON, John
(Club Professional)
Lee On The Solent
£14.00 for 30 minutes

RODGERS, Peter
(Club Professional)
Barton-On-Sea
£12.00 for 30 minutes

ROSS, Laurance
(Club Professional)
Fareham Woods

SCOTT, Malcolm
(Professional)
Alresford

SLADE, John
(Professional)
Dibden Golf Ctre
£13.00 for 30 minutes

SMITH, Paul
(Professional)
Dibden Golf Ctre
£13.00 for 30 minutes

STRICKET, Chris
(Club Professional)
Fleming Park

TESCHNER, Heath
(Club Professional)
Dunwood Manor

TYE, W P
(Professional)
Burley

WARD, S
(Club Professional)
Bishopswood

WARICK, Ian
(Club Professional)
County
£22.00 for 60 minutes

WATSON, Scott
(Club Professional)
Basingstoke

WILLIAMS, Mark
(Club Professional)
Paultons Golf Centre

YOUNG, Finlay
(Professional)
Winchester (Royal)
£14.00 for 30 minutes

YOUNG, Ian
(Professional)
Stoneham

HEREFORDSHIRE

BROOKES, Phil
(Club Professional)
Grove
£12.00 for 30 minutes

FERRIDAY, Andrew
(Club Professional)
Leominster

GEALY, Andy
(Club Professional)
Kington

GEALY, Andy
(Professional)
Summerhill

LITCHFIELD, E
(Professional)
South Herefordshire

STOKES, James
(Club Professional)
Brampton Golf
£12.00 for 60 minutes

HERTFORDSHIRE

AINSWORTH, Andrew
(Club Professional)
Ashridge

ALLEN, Nick
(Club Professional)
Little Hay
£16.00 for 30 minutes

ARNOTT, Henry
(Professional)

Chesfield Downs

ATKINSON, Graham
(Club Professional)
Bushey Golf Course
£15.00 for 30 minutes

BARKER, Stephen
(Club Professional)
Stevenage
£13.00 for 30 minutes

BATES, Jamie
(Club Professional)
Barkway Park
£15.00 for 30 minutes

BRYAN, Stephen M
(Club Professional)
Bishops Stortford
£40.00 for 60 minutes

CLARK, Sean
(Club Professional)
Royston
£30.00 for 60 minutes

CORLASS, Michael
(Professional)
Panshanger Golf Complex
£15.00 for 30 minutes

CULMER, Glen
(Club Professional)
East Herts
£15.00 for 30 minutes

DOBBINS, Alan
(Club Professional)
Rickmansworth
£19.00 for 30 minutes

FARMER, Lawrence
(Club Professional)
Moor Park

FERNLEY, Jane
(Club Professional)
Chesfield Downs

FITZSIMMONS, Daniel
(Club Professional)
Harpenden Common

GLEESON, David
(Club Professional)
Porter's Park

GREEN, Matthew
(Professional)
Whipsnade Park

HASTINGS, D
(Professional)
Kingsway

HOLBA, Maximilian
(Assistant Professional)
Stevenage
£13.00 for 30 minutes

HUGGETT, Geoff
(Club Professional)
Whaddon
£12.95 for 30 minutes

HUNTER, Stephen
(Head Professional)
Redbourn

JELLEY, Ian
(Club Professional)
Brookmans Park
£10.00 - £13.00 for 30 minutes

JONES, Peter
(Club Professional)
Hadley Wood

🌑 **LAURENCE,** Craig
(Club Professional)
Manor of Groves
£15.00 for 30 minutes

🌑 **LEWIS,** Bryan
(Club Professional)
Panshanger Golf Complex
£15.00 for 30 minutes

🌑 **LOVEGROVE,** Mike
(Club Professional)
Penfold Park
£25.00 for 30 minutes

🌑 **MACRAE,** Mark
(Professional)
Hertfordshire
£27.00 for 60 minutes

🌑 **MCEVOY,** Peter
(Club Professional)
Old Fold Manor

🌑 **PARFALENENT,** Nick
(Club Professional)
Lamerwood Country Club
£15.00 for 30 minutes

🌑 **PARKER,** G
(Professional)
Knebworth

🌑 **PARKER,** Ian
(Club Professional)
Mill Green Golf Club

🌑 **PERRY,** Michael
(Professional)
Little Hay
£16.00 for 30 minutes

🌑 **PERRY,** Roland
(Club Professional)
Whipsnade Park

🌑 **PLUMB,** Steve
(Club Professional)
Aldwickbury Park
£32.00 for 60 minutes

🌑 **PORTER,** Martin
(Club Professional)
Arkley
£20.00 for 60 minutes

🌑 **PROUDFOOT,** Basil
(Club Professional)
Berkhamsted

🌑 **PROUDFOOT,** Stephen
(Club Professional)
Batchworth Park
£17.00 for 30 minutes

🌑 **PUTTICK,** Barney
(Professional)
Mid-Herts

🌑 **SAXON-MILLS,** John
(Professional)
Heydon Grange

🌑 **SHEARN,** Adrian
(Club Professional)
Hertfordshire
£27.00 for 60 minutes

🌑 **SMITH,** David
(Professional)
Hertfordshire
£27.00 for 60 minutes

🌑 **TOILEY,** Gary
(Club Professional)
Danesbury Park
£20.00 for 60 minutes

🌑 **WALL,** M

(Club Professional)
Chadwell Springs

🌑 **WHITE,** M
(Club Professional)
Shendish Manor
£15.00 for 30 minutes

🌑 **WOOD,** Keith
(Club Professional)
Brocket Hall
£20.00 for 30 minutes

🌑 **WRIGHT,** James
(Club Professional)
Oxhey Park
£17.50 for 45 minutes

ISLE OF MAN

🌑 **CROWE,** Murray
(Professional)
Castletown Golf Links

🌑 **DYSON,** Andrew
(Club Professional)
Mount Murray

🌑 **JONES,** D
(Professional)
King Edward Bay

ISLE OF WIGHT

🌑 **HAMMOND,** Peter
(Club Professional)
Shanklin & Sandown

🌑 **HAYWOOD,** Simon
(Club Professional)
Westridge
£20.00 for 60 minutes

KENT

🌑 **BARBOUR,** Derek
(Club Professional)
Princes
£20.00 - £30.00 for 60 minutes

🌑 **BARTON,** Mike
(Club Professional)
Tunbridge Wells

🌑 **BATCHELOR,** Larry
(Club Professional)
Southern Valley
£15.00 for 40 minutes

🌑 **BOWEN,** Tony
(Club Professional)
Homelands
£12.50 for 60 minutes

🌑 **BRITZ,** Tienie
(Club Professional)
Broome Park
£15.00 for 30 minutes

🌑 **BROOKS,** Andrew
(Club Professional)
St. George's (Royal)

🌑 **BROTHERTON,** John
(Club Professional)
Chestfield
£15.00 - £18.00 for 45 minutes

🌑 **BUGG,** David
(Club Professional)
Mote Park Golf Hut

🌑 **CAMPBELL,** Ewan
(Club Professional)
Westerham
£22.00 - £32.00 for 45 minutes

🌑 **CHILCOTT,** Mark
(Club Professional)

London Beach
£25 for 30 minutes

🌑 **CHILD,** Nigel
(Club Professional)
Cherry Lodge
£25.00 for 60 minutes

🌑 **COLLINS,** Tony
(Club Professional)
Hawkhurst
£19.50 for 30 minutes

🌑 **COPSEY,** David
(Club Professional)
Darenth Valley
£16.00 for 30 minutes

🌑 **CORNISH,** James
(Club Professional)
Ridge Golf Club
£15.00 - £18.00 for 60 minutes

🌑 **CORNWELL,** Roger
(Club Professional)
Upchurch River Valley
£12.00 for 30 minutes

🌑 **COWIE,** Cameron
(Club Professional)
Ashford
£30.00 for 60 minutes

🌑 **DENHAM,** John
(Club Professional)
Beckenham Place Park
£30.00 for 60 minutes

🌑 **DORDOY,** S
(Professional)
Herne Bay

🌑 **DUNGATE,** Trevor
(Club Professional)
Boughton
£24.00 for 60 minutes

🌑 **EDWARDS,** Paul
(Club Professional)
Austin Lodge

🌑 **EVERARD,** Paul
(Club Professional)
Canterbury
£30.00 for 60 minutes

🌑 **FIDLER,** Roger
(Club Professional)
West Kent

🌑 **FITCHIE,** Leigh
(Assistant Professional)
Rochester & Cobham
£16.00 for 30 minutes

🌑 **FOSTON,** Paul
(Club Professional)
Cobtree Manor Park
£20.00 - £40.00 for 60 minutes

🌑 **FOX,** Richard
(Club Professional)
Deangate Ridge
£25.00 for 60 minutes

🌑 **FRENCH,** Danny
(Club Professional)
Chart Hills
£25.00 for 60 minutes

🌑 **GARGARO,** James
(Assistant Professional)
Rochester & Cobham
£16.00 for 30 minutes

🌑 **GIANNANDREA,** Raphael
(Club Professional)
Cray Valley
£15.00 for 30 minutes

Hertfordshire — Kent

Professionals by **COUNTY** in **England**

GREGORY, John
(Club Professional)
Dartford

HANLON, Fred
(Club Professional)
Pedham Place Golf Ctre
£25.00 for 60 minutes

HARRIS, Andrew
(Club Professional)
Roundwood Hall
£12.50 for 30 minutes

HIGGINS, Iain
(Club Professional)
Rochester & Cobham
£16.00 for 30 minutes

HILL, Trevor
(Club Professional)
Ashford
£30.00 for 60 minutes

HINTON, Kevin
(Club Professional)
Holtye
£15.00 for 30 minutes

HODGESON, Alan
(Club Professional)
Bromley

HODGSON, Chris
(Club Professional)
Etchinghill
£12.00 for 60 minutes

HUNTER, Rupert
(Professional)
Hilden Europro
£15.00 for 20 minutes

IMPETT, Brian
(Club Professional)
Lamberhurst
£20.00 for 60 minutes

JARVIS, Matt
(Professional)
Hilden Europro
£15.00 for 20 minutes

JENKINS, Colin
(Club Professional)
Staplehurst Golfing Park
£15.00 for 30 minutes

JONES, Andrew
(Club Professional)
Littlestone
£15.00 for 30 minutes

JONES, Andrew
(Club Professional)
Romney Warren
£15.00 for 30 minutes

KELSALL, Kyle
(Club Professional)
Tenterden
£15.00 for 30 minutes

LAMBERT, Duncan
(Club Professional)
West Malling
£20.00 for 45 minutes

LEE, Nigel
(Head Professional)
Chelsfield Lakes Golf Ctre

LEWIS, David
(Club Professional)
Barnehurst

LONGMUIR, Bill
(Professional)

London

LYONS, Paul
(Club Professional)
Sweetwoods Park
£20.00 for 30 minutes

MCKILLOP, Cameron
(Club Professional)
Fawkham Valley Golf Club

MCNALLY, Nick
(Club Professional)
Tudor Park
£20.00 for 30 minutes

MELLOR, Ally
(Club Professional)
Nizels

MITCHELL, Ron
(Club Professional)
Pedham Place Golf Ctre
£25.00 for 60 minutes

MOGER, Paul
(Club Professional)
Edenbridge

PAGET, Mathew
(Club Professional)
Walmer & Kingsdown
£12.50 - £15.00 for 30 minutes

PURVES, Steve
(Club Professional)
Leeds Castle

REMY, Peter
(Club Professional)
High Elms

REYNOLDS, Andrew
(Professional)
Cinque Ports (Royal)

SCOTT, Derek
(Club Professional)
St. Agustines
£15.00 for 30 minutes

SHERMAN, Hugh
(Club Professional)
Ashford

SIMPSON, Tim
(Club Professional)
Bearsted
£19.00 for 60 minutes

SLADE, Brian
(Club Professional)
Villa
£15.00 for 30 minutes

SMITH, Stuart
(Club Professional)
Lydd

STAFF, Colin
(Club Professional)
Langley Park
£30.00 for 60 minutes

STANDFORD, L
(Club Professional)
Sheerness
£15.00 for 60 minutes

STEWART, Gary
(Club Professional)
Ruxley Park
£15.00 for 30 minutes

STURGEON, R
(Professional)
Westerham
£22.00 - £32.00 for 45 minutes

SYKES, Phil
(Club Professional)
Knole Park
£35.00 for 60 minutes

TAYLOR, Mick
(Club Professional)
Shortlands
£25.00 for 60 minutes

TAYLOR, Ross
(Club Professional)
Redlibbets
£20.00 for 40 minutes

WALLEY, Mike
(Club Professional)
Ruxley Park
£15.00 for 30 minutes

WATT, Mark
(Club Professional)
Lullingstone Park
£30.00 for 60 minutes

WAY, Nicky
(Club Professional)
Hilden Europro
£15.00 for 20 minutes

WOOD, Simon
(Club Professional)
Moatlands
£15.00 for 30 minutes

WORLEY, Mike
(Club Professional)
Cray Valley
£15.00 for 30 minutes

LANCASHIRE

ACCLETON, Frank
(Club Professional)
Castle Hawk
£24.00 for 60 minutes

ATKISS, Phil
(Club Professional)
Mossock Hall
£20.00 for 60 minutes

BENSON, Gareth
(Club Professional)
Westhoughton

BIRCHDNOUGH, Eddie
(Club Professional)
Lytham & St Annes (Royal)

BONEHILL, David
(Club Professional)
Ashton
£15.00 for 60 minutes

BOOTH, Andrew
(Assistant Professional)
Knott End
£20.00 for 60 minutes

BOWRING, Craig
(Club Professional)
Castle Hawk
£24.00 for 60 minutes

BOYLE, Colin
(Club Professional)
Ashton-under-Lyne
£16.00 for 60 minutes

BRADLEY, Mark
(Club Professional)
Ingol
£19.50 for 60 minutes

BRAZELL, Neil
(Club Professional)
Hindley Hall

£24.00 for 60 minutes

🍂 **BURGESS,** Colin
(Club Professional)
Leyland

🍂 **CLARKE,** David
(Club Professional)
Shaw Hill

🍂 **COOPE,** Gary
(Club Professional)
Mytton Fold
£14.00 for 30 minutes on the practice ground.

🍂 **DANCHIN,** Stuart
(Club Professional)
Dean Wood
£24.00 for 60 minutes

🍂 **DONE,** Ryan
(Club Professional)
Heysham

🍂 **DUNCAN,** Andrew
(Club Professional)
Bolton
£20.00 for 60 minutes

🍂 **ESCLAPEZ,** Jon
(Club Professional)
Hurlston

🍂 **FLETCHER,** Simon
(Professional)
Morecambe

🍂 **FUREY,** Ged
(Club Professional)
Pleasington

🍂 **GREENBANK,** A
(Club Professional)
Preston

🍂 **GREENOUGH,** Mike
(Club Professional)
Ashton & Lea

🍂 **HARLING,** William
(Club Professional)
Accrington & District
£20.00 for 60 minutes

🍂 **HEMMINGS,** Stuart
(Assistant Professional)
Ingol
£19.50 for 60 minutes

🍂 **HOWARTH,** Tony
(Professional)
Great Lever & Farnworth

🍂 **HUDSON,** R
(Professional)
Herons Reach

🍂 **HUNT,** Jamie
(Club Professional)
Whalley
£26.00 for 60 minutes

🍂 **KERSHAW,** Tim
(Club Professional)
Standish Court

🍂 **LANCASTER,** Andrew
(Club Professional)
Lytham Green

🍂 **MARTINDALE,** David
(Club Professional)
Deane

🍂 **MCGARVEY,** Neil
(Professional)
Fleetwood
£24.00 for 60 minutes

🍂 **MCLAUGHLIN,** Steve
(Club Professional)
Fleetwood
£24.00 for 60 minutes

🍂 **NICHOLLS,** S
(PGA Professional)
Rosendale Golf Club

🍂 **PARANOMOS,** Nick
(Professional)
Fishwick Hall

🍂 **PURDIE,** Brian
(Club Professional)
Blackpool Park

🍂 **PYE,** Andrew
(Professional)
Ashton
£15.00 for 60 minutes

🍂 **RODWELL,** Alan
(Club Professional)
Blackburn

🍂 **ROPER,** Gareth
(Club Professional)
Charnock Richard
£20.00 for 60 minutes

🍂 **ROSS,** Martin
(Professional)
Marsden Park Public

🍂 **SEED,** Jason
(Club Professional)
Greenmount
£24.00 for 60 minutes

🍂 **SUMNER,** Nigel
(Club Professional)
Nelson

🍂 **SUTCLIFFE,** David
(Club Professional)
Lancaster

🍂 **TAYLOR,** K
(Club Professional)
Blackburn

🍂 **TAYLOR,** Lee
(Professional)
Charnock Richard
£20.00 for 60 minutes

🍂 **TREADGOLD,** Gary
(Club Professional)
Dunscar
£25.00 for 60 minutes

🍂 **TWISSELL,** J
(Club Professional)
Clitheroe

🍂 **VIPOND,** Michael
(Professional)
Pikefold
£30.00 for 60 minutes

🍂 **WALKER,** Paul
(Club Professional)
Knott End
£20.00 for 60 minutes

🍂 **WARD,** Brenden
(Club Professional)
Blackpool North Shore

🍂 **WEBSTER,** Daniel
(Club Professional)
St. Annes Old Links

LEICESTERSHIRE

🍂 **BLAND,** Nevil
(Professional)
Hinckley

£28.00 for 60 minutes

🍂 **BUTLER,** David
(Golf Professional)
Western

🍂 **BYRNE,** Sean
(Club Professional)
Beedles Lake
£25.00 for 60 minutes

🍂 **CLARK,** Dave
(Club Professional)
Birstall

🍂 **CLIFFORD,** Adrian
(Club Professional)
Stoke Albany

🍂 **CURTIS,** Neil
(Club Professional)
Kirby Muxloe

🍂 **FENWICK,** Andrew
(Assistant Professional)
Leicester
£17.00 for 60 minutes

🍂 **FITZPATRICK,** Dominic
(Club Professional)
Glen Gorse

🍂 **HETHERINGTON,** James
(Club Professional)
Melton Mowbray

🍂 **JONES,** Andrew
(Professional)
Leicester
£17.00 for 60 minutes

🍂 **JONES,** Darren
(Club Professional)
Leicester
£17.00 for 60 minutes

🍂 **JONES,** Richard
(Club Professional)
Hinckley
£28.00 for 60 minutes

🍂 **LARRATT,** Bob
(Club Professional)
Kibworth

🍂 **MEE,** David
(Club Professional)
Longcliffe
£14.00 for 30 minutes

🍂 **MELVIN,** N
(Professional)
Kilworth Springs

🍂 **MORRISS,** Bryn
(Club Professional)
Blackthorn Wood
£17.00 for 60 minutes

🍂 **NEAL,** Syke
(Touring Professional)
Beedles Lake
£25.00 for 60 minutes

🍂 **OAKLEY,** Nick
(Professional)
Hinckley
£28.00 for 60 minutes

🍂 **RAITT,** David
(Club Professional)
Whetstone
£20.00 for 60 minutes

🍂 **SELLEARS,** Peter
(Club Professional)
Lingdale
£15.00 for 30 minutes

ULYETT, Matthew
(Club Professional)
Park Hill

WELLS, Andrew
(Club Professional)
Oadby

WHIPHAM, Bruce
(Club Professional)
Kirby Muxloe

WOOD, Simon
(Club Professional)
Scraptoft

LINCOLNSHIRE

BLUNDELL, Allan
(Club Professional)
Louth

BOOTH, Paul
(Professional)
Sleaford

BURNETT, Ian
(Club Professional)
Luffenham Heath

CARTER, Ashley
(Club Professional)
Lincoln
£22.00 for 40 minutes

CHAMBERLAIN, Peter
(Club Professional)
South Kyme
£14.50 for 30 minutes

CHESTER, A M
(Professional)
Market Rasen & District

CORNELIUS, John
(Club Professional)
North Shore

DARROCH, James
(Club Professional)
Rutland County

DAVIES, Glenn
(Club Professional)
Burghley Park

DOWE, Angus
(Professional)
Stoke Rochford

ELLIOT, Campbell
(Professional)
Woodhall Spa
With Nick Hiom for 60 minutes £29.00
and with Campbell Elliot for 60 minutes
£35.00

HOLM, Nick
(Professional)
Woodhall Spa
With Nick Hiom for 60 minutes £29.00
and with Campbell Elliot for 60 minutes
£35.00

HUNTER, Richard
(Club Professional)
Carholme

HUTTON, David
(Club Professional)
Gedney Hill

HUTTON, Tim
(Club Professional)
Sudbrook Moor
£12.00 for 30 minutes

JACKSON, Mark
(Club Professional)

Toft Hotel
£18.00 – £28.00 for 60 minutes

LAWIE, Robin
(Club Professional)
Seacroft
£15.00 for 60 minutes

LESLIE, Gary
(Club Professional)
Welton Manor Golf Ctre

MCKEE, Brian
(Club Professional)
Belton Park
£12.00 for 40 minutes

MURRAY, John
(Club Professional)
Millfield Golf

PAYNE, Jim
(Club Professional)
Sandilands & Leisure

SAYERS, Steve
(Club Professional)
Belton Woods

SHARP, Eric
(Club Professional)
Kenwick Park
£20.00 for 60 minutes

SQUIRES, T
(Club Professional)
Boston

TASKER, Lee
(Club Professional)
Pottergate
£10.00 – £12.00 for 30 minutes

TAYLOR, Graham
(Club Professional)
Owmby
£10.00 for 30 minutes

WILLIAMSON, S J
(Club Professional)
Canwick Park

WILSON, James
(Club Professional)
Sleaford

LINCOLNSHIRE (NORTH EAST)

BURKITT, Nigel
(Club Professional)
Waltham Windmill

HARDING, Nick
(Club Professional)
Immingham

LINCOLNSHIRE (NORTH)

BREWER, Stewart
(Club Professional)
Elsham

EDWARDS, David
(Professional)
Forest Pines

MCKIERNAN, Richard
(Professional)
Holme Hall

MILLER, Andrew
(Club Professional)
Ashby Decoy
£16.00 for 60 minutes

WORRALL, Dean
(Club Professional)
Ashby Decoy
£16.00 for 60 minutes

LONDON

GERKEN, Richard
(Club Professional)
Lee Valley

LONDON (GREATER)

ANDREWS, Adrian
(Club Professional)
Bush Hill Park
£30.00 for 60 minutes

BAILLIE, David
(Club Professional)
Dulwich & Sydenham Hill

BEAL, David
(Club Professional)
Mill Hill

BOWN, David
(Club Professional)
Richmond Park

BOYLE, Hugh
(Professional)
Wimbledon (Royal)

BRETT, Gary
(Club Professional)
Eltham Warren

BROTHERTON, David
(Club Professional)
Shooters Hill
£14.00 for 60 minutes

BROWN, Peter
(Club Professional)
Hampstead
£34.00 for 60 minutes

BRYANT, Peter
(Club Professional)
Brent Valley Public
£30.00 for 60 minutes

BUTLER, David
(Club Professional)
Coombe Wood

COE, John
(Club Professional)
Humax
£15.00 for 60 minutes

DEAL, Matt
(Club Professional)
Hendon
£30.00 for 60 minutes

DEFOY, C
(Club Professional)
Coombe Hill
£25.00 for 30 minutes

FICKLING, Lee
(Club Professional)
Enfield

GEORGE, Freddy
(Club Professional)
North Middlesex

HAWKINS, David
(Club Professional)
Wanstead

HENBERY, Malcolm
(Club Professional)
Dukes Meadow
£34.00 for 60 minutes

HILL, Stewart
(Club Professional)
Richmond Park

HOLDSWORTH, Chris

(Club Professional)
Northwood

JOYCE, Robert
(Club Professional)
West Essex

JUKES, Jeff
(Club Professional)
Wimbledon Common
£30.00 for 60 minutes

KEENAN, Paul
(Professional)
Brent Valley Public
£30.00 for 60 minutes

LEE, Darren
(Touring Professional)
Wanstead

LEWIS, D
(Club Professional)
Whitewebbs

MITCHELL, Bobby
(Professional)
South Herts

MORGAN, Andrew
(Club Professional)
Richmond Park

PAGE, Sarah
(Professional)
Bush Hill Park
£30.00 for 60 minutes

PARTLEK, Mark
(Professional)
Shooters Hill
£14.00 for 60 minutes

PRIVATE, Fred
(Club Professional)
Aquarius
£30.00 for 60 minutes

ROBERTS, Len
(Club Professional)
Hampton Court Palace Golf Club
£20.00 for 45 minutes

SMILLIE, Cameron
(Club Professional)
Haste Hill
£15.00 for 30 minutes

SMITH, Neil
(Professional)
Wyke Green

SQUIRES, Simon
(Professional)
Trent Park Golf Club
£18.00 for 30 minutes

SULLIVAN, Craig
(Professional)
Hendon
£30.00 for 60 minutes

TAYNOR, Andrew
(Club Professional)
Chingford
£20.00 for 30 minutes

TRAYNOR, Andy
(Club Professional)
Epping Forest (Royal)

TURNER, Robin
(Club Professional)
Highgate
£35.00 for 60 minutes

WELLER, Ashley
(Professional)
Hampton Court Palace Golf Club

£20.00 for 45 minutes

WHALE, Kevin
(Club Professional)
Central London
£32.00 for 60 minutes

WICKELOW, N
(Club Professional)
Crews Hill

WILTON, David
(Club Professional)
Muswell Hill

WINDGROVE, Dean
(Club Professional)
Wimbledon Park

WOODROFFE, John
(Professional)
Central London
£32.00 for 60 minutes

WRIGHT, Phil
(Assistant Professional)
Coombe Wood

MANCHESTER (GREATER)

ATKINSON, Chris
(Club Professional)
Oldham
£20.00 for 60 minutes

BUTLER, Dean
(Club Professional)
Davyhulme Park

CONNOR, Brian
(Club Professional)
Manchester
£26.00 for 60 minutes

COUSIN, Ceri
(Club Professional)
Worsley

CUPPELLO, Tony
(Club Professional)
Brookdale
£30.00 for 60 minutes

CURRIE, Scott
(Club Professional)
Boysnope Park
£25.00 for 60 minutes

DANCE, Mark
(Club Professional)
Stand

GOULD, Craig
(Club Professional)
Blackley
£20.00 for 60 minutes

HOLINGSWORTH, Michael
(Club Professional)
Denton
£25 for 60 minutes

JOHNSON, Robert
(Club Professional)
Saddleworth

JONES, Mike
(Club Professional)
Heaton Park
£35.00 for 60 minutes

LOMAX, S
(Professional)
Brackley

MARONEY, Colin
(Professional)
Heaton Park
£35.00 for 60 minutes

MELLING, David
(Club Professional)
Crompton & Royton

MORLEY, Terry
(Club Professional)
Ellesmere

MORRIS, Carl
(Club Professional)
Heaton Park
£35.00 for 60 minutes

PELL, Jason
(Professional)
New North Manchester

PENNY, Roy
(Club Professional)
Werneth
£30.00 for 60 minutes

REEVES, Paul
(Club Professional)
Whitefield

SCREETON, David
(Club Professional)
Worsley Park

VALENTINE, David
(Club Professional)
Chorlton-cum-Hardy
£30.00 for 60 minutes

WAKEFIELD, S
(Professional)
Prestwich

WARE, David
(Club Professional)
Flixton

WILSON, Jimmy
(Club Professional)
Swinton Park

MERSEYSIDE

ADAMS, M
(Club Professional)
Wallasey
£15.00 for 30 minutes

AYRE, Andrew
(Club Professional)
Leasowe

BERRY, Geoff
(Club Professional)
Bromborough
£15.00 for 30 minutes

BISBURY, C
(Professional)
Brackenwood

BRADSHAW, Alan
(Club Professional)
Bootle

BURBIDGE, Richard
(Club Professional)
Blundells Hill
£25.00 for 60 minutes

BUTLER, Gary
(Head Professional)
Formby

COPEMAN, G
(Club Professional)
Southport Old Links
£15.00 for 60 minutes

DICKENSON, Paul
(Club Professional)
Houghwood
£12.50 for 30 minutes

London (Greater) — Merseyside

Professionals by **COUNTY** in England

DISBURY, Colin
(Club Professional)
Arrowe Park
£12.50 for 30 minutes

DONOGHUE, John
(Club Professional)
Hesketh

DUFFY, Scot
(Club Professional)
Aintree
£26.00 for 60 minutes

EDGE, Gary
(Club Professional)
West Lancashire

FLETCHER, Bill
(Club Professional)
Southport Municipal
£12.50 for 30 minutes

GIBBONS, Alan
(Assistant Professional)
Caldy
£15.00 for 30 minutes

HASTINGS, Tim
(Professional)
West Lancashire

HEGGARTY, John
(Club Professional)
Liverpool (Royal)

HODGKINSON, Brian
(Club Professional)
Birkdale (Royal)

HOOTON, Simon
(Club Professional)
Hoylake Municipal

JONES, Daniel
(Club Professional)
Sherdley Park Municipal
£10.00 for 30 minutes

KEARNEY, Ian
(Assistant Professional)
Formby

KENWRIGHT, Peter
(Club Professional)
Haydock Park

LAMB, Ken
(Head Professional)
Brackenwood Municipal

LARGE, Barry
(Club Professional)
Allerton
£15.00 for 60 minutes

LLOYD, David
(Club Professional)
Formby Hall

MACFARLANE, Neil
(Club Professional)
Bidston
£12.00 for 45 minutes

MARSHALL, James
(Touring Professional)
Hesketh

PARR, Nigel
(Club Professional)
Childwall
£15.00 for 30 minutes

PAYNE, Jim
(Club Professional)
Southport & Ainsdale
£20.00 for 60 minutes

SARGENT, Nick
(Professional)
Eastham Lodge

SLATTERY, Lee
(Touring Professional)
Hesketh

THOMPSON, A
(Club Professional)
Heswall
£22.50 for 30 minutes

THOMPSON, Robin
(Club Professional)
Prenton
£24.00 for 60 minutes

WESTON, Dave
(Club Professional)
Liverpool Municipal
£20.00 for 60 minutes

WHELLER, Dene
(Assistant Professional)
Formby

MIDLANDS (WEST)

ANDERSON, John
(Professional)
Little Aston

ATKINSON, Tim
(Club Professional)
Widney Manor
£12.00 for 30 minutes

BOTTRILL, S
(Club Professional)
Shirley
£30.00 for 60 minutes. £15.00 for 30
minutes

BOWNES, Andrew
(Professional)
North Warwickshire

CLARK, Finlay
(Club Professional)
North Worcestershire
£15.00 for 40 minutes

COULSON, Marc
(Club Professional)
Stoneleigh Deer Park

CUNDY, Jamie
(Club Professional)
Edgbaston
£15.00 for 60 minutes

DANCE, Richard J
(Club Professional)
Bloxwich

GLEDHILL, Chris
(Club Professional)
Brandon Wood Municipal

GRIER, Rob
(Club Professional)
Stonebridge

GRIFFIN, Martin
(Professional)
Moseley

HARVEY, A
(Club Professional)
Robin Hood
£24.00 for 60 minutes

HAYES, Jerry
(Club Professional)
Sutton Coldfield

HAYES, Jerry
(Club Professional)

Sutton Coldfield Ladies
£20.00 for 60 minutes

HERBETT, Mike
(Club Professional)
Fulford Heath

JOYCE, Simon
(Club Professional)
Dartmouth

MALE, Mark
(Club Professional)
Stourbridge

MOUNTFORD, Richard
(Professional)
Ladbrook Park

NICHOLAS, Jon
(Club Professional)
Halesowen

PARTRIDGE, Alan
(Professional)
Moor Hall

PARTRIDGE, Alan
(Professional)
Wishaw

QUARTERMAN, A
(Professional)
Harborne

REAY, John
(Club Professional)
Stoneleigh Deer Park

RHODES, J
(Club Professional)
South Staffordshire

SELWYN-SMITH, Neil
(Club Professional)
Hawkesbury Golf Centre
£15.00 for 60 minutes

SHORT, Trevor
(Club Professional)
Boldmere
£25.00 for 60 minutes

SMITH, Simon
(Club Professional)
Aston Wood
£24.00 - £30.00 for 60 minutes

TUDOR, Damian
(Club Professional)
Forest of Arden

WICKETTS, C J
(Club Professional)
Walmley

WYLIE, Nigel
(Club Professional)
Sandwell Park
£12.00 for 60 minutes

NORFOLK

ABBOTT, P
(Professional)
Wensum Valley
£10.00 - £12.00 for 30 minutes

ALLEN, Mark
(Club Professional)
Eaton

CLARKE, Martyn
(Club Professional)
Fakenham
£12.00 for 30 miutes

CURTIS, Robert
(Club Professional)

Dereham

DICKSEE, Simon
(Head Professional)
Barnham Broom

DODDS, James
(Club Professional)
Hunstanton

FEW, Michael
(Club Professional)
Weston Park
£20.00 for 30 minutes

FIELD, Peter
(Professional)
Swaffham

FUTTER, Dean
(Club Professional)
Norwich (Royal)
£15.00 for 60 minutes

HEMSLEY, Alan
(Club Professional)
Richmond Park
£12.00 for 30 minutes

HILL, James
(Club Professional)
Great Yarmouth & Caister

IRESON, Guy
(Club Professional)
Sprowston Manor
£15.00 for 30 minutes

JUBB, M W
(Club Professional)
Sheringham

KITLEY, Gary
(Club Professional)
Thetford
£10.00 - £14.00 for 35 minutes

MITCHELL, Neil
(Club Professional)
Feltwell

PATTERSON, L
(Club Professional)
Cromer (Royal)

PICKERELL, N
(Club Professional)
Eagles
£15.00 for 60 minutes

POTTER, Chris
(Club Professional)
Bawburgh

POTTER, Gary
(Club Professional)
Dunham

RAYNER, Simon
(Club Professional)
West Norfolk (Royal)

REYNOLDS, John
(Club Professional)
King's Lynn

SCHULVER, Syer
(Club Professional)
Caldecott Hall
£10.00 for 30 minutes

SHEARD, Alison
(Professional)
Ryston Park

SYMMONS, T
(Club Professional)
Mundesley

TAYLOR, Nigel

(Professional)
Diss

WHITE, Steve
(Club Professional)
Middleton Hall

WHITTLE, Peter
(Club Professional)
Wensum Valley
£10.00 - £12.00 for 30 minutes

YOUNG, Andrew
(Club Professional)
Costessey Park

NORTHAMPTONSHIRE

ARMSTRONG, P
(Club Professional)
Kingsthorpe

BAREHAM, Henry
(Club Professional)
Collingtree Park

BRADBROOK, Jeff
(Club Professional)
Corby Public

CARTER, Alan
(Club Professional)
Collingtree Park

CLIFFORD, David
(Club Professional)
Wellingborough
£15.00 for 60 minutes

CORBY, John
(Club Professional)
Delapre Park Golf Complex
£19.00 - £25.00 for 60 minutes

CUDDIHY, John
(Professional)
Delapre Park Golf Complex
£19.00 - £25.00 for 60 minutes

DICKENS, K
(Club Professional)
Northampton
£25.00 for 60 minutes

HUDSON, Richard
(Club Professional)
Brampton Heath
£10.00 - £15.00 for 30 minutes

LILLY, Simon
(Touring Professional)
Wellingborough
£15.00 for 60 minutes

MACHIN, Peter
(Club Professional)
Pytchley Golf Lodge

MUDGE, Richard
(Club Professional)
Staverton Park

POOK, Geoff
(Club Professional)
Collingtree Park

ROSE, Shane
(Club Professional)
Cold Ashby
£15.00 for 60 minutes

ROUSE, Tim
(Club Professional)
Northamptonshire County
£14.00 for 30 minutes

SAINSBURY, Carl
(Club Professional)
Brampton Heath

£10.00 - £15.00 for 30 minutes

NORTHUMBERLAND

BROWN, Andrew
(Club Professional)
Blyth

CRAWFORD, John
(Club Professional)
Prudhoe

CURRY, David
(Club Professional)
Linden Hall

FORSTER, Martin
(Club Professional)
Hexham

JACKSON, Martin
(Club Professional)
Morpeth

MATHER, D
(Club Professional)
Stocksfield
£24.00 for 60 minutes

MCNALLY, Steve
(Club Professional)
Burgham

ROBINSON, Gordon
(Head Teaching Professional)
Slaley Hall Golf Course
£15.00 for 30 minutes

TERRAS, Paul
(Club Professional)
Berwick
£12.00 for 30 minutes

WAUGH, Ian
(Club Professional)
Tynedale
£12.00 for 60 minutes

WEBB, M
(Club Professional)
Bedlingtonshire

NOTTINGHAMSHIRE

BARKER, Jasen
(Club Professional)
Mapperley

BETTERIDGE, Stuart
(Club Professional)
Kilton Forest

CLAY, J
(Professional)
Trent Lock
£12.00 for 30 minutes

DREW, Paul
(Club Professional)
Springwater

HALL, K
(Professional)
Sherwood Forest

HALL, Ken
(Club Professional)
Sherwood Forest

HERNON, Nick
(Club Professional)
Stanton On The Wolds
£13.00 for 30 minutes

HURT, B
(Professional)
Oakmere Park
£14.00 for 30 minutes

Norfolk — Nottinghamshire

Professionals by COUNTY in England

JACKSON, Simon
(Professional)
Trent Lock
£12.00 for 30 minutes

JOHNS, Steve
(Professional)
Ruddington Grange

KING, John R
(Club Professional)
Lindrick
£15.00 - £25.00 for 60 minutes

KNIGHT, A
(Professional)
Stanton On The Wolds
£13.00 for 30 minutes

LOCKLEY, P
(Club Professional)
Newark

LOWER, J
(Club Professional)
Wollaton Park
£15.00 - £20.00 for 45 minutes

MACEY, Robert
(Club Professional)
Ramsdale Park
£12.00 for 30 minutes

MEADE, S
(Club Professional)
Southwell
£12.00 - £14.00 for 30 minutes

MORRIS, C
(Club Professional)
Retford
£12.00 for 30 minutes

RAWLINGS, Lee
(Club Professional)
Bulwell Forest
£12.00 for 30 minutes

RIDLEY, David
(Club Professional)
Coxmoor

SIMPSON, Rob
(Club Professional)
Ruddington Grange

SMITH, Robert
(Club Professional)
Cotgrave Place
£25.00 for 60 minutes

SNELL, C
(Club Professional)
College Pines
£30.00 for 60 minutes

ST JOHN-JONES, D
(Club Professional)
Oakmere Park
£14.00 for 30 minutes

STAPLES, John
(Club Professional)
Edwalton Municipal
£18.00 for 60 minutes

TAYLOR, Mark
(Club Professional)
Trent Lock
£12.00 for 30 minutes

THOMAS, Alasdair
(Club Professional)
Notts
£12.00 for 60 minutes

THOMAS, Kirsty
(Club Professional)

Riverside

THOMPSON, James
(Professional)
Rufford Park Golf Ctre
£15.00 for 30 minutes

THORNTON, Paul
(Club Professional)
Norwood Park
£12.00 for 30 minutes

VAUGHAN, John
(Club Professional)
Rufford Park Golf Ctre
£15.00 for 30 minutes

WAKE, J
(Professional)
Wollaton Park
£15.00 - £20.00 for 45 minutes

WARDLE, Alan
(Club Professional)
Beeston Fields

WEATHERHEAD, Carl
(Club Professional)
Worksop
Details on application

WILSON, Paul
(Club Professional)
Chilwell Manor
£13.00 for 30 minutes

OXFORDSHIRE

BROWN, Alistair
(Club Professional)
Brailes

CRAIK, Derek
(Club Professional)
Frilford Heath
£24.00 - £28.00 for 60 minutes

DUNN, Jonathan
(Club Professional)
Badgemore Park

FINCHER, J
(Club Professional)
Lyneham
£12.00 for 30 minutes

GOODMAN, Julian
(Club Professional)
Waterstock

HOWELL, Mark
(Club Professional)
Henley

HOWETT, Richard
(Club Professional)
Hinksey Heights
£35.00 for 60 minutes

KINGSLEY PGA, Peter
(Club Professional)
Banbury Golf Ctre

KINGSTON, Joe
(Professional)
Cherwell Edge
£20.00 for 60 minutes

NOTLEY, Terry
(Club Professional)
Aspect Park

PARKER, Steve
(Club Professional)
Carswell
£36.00 for 60 minutes

PENNOCK, Tony
(Club Professional)

Rye Hill
£14.00 for 40 minutes

REFFIN, David
(Club Professional)
Huntercombe
£40.00 for 60 minutes

ROBBINS, Geoff
(PGA Professional)
Faringdon
£30.00 for 60 minutes

SCOTT, Daryl
(Professional)
Dog

SOUTER, Adam
(Club Professional)
Witney Lakes
£15.00 for 30 minutes

WALTERS, A
(Club Professional)
Hadden Hill
£16.00 for 30 minutes

WILLIAMS, Tony
(Club Professional)
Studley Wood
£30.00 for 60 minutes

RUTLAND

PENGELLY, John
(Club Professional)
Greetham Valley
£12.00 for 30 minutes

SHROPSHIRE

BATEMAN, Dan
(Club Professional)
Telford

CARPENTER, Scott
(Club Professional)
Mile End

DORAN, I
(Professional)
Meole Brace

DOVAN, Ian
(Club Professional)
Arscott

FLANNIGAN, J
(Club Professional)
Shifnal

HINTON, Paul
(Club Professional)
Bridgnorth
£20.00 for 60 minutes

HOUSDEN, Keith
(Club Professional)
Wrekin

JONES, Jon
(Touring Professional)
Cleobury Mortimer
£25.00 for 60 minutes

PAYNE, Martin
(Club Professional)
Cleobury Mortimer
£25.00 for 60 minutes

PRICE, Russell
(Club Professional)
Ludlow

RUSSELL, Stephen
(Club Professional)
Worfield

SEAL, Peter

(Club Professional)
Shrewbury
£20.00 for 40 minutes

SKELTON, David
(Club Professional)
Oswestry

STRANGE, Alan
(Club Professional)
Brow

TOWNSEND, James
(Club Professional)
Church Stretton

SOMERSET

BISHOP, Adrian
(Club Professional)
Wells

COOMBE, Graham
(Club Professional)
Isle Of Wedmore

CROWTHER SMITH, Mark
(Club Professional)
Burnham & Berrow

DRIVER, Duncan
(Club Professional)
Windwhistle
£10.00 for 30 minutes

ENGLAND, Andrew
(Club Professional)
Wheathill

ENGLAND, Andrew
(Club Professional)
Wincanton
£32.00 for 60 minutes

GARDNER, Russell
(Club Professional)
Oake Manor

GOYMER, John
(Club Professional)
Wheathill

HAYES, Andrew
(Club Professional)
Long Sutton
£20.00 for 60 minutes

HAYNES, David
(Club Professional)
Brean
£30.00 for 60 minutes

KEITCH, Martin
(Club Professional)
Taunton Vale

KITE, Geoff
(Club Professional)
Yeovil
£18.00 - £30.00 for 60 minutes

MAHER, Graham
(Professional)
Brean
£30.00 for 60 minutes

MILNE, G
(Professional)
Taunton & Pickeridge

READ, Ian
(Club Professional)
Minehead & West Somerset
£21.00 for 60 minutes

STEADMAN, Michael
(Club Professional)
Vivary Park
£25.00 for 60 minutes

WIXON, Nigel
(Club Professional)
Enmore Park
£20.00 for 60 minutes

SOMERSET (NORTH)

LABAND, Mike
(Club Professional)
Weston

STAFFORDSHIRE

ALCOCK, Wayne
(Club Professional)
Tamworth Municipal

ARNOLD, Simon
(Club Professional)
Wolstanton

BENSON, Ian
(Club Professional)
Leek

BROWN, Richard
(Club Professional)
Alsager

DUNK, David
(Club Professional)
Cannock Park
£12.00 for 30 minutes

GREEN, James
(Head Professional)
Chase

HADFIELD, Steve
(Club Professional)
Craythorne

HYDE, Neale
(Club Professional)
Westwood

JOHNSON, Bob
(Club Professional)
Brocton Hall
£10.50 for 30 minutes

MCCANDLESS, Adam
(Club Professional)
Uttoxeter
£19.00 for 60 minutes

ODELL, Richard
(Club Professional)
Branston
£27.50 for 60 minutes

O'HANLON, Richard
(Club Professional)
St. Thomas' Priory

RIMMER, Brian
(Club Professional)
Trentham Park

ROGERS, Ian
(Club Professional)
Barlaston

SHELDON, Lee
(Club Professional)
Branston
£27.50 for 60 minutes

STAFFORD, Gary
(Club Professional)
Burton On Trent

STANLEY, Chris
(PGA Professional)
Seedy Mill

STURE, Jacob
(Club Professional)
Branston

£27.50 for 60 minutes

SYMONDS, Paul
(Club Professional)
Newcastle-Under-Lyme

WILSON, Sandy
(Professional)
Trentham

SUFFOLK

ALAN, Brian
(Club Professional)
Southwold
£20.00 for 60 minutes

ALDRED, Chris
(Club Professional)
Flempton
£30.00 for 60 minutes

COOPER, Tim
(Professional)
Newton Green
£32.00 for 60 minutes

DOWLAND, Jamie
(Assistant Professional)
Suffolk Golf
£14.00 for 30 minutes

HALL, Stephen
(Club Professional)
Suffolk Golf
£14.00 for 30 minutes

HARRISON, Simon
(Club Professional)
Halesworth
£25.00 for 60 minutes

HAWKINS, Malcolm
(Club Professional)
Worlington & Newmarket (Royal)
£24.00 for 60 minutes

HUBERT, Adrian
(Club Professional)
Woodbridge

JACKSON, N
(Professional)
Cretingham
£24.00 for 60 minutes

JILLINGS, Mark
(Club Professional)
Bury St Edmunds

LUCAS, Alex
(Professional)
Fynn Valley
£30.00 for 60 minutes

MACPHERSON, Ian
(Club Professional)
Felixstowe Ferry
£30.00 for 60 minutes

MCNEIL, Nick
(Club Professional)
Rushmere

ROBERTSON, Stuart
(Club Professional)
Ufford Park

SPINK, Alistair
(Professional)
Hintlesham Hall

TAYLOR, Robert
(Club Professional)
Brettvale
£30.00 for 60 minutes

VINCE, Kelvin
(Club Professional)

Shropshire — Suffolk

Professionals by COUNTY in England

Fynn Valley
£30.00 for 60 minutes

🦢 **WHYMARK,** Stephen
(Club Professional)
Ipswich

🦢 **WILBY,** Paul
(Touring Professional)
Fynn Valley
£30.00 for 60 minutes

SURREY

🦢 **ANDREWS,** S
(Club Professional)
Wildwood Country Club
£16.00 for 30 minutes

🦢 **ARNOLD,** Janice
(Club Professional)
Rusper
£16.00 for 30 minutes

🦢 **BARBER,** Alan
(Club Professional)
Windlesham

🦢 **BEDWARD,** Neal
(Club Professional)
Horne Park
£15.00 for 30 minutes

🦢 **BENNETT,** Jeremy
(Club Professional)
Windlesham

🦢 **BEVERAGE,** M
(Professional)
Sandown Golf Ctre
£30.00 for 60 minutes

🦢 **BIANCO,** Carl
(Club Professional)
Woking

🦢 **BRENNAN,** A
(Professional)
Drift

🦢 **BREWER,** D
(Club Professional)
Pyrford Golf Club
£20.00 - £30.00 for 60 minutes

🦢 **BREWER,** Darren
(Club Professional)
Traditions Golf Course
£15.00 for 30 minutes

🦢 **BURKE,** Neil
(Club Professional)
Surrey Golf & Fitness
£15.00 for 60 minutes

🦢 **BURTON,** Maxine
(Club Professional)
Hurtmore
£18.00 for 30 minutes

🦢 **CARTER,** Adrian
(Club Professional)
Bowenhurst
£15.00 for 30 minutes

🦢 **CHRISTINE,** Jim
(Professional)
Worplesdon

🦢 **CHURCHILL,** Malcolm
(Club Professional)
Selsdon Park

🦢 **COOMBES,** Tim
(Club Professional)
Chobham

🦢 **COWLISHAW,** Grahame
(Club Professional)

Farnham
£35.00 for 60 minutes

🦢 **CREANTER,** Paul
(Club Professional)
Milford Golf Club
17.50 for 30 minutes

🦢 **DICKMAN,** Roger
(Club Professional)
Banstead Downs
£20.00 for 60 minutes

🦢 **DOWDELL,** Mark
(Club Professional)
Shillinglee Park

🦢 **EDGAR,** James
(Club Professional)
Redhill Golf Ctre
£14.00 for 30 minutes

🦢 **ELVIDGE,** VR
(Professional)
New Zealand

🦢 **FINNEY,** M
(Club Professional)
Ashford Manor

🦢 **FORSYTH,** C
(Club Professional)
Reigate Hill
£18.00 for 30 minutes

🦢 **GADD,** N
(Club Professional)
Moore Place
£20.00 for 45 minutes

🦢 **GOLDING,** Ian
(Club Professional)
Woodcote Park
£20.00 for 60 minutes

🦢 **GOOD,** A
(Club Professional)
Foxhills Golf
£15.00 - £25.00 for 30 minutes

🦢 **GOOD,** John
(Club Professional)
Addington Court Golf Club

🦢 **GOUDIE,** R
(Club Professional)
Epsom

🦢 **GRAHAM,** Scott
(Club Professional)
Farleigh Court

🦢 **GREASLEY,** L
(Club Professional)
Drift

🦢 **HARDAWAY,** Alistair
(Professional)
Sunbury

🦢 **HIRST,** Martin
(Head Professional)
Horton Park Golf
£15.00 for 30 minutes

🦢 **HOATSON,** S
(Club Professional)
Effingham
£20.00 for 30 minutes

🦢 **HOWARD,** Matt
(Professional)
Farnham
£35.00 for 60 minutes

🦢 **HUTTON,** R
(Club Professional)
Hersham Village
£35.00 for 60 minutes

🦢 **JANES,** M
(Club Professional)
Chessington
£17.00 for 60 minutes

🦢 **JOHNSON,** L
(Club Professional)
Burhill

🦢 **JONES,** R
(Club Professional)
Thames Ditton & Esher
£15.00 for 30 minutes

🦢 **LINTOTT,** Dean
(Professional)
Puttenham
£15.00 for 60 minutes

🦢 **LONGMUIR,** T
(Club Professional)
Cranleigh
£15.00 for 30 minutes

🦢 **MASTERTON,** Grant
(Professional)
Chiddingfold
£15.00 for 30 minutes

🦢 **MAXWELL,** Keith
(Professional)
Sunningdale

🦢 **MCCOLGAN,** Adrian
(Professional)
Traditions Golf Course
£15.00 for 30 minutes

🦢 **MCPHERSON,** Ken
(Club Professional)
Walton Heath

🦢 **MILTON,** K
(Club Professional)
Broadwater Park
£20.00 for 30 minutes

🦢 **MORLEY,** Chris
(Club Professional)
Lingfield Park

🦢 **MUCKLOW,** Lee
(Club Professional)
Windlesham

🦢 **MULRANEY,** Steve
(Club Professional)
Addington Court Golf Club

🦢 **MURTON,** G
(Club Professional)
Oak Park Golf Club
£15.00 for 30 minutes

🦢 **OGILVY,** N
(Club Professional)
Hindhead

🦢 **PEDDIE,** G
(Club Professional)
Bramley
£18.00 members and £25.00 non
members.

🦢 **PIKE,** Warren
(Club Professional)
Redhill & Reigate

🦢 **POWELL,** Tim
(Club Professional)
Hoebridge

🦢 **PUGH,** Denis
(Club Professional)
Wisley

🦢 **RALPH,** Glenn
(Club Professional)
Camberley Heath

REGAN, David
(Club Professional)
West Byfleet

RENNIE, David
(Professional)
Wentworth

SARGEANT, Rae
(Club Professional)
Gatton Manor

SEFTON, P
(Club Professional)
Pine Ridge Golf Ctre

SHERIDAN, F
(Club Professional)
Hazelwood Golf Ctre

SIMMONS, Gary
(Club Professional)
Puttenham
£15.00 for 60 minutes

SIMS, T
(Club Professional)
Kingswood
£17.50 for 30 minutes

SKIMMER, J
(Club Professional)
Sandown Golf Ctre
£30.00 for 60 minutes

STILLWELL, E
(Club Professional)
Croham Hurst
£27.00 for 60 minutes

STOTT, H
(Club Professional)
Laleham

STOW, Peter
(Professional)
Hankley Common

TALBOT, P
(Club Professional)
Mid-Surrey (Royal)

TAWSE, A
(Club Professional)
West Surrey

TEDDER, P
(Club Professional)
Sutton Green
£17.50 for 30 minutes

TERRELL, John
(Professional)
Horton Park Golf
£15.00 for 30 minutes

THOMAS, David
(Club Professional)
Windlermere

TOCHER, Andy
(Club Professional)
Betchworth Park

TORBETT, Gary
(Club Professional)
Chipstead

WALKER, Stuart
(Professional)
Horton Park Golf
£15.00 for 30 minutes

WALLIS, Gary
(Club Professional)
Chiddingfold
£15.00 for 30 minutes

WILLIAMS, Roger

(Club Professional)
Addington Palace

SUSSEX (EAST)

ANDREWS, James
(Club Professional)
Sedlescombe
£15.00 - £30.00 for 30 minutes

ANDREWS, M
(Club Professional)
Highwoods
£15.00 for 30 minutes

BONSALL, Phil
(Club Professional)
Brighton & Hove

CHARMAN, Paul
(Club Professional)
Dale Hill
£32.00 for 60 minutes

CHARMAN, Paul
(Club Professional)
Waterhall
£13.00 for 30 minutes

CONNELL, Chris
(Professional)
Mid Sussex
£15.00 for 30 minutes

COOK, D
(Club Professional)
West Hove

CREASEY, Sean
(Club Professional)
Battle
£14.00 for 30 minutes

DOBSON, Paul
(Club Professional)
Lewes

EDWARDS, David
(Club Professional)
Boars Head
£14.00 for 30 minutes

FINCH, Barrie
(Club Professional)
Eastbourne Golfing Park
£15.00 for 60 minutes

GODIN, Nick
(Club Professional)
Dewlands Manor

LANDSBOROUGH, Martyn
(Club Professional)
Ashdown Forest (Royal)
£18.00 for 30 minutes

LEE, Michael
(Professional)
Rye

LEWIS, Phil
(Club Professional)
Eastbourne Golfing Park
£15.00 for 60 minutes

MACLENNAN, Sarah
(PGA Professional)
East Sussex National
£50.00 for 60 minutes

MARSHALL, Terry
(Club Professional)
Eastbourne Downs

MARTIN, Simon
(Club Professional)
Benfield Valley

MILLS, David

(Club Professional)
Seaford
£30.00 for 60 minutes

MOORE, Troy
(Club Professional)
Willingdon
£12.00 for 40 minutes

NAYLOR, Iain
(Golf Professional)
East Sussex National
£50.00 for 60 minutes

NEWNHAM, D
(Club Professional)
Crowborough Beacon
£15.00 for 30 minutes

PEARSON, Ian
(Club Professional)
Peacehaven

PORTER, Ben
(Club Professional)
Eastbourne Golfing Park
£15.00 for 60 minutes

SIM, J
(Club Professional)
Cooden Beach
£15.00 for 30 minutes

STUART - WILLIAM, Mark
(Club Professional)
East Brighton

TYSON, Alan
(Assistant Professional)
Horam Park
£17.00 with Giles Velvick for 30 minutes and £15.00 with Alan Tyson for 30 minutes

VELVICK, Giles
(PGA Professional)
Horam Park
£17.00 with Giles Velvick for 30 minutes and £15.00 with Alan Tyson for 30 minutes

WOOD, Mark
(Professional)
Wellshurst
£15.00 for 60 minutes

SUSSEX (WEST)

BASSIL, Steve
(Club Professional)
Bognor Regis

BEECH, Richard
(Club Professional)
Avisford Park
£20.00 for 60 minutes

BLANSHARD, Simon
(Club Professional)
Hillbarn
£20 for 60 minutes

BLANSHARD, Simon
(Professional)
Brooklands Park

BUCKLEY, Simon
(Club Professional)
Ham Manor
£18.00 for 30 minutes

CALLAN, Callum
(Club Professional)
Cottesmore
£18.00 for 30 minutes

CLINGAN, Tony
(Club Professional)

Surrey — Sussex (West)

Professionals by **COUNTY** in England

Rookwood
£24.00 for 60 minutes

CLINGAN, Tony
(Club Professional)
Slinfold Park

COUSINS, Lorraine
(Professional)
Horsham Golf
£28.00 for 60 minutes

EARL, Jonathan
(Club Professional)
Ifield

FIRKINS, Bernard
(Professional)
Cuckfield

FIT, Alastair
(Professional)
Horsham Golf
£28.00 for 60 minutes

GREEN, M
(Club Professional)
Paxhill Park

GRINDLEY, Peter
(Club Professional)
Selsey
£24.00 for 60 minutes

HOBBS, David
(Club Professional)
Chartham Park
£22.00 for 60 minutes

LITTLE, John
(Club Professional)
Petworth
£20.00 for 60 minutes

MACDONALD, Keith
(Club Professional)
Goodwood
£30.00 for 60 minutes

MCQUITTY, Guy
(Club Professional)
Littlehampton Golf

PACKHAM, Tim
(Club Professional)
West Sussex
£20.00 for 30 minutes

ROLLEY, Steven
(Club Professional)
Worthing

SLINGER, John
(Professional)
Chichester
£12.50 for 60 minutes

STREET, Wallace
(Club Professional)
Singing Hills
£36.00 for 60 minutes

TRUSSELL, Sean
(Club Professional)
Tilgate Forest
£28.00 for 60 minutes

TUCKER, Clive
(Professional)
Mannings Heath

WILLIAMS, Ian
(Professional)
West Chiltington

TYNE AND WEAR

CARLAW, Philip
(Club Professional)
Boldon

MCKENNA, Steve
(Club Professional)
Newcastle

PATTERSON, David
(Club Professional)
George Washington

RICHARDSON, Sean
(Club Professional)
Boldon

ROBSON-CROSBY, Alan
(Club Professional)
Ponteland

WARWICKSHIRE

GILKS, Nicholas
(Professional)
Bramcote Waters
£14.00 for 30 minutes

HAYER, Karl
(Head Professional)
Welcombe Hotel

MELLOR, Julian
(Club Professional)
Leamington & County
£30.00 for 60 minutes

PECK, Danny
(Club Professional)
Warwickshire

PRICE, Darren
(Club Professional)
Whitefields

SALTER, Jonathan
(Club Professional)
Nuneaton

YATES, Steve
(Club Professional)
Kenilworth

WILTSHIRE

AMOR, Simon
(Professional)
Marlborough

BLAKE, Richard
(Club Professional)
Upavon
£20.00 - £32.00 for 60 minutes

BOLT, Ian
(Professional)
Cricklade

BUTLER, A
(Club Professional)
Kingsdown
£22.00 for 60 minutes

CAVE, J
(Club Professional)
Salisbury & South Wilts
£15.00 for 30 minutes

FLOYD, Matthew
(Professional)
Wrag Barn
£30.00 for 60 minutes

GOSDEN, Terry
(Club Professional)
Tidworth Garrison
£30.00 for 60 minutes

GRAY, Andy
(Club Professional)
Wiltshire

GREEN, Peter
(Club Professional)
Manor House

ISAACS, Tony
(Club Professional)
Thoulstone Park

KARROLL, D
(Club Professional)
Oaksey

LOUGHREY, Barry
(Club Professional)
Wrag Barn
£30.00 for 60 minutes

MCOMISH, S
(Professional)
Kingsdown
£22.00 for 60 minutes

MORTIMER, Richard
(Professional)
Upavon
£20.00 - £32.00 for 60 minutes

PEARS, C
(Club Professional)
Brinkworth

POCOCK, T
(Club Professional)
Shrivenham Park
£15.00 for 30 minutes

POCOCK, T
(Professional)
Shrivenham Park
£15.00 for 30 minutes

SANDRY, B
(Club Professional)
Broome Manor
£15.00 for 30 minutes

SAWYER, G
(Professional)
Bradford-on-Avon

TAYLOR, Max
(Head Professional)
Bowood

TESCHNER, G
(Professional)
Salisbury & South Wilts
£15.00 for 30 minutes

VALENTINE, T
(Professional)
Whitley
£12.00 for 30 minutes

WALTERS, Michael
(Club Professional)
Erlestoke Sands
£18.00 for 45 minutes

WELDING, I
(Club Professional)
High Post
£15.00 for 30 minutes

WHITE, Mark
(Club Professional)
Hamptworth
£15.00 for 60 minutes

WORCESTERSHIRE

CUNDY, Phil
(Club Professional)
Little Lakes
£25.00 for 60 minutes

DOWN, David
(Club Professional)
Redditch

£13.00 for 30 minutes

FREEMAN, Martyn
(Club Professional)
Broadway

GREY, William
(Golf Professional)
Bewdley Pines

HOARE, Angus
(Club Professional)
Wharton Park

KNOWLES, Chris
(Club Professional)
Sapey

LAING, M A
(Club Professional)
Little Lakes

LONG, Graeme
(Club Professional)
Bromsgrove
£16.50 for 30 minutes

MALONE, Declane
(Club Professional)
Abbey Hotel

PRICE, Simon
(Club Professional)
Wyre Forest
£12.50 for 30 minutes

STEWART, David
(Club Professional)
Pitcheroak
£12.00 for 30 minutes

WHITING, Adam
(Assistant Professional)
Little Lakes
£25.00 for 60 minutes

WOODWARD, Mark
(Club Professional)
Perdiswell Park Golf Course
£24.00 for 60 minutes

YORKSHIRE (EAST)

ASHBY, Alex
(Club Professional)
Beverley & East Riding

BININGTON, Paul
(Club Professional)
Hainsworth Park
£24.00 for 60 minutes

BUNDY, Nigel
(Club Professional)
Boothferry Park

CALUM, James
(Club Professional)
Cherry Burton
£25.00 for 60 minutes

FIELDSEND, Grahame
(Professional)
Hessle

HOWARTH, Anthony
(Club Professional)
Bridlington
£25.00 for 60 minutes

MACKINDER, Steve
(Club Professional)
Cave Castle

SMEE, Mike
(PGA Professional)
Ganstead Park

WRIGHT, Stretton

(Club Professional)
Hornsea

YORKSHIRE (NORTH)

BRADLEY, Phil
(Club Professional)
Forest Of Galtres

BROWN, G
(Club Professional)
Ganton

BURDETT, Steve
(Club Professional)
Heworth
£10.00 for 60 minutes

DELLER, S N
(Club Professional)
North Cliff

FOOTMAN, Steve
(Club Professional)
Scarthingwell
£25.00 for 60 minutes

HARRISON, Phil
(Club Professional)
Aldwark Manor
£20 for 60 minutes

HARRISON, Phil
(Touring Professional)
Aldwark Manor
£20 for 60 minutes

JOHNSON, Tony
(PGA Professional)
Bedale

MALLISON, Ben
(Professional)
Skipton

MARSHALL, Andy
(Professional)
Catterick

MASON, Tony
(Club Professional)
Whitby

MOORE, Mark
(Club Professional)
Rudding Park
£30.00 for 60 minutes

PADGETT, David
(Club Professional)
Pannal

PLATT, Geoff
(Professional)
Aldwark Manor
£20 for 60 minutes

ROBINSON, Peter
(Club Professional)
Skipton

SIMPSON, M
(Club Professional)
Spofforth
£10.00 for 60 minutes

SKINGLE, Tony
(Club Professional)
Scarborough South Cliff

THOMPSON, Graham
(Club Professional)
Cocksford
£22.50 for 60 minutes

TOWNHILL, Joe
(Club Professional)
Kilnwick Percy
£18.00 for 60 minutes

TOWNHILL, Joe
(Club Professional)
Oaks
£11.00 for 60 minutes

TURNER, Nick
(Professional)
Scarthingwell
£25.00 for 60 minutes

TYSON, Chris
(Club Professional)
Kirkbymoorside

YORKSHIRE (SOUTH)

AUDSLEY, Paul
(Club Professional)
Hickleton

BALL, Pete
(Professional)
Birley Wood

CARNALL, Andrew
(Professional)
Birley Wood

DRURY, J
(Club Professional)
Kingswood
£10.00 for 30 minutes

HORSMAN, Lewis
(Club Professional)
Hillsborough
£20.00 for 60 minutes

KIRK, Ian
(Club Professional)
Tankersley Park

LASZKOWICZ, Jason
(Club Professional)
Robin Hood

RIPLEY, Jason
(Club Professional)
Rother Valley Golf

SHAW, Steve
(Club Professional)
Doncaster Town Moor

TAYLOR, Nic
(Club Professional)
Sitwell

WOOLHOUSE, Robert
(Assistant Professional)
Hillsborough
£20.00 for 60 minutes

YORKSHIRE (WEST)

ALISON, Michael
(Club Professional)
Halifax

BARBER, Nigel
(Club Professional)
West Bradford

BOOTH, Simon
(Club Professional)
Horsforth

BOTTOMLEY, Ian
(Club Professional)
Fardew

BRADLEY, Mike
(Club Professional)
Keighley

CARMEN, Paul
(Club Professional)
Huddersfield
£30.00 for 60 minutes

Worcestershire — Yorkshire (West)

Professionals by **COUNTY** in **England**

Professionals by **COUNTY** in **England**   Yorkshire (West) — Yorkshire (West)

CHAPMAN, David
(Club Professional)
Outlane
£20.00 for 60 minutes

COBBETT, Alastair
(Club Professional)
Mid Yorkshire

COOKE, Paul
(Club Professional)
South Bradford

COVERLEY, Jamie
(Club Professional)
Crosland Heath

DAVIES, Paul
(Professional)
Meltham
£30.00 for 60 minutes

DAY, Gary
(Club Professional)
Manor
£23.40 for 60 minutes.

EVERETT, Paul
(Club Professional)
Crow Nest Park
£22.00 for 60 minutes

FINDLATER, Ken
(Professional)
Garforth

FIRTH, Ray
(Club Professional)
Bingley St Ives

GREEN, John
(Professional)
Alwoodley

GROMIT, Steven
(Club Professional)
Oulton Park
£18.00 for 60 minutes

HARVEY, Neil
(Club Professional)
Leeds Golf Ctre
£30.00 for 60 minutes

HAWORTH, Julian
(Club Professional)
Willow Valley
£12.50 for 60 minutes

HIGGINBOTTOM, Michael
(Club Professional)
Woodsome Hall
£40.00 for 60 minutes

HILLAS, Mick
(Club Professional)
Northcliffe

HIRST, Nigel
(Professional)
Dewsbury District

HOLLAND, R
(Professional)
Whitwood

HOLLAND, Roger
(Professional)
Pontefract

HOULGATE, F
(Professional)
Normanton

INGRAM, Andy
(Professional)
Otley
£12.00 for 60 minutes

KERSHAW, Robert
(Club Professional)
Lightcliffe

KRYZWICKI, Nick
(Club Professional)
Elland
£20.00 for 60 minutes

KRYZWICKI, Nick
(Club Professional)
Marsden

LEEMING, Nick
(Club Professional)
Longley Park

LEWIS, Michael
(Club Professional)
South Leeds

LOCKETT, Warren
(Club Professional)
Woodhall Hills

LONGSTER, Simon
(Club Professional)
Leeds

MASTERS, Richard
(Club Professional)
Baildon

O'BRIEN, Kieran
(Professional)
Willow Valley
£12.50 for 60 minutes

PAPE, James
(Club Professional)
Roundhay
£30.00 for 60 minutes

PARRY, Bob
(Professional)
Shipley
£13.50 for 60 minutes

PEARSON, Mark
(Club Professional)
Cookridge Hall Golf Club

STEAD, Nathan
(Professional)
Otley
£12.00 for 60 minutes

WATKINSON, Gary
(Club Professional)
Howley Hall
£20.00 for 60 minutes

WOOD, Peter
(Professional)
Bradley Hall

WRIGHT, Ian
(Club Professional)
Wakefield
£30.00 for 60 minutes

COUNTY CARLOW

BULGER, Jimmy
(Professional)
Mount Wolseley Hotel

GILBERT, Andrew
(Professional)
Carlow

COUNTY CLARE

O'CONNOR, Sean
(Club Professional)
Kilrush

SHAW, Brian
(Club Professional)
Doonbeg

COUNTY CORK

BRODERICK, Gee
(Club Professional)
Kinsale
£15.00 for 60 minutes

CONWAY, Sean
(Professional)
Mallow

DONOVAN, Morgan D
(Professional)
Harbour Point

HICKEY, Peter
(Professional)
Cork

LEHANE, Martin
(Club Professional)
Muskerry

MURPHY, Batt
(Club Professional)
Monkstown

NICHOLSON, Garry
(Club Professional)
Douglas
£20.00 for 60 minutes

RYAN, Michael
(Club Professional)
Frankfield

SUGRUE, John
(Professional)
Kinsale
£15.00 for 60 minutes

COUNTY DONEGAL

MCBRIARTY, S
(Club Professional)
North West

ROBINSON, David T
(Club Professional)
Bundoran

COUNTY DUBLIN

ALLAN, Michael
(Club Professional)
Leopardstown
£40.00 for 60 minutes

BAMFORD, Sue
(Club Professional)
Open
£15.00 for 60 minutes

BOSHELL, Brian
(Club Professional)
Hollystown Golf

CALLAN, Mark
(Club Professional)

Clontarf
£20.00 for 30 minutes

CROFTON, Andrew
(Club Professional)
Edmondstown

DUNCAN, Gary
(Club Professional)
Grange Castle

KINSELLA, D
(Club Professional)
Castle

MURPHY, Tom
(Professional)
Kilternan

MURRAY, John
(Club Professional)
Malahide
£30.00 for 60 minutes

NOBLE, Bill
(Professional)
Open
£15.00 for 60 minutes

O'CONNOR, Christy
(Club Professional)
Christy O'Connor

O'CONNOR, Peter
(Club Professional)
Christy O'Connor

O'DONNELL, Karl
(Club Professional)
Newlands

O'HARA, Brian
(Club Professional)
Rathfarnham

COUNTY GALWAY

O'NEILL, Hugh
(Club Professional)
Connemara
£15.00 for 30 minutes

COUNTY KERRY

BOWMAN, Jamie
(Club Professional)
Ring Of Kerry

COVENEY, Tom
(Professional)
Killarney

HIGGINS, Liam
(Professional)
Waterville House & Golf Links

O'CALLAGHAN, Brian
(Professional)
Ballybunion
By appointment. Contact for details.

O'CONNOR, Dermot
(Club Professional)
Ceann Sibéal

O'MEARA, Alan
(Pga Golf Professional)
Ross Golf
£15.00 for 30 minutes

COUNTY KILDARE

EGAN, Gerry
(Club Professional)
Castlewarden

JONES, Ernie
(Club Professional)
K Club

£35.00 for 30 minutes

O'HAGAN, Peter
(Club Professional)
Highfield
£30.00 for 60 minutes

COUNTY KILKENNY

MCDERMOT, Brendan
(Club Professional)
Mount Juliet
£50.00 for minutes

COUNTY LIMERICK

CASSIDY, Noel
(Club Professional)
Castletroy

CASSIDY, Noel
(Professional)
Rathbane
£30.00 for 60 minutes

HARRINGTON, Lee
(Club Professional)
Limerick

MOWBRAY, Ian
(Club Professional)
Abbeyfeale
£14.00 for 60 minutes

COUNTY LOUTH

CARROLL, David
(Club Professional)
Seapoint

MCGUIRK, Paddy
(Club Professional)
Louth (County)

COUNTY MEATH

WHISTON, Adam
(Professional)
Tara (Royal)

COUNTY MONAGHAN

CASSIDY, Maurice
(PGA Professional)
Nuremore Hotel

COUNTY ROSCOMMON

QUINN, Martin
(Professional)
Athlone

COUNTY SLIGO

ROBINSON, Jim
(Club Professional)
Sligo (County)

COUNTY TIPPERARY

FORAN, Dominic
(Club Professional)
Cashel Golf Range

MCBRIDE, James
(Club Professional)
Ballykisteen
£30.00 for 60 minutes. £15.00 for 30
minutes

COUNTY WATERFORD

DOOLEY, John
(Club Professional)
Faithlegg
£22.00 for 60 minutes

DOOLEY, John
(Touring Professional)

County Carlow — County Waterford

Professionals by COUNTY in Ireland

Faithlegg
£22.00 for 60 minutes

🌑 HAYES, David
(Club Professional)
Dungarvan
£15.00 for 30 minutes

🌑 KIELY, Derry
(Club Professional)
Dunmore East

🌑 KIELY, Derry
(Club Professional)
Tramore

COUNTY WEXFORD

🌑 YOUNG, Johnny
(Club Professional)
Rosslare

COUNTY WICKLOW

🌑 DALY, David
(Club Professional)
Wicklow

🌑 D'ARCY, Eamonn
(Touring Professional)
Druids Glen

🌑 DHOMMEE, Willy
(Professional)
Rathsallagh
£50.00 for 60 minutes

🌑 DUIGNAN, Peter
(Club Professional)
Charlesland

🌑 GERAGHTY, Patrick
(Touring Professional)
Boystown

🌑 JONES, Peter
(Club Professional)
Coollattin
£15.00 for 15 minutes

🌑 LUNNY, Gavin
(Touring Professional)
Rathsallagh
£50.00 for 60 minutes

🌑 MCDAID, Brendan
(Club Professional)
Rathsallagh
£50.00 for 60 minutes

🌑 MONAGHAN, Ciaran
(Club Professional)
Druids Glen

🌑 THOMPSON, Paul
(Club Professional)
Powerscourt
£25.00 for 30 minutes

COUNTY ANTRIM

CALDER, C
(Club Professional)
Down Royal Park
£10.00 for 30 minutes

COLLINS, Phil
(Club Professional)
Galgorm Castle
£15.00 for 30 minutes

FAREWEATHER, Gordon
(Club Professional)
Knock
£20.00 for 60 minutes

FARR, Colin
(Club Professional)
Whitehead
£15.00 for 30 minutes

GRAY, K
(Professional)
Gilnahirk

HAMILL, Stephen
(Club Professional)
Allen Park
£15.00 for 40 minutes.

HANILL, S
(Club Professional)
Lisburn
£12.00 for 30 minutes

HUTTON, Robert
(Club Professional)
Cliftonville
£14.00 for 30 minutes

KELLY, Maurice
(Professional)
Belvoir Park

LOUGHREY, Geoff
(Club Professional)
Mount Ober

MCBRIDE, Joseph
(Club Professional)
Temple Club

MCLAUGHLIN, Ian
(Club Professional)
Ballycastle
£10.00 for 30 minutes

MCNEILL, Gary
(Club Professional)
Portrush (Royal)

MERCER, Gary
(Professional)
Lisburn
£12.00 for 30 minutes

REVIE, Ken
(Club Professional)
Ballymena
£24.00 for 60 minutes

SKIELLEN, Ray
(Club Professional)
Greenacres Golf Ctre

WALKER, Bob
(Club Professional)
Cairndhu

WHITFORD, Richard
(Professional)
Knock
£20.00 for 60 minutes

COUNTY ARMAGH

STEVENSON, P
(Club Professional)
Portadown

STEVENSON, Paul
(Professional)
Tandragee
£12.00 for 60 minutes

COUNTY DOWN

DREW, Gordon
(Club Professional)
Donaghadee

FARRELL, Phillip
(Club Professional)
Ardglass
£30.00 for 60 minutes

GRAY, Paul
(Club Professional)
Holywood
£13.00 for 30 minutes

HANNA, Debbie
(Club Professional)
Blackwood Golf Ctre

LOUGHRAN, Thomas
(Club Professional)
Carnalea
£30.00 for 60 minutes

MCCRYSTAL, Paul
(Club Professional)
Scrabo
£12.00 for 30 minutes

MONEY, E
(Club Professional)
Ashfield

PEDEN, Jonathan
(Club Professional)
Kirkistown Castle

SHAW, Nigel
(Club Professional)
Warrenpoint
£25.00 for 60 minutes

WHITSON, Kevan
(Club Professional)
Down (Royal County)
£25.00 for 30 minutes.

COUNTY FERMANAGH

TRAINOR, Patrick
(Club Professional)
Ashwoods
£10.00 for 30 minutes

COUNTY LONDONDERRY

DOHERTY, Michael
(Club Professional)
Derry
£15.00 for 30 minutes

HUNTER, Alan
(Professional)
Portstewart

MCLAUGHLIN, Kieran
(Club Professional)
Foyle
£12.00 for 60 minutes

REVIE, Ken
(Club Professional)
Brown Trout

TEAGUE, V
(Professional)
Moyola Park

COUNTY TYRONE

CHAMBERS, Gary
(Professional)
Killymoon

MCGIRR, Kevin
(Club Professional)
Springhill
£6.00 for 60 minutes

ABERDEEN (CITY OF)

BRATTON, Ian
(Club Professional)
East Aberdeenshire
£16.00 for 30 minutes

COUTTS, Frank
(PGA Professional)
Deeside

DAVIDSON, B
(Professional)
Kings Links Golf Ctre

DAVIDSON, B
(Professional)
Northern

FORBES, Gary
(Club Professional)
Murcar

LAWRIE, Paul
(Touring Professional)
Meldrum House
£30.00 for 60 minutes

THOMPSON, Muriel
(Professional)
Portlethen

ABERDEENSHIRE

LEES, Mark
(Professional)
Inverurie
£30.00 for 60 minutes

LOVE, Hamish
(Club Professional)
Oldmeldrum

LOVIE, Patrick
(Club Professional)
Inchmarlo Golf Ctre
£15.00 for 30 minutes

MANN, David
(Professional)
Peterculter
£14.00 for a 40 minute lesson for adults and £8.00 for a 40 minute lesson for juniors.

NAYLOR, David
(Club Professional)
Banchory
£16.00 for 30 minutes

PENNET, John
(Professional)
Braemar

SMITH, Robin
(Club Professional)
Turriff

STRACHAN, Bob
(Club Professional)
Duff House Royal

VANNEL, Dean G
(Professional)
Peterculter
£14.00 for a 40 minute lesson for adults and £8.00 for a 40 minute lesson for juniors.

WRIGHT, Innes
(Club Professional)
Aboyne

YULE, Bill
(Club Professional)
Ballater

ANGUS

BOYD, Jason J
(Club Professional)
Montrose Links Trust

DALLAS, Karyn
(Club Professional)
Kirriemuir
£30.00 for 60 minutes

EWART, Linsey
(Club Professional)
Arbroath
£30.00 for 60 minutes

EWART, Linsey
(Professional)
Arbroath
£30.00 for 60 minutes

HANNA, Ian
(Club Professional)
Arbroath
£30.00 for 60 minutes

LOCHHEAD, Gary
(Professional)
Panmure

MACINTOSH, Nim
(Club Professional)
Panmure

MCLEOD, Ian
(Professional)
Monifieth Golf Links
£25.00 for 60 minutes

MCNIVEN, Peter
(Professional)
Forfar

RENNIE, Stephen
(Professional)
Brechin Golf & Squash Club
£14.00 for 60 minutes

WEBSTER, Alastair
(Club Professional)
Edzell

ARGYLL AND BUTE

CAMPBELL, Ken
(Club Professional)
Dunaverty

CAMPBELL, Ken
(Club Professional)
Machrihanish
£15.00 for 60 minutes

DOUGAL, Jim
(Club Professional)
Rothesay

FARRELL, Robert
(Club Professional)
Cardross
£10.00 - £15.00 for 30 minutes

FOTHERINGHAM, David
(Club Professional)
Helensburgh

WEIR, Russell
(Club Professional)
Cowal

AYRSHIRE (NORTH)

BOND, Peter
(Club Professional)
Ravenspark
£15.00 for 30 minutes

DOCHERTY, Kenneth
(Club Professional)

Largs

LEE, Hal
(Club Professional)
Millport
£12.00 for 30 minutes

MCCALLE, P
(Club Professional)
Brodick

MCQUEEN, Greg
(Club Professional)
Routenburn
£12.50 for 30 minutes

RODGERS, Bob
(Club Professional)
Auchenharvie
£12.00 for 30 minutes

RODGERS, Paul
(Touring Professional)
Auchenharvie
£12.00 for 30 minutes

ROSS, Graham
(Club Professional)
West Kilbride
£14.00 for 30 minutes

STEVEN, Jack
(Club Professional)
Glasgow Gailes

AYRSHIRE (SOUTH)

ANDERSON, R B
(Club Professional)
Troon (Royal)

CHEYNEY, Philip
(Club Professional)
Dalmilling
£14.50 for 40 minutes

FORBES, Steven
(Club Professional)
Brunston Castle
£15.00 for 30 minutes

GORDON, Richard
(Club Professional)
Belleisle & Seafield
£12.00 for 30 minutes

HOWIE, G
(Professional)
Kilmarnock

RENNIE, Frank
(Club Professional)
Prestwick

CLACKMANNANSHIRE

BENNETT, Bill
(Club Professional)
Alloa
£15.00 for 30 minutes

BOYCE, David
(Club Professional)
Braehead
£16.00 for 30 minutes

HERD, David
(Professional)
Alloa
£15.00 for 30 minutes

SALMONI, Keith
(Club Professional)
Muckhart

DUMFRIES AND GALLOWAY

DAVIDSON, J T
(Club Professional)

Thornhill
£20.00 for 60 minutes

DAVIDSON, Jim
(Club Professional)
Pines
£16.00 for 60 minutes

DICK, Gareth
(Club Professional)
Powfoot

FERGUSSON, Joe
(Club Professional)
Galloway

GEMMEL, Brian
(Club Professional)
Pines
£16.00 for 60 minutes

GRAY, Gordon
(Club Professional)
Park Tongland
£12.50 for 60 minutes

GRAY, Gordon
(Touring Professional)
Park Tongland
£12.50 for 60 minutes

SYME, Stuart
(Club Professional)
Dumfries & County

EDINBURGH (CITY OF)

COLGUHOUN, Neil
(Club Professional)
Merchants Of Edinburgh

FYVIE, Richard
(Club Professional)
Swanston

GRAHAM, Neal
(Head Professional)
Dalmahoy

MACKENZIE, Brian
(Club Professional)
Bruntsfield Golf Club
£15.00 for 60 minutes

MCGHEE, B
(Club Professional)
Craigmillar Park

MORRIS, Chris
(Professional)
Kingsknowe

MUNGALL, Kurt
(Club Professional)
Lothianburn

MURRAY, John
(Club Professional)
Turnhouse

FALKIRK

CHILLAS, J
(Professional)
Glenbervie

FIFE

BROOKES, Paul
(Club Professional)
Pitreavie
£12.00 for 60 minutes

CAIRA, Anthony
(Club Professional)
Kirkcaldy

CAMPBELL, Stuart
(Club Professional)

Scotscraig

CRAIG, Steven
(Professional)
Balbirnie Park
£30.00 for 60 minutes

DONNELLY, Craig
(Club Professional)
Balbirnie Park
£30.00 for 60 minutes

GEMMELL, David
(Club Professional)
Canmore
£15.00 for 40 minutes

GOLDIE, Martin
(Club Professional)
Lochgelly
£30.00 for 60 minutes

GRAY, Martin
(Club Professional)
Ladybank

HUTTON, Andy
(Club Professional)
Charleton
£25.00 for 60 minutes

LENNIE, Graeme
(Club Professional)
Crail

MCCALUM, Gordon
(Club Professional)
Aberdour

MCDOWALL, Graeme
(PGA Professional)
Elmwood

NUGENT, Chris
(Club Professional)
Dunfermline
£30.00 for 60 minutes

WALKER, Ron
(Club Professional)
Dukes
£30.00 for 30 minutes

WEBSTER, David
(Club Professional)
Lundin
£20.00 for 30 minutes

WHYTE, Gregor
(Club Professional)
Dunnikier
£30.00 for 60 minutes

GLASGOW (CITY OF)

BARNETT, Steve
(Club Professional)
Hayston

BRENNAN, Mark
(Club Professional)
Campsie

DARROCH, Iain
(Club Professional)
Eastwood

DUFFY, Chris
(Professional)
Windyhill

EVERETT, Craig
(Club Professional)
Esporta Dougalston

MARSHALL, Stewart
(Club Professional)
Williamwood

MCALISTER, J
(Professional)
Haggs Castle

MCCALLUM, Jim
(Club Professional)
Lenzie

MCWADE, K
(Professional)
Bonnyton

RUSSELL, Stuart
(Club Professional)
East Renfrewshire

SCOTT, David
(Club Professional)
Douglas Park

STEVELY, K
(Club Professional)
Cawder

STEVEN, Jack
(Club Professional)
Glasgow

TAGGART, Gary
(Club Professional)
Lethamhill

TAIT, Alan
(Professional)
Westerwood

WILLIAMSON, Duncan
(Club Professional)
Kirkhill
£9.00 for 30 minutes

HIGHLANDS

FYFE, R P
(Golf Professional)
Nairn

HENDERSON, R
(Club Professional)
Newtonmore

INGRAM, James
(Club Professional)
Boat Of Garten

PIGGOT, Martin
(Club Professional)
Loch Ness

SKINNER, Andrew
(Professional)
Dornoch (Royal)

STEWART, G
(Touring Professional)
Inverness
£20.00 for 60 minutes

THOMPSON, A P
(Club Professional)
Inverness
£20.00 for 60 minutes

THOMSON, David
(Professional)
Carnegie

URQUHART, M
(Touring Professional)
Inverness
£20.00 for 60 minutes

INVERCLYDE

CLARK, G
(Club Professional)
Gourock

Dumfries And Galloway — Inverclyde

Professionals by COUNTY in Scotland

LANARKSHIRE (NORTH)

KING, Graham
(Club Professional)
Easter Moffat

STRACHAN, John
(Professional)
Shotts

LANARKSHIRE (SOUTH)

RAE, Ian
(Professional)
Hollandbush

WHITE, Alan
(Club Professional)
Lanark
£30.00 for 60 minutes

LOTHIAN (EAST)

HUISH, David
(Club Professional)
North Berwick

HUME, Jimmy
(Club Professional)
Gullane

MONTGOMERY, Jacky
(Club Professional)
Dunbar

PHILLIPS, Kevin
(Professional)
Winterfield

SANDILANDS, John
(Club Professional)
Haddington
£12.00 for 30 minutes

SMALL, Derek
(Club Professional)
Castle Park
£20.00 for 60 minutes

WARDELL, Paul
(Club Professional)
Whitekirk
£14.00 for 60 minutes

LOTHIAN (MID)

JONES, Cliff
(Professional)
Glencorse

MANN, Frazer
(Club Professional)
Musselburgh

MURDOCH, Alan
(Professional)
Kings Acre
£40.00 for 60 minutes

LOTHIAN (WEST)

DUMBER, Brian
(Club Professional)
Deer Park

LEIGHTON, Malcolm
(Club Professional)
Greenburn
£20.00 for 60 minutes

MARSHALL, Andy
(Club Professional)
Bridgecastle
£25.00 for 60 minutes

ROSIE, Steven
(Club Professional)
Linlithgow

STRACHAN, S
(Club Professional)
Bathgate

TAYLOR, Ian
(Club Professional)
West Lothian

MORAY

AIRD, Sandy
(Club Professional)
Forres
£15.00 for 30 minutes

THOMSON, Alistair
(Club Professional)
Moray

PERTH AND KINROSS

BAKER, Gavin
(Professional)
Auchterarder

DERNIE, Charles
(Professional)
Blairgowrie

DOTT, Colin
(Professional)
Taymouth Castle

DOTT, Gavin
(PGA Professional)
Taymouth Castle

MUIR, Ian
(Club Professional)
Craigie Hill

MURCHIE, David
(Club Professional)
Crieff

REID, Alan
(Club Professional)
Lynedoch & Murrayshall

SMITH, Colin
(Club Professional)
Strathmore Golf Ctre
£30.00 for 60 minutes

SMITH, Sandy
(Professional)
Gleneagles

YOUNG, Brian
(Professional)
Strathmore Golf Ctre
£30.00 for 60 minutes

RENFREWSHIRE

BOSWELL, G
(Club Professional)
Gleddoch
£15.00 - £20.00 for 30 minutes

BOWMAN, R
(Club Professional)
Elderslie

CAMPBELL, K
(Club Professional)
Gleddoch
£15.00 - £20.00 for 30 minutes

GARRETT, S
(Professional)
Gleddoch
£15.00 - £20.00 for 30 minutes

LOGAN, Alan J
(Club Professional)
Cochrane Castle

MUNRO, C

(Club Professional)
Ralston
£14.00 for 30 minutes

REILLY, Gerry
(Club Professional)
Lochwinnoch

STEWART, Gordon
(Club Professional)
Paisley
£12.00 - £15.00 for 30 minutes

THOMPSON, P
(Professional)
Erskine

THOMPSON, Stephen
(Professional)
Renfrew

SCOTTISH BORDERS

IMLAH, Craig
(Club Professional)
Peebles

LOBBAN, Keith
(Club Professional)
Hirsel
£25.00 for 60 minutes

MALTMAN, Craig
(Touring Professional)
Eyemouth

MONTGOMERIE, Craig
(Club Professional)
Roxburghe

TERRAS, Paul
(Club Professional)
Eyemouth

WRIGHT, Ian
(Club Professional)
West Linton
£15.00 for 30 minutes

STIRLING

BAXTER, Keith
(Club Professional)
Buchanan Castle

BRIDGEND

WARNE, Leon
(Club Professional)
Grove
£16.00 for 60 minutes

CAERPHILLY

BEBB, Sion
(Club Professional)
Castell Heights

CARMARTHENSHIRE

EVANS, Neil
(Club Professional)
Glyn Abbey

GILLIS, Pat
(Club Professional)
Carmarthen
£10.00 for 30 minutes.

THOMAS, David
(Professional)
Carmarthen
£10.00 for 30 minutes.

CEREDIGION

DIAMOND, Paul
(Club Professional)
Penrhos
£12.00 for 30 minutes

LEWIS, John
(Club Professional)
Borth & Ynyslas
£10.00 for 30 minutes

MCCLOUD, Jim
(Club Professional)
Aberystwyth

PARSONS, Colin
(Club Professional)
Cardigan

PARSONS, Steve
(Club Professional)
Cwmrhydneuadd

CONWY

BRADBURY, R A
(Club Professional)
North Wales
£15.00 for 60 minutes

LEES, Peter
(Club Professional)
Conwy

MACARA, Mike
(Club Professional)
Rhos-On-Sea
£15.00 for 30 minutes

RUNCIE, Iain
(Club Professional)
Abergele

WILLIAMS, Mark
(Assistant Professional)
Rhos-On-Sea
£15.00 for 30 minutes

DENBIGHSHIRE

CARR, Andrew
(Club Professional)
Rhuddlan

COOPER, Wayne
(Assistant Professional)
Prestatyn
£18.00 for 60 minutes

ELLIS, Matthew
(Touring Professional)
Vale Of Llangollen

HUGHES, Richard
(Club Professional)
St. Melyd
£24.00 for 60 minutes

JONES, M
(Club Professional)
Ruthin-Pwllglas

JONES, Mike
(Club Professional)
Denbigh
£12.00 for 60 minutes

LEAH, Tim
(Club Professional)
Rhyl
£10.00 for 60 minutes

STATON, Malcolm
(Club Professional)
Prestatyn
£18.00 for 60 minutes

THORNE, David
(Club Professional)
Vale Of Llangollen

FLINTSHIRE

ASHTON, David
(Club Professional)
Padeswood & Buckley
£10.00 per day

DAVIES, Tony
(Club Professional)
Old Padeswood

JORDAN, Mark
(Club Professional)
Mold
£4.00

LEWIS, B
(Professional)
Northop
£15.00 for 60 minutes

NORWOOD, Alan
(Club Professional)
Kinsale
£30.00 for 60 minutes

PARSLEY, Matt
(Club Professional)
Holywell

PRITCHARD, M
(Club Professional)
Northop
£15.00 for 60 minutes

GLAMORGAN (VALE OF)

BIRCH, Stephen
(Club Professional)
Cottrell Park
£15.00 for 60 minutes

CLARK, D
(Club Professional)
Peterstone Lakes
£12.50 for 30 minutes

CLARK, Eddie
(Club Professional)
Whitchurch

HANSON, Terry
(Professional)
Cardiff

HARRIS, Jason
(Club Professional)
Wenvoe Castle

JOHNSON, Peter
(Club Professional)
Vale Of Glamorgan

JONES, A
(Professional)
Llanishen

PALMER, Alan
(Club Professional)
Aberdare

TAYLOR, Jestyn
(Club Professional)
St. Andrews Major
£10.00 for 30 minutes

GWYNEDD

BARNETT, Andrew
(Touring Professional)
Harlech
£30.00 for 60 minutes

BARNETT, John
(Club Professional)
Harlech
£30.00 for 60 minutes

DAVIES, John
(Professional)
Aberdovey

FROOM, J
(Club Professional)
Nefyn & District

HILL, Ainsley
(Professional)
Harlech
£30.00 for 60 minutes

JONES, A
(Club Professional)
Abersoch

OWEN, Aled
(Club Professional)
Caernarfon (Royal Town of)
£12.00 for 30 minutes

PILKINGTON, J
(Professional)
Pwllheli

ISLE OF ANGLESEY

BRUNT, Paul
(Club Professional)
Storws Wen
£25.00 for 60 minutes

BURNS, John
(Club Professional)
Bull Bay

ELLIOT, Steve
(Professional)
Holyhead

GADSBY, D
(Professional)
Prince's
£10.00 for 60 minutes

LOVELL, Paul
(Club Professional)
Anglesey

MATON, Peter
(Professional)
Prince's
£10.00 for 60 minutes

MONMOUTHSHIRE

ASHMEAD, Alan

Bridgend — Monmouthshire

Professionals by COUNTY in Wales

(Club Professional)
Wernddu
£20.00 for 60 minutes

🌑 CACE, Garath
(Club Professional)
Raglan Parc
£12.00 for 30 minutes

🌑 DAVIES, Michael
(Club Professional)
Alice Springs
£20.00 for 60 minutes

🌑 DUN, Craig
(Club Professional)
St. Pierre

🌑 EDWARDS, Brian
(Club Professional)
Monmouthshire

🌑 GIRLING, Brian
(Club Professional)
Monmouth
£10.00 for 60 minutes

🌑 HOWARD, James
(Club Professional)
Pontypool

🌑 PAGETT, Lee
(Club Professional)
Shirenewton
£30.00 for 60 minutes

🌑 PRITCHARD, A
(Club Professional)
Woodlake Park
£20.00 for 60 minutes

🌑 SKUSE, John
(Club Professional)
Dewstow
£30.00 for 60 minutes

🌑 SMITH, Wil
(Professional)
Alice Springs
£20.00 for 60 minutes

NEATH PORT TALBOT

🌑 BENNETT, E M
(Club Professional)
Neath

🌑 DAY, Mike
(Professional)
Swansea Bay Golf Shop

🌑 EVANS, Neil
(Club Professional)
Glynneath

🌑 WOOTTON, M
(Club Professional)
Lakeside
£12.00 for 30 minutes

NEWPORT

🌑 LYNCH, Jim
(Club Professional)
Caerleon

🌑 MORGAN, Merfyn
(Club Professional)
Tredegar Park
£20.00 for 60 minutes

🌑 PATIENCE, Scott
(Club Professional)
Celtic Manor
£35.00 for 60 minutes

🌑 PRICE, Stephen
(Club Professional)
Llanwern

PEMBROKESHIRE

🌑 HAWKEY, M
(Club Professional)
Tenby

🌑 LAIDLER, Steven
(Club Professional)
Trefloyne
£12.00 for 30 minutes

🌑 NOOTT, Julian
(Club Professional)
Newport
£15.00 for 45 minutes

🌑 PARSONS, S
(Club Professional)
Priskilly
£12.50 for 45 minutes

🌑 PILE, Alex
(Club Professional)
Haverfordwest
£10.00 for 60 minutes

🌑 VAUGHAN, Wesley
(Professional)
Haverfordwest
£10.00 for 60 minutes

POWYS

🌑 BARLOW, Bob
(Club Professional)
Welshpool

🌑 DAVIS, Richard
(Professional)
Cradoc

🌑 EDWARDS, Simon
(Club Professional)
Builth Wells
£15.00 for 30 minutes

🌑 OWEN, D P
(Club Professional)
St. Giles

RHONDDA CYNON TAFF

🌑 BEBB, Gareth
(Club Professional)
Rhondda

🌑 PHILLIPS, M D
(Club Professional)
Llantrisant & Pontyclun

🌑 WILLS, Marcus
(Club Professional)
Mountain Ash
£12.00 for 30 minutes

SWANSEA

🌑 BAVEN, Andrew
(Professional)
Pennard
£8.00 - £15.00 for 30 minutes

🌑 BENNETT, Mike
(Club Professional)
Pennard
£8.00 - £15.00 for 30 minutes

🌑 CLEWETT, J
(Club Professional)
Clyne
£10.00 for 30 minutes

🌑 EVANS, Mark
(Club Professional)
Langland Bay
£15.00 for 30 minutes

🌑 HUGHES, Gary
(Club Professional)

Fairwood Park

🌑 REES, Deryl
(Club Professional)
Morriston
£10.00 for 30 minutes

🌑 WILLIAMSON, A
(Club Professional)
Gower
£12.00 for 30 minutes

TORFAEN

🌑 STEBBINGS, Peter
(Club Professional)
Green Meadow
£20.00 for 60 minutes

WREXHAM

🌑 LARKIN, David
(Club Professional)
Clays Golf Ctre
£28.00 for 60 minutes

🌑 MADDISON, Mark
(Club Professional)
Chirk

🌑 WILLIAMS, Paul
(Club Professional)
Wrexham

Monmouthshire — Wrexham

Professionals by COUNTY in Wales

SECTION 12b

This section allows you to select golf professionals alphabetically, detailing the club they belong to.

e.g Skingle, Tony
Scarborough South Cliff

GolfWorld Directory

ABBOTT, P
Wensum Valley
Norfolk

ACCLETON, Frank
Castle Hawk
Lancashire

ADAMS, David
Hallowes
Derbyshire

ADAMS, M
Wallasey
Merseyside

ADAMS, Richard
South Winchester
Hampshire

ADWICK, Stewart
Padbrook Park
Devon

AINSWORTH, Andrew
Ashridge
Hertfordshire

AIRD, Sandy
Forres
Moray

ALAN, Brian
Southwold
Suffolk

ALCOCK, Wayne
Tamworth Municipal
Staffordshire

ALDRED, Chris
Flempton
Suffolk

ALISON, Michael
Halifax
Yorkshire (West)

ALLAN, Michael
Leopardstown
County Dublin

ALLEN, Mark
Eaton
Norfolk

ALLEN, Nick
Little Hay
Hertfordshire

ALLEN, Norman
Cotswold Hills
Gloucestershire

ALLISS, Gary
Trevose
Cornwall

AMIET, Scott
Teign Valley
Devon

AMOR, Simon
Marlborough
Wiltshire

ANDERSON, John
Little Aston
Midlands (West)

ANDERSON, P
Berkshire
Berkshire

ANDERSON, R B
Troon (Royal)
Ayrshire (South)

ANDREWS, Adrian
Bush Hill Park
London (Greater)

ANDREWS, James
Sedlescombe
Sussex (East)

ANDREWS, M
Highwoods
Sussex (East)

ANDREWS, S
Wildwood Country Club
Surrey

ANGEL, Mark
Colchester
Essex

ARMSTRONG, P
Kingsthorpe
Northamptonshire

ARNOLD, Janice
Rusper
Surrey

ARNOLD, Simon
Wolstanton
Staffordshire

ARNOTT, Henry
Chesfield Downs
Hertfordshire

ASHBY, Alex
Beverley & East Riding
Yorkshire (East)

ASHMEAD, Alan
Wernddu
Monmouthshire

ASHTON, David
Padeswood & Buckley
Flintshire

ATKINSON, Chris
Oldham
Manchester (Greater)

ATKINSON, Graham
Bushey Golf Course
Hertfordshire

ATKINSON, Tim
Widney Manor
Midlands (West)

ATKISS, Phil
Mossock Hall
Lancashire

AUDSLEY, Paul
Hickleton
Yorkshire (South)

AYRE, Andrew
Leasowe
Merseyside

BAGULEY, Andrew
Leigh
Cheshire

BAILLIE, David
Dulwich & Sydenham Hill
London (Greater)

BAKER, C
High Beech
Essex

BAKER, Gavin
Auchterarder
Perth And Kinross

BALFOUR, Martin
Donnington Valley
Berkshire

BALFOUR, Martin
Winchester (Royal)
Hampshire

BALL, Pete
Birley Wood
Yorkshire (South)

BALLARD, R
Forest Hills
Gloucestershire

BAMBOROUGH, Ian
Gog Magog
Cambridgeshire

BAMFORD, Sue
Open
County Dublin

BANTING, Jason
Portsmouth
Hampshire

BARBER, Alan
Windlesham
Surrey

BARBER, Nigel
West Bradford
Yorkshire (West)

BARBOUR, Derek
Princes
Kent

BAREHAM, Henry
Collingtree Park
Northamptonshire

BARHAM, P
Crondon Park
Essex

BARKER, Jasen
Mapperley
Nottinghamshire

BARKER, Stephen
Stevenage
Hertfordshire

BARLOW, Bob
Welshpool
Powys

BARNETT, Andrew
Harlech
Gwynedd

BARNETT, John
Harlech
Gwynedd

BARNETT, Steve
Hayston
Glasgow (City of)

BARR, Matthew
Gerrards Cross
Buckinghamshire

BARRINGTON, Paul
Kendleshire
Bristol

BARTER, Tim
Botley Park
Hampshire

BARTON, Mike
Tunbridge Wells
Kent

BASSIL, Steve
Bognor Regis
Sussex (West)

BATCHELOR, Larry
Southern Valley
Kent

BATEMAN, Dan
Telford
Shropshire

BATES, Jamie
Barkway Park
Hertfordshire

BAVEN, Andrew
Pennard
Swansea

BAXTER, Keith
Buchanan Castle
Stirling

BEAL, David
Mill Hill
London (Greater)

BEBB, Gareth
Rhondda
Rhondda Cynon Taff

BEBB, Sion
Castell Heights
Caerphilly

BEDWARD, Neal
Horne Park
Surrey

BEECH, Richard
Avisford Park
Sussex (West)

BEER, Nigel
Woodspring
Bristol

BENFLEET, Ben
Southampton Municipal
Hampshire

BENNETT, Bill
Alloa
Clackmannanshire

BENNETT, E M
Neath
Neath Port Talbot

BENNETT, Jeremy
Windlesham
Surrey

BENNETT, Mike
Pennard
Swansea

BENSON, Gareth
Westhoughton
Lancashire

BENSON, Ian
Blacknest
Hampshire

BENSON, Ian
Leek
Staffordshire

BERRY, Geoff
Bromborough
Merseyside

BERRY, P
Millers Barn Golf Park
Essex

BETTERIDGE, Stuart
Kilton Forest
Nottinghamshire

BEVERAGE, M
Sandown Golf Ctre
Surrey

BIANCO, Carl
Woking
Surrey

BICKNELL, Nigel
Truro
Cornwall

BININGTON, Paul
Hainsworth Park
Yorkshire (East)

BIRCH, Stephen
Cottrell Park
Glamorgan (Vale of)

BIRCHDNOUGH, Eddie
Lytham & St Annes (Royal)
Lancashire

BIRD, Willie
Chevin
Derbyshire

BISBURY, C
Brackenwood
Merseyside

BISHOP, Adrian
Wells
Somerset

BLACK, Andrew
Lyme Regis
Dorset

BLACKBURN, A
Hanover
Essex

BLACKBURN, J
Mendip Spring
Bristol

BLACKLOCK, Luther
Woburn
Buckinghamshire

BLAINEY, M
Billingbear Park
Berkshire

BLAKE, Richard
Upavon
Wiltshire

BLAND, Nevil
Hinckley
Leicestershire

BLANNIN, Ryan
Farrington
Bristol

BLANSHARD, Simon
Brooklands Park
Sussex (West)

BLANSHARD, Simon
Hillbarn
Sussex (West)

BLUNDELL, Allan
Louth
Lincolnshire

BLUNDELL, Phil
Mullion
Cornwall

BOARD, Ray
Chigwell
Essex

BOAST, Charlie
Tewkesbury Park
Gloucestershire

BOLAND, N
Shipton
Gloucestershire

BOLT, Ian
Cricklade
Wiltshire

BOLTON, R
Burnham Beeches
Berkshire

BOND, Keith
Abbey Hill
Buckinghamshire

BOND, Peter
Ravenspark
Ayrshire (North)

BONEHILL, David
Ashton
Lancashire

BONSALL, Phil
Brighton & Hove
Sussex (East)

BOOTH, Andrew
Knott End
Lancashire

BOOTH, Paul
Sleaford
Lincolnshire

BOOTH, Simon
Horsforth
Yorkshire (West)

BOSHELL, Brian
Hollystown Golf
County Dublin

BOSWELL, G
Gleddoch
Renfrewshire

BOTTOMLEY, Ian
Fardew
Yorkshire (West)

BOTTOMLEY, Ian
Fardew
Yorkshire (West)

BOTTRILL, S
Shirley
Midlands (West)

BOUNDY, Mark
Trethorne
Cornwall

BOWEN, Jason
Wokefield Park
Berkshire

BOWEN, Tony
Homelands
Kent

BOWMAN, Jamie
Ring Of Kerry
County Kerry

BOWMAN, R
Elderslie
Renfrewshire

BOWN, David
Richmond Park
London (Greater)

BOWNES, Andrew
North Warwickshire
Midlands (West)

BOWRING, Craig
Castle Hawk
Lancashire

BOWRING, Peter
Alderley Edge
Cheshire

BOYCE, David
Braehead
Clackmannanshire

BOYD, Jason J
Montrose Links Trust
Angus

BOYLE, Colin
Ashton-under-Lyne
Lancashire

BOYLE, Hugh
Wimbledon (Royal)
London (Greater)

BRADBROOK, Jeff
Corby Public
Northamptonshire

BRADBURY, R A
North Wales
Conwy

BRADBURY, Steven
Aldersey Green
Cheshire

BRADLEY, Mark
Ingol
Lancashire

BRADLEY, Mike
Keighley
Yorkshire (West)

BRADLEY, Phil
Forest Of Galtres
Yorkshire (North)

BRADSHAW, Alan
Bootle
Merseyside

BRAND, G M
Knowle
Bristol

BRANT, Jason
Castle Royle
Berkshire

BRATLEY, Neil
Wellow
Hampshire

BRATTON, Ian
East Aberdeenshire
Aberdeen (City of)

BRAZELL, Neil
Hindley Hall
Lancashire

BRENNAN, A
Drift
Surrey

BRENNAN, Mark
Campsie
Glasgow (City of)

BRETT, Gary
Eltham Warren
London (Greater)

BREWER, D
Pyrford Golf Club
Surrey

BREWER, Darren
Traditions Golf Course
Surrey

BREWER, Stewart
Elsham
Lincolnshire (North)

BRIGGS, Alastair
Test Valley
Hampshire

BRITZ, Tienie
Broome Park
Kent

BROADLEY, Gary
Mellor & Townscliffe
Cheshire

BRODERICK, Gee
Kinsale
County Cork

BROOK, Andrew S
Hunley Hall
Cleveland

BROOK, Chris
Parley
Dorset

BROOKES, David
Warren
Essex

BROOKES, Paul
Pitreavie
Fife

BROOKES, Phil
Grove
Herefordshire

BROOKS, Andrew
St. George's (Royal)
Kent

BROOKS, Mark
Kendleshire
Bristol

BROTHERTON, David
Shooters Hill
London (Greater)

BROTHERTON, John
Chestfield
Kent

BROWN, Alistair
Brailes
Oxfordshire

BROWN, Andrew
Blyth
Northumberland

BROWN, Derek
Furzeley
Hampshire

BROWN, G
Ganton
Yorkshire (North)

BROWN, Gary
Buxton & High Peak
Derbyshire

BROWN, Ian
Newent
Gloucestershire

BROWN, Paul
Alton
Hampshire

BROWN, Peter
Hampstead
London (Greater)

BROWN, Richard
Alsager
Staffordshire

BROWN, Robert
Tournerbury Golf Ctre
Hampshire

BROWN, Stewart
March
Cambridgeshire

BRUNT, Paul
Storws Wen
Isle of Anglesey

BRUNTON, D
Ringway
Cheshire

BRYAN, Stephen M
Bishops Stortford
Hertfordshire

BRYANT, Peter
Brent Valley Public
London (Greater)

BRYDEN, Phillip
Tournerbury Golf Ctre
Hampshire

BUCKLEY, Simon
Ham Manor
Sussex (West)

BUGG, D
West Park
Essex

Bottrill — Bugg

Professionals Alphabetically

BUGG, David
Mote Park Golf Hut
Kent

BULGER, Jimmy
Mount Wolseley Hotel
County Carlow

BUNDY, Nigel
Boothferry Park
Yorkshire (East)

BUNYAN, Terry
Chalgrave Manor
Bedfordshire

BURBIDGE, Richard
Blundells Hill
Merseyside

BURDETT, Steve
Heworth
Yorkshire (North)

BURGESS, Colin
Leyland
Lancashire

BURKE, Neil
Surrey Golf & Fitness
Surrey

BURKITT, Nigel
Waltham Windmill
Lincolnshire (North East)

BURNETT, Ian
Luffenham Heath
Lincolnshire

BURNS, John
Bull Bay
Isle of Anglesey

BURROWS, Graham
Boyce Hill
Essex

BURTON, Douglas
Mapledurham
Berkshire

BURTON, Maxine
Hurtmore
Surrey

BUSHELL, Paul
Stinchcombe Hill
Gloucestershire

BUTLER, A
Kingsdown
Wiltshire

BUTLER, David
Coombe Wood
London (Greater)

BUTLER, David
Western
Leicestershire

BUTLER, Dean
Davyhulme Park
Manchester (Greater)

BUTLER, Gary
Formby
Merseyside

BYRNE, Sean
Beedles Lake
Leicestershire

CACE, Garath
Raglan Parc
Monmouthshire

CADE, Reg
Ashbury
Devon

CAIRA, Anthony
Kirkcaldy
Fife

CALDER, C
Down Royal Park
County Antrim

CALLAN, Callum
Cottesmore
Sussex (West)

CALLAN, Mark
Clontarf
County Dublin

CALUM, James
Cherry Burton
Yorkshire (East)

CAMERON, A
Orchard
Gloucestershire

CAMERON, Rod
Meon Valley
Hampshire

CAMPBELL, Ian
Calcot Park
Berkshire

CAMPBELL, K
Gleddoch
Renfrewshire

CAMPBELL, Ken
Dunaverty
Argyll and Bute

CAMPBELL, Ken
Machrihanish
Argyll and Bute

CAMPBELL, Maurice
Leighton Buzzard
Bedfordshire

CAMPBELL, Stuart
Scotscraig
Fife

CANNON, S
Hedsor
Buckinghamshire

CARDY, Steven
Burnham-on-Crouch
Essex

CARLAW, Philip
Boldon
Tyne And Wear

CARMEN, Paul
Huddersfield
Yorkshire (West)

CARNALL, Andrew
Birley Wood
Yorkshire (South)

CARNALL, J
Barlborough Links
Derbyshire

CARPENTER, Scott
Mile End
Shropshire

CARR, Andrew
Rhuddlan
Denbighshire

CARROLL, David
Seapoint
County Louth

CARTER, Adrian
Bowenhurst
Surrey

CARTER, Alan
Collingtree Park
Northamptonshire

CARTER, Ashley
Lincoln
Lincolnshire

CASEY, Gary
Thorpe Wood
Cambridgeshire

CASSIDY, Maurice
Nuremore Hotel
County Monaghan

CASSIDY, Noel
Castletroy
County Limerick

CASSIDY, Noel
Rathbane
County Limerick

CAVE, J
Salisbury & South Wilts
Wiltshire

CHAMBERLAIN, Peter
South Kyme
Lincolnshire

CHAMBERS, Gary
Killymoon
County Tyrone

CHAPMAN, David
Outlane
Yorkshire (West)

CHAPMAN, Peter
Four Marks
Hampshire

CHARMAN, Paul
Dale Hill
Sussex (East)

CHARMAN, Paul
Waterhall
Sussex (East)

CHESTER, A M
Market Rasen & District
Lincolnshire

CHEYNEY, Philip
Dalmilling
Ayrshire (South)

CHILCOTT, Mark
London Beach
Kent

CHILD, Nigel
Cherry Lodge
Kent

CHILLAS, J
Glenbervie
Falkirk

CHOLTON, Darren
Tilsworth
Bedfordshire

CHRISTINE, Jim
Worplesdon
Surrey

CHURCHILL, Malcolm
Selsdon Park
Surrey

CLARK, D
Peterstone Lakes
Glamorgan (Vale of)

CLARK, Dave
Birstall
Leicestershire

CLARK, Eddie
Whitchurch
Glamorgan (Vale of)

CLARK, Finlay
North Worcestershire
Midlands (West)

CLARK, G
Gourock
Inverclyde

CLARK, Philip
Sherdons
Gloucestershire

CLARK, Sean
Royston
Hertfordshire

CLARKE, David
Shaw Hill
Lancashire

CLARKE, Martyn
Fakenham
Norfolk

CLAY, J
Trent Lock
Nottinghamshire

CLAY, Stephen
Blackmoor
Hampshire

CLAYTON, Richard
Loughton
Essex

CLEMONS, Michael
Cambridge Meridian
Cambridgeshire

CLEWETT, J
Clyne
Swansea

CLIFFORD, Adrian
Stoke Albany
Leicestershire

CLIFFORD, David
Wellingborough
Northamptonshire

CLINGAN, Colin
Windmill Hill
Buckinghamshire

CLINGAN, Tony
Rookwood
Sussex (West)

CLINGAN, Tony
Slinfold Park
Sussex (West)

COBBETT, Alastair
Mid Yorkshire
Yorkshire (West)

COCKER, Lee
Essex
Essex

COE, John
Humax
London (Greater)

COGLE, Eddie
South Beds
Bedfordshire

COLE, Chris
Beamish Park
County Durham

COLE, S
Hartswood
Essex

COLGUHOUN, Neil
Merchants Of Edinburgh
Edinburgh (City of)

COLLINS, Phil
Galgorm Castle
County Antrim

COLLINS, Tony
Hawkhurst
Kent

CONGDON, Damian
Dudsbury
Dorset

CONLEY, G
Army
Hampshire

CONNELL, Chris
Mid Sussex
Sussex (East)

CONNOLLY, Steve
Abbotsley
Cambridgeshire

CONNOR, Brian
Manchester
Manchester (Greater)

CONWAY, Sean
Mallow
County Cork

COOK, D
West Hove
Sussex (East)

COOKE, Paul
South Bradford
Yorkshire (West)

COOMBE, Graham
Isle Of Wedmore
Somerset

COOMBES, Tim
Chobham
Surrey

COOPE, Gary
Mytton Fold
Lancashire

COOPER, Tim
Newton Green
Suffolk

COOPER, Wayne
Prestatyn
Denbighshire

COPEMAN, G
Southport Old Links
Merseyside

COPSEY, David
Darenth Valley
Kent

CORBALLY, Steve
Durham City
County Durham

CORBY, John
Delapre Park Golf Complex
Northamptonshire

CORCORAN, Lee
Mollington Grange
Cheshire

CORLASS, Michael
Panshanger Golf Complex
Hertfordshire

CORNELIUS, John
North Shore
Lincolnshire

CORNISH, James
Ridge Golf Club
Kent

CORNWELL, Roger
Upchurch River Valley
Kent

COULSON, Marc
Stoneleigh Deer Park
Midlands (West)

COUSIN, Ceri
Worsley
Manchester (Greater)

COUSINS, Lorraine
Horsham Golf
Sussex (West)

COUTTS, Frank
Deeside
Aberdeen (City of)

COVENEY, Tom
Killarney
County Kerry

COVERLEY, Jamie
Crosland Heath
Yorkshire (West)

COWELL, Sean
South Moor
County Durham

COWGILL, Jon
Farrington
Bristol

COWIE, Cameron
Ashford
Kent

Chillas — Cowie

Professionals Alphabetically

COWLISHAW, Grahame
Farnham
Surrey

COXON, Tim
Mickleover
Derbyshire

CRAIG, Malcolm
Newton Abbot
Devon

CRAIG, Steven
Balbirnie Park
Fife

CRAIK, Derek
Frilford Heath
Oxfordshire

CRAWFORD, John
Prudhoe
Northumberland

CREANTER, Paul
Milford Golf Club
Surrey

CREASEY, Sean
Battle
Sussex (East)

CROFTON, Andrew
Edmondstown
County Dublin

CRONIN, Stewart
Hampshire
Hampshire

CROSS, Carl P
New Mills
Cheshire

CROWE, Murray
Castletown Golf Links
Isle of Man

CROWTHER SMITH, Mark
Burnham & Berrow
Somerset

CUDDIHY, John
Delapre Park Golf Complex
Northamptonshire

CULLEN, A J
Newquay
Cornwall

CULLEN, Andrew
Roserrow
Cornwall

CULLEN, David
Chapel-en-le-Frith
Derbyshire

CULMER, Glen
East Herts
Hertfordshire

CUNDY, Jamie
Edgbaston
Midlands (West)

CUNDY, Phil
Little Lakes
Worcestershire

CUPPELLO, Tony
Brookdale
Manchester (Greater)

CURRIE, Alisdair
Brampton Park
Cambridgeshire

CURRIE, Scott
Boysnope Park
Manchester (Greater)

CURRY, Andrew
Hobbs Cross
Essex

CURRY, David
Linden Hall
Northumberland

CURTIS, Neil
Kirby Muxloe
Leicestershire

CURTIS, Robert
Dereham
Norfolk

DALLAS, Karyn
Kirriemuir
Angus

DALY, David
Wicklow
County Wicklow

DANCE, Mark
Stand
Manchester (Greater)

DANCE, Richard J
Bloxwich
Midlands (West)

DANCHIN, Stuart
Dean Wood
Lancashire

D'ARCY, Eamonn
Druids Glen
County Wicklow

DARROCH, Iain
Eastwood
Glasgow (City of)

DARROCH, James
Rutland County
Lincolnshire

DAVIDSON, B
Kings Links Golf Ctre
Aberdeen (City of)

DAVIDSON, B
Northern
Aberdeen (City of)

DAVIDSON, J T
Thornhill
Dumfries And Galloway

DAVIDSON, Jim
Pines
Dumfries And Galloway

DAVIES, Glenn
Burghley Park
Lincolnshire

DAVIES, John
Aberdovey
Gwynedd

DAVIES, Jon
Woburn
Buckinghamshire

DAVIES, Mark
Ilfracombe
Devon

DAVIES, Michael
Alice Springs
Monmouthshire

DAVIES, Paul
Meltham
Yorkshire (West)

DAVIES, Rob
Mentmore
Bedfordshire

DAVIES, Tony
Old Padeswood
Flintshire

DAVIS, Philip
Saffron Walden
Essex

DAWSON, Peter
South Winchester
Hampshire

DAY, Gary
Manor
Yorkshire (West)

DAY, Mike
Swansea Bay Golf Shop
Neath Port Talbot

DE BRUIN, Chris
Tylney Park
Hampshire

DEAL, Matt
Hendon
London (Greater)

DEFOY, C
Coombe Hill
London (Greater)

DELLER, S N
North Cliff
Yorkshire (North)

DENHAM, John
Beckenham Place Park
Kent

DENNIS, Paul
Dunham Forest
Cheshire

DERNIE, Charles
Blairgowrie
Perth And Kinross

DEWHURST, Stephen
Mobberley
Cheshire

DHOMMEE, Willy
Rathsallagh
County Wicklow

DIAMOND, Paul
Penrhos
Ceredigion

DICK, Gareth
Powfoot
Dumfries And Galloway

DICKENS, K
Northampton
Northamptonshire

Cowlishaw — Dickens

Professionals Alphabetically

DICKENSON, Paul
Houghwood
Merseyside

DICKMAN, Roger
Banstead Downs
Surrey

DICKS, Wendy
Regiment
Essex

DICKSEE, Simon
Barnham Broom
Norfolk

DILLEY, Craig
Darlington
County Durham

DISBURY, Colin
Arrowe Park
Merseyside

DISNEY, Stuart
Torquay
Devon

DIXON, Geraint
Lyshott Heath
Bedfordshire

DOBBINS, Alan
Rickmansworth
Hertfordshire

DOBSON, Paul
Lewes
Sussex (East)

DOCHERTY, Kenneth
Largs
Ayrshire (North)

DODD, Mike
Ferndown Forest
Dorset

DODDS, James
Hunstanton
Norfolk

DOHERTY, Michael
Derry
County Londonderry

DONALDSON, Craig
Cleveland
Cleveland

DONE, Ryan
Heysham
Lancashire

DONNELLY, Craig
Balbirnie Park
Fife

DONOGHUE, John
Hesketh
Merseyside

DONOVAN, Morgan D
Harbour Point
County Cork

DOOLEY, John
Faithlegg
County Waterford

DOOLEY, John
Faithlegg
County Waterford

DORAN, I
Meole Brace
Shropshire

DORDOY, S
Herne Bay
Kent

DOTT, Colin
Taymouth Castle
Perth And Kinross

DOTT, Gavin
Hallowes
Derbyshire

DOTT, Gavin
Taymouth Castle
Perth And Kinross

DOUGAL, Jim
Rothesay
Argyll and Bute

DOUGAN, Steven
Dartmouth
Devon

DOVAN, Ian
Arscott
Shropshire

DOWDELL, Mark
Shillinglee Park
Surrey

DOWE, Angus
Stoke Rochford
Lincolnshire

DOWLAND, Jamie
Suffolk Golf
Suffolk

DOWN, David
Redditch
Worcestershire

DREW, Gordon
Donaghadee
County Down

DREW, Paul
Springwater
Nottinghamshire

DRIVER, Duncan
Windwhistle
Somerset

DRURY, J
Kingswood
Yorkshire (South)

DUFFIN, Andrew
Clacton
Essex

DUFFY, Chris
Windyhill
Glasgow (City of)

DUFFY, Scot
Aintree
Merseyside

DUIGNAN, Peter
Charlesland
County Wicklow

DUMBER, Brian
Deer Park
Lothian (West)

DUMBRECK, James
Tehidy
Cornwall

DUN, Craig
St. Pierre
Monmouthshire

DUNCAN, Andrew
Bolton
Lancashire

DUNCAN, Gary
Grange Castle
County Dublin

DUNGATE, Trevor
Boughton
Kent

DUNK, David
Cannock Park
Staffordshire

DUNN, Philip
Hallowes
Derbyshire

DUNROE, Neil
Eaton
Cheshire

DYSON, Andrew
Mount Murray
Isle of Man

EADY, P
Epping Forest
Essex

EARL, Jonathan
Ifield
Sussex (West)

EDGAR, James
Redhill Golf Ctre
Surrey

EDGE, Gary
West Lancashire
Merseyside

EDWARDS, Brian
Monmouthshire
Monmouthshire

EDWARDS, David
Boars Head
Sussex (East)

EDWARDS, David
Forest Pines
Lincolnshire (North)

EDWARDS, Paul
Austin Lodge
Kent

EDWARDS, Scott
Wickham Park
Hampshire

EDWARDS, Simon
Builth Wells
Powys

EGAN, Gerry
Castlewarden
County Kildare

ELLIOT, Campbell
Woodhall Spa
Lincolnshire

Dickenson — Elliot

Professionals Alphabetically

ELLIOT, Steve
Holyhead
Isle of Anglesey

ELLIS, Brent
Shirehampton Park
Bristol

ELLIS, Matthew
Vale Of Llangollen
Denbighshire

ELLIS, Nick
Naunton Downs
Gloucestershire

ELVIDGE, VR
New Zealand
Surrey

EMERSON, Gary
Broadstone
Dorset

ENGELMAN, Adrienne
Cambridge
Cambridgeshire

ENGLAND, Andrew
Wheathill
Somerset

ENGLAND, Andrew
Wincanton
Somerset

ESCLAPEZ, Jon
Hurlston
Lancashire

EVANS, Gary
Mill Ride
Berkshire

EVANS, Mark
Langland Bay
Swansea

EVANS, Neil
Glyn Abbey
Carmarthenshire

EVANS, Neil
Glynneath
Neath Port Talbot

EVERARD, Paul
Canterbury
Kent

EVERETT, Craig
Esporta Dougalston
Glasgow (City of)

EVERETT, Darren
Portmore Golf Park
Devon

EVERETT, Paul
Crow Nest Park
Yorkshire (West)

EWART, Linsey
Arbroath
Angus

EWART, Linsey
Arbroath
Angus

EYRE, Peter
Mere
Cheshire

FAIRWEATHER, Colin
Benton Hall
Essex

FANNON, Andrew
Dummer
Hampshire

FAREWEATHER, Gordon
Knock
County Antrim

FARMER, Lawrence
Moor Park
Hertfordshire

FARR, Colin
Whitehead
County Antrim

FARRANCE, Paul
Antrobus
Cheshire

FARRELL, Phillip
Ardglass
County Down

FARRELL, Robert
Cardross
Argyll and Bute

FARROW, William
Hennerton
Berkshire

FENWICK, Andrew
Leicester
Leicestershire

FERGUSSON, Joe
Galloway
Dumfries And Galloway

FERNLEY, Jane
Chesfield Downs
Hertfordshire

FERRIDAY, Andrew
Leominster
Herefordshire

FEW, Michael
Weston Park
Norfolk

FICKLING, Lee
Enfield
London (Greater)

FIDLER, Roger
West Kent
Kent

FIELD, Peter
Swaffham
Norfolk

FIELDSEND, Grahame
Hessle
Yorkshire (East)

FINCH, Barrie
Eastbourne Golfing Park
Sussex (East)

FINCH, Howard
Crediton
Devon

FINCHER, J
Lyneham
Oxfordshire

FINDLATER, Ken
Garforth
Yorkshire (West)

FINNEY, M
Ashford Manor
Surrey

FIRKINS, Bernard
Cuckfield
Sussex (West)

FIRTH, Ray
Bingley St Ives
Yorkshire (West)

FIT, Alastair
Horsham Golf
Sussex (West)

FITCHIE, Leigh
Rochester & Cobham
Kent

FITTON, Dennis
Thorpe Wood
Cambridgeshire

FITZPATRICK, Dominic
Glen Gorse
Leicestershire

FITZSIMMONS, Daniel
Harpenden Common
Hertfordshire

FLANNIGAN, J
Shifnal
Shropshire

FLETCHER, Bill
Southport Municipal
Merseyside

FLETCHER, David
Chester-Le-Street
County Durham

FLETCHER, Simon
Morecambe
Lancashire

FLOYD, Matthew
Wrag Barn
Wiltshire

FLYNN, Patrick
Woburn
Buckinghamshire

FOOTMAN, Steve
Scarthingwell
Yorkshire (North)

FORAN, Dominic
Cashel Golf Range
County Tipperary

FORBES, Gary
Murcar
Aberdeen (City of)

FORBES, Steven
Brunston Castle
Ayrshire (South)

FORSTER, Martin
Hexham
Northumberland

FORSYTH, C
Reigate Hill
Surrey

Elliot — Forsyth

Professionals Alphabetically

FOSTON, Paul
Cobtree Manor Park
Kent

FOTHERINGHAM, David
Helensburgh
Argyll and Bute

FOTHERINGHAM, Scott
Reading
Berkshire

FOX, Richard
Deangate Ridge
Kent

FRANKLIN, A
Runcorn
Cheshire

FREEMAN, Bob
Reddish Vale
Cheshire

FREEMAN, Martyn
Broadway
Worcestershire

FRENCH, Danny
Chart Hills
Kent

FROOM, J
Nefyn & District
Gwynedd

FUREY, Ged
Pleasington
Lancashire

FUTTER, Dean
Norwich (Royal)
Norfolk

FYFE, R P
Nairn
Highlands

FYVIE, Richard
Swanston
Edinburgh (City of)

GADD, N
Moore Place
Surrey

GADD, Ray
Hayling
Hampshire

GADSBY, D
Prince's
Isle of Anglesey

GALLAGHER, Mike
Peterborough Milton
Cambridgeshire

GARDNER, Peter
Upton-By-Chester
Cheshire

GARDNER, Russell
Oake Manor
Somerset

GARGARO, James
Rochester & Cobham
Kent

GARRATT, Peter
Cirencester
Gloucestershire

GARRETT, S
Gleddoch
Renfrewshire

GATHERCOLE, James
Essex
Essex

GEALY, Andy
Kington
Herefordshire

GEALY, Andy
Summerhill
Herefordshire

GEARY, Steve
Maidenhead
Berkshire

GEMMEL, Brian
Pines
Dumfries And Galloway

GEMMELL, David
Canmore
Fife

GEORGE, Andrew
Ely City
Cambridgeshire

GEORGE, Freddy
North Middlesex
London (Greater)

GERAGHTY, Patrick
Boystown
County Wicklow

GERKEN, Richard
Lee Valley
London

GIANNANDREA, Raphael
Cray Valley
Kent

GIBBINS, Peter
Chartridge Park
Buckinghamshire

GIBBONS, Alan
Caldy
Merseyside

GILBERT, Andrew
Carlow
County Carlow

GILKS, Nicholas
Bramcote Waters
Warwickshire

GILL, Chris
Crediton
Devon

GILLESPY, Ken
Parley
Dorset

GILLICK, Chris
Gloucester
Gloucestershire

GILLIS, Pat
Carmarthen
Carmarthenshire

GIRLING, Brian
Monmouth
Monmouthshire

GIVENS, Ralph
Stressholme
County Durham

GLEDHILL, Chris
Brandon Wood Municipal
Midlands (West)

GLEESON, David
Porter's Park
Hertfordshire

GLENN, Danny
Epping
Essex

GOBLE, Guy
Aylesbury Vale
Bedfordshire

GODDARD, Chris
Romford
Essex

GODIN, Nick
Dewlands Manor
Sussex (East)

GODLEMAN, Ian
Datchet
Berkshire

GOLDIE, Martin
Lochgelly
Fife

GOLDING, Ian
Woodcote Park
Surrey

GOOD, A
Foxhills Golf
Surrey

GOOD, John
Addington Court Golf Club
Surrey

GOODMAN, Julian
Waterstock
Oxfordshire

GORDON, Richard
Belleisle & Seafield
Ayrshire (South)

GOSDEN, Terry
Tidworth Garrison
Wiltshire

GOSLING, David
Cotswold Edge
Gloucestershire

GOUDIE, R
Epsom
Surrey

GOULD, Craig
Blackley
Manchester (Greater)

GOULD, Steve
Fingle Glen
Devon

GOULDS, Steven
Portmore Golf Park
Devon

GOYMER, John
Wheathill
Somerset

GRAHAM, J
Silloth
Cumbria

GRAHAM, Neal
Dalmahoy
Edinburgh (City of)

GRAHAM, Scott
Farleigh Court
Surrey

GRAY, Andy
Wiltshire
Wiltshire

GRAY, Gordon
Park Tongland
Dumfries And Galloway

GRAY, Gordon
Park Tongland
Dumfries And Galloway

GRAY, K
Gilnahirk
County Antrim

GRAY, Martin
Ladybank
Fife

GRAY, Paul
Holywood
County Down

GREASLEY, L
Drift
Surrey

GREEN, James
Chase
Staffordshire

GREEN, John
Alwoodley
Yorkshire (West)

GREEN, M
Paxhill Park
Sussex (West)

GREEN, Matthew
Whipsnade Park
Hertfordshire

GREEN, Peter
Manor House
Wiltshire

GREEN, Phil
Three Rivers
Essex

GREEN, Robert
Nazeing
Essex

GREENBANK, A
Preston
Lancashire

GREENOUGH, Mike
Ashton & Lea
Lancashire

GREGORY, John
Dartford
Kent

GREY, Andy
Forest Of Dean
Gloucestershire

GREY, William
Bewdley Pines
Worcestershire

GRICE, Phil
Lexden
Essex

GRIER, Rob
Stonebridge
Midlands (West)

GRIFFIN, Martin
Moseley
Midlands (West)

GRINDLEY, Peter
Selsey
Sussex (West)

GROAT, Jason
Warley Park
Essex

GROMIT, Steven
Oulton Park
Yorkshire (West)

GRUBB, Tony
Rodway Hill
Gloucestershire

HACKER, Danny
Wokefield Park
Berkshire

HADDON, F
Lilley Brook
Gloucestershire

HADFIELD, Steve
Craythorne
Staffordshire

HADLAND, Jason
Goring and Streatley
Berkshire

HALL, Alan
Priors
Essex

HALL, Alan
Stapleford Abbotts Golf Club
Essex

HALL, Andrew
Sand Martins
Berkshire

HALL, K
Sherwood Forest
Nottinghamshire

HALL, Ken
Sherwood Forest
Nottinghamshire

HALL, Stephen
Suffolk Golf
Suffolk

HALLAM, Neville
Shirland
Derbyshire

HAMILL, Stephen
Allen Park
County Antrim

HAMMOND, Peter
Shanklin & Sandown
Isle of Wight

HANILL, S
Lisburn
County Antrim

HANLON, Fred
Pedham Place Golf Ctre
Kent

HANNA, Debbie
Blackwood Golf Ctre
County Down

HANNA, Ian
Arbroath
Angus

HANSON, Terry
Cardiff
Glamorgan (Vale of)

HARDAWAY, Alistair
Sunbury
Surrey

HARDING, Nick
Immingham
Lincolnshire (North East)

HARLING, William
Accrington & District
Lancashire

HARRINGTON, Lee
Limerick
County Limerick

HARRIS, Andrew
Roundwood Hall
Kent

HARRIS, Danny
New Forest
Hampshire

HARRIS, David
Newbury & Crookham
Berkshire

HARRIS, Jason
Wenvoe Castle
Glamorgan (Vale of)

HARRISON, Phil
Aldwark Manor
Yorkshire (North)

HARRISON, Phil
Aldwark Manor
Yorkshire (North)

HARRISON, Simon
Halesworth
Suffolk

HARRISON, Steve
Eden
Cumbria

HART, David
Lambourne Club
Berkshire

HART, Mike
Long Ashton
Bristol

HARTLEY, Alan
Roseberry Grange
County Durham

HARVEY, A
Robin Hood
Midlands (West)

HARVEY, Neil
Leeds Golf Ctre
Yorkshire (West)

HASTINGS, D
Kingsway
Hertfordshire

HASTINGS, Tim
West Lancashire
Merseyside

HAWKEY, M
Tenby
Pembrokeshire

HAWKINS, David
Wanstead
London (Greater)

HAWKINS, Malcolm
Worlington & Newmarket (Royal)
Suffolk

HAWORTH, Julian
Willow Valley
Yorkshire (West)

HAWTON, Michael
Tiverton
Devon

HAYER, Karl
Welcombe Hotel
Warwickshire

HAYES, Andrew
Long Sutton
Somerset

HAYES, David
Dungarvan
County Waterford

HAYES, Jerry
Sutton Coldfield
Midlands (West)

HAYES, Jerry
Sutton Coldfield Ladies
Midlands (West)

HAYNES, David
Brean
Somerset

HAYWOOD, Simon
Westridge
Isle of Wight

HEALY, Terry
Great Salterns
Hampshire

HECTOR, W
Seaton Carew
Cleveland

HEGGARTY, John
Liverpool (Royal)
Merseyside

HEGGIE, Martin
Carlisle
Cumbria

HEMMINGS, Stuart
Ingol
Lancashire

HEMSLEY, Alan
Richmond Park
Norfolk

HENBERY, Malcolm
Dukes Meadow
London (Greater)

HENDERSON, Nigel
Entry Hill
Bath & Somerset (North East)

HENDERSON, R
Newtonmore
Highlands

HENNERSY, Justin
Hurst
Berkshire

HENRY, Kieron Stevenson
Old Thorns
Hampshire

HERBETT, Mike
Fulford Heath
Midlands (West)

HERD, David
Alloa
Clackmannanshire

HERNON, Nick
Stanton On The Wolds
Nottinghamshire

HERRING, Richard
North Devon (Royal)
Devon

HETHERINGTON, James
Melton Mowbray
Leicestershire

HICKEY, Peter
Cork
County Cork

HIGGINBOTTOM, Michael
Woodsome Hall
Yorkshire (West)

HIGGINS, Iain
Rochester & Cobham
Kent

HIGGINS, Liam
Waterville House & Golf Links
County Kerry

HILL, Ainsley
Harlech
Gwynedd

HILL, James
Great Yarmouth & Caister
Norfolk

HILL, Richard
Boscombe Ladies
Dorset

HILL, Stewart
Richmond Park
London (Greater)

HILL, Stuart
Swinley Forest
Berkshire

HILL, Trevor
Ashford
Kent

HILLAS, Mick
Northcliffe
Yorkshire (West)

HINTON, Kevin
Holtye
Kent

HINTON, Paul
Bridgnorth
Shropshire

HIRST, Martin
Horton Park Golf
Surrey

HIRST, Nigel
Dewsbury District
Yorkshire (West)

HOARE, Angus
Wharton Park
Worcestershire

HOATSON, S
Effingham
Surrey

HOBBS, David
Chartham Park
Sussex (West)

HODGESON, Alan
Bromley
Kent

HODGKINSON, Brian
Birkdale (Royal)
Merseyside

HODGSON, Chris
Etchinghill
Kent

HOLBA, Maximilian
Stevenage
Hertfordshire

HOLDSWORTH, Chris
Northwood
London (Greater)

HOLINGSWORTH, Michael
Denton
Manchester (Greater)

HOLLAND, R
Whitwood
Yorkshire (West)

HOLLAND, Roger
Pontefract
Yorkshire (West)

HOLM, Nick
Woodhall Spa
Lincolnshire

HOLMAN, Neil
Churston
Devon

HONAN, Derwin
East Dorset
Dorset

HOOTON, Simon
Hoylake Municipal
Merseyside

HOPE, Alan
Middlesbrough Municipal
Cleveland

HOPKIN, John
Maylands
Essex

Harvey — Hopkin

Professionals Alphabetically

HOPLEY, J
Gatley
Cheshire

HORSMAN, Lewis
Hillsborough
Yorkshire (South)

HOULGATE, F
Normanton
Yorkshire (West)

HOUSDEN, Keith
Wrekin
Shropshire

HOWARD, Ashley
Orton Meadows
Cambridgeshire

HOWARD, James
Pontypool
Monmouthshire

HOWARD, Matt
Farnham
Surrey

HOWARTH, Anthony
Bridlington
Yorkshire (East)

HOWARTH, Tony
Great Lever & Farnworth
Lancashire

HOWELL, Mark
Henley
Oxfordshire

HOWETT, Richard
Hinksey Heights
Oxfordshire

HOWIE, G
Kilmarnock
Ayrshire (South)

HUBBARD, Simon
Thornbury Golf
Bristol

HUBERT, Adrian
Woodbridge
Suffolk

HUDSON, C
Army
Hampshire

HUDSON, John
Braxted Park
Essex

HUDSON, R
Herons Reach
Lancashire

HUDSON, Richard
Brampton Heath
Northamptonshire

HUGGETT, Geoff
Cambridge
Cambridgeshire

HUGGETT, Geoff
Whaddon
Hertfordshire

HUGHES, Gary
Fairwood Park
Swansea

HUGHES, Richard
St. Melyd
Denbighshire

HUISH, David
North Berwick
Lothian (East)

HUME, Jimmy
Gullane
Lothian (East)

HUNT, Jamie
Whalley
Lancashire

HUNT, Tony
Crane Valley
Dorset

HUNTER, Alan
Portstewart
County Londonderry

HUNTER, Richard
Carholme
Lincolnshire

HUNTER, Rupert
Hilden Europro
Kent

HUNTER, Stephen
Redbourn
Hertfordshire

HUNTER, Steven
Winchester (Royal)
Hampshire

HURT, B
Oakmere Park
Nottinghamshire

HUTTON, Andy
Charleton
Fife

HUTTON, David
Gedney Hill
Lincolnshire

HUTTON, R
Hersham Village
Surrey

HUTTON, Robert
Cliftonville
County Antrim

HUTTON, Tim
Sudbrook Moor
Lincolnshire

HYDE, Neale
Westwood
Staffordshire

HYLAND, Andy
Broughton Heath
Derbyshire

IDDON, Colin
Heyrose
Cheshire

IMLAH, Craig
Peebles
Scottish Borders

IMPETT, Brian
Lamberhurst
Kent

INGRAM, Andy
Otley
Yorkshire (West)

INGRAM, James
Boat Of Garten
Highlands

INGUS, Euan
Bearwood Lakes
Berkshire

IRESON, Guy
Sprowston Manor
Norfolk

IRON, Greg
Wavendon Golf Ctre
Buckinghamshire

ISAACS, Tony
Thoulstone Park
Wiltshire

JACKSON, Lee
Harleyford
Buckinghamshire

JACKSON, Mark
Toft Hotel
Lincolnshire

JACKSON, Martin
Morpeth
Northumberland

JACKSON, N
Cretingham
Suffolk

JACKSON, Peter
Castle Eden
Cleveland

JACKSON, Simon
Trent Lock
Nottinghamshire

JANES, M
Chessington
Surrey

JARRETT, Sarah
Tickenham
Bristol

JARVIS, Matt
Hilden Europro
Kent

JEFFERIES, Simon
Okehampton
Devon

JELLEY, Ian
Brookmans Park
Hertfordshire

JENKINS, Colin
Staplehurst Golfing Park
Kent

JENNINGS, Paul
Risebridge
Essex

JILLINGS, Mark
Bury St Edmunds
Suffolk

JOHNS, Steve
Ruddington Grange
Nottinghamshire

JOHNSON, Bob
Brocton Hall
Staffordshire

JOHNSON, David
Lavender Park
Berkshire

JOHNSON, Glen
Hennerton
Berkshire

JOHNSON, L
Burhill
Surrey

JOHNSON, Peter
Vale Of Glamorgan
Glamorgan (Vale of)

JOHNSON, Robert
Saddleworth
Manchester (Greater)

JOHNSON, Tony
Bedale
Yorkshire (North)

JOINER, Paul
Orsett
Essex

JONES, A
Abersoch
Gwynedd

JONES, A
Llanishen
Glamorgan (Vale of)

JONES, Andrew
Leicester
Leicestershire

JONES, Andrew
Littlestone
Kent

JONES, Andrew
Romney Warren
Kent

JONES, Cliff
Glencorse
Lothian (Mid)

JONES, D
King Edward Bay
Isle of Man

JONES, Daniel
Sherdley Park Municipal
Merseyside

JONES, Darren
Leicester
Leicestershire

JONES, Ernie
K Club
County Kildare

JONES, Jon
Cleobury Mortimer
Shropshire

JONES, M
Ruthin-Pwllglas
Denbighshire

JONES, Mike
Denbigh
Denbighshire

JONES, Mike
Heaton Park
Manchester (Greater)

JONES, Peter
Coollattin
County Wicklow

JONES, Peter
Hadley Wood
Hertfordshire

JONES, R
Thames Ditton & Esher
Surrey

JONES, Richard
Hinckley
Leicestershire

JORDAN, Mark
Mold
Flintshire

JOYCE, Robert
West Essex
London (Greater)

JOYCE, Simon
Dartmouth
Midlands (West)

JUKES, Jeff
Wimbledon Common
London (Greater)

KAMINSKI, Chris
Lostwithiel
Cornwall

KARROLL, D
Oaksey
Wiltshire

KEARNEY, Ian
Formby
Merseyside

KEENAN, Paul
Brent Valley Public
London (Greater)

KEITCH, Martin
Taunton Vale
Somerset

KELLY, Maurice
Belvoir Park
County Antrim

KELSALL, Kyle
Tenterden
Kent

KEMP, Mervyn
Fingle Glen
Devon

KENNEDY, John
Wexham Park
Berkshire

KENWRIGHT, Peter
Haydock Park
Merseyside

KERSHAW, Robert
Lightcliffe
Yorkshire (West)

KERSHAW, Tim
Standish Court
Lancashire

KEY, Gary
Appleby
Cumbria

KEYS, Richard
Oundle
Cambridgeshire

KIDDIE, Frank
Elton Furze
Cambridgeshire

KIELY, Derry
Dunmore East
County Waterford

KIELY, Derry
Tramore
County Waterford

KILLING, Andrew
Thorney Park
Buckinghamshire

KING, Graham
Easter Moffat
Lanarkshire (North)

KING, John R
Lindrick
Nottinghamshire

KINGSLEY PGA, Peter
Banbury Golf Ctre
Oxfordshire

KINGSTON, Joe
Cherwell Edge
Oxfordshire

KINSELLA, D
Castle
County Dublin

KIRK, Ian
Tankersley Park
Yorkshire (South)

KITE, Geoff
Yeovil
Somerset

KITLEY, Gary
Thetford
Norfolk

KLEPACZ, P
Rowlands Castle
Hampshire

KNIGHT, A
Stanton On The Wolds
Nottinghamshire

KNOWLES, Chris
Sapey
Worcestershire

KRYZWICKI, Nick
Elland
Yorkshire (West)

KRYZWICKI, Nick
Marsden
Yorkshire (West)

LABAND, Mike
Weston
Somerset (North)

LAIDLER, Steven
Trefloyne
Pembrokeshire

Johnson — Laidler

Professionals Alphabetically

LAING, M A
Little Lakes
Worcestershire

LAITT, C
Birch Grove
Essex

LAMB, Jonathan
Woburn
Buckinghamshire

LAMB, Ken
Brackenwood Municipal
Merseyside

LAMBERT, Duncan
West Malling
Kent

LANCASTER, Andrew
Lytham Green
Lancashire

LANDSBOROUGH, Martyn
Ashdown Forest (Royal)
Sussex (East)

LANGMEAD, James
Hele Park Golf Ctre
Devon

LARGE, Barry
Allerton
Merseyside

LARKIN, David
Clays Golf Ctre
Wrexham

LARRATT, Bob
Kibworth
Leicestershire

LASZKOWICZ, Jason
Robin Hood
Yorkshire (South)

LATHAM, James
Cotswold Hills
Gloucestershire

LAUGHER, Peter
Thurlestone
Devon

LAURENCE, Craig
Manor of Groves
Hertfordshire

LAWIE, Robin
Seacroft
Lincolnshire

LAWRIE, Paul
Meldrum House
Aberdeen (City of)

LEAH, Tim
Rhyl
Denbighshire

LEE, Darren
Wanstead
London (Greater)

LEE, Geoffrey
Liphook
Hampshire

LEE, Hal
Millport
Ayrshire (North)

LEE, Michael
Rye
Sussex (East)

LEE, Nigel
Chelsfield Lakes Golf Ctre
Kent

LEEMING, Nick
Longley Park
Yorkshire (West)

LEES, Mark
Inverurie
Aberdeenshire

LEES, Peter
Conwy
Conwy

LEHANE, Martin
Muskerry
County Cork

LEIGHTON, Malcolm
Greenburn
Lothian (West)

LENAGHAN, Gary
Woburn
Buckinghamshire

LENNIE, Graeme
Crail
Fife

LESLIE, Gary
Welton Manor Golf Ctre
Lincolnshire

LEVERMORE, Stuart
Clacton
Essex

LEWIS, B
Northop
Flintshire

LEWIS, Bryan
Panshanger Golf Complex
Hertfordshire

LEWIS, D
Whitewebbs
London (Greater)

LEWIS, David
Barnehurst
Kent

LEWIS, John
Borth & Ynyslas
Ceredigion

LEWIS, Michael
South Leeds
Yorkshire (West)

LEWIS, Phil
Eastbourne Golfing Park
Sussex (East)

LEWIS, R
Manor House
Devon

LEYTON, Stuart
Abridge
Essex

LILLY, Simon
Wellingborough
Northamptonshire

LINTOTT, Dean
Puttenham
Surrey

LITCHFIELD, E
South Herefordshire
Herefordshire

LITTLE, John
Petworth
Sussex (West)

LLOYD, David
Formby Hall
Merseyside

LOBBAN, Keith
Hirsel
Scottish Borders

LOCHHEAD, Gary
Panmure
Angus

LOCHRIE, Des
Weymouth
Dorset

LOCKETT, Warren
Woodhall Hills
Yorkshire (West)

LOCKLEY, P
Newark
Nottinghamshire

LOGAN, Alan J
Cochrane Castle
Renfrewshire

LOMAX, S
Brackley
Manchester (Greater)

LONG, Graeme
Bromsgrove
Worcestershire

LONGMUIR, Bill
London
Kent

LONGMUIR, T
Cranleigh
Surrey

LONGSTER, Simon
Leeds
Yorkshire (West)

LOOMS, Ian
Blue Mountain Golf Centre
Berkshire

LOUGHRAN, Thomas
Carnalea
County Down

LOUGHREY, Barry
Wrag Barn
Wiltshire

LOUGHREY, Geoff
Mount Ober
County Antrim

LOVE, Hamish
Oldmeldrum
Aberdeenshire

LOVEGROVE, Mike
Penfold Park
Hertfordshire

LOVELL, Paul
Anglesey
Isle of Anglesey

LOVIE, Patrick
Inchmarlo Golf Ctre
Aberdeenshire

LOWE, Jamie
Lexden
Essex

LOWER, J
Wollaton Park
Nottinghamshire

LOWRY, Simon
Princes Risborough
Buckinghamshire

LUCAS, Alex
Fynn Valley
Suffolk

LUNNY, Gavin
Rathsallagh
County Wicklow

LYLE, Graham
Horsley Lodge
Derbyshire

LYNCH, Jim
Caerleon
Newport

LYONS, Paul
Sweetwoods Park
Kent

MACARA, Mike
Rhos-On-Sea
Conwy

MACDONALD, Alastair
Looe
Cornwall

MACDONALD, Keith
Goodwood
Sussex (West)

MACEY, Robert
Ramsdale Park
Nottinghamshire

MACFARLANE, Neil
Bidston
Merseyside

MACHIN, Peter
Pytchley Golf Lodge
Northamptonshire

MACINTOSH, Nim
Panmure
Angus

MACKENZIE, Albert
Saunton
Devon

MACKENZIE, Albert
Saunton
Devon

MACKENZIE, Brian
Bruntsfield Golf Club
Edinburgh (City of)

MACKINDER, Steve
Cave Castle
Yorkshire (East)

MACLENNAN, Sarah
East Sussex National
Sussex (East)

MACPHERSON, Ian
Felixstowe Ferry
Suffolk

MACRAE, Mark
Hertfordshire
Hertfordshire

MADDISON, Mark
Chirk
Wrexham

MAHER, Graham
Brean
Somerset

MALE, Mark
Stourbridge
Midlands (West)

MALLISON, Ben
Skipton
Yorkshire (North)

MALONE, Declane
Abbey Hotel
Worcestershire

MALTMAN, Craig
Eyemouth
Scottish Borders

MANN, David
Peterculter
Aberdeenshire

MANN, Frazer
Musselburgh
Lothian (Mid)

MANNION, Mike
Woodcray Manor
Berkshire

MANSON, Peter
Bristol & Clifton
Bristol

MARCH, Dave
Regiment
Essex

MARCH, Dave
Regiment
Essex

MARONEY, Colin
Heaton Park
Manchester (Greater)

MARSH, Adrian
Mendip
Bath & Somerset (North East)

MARSH, Simon
Heaton Moor
Cheshire

MARSHALL, Andy
Bridgecastle
Lothian (West)

MARSHALL, Andy
Catterick
Yorkshire (North)

MARSHALL, James
Hesketh
Merseyside

MARSHALL, Stewart
Williamwood
Glasgow (City of)

MARSHALL, Terry
Eastbourne Downs
Sussex (East)

MARTIN, Simon
Benfield Valley
Sussex (East)

MARTINDALE, David
Deane
Lancashire

MASON, Tony
Whitby
Yorkshire (North)

MASTERS, Richard
Baildon
Yorkshire (West)

MASTERTON, Grant
Chiddingfold
Surrey

MATHER, D
Stocksfield
Northumberland

MATON, Peter
Prince's
Isle of Anglesey

MAXWELL, Keith
Sunningdale
Surrey

MCALISTER, J
Haggs Castle
Glasgow (City of)

MCARTHY, D
Brailsford
Derbyshire

MCASKELL, Scott
Elfordleigh
Devon

MCBRIARTY, S
North West
County Donegal

MCBRIDE, James
Ballykisteen
County Tipperary

MCBRIDE, Joseph
Temple Club
County Antrim

MCBRIDE, Pete
Lexden
Essex

MCCALLE, P
Brodick
Ayrshire (North)

MCCALLUM, Jim
Lenzie
Glasgow (City of)

MCCALUM, Gordon
Aberdour
Fife

MCCANDLESS, Adam
Uttoxeter
Staffordshire

MCCARTHY, Glynn
Stockwood Park
Bedfordshire

MCCARTHY, Stephen
Lymm
Cheshire

MCCLOUD, Jim
Aberystwyth
Ceredigion

MCCOLGAN, Adrian
Traditions Golf Course
Surrey

MCCOLL, Bill
Thorpe Hall
Essex

MCCRYSTAL, Paul
Scrabo
County Down

MCDAID, Brendan
Rathsallagh
County Wicklow

MCDERMOT, Brendan
Mount Juliet
County Kilkenny

MCDOUGALL, R
Sonning
Berkshire

MCDOWALL, Graeme
Elmwood
Fife

MCEVOY, Peter
Old Fold Manor
Hertfordshire

MCEWAN, Murdoch
Frome Golf Club
Bath & Somerset (North East)

MCGARVEY, Neil
Fleetwood
Lancashire

MCGHEE, B
Craigmillar Park
Edinburgh (City of)

MCGHEE, Jimmy
Willingcott
Devon

MCGINN, Alan
Canons Brook
Essex

MCGIRR, Kevin
Springhill
County Tyrone

MCGUIRK, Paddy
Louth (County)
County Louth

MCKEE, Brian
Belton Park
Lincolnshire

MCKENNA, Steve
Newcastle
Tyne And Wear

MCKIERNAN, Richard
Holme Hall
Lincolnshire (North)

MCKILLOP, Cameron
Fawkham Valley Golf Club
Kent

MCLAUGHLIN, Ian
Ballycastle
County Antrim

MCLAUGHLIN, Kieran
Foyle
County Londonderry

MCLAUGHLIN, Steve
Fleetwood
Lancashire

MCLEAN, Mike
Chesterfield
Derbyshire

MCLEOD, Gordon
Tytherington
Cheshire

MCLEOD, Ian
Monifieth Golf Links
Angus

MCNALLY, Nick
Tudor Park
Kent

MCNALLY, Steve
Burgham
Northumberland

MCNEIL, Nick
Rushmere
Suffolk

MCNEILL, Gary
Portrush (Royal)
County Antrim

MCNIVEN, Peter
Forfar
Angus

MCOMISH, S
Kingsdown
Wiltshire

MCPHERSON, Ken
Walton Heath
Surrey

MCQUEEN, Greg
Routenburn
Ayrshire (North)

MCQUITTY, Guy
Littlehampton Golf
Sussex (West)

MCSHERRY, Tim
Yelverton
Devon

MCWADE, K
Bonnyton
Glasgow (City of)

MEADE, S
Southwell
Nottinghamshire

MEE, David
Longcliffe
Leicestershire

MELLING, David
Crompton & Royton
Manchester (Greater)

MELLOR, Ally
Nizels
Kent

MELLOR, Julian
Leamington & County
Warwickshire

MELVIN, N
Kilworth Springs
Leicestershire

MERCER, Gary
Lisburn
County Antrim

MICHELL, D
Perranporth
Cornwall

MILES, David
Bournemouth & Meyrick
Dorset

MILES, Jane
Parley
Dorset

MILLER, Andrew
Ashby Decoy
Lincolnshire (North)

MILLS, David
Seaford
Sussex (East)

MILNE, G
Taunton & Pickeridge
Somerset

MILTON, K
Broadwater Park
Surrey

MITCHELL, Bobby
South Herts
London (Greater)

MITCHELL, Jason
Orton Meadows
Cambridgeshire

MITCHELL, Neil
Feltwell
Norfolk

MITCHELL, Nick
Newbury Racecourse
Berkshire

MITCHELL, Paul
Bristol & Clifton
Bristol

MITCHELL, Ron
Pedham Place Golf Ctre
Kent

MOGER, Paul
Edenbridge
Kent

MONAGHAN, Ciaran
Druids Glen
County Wicklow

MONCUR, Terry
Langdon Hills Golf Ctre
Essex

MONTGOMERIE, Craig
Roxburghe
Scottish Borders

MONTGOMERY, Jacky
Dunbar
Lothian (East)

MOON, David
St. Mellion International
Cornwall

MOORE, Mark
Rudding Park
Yorkshire (North)

MOORE, Troy
Willingdon
Sussex (East)

MORGAN, Andrew
Richmond Park
London (Greater)

MORGAN, Merfyn
Tredegar Park
Newport

MORLEY, Chris
Lingfield Park
Surrey

MORLEY, Terry
Ellesmere
Manchester (Greater)

MORRIS, C
Retford
Nottinghamshire

MORRIS, Carl
Heaton Park
Manchester (Greater)

MORRIS, G C
Harewood Downs
Buckinghamshire

MORRISS, Bryn
Blackthorn Wood
Leicestershire

MORTIMER, Richard
Upavon
Wiltshire

MOSS, R
Mendip Spring
Bristol

MOUNTFORD, Richard
Ladbrook Park
Midlands (West)

MOWBRAY, Ian
Abbeyfeale
County Limerick

MUCKLOW, Lee
Windlesham
Surrey

MUDGE, Richard
Staverton Park
Northamptonshire

MUIR, Ian
Craigie Hill
Perth And Kinross

MULRANEY, Steve
Addington Court Golf Club
Surrey

MUNGALL, Kurt
Lothianburn
Edinburgh (City of)

MUNRO, C
Ralston
Renfrewshire

MURCHIE, David
Crieff
Perth And Kinross

MURDOCH, Alan
Kings Acre
Lothian (Mid)

MURPHY, Batt
Monkstown
County Cork

MURPHY, Tom
Kilternan
County Dublin

MURRAY, Alex
Tall Pines
Bristol

MURRAY, John
Malahide
County Dublin

MURRAY, John
Millfield Golf
Lincolnshire

MURRAY, John
Turnhouse
Edinburgh (City of)

MURTON, G
Oak Park Golf Club
Surrey

MYERS, D
Marple
Cheshire

NASH, Tony
Lostwithiel
Cornwall

NAYLOR, David
Banchory
Aberdeenshire

NAYLOR, David
Houldsworth
Cheshire

NAYLOR, Iain
East Sussex National
Sussex (East)

NEAL, Syke
Beedles Lake
Leicestershire

NEIL, Russell
Mill Ride
Berkshire

NEVE, Jason
Cams Hall Estate Golf Club
Hampshire

NEWMAN, Lee
Theale Golf Ctre
Berkshire

NEWNHAM, D
Crowborough Beacon
Sussex (East)

NICHOLAS, Jon
Halesowen
Midlands (West)

NICHOLAS, Kevin
Pavenham
Bedfordshire

NICHOLLS, S
Rosendale Golf Club
Lancashire

NICHOLSON, Garry
Douglas
County Cork

NOBLE, Bill
Open
County Dublin

NOOTT, Julian
Newport
Pembrokeshire

NORCOTT, Gary
Davenport
Cheshire

NORWOOD, Alan
Kinsale
Flintshire

NOTLEY, Terry
Aspect Park
Oxfordshire

NUGENT, Chris
Dunfermline
Fife

OAKLEY, Nick
Hinckley
Leicestershire

O'BRIEN, Kieran
Willow Valley
Yorkshire (West)

O'CALLAGHAN, Brian
Ballybunion
County Kerry

O'CONNER, Sean
Pryors Hayes
Cheshire

O'CONNOR, Christy
Christy O'Connor
County Dublin

O'CONNOR, Dermot
Ceann Sibeal
County Kerry

O'CONNOR, Peter
Christy O'Connor
County Dublin

O'CONNOR, Sean
Kilrush
County Clare

ODELL, Richard
Branston
Staffordshire

O'DONNELL, Karl
Newlands
County Dublin

OGILVY, N
Hindhead
Surrey

O'HAGAN, Peter
Highfield
County Kildare

Montgomery — O'Hagan

Professionals Alphabetically

O'HANLON, Richard
St. Thomas' Priory
Staffordshire

O'HARA, Brian
Rathfarnham
County Dublin

OLIPHANT, Andrew
Wynyard Club
Cleveland

O'MEARA, Alan
Ross Golf
County Kerry

O'NEILL, Hugh
Connemara
County Galway

ORD, Jack
Consett & District
County Durham

OWEN, Aled
Caernarfon (Royal Town of)
Gwynedd

OWEN, D P
St. Giles
Powys

PACKHAM, Tim
West Sussex
Sussex (West)

PADGETT, David
Pannal
Yorkshire (North)

PAGE, Rob
Bowood
Cornwall

PAGE, Sarah
Bush Hill Park
London (Greater)

PAGET, Mathew
Walmer & Kingsdown
Kent

PAGETT, Lee
Shirenewton
Monmouthshire

PALMER, Alan
Aberdare
Glamorgan (Vale of)

PAPE, James
Roundhay
Yorkshire (West)

PARANOMOS, Nick
Fishwick Hall
Lancashire

PARCELL, Tony
Braintree
Essex

PARKER, G
Knebworth
Hertfordshire

PARKER, Iain
Ferndown
Dorset

PARKER, Ian
Mill Green Golf Club
Hertfordshire

PARKER, John
Sherdons
Gloucestershire

PARKER, Steve
Carswell
Oxfordshire

PARR, Nigel
Childdwall
Merseyside

PARRY, Bob
Shipley
Yorkshire (West)

PARRY, Bob
Shipley
Yorkshire (West)

PARSLEY, Matt
Holywell
Flintshire

PARSONS, Colin
Cardigan
Ceredigion

PARSONS, David
Bridport & West Dorset
Dorset

PARSONS, S
Priskilly
Pembrokeshire

PARSONS, Steve
Cwmrhydneuadd
Ceredigion

PARTLEK, Mark
Shooters Hill
London (Greater)

PARTRIDGE, Alan
Moor Hall
Midlands (West)

PARTRIDGE, Alan
Wishaw
Midlands (West)

PATIENCE, Scott
Celtic Manor
Newport

PATTERSON, David
George Washington
Tyne and Wear

PATTERSON, L
Cromer (Royal)
Norfolk

PAYNE, Jim
Sandilands & Leisure
Lincolnshire

PAYNE, Jim
Southport & Ainsdale
Merseyside

PAYNE, Martin
Cleobury Mortimer
Shropshire

PAYNE, Warwick
Tilsworth
Bedfordshire

PEARCE, Darren
Barnard Castle
County Durham

PEARCE, Trevor
East Horton Golf Ctre
Hampshire

PEARS, C
Brinkworth
Wiltshire

PEARSON, Ian
Peacehaven
Sussex (East)

PEARSON, Mark
Cookridge Hall Golf Club
Yorkshire (West)

PECK, Danny
Warwickshire
Warwickshire

PEDDIE, G
Bramley
Surrey

PEDEN, Jonathan
Kirkistown Castle
County Down

PELL, Jason
New North Manchester
Manchester (Greater)

PENGELLY, John
Greetham Valley
Rutland

PENNET, John
Braemar
Aberdeenshire

PENNOCK, Tony
Rye Hill
Oxfordshire

PENNY, Roy
Werneth
Manchester (Greater)

PERKINS, Martin
Tydd St Giles
Cambridgeshire

PERRY, Michael
Little Hay
Hertfordshire

PERRY, Roland
Whipsnade Park
Hertfordshire

PHILLIPS, Kevin
Winterfield
Lothian (East)

PHILLIPS, M D
Llantrisant & Pontyclun
Rhondda Cynon Taff

PICKERELL, N
Eagles
Norfolk

PICKERING, A J
Grange-Over-Sands
Cumbria

PICKETT, Kevin
Hilton Puckrup Hall
Gloucestershire

PIGGOT, Martin
Loch Ness
Highlands

O'Hanlon — Piggot

Professionals Alphabetically

PIKE, Gary
Forrester Park
Essex

PIKE, Warren
Redhill & Reigate
Surrey

PILE, Alex
Haverfordwest
Pembrokeshire

PILKINGTON, J
Pwllheli
Gwynedd

PITTS, T
St. Austell
Cornwall

PLATT, Geoff
Aldwark Manor
Yorkshire (North)

PLUMB, Steve
Aldwickbury Park

PLUMB, Steve
Aldwickbury Park
Hertfordshire

POCOCK, T
Shrivenham Park
Wiltshire

POCOCK, T
Shrivenham Park
Wiltshire

POOK, Geoff
Collingtree Park
Northamptonshire

POOLE, D
Whitsand Bay
Cornwall

PORTER, Ben
Eastbourne Golfing Park
Sussex (East)

PORTER, George
North Hants Fleet
Hampshire

PORTER, Lee
Hylands Golf Complex
Essex

PORTER, Martin
Arkley
Hertfordshire

PORTER, Roy
Top Meadow
Essex

PORTER, Steve
North Hants Fleet
Hampshire

POTTER, Chris
Bawburgh
Norfolk

POTTER, Gary
Dunham
Norfolk

POULTER, Ian
Leighton Buzzard
Bedfordshire

POWELL, Tim

Hoebridge
Surrey

PRICE, Darren
Whitefields
Warwickshire

PRICE, Russell
Ludlow
Shropshire

PRICE, Simon
Wyre Forest
Worcestershire

PRICE, Stephen
Llanwern
Newport

PRICE, Stephen
Llanwern
Newport

PRITCHARD, A
Woodlake Park
Monmouthshire

PRITCHARD, M
Northop
Flintshire

PRIVATE, Fred
Aquarius
London (Greater)

PROUDFOOT, Basil
Berkhamsted
Hertfordshire

PROUDFOOT, Stephen
Batchworth Park
Hertfordshire

PROWSE, Darren
Warren
Devon

PUGH, Denis
Wisley
Surrey

PURDIE, Brian
Blackpool Park
Lancashire

PURTON, James
Deanwood Park
Berkshire

PURVES, Steve
Leeds Castle
Kent

PUTTICK, Barney
Mid-Herts
Hertfordshire

PYE, Andrew
Ashton
Lancashire

QUARTERMAN, A
Harborne
Midlands (West)

QUINN, Martin
Athlone
County Roscommon

RAE, Ian
Hollandbush
Lanarkshire (South)

RAITT, David

Whetstone
Leicestershire

RAJ, Michael
Reading
Berkshire

RALPH, Glenn
Camberley Heath
Surrey

RANSON, D
Crane Valley
Dorset

RASTALL, Tim
Mottram Hall
Cheshire

RAWLINGS, Lee
Bulwell Forest
Nottinghamshire

RAYNER, Simon
West Norfolk (Royal)
Norfolk

READ, Ian
Minehead & West Somerset
Somerset

REAY, John
Stoneleigh Deer Park
Midlands (West)

REES, Deryl
Morriston
Swansea

REEVES, Paul
Whitefield
Manchester (Greater)

REFFIN, David
Huntercombe
Oxfordshire

REGAN, David
West Byfleet
Surrey

REHAAG, Domonic
Tavistock
Devon

REID, Alan
Lynedoch & Murrayshall
Perth And Kinross

REID, Matt
Mardyke Valley Golf Ctre
Essex

REILLY, Gerry
Lochwinnoch
Renfrewshire

REMY, Peter
High Elms
Kent

RENNIE, David
Wentworth
Surrey

RENNIE, Frank
Prestwick
Ayrshire (South)

RENNIE, Stephen
Brechin Golf & Squash Club
Angus

REVIE, Ken

Pike — Revie

Professionals Alphabetically

Ballymena
County Antrim

🍂 REVIE, Ken
Brown Trout
County Londonderry

🍂 REYNOLDS, Andrew
Cinque Ports (Royal)
Kent

🍂 REYNOLDS, John
King's Lynn
Norfolk

🍂 RHODES, J
South Staffordshire
Midlands (West)

🍂 RICHARDS, Alan
Woodbury Park
Devon

🍂 RICHARDS, Glenn
Wrangaton
Devon

🍂 RICHARDS, John
Stockwood Vale
Bristol

🍂 RICHARDSON, Gerry
Mowsbury
Bedfordshire

🍂 RICHARDSON, John
Lee On The Solent
Hampshire

🍂 RICHARDSON, Sean
Boldon
Tyne And Wear

🍂 RIDLEY, David
Coxmoor
Nottinghamshire

🍂 RIDYARD, David
Dinnaton
Devon

🍂 RILEY, Nick
Henbury
Bristol

🍂 RIPLEY, Jason
Rother Valley Golf
Yorkshire (South)

🍂 ROBBINS, Geoff
Faringdon
Oxfordshire

🍂 ROBERTS, Len
Hampton Court Palace Golf Club
London (Greater)

🍂 ROBERTS, Mike
Mount Pleasant
Bedfordshire

🍂 ROBERTSON, Stuart
Ufford Park
Suffolk

🍂 ROBINSON, Darren
Filton
Bristol

🍂 ROBINSON, David T
Bundoran
County Donegal

🍂 ROBINSON, Gordon

Slaley Hall Golf Course
Northumberland

🍂 ROBINSON, Jim
Sligo (County)
County Sligo

🍂 ROBINSON, Peter
Skipton
Yorkshire (North)

🍂 ROBLIN, Henry
Bunsay Downs
Essex

🍂 ROBSON-CROSBY, Alan
Ponteland
Tyne And Wear

🍂 RODGERS, Bob
Auchenharvie
Ayrshire (North)

🍂 RODGERS, Paul
Auchenharvie
Ayrshire (North)

🍂 RODGERS, Peter
Barton-On-Sea
Hampshire

🍂 RODWELL, Alan
Blackburn
Lancashire

🍂 RODWELL, Alan
Blackburn

🍂 ROE, Arthur
East Berkshire
Berkshire

🍂 ROGERS, Ian
Barlaston
Staffordshire

🍂 ROGERS, Nick
Came Down
Dorset

🍂 ROLLEY, Steven
Worthing
Sussex (West)

🍂 ROOKE, W S M
Windermere
Cumbria

🍂 ROPER, Gareth
Charnock Richard
Lancashire

🍂 ROSE, Shane
Cold Ashby
Northamptonshire

🍂 ROSIE, Steven
Linlithgow
Lothian (West)

🍂 ROSS, Graham
West Kilbride
Ayrshire (North)

🍂 ROSS, Laurance
Fareham Woods
Hampshire

🍂 ROSS, Martin
Marsden Park Public
Lancashire

🍂 ROUND, Peter
St. Neots

Cambridgeshire

🍂 ROUSE, Tim
Northamptonshire County
Northamptonshire

🍂 ROWE, Mark
Carlyon Bay
Cornwall

🍂 ROWETT, Mike
Exeter
Devon

🍂 RUDD, Sean
Seascale
Cumbria

🍂 RUNCIE, Iain
Abergele
Conwy

🍂 RUSSELL, Stephen
Worfield
Shropshire

🍂 RUSSELL, Stuart
East Renfrewshire
Glasgow (City of)

🍂 RUTH, Martin
Torquay
Devon

🍂 RUTHERFORD, Carl
Caversham Heath
Berkshire

🍂 RYAN, Michael
Frankfield
County Cork

🍂 RYAN, N
Ringway
Cheshire

🍂 SAARY, Alex
Aylesbury
Buckinghamshire

🍂 SAINSBURY, Carl
Brampton Heath
Northamptonshire

🍂 SALMONI, Keith
Muckhart
Clackmannanshire

🍂 SALTER, Jonathan
Nuneaton
Warwickshire

🍂 SANDILANDS, John
Haddington
Lothian (East)

🍂 SANDRY, B
Broome Manor
Wiltshire

🍂 SARGEANT, Rae
Gatton Manor
Surrey

🍂 SARGENT, Nick
Eastham Lodge
Merseyside

🍂 SAWYER, G
Bradford-on-Avon
Wiltshire

🍂 SAXON-MILLS, John
Heydon Grange

Revie — Saxon-Mills

Professionals Alphabetically

Hertfordshire

🏌 **SAYERS**, Steve
Belton Woods
Lincolnshire

🏌 **SCHULVER**, Syer
Caldecott Hall
Norfolk

🏌 **SCOTT**, Daryl
Dog
Oxfordshire

🏌 **SCOTT**, David
Douglas Park
Glasgow (City of)

🏌 **SCOTT**, Derek
St. Agustines
Kent

🏌 **SCOTT**, Malcolm
Alresford
Hampshire

🏌 **SCOTT**, Peter
Kendal
Cumbria

🏌 **SCOTT**, Stewart
Ramsey Club
Cambridgeshire

🏌 **SCREETON**, David
Worsley Park
Manchester (Greater)

🏌 **SEAL**, Peter
Shrewbury
Shropshire

🏌 **SEED**, Jason
Greenmount
Lancashire

🏌 **SEFTON**, P
Pine Ridge Golf Ctre
Surrey

🏌 **SELLEARS**, Peter
Lingdale
Leicestershire

🏌 **SELWYN-SMITH**, Neil
Hawkesbury Golf Centre
Midlands (West)

🏌 **SHARP**, Eric
Kenwick Park
Lincolnshire

🏌 **SHAW**, Brian
Doonbeg
County Clare

🏌 **SHAW**, Nigel
Warrenpoint
County Down

🏌 **SHAW**, Steve
Doncaster Town Moor
Yorkshire (South)

🏌 **SHEARD**, Alison
Ryston Park
Norfolk

🏌 **SHEARN**, Adrian
Hertfordshire
Hertfordshire

🏌 **SHELDON**, Lee
Branston

Staffordshire

🏌 **SHERIDAN**, F
Hazelwood Golf Ctre
Surrey

🏌 **SHERMAN**, Hugh
Ashford
Kent

🏌 **SHERRATT**, Simon
Maywood
Derbyshire

🏌 **SHORT**, James
Stockwood Park
Bedfordshire

🏌 **SHORT**, Trevor
Boldmere
Midlands (West)

🏌 **SIM**, J
Cooden Beach
Sussex (East)

🏌 **SIMMONS**, Gary
Puttenham
Surrey

🏌 **SIMPSON**, M
Spofforth
Yorkshire (North)

🏌 **SIMPSON**, Paul
West Berkshire
Berkshire

🏌 **SIMPSON**, Rob
Ruddington Grange
Nottinghamshire

🏌 **SIMPSON**, Tim
Bearsted
Kent

🏌 **SIMS**, T
Kingswood
Surrey

🏌 **SINCLAIR**, Ian
Channels
Essex

🏌 **SKELTON**, David
Oswestry
Shropshire

🏌 **SKIELLEN**, Ray
Greenacres Golf Ctre
County Antrim

🏌 **SKIFFINGTON**, David
Bishop Auckland
County Durham

🏌 **SKIMMER**, J
Sandown Golf Ctre
Surrey

🏌 **SKINGLE**, Tony
Scarborough South Cliff
Yorkshire (North)

🏌 **SKINNER**, Andrew
Dornoch (Royal)
Highlands

🏌 **SKUSE**, John
Dewstow
Monmouthshire

🏌 **SLADE**, Brian
Villa

Kent

🏌 **SLADE**, John
Dibden Golf Ctre
Hampshire

🏌 **SLATTERY**, Lee
Hesketh
Merseyside

🏌 **SLINGER**, John
Chichester
Sussex (West)

🏌 **SMALL**, Derek
Castle Park
Lothian (East)

🏌 **SMEE**, Mike
Ganstead Park
Yorkshire (East)

🏌 **SMILLIE**, Cameron
Haste Hill
London (Greater)

🏌 **SMITH**, Adrian
Tickenham
Bristol

🏌 **SMITH**, Andrew
Ashbourne
Derbyshire

🏌 **SMITH**, Colin
Strathmore Golf Ctre
Perth And Kinross

🏌 **SMITH**, David
Hertfordshire
Hertfordshire

🏌 **SMITH**, Gary
Wokefield Park
Berkshire

🏌 **SMITH**, Ian
Sutton Hall
Cheshire

🏌 **SMITH**, Mike
Ulverston
Cumbria

🏌 **SMITH**, Neil
Wyke Green
London (Greater)

🏌 **SMITH**, Paul
Dibden Golf Ctre
Hampshire

🏌 **SMITH**, Robert
Cotgrave Place
Nottinghamshire

🏌 **SMITH**, Robin
Turriff
Aberdeenshire

🏌 **SMITH**, Sandy
Gleneagles
Perth And Kinross

🏌 **SMITH**, Simon
Aston Wood
Midlands (West)

🏌 **SMITH**, Stuart
Lydd
Kent

🏌 **SMITH**, Wil
Alice Springs

Saxon-Mills — Smith

Professionals Alphabetically

Monmouthshire

SNELL, C
College Pines
Nottinghamshire

SOUTER, Adam
Witney Lakes
Oxfordshire

SPINK, Alistair
Hintlesham Hall
Suffolk

SPROSTON, Anthony
High Legh Park
Cheshire

SQUIRES, Simon
Trent Park Golf Club
London (Greater)

SQUIRES, T
Boston
Lincolnshire

ST JOHN-JONES, D
Oakmere Park
Nottinghamshire

STAFF, Colin
Langley Park
Kent

STAFFORD, Gary
Burton On Trent
Staffordshire

STANLEY, Chris
Seedy Mill
Staffordshire

STAPLES, John
Edwalton Municipal
Nottinghamshire

STATHAM, Judy
Portal Premier
Cheshire

STATHAM, N
Wessex Golf Ctre
Dorset

STATON, Malcolm
Prestatyn
Denbighshire

STEAD, Nathan
Otley
Yorkshire (West)

STEADMAN, Michael
Vivary Park
Somerset

STEBBINGS, Peter
Green Meadow
Torfaen

STEELE, C
Minchinhampton
Gloucestershire

STEELS, Damon
Breadsall Priory
Derbyshire

STEVELY, K
Cawder
Glasgow (City of)

STEVEN, Jack
Glasgow

Glasgow (City of)

STEVEN, Jack
Glasgow Gailes
Ayrshire (North)

STEVENSON, Andy
Mersey Valley
Cheshire

STEVENSON, P
Portadown
County Armagh

STEVENSON, Paul
Tandragee
County Armagh

STEWART, David
Pitcheroak
Worcestershire

STEWART, G
Inverness
Highlands

STEWART, Gary
Ruxley Park
Kent

STEWART, Gary
South Essex
Essex

STEWART, Gordon
Paisley
Renfrewshire

STEWART, M
Sale
Cheshire

STIFF, Sean
Broughton Heath
Derbyshire

STILLWELL, E
Croham Hurst
Surrey

STOCKDALE, Richard
Vale Royal Abbey
Cheshire

STOKES, James
Brampton Golf
Herefordshire

STOTT, H
Laleham
Surrey

STOW, Peter
Hankley Common
Surrey

STRACHAN, Bob
Duff House Royal
Aberdeenshire

STRACHAN, John
Shotts
Lanarkshire (North)

STRACHAN, S
Bathgate
Lothian (West)

STRANGE, Alan
Brow
Shropshire

STREET, Wallace
Singing Hills

Sussex (West)

STRICKET, Chris
Fleming Park
Hampshire

STUART - WILLIAM, Mark
East Brighton
Sussex (East)

STUPPLE, Mike
Parley
Dorset

STURE, Jacob
Branston
Staffordshire

SUGRUE, John
Kinsale
County Cork

SULLIVAN, Craig
Hendon
London (Greater)

SUMMERS, Malcolm
Mowsbury
Bedfordshire

SUMNER, Nigel
Nelson
Lancashire

SUTCLIFFE, David
Lancaster
Lancashire

SWAIN, Geoff
Baron & Baroness
Bedfordshire

SYKES, Phil
Knole Park
Kent

SYME, Stuart
Dumfries & County
Dumfries And Galloway

SYMMONS, T
Mundesley
Norfolk

SYMONDS, Paul
Newcastle-Under-Lyme
Staffordshire

TAGGART, Gary
Lethamhill
Glasgow (City of)

TAIT, Alan
Westerwood
Glasgow (City of)

TALBOT, P
Mid-Surrey (Royal)
Surrey

TAPLEY, Tim
Entry Hill
Bath & Somerset (North East)

TAPPER, Gaele
Sidmouth
Devon

TASKER, Lee
Pottergate
Lincolnshire

TATTERSALL, Roger
Bedford & County

Bedfordshire

TAWSE, A
West Surrey
Surrey

TAYLOR, Graham
Owmby
Lincolnshire

TAYLOR, Ian
West Lothian
Lothian (West)

TAYLOR, Jestyn
St. Andrews Major
Glamorgan (Vale of)

TAYLOR, K
Blackburn
Lancashire

TAYLOR, K
Blackburn
Lancashire

TAYLOR, Lee
Charnock Richard
Lancashire

TAYLOR, Mark
Trent Lock
Nottinghamshire

TAYLOR, Max
Bowood
Wiltshire

TAYLOR, Mick
Shortlands
Kent

TAYLOR, Nic
Sitwell
Yorkshire (South)

TAYLOR, Nigel
Diss
Norfolk

TAYLOR, P
Sickleholme
Derbyshire

TAYLOR, Robert
Brettvale
Suffolk

TAYLOR, Robert
Colne Valley
Essex

TAYLOR, Ross
Redlibbets
Kent

TAYLOR, Tony
Macclesfield
Cheshire

TAYNOR, Andrew
Chingford
London (Greater)

TEAGUE, V
Moyola Park
County Londonderry

TEDDER, P
Sutton Green
Surrey

TEMPLEMAN, Mark
Thorney
Cambridgeshire

TERRAS, Paul
Berwick
Northumberland

TERRAS, Paul
Eyemouth
Scottish Borders

TERRELL, John
Horton Park Golf
Surrey

TESCHNEL, Karl
Iver
Buckinghamshire

TESCHNEL, Karl
Iver
Buckinghamshire

TESCHNER, G
Salisbury & South Wilts
Wiltshire

TESCHNER, Heath
Dunwood Manor
Hampshire

THATCHER, Alistair
Oakland Park
Buckinghamshire

THOMAS, Alasdair
Notts
Nottinghamshire

THOMAS, David
Carmarthen
Carmarthenshire

THOMAS, David
Windlermere
Surrey

THOMAS, Kirsty
Riverside
Nottinghamshire

THOMAS, Mark
Dudsbury
Dorset

THOMPSON, A
Heswall
Merseyside

THOMPSON, A P
Inverness
Highlands

THOMPSON, Graham
Cocksford
Yorkshire (North)

THOMPSON, James
Rufford Park Golf Ctre
Nottinghamshire

THOMPSON, Martyn
Parkstone
Dorset

THOMPSON, Muriel
Portlethen
Aberdeen (City of)

THOMPSON, P
Erskine
Renfrewshire

THOMPSON, Paul
Powerscourt
County Wicklow

THOMPSON, Peter
Parley
Dorset

THOMPSON, Robin
Prenton
Merseyside

THOMPSON, Stephen
Renfrew
Renfrewshire

THOMPSON, Zac
Bedford
Bedfordshire

THOMPSON-GREEN, Tim
Tracy Park
Bristol

THOMSON, Alistair
Moray
Moray

THOMSON, Andrew
Otter Valley Golf Ctre
Devon

THOMSON, David
Carnegie
Highlands

THOMSON, Scott
Girton
Cambridgeshire

THORNE, David
Vale Of Llangollen
Denbighshire

THORNTON, Paul
Norwood Park
Nottinghamshire

TINGY, David
Hylands Golf Complex
Essex

TOCHER, Andy
Betchworth Park
Surrey

TOILEY, Gary
Danesbury Park
Hertfordshire

TOKELY, Nigel
Broadstone
Dorset

TONGE, Graham
Frodsham
Cheshire

TORBETT, Gary
Chipstead
Surrey

TOWNHILL, Joe
Kilnwick Percy
Yorkshire (North)

TOWNHILL, Joe
Oaks
Yorkshire (North)

TOWNSEND, James
Church Stretton
Shropshire

TOZER, J
Launceston
Cornwall

Tattersall — Tozer

Professionals Alphabetically

TRAINOR, Patrick
Ashwoods
County Fermanagh

TRAYNOR, Andy
Epping Forest (Royal)
London (Greater)

TREADGOLD, Gary
Dunscar
Lancashire

TROAKE, Russ
Elfordleigh
Devon

TRUSSELL, Sean
Tilgate Forest
Sussex (West)

TUCKER, Clive
Mannings Heath
Sussex (West)

TUDDENHAM, Roger
Canford Magna
Dorset

TUDOR, Damian
Forest of Arden
Midlands (West)

TURNER, D
Carus Green
Cumbria

TURNER, D
Ringway
Cheshire

TURNER, Nick
Scarthingwell
Yorkshire (North)

TURNER, Robin
Highgate
London (Greater)

TWISSELL, J
Clitheroe
Lancashire

TYE, W P
Burley
Hampshire

TYSON, Alan
Horam Park
Sussex (East)

TYSON, Chris
Kirkbymoorside
Yorkshire (North)

TYSON, Martin
Dainton Park
Devon

ULYETT, Matthew
Park Hill
Leicestershire

UNDERWOOD, Trevor
East Devon
Devon

URE, Michael
Billingham
Cleveland

URQUHART, M
Inverness
Highlands

UTTERIDGE, M
Castle Point
Essex

VALENTINE, David
Chorlton-cum-Hardy
Manchester (Greater)

VALENTINE, Kevin
Alvaston Hall
Cheshire

VALENTINE, T
Whitley
Wiltshire

VANNEL, Dean G
Peterculter
Aberdeenshire

VAUGHAN, John
Rufford Park Golf Ctre
Nottinghamshire

VAUGHAN, Wesley
Haverfordwest
Pembrokeshire

VAUGHN, Lee
Thorpe Wood
Cambridgeshire

VELVICK, Giles
Horam Park
Sussex (East)

VINCE, Kelvin
Fynn Valley
Suffolk

VIPOND, Michael
Pikefold
Lancashire

WAKE, J
Wollaton Park
Nottinghamshire

WAKEFIELD, S
Prestwich
Manchester (Greater)

WALKER, Bob
Cairndhu
County Antrim

WALKER, Graham
Barlborough Links
Derbyshire

WALKER, Paul
Knott End
Lancashire

WALKER, Ron
Dukes
Fife

WALKER, Stuart
Horton Park Golf
Surrey

WALKER (OBE), Nicky
Warren
Essex

WALL, M
Chadwell Springs
Hertfordshire

WALLEY, Mike
Ruxley Park
Kent

WALLIS, Gary
Chiddingfold
Surrey

WALTERS, A
Hadden Hill
Oxfordshire

WALTERS, Michael
Erlestoke Sands
Wiltshire

WARD, Brenden
Blackpool North Shore
Lancashire

WARD, Ken
Whiteleaf
Buckinghamshire

WARD, Peter
Teignmouth
Devon

WARD, S
Bishopswood
Hampshire

WARDELL, Paul
Whitekirk
Lothian (East)

WARDLE, Alan
Beeston Fields
Nottinghamshire

WARE, David
Flixton
Manchester (Greater)

WAREING, Keith
Distington Golf
Cumbria

WARICK, Ian
County
Hampshire

WARN, Ian
Regiment
Essex

WARN, Ian
Regiment
Essex

WARNE, Leon
Grove
Bridgend

WATERMAN, Scott
Lakeside Lodge
Cambridgeshire

WATKINSON, Gary
Howley Hall
Yorkshire (West)

WATSON, Craig
Bourn
Cambridgeshire

WATSON, Paul
Flackwell Heath
Buckinghamshire

WATSON, Scott
Basingstoke
Hampshire

WATT, Mark
Lullingstone Park
Kent

WATTS, Ian
Cannons Court
Gloucestershire

WATTS, Robert
Lambourne Club
Berkshire

WAUGH, Ian
Tynedale
Northumberland

WAY, Nicky
Hilden Europro
Kent

WEATHERHEAD, Carl
Worksop
Nottinghamshire

WEBB, Graham
Holsworthy
Devon

WEBB, M
Bedlingtonshire
Northumberland

WEBB, Nick
Tilsworth
Bedfordshire

WEBSTER, Alastair
Edzell
Angus

WEBSTER, Daniel
St. Annes Old Links
Lancashire

WEBSTER, David
Lundin
Fife

WEIR, Russell
Cowal
Argyll and Bute

WELCH, Mark
Chelmsford
Essex

WELDING, I
High Post
Wiltshire

WELDON, Michael
Dunstable Downs
Bedfordshire

WELLER, Ashley
Hampton Court Palace Golf Club
London (Greater)

WELLS, Andrew
Oadby
Leicestershire

WESSELINGH, Paul
Kedleston Park
Derbyshire

WESTON, Dave
Liverpool Municipal
Merseyside

WHALE, Kevin
Central London
London (Greater)

WHEELER, David
Malkins Bank
Cheshire

WHELLER, Dene
Formby
Merseyside

WHIDDON, John
Gloucester
Gloucestershire

WHIPHAM, Bruce
Kirby Muxloe
Leicestershire

WHISTON, Adam
Tara (Royal)
County Meath

WHITE, Alan
Lanark
Lanarkshire (South)

WHITE, Alex
Tilsworth
Bedfordshire

WHITE, Alistair
Ascot (Royal)
Berkshire

WHITE, Andrew
Oak Leaf
County Durham

WHITE, M
Shendish Manor
Hertfordshire

WHITE, Mark
Hamptworth
Wiltshire

WHITE, Steve
Middleton Hall
Norfolk

WHITEHALL, A
Barrow
Cumbria

WHITELEY, J
Temple
Berkshire

WHITFORD, Richard
Knock
County Antrim

WHITING, Adam
Little Lakes
Worcestershire

WHITLEY, Neville
Sparkwell
Devon

WHITSON, Kevan
Down (Royal County)
County Down

WHITTLE, Peter
Wensum Valley
Norfolk

WHYMARK, Stephen
Ipswich
Suffolk

WHYTE, Gregor
Dunnikier
Fife

WICKELOW, N
Crews Hill
London (Greater)

WICKETTS, C J
Walmley
Midlands (West)

WILBY, Paul
Fynn Valley
Suffolk

WILD, Terry
Mill Ride
Berkshire

WILKINSON, Stewart
Brampton
Cumbria

WILLIAMS, G
Parasampia
Berkshire

WILLIAMS, Greg
Pavenham
Bedfordshire

WILLIAMS, Ian
West Chiltington
Sussex (West)

WILLIAMS, Mark
Paultons Golf Centre
Hampshire

WILLIAMS, Mark
Rhos-On-Sea
Conwy

WILLIAMS, Michael
Ashton-on-Mersey
Cheshire

WILLIAMS, Nick
St. Enodoc
Cornwall

WILLIAMS, Paul
Mount Pleasant
Bedfordshire

WILLIAMS, Paul
Wrexham
Wrexham

WILLIAMS, Roger
Addington Palace
Surrey

WILLIAMS, Tony
Studley Wood
Oxfordshire

WILLIAMSON, A
Gower
Swansea

WILLIAMSON, Duncan
Kirkhill
Glasgow (City of)

WILLIAMSON, Roy
Casterton
Cumbria

WILLIAMSON, S J
Canwick Park
Lincolnshire

WILLS, Marcus
Mountain Ash
Rhondda Cynon Taff

WILSON, Ernie
Woodham
County Durham

Watts — Wilson

Professionals Alphabetically

WILSON, James
Sleaford
Lincolnshire

WILSON, Jimmy
Swinton Park
Manchester (Greater)

WILSON, Paul
Chilwell Manor
Nottinghamshire

WILSON, Sandy
Trentham
Staffordshire

WILTON, David
Muswell Hill
London (Greater)

WINDGROVE, Dean
Wimbledon Park
London (Greater)

WIXON, Nigel
Enmore Park
Somerset

WOOD, Keith
Brocket Hall
Hertfordshire

WOOD, Keith
Ramada Hotel
Gloucestershire

WOOD, Mark
Wellshurst
Sussex (East)

WOOD, Peter
Bradley Hall
Yorkshire (West)

WOOD, Simon
Moatlands
Kent

WOOD, Simon
Scraptoft
Leicestershire

WOODROFFE, John
Central London
London (Greater)

WOODWARD, Mark
Perdiswell Park Golf Course
Worcestershire

WOOLHOUSE, Robert
Hillsborough
Yorkshire (South)

WOOTTON, M
Lakeside
Neath Port Talbot

WORLEY, Mike
Cray Valley
Kent

WORRALL, Dean
Ashby Decoy
Lincolnshire (North)

WRIGHT, Ian
Wakefield
Yorkshire (West)

WRIGHT, Ian
West Linton
Scottish Borders

WRIGHT, Innes
Aboyne
Aberdeenshire

WRIGHT, James
Oxhey Park
Hertfordshire

WRIGHT, Phil
Coombe Wood
London (Greater)

WRIGHT, Stretton
Hornsea
Yorkshire (East)

WRIGLEY, Ian
Dunham Forest
Cheshire

WYLIE, Nigel
Sandwell Park
Midlands (West)

YATES, Steve
Kenilworth
Warwickshire

YEO, John
Bude & North Cornwall
Cornwall

YOUNG, Andrew
Costessey Park
Norfolk

YOUNG, Bobby
Peover
Cheshire

YOUNG, Brian
Strathmore Golf Ctre
Perth And Kinross

YOUNG, Finlay
Winchester (Royal)
Hampshire

YOUNG, Ian
Stoneham
Hampshire

YOUNG, Johnny
Rosslare
County Wexford

YULE, Bill
Ballater
Aberdeenshire

Wilson — Yule

Professionals Alphabetically

SECTION 13

*Additional useful contact
details, retailers, suppliers
of golf equipment, driving
ranges and pitch and putt
courses.*

*Listed by Company type
by Country by County.*

DRIVING RANGES

ENGLAND

BERKSHIRE

⛳ **BRAYWICK GOLF PARK,** Braywick Road, Maidenhead, **BERKSHIRE,** SL6 1BN
(T) 01628 676910

⛳ **LEADERBOARD GOLF CENTRE,** Richfield Avenue, Reading, **BERKSHIRE,** RG1 8EQ
(T) 0118 957 5655

⛳ **RICHFIELD DRIVING RANGE LTD,** Rivermead, Richfield Ave, Reading, **BERKSHIRE,** RG1 8EQ
(T) 0118 9573700

⛳ **TRY GOLF,** Blue Mountain Golf Centre, 1 Wood Lane, Binfield, Bracknell, **BERKSHIRE,** RG42 4EX
(T) 01344 488858

BRISTOL

⛳ **HAMBROOK GOLF RANGE,** Commonmead Lane, Hambrook, Bristol, **BRISTOL,** BS16 1QQ
(T) 0117 970 1116

CAMBRIDGESHIRE

⛳ **SWINGERS '92,** East Of England Showground, Oundle Road, Alwalton, Peterborough, **CAMBRIDGESHIRE,** PE2 6XE
(T) 01733 239911

CHESHIRE

⛳ **BANNEL GOLF RANGE,** Mold Road, Broughton, Chester, **CHESHIRE,** CH4 0EW
(T) 01244 544639

⛳ **CHESTER GOLF RANGE,** Chester Road, Bretton, Chester, **CHESHIRE,** CH4 0DF
(T) 01244 681605

⛳ **CRANFORD GOLF CENTRE & DRIVING RANGE,** Harwood Road, Stockport, **CHESHIRE,** SK4 3AW
(T) 0161 432 8242

⛳ **DRIVETIME GOLF STORE,** Centre Park, Slutchers Lane, Warrington, **CHESHIRE,** WA1 1QL
(T) 01925 234800

⛳ **EATON HILL GOLF DRIVING RANGE,** Forest Road, Tarporley, **CHESHIRE,** CW6 0JA
(T) 01829 732482

⛳ **ELTON GOLF DRIVING RANGE,** Hall Lane, Elton, Sandbach, **CHESHIRE,** CW11 3TT
(T) 01270 526200

⛳ **HARTFORD GOLF RANGE,** Burrows Hill, Hartford, Northwich, **CHESHIRE,** CW8 3AA
(T) 01606 871162

⛳ **SANDFIELD GOLF RANGE,** Ince Lane, Wimbolds Trafford, Chester, **CHESHIRE,** CH2 4JP
(T) 01244 301752

⛳ **STROKEPLAY DRIVING RANGE,** Stockport Road, Timperley, Altrincham, **CHESHIRE,** WA15 7LP
(T) 0161 927 7504

⛳ **SUTTON FIELDS CENTRE,** Chester Road, Sutton Weaver, Runcorn, **CHESHIRE,** WA7 3EY
(T) 01928 791001

⛳ **SYCAMORES GOLF CENTRE,** Ashton Rd Farm, Ashton Rd, Golborne, Warrington, **CHESHIRE,** WA3 3UU
(T) 01942 717665

⛳ **WOODSIDE GOLF DRIVING RANGE,** Knutsford Road, Cranage, Crewe, **CHESHIRE,** CW4 8HJ
(T) 01477 532388

CORNWALL

⛳ **CORNWALL GOLF CENTRE,** Carminnow Cross, Bodmin, **CORNWALL,** PL30 4AW
(T) 01208 77588

⛳ **HAYLE GOLF RANGE,** 1 Wheal Alfred Road, Hayle, **CORNWALL,** TR27 5JT
(T) 01736 753655

⛳ **MITHIAN GOLF DRIVING RANGE,** Fairview Farm, Mithian Downs, St. Agnes, **CORNWALL,** TR5 0PY
(T) 01872 553833

CUMBRIA

⛳ **KENDAL GOLF DRIVING RANGE,** Oxenholme Road, Kendal, **CUMBRIA,** LA9 7HG
(T) 01539 733933

⛳ **PENRITH GOLF CENTRE & DRIVING RANGE,** Redhills, Penrith, **CUMBRIA,** CA11 0DR
(T) 01768 892167

⛳ **STROKE ONE DRIVING RANGE,** Thwaite Flat, Barrow-in-Furness, **CUMBRIA,** LA14 4QH
(T) 01229 464164

DERBYSHIRE

⛳ **DERBY GOLF CENTRE,** Borrowash Road, Spondon, Derby, **DERBYSHIRE,** DE21 7PH
(T) 01332 661414

⛳ **DRONFIELD DRIVING RANGE,** Callywhite Lane, Dronfield, **DERBYSHIRE,** S18 2XH
(T) 01246 291828

⛳ **PEAK PRACTICE,** Barns farm, Fairfield, Buxton, **DERBYSHIRE,** SK17 7HW
(T) 01298 74444

DEVON

⛳ **CLIFTON HILL,** Clifton Hill, Exeter, **DEVON,** EX1 2DJ
(T) 01392 493196

⛳ **ILFRACOMBE & WOOLACOMBE GOLF RANGE,** Woolacombe, **DEVON,** EX34 7HF
(T) 01271 866222

⛳ **TIVERTON PARKWAY GOLF DRIVING RANGE,** Sampford Peverell, Tiverton, **DEVON,** EX16 7EH
(T) 01884 820825

⛳ **TORBAY GOLF CENTRE LTD,** Grange Road, Paignton, **DEVON,** TQ4 7JT
(T) 01803 528728

⛳ **YELVERTON GOLF DRIVING RANGE,** Abbey Lane, Crapstone, Yelverton, **DEVON,** PL20 7PU
(T) 01822 855526

DORSET

⛳ **BOURNEMOUTH GOLF DRIVING RANGE,** Parley, Christchurch, **DORSET,** BH23 6BB
(T) 01202 593131

⛳ **GOLF ACADEMY,** Canford Magna Golf Club, Knighton Lane, Wimborne, **DORSET,** BH21 3AS
(T) 01202 591212

⛳ **TWYFORD GOLFING RANGE,** Brach Farm, Twyford, Shaftesbury, **DORSET,** SP7 0JN
(T) 01747 811356

ESSEX

⛳ **BELVEDERE GOLF RANGE,** Hardings Elms Road, Crays Hill, Billericay, **ESSEX,** CM11 2UH
(T) 01268 286612

⛳ **COLCHESTER GOLF RANGE,** Old Ipswich Road, Ardleigh, Colchester, **ESSEX,** CO7 7QR
(T) 01206 230974

⛳ **ELSENHAM GOLF CENTRE,** Henham Road, Elsenham, Bishop's Stortford, **ESSEX,** CM22 6DH
(T) 01279 812865

⛳ **EPPING GOLF RANGE,** Upland Road, Thornwood, Epping, **ESSEX,** CM16 6NL
(T) 01992 570707

⛳ **EUROPEAN GOLF & LEISURE CLUB,** St. James Ctre, East Rd, Harlow, **ESSEX,** CM20 2SX
(T) 01279 420460

⛳ **HANFORD VIEW GOLF RANGE,** Clacton Road, Little Oakley, Harwich, **ESSEX,** CO12 5JJ
(T) 01255 886892

⛳ **HOCKLEY DRIVING RANGE,** Aldermans Hill, Hockley, **ESSEX,** SS5 4RP
(T) 01702 207218

⛳ **LEIGH GOLF RANGE,** Leigh Marshes, Leigh-on-Sea, **ESSEX,** SS9 2ER
(T) 01702 710586

Driving Ranges — Driving Ranges

Useful Addresses

⛳ **NORTH WEALD GOLF SCHOOL,** North
Weald Golf Range/Merlin Way, North Weald
Airfield, Epping, **ESSEX,** CM16 4BZ
(T) 01992 522188

⛳ **RAYLEIGH GOLF RANGE,** Rear Of
Carpenters Arms, Old London Road,
Rawreth, Wickford, **ESSEX,** SS11 8TZ
(T) 01268 781706

⛳ **SWINGFIELD FAMILY GOLF CENTRE,**
Pro Shop, Steeple Road, Latchingdon,
Chelmsford, **ESSEX,** CM3 6LD
(T) 01621 744473

⛳ **TIPTREE GOLF DRIVING RANGE,**
Newbridge Road, Tiptree, Colchester,
ESSEX, CO5 0HZ
(T) 01621 819374

⛳ **WARREN PARK GOLF CENTRE,**
Whalebone Lane North, Romford, **ESSEX,**
RM6 6SB
(T) 0208 597 1120

⛳ **WOODHAM MORTIMER GOLF
RANGE,** Burnham Road, Woodham
Mortimer, Maldon, **ESSEX,** CM9 6SR
(T) 01245 222276

HAMPSHIRE

⛳ **A G PHILLIPS & SON LTD,** Tournerbury
Lane, Hayling Island, **HAMPSHIRE,** PO11
9DL
(T) 02392 468613

⛳ **ANDREW STUBBS,** Chestnut Avenue,
Eastleigh, **HAMPSHIRE,** SO50 5BT
(T) 02380 616550

⛳ **DENMEAD GOLF DRIVING RANGE,**
Glenfield Stud, Furzeley Road,
Waterlooville, **HAMPSHIRE,** PO7 6TX
(T) 02392 268884

HEREFORDSHIRE

⛳ **HEREFORD DRIVING RANGE & GOLF
CENTRE,** Hill Barn, Lyde, Hereford,
HEREFORDSHIRE, HR4 8AB
(T) 01432 265666

HERTFORDSHIRE

⛳ **A1 GOLF DRIVING RANGE,** Rowley
Lane, Barnet, **HERTFORDSHIRE,** EN5 3HW
(T) 0208 447 1411

⛳ **RADLETT GOLF CENTRE,** Harper Lane,
Radlett, **HERTFORDSHIRE,** WD7 7HU
(T) 01923 852557

⛳ **TOP GOLF GAMES CENTRE,** Bushey
Mill Lane, Watford, **HERTFORDSHIRE,**
WD24 7PD
(T) 01923 222045

KENT

⛳ **GREENSOLE GOLF PRACTICE
CENTRE,** Manston Road, Manston,
Ramsgate, **KENT,** CT12 5BE
(T) 01843 590005

⛳ **HERNE BAY GOLF DRIVING RANGE,**
Bullockstone Road, Herne Bay, **KENT,** CT6
7NN
(T) 01227 742742

⛳ **SHEERNESS DRIVING RANGE,** Halfway
Road, Minster on Sea, Sheerness, **KENT,**
ME12 3AA
(T) 01795 581425

⛳ **SWANLEY GOLF CENTRE,** Beechenlea
Lane, Swanley, **KENT,** BR8 8DR
(T) 01322 615126

⛳ **SWANMEAD GOLF DRIVING RANGE,**
Cannon Lane, Tonbridge, **KENT,** TN9 1PP
(T) 01732 353281

⛳ **THAMES VIEW GOLF CENTRE,** Thong
Lane, Gravesend, **KENT,** DA12 4LG
(T) 01474 335002

⛳ **WORLD OF GOLF,** A20 Sidcup By
Passage, Chislehurst, **KENT,** BR7 6RP
(T) 0208 309 0181

LANCASHIRE

⛳ **BLACKBURN GOLF DRIVING RANGE,**
Haslingden Road, Blackburn,
LANCASHIRE, BB2 3HJ
(T) 01254 581996

⛳ **CASTLE HAWK,** Chadwick Lane,
Rochdale, **LANCASHIRE,** OL11 3BY
(T) 01706 640841

⛳ **CHORLEY GOLF DRIVING RANGE,**
Brookfields, Chancery Road, Chorley,
LANCASHIRE, PR7 1XP
(T) 01257 233942

⛳ **DOUGLAS VALLEY GOLF DRIVING
RANGE,** A6 Blackrod By Passage,
Blackrod, Bolton, **LANCASHIRE,** BL6 5HX
(T) 01257 474844

⛳ **KEARSLEY GOLF RANGE,** Moss Lane,
Kearsley, Bolton, **LANCASHIRE,** BL4 8SF
(T) 01204 575726

⛳ **LEE VALLEY GOLF,** Lee Lane, Rishton,
Blackburn, **LANCASHIRE,** BB1 4AJ
(T) 01254 884222

⛳ **LEISURE LAKES GOLF DRIVING
RANGE,** Mere Brow, Preston,
LANCASHIRE, PR4 6LA
(T) 01772 815842

⛳ **LUCKY STRIKE GOLF DRIVING
RANGE,** Lytham Road, Warton, Preston,
LANCASHIRE, PR4 1TE
(T) 01772 631621

⛳ **PHOENIX SPORTING & LEISURE
CENTRE,** North Drive, Thornton-
Cleveleys, **LANCASHIRE,** FY5 3AJ
(T) 01253 854846

⛳ **PRESTON GOLF DRIVING RANGE,**
Lightfoot Lane, Fulwood, Preston,
LANCASHIRE, PR4 0AE
(T) 01772 861827

⛳ **TWINBROOK GOLF RANGE,** Lincoln
Way, Clitheroe, **LANCASHIRE,** BB7 1QD
(T) 01200 444902

LEICESTERSHIRE

⛳ **CHARNWOOD GOLF & LEISURE
CENTRE,** Derby Road, Loughborough,
LEICESTERSHIRE, LE11 5AD
(T) 01509 610022

⛳ **DISCOVERY GOLF & LEISURE LTD,**
Ashby Road, Coalville, **LEICESTERSHIRE,**
LE67 3LA
(T) 01530 811622

LINCOLNSHIRE

⛳ **BOSTON WEST GOLF CENTRE LTD,**
Hubberts Bridge, Boston, **LINCOLNSHIRE,**
PE20 3QX
(T) 01205 290670

⛳ **ELMS GOLF CENTRE,** Croft Bank, Croft,
Wainfleet, Skegness, **LINCOLNSHIRE,**
PE24 4AW
(T) 01754 881230

LINCOLNSHIRE (NORTH EAST)

⛳ **COUNTY GOLF DRIVING RANGE,**
Cheapside, Waltham, Grimsby,
LINCOLNSHIRE (NORTH EAST), DN37
0JS
(T) 01472 821883

⛳ **SWINGTIME,** Cromwell Road, Grimsby,
LINCOLNSHIRE (NORTH EAST), DN31
2BH
(T) 01472 250555

LONDON (GREATER)

⛳ **CHINGFORD GOLF RANGE,** Waltham
Way, London, **LONDON (GREATER),** E4
8AQ
(T) 0208 529 2409

⛳ **CHISWICK BRIDGE GOLF RANGE,**
Dukes Meadows, London, **LONDON
(GREATER),** W4 2SH
(T) 0208 995 0537

⛳ **EALING GOLF RANGE,** Rowdell Road,
Northolt, **LONDON (GREATER),** UB5 6AG
(T) 0208 845 4967

⛳ **GOLFER LTD,** Woolwich Manor Way,
London, **LONDON (GREATER),** E6 5LJ
(T) 0207 511 3404

⛳ **KNIGHTSBRIDGE GOLF SCHOOL,** 47
Lowndes Square, London, **LONDON
(GREATER),** SW1X 9JU
(T) 0207 235 2468

⛳ **METRO GOLF,** Great North Way, London,
LONDON (GREATER), NW4 1PS
(T) 0208 202 1202

⛳ **REGENTS PARK GOLF & TENNIS
SCHOOL,** Outer Circle, Regents Pk,
London, **LONDON (GREATER),** NW1 4RL
(T) 020 77240643

⚲ **UK DRIVING RANGES LTD,** The Old Potato Yard, York Way, London, **LONDON (GREATER),** N1 0AS
(T) 0207 837 1616

MANCHESTER

⚲ **PLAY GOLF EXPERIENCE,** Old Pk Lane, The Trafford Centre, Manchester, **MANCHESTER,** M17 8AP
(T) 0161 749 7000

MANCHESTER (GREATER)

⚲ **ASTLEY GOLF RANGE,** Manchester Road, Astley, Tyldesley, Manchester, **MANCHESTER (GREATER),** M29 7EJ
(T) 01942 889436

⚲ **BARDSLEY PARK GOLF CENTRE,** Knott Lanes, Bardsley, Oldham, **MANCHESTER (GREATER),** OL8 3JD
(T) 0161 6272463

⚲ **CARRINGTON GOLF RANGE,** Ackers Lane, Carrington, Manchester, **MANCHESTER (GREATER),** M31 4AW
(T) 0161 775 7655

MERSEYSIDE

⚲ **FORMBY GOLF CENTRE,** Moss Side, Formby, Liverpool, **MERSEYSIDE,** L37 0AF
(T) 01704 875952

⚲ **LIVERPOOL GOLF DRIVING RANGE,** Caldway Drive, Liverpool, **MERSEYSIDE,** L27 0YB
(T) 0151 487 3744

⚲ **MORETON HILLS GOLF CENTRE,** Tarran Way South, Tarran Industrial Estate, Wirral, **MERSEYSIDE,** CH46 4TP
(T) 0151 677 6606

⚲ **PORT SUNLIGHT GOLF DRIVING RANGE,** Port Sunlight, Wirral, **MERSEYSIDE,** CH62 4SY
(T) 0151 643 8751

⚲ **PRENTON GOLF DRIVING RANGE,** Prenton Dell Road, Prenton, **MERSEYSIDE,** CH43 3BS
(T) 0151 609 0669

MIDLANDS (WEST)

⚲ **FISHLEY PARK GOLF RANGE,** Fishley Lane, Pelsall, Walsall, **MIDLANDS (WEST),** WS3 5AE
(T) 01922 685279

⚲ **FOUR ASHES GOLF CENTRE,** Four Ashes Road, Dorridge, Solihull, **MIDLANDS (WEST),** B93 8NQ
(T) 01564 779055

⚲ **HALESOWEN GOLF RANGE,** Quarry Lane, Halesowen, **MIDLANDS (WEST),** B63 4PB
(T) 0121 550 2920

⚲ **HOST CENTRE,** Booths Lane, Birmingham, **MIDLANDS (WEST),** B42 2RG
(T) 0121 360 7600

⚲ **JOHN REAY,** Sandpits Lane, Coventry, **MIDLANDS (WEST),** CV6 2FR
(T) 02476 333920

⚲ **SANDWELL PINES GOLF CENTRE,** Allsopps Hill, Tippity Green, Rowley Regis, **MIDLANDS (WEST),** B65 9AA
(T) 0121 559 0353

⚲ **WAST HILLS GOLF CENTRE,** 300 Redhill Road, Kings Norton, Birmingham, **MIDLANDS (WEST),** B38 9EL
(T) 0121 459 7767

NORFOLK

⚲ **FAKENHAM DRIVING RANGE,** Burnham Market Road, Sculthorpe, Fakenham, **NORFOLK,** NR21 9SA
(T) 01328 856614

NORTHUMBERLAND

⚲ **GUBEON GOLF CENTRE LTD,** Walton Road, Morpeth, **NORTHUMBERLAND,** NE61 3YJ
(T) 01670 519090

⚲ **ST GEORGES GOLF DRIVING RANGE,** Hallyards Farm, Mickley, Stocksfield, **NORTHUMBERLAND,** NE43 7LR
(T) 01661 843044

NOTTINGHAMSHIRE

⚲ **MANSFIELD FAMILY GOLF CENTRE,** Jubilee Way North, Mansfield, **NOTTINGHAMSHIRE,** NG18 3PJ
(T) 01623 422764

⚲ **P LOCKLEY,** The Showground, Lincoln Road, Winthorpe, Newark, **NOTTINGHAMSHIRE,** NG24 2NY
(T) 01636 702161

⚲ **RIVERBANK DRIVING RANGE,** Riverbank Farm, Fackley Road, Teversal, Sutton-in-Ashfield, **NOTTINGHAMSHIRE,** NG17 3HN
(T) 01623 514500

OXFORDSHIRE

⚲ **DRAYTON LEISURE GOLF DRIVING RANGE,** Drayton Lodge Farm, Warwick Road, Banbury, **OXFORDSHIRE,** OX17 1HJ
(T) 01295 730242

⚲ **HEATHFIELD GOLF CENTRE,** Heathfield Village, Bletchingdon, Kidlington, **OXFORDSHIRE,** OX5 3DX
(T) 01869 351552

⚲ **HILLSIDE FARM GOLF DRIVING RANGE,** Hillside Farm, Banbury Road, Bloxham, Banbury, **OXFORDSHIRE,** OX15 4PF
(T) 01295 720361

⚲ **SMOKE ACRE GOLF DRIVING RANGE,** Woodway Road, Blewbury, Didcot, **OXFORDSHIRE,** OX11 9HW
(T) 01235 850575

⚲ **SOUTHFIELDS GOLF RANGE,** A D Business Centre/Beadle Trading Estate, Hithercroft Road, Wallingford, **OXFORDSHIRE,** OX10 9EZ
(T) 01844 214285

SHROPSHIRE

⚲ **AQUALATE GOLF CENTRE,** Stafford Road, Newport, **SHROPSHIRE,** TF10 9BY
(T) 01952 811699

⚲ **HIGHLEY GOLF RANGE,** Netherfield Farm, New England Lane, Highley, Bridgnorth, **SHROPSHIRE,** WV16 6ET
(T) 01746 862500

⚲ **SHREWSBURY GOLF DRIVING RANGE LTD,** Telford Way, Shrewsbury, **SHROPSHIRE,** SY2 5XQ
(T) 01743 354975

SOMERSET

⚲ **CLEVEDON GOLF CENTRE,** Stileway Farm, Lower Strode Road, Clevedon, **SOMERSET,** BS21 6UU
(T) 01275 340342

⚲ **SWINGRITE,** Haydon Lane, Haydon, Taunton, **SOMERSET,** TA3 5AB
(T) 01823 442600

⚲ **WESTON GOLF CENTRE,** Weston Links, Weston-super-Mare, **SOMERSET,** BS23 3WL
(T) 01934 613423

⚲ **WESTON SUPER RANGE,** Wolvershill Road, Banwell, **SOMERSET,** BS29 6LH
(T) 01934 823382

STAFFORDSHIRE

⚲ **BELMONT GOLF DRIVING RANGE,** Tutbury Road, Needwood, Burton-on-Trent, **STAFFORDSHIRE,** DE13 9PH
(T) 01283 814381

⚲ **KEELE DRIVING RANGE & GOLF SHOP,** Keele Road, Newcastle, **STAFFORDSHIRE,** ST5 5AB
(T) 01782 717417

⚲ **LIGHTWOOD GOLF DRIVING RANGE,** Woodpark Lane, Stoke-on-Trent, **STAFFORDSHIRE,** ST3 4AD
(T) 01782 335812

⚲ **SOUTH POPLARS GOLF CENTRE,** Newlands Lane, Cannock, **STAFFORDSHIRE,** WS12 5HH
(T) 01543 277999

⚲ **SWINDON RIDGE GOLF DRIVING RANGE,** Bridgnorth Road, Swindon, Dudley, **STAFFORDSHIRE,** DY3 4PU
(T) 01902 896191

⚲ **SWINGERS GOLF CENTRE,** Darnford Lane, Lichfield, **STAFFORDSHIRE,** WS14 9JG
(T) 01543 419416

Driving Ranges — Driving Ranges

Useful Addresses

⛳ **TRENTHAM GARDENS GOLF DRIVING RANGE,** Stone Road, Stoke-on-Trent, **STAFFORDSHIRE,** ST4 8AX
(T) 01782 644606

SUFFOLK

⛳ **BECK ROW GOLF DRIVING RANGE,** Kenny Hill, Bury St. Edmunds, **SUFFOLK,** IP28 8DS
(T) 01638 718972

⛳ **BOURNE HILL GOLF CENTRE LTD,** Bourne Hill, Wherstead, Ipswich, **SUFFOLK,** IP2 8ND
(T) 01473 683233

⛳ **BURY GOLF RANGE,** Rushbrooke Lane, Bury St. Edmunds, **SUFFOLK,** IP33 2RR
(T) 01284 723894

⛳ **FELIXSTOWE GOLF RANGE,** Gulpher Road, Felixstowe, **SUFFOLK,** IP11 9RD
(T) 01394 282135

⛳ **OLD JOE'S,** Greys Hall, Grays Hall Corner, Great Cornard, Sudbury, **SUFFOLK,** CO10 0QG
(T) 01787 374807

⛳ **STONHAM BARNS GOLF CENTRE,** Stonham Barns, Pettaugh Road, Stonham Aspal, Stowmarket, **SUFFOLK,** IP14 6AT
(T) 01449 711545

SURREY

⛳ **CROYDON GOLF DRIVING RANGE LTD,** 175 Long Lane, Croydon, **SURREY,** CR0 7TE
(T) 0208 656 1690

⛳ **HAGEN INTERNATIONAL (UK) LTD,** Pinetree Lodge, Heath House Road, Woking, **SURREY,** GU22 0QU
(T) 01483 476964

⛳ **PACHESHAM PARK GOLF CENTRE,** Oaklawn Road, Leatherhead, **SURREY,** KT22 0BT
(T) 01372 843453

SUSSEX (WEST)

⛳ **SLINFOLD PARK,** Stane Street, Slinfold, Horsham, **SUSSEX (WEST),** RH13 7RE
(T) 01403 791555

TYNE AND WEAR

⛳ **BEGGARS WOOD DRIVING RANGE,** Beggarswood, Coach Road, Gateshead, **TYNE AND WEAR,** NE11 0HE
(T) 0191 460 3633

⛳ **COCKEN LODGE DRIVING RANGE,** Leamside, Houghton le Spring, **TYNE AND WEAR,** DH4 6OP
(T) 0191 584 1053

⛳ **GOSFORTH PARK GOLFING COMPLEX,** High Gosforth Park, Newcastle upon Tyne, **TYNE AND WEAR,** NE3 5HQ
(T) 0191 236 4867

⛳ **SUNDERLAND DRIVING RANGE,** Athenaeum House, Newcastle Road, Sunderland, **TYNE AND WEAR,** SR5 1JT
(T) 0191 516 8600

WARWICKSHIRE

⛳ **ALCESTER GOLF CENTRE,** Old Stratford Road, Oversley Green, Alcester, **WARWICKSHIRE,** B49 6LN
(T) 01789 400942

⛳ **BRAMCOTE GOLF DRIVING RANGE LTD,** Bazzard Road, Bramcote, Nuneaton, **WARWICKSHIRE,** CV11 6QJ
(T) 01455 221341

⛳ **LEAM VALLEY GOLF CENTRE,** Southam Road, Kytes Hardwick, Rugby, **WARWICKSHIRE,** CV23 8AA
(T) 01788 522765

⛳ **M J M GOLF CENTRE,** Brickyard Lane, Studley, **WARWICKSHIRE,** B80 7EE
(T) 01527 857129

⛳ **WARWICK GOLF CENTRE,** Warwick Racecourse, Warwick, **WARWICKSHIRE,** CV34 6HW
(T) 01926 494316

WILTSHIRE

⛳ **GOLF ACADEMY,** Tiddly Wink, Yatton Keynell, Chippenham, **WILTSHIRE,** SN14 7BY
(T) 01249 783121

⛳ **SALISBURY GOLF DRIVING RANGE LTD,** 1 Cricket Field Cottages, Wilton Road, Salisbury, **WILTSHIRE,** SP2 9NS
(T) 01722 410209

⛳ **WINGFIELD GOLF DRIVING RANGE,** Trowbridge Road, Wingfield, Trowbridge, **WILTSHIRE,** BA14 9LE
(T) 01225 776365

WORCESTERSHIRE

⛳ **DROITWICH GOLF CENTRE,** Copcut Lane, Copcut, Droitwich, **WORCESTERSHIRE,** WR9 7JB
(T) 01905 797190

⛳ **INKBERROW GOLF CENTRE,** Holberrow Green, Redditch, **WORCESTERSHIRE,** B96 6SF
(T) 01386 793053

⛳ **OLDINGTON GOLF RANGE,** Zortech Avenue, Kidderminster, **WORCESTERSHIRE,** DY11 7EX
(T) 01562 861841

⛳ **WORCESTER GOLF RANGE,** Weir Lane, Worcester, **WORCESTERSHIRE,** WR2 4AY
(T) 01905 421213

WREXHAM

⛳ **LLAY GOLF DRIVING RANGE,** Llay New Road, Llay, Wrexham, **WREXHAM,** LL12 0TE
(T) 01978 853009

YORKSHIRE (EAST)

⛳ **COUNTRY GOLF,** East Carr Road, Hull, **YORKSHIRE (EAST),** HU8 9LR
(T) 01482 784986

⛳ **SPALDINGTON GOLF CENTRE LTD,** Driving Range, Spaldington Lane, Spaldington, Goole, **YORKSHIRE (EAST),** DN14 7NG
(T) 01430 432484

YORKSHIRE (NORTH)

⛳ **RUDDING PARK GOLF DRIVING RANGE,** Follifoot, Harrogate, **YORKSHIRE (NORTH),** HG3 1DJ
(T) 01423 873400

⛳ **SCALM PARK DRIVING RANGE,** Scalm Park, Wistow Common, Selby, **YORKSHIRE (NORTH),** YO8 3RD
(T) 01757 210846

⛳ **SCOTTON GOLF DRIVING RANGE,** Low Moor Lane, Scotton, Knaresborough, **YORKSHIRE (NORTH),** HG5 9HZ
(T) 01423 868943

⛳ **WHITEHILLS GOLF DRIVING RANGE,** Whitehills, Stirton, Skipton, **YORKSHIRE (NORTH),** BD23 3LH
(T) 01756 793325

YORKSHIRE (SOUTH)

⛳ **DONCASTER GOLF DRIVING RANGE,** Armthorpe Lane, Barnby Dun, Doncaster, **YORKSHIRE (SOUTH),** DN3 1LZ
(T) 01302 883265

⛳ **MOORE VIEW GOLF CENTRE,** Bradway Road, Sheffield, **YORKSHIRE (SOUTH),** S17 4QU
(T) 0114 236 1195

⛳ **SANDHILL GOLF RANGE,** Middlecliffe Lane, Little Houghton, Barnsley, **YORKSHIRE (SOUTH),** S72 0HW
(T) 01226 751775

⛳ **WOODLANDS,** Lee Lane, Royston, Barnsley, **YORKSHIRE (SOUTH),** S71 4RT
(T) 01226 390779

YORKSHIRE (WEST)

⛳ **DENHOLME HOUSE GOLF DRIVING RANGE,** Halifax Road, Denholme, Bradford, **YORKSHIRE (WEST),** BD13 4EN
(T) 01274 831782

⛳ **GARFORTH GOLF DRIVING RANGE,** Long Lane, Garforth, Leeds, **YORKSHIRE (WEST),** LS25 2DS
(T) 0113 287 1111

⛳ **GHYLLBECK GOLF DRIVING RANGE LTD,** Esholt Lane, Baildon, Shipley, **YORKSHIRE (WEST),** BD17 7RJ
(T) 01274 530338

⛳ **SILSDEN GOLF DRIVING RANGE,** Keighley Road, Silsden, Keighley, **YORKSHIRE (WEST),** BD20 0EH
(T) 01535 655720

Driving Ranges — Driving Ranges

Useful Addresses

⛳ **STADIUM GOLF,** Stadium Way, Huddersfield, **YORKSHIRE (WEST),** HD1 6PG
(T) 01484 452564

⛳ **WALTON GOLF CENTRE,** Common Lane, Walton, Wakefield, **YORKSHIRE (WEST),** WF2 6PS
(T) 01924 253155

IRELAND
COUNTY CARLOW

⛳ **CARLOW GOLF RANGE,** Leighlin Rd, Crossneen, **COUNTY CARLOW,**
(T) 0503 41683

COUNTY CORK

⛳ **BLARNEY GOLF RANGE,** Blarney, **COUNTY CORK,**
(T) 021 4382060

⛳ **CARRIGDHOUN GOLF RANGE,** Ringaskiddy Rd, Carrigaline, Cork, **COUNTY CORK,**
(T) 021 4371303

⛳ **DUHALLOW DRIVING RANGE,** Rossacon Newmarket, **COUNTY CORK,**
(T) 029 51105

⛳ **FRANKFIELD GOLF CLUB & DRIVING RANGE,** Frankfield Grange, Douglas, **COUNTY CORK,**
(T) 021 4363124

⛳ **KILCULLY GOLF RANGE,** Kilcully, **COUNTY CORK,**
(T) 021 4394475

⛳ **MALLOW GOLF RANGE,** Copstown, Mallow, **COUNTY CORK,**
(T) 022 27894

⛳ **ROSSCARBERY GOLF DRIVING RANGE,** Rosscarbery, **COUNTY CORK,**
(T) 023 48054

⛳ **WOODVIEW GOLF DRIVING RANGE,** Jamesbrook East Ferry, Midleton, **COUNTY CORK,**
(T) 021 4652573

COUNTY DUBLIN

⛳ **ELMGREEN DRIVING RANGE,** Castleknock, Dublin, **COUNTY DUBLIN,**
(T) 01 8200797

COUNTY GALWAY

⛳ **GALWAY GOLF RANGE,** Knocknacarra, Salthill, **COUNTY GALWAY,**
(T) 091 526737

COUNTY KERRY

⛳ **BARRADUFF GOLF DRIVING RANGE,** Killarney, **COUNTY KERRY,**
(T) 064 54656

⛳ **KERRIES GOLF RANGE,** The Kerries, Tralee, **COUNTY KERRY,**
(T) 066 7129543

COUNTY KILDARE

⛳ **CELBRIDGE GOLF RANGE,** Dublin Rd, Celbridge, **COUNTY KILDARE,**
(T) 01 6288833

⛳ **NAAS DRIVING RANGE,** Kerdiffstown, Naas, **COUNTY KILDARE,**
(T) 045 874489

COUNTY LIMERICK

⛳ **LIMERICK DRIVING RANGE,** Coonagh Coonagh, Limerick, **COUNTY LIMERICK,**
(T) 061 455584

COUNTY LONGFORD

⛳ **LONGFORD GOLF RANGE,** Dublin Rd, **COUNTY LONGFORD,**
(T) 043 47378

COUNTY MAYO

⛳ **BALLINA GOLF PRACTICE RANGE,** Crossmolina Rd, Ballina, **COUNTY MAYO,**
(T) 096 72803

⛳ **MAYO GOLF DRIVING RANGE,** Curradrish Turlough Rd, Castlebar, **COUNTY MAYO,**
(T) 094 22327

COUNTY MONAGHAN

⛳ **INNISKEEN GOLF RANGE,** Knock Inniskeen, **COUNTY MONAGHAN,**
(T) 042 9378425

⛳ **MONAGHAN GOLF DRIVING RANGE,** Cormeen, **COUNTY MONAGHAN,**
(T) 047 84909

COUNTY WATERFORD

⛳ **CONSORT MANOR DRIVING RANGE,** Killottern, Butlerstown, **COUNTY WATERFORD,**
(T) 051 354939

COUNTY WESTMEATH

⛳ **MULLINGAR GOLF DRIVING RANGE,** Ballymahon Rd, Mullingar, **COUNTY WESTMEATH,**
(T) 044 48529

COUNTY WICKLOW

⛳ **GREYSTONES DRIVING RANGE,** South Beach, Greystones, **COUNTY WICKLOW,**
(T) 01 2873225

NORTHERN IRELAND
COUNTY ANTRIM

⛳ **KNOCKBRACKEN GOLF ACADEMY,** 24 Ballymaconaghy Road, Belfast, **COUNTY ANTRIM,** BT8 6SB
(T) 02890 701648

⛳ **LAGANVIEW GOLF CENTRE,** 24 Ballyskeagh Road, Lisburn, **COUNTY ANTRIM,** BT27 5SY
(T) 02890 612332

⛳ **NEWFORGE LANE GOLF CENTRE,** 22 Newforge Lane, Belfast, **COUNTY ANTRIM,** BT9 5NW
(T) 02890 683174

⛳ **WHITEHEAD GOLF DRIVING RANGE,** Slaughterford Rd, Whitehead, Carrickfergus, **COUNTY ANTRIM,** BT38 9TG
(T) 028 93353139

COUNTY DOWN

⛳ **BRADSHAWS BRAE,** 115 Belfast Road, Newtownards, **COUNTY DOWN,** BT23 4TS
(T) 02891 813484

⛳ **GROOMSPORT GOLF CENTRE,** 101 Springwell Road, Bangor, **COUNTY DOWN,** BT19 6LX
(T) 02891 473586

⛳ **PARKVIEW GOLF CENTRE,** 12 Comber Road, Hillsborough, **COUNTY DOWN,** BT26 6LN
(T) 02892 689902

⛳ **PAT TRAINOR GOLF ACADEMY,** 45 Milltown Street, Warrenpoint, Newry, **COUNTY DOWN,** BT34 3PU
(T) 02841 773247

COUNTY LONDONDERRY

⛳ **TOBERMORE GOLF DRIVING RANGE,** Maghera Road, Tobermore, Magherafelt, **COUNTY LONDONDERRY,** BT45 5QB
(T) 02879 645406

SCOTLAND
ABERDEENSHIRE

⛳ **KINGS LINKS GOLF CENTRE,** Golf Road, Aberdeen, **ABERDEENSHIRE,** AB24 1RZ
(T) 01224 641644

ARGYLL AND BUTE

⛳ **WORLD OF GOLF,** 2700 Great Western Road, Clydebank, **ARGYLL AND BUTE,** G81 2XT
(T) 0141 944 0444

EDINBURGH (CITY OF)

⛳ **BRAID HILLS GOLF SHOP & GOLF RANGE,** 91 Liberton Drive, Edinburgh, **EDINBURGH (CITY OF),** EH16 6NS
(T) 0131 658 1111

FALKIRK

⛳ **FORTH VIEW GOLF ACADEMY,** Airth Mills, Airth, Falkirk, **FALKIRK,** FK2 8JG
(T) 01324 831112

FIFE

⛳ **FORRESTER COUNTRY PARK GOLF DRIVING RANGE,** Pitdinnie Road, Cairneyhill, Dunfermline, **FIFE,** KY12 8RF
(T) 01383 880505

⛳ **WELLSGREEN GOLF RANGE,** Windygates, Leven, **FIFE,** KY8 5RU
(T) 01592 712435

Driving Ranges — Driving Ranges

Useful Addresses

Driving Ranges — Golf Equipment Manufacturers

Useful Addresses

GLASGOW (CITY OF)

BISHOPBRIGGS GOLF RANGE LTD, Crosshill Road, Bishopbriggs, Glasgow, **GLASGOW (CITY OF),** G64 2PZ
(T) 0141 762 4883

GARY MITCHELL, Blantyre Ferme Road, Uddingston, Glasgow, **GLASGOW (CITY OF),** G71 7RR
(T) 0141 641 8899

HIGHLAND

FAIRWAYS LEISURE LTD, Castleheather, Inverness, **HIGHLAND,** IV2 6AA
(T) 01463 713335

LANARKSHIRE (SOUTH)

NINETEENTH HOLE (THE), Golf Range, Mote Hill, Hamilton, **LANARKSHIRE (SOUTH),** ML3 6BY
(T) 01698 286505

STRATHCLYDE PARK GOLF CENTRE, Mote Hill, Hamilton, **LANARKSHIRE (SOUTH),** ML3 6BY
(T) 01698 285511

LOTHIAN (EAST)

EAST LOTHIAN GOLF RANGE, Meadowmill Sports Complex, Tranent, **LOTHIAN (EAST),** EH33 1LZ
(T) 01875 616100

LOTHIAN (MID)

MELVILLE GOLF CENTRE, Lasswade, **LOTHIAN (MID),** EH18 1AN
(T) 0131 663 8038

LOTHIAN (WEST)

KINGSFIELD GOLF DRIVING RANGE, Kingsfield Farm, Linlithgow, **LOTHIAN (WEST),** EH49 7LS
(T) 01506 671607

PERTH AND KINROSS

MIDDLEBANK GOLF DRIVING RANGE, Middlebank Farm, Errol, Perth, **PERTH AND KINROSS,** PH2 7SX
(T) 01821 670335

NOAH'S ARK GOLF CENTRE, Newhouse Lodge, Newhouse Farm, Perth, **PERTH AND KINROSS,** PH1 1QF
(T) 01738 440678

RENFREWSHIRE

CASTLE GOLF DRIVING RANGE, Rannoch Road, Johnstone, **RENFREWSHIRE,** PA5 0SP
(T) 01505 383599

JOHN MULGREW'S EUROPRO GOLF CENTRE, Inchinnan Road, Renfrew, **RENFREWSHIRE,** PA4 9EG
(T) 0141 886 7477

SCOTTISH BORDERS

DOUGLAS T E, Glendearg, Galashiels, **SCOTTISH BORDERS,** TD1 2NR
(T) 01896 752413

MOUNTHOOLY GOLF DRIVING RANGE, Mounthooly Farm, Jedburgh, **SCOTTISH BORDERS,** TD8 6TJ
(T) 01835 850787

SHETLAND ISLANDS

MOOR PARK FAMILY GOLF CENTRE, Setter, Gulberwick, Shetland, **SHETLAND ISLANDS,** ZE2 9JX
(T) 01595 696933

STIRLING

BRUCEFIELDS FAMILY GOLF LTD, Pirnhall Road, Bannockburn, Stirling, **STIRLING,** FK7 8EH
(T) 01786 818184

WALES

BRIDGEND

CYNFFIG GOLF DRIVING RANGE, Parc Newydd Farm, Moor Lane, Nottage, Porthcawl, **BRIDGEND,** CF36 3EX
(T) 01656 773406

CAERPHILLY

RIDGEWAY GOLF RANGE, Caerphilly Mountain, Thornhill, Caerphilly, **CAERPHILLY,** CF83 1LY
(T) 02920 882255

CARMARTHENSHIRE

TYCROES GOLF RANGE, Llwynceibren, Capel Hendre, Ammanford, **CARMARTHENSHIRE,** SA18 3RH
(T) 01269 597575

CEREDIGION

GOWERTON GOLF RANGE, Victoria Road, Gowerton, Swansea, **CEREDIGION,** SA4 3AB
(T) 01792 875188

GLAMORGAN (VALE OF)

BEGAN PARK GOLF CENTRE, Began Road, Old St. Mellons, Cardiff, **GLAMORGAN (VALE OF),** CF3 6XJ
(T) 02920 361122

HENSOL GOLF ACADEMY, Duffryn Bach, Clawddcoch, Cowbridge, **GLAMORGAN (VALE OF),** CF71 7UP
(T) 01443 226901

GWYNEDD

LLYN GOLF CENTRE, Penrhos, Pwllheli, **GWYNEDD,** LL53 7HG
(T) 01758 701200

PORTHMADOG GOLFING RANGE, Porthmadog, **GWYNEDD,** LL49 9SL
(T) 01766 514499

TREBORTH DRIVING RANGE, Rivendell, Treborth Road, Bangor, **GWYNEDD,** LL57 2RX
(T) 01248 371170

ISLE OF ANGLESEY

PENRHYN GOLF COMPLEX, Llanddaniel, Gaerwen, **ISLE OF ANGLESEY,** LL60 6NN
(T) 01248 421150

NEATH PORT TALBOT

LAKE SIDE DRIVING RANGE, Water Street, Margam, Port Talbot, **NEATH PORT TALBOT,** SA13 2PA
(T) 01639 888400

PEMBROKESHIRE

MAYFIELD, Clareston Farm, Freystrop, Haverfordwest, **PEMBROKESHIRE,** SA62 4NN
(T) 01437 764300

RHONDDA CYNON TAFF

RHONDDA DRIVING RANGE, Pontygwaith, Ferndale, **RHONDDA CYNON TAFF,** CF43 3PW
(T) 01443 441544

TORFAEN

TALYWAIN GOLF CENTRE, Albert Road, Talywain, Pontypool, **TORFAEN,** NP4 7RJ
(T) 01495 775125

GOLF EQUIPMENT MANUFACTURERS

ENGLAND

BEDFORDSHIRE

BETTER METHODS (EUROPE) LTD, 7 Halfway Avenue, Luton, **BEDFORDSHIRE,** LU4 8RA
(T) 01582 758444

L.B. DISCOUNT GOLF, 85 Hockliffe Street, Leighton Buzzard, **BEDFORDSHIRE,** LU7 8EZ
(T) 01525 333030

PEERLESS GOLF CLUBS, 12 Fenlake Road Industrial Estate, Fenlake Road, Bedford, **BEDFORDSHIRE,** MK42 0HB
(T) 01234 347422

BERKSHIRE

AMENITY TECHNOLOGY PRODUCTS LTD, 5 Arkwright Road, Reading, **BERKSHIRE,** RG2 0LU
(T) 0118 931 1111

D GRAY, 159 Old Woosehill Lane, Wokingham, **BERKSHIRE,** RG41 3HR
(T) 0118 989 3047

GOLF LTD, Bishop Centre, Bath Road, Taplow, Maidenhead, **BERKSHIRE,** SL6 0NY
(T) 0800 616462

INDOOR GOLF DESIGNS, 67 Lower Henley Road, Caversham, Reading, **BERKSHIRE,** RG4 5LD
(T) 0118 947 3089

RPK TURF CARE SUPPLIES, 25 The Junipers, Wokingham, **BERKSHIRE,** RG41 4UX
(T) 0118 989 2329

W G THOMAS, Cartref Farm, Wokingham Road, Hurst, Reading, **BERKSHIRE,** RG10 0RU
(T) 0118 934 3728

BRISTOL

FORMULA ONE GOLF, Yew Tree Farm, Nupdown Lane, Oldbury-on-Severn, Bristol, **BRISTOL,** BS35 1RS
(T) 01454 269219

BUCKINGHAMSHIRE

CUSTOM GOLF CONCEPT, Golf Workshop, Westcott Venture Pk, Westcott, Aylesbury, **BUCKINGHAMSHIRE,** HP18 0XB
(T) 01296 770773

H PATTISON LTD, Pattison House, Addison Road, Chesham, **BUCKINGHAMSHIRE,** HP5 2BD
(T) 01494 794646

JACK BARKER GOLF CO, Administration, 14 The Green, Newport Pagnell, **BUCKINGHAMSHIRE,** MK16 0JW
(T) 01908 217500

MACGREGOR GOLF (EUROPE), Coronation Road, Cressex Business Park, High Wycombe, **BUCKINGHAMSHIRE,** HP12 3TA
(T) 01494 755900

PINPOINT GREEN SYSTEMS LTD, 153 Bellingdon Road, Chesham, **BUCKINGHAMSHIRE,** HP5 2NN
(T) 01494 773757

R D A SMITH, 1 Chicheley Street, Newport Pagnell, **BUCKINGHAMSHIRE,** MK16 9AP
(T) 01908 616617

REFUGEES, 3 Linton Cl, Heelands, Milton Keynes, **BUCKINGHAMSHIRE,** MK13 7NR
(T) 01908 321814

SLAGTER GOLF DESIGN LTD, 108 Marys Mead, Hazlemere, High Wycombe, **BUCKINGHAMSHIRE,** HP15 7DY
(T) 01494 715000

STANDARD GOLF (UK) LTD, 554 Ipswich Road, Slough, **BUCKINGHAMSHIRE,** SL1 4EP
(T) 01753 537410

UK GOLF SERVICES LTD, PO Box 1039, Gerrards Cross, **BUCKINGHAMSHIRE,** SL9 7UU
(T) 01753 891661

CAMBRIDGESHIRE

GOLF XCHANGE, Unit 21a Uplands Industrial Estate, Mere Way, Wyton, Huntingdon, **CAMBRIDGESHIRE,** PE28 2DY
(T) 01480 458900

GOLFSMITH LYNX EUROPE, Ormond House, Nuffield Road, St. Ives, **CAMBRIDGESHIRE,** PE27 3LX
(T) 01480 308800

TOMOZUI GOLF, 4 Maxwell Road, Peterborough, **CAMBRIDGESHIRE,** PE2 7JB
(T) 01733 371020

CHESHIRE

ACE GOLF & LEISURE LTD, 217 Birchfield Road, Widnes, **CHESHIRE,** WA8 9AH
(T) 0151 423 3400

ACORN EQUIPMENT UK, Birchbrook Road, Lymm, **CHESHIRE,** WA13 9SA
(T) 01925 757005

DL TEE PRODUCTS, Unit 2, Hampton Heath Industrial Estate, Hampton, Malpas, **CHESHIRE,** SY14 8LU
(T) 01948 820488

FORE GOLF DISCOUNT, Warrington Road, High Legh, Knutsford, **CHESHIRE,** WA16 0WA
(T) 01565 830555

GRAHAM TONGE, Simons Lane, Frodsham, **CHESHIRE,** WA6 6HE
(T) 01928 739442

KADDI-FIX, Unit 2 Millers Lane, Lymm, **CHESHIRE,** WA13 9RG
(T) 01925 756223

POWERLOYAL UK LTD, Nantwich Road, Stanthorne, Middlewich, **CHESHIRE,** CW10 0LH
(T) 01606 841112

STOCKPORT GOLF DEPOT, Meadow Mill, Water Street, Stockport, **CHESHIRE,** SK1 2BY
(T) 0161 480 2007

CLEVELAND

CADDI-LAC ELECTRIC GOLF TROLLY'S, 17 Bonlea Trading Estate, Thornaby, Stockton-on-Tees, **CLEVELAND,** TS17 7AQ
(T) 01642 616746

CUMBRIA

LAKELAND GOLF, Stroke One Driving Range/Hawthwaite Lane, Park Road, Thwaite Flat, Barrow-in-Furness, **CUMBRIA,** LA14 4QH
(T) 01229 464164

DAGENHAM

EAGLE GOLF PRODUCTS & SERVICES, Rear Of 145 Becontree Avenue, Dagenham, **DAGENHAM,** RM8 2UL
(T) 0208 599 7152

DERBYSHIRE

BELPER GOLF CENTRE, 110a Bridge Street, Belper, **DERBYSHIRE,** DE56 1AZ
(T) 01773 827884

CAMPLYON TRADING CO LTD, Norbury Manor, Norbury, Ashbourne, **DERBYSHIRE,** DE6 2ED
(T) 01335 324600

GOLF INDUSTRIES LTD, Unit 3 Slater Avenue, Derby, **DERBYSHIRE,** DE1 1GT
(T) 0800 197 0655

LONGRIDGE GOLF CO LTD, Unit 11 Westminster Industrial Estate, Measham, Swadlincote, **DERBYSHIRE,** DE12 7DS
(T) 01530 273222

POWERMADE DESIGNS LTD, Unit 17 First Stage House, Brimington Rd North, Old Whittington, Chesterfield, **DERBYSHIRE,** S41 9JE
(T) 01246 540044

PRESTIGE GOLF (UK) LTD, 3 Barton Road, Long Eaton, Nottingham, **DERBYSHIRE,** NG10 2FN
(T) 0115 972 7898

DEVON

ALL GOLF.CO.UK, Taw Croft, Chawleigh, Chulmleigh, **DEVON,** EX18 7JY
(T) 01769 580301

DISCOUNT GOLF, High Bullen Hotel, Chittlehamholt, Umberleigh, **DEVON,** EX37 9HD
(T) 01769 540530

PLAY IT AGAIN SPORTS, 3 Staples Mews, Exeter Road, Exmouth, **DEVON,** EX8 1PL
(T) 01395 270780

POWER CADDIE CENTRE, Pottery Road, Bovey Tracey, Newton Abbot, **DEVON,** TQ13 9DS
(T) 01626 834831

DORSET

STRIKE RITE, Companies House, Ringwood Road, Bransgore, Christchurch, **DORSET,** BH23 8JQ
(T) 01425 673555

ESSEX

AMERICAN GOLF DISCOUNT CENTRE, 97-101 Main Road, Romford, **ESSEX,** RM2 6DP
(T) 01708 756611

ASHWORTH UK LTD, Unit 4 Capitol Industrial Centre, Off Hodgson Way, Wickford, **ESSEX,** SS11 8YX
(T) 01268 561874

ATLANTIC GOLF GROUP, Westside Centre, London Road, Stanway, Colchester, **ESSEX,** CO3 5PH
(T) 01206 504030

BALLPIC LTD, 21 Nobel Square, Burnt Mills Industrial Estate, Basildon, **ESSEX,** SS13 1LP
(T) 01268 725888

FORRESTER PARK GOLF & TENNIS CLUB, Golf Shop, Beckingham Road, Great Totham, Maldon, **ESSEX,** CM9 8EA
(T) 01621 893456

Golf Equipment Manufacturers — Golf Equipment Manufacturers

Useful Addresses

GOLF BUDDIES, Lower Park Road, Wickford, **ESSEX**, SS12 9EJ
(T) 07071 888111

JOHN LEE, 21 Lawrence Road, Romford, **ESSEX**, RM2 5SS
(T) 01708 479739

LAKEBALLS.NET, Abbeyrose House, 181 High Street, Ongar, **ESSEX**, CM5 9JG
(T) 01277 366092

PLUMLINE QUALITY PRODUCTS, Thorndon Cottages, Thorndon Gate, Ingrave, Brentwood, **ESSEX**, CM13 3RG
(T) 01277 812033

ROMFORD GOLF CENTRE, 46 North Street, Romford, **ESSEX**, RM1 1QS
(T) 01708 737393

S CIPA, 114 Hall Lane, Upminster, **ESSEX**, RM14 1AU
(T) 01708 220000

UNEEK PROMOTIONS LTD, 15 Temple Farm Industrial Estate, Craftsman Square, Temple Farm Industrial Estate, Southend-on-Sea, **ESSEX**, SS2 5RH
(T) 01702 309208

WATKINSON DAVID, Unit F9/Briarsford, Perry Road, Witham, **ESSEX**, CM8 3UY
(T) 01376 519909

GLOUCESTERSHIRE

GAMBETTIBARRE UK LTD, Birdlip, Gloucester, **GLOUCESTERSHIRE**, GL4 8JH
(T) 01452 863007

SYNERGY WORKS LTD, 9 Alexandra Way, Ashchurch, Tewkesbury, **GLOUCESTERSHIRE**, GL20 8NB
(T) 01684 296544

HAMPSHIRE

CLEVELAND GOLF, Ringway House, Bell Road, Basingstoke, **HAMPSHIRE**, RG24 8FB
(T) 01256 338683

DAVID HICKS ULTIMATE PUTTERS LTD, Gore Rd Industrial Estate, New Milton, **HAMPSHIRE**, BH25 6TH
(T) 01425 623232

GOLF DIRECT UK, 7 Nightingale Cl, West Wellow, Romsey, **HAMPSHIRE**, SO51 6BZ
(T) 01794 323303

GOLF-TECH SERVICES, 45 Kilmiston Drive, Fareham, **HAMPSHIRE**, PO16 3EG
(T) 01329 829158

HARRISON GOLF, 48 The Causeway, Fareham, **HAMPSHIRE**, PO16 8RW
(T) 01329 280179

LAWIA UK, Liphook Road, Lindford, Bordon, **HAMPSHIRE**, GU35 0PG
(T) 01420 488828

SALOMAN TAYLOR MADE LTD, Annacy House/Unit K The Loddon Centre, Wade Road, Basingstoke, **HAMPSHIRE**, RG24 8FL
(T) 01256 479555

SOLENT SOUVENIRS, Hamble Bank, 40 Newtown Road, Warsash, Southampton, **HAMPSHIRE**, SO31 9FZ
(T) 01489 577985

HEREFORDSHIRE

T H WATSON LTD, Claypitts House, Much Birch, Hereford, **HEREFORDSHIRE**, HR2 8HX
(T) 01981 540931

HERTFORDSHIRE

C B DESIGNS INTERNATIONAL LTD, 66B Sydney Road, Watford, **HERTFORDSHIRE**, WD18 7QX
(T) 01923 331677

CADDY MATIC SALES SERVICE CENTRE, Bushey Golf & Country Club, High Street, Bushey, Watford, **HERTFORDSHIRE**, WD23 1BJ
(T) 0208 421 8182

DANE STYLE AS LTD, 194 High Road, Broxbourne, **HERTFORDSHIRE**, EN10 6QF
(T) 01992 471300

GOSLING GOLF RANGE, The Gosling Stadium, Stanborough Road, Welwyn Garden City, **HERTFORDSHIRE**, AL8 6XE
(T) 01707 323443

RHOLER 2000 LTD, Arlingham House, St. Albans Road, South Mimms, Potters Bar, **HERTFORDSHIRE**, EN6 3PH
(T) 01707 645200

KENT

BETA GOLF PRODUCTS, The Old School House, Linton Hill, Linton, Maidstone, **KENT**, ME17 4AP
(T) 01622 749958

C B WORLD OF GOLF, Golf House, Horsewash Lane, Rochester, **KENT**, ME1 1EE
(T) 01634 880061

GOLF UNLIMITED, 1 Mill Row, Bexley High Street, Bexley, **KENT**, DA5 1LA
(T) 01322 526066

I.G.D.C., 50 High Street, Orpington, **KENT**, BR6 0JQ
(T) 01689 817856

MARK FOREMAN, Singlewell Road, Gravesend, **KENT**, DA11 7RB
(T) 01474 332810

PHILIP SPARKS, Manston Road, Manston, Ramsgate, **KENT**, CT12 5BE
(T) 01843 590005

SIMPLY GOLF, Unit 2/Goblands Farm, Court Lane, Hadlow, Tonbridge, **KENT**, TN11 0DP
(T) 01732 852322

SUNDRIDGE GOLF LTD, Buttercock Wharf, Vicarage Lane, Hoo, Rochester, **KENT**, ME3 9LW
(T) 01634 252141

TRAVEL CLUB, 48 Barnfield Wood Road, Beckenham, **KENT**, BR3 6SU
(T) 0208 658 2226

LANCASHIRE

CAD GOLF, Unit 20 Hope Enterprise Centre, Scot Lane, Wigan, **LANCASHIRE**, WN5 0PN
(T) 01942 733858

CADILEC, Haigh Road, Aspull, Wigan, **LANCASHIRE**, WN2 1XH
(T) 01942 833510

CHALLENGER GOLF, Swansea Mill, Mill Lane, Whittle-le-Woods, Chorley, **LANCASHIRE**, PR6 7LX
(T) 01252 248700

CLUBHOUSE GOLF DISCOUNT, 5 Cavendish Street, Ashton-under-Lyne, **LANCASHIRE**, OL6 7QL
(T) 0161 339 6686

FAIRWAY PRODUCTS, Peel Mills, Gordon Street, Bury, **LANCASHIRE**, BL9 0LS
(T) 0161 763 7060

GOLF DISCOUNT CENTRE (BLACKPOOL) LTD, 3-5 Caunce Street, Blackpool, **LANCASHIRE**, FY1 3DN
(T) 01253 622262

IDENTITY EUROPE LTD, 317 Chorley New Road, Bolton, **LANCASHIRE**, BL1 5GE
(T) 01204 496006

M I S NORTHWEST, Enterprise Buildings, White Street, Pemberton, Wigan, **LANCASHIRE**, WN5 8JW
(T) 01942 704141

MITSUSHIBA (UK) LTD, Unit 504 Phoenix Close, Phoenix Park Industrial Estate, Heywood, **LANCASHIRE**, OL10 2JG
(T) 01706 623139

NORMAN MARSHALL, Mere Brow, Preston, **LANCASHIRE**, PR4 6LA
(T) 01772 815842

PRO-BALL GOLF, Bank Lodge, 148 Liverpool Road, Longton, Preston, **LANCASHIRE**, PR4 5AU
(T) 01772 611226

SECOND CHANCE LTD, Second Chance House, Unit A Scafell Road, Queensway Industrial Estate, Lytham St. Annes, **LANCASHIRE**, FY8 3HE
(T) 01253 724495

TEE RANGE GOLF CO LTD, Unit 7 Kirby Road, Lomeshaye Industrial Estate, Nelson, **LANCASHIRE**, BB9 6RS
(T) 01282 617829

VOCO (UK) LTD, Palmer House/4 Plantation Road, Burscough Industrial Estate, Ormskirk, **LANCASHIRE,** L40 8JT
(T) 01704 894688

LEICESTERSHIRE

ADVERTEES, 39 Waterfall Way, Barwell, Leicester, **LEICESTERSHIRE,** LE9 8EH
(T) 01455 843691

BEST NET LTD, Sunnydene Works, Woodland Avenue, Hinckley, **LEICESTERSHIRE,** LE10 2BD
(T) 01455 233882

FRASER PRODUCTS, 33 Turn Street, Syston, Leicester, **LEICESTERSHIRE,** LE7 1HP
(T) 0116 269 3609

JEFFREY KIBBLE, The Limes, 37-39 Coventry Road, Sharnford, Hinckley, **LEICESTERSHIRE,** LE10 3PG
(T) 01455 272231

MACNEILL ENGINEERING, Unit 54-55 The Warren, East Goscote, Leicester, **LEICESTERSHIRE,** LE7 3XA
(T) 0116 269 6006

RANGE ENGINEERING PRODUCTS, 35 Grosvenor Cresent, Oadby, Leicester, **LEICESTERSHIRE,** LE2 5FP
(T) 0116 271 0477

LINCOLNSHIRE

PING EUROPE LTD, Corringham Road, Gainsborough, **LINCOLNSHIRE,** DN21 1XZ
(T) 01427 615405

LONDON (GREATER)

BROCKLEY HILL GOLF PARK, Brockley Hill, Stanmore, **LONDON (GREATER),** HA7 4LR
(T) 0208 420 6222

CAPITAL T LTD, 4 Redcliffe Place, London, **LONDON (GREATER),** SW10 9DD
(T) 0207 349 8898

GOLFERS FRIEND, Unit 31 26-28 Queensway, Enfield, **LONDON (GREATER),** EN3 4SA
(T) 0208 805 9099

K GOLF & LEISURE, Gateway House, Regents Park Road, London, **LONDON (GREATER),** N3 2LN
(T) 0208 343 2115

MBA DEVELOPMENTS, 170 Woodcock Hill, Harrow, **LONDON (GREATER),** HA3 0NY
(T) 0208 908 0595

NORTH CIRCULAR GOLF, Unit G1 Skillion Business Centre, Harbet Road, London, **LONDON (GREATER),** N18 3BP
(T) 0208 884 1344

TEE SETTER LTD, 14 Duck Lees Lane Industrial Estate, Duck Lees Lane, Enfield, **LONDON (GREATER),** EN3 7SR
(T) 0208 443 1631

WORLD GOLF SYSTEMS LTD, Canada House Business Centre, 272 Field End Road, Ruislip, **LONDON (GREATER),** HA4 9NA
(T) 0208 582 0435

MANCHESTER (GREATER)

COUNTY GOLF CENTRES, 163a Kingsway, Manchester, **MANCHESTER (GREATER),** M19 2ND
(T) 0161 225 1481

UK GOLF DISCOUNT LTD, Stakehill Industrial Estate, Middleton, Manchester, **MANCHESTER (GREATER),** M24 2RW
(T) 0161 653 7500

MERSEYSIDE

GOLF MATS UK LTD, 42 Hillsview Road, Southport, **MERSEYSIDE,** PR8 3PN
(T) 01704 571271

SOUTHPORT GOLF COMPLEX, 25-27 Shakespeare Street, Southport, **MERSEYSIDE,** PR8 5AB
(T) 01704 544312

MIDLANDS (WEST)

ALAN MORGAN, Blackhorse Road, Longford, Coventry, **MIDLANDS (WEST),** CV6 6HG
(T) 02476 360580

ALDILA LTD, 12 Heather Road, Binley Woods, Coventry, **MIDLANDS (WEST),** CV3 2DE
(T) 02476 545651

BAKER & DAVIES, Sargent Turner Industrial Estate, Bromley Street, Stourbridge, **MIDLANDS (WEST),** DY9 8HX
(T) 01384 891788

CADI STAT LTD, Oban Road, Coventry, **MIDLANDS (WEST),** CV6 6HH
(T) 02476 361900

ELECTRA CADDIE, Sharrocks Street, Wolverhampton, **MIDLANDS (WEST),** WV1 3RP
(T) 01902 870077

HAROLD BIRD & SON, Pinseeker Golf Equipment, Northgate, Aldridge, Walsall, **MIDLANDS (WEST),** WS9 8UB
(T) 01922 451444

K B PRODUCTS, Branston Court, Branston Street, Birmingham, **MIDLANDS (WEST),** B18 6BA
(T) 0121 608 4050

PROSIMMON GOLF (UK) PTY LTD, Unit 21/Monkspath Business Pk, Highlands Road, Shirley, Solihull, **MIDLANDS (WEST),** B90 4NZ
(T) 0121 744 9551

NORTHAMPTONSHIRE

GOLFLAND, 3 St Peters Square, Northampton, **NORTHAMPTONSHIRE,** NN1 1PS
(T) 01604 239755

NOTTINGHAMSHIRE

PAUL THORNTON, Norwood Hall, Halam Road, Southwell, **NOTTINGHAMSHIRE,** NG25 0PF
(T) 01636 816626

SWINGOPTIMISER, 5/Redwood Court, Salisbury Street, Nottingham, **NOTTINGHAMSHIRE,** NG7 2BQ
(T) 0115 978 3172

OXFORDSHIRE

NEVADA BOBS, Unit 2b Launton Road Retail Park, Launton Road, Bicester, **OXFORDSHIRE,** OX26 4PS
(T) 01869 243990

STEVE HUTCHINSON, Sutton Lane, Lower Brailes, Banbury, **OXFORDSHIRE,** OX15 5BB
(T) 01608 685633

SHROPSHIRE

ON COURSE MATTING, Chapel House Farm, Cockshutt, Ellesmere, **SHROPSHIRE,** SY12 0JJ
(T) 01939 270500

THINK GOLF LTD, Unit 3, 10 Haygate Road, Wellington, Telford, **SHROPSHIRE,** TF1 1QA
(T) 01952 251669

SOMERSET

MACKENZIE GOLFWORKS, Old Church Farm, School Street, Drayton, Langport, **SOMERSET,** TA10 0LH
(T) 01458 252100

STARTING NEW AT GOLF, Higher Hurcot House, Hurcot, Somerton, **SOMERSET,** TA11 6AA
(T) 01458 270064

TRANSLINE SPORTS LTD, Unit 5 Bridgwater Court, Oldmixon Cresent, Weston-super-Mare, **SOMERSET,** BS24 9AY
(T) 01934 642214

STAFFORDSHIRE

ELECTRA CADDIE, Valley Road Works, Dudley, **STAFFORDSHIRE,** DY3 1DT
(T) 01902 673360

HIPPO GOLF (EUROPE) LTD, Moseley Street, Burton-on-Trent, **STAFFORDSHIRE,** DE14 1DW
(T) 01283 509795

PERSONAL TOUCH GOLF CENTRE, 159a Marston Road, Stafford, **STAFFORDSHIRE,** ST16 3BS
(T) 01785 225920

ROILE COMMODITIES DIRECT LTD, 50 Britannia Way, Britannia Enterprise Park, Lichfield, **STAFFORDSHIRE,** WS14 9UY
(T) 01543 418849

ROTANET LTD, Unit 18 Town Yard Industrial Estate, Station Street, Leek, **STAFFORDSHIRE,** ST13 8BF
(T) 01538 381010

Golf Equipment Manufacturers — Golf Equipment Manufacturers

Useful Addresses

SUFFOLK

GOLF DIRECT, Bourne Hill, Wherstead, Ipswich, **SUFFOLK**, IP2 8ND
(T) 01473 683233

GOLF MOTO, 59 Bramford Road, Ipswich, **SUFFOLK**, IP1 2LU
(T) 01473 254419

KADDY TECH, The Forge, Bredfield, Woodbridge, **SUFFOLK**, IP13 6AE
(T) 01394 387422

PARQUE DA FLORESTA HOLIDAYS, 468 Woodbridge Road, Ipswich, **SUFFOLK**, IP4 4QA
(T) 01473 713318

ROBBINS RETRIEVER CO LTD, Mill End, Low Road, Eyke, Woodbridge, **SUFFOLK**, IP12 2QF
(T) 01394 461557

SOFTSPIKES UK, The Old Wool Warehouse, St Andrews Street South, Bury St. Edmunds, **SUFFOLK**, IP33 3AQ
(T) 01284 766660

WESTGOLF, 1 Bull Lane Industrial Estate, Bull Lane, Acton, Sudbury, **SUFFOLK**, CO10 0BD
(T) 01787 372536

SURREY

CALLAWAY GOLF EUROPE LTD, Unit 27 Barwell Business Pk, Leatherhead Road, Chessington, **SURREY**, KT9 2NY
(T) 0208 391 0111

DOUG MCCLELLAND GOLF STORE LTD, Downs Farm, Reigate Road, Epsom, **SURREY**, KT17 3BY
(T) 0208 786 8988

EAGLE PROMOTIONS LTD, Eagle Ho /1 Clearway Court, 139-141 Croydon Road, Caterham, **SURREY**, CR3 6PF
(T) 01883 344244

FROM TEE TO GREEN, 21 Woodmansterne Street, Banstead, **SURREY**, SM7 3NN
(T) 01737 353570

GATWICK GOLF CENTRE, 44 Brighton Road, Salfords, Redhill, **SURREY**, RH1 5BX
(T) 01293 821234

GOLF AVENUE LTD, 144 High Street, Godalming, **SURREY**, GU7 1AB
(T) 01483 428770

GOLF BUSINESS LTD, 111 Chertsey Road, Byfleet, West Byfleet, **SURREY**, KT14 7AX
(T) 01932 336889

GOLF PRO INTERNATIONAL LTD, 289-291 Wickham Road, Croydon, **SURREY**, CR0 8BF
(T) 0208 777 2444

J & J GOLF CLUBS REPAIRS, Redhill Road, Cobham, **SURREY**, KT11 1EF
(T) 01932 863644

J E GOLF PROMOTIONS, Unit 4 Foxhills Farm, Longcross Road, Longcross, Chertsey, **SURREY**, KT16 0DN
(T) 01932 877501

N L R, 162 Portsmouth Road, Cobham, **SURREY**, KT11 1HS
(T) 01932 888919

REIGATE GOLF CENTRE, 24 Church Street, Reigate, **SURREY**, RH2 0HD
(T) 01737 242345

RIO GOLF LTD, 31 Old Woking Road, West Byfleet, **SURREY**, KT14 6LG
(T) 01932 336996

SR DESIGNS LTD, 1 Hook Hill Park, Woking, **SURREY**, GU22 0PX
(T) 01483 750611

STRAKERS GOLF STATIONERY, 5 Manor Road, Reigate, **SURREY**, RH2 9LA
(T) 01737 226016

SUSSEX (EAST)

CLUBHOUSE, 146 Mackie Avenue, Brighton, **SUSSEX (EAST)**, BN1 8SB
(T) 01273 232293

GOLF DIRECT, Unit 4 98 Goldstone Villas, Hove, **SUSSEX (EAST)**, BN3 3RU
(T) 01273 202122

H M T PLASTICS LTD, 31a Framfield Road, Uckfield, **SUSSEX (EAST)**, TN22 5AH
(T) 01825 769393

MERIDIAN (LUTON) LTD, P O Box 28, Uckfield, **SUSSEX (EAST)**, TN22 3WL
(T) 01825 732111

SUSSEX GOLF CENTRE, Ditchling Road, Brighton, **SUSSEX (EAST)**, BN1 7HS
(T) 01273 552010

TANDRIC LTD, Old Grange House, Southview Road, Crowborough, **SUSSEX (EAST)**, TN6 1HF
(T) 01892 665930

SUSSEX (WEST)

CRAWLEY GOLF REPAIRS, Unit 8 Reynolds Road, Crawley, **SUSSEX (WEST)**, RH11 7HA
(T) 01293 521706

DELTA GOLF CO UK LTD, Bolney Grange Industrial Estate, Unit 30 Stairbridge Lane, Bolney, Haywards Heath, **SUSSEX (WEST)**, RH17 5PA
(T) 01444 241675

GRAMPIAN GOLFWORKS, Appledram Barns, Birdham Road, Chichester, **SUSSEX (WEST)**, PO20 7EQ
(T) 01243 538777

JD GOLF, 4 Sussex Street, Wick, Littlehampton, **SUSSEX (WEST)**, BN17 6JD
(T) 01903 715706

PARAIDE UK LTD, Unit 1b/Independent Business Pk, Imberhorne Lane, East Grinstead, **SUSSEX (WEST)**, RH19 1TU
(T) 01342 331356

PEASE POTTAGE GOLF RANGE, Horsham Road, Pease Pottage, Crawley, **SUSSEX (WEST)**, RH11 9SG
(T) 01293 531531

PENFOLD GOLF, Accounts & Sales, PO Box 134, East Grinstead, **SUSSEX (WEST)**, RH19 1YH
(T) 01494 794646

SPORTMASTER LTD, Drayton House, Drayton Lane, Drayton, Chichester, **SUSSEX (WEST)**, PO20 6EW
(T) 01243 780801

SWANSEA

GOLF CENTRE, Unit 9 Plasmarl Industrial Estate, Beaufort Road, Plasmarl, Swansea, **SWANSEA**, SA6 8JG
(T) 01792 771813

TYNE AND WEAR

CUTTER & BUCK B V, North Sands Business Centre, Liberty Way, Sunderland, **TYNE AND WEAR**, SR6 0QA
(T) 0191 567 6700

GOLF TARGET CO LTD, Matfen Hall Workshops, Matfen, Newcastle upon Tyne, **TYNE AND WEAR**, NE20 0RH
(T) 01661 886774

KADDY CARE, Bushes Yard/Fox Hunters Industrial Estate, Fox Hunters Road, Whitley Bay, **TYNE AND WEAR**, NE25 8UG
(T) 0191 251 2011

PHIPPS GOLF, Dipe Lane, East Boldon, **TYNE AND WEAR**, NE36 0PQ
(T) 0191 5190157

TYNEBUILT GOLF, 252 Wardroper House, Greenford Road, Newcastle upon Tyne, **TYNE AND WEAR**, NE6 3XJ
(T) 0191 234 0033

WARWICKSHIRE

A1 JUST GOLF, 4 Spencer Street, Leamington Spa, **WARWICKSHIRE**, CV31 3NF
(T) 01926 889990

BAGS UK LTD, 2 Cherwell Way, Rugby, **WARWICKSHIRE**, CV23 9SU
(T) 01788 546338

BRITISH GOLF INDUSTRY ASSOCIATION, Stoneleigh Park Pavilion, National Agricultural Centre, Stoneleigh Park, Kenilworth, **WARWICKSHIRE**, CV8 2RF
(T) 02476 417141

TACIT, 48 Hillmorton Road, Rugby, **WARWICKSHIRE**, CV22 5AD
(T) 01788 568818

WILTSHIRE

BIRDIE GOLF LTD, 15 Market Place, Warminster, **WILTSHIRE,** BA12 9AY
(T) 01985 216011

CARDIN GOLF, Highworth Golf Centre, Swindon Road, Highworth, Swindon, **WILTSHIRE,** SN6 7SJ
(T) 01793 766014

GOLF TECH LTD, Unit 5 Woodside Road, South Marston Industrial Estat, Swindon, **WILTSHIRE,** SN3 4WA
(T) 01793 822566

M C GOLF SUPPLIES, 29 Brakspear Drive, Corsham, **WILTSHIRE,** SN13 9NE
(T) 01249 715634

WORCESTERSHIRE

NEVADA BOBS, Unit 7 Sherriff St Trading Estate, Worcester, **WORCESTERSHIRE,** WR4 9AB
(T) 01905 610227

NORTHWICK TROLLEY SERVICES, 2 New Street, Evesham, **WORCESTERSHIRE,** WR11 5AX
(T) 01386 446423

SMITH RUSSELL & ASSOCIATES LTD, 18 Cornfield Avenue, Stoke Heath, Bromsgrove, **WORCESTERSHIRE,** B60 3QU
(T) 01527 875750

SPECTRUM GOLF PERSONALISED PRODUCTS, Skirgens Farm, Hanbury, Redditch, **WORCESTERSHIRE,** B96 6RD
(T) 01527 821218

YORKSHIRE (EAST)

CRANSWICK CLUBS, 33 Laburnum Avenue, Cranswick, Driffield, **YORKSHIRE (EAST),** YO25 9QH
(T) 01377 271717

FERN HOUSE MARKETING LTD, The Fernery, Reedness, Goole, **YORKSHIRE (EAST),** DN14 8EW
(T) 01405 704840

YORKSHIRE (NORTH)

GREENHILL LEISURE PRODUCTS, Harmby Road, Leyburn, **YORKSHIRE (NORTH),** DL8 5QA
(T) 01969 624324

GREENKEEPING SUPPLY CO, 4 Speedwell Glade, Harrogate, **YORKSHIRE (NORTH),** HG3 2HE
(T) 01423 522969

PAOLO GOLF, Unit 3 Fulford Road, York, **YORKSHIRE (NORTH),** YO1 4NS
(T) 01904 642462

YORKSHIRE (SOUTH)

CADDY SHACKS, Manor Farm House, Spring Lane, Sprotbrough, Doncaster, **YORKSHIRE (SOUTH),** DN5 7QN
(T) 01302 570031

DARTON GOLF CLUB REPAIRS, Unit 47 The Brampton Centre, Brampton Road, Wath-upon-Dearne, Rotherham, **YORKSHIRE (SOUTH),** S63 6BB
(T) 01709 877008

GOLFING LINX LTD, Anston House, 73 Ryton Road, Anston, Sheffield, **YORKSHIRE (SOUTH),** S25 4DL
(T) 01909 560387

GOLFWEAR (UK), Club House, Upper Wortley Road, Rotherham, **YORKSHIRE (SOUTH),** S61 2SJ
(T) 01709 555999

YORKSHIRE (WEST)

AFFORDABLE GOLF, 16 Gillygate, Pontefract, **YORKSHIRE (WEST),** WF8 1PQ
(T) 01977 602189

AID TO GOLF, Spring House, Spring Gardens Lane, Keighley, **YORKSHIRE (WEST),** BD20 6LB
(T) 01535 611145

AILSA GOLF LTD, 109C Elephant & Castle Yard, Westgate, Wakefield, **YORKSHIRE (WEST),** WF1 1HQ
(T) 01924 381948

CARDIN GOLF, Unit 2 Oakwell Court, Oakwell Way, Birstall, Batley, **YORKSHIRE (WEST),** WF17 9LU
(T) 01924 471809

CARPETITION LTD, 14 Kaffir Road, Huddersfield, **YORKSHIRE (WEST),** HD2 2AN
(T) 01484 428777

EAGLE GOLF CENTRE, 587 Harehills Lane, Leeds, **YORKSHIRE (WEST),** LS9 6NQ
(T) 0113 248 5851

HAZZAD GOLF, 17 Stott Hill, Bradford, **YORKSHIRE (WEST),** BD1 4EH
(T) 01274 370129

MIDAS GOLF, Unit 3B, Park Mill Way, Clayton West, Huddersfield, **YORKSHIRE (WEST),** HD8 9XJ
(T) 01484 864888

OXYGEN SPORTS & LESUIRE PLC, Regal House, Bow Beck, Bradford, **YORKSHIRE (WEST),** BD4 8SL
(T) 0161 728 3522

PETER CLARKE GOLF, Unit 2 Britannia Works, Skinner Lane, Pontefract, **YORKSHIRE (WEST),** WF8 1HU
(T) 01977 602883

SHAY GRANGE GOLF CENTRE, Long Lane, Off Bingley Road, Bradford, **YORKSHIRE (WEST),** BD9 6RX
(T) 01274 491945

STROKE OF GENIUS, Bretton Street, Dewsbury, **YORKSHIRE (WEST),** WF12 9DB
(T) 01924 488800

U S P BRANDS LTD, Clayton Works, Pepper Road, Leeds, **YORKSHIRE (WEST),** LS10 2EU
(T) 0113 387 7700

NORTHERN IRELAND

COUNTY ANTRIM

B NEILL, 23a Lambeg Road, Lisburn, **COUNTY ANTRIM,** BT27 4QA
(T) 02892 677993

E-CADDY (EUROPE) LTD, Ballymoney Enterprise Centre, 2 Riada Avenue, Ballymoney, **COUNTY ANTRIM,** BT53 7LH
(T) 02827 669539

GOLF NETWORK, Unit 6, Rathenraw Industrial Estate, Antrim, **COUNTY ANTRIM,** BT41 2SJ
(T) 02890 460333

KISSOCK MORTON AGENCIES, Unit 14a Boucher Business Centre, Apollo Road, Belfast, **COUNTY ANTRIM,** BT12 6HP
(T) 02890 666799

COUNTY DOWN

BOYD GOLF COURSE ACCESSORIES, 67 Grays Hill, Bangor, **COUNTY DOWN,** BT20 3BB
(T) 02891 271163

COUNTY TYRONE

IRVINE GOLF & SPORTS, 135 Clabby Road, Clabby, Fivamiletown, **COUNTY TYRONE,** BT75 0RF
(T) 02889 521206

SCOTLAND

ABERDEEN (CITY OF)

GO GOLF DISTRIBUTIONS LTD, 24 Carden Place, Aberdeen, **ABERDEEN (CITY OF),** AB10 1UQ
(T) 01224 588225

ANGUS

DAVID LOW SPORTS CO LTD, Links Avenue, Carnoustie, **ANGUS,** DD7 7HR
(T) 01241 853439

GOLF TRAP, 28 Union Street, Dundee, **ANGUS,** DD1 4BE
(T) 01382 201098

AYRSHIRE (NORTH)

TOUCH GOLF, 18 Bell Cr, Irvine, **AYRSHIRE (NORTH),** KA12 9JR
(T) 01294 278366

AYRSHIRE (SOUTH)

KIMS, Shaw Farm, 6 Cargill Drive, Prestwick, **AYRSHIRE (SOUTH),** KA9 2TE
(T) 01292 479699

TARTAN GOLF LTD, 16 Brewery Road, Kilmarnock, **AYRSHIRE (SOUTH),** KA1 3HZ
(T) 01563 574600

Golf Equipment Manufacturers — Golf Equipment Manufacturers

Useful Addresses

DUMFRIES AND GALLOWAY

LEA PRODUCTS, Caldow Lodge, Corsock, Castle Douglas, **DUMFRIES AND GALLOWAY,** DG7 3EB
(T) 01644 440286

EDINBURGH (CITY OF)

FIRST TEE, 3c Lutton Place, Edinburgh, **EDINBURGH (CITY OF),** EH8 9PD
(T) 0131 667 4153

J G GOLF CLASSICS, 17 Blackford Hill Grove, Edinburgh, **EDINBURGH (CITY OF),** EH9 3HA
(T) 0131 662 1600

FIFE

A & M LAWRIE, 4 Hawkslaw Trading Estate, Riverside Road, Leven, **FIFE,** KY8 4LT
(T) 01333 330480

ARISTOCRAT GOLF CLUBS, 5 Greenside Court, St. Andrews, **FIFE,** KY16 9UG
(T) 01334 474217

DAVID LOW SPORTS CO LTD, 6 Golf Place, St. Andrews, **FIFE,** KY16 9JA
(T) 01334 474119

HERITAGE GOLF OF ST ANDREWS LTD, Unit 5/8/Argyle Business Pk, Largo Road, St. Andrews, **FIFE,** KY16 8PJ
(T) 01334 472266

MEIKLEJOHN I.G & CO LTD, Kingslaw Works, Junction Road, Kirkcaldy, **FIFE,** KY1 2BW
(T) 01592 651054

MERLIN GOLF LTD, Merlin Way, Hillend, Dunfermline, **FIFE,** KY11 9JY
(T) 01383 821133

GLASGOW (CITY OF)

GOLF 2000, 60-64 Lymburn Street, Glasgow, **GLASGOW (CITY OF),** G3 8PD
(T) 0141 226 3444

GOLF CLINIC, 57 Miller Street, Glasgow, **GLASGOW (CITY OF),** G1 1EB
(T) 0141 221 7374

JOHN LETTERS OF SCOTLAND, 1-3 Earl Haig Road, Hillington Industrial Estate, Glasgow, **GLASGOW (CITY OF),** G52 4JU
(T) 0141 882 9923

SUNDERLAND OF SCOTLAND LTD, 10-14 West Nile Street, Glasgow, **GLASGOW (CITY OF),** G1 2PP
(T) 0141 572 5220

HIGHLAND

KING OF CLUBS, Sunnyside, Culloden Moor, Inverness, **HIGHLAND,** IV2 5EE
(T) 01463 790476

LANARKSHIRE (NORTH)

CADDY SHACK, Cumbernauld Golf Range/The Stables, Palacerigg Road, Cumbernauld, Glasgow, **LANARKSHIRE (NORTH),** G67 3HU
(T) 01236 780351

LANARKSHIRE (SOUTH)

IAN RAE, New Trows Road, Lesmahagow, Lanark, **LANARKSHIRE (SOUTH),** ML11 0JS
(T) 01555 893646

LYNX GOLF (EUROPE) LTD, 9-11 Langlands Place, Kelvin South Business Park, East Kilbride, Glasgow, **LANARKSHIRE (SOUTH),** G75 0YF
(T) 01355 235762

LOTHIAN (EAST)

BEN SAYERS/CALEDONIAN GOLF GROUP, 1 Tantallon Road, North Berwick, **LOTHIAN (EAST),** EH39 5NF
(T) 01620 892219

GOLF CLUB REPAIRS, 10 Elcho Ter, Aberlady, Longniddry, **LOTHIAN (EAST),** EH32 0RH
(T) 01875 870664

WINTERFIELD GOLF & RECREATIONAL CLUB, North Road, Dunbar, **LOTHIAN (EAST),** EH42 1AU
(T) 01368 863562

LOTHIAN (MID)

GOLF CENTRE (EDINBURGH) LTD, 58 Dairy Road, Edinburgh, **LOTHIAN (MID),** EH11 2AY
(T) 0131 337 5888

PERTH AND KINROSS

CRAFTSMAN QUALITY LOCKERS LTD, Ancaster Business Centre, Cross Street, Callander, **PERTH AND KINROSS,** FK17 8EA
(T) 01877 331738

STIRLING

BAXTER KEITH, Drymen, Glasgow, **STIRLING,** G63 0HY
(T) 01360 660330

WALES

BRIDGEND

CADDY CARE, 31 Village Farm Road, Village Farm Industrial Estate, Pyle, Bridgend, **BRIDGEND,** CF33 6BL
(T) 07971 295932

CONWY

LOGAN GOLF INTERNATIONAL, 290 Conway Road, Mochdre, Colwyn Bay, **CONWY,** LL28 5DS
(T) 01492 546555

DENBIGHSHIRE

LOGAN GOLF INTERNATIONAL, 111 Grange Road, Rhyl, **DENBIGHSHIRE,** LL18 4DA
(T) 01745 369200

POWYS

P G S GOLF EUROPE, Golf Links Road, Builth Wells, **POWYS,** LD2 3NF
(T) 01982 551155

RHONDDA CYNON TAFF

A W PALMER, 61 Aber-Nant Road, Aberdare, **RHONDDA CYNON TAFF,** CF44 0PY
(T) 01685 876316

GOLF SHOPS

ENGLAND

BEDFORDSHIRE

AMERICAN GOLF DISCOUNT CENTRE, Hills Lane, Biggleswade, **BEDFORDSHIRE,** SG18 9AY
(T) 01767 318040

BEADLOW MANOR GOLF SHOP, Beadlow Manor, Beadlow, Shefford, **BEDFORDSHIRE,** SG17 5PH
(T) 01525 860666

CENTRAL GOLF, 254 Hockliffe Road, Leighton Buzzard, **BEDFORDSHIRE,** LU7 8XL
(T) 01525 853300

FACTORY GOLF SHOPS, 15a Vandyke Road, Leighton Buzzard, **BEDFORDSHIRE,** LU7 8HG
(T) 01525 382233

GOLF FORE U, Unit 10C3/Elstow Storage Depot, Ampthill Road, Kempston Hardwick, Bedford, **BEDFORDSHIRE,** MK45 3NL
(T) 01234 742865

GUY GOBLE, Stewkley Road, Wing, Leighton Buzzard, **BEDFORDSHIRE,** LU7 0UJ
(T) 01525 240197

MICHAEL WELDON, Whipsnade Road, Kensworth, Dunstable, **BEDFORDSHIRE,** LU6 2NB
(T) 01582 662806

NEVADA BOB'S, 2-4 Poynters Road, Luton, **BEDFORDSHIRE,** LU4 0LA
(T) 01582 499999

PETER ROUND, Biggleswade Road, Sutton, Sandy, **BEDFORDSHIRE,** SG19 2LY
(T) 01767 260094

PRIDEFIELDS LTD, 15b Vandyke Road, Leighton Buzzard, **BEDFORDSHIRE,** LU7 8HG
(T) 01525 851941

BERKSHIRE

BOSTON GOLF TEE CO LTD, Eagle House, Berkeley Business Pk, Wokingham, **BERKSHIRE,** RG40 4YJ
(T) 0118 973 5656

CAMA GOLF, Holme Grange Craft Village, Heathlands Road, Wokingham, **BERKSHIRE,** RG40 3AW
(T) 0118 978 1156

Useful Addresses　　　Golf Equipment Manufacturers — Golf Shops

⛳ **CML GOLF,** 367 Wokingham Road, Earley, Reading, **BERKSHIRE,** RG6 7EH
(T) 0118 935 2783

⛳ **GOLF DISCOUNT CENTRE,** 7/Broomhall Buildings, Chobham Road, Ascot, **BERKSHIRE,** SL5 0DU
(T) 01344 872020

⛳ **GOLF PROFESSIONAL SHOP,** Rectory Road, Streatley, Reading, **BERKSHIRE,** RG8 9QA
(T) 01491 873715

⛳ **GOLFERS DISCOUNT,** 8 William Street, Windsor, **BERKSHIRE,** SL4 1BA
(T) 01753 840233

⛳ **GOLFLAND,** Gowring House, Market Street, Bracknell, **BERKSHIRE,** RG12 1JG
(T) 01344 485444

⛳ **GRASS ROOTS TRADING CO LTD,** Ivanhoe Road, Finchampstead, Wokingham, **BERKSHIRE,** RG40 4QQ
(T) 0118 973 6600

⛳ **J R M GOLFING,** 5 Galaxy House, New Greenham Pk, Greenham, Thatcham, **BERKSHIRE,** RG19 6HW
(T) 01635 817417

⛳ **MADE TO MEASURE GOLF SERVICES,** 39, New Greenham Pk, Greenham, Thatcham, **BERKSHIRE,** RG19 6HW
(T) 01635 817503

⛳ **NEVADA BOB'S,** 79 Northumberland Avenue, Reading, **BERKSHIRE,** RG2 7PT
(T) 0118 987 3858

⛳ **SUNNINGDALE GOLF SHOP,** Ridgemount Road, Ascot, **BERKSHIRE,** SL5 9RR
(T) 01344 620128

BRISTOL

⛳ **BRISTOL GOLF CENTRE,** 2-3 Waring House, Redcliff Hill, Bristol, **BRISTOL,** BS1 6TB
(T) 0117 921 1692

⛳ **G BRAND,** Fairway, Bristol, **BRISTOL,** BS4 5DF
(T) 0117 977 9193

⛳ **JOHN RICHARDS,** Stockwood Lane, Keynsham, Bristol, **BRISTOL,** BS31 2ER
(T) 0117 986 6505

⛳ **MASTERS GOLF CO LTD,** 1 Harbour Rd Trading Estate, Portishead, Bristol, **BRISTOL,** BS20 7BL
(T) 01275 818190

⛳ **NEVADA BOB'S,** Unit 10/Cribbs Causeway Retail Pk, Lysander Road, Patchway, Bristol, **BRISTOL,** BS34 5UL
(T) 0117 949 9949

⛳ **PROFESSIONAL GOLF SHOP,** Horton Road, Chipping Sodbury, Bristol, **BRISTOL,** BS37 6PU
(T) 01454 314087

BUCKINGHAMSHIRE

⛳ **CARDIN GOLF,** Knebworth Gate, Giffard Park, Milton Keynes, **BUCKINGHAMSHIRE,** MK14 5QD
(T) 01908 618856

⛳ **FLACKWELL HEATH PROFESSIONAL SHOP,** Treadaway Road, Flackwell Heath, High Wycombe, **BUCKINGHAMSHIRE,** HP10 9PE
(T) 01628 523017

⛳ **FOREMOST GOLF STORE,** Capital House, The Broadway, Farnham Common, Slough, **BUCKINGHAMSHIRE,** SL2 3PQ
(T) 01753 642799

⛳ **GRAHAM HEPSWORTH,** Galleymead Road, Colnbrook, Slough, **BUCKINGHAMSHIRE,** SL3 0EN
(T) 01753 685127

⛳ **MIKE BROS,** Longbottom Lane, Jordans, Beaconsfield, **BUCKINGHAMSHIRE,** HP9 2UR
(T) 01494 676616

⛳ **NEVADA BOB'S,** Farnham Road, Slough, **BUCKINGHAMSHIRE,** SL1 3TA
(T) 01753 531521

⛳ **NEVADA BOB'S,** 25 The Stacey Bushes Trading Centre, Erica Road, Stacey Bushes, Milton Keynes, **BUCKINGHAMSHIRE,** MK12 6HS
(T) 01908 318600

⛳ **PRINCES RISBOROUGH PRO SHOP,** Lee Road, Saunderton Lee, Princes Risborough, **BUCKINGHAMSHIRE,** HP27 9NX
(T) 01844 274567

⛳ **TOM GATES,** Tingewick Road, Tingewick, Buckingham, **BUCKINGHAMSHIRE,** MK18 4AE
(T) 01280 815210

⛳ **WAVENDON GOLF CENTRE,** Lower End Road, Wavendon, Milton Keynes, **BUCKINGHAMSHIRE,** MK17 8DA
(T) 01908 281296

CAMBRIDGESHIRE

⛳ **ETON LTD,** Units 1 & 2/The Stirling Centre, Stirling Way, Market Deeping, Peterborough, **CAMBRIDGESHIRE,** PE6 8EQ
(T) 01778 341555

⛳ **GOLFERS WORLD,** Lancaster Way Business Park, Ely, **CAMBRIDGESHIRE,** CB6 3NW
(T) 01353 669901

⛳ **JAY DEE GOLF CENTRE,** Cambridge Road, Hemingford Abbots, Huntingdon, **CAMBRIDGESHIRE,** PE28 9HQ
(T) 01480 492939

⛳ **MICHAEL CLEMONS,** Comberton Road, Toft, Cambridge, **CAMBRIDGESHIRE,** CB3 7RY
(T) 01223 264702

⛳ **NEVADA BOB'S,** Star Mews, Star Road, Peterborough, **CAMBRIDGESHIRE,** PE1 5HY
(T) 01733 310600

⛳ **PAULO GOLF,** Cowley Road, Cambridge, **CAMBRIDGESHIRE,** CB4 0DL
(T) 01223 425000

⛳ **QUEENS MOAT HOUSES (CAMBRIDGE) LTD,** Bar Hill, Bar Hill, Cambridge, **CAMBRIDGESHIRE,** CB3 8EU
(T) 01954 780098

CHESHIRE

⛳ **AMERICAN GOLF DISCOUNT CENTRE,** Deeside Lane, Sealand, Chester, **CHESHIRE,** CH1 6BP
(T) 01244 881800

⛳ **AMERICAN GOLF DISCOUNT CENTRE,** 384 Washway Road, Sale, **CHESHIRE,** M33 4JH
(T) 0161 962 8274

⛳ **AMERICAN GOLF DISCOUNT CENTRE,** Queens Pk Drive, Crewe, **CHESHIRE,** CW2 7SU
(T) 01270 666724

⛳ **AMERICAN GOLF DISCOUNT CENTRE,** Slutchers Lane, Centre Pk, Warrington, **CHESHIRE,** WA1 1QL
(T) 01925 573345

⛳ **AMERICAN GOLF DISCOUNT CENTRE,** 41 Manchester Road, Woolston, Warrington, **CHESHIRE,** WA1 4AE
(T) 01925 818166

⛳ **AMERICAN GOLF DISCOUNT CENTRE,** 1030 Europa Boulevard, Westbrook, Warrington, **CHESHIRE,** WA5 5YW
(T) 01925 488400

⛳ **AMERICAN GOLF DISCOUNT CENTRE,** 234 London Road, Hazel Grove, Stockport, **CHESHIRE,** SK7 4DA
(T) 0161 456 6666

⛳ **AMERICAN GOLF DISCOUNT CENTRE,** 62 Tarvin Road, Boughton, Chester, **CHESHIRE,** CH3 5DZ
(T) 01244 400040

⛳ **CLUB GOLF,** 175 Orford Lane, Warrington, **CHESHIRE,** WA2 7BA
(T) 01925 489367

⛳ **DISCOUNT GOLF LTD,** 20 Clarendon Court, Winwick Quay, Warrington, **CHESHIRE,** WA2 8QP
(T) 01925 636086

⛳ **EDWIN WATTS GOLF DISCOUNTS LTD,** Chaser Court/Greyhound Park, Sealand Road, Chester, **CHESHIRE,** CH1 4QQ
(T) 01244 390827

⛳ **FARRANCE GOLF SHOP,** Foggs Lane, Antrobus, Northwich, **CHESHIRE,** CW9 6JQ
(T) 01925 730900

Golf Shops — Golf Shops

Useful Addresses

FORE GOLF, Deeside Lane, Sealand, Chester, **CHESHIRE**, CH1 6BP
(T) 01244 881604

GOLF 2000 LTD, 2 Woodlands Road, Wilmslow, **CHESHIRE**, SK9 5QB
(T) 01625 549549

GOLF GALLERY, 50 Lower Bridge Street, Chester, **CHESHIRE**, CH1 1RS
(T) 01244 403046

GOLF SHOP, 245 Edleston Road, Crewe, **CHESHIRE**, CW2 7EA
(T) 01270 505400

GRASS ROOTS, Unit 10/Pear Mill Industrial Estate, Stockport Rd West, Bredbury, Stockport, **CHESHIRE**, SK6 2BP
(T) 0161 406 8898

HEATON MOOR PROFESSIONAL SHOP, Mauldeth Road, Stockport, **CHESHIRE**, SK4 3NX
(T) 0161 432 0846

JASON O'BRIEN, Highfield Road, Widnes, **CHESHIRE**, WA8 7DT
(T) 0151 420 7467

K W GOLF, 141 Bewsey Road, Warrington, **CHESHIRE**, WA5 5LG
(T) 01925 638652

NEVADA BOB'S, 4-8 St Anns Parade, Wilmslow, **CHESHIRE**, SK9 1HG
(T) 01625 536367

NICK SUMMERFIELD, Macclesfield Road, Prestbury, Macclesfield, **CHESHIRE**, SK10 4BJ
(T) 01625 828242

PETER EYRE, Mere Golf & Country Club, Chester Road, Mere, Knutsford, **CHESHIRE**, WA16 6LJ
(T) 01565 830219

POULTON PARK GOLF SHOP, Dig Lane, Croft, Warrington, **CHESHIRE**, WA2 0SH
(T) 01925 825220

S PARKINSON & CO, Tanners Lane, Golborne, Warrington, **CHESHIRE**, WA3 3AN
(T) 01942 722080

SALE PRO SHOP, Sale Lodge, Golf Road, Sale, **CHESHIRE**, M33 2XU
(T) 0161 973 1730

SCOTTSDALE GOLF UK LTD, 148 Cross Street, Sale, **CHESHIRE**, M33 7AQ
(T) 0161 969 4644

T GILBERT, 27 Cranston Drive, Sale, **CHESHIRE**, M33 2PB
(T) 0161 973 9953

TFG GOLF SHOP, 1 Cross Lane Farm Cottage, Widnes Road, Cuerdley, Warrington, **CHESHIRE**, WA5 2UW
(T) 01925 791790

TONY STEVENS, Pott Shrigley, Macclesfield, **CHESHIRE**, SK10 5SB
(T) 01625 575626

WIDNES GOLF CENTRE, Unit 15 St Michaels Industrial Estate, Widnes, **CHESHIRE**, WA8 8TL
(T) 0151 257 9381

CLEVELAND

GOLF CENTRE, Tees Road, Hartlepool, **CLEVELAND**, TS25 1DD
(T) 01429 864511

GOLF SHOP, Middlesbrough Municipal Golf Centre, Ladgate Lane, Middlesbrough, **CLEVELAND**, TS5 7YZ
(T) 01642 300720

MIKE NUTTER, 251 Linthorpe Road, Middlesbrough, **CLEVELAND**, TS1 4AT
(T) 01642 252552

NEVADA BOB'S, 33 Station Street, Middlesbrough, **CLEVELAND**, TS1 1SR
(T) 01642 224000

CORNWALL

CARDIN GOLF, Pool Trading Estate, Dudnance Lane, Pool, Redruth, **CORNWALL**, TR15 3QW
(T) 01209 715715

COUNTY DURHAM

LEDA GOLF DISCOUNT CENTRE, Klondyke Garden Centre, Lambton Park, Chester le Street, **COUNTY DURHAM**, DH3 4PZ
(T) 0191 385 4545

PROFESSIONAL SHOP, Lumley Links, Chester le Street, **COUNTY DURHAM**, DH3 4NS
(T) 0191 389 0157

R W CHIVERS & CO, 153A Newgate Street, Bishop Auckland, **COUNTY DURHAM**, DL14 7EN
(T) 01388 451585

CUMBRIA

APPLEBY GOLF SHOP, Brackenber, Appleby-in-Westmorland, **CUMBRIA**, CA16 6LP
(T) 017683 52922

CARLISLE GOLF CENTRE, Arch 1 Viaduct Estate Road, Carlisle, **CUMBRIA**, CA2 5BN
(T) 01228 511534

GOLF GALORE, 42 Cecil Street, Carlisle, **CUMBRIA**, CA1 1NT
(T) 01228 533022

GOLF SHOP, 118 Market Street, Dalton-in-Furness, **CUMBRIA**, LA15 8RE
(T) 01229 465372

LAKES GOLF SHOP, Kendal Road, Bowness-on-Windermere, Windermere, **CUMBRIA**, LA23 3FB
(T) 015394 48370

DERBYSHIRE

ALFRETON PRO SHOP, Wingfield Road, Oakerthorpe, Alfreton, **DERBYSHIRE**, DE55 7LH
(T) 01773 831901

ARROW ACCESSORIES, Unit 11 Westminster Industrial Estate, Measham, Swadlincote, **DERBYSHIRE**, DE12 7DS
(T) 01530 273111

TROLL GOLF LTD, Unit 15 1st Stage House, Chesterfield, **DERBYSHIRE**, S41 9BN
(T) 01246 455255

WOODS GOLF SHOP, 419b Sheffield Road, Chesterfield, **DERBYSHIRE**, S41 8LT
(T) 01246 268055

DEVON

AMERICAN GOLF DISCOUNT CENTRE, Unit 5-8 Sugermill Business Pk, Billacombe Road, Plymouth, **DEVON**, PL9 7HT
(T) 01752 481288

CARDIN GOLF, 9 West Street, Exeter, **DEVON**, EX1 1BB
(T) 01392 211831

DISCOUNT GOLF, 58 Boutport Street, Barnstaple, **DEVON**, EX31 1SH
(T) 01271 324220

GOLF CENTRE, Unit 56 Faraday Mill Business Park, Faraday Road, Plymouth, **DEVON**, PL4 0ST
(T) 01752 254573

GOLF GALLERY, 21 Westcombe, Bideford, **DEVON**, EX39 3JQ
(T) 01237 422097

GOLF LOCKER ROOM, 252 Torquay Road, Paignton, **DEVON**, TQ3 2EZ
(T) 01803 521665

GOLF WORKSHOP, Unit 5B, Mullacott Industrial Estate, Ilfracombe, **DEVON**, EX34 8PL
(T) 01271 879139

JAMES LANGMEAD, Ashburton Road, Newton Abbot, **DEVON**, TQ12 6JN
(T) 01626 351681

MIKE ROWETT, Exeter Golf & Country Club, Topsham Road, Exeter, **DEVON**, EX2 7AE
(T) 01392 875028

NEVADA BOB'S, Kennaware Warehouse, Commercial Road, Exeter, **DEVON**, EX2 4AE
(T) 01392 216111

PERFECTION PUTTING, 4 Manor Vale Road, Galmpton, Brixham, **DEVON**, TQ5 0PA
(T) 01803 842385

PREMIER GOLF LTD, 89a Queen Street, Newton Abbot, **DEVON**, TQ12 2BG
(T) 01626 335772

⛳ **PROFESSIONAL SHOP,** Down Road, Tavistock, **DEVON,** PL19 9AQ
(T) 01822 612316

⛳ **RICHARD LEWIS,** North Bovey, Newton Abbot, **DEVON,** TQ13 8RE
(T) 01647 440998

⛳ **S JEFFERIES,** Tors Road, Okehampton, **DEVON,** EX20 1EF
(T) 01837 53541

⛳ **STADDON HEIGHTS GOLF PROFESSIONAL SHOP,** Staddon Heights, Plymouth, **DEVON,** PL9 9SP
(T) 01752 492630

⛳ **TORBAY PRO GOLF,** 250 Union Street, Torquay, **DEVON,** TQ2 5QU
(T) 01803 213444

⛳ **YELVERTON GOLF SHOP,** Golf Links Road, Yelverton, **DEVON,** PL20 6BN
(T) 01822 853593

DORSET

⛳ **AMERICAN GOLF DISCOUNT CENTRE,** 130-138 Holdenhurst Road, Bournemouth, **DORSET,** BH8 8AW
(T) 01202 311300

⛳ **GOLF SHOP,** 19 Church Street, Christchurch, **DORSET,** BH23 1BW
(T) 01202 474828

⛳ **GOLF SHOP,** 135a Commercial Road, Poole, **DORSET,** BH14 0JD
(T) 01202 731143

⛳ **GOLFING LADIES,** 177 New Road, West Parley, Ferndown, **DORSET,** BH22 8ED
(T) 01202 573941

⛳ **GOLFMARK,** 417c Lymington Road, Highcliffe, Christchurch, **DORSET,** BH23 5EN
(T) 07879 462211

⛳ **NIGEL TOKELY,** Wentworth Drive, Off Station Approach, Broadstone, **DORSET,** BH18 8DQ
(T) 01202 692835

⛳ **PREMIERE SOCCER & GOLF LTD,** Unit 10/Albany Pk, Cabot Lane, Poole, **DORSET,** BH17 7BX
(T) 01202 600043

⛳ **T S INTERNATIONAL,** 1/Cedar Trade Pk, Cobham Road, Ferndown Industrial Estate, Wimborne, **DORSET,** BH21 7SD
(T) 01202 894555

ESSEX

⛳ **ALAN MCGINN,** Elizabeth Way, Harlow, **ESSEX,** CM19 5BE
(T) 01279 418357

⛳ **AMERICAN GOLF DISCOUNT CENTRE,** Charter Way, Braintree, **ESSEX,** CM7 9YH
(T) 01376 349000

⛳ **BEN CHARLES,** A16 Cowdray Centre, Cowdray Avenue, Colchester, **ESSEX,** CO1 1BH
(T) 01206 369268

⛳ **BENTLEY PROFESSIONAL GOLF SHOP,** Ongar Road, Pilgrims Hatch, Brentwood, **ESSEX,** CM15 9SS
(T) 01277 372933

⛳ **BOYCE HILL PROFESSIONAL SHOP,** Vicarage Hill, Benfleet, **ESSEX,** SS7 1PD
(T) 01268 752565

⛳ **BRIAN WHITE,** Ingrave, Brentwood, **ESSEX,** CM13 3RH
(T) 01277 810736

⛳ **CANON GOLF & LEISURE,** 78 Roundhills, Waltham Abbey, **ESSEX,** EN9 1UU
(T) 01992 769300

⛳ **CHANNELS GOLF SHOP,** Belsteads Farm Lane, Little Waltham, Chelmsford, **ESSEX,** CM3 3PT
(T) 01245 441056

⛳ **CLUBGOLF,** Tunnel Industrial Estate, London Road, Grays, **ESSEX,** RM20 3HH
(T) 01708 866122

⛳ **CUSTOM CLUBS OF EPPING,** 240A High Street, Epping, **ESSEX,** CM16 4AP
(T) 01992 570548

⛳ **FAIRLOP WATERS,** Golf Shop/Lake, Forest Road, Ilford, **ESSEX,** IG6 3HN
(T) 0208 501 1881

⛳ **GOLF & LEISURE HOUSE,** 2-4 Crown Street, Brentwood, **ESSEX,** CM14 4BA
(T) 01277 221253

⛳ **GOLF CADDY,** 7 Earls Hall Parade, Prince Avenue, Southend-on-Sea, **ESSEX,** SS2 6NW
(T) 01702 342396

⛳ **GOLF CADDY,** 88 High Street, Hadleigh, Benfleet, **ESSEX,** SS7 2PB
(T) 01702 553455

⛳ **GOLF FACTORY,** 8 Faringdon Gr, Faringdon Avenue, Romford, **ESSEX,** RM3 8TD
(T) 01708 377617

⛳ **GOLF SHOP,** Unit K5, Market Road, Chelmsford, **ESSEX,** CM1 1XA
(T) 01245 252131

⛳ **GOLF TRADE CENTRE,** 173 Western Road, Billericay, **ESSEX,** CM12 9JD
(T) 01277 633233

⛳ **LAKESIDE GOLF,** 2 Thurrock Lakeside Shopping Centre, West Thurrock, Grays, **ESSEX,** RM20 2ZF
(T) 01708 890461

⛳ **NEVADA BOB'S,** St James Centre, East Road, Harlow, **ESSEX,** CM20 2SX
(T) 01279 432288

⛳ **NEVADA BOB'S,** 73-75 London Road, Copford, Colchester, **ESSEX,** CO6 1LG
(T) 01206 212752

⛳ **NEVADA BOB'S,** Tunnel Industrial Estate, Weston Avenue, Grays, **ESSEX,** RM20 3HH
(T) 01708 890698

⛳ **PAN EUROPEAN (GOLF) PROMOTIONS,** Old Mill Works, High Street, Maldon, **ESSEX,** CM9 7EY
(T) 01621 851700

⛳ **PRO SHOP,** West Road, Clacton-on-Sea, **ESSEX,** CO15 1AJ
(T) 01255 426304

⛳ **SAFFRON WALDEN PRO-GOLF SHOP,** Windmill Hill, Saffron Walden, **ESSEX,** CB10 1BX
(T) 01799 527728

⛳ **STAPLEFORD ABBOTTS GOLF SHOP,** Tysea Hill, Stapleford Abbotts, Romford, **ESSEX,** RM4 1JU
(T) 01708 381108

⛳ **TOUR GOLF,** Unit 1a/Elm House, Church Road, Harold Wood, Romford, **ESSEX,** RM3 0JU
(T) 01708 378411

GLOUCESTERSHIRE

⛳ **CITY GOLF AND LEISURE,** 152 Southgate Street, Gloucester, **GLOUCESTERSHIRE,** GL1 2EX
(T) 01452 414034

⛳ **CLUB MASTERS,** Dundry Nurseries, Bamfurlong Lane, Cheltenham, **GLOUCESTERSHIRE,** GL51 6SL
(T) 01452 715007

⛳ **COTSWOLD HILLS PROFESSIONAL SHOP,** Ullenwood, Cheltenham, **GLOUCESTERSHIRE,** GL53 9QT
(T) 01242 515263

⛳ **EUROPRO GOLF CENTRE,** Matson Lane, Matson, Gloucester, **GLOUCESTERSHIRE,** GL4 6EA
(T) 01452 414131

⛳ **GLOUCESTER GOLF CENTRE FACTORY OUTLET,** Barnwood Business Centre, Barnett Way, Barnwood, Gloucester, **GLOUCESTERSHIRE,** GL4 3RT
(T) 01452 613864

⛳ **GLOUCESTER GOLF SHOP,** Matson Lane, Matson, Gloucester, **GLOUCESTERSHIRE,** GL4 6EA
(T) 01452 411331

⛳ **GOLF LINKS,** Beechwood Shopping Centre, 123 High Street, Cheltenham, **GLOUCESTERSHIRE,** GL50 1DQ
(T) 01242 529888

⛳ **REGAL,** Lincoln Green Lane, Tewkesbury, **GLOUCESTERSHIRE,** GL20 7DN
(T) 01684 294892

Golf Shops — Golf Shops

Useful Addresses

SIGMA GOLF (UK) LTD, Barnwood Business Centre, Barnett Way, Barnwood, Gloucester, **GLOUCESTERSHIRE,** GL4 3RT
(T) 01452 611888

HAMPSHIRE

AMERICAN GOLF DISCOUNT CENTRE, 411 Millbrook Road West, Southampton, **HAMPSHIRE,** SO15 0HX
(T) 02380 511000

AURIOL POWERDRIVE, Mill Lane, Passfield, Liphook, **HAMPSHIRE,** GU30 7RR
(T) 01428 751446

CLUB SPORTS, Solent Business Centre, Millbrook Road West, Southampton, **HAMPSHIRE,** SO15 0HW
(T) 02380 702654

DUNWOOD MANOR PRO SHOP, Danes Road, Awbridge, Romsey, **HAMPSHIRE,** SO51 0GF
(T) 01794 340663

GLENDALE GOLF, Unit 12 Apex Centre, Speedfields Pk, Fareham, **HAMPSHIRE,** PO14 1TP
(T) 01329 828805

GOLFLAND, Ketts House, Winchester Road, Chandler's Ford, Eastleigh, **HAMPSHIRE,** SO53 2FZ
(T) 02380 274343

HOLE IN ONE GOLF SHOP, 3 Firgrove Parade, Farnborough, **HAMPSHIRE,** GU14 7RE
(T) 01252 517658

NEVADA BOB'S, 53 Northern Road, Portsmouth, **HAMPSHIRE,** PO6 3DN
(T) 02392 384828

NEVADA BOB'S, Unit 3 Chestnut Avenue Retail Park, Chesnut Avenue, Eastleigh, **HAMPSHIRE,** SO50 9HP
(T) 02380 629595

NEVADA BOB'S, 5 Queens Road, Farnborough, **HAMPSHIRE,** GU14 6DJ
(T) 01252 547747

RICHARD BENFIELD, Winchester Road, Ampfield, Romsey, **HAMPSHIRE,** SO51 9BQ
(T) 01794 368750

ROYAL WINCHESTER, Sarum Road, Winchester, **HAMPSHIRE,** SO22 5QE
(T) 01962 862473

SOUTHWICK PARK GOLF SHOP, Pinsley Drive, Southwick, Fareham, **HAMPSHIRE,** PO17 6EL
(T) 02392 380442

HEREFORDSHIRE

AMERICAN GOLF DISCOUNT CENTRE, Bushey Mill Lane, Bushey, **HEREFORDSHIRE,** WD23 2AB
(T) 01923 255591

EUROPEAN DISCOUNT GOLF, Hill Barn, Lyde, Hereford, **HEREFORDSHIRE,** HR4 8AB
(T) 01432 371561

PRO GOLF OF HEREFORD, Unit 16 Beech Business Park, Tillington Road, Hereford, **HEREFORDSHIRE,** HR4 9QJ
(T) 01432 351376

HERTFORDSHIRE

AMERICAN GOLF DISCOUNT CENTRE, Cambridge Road, Melbourn, Royston, **HERTFORDSHIRE,** SG8 6EY
(T) 01763 262943

ANDREW AINSWORTH ASHRIDGE PRO-SHOP, Little Gaddesden, Little Gaddesden, Berkhamsted, **HERTFORDSHIRE,** HP4 1LY
(T) 01442 842307

BERKHAMSTED GOLF SHOP, 238 High Street, Berkhamsted, **HERTFORDSHIRE,** HP4 1AG
(T) 01442 866678

BISHOPS STORTFORD GOLF SHOP, Dunmow Road, Bishop's Stortford, **HERTFORDSHIRE,** CM23 5HP
(T) 01279 651324

CADDIESHACK LTD, Stocks Road, Aldbury, Tring, **HERTFORDSHIRE,** HP23 5RX
(T) 01442 851341

CARDIN GOLF, Beatty Road, Waltham Cross, **HERTFORDSHIRE,** EN8 7UD
(T) 01992 711926

COMPLETE GOLFER, Moor Pk, Rickmansworth, **HERTFORDSHIRE,** WD3 1QN
(T) 01923 774113

G & J PGA GOLF, Darkes Lane, Potters Bar, **HERTFORDSHIRE,** EN6 1DF
(T) 01707 652987

GOLF PRO, 54a High Street, Redbourn, St. Albans, **HERTFORDSHIRE,** AL3 7LN
(T) 01582 794183

HAMSHAW'S LTD, 26 Beech Road, St. Albans, **HERTFORDSHIRE,** AL3 5AS
(T) 01727 853627

PAOLO GOLF, 69 High Street, Potters Bar, **HERTFORDSHIRE,** EN6 5AS
(T) 01707 642333

RULE JOHN PROFESSIONAL SHOP, Hartsbourne Avenue, Bushey, Watford, **HERTFORDSHIRE,** WD23 1JW
(T) 0208 950 2836

ISLE OF WIGHT

GOLF SHOP, 61 Pyle Street, Newport, **ISLE OF WIGHT,** PO30 1UL
(T) 01983 532422

KENT

AMERICAN GOLF DISCOUNT CENTRE, 5-9 Tonbridge Road, Maidstone, **KENT,** ME16 8RL
(T) 01622 690790

BEAVER GOLF WORKS, 27-29 Crayford High Street, Dartford, **KENT,** DA1 4HH
(T) 01322 559966

BIRCHWOOD PARK GOLF CENTRE, London Golf Centre, Birchwood Road, Dartford, **KENT,** DA2 7HJ
(T) 01322 664500

C T'S GOLF SHOP, 1 Stanley Way, Orpington, **KENT,** BR5 2HE
(T) 01689 890077

CHATHAM GOLF CENTRE LTD, Street End Road, Chatham, **KENT,** ME5 0BG
(T) 01634 848925

CLUBGOLF, L062b/Unit, Lower Thames Walk, Bluewater, Greenhithe, **KENT,** DA9 9SJ
(T) 01322 382111

D LAMBERT, Trottiscliffe Road, Addington, West Malling, **KENT,** ME19 5AR
(T) 01732 844022

DRIVING AMBITIONS GOLF CO, 4 Senacre Square, Maidstone, **KENT,** ME15 8QF
(T) 01622 681700

EVM LTD, North Street, Headcorn, Ashford, **KENT,** TN27 9NN
(T) 01622 891334

GOLF PROFESSIONAL SHOP, St. Georges Lodge, Royal St. Georges Golf Club, Sandwich Bay, Sandwich, **KENT,** CT13 9PB
(T) 01304 615236

GOLF WORKSHOP, Millroom/Charmwood Farm, Charmwood Lane, Orpington, **KENT,** BR6 7SA
(T) 01689 855660

GOLF ZONE, 14 Blackfen Parade, Blackfen Road, Sidcup, **KENT,** DA15 9LU
(T) 0208 298 7532

HILL BILLY POWERED GOLF TROLLEY, Unit 32 Joseph Wilson Industrial Estate, Millstrood Road, Whitstable, **KENT,** CT5 3PS
(T) 01227 771910

HUGH SHERMAN, Sandyhurst Lane, Ashford, **KENT,** TN25 4NT
(T) 01233 629644

JOHN HEARN, Golf Shop, Wormdale Hill, Newington, Sittingbourne, **KENT,** ME9 7PX
(T) 01795 842775

LINKS GOLF (SANDWICH), 15 The Butchery, Sandwich, **KENT,** CT13 9DL
(T) 01304 619881

LOFT & LIE GOLF STORE, Jack Nicholaus Golf Centre, Thong Lane, Gravesend, **KENT,** DA12 4LF
(T) 01474 327555

MARK LAWRENCE PROFESSIONAL GOLF SHOP, Camden Place, Camden Park Road, Chislehurst, **KENT,** BR7 5HJ
(T) 0208 467 6798

MEDWAY GOLF CENTRE LTD, Unit 1 24a Longley Road, Rainham, Gillingham, **KENT,** ME8 7RU
(T) 01634 262002

NEVADA BOB'S, Unit 3, 26 Maynard Road, Wincheap Industrial Estate, Canterbury, **KENT,** CT1 3RH
(T) 01227 470703

NEVADA BOB'S, 363-369 Crofton Road, Orpington, **KENT,** BR6 8NR
(T) 01689 818741

NEVADA BOB'S, 11 Union Square, Eridge Road, Tunbridge Wells, **KENT,** TN4 8HE
(T) 01892 520262

POWAKADDY INTERNATIONAL LTD, Unit 4 Sittingbourne Industrial Park, Crown Quay Lane, Sittingbourne, **KENT,** ME10 3JH
(T) 01795 473555

PROFESSIONAL SHOP, Woodlands Road, Gillingham, **KENT,** ME7 2AP
(T) 01634 855862

PROFESSIONAL SHOP, Power Station Road, Minster on Sea, Sheerness, **KENT,** ME12 3DN
(T) 01795 583060

PROFESSIONAL SHOP, Canterbury Road, Etchinghill, Folkestone, **KENT,** CT18 8FA
(T) 01303 863966

TC GOLF SHOP, Swanmead Driving Range, Cannon Lane, Tonbridge, **KENT,** TN9 1PP
(T) 01732 365148

TUDOR PARK GOLF SHOP, Ashford Road, Bearsted, Maidstone, **KENT,** ME14 4NQ
(T) 01622 739412

WEALD OF KENT, Golf Shop, Maidstone Road, Headcorn, Ashford, **KENT,** TN27 9PT
(T) 01622 890866

KINGSTON UPON THAMES

AMERICAN GOLF DISCOUNT CENTRE, 11-13 Coombe Road, Kingston upon Thames, **KINGSTON UPON THAMES,** KT2 7AB
(T) 0208 974 9774

COOMBE WOOD PROFESSIONAL SHOP, George Road, Kingston upon Thames, **KINGSTON UPON THAMES,** KT2 7NS
(T) 0208 942 6764

LANCASHIRE

A J LAVERTY, Edenfield Road, Rochdale, **LANCASHIRE,** OL11 5YR
(T) 01706 522104

AMERICAN GOLF DISCOUNT CENTRE, 28 The Linkway, Horwich, Bolton, **LANCASHIRE,** BL6 6JA
(T) 01204 699666

AMERICAN GOLF DISCOUNT CENTRE, 320-322 North Road, Preston, **LANCASHIRE,** PR1 8AE
(T) 01772 200333

AMERICAN GOLF DISCOUNT CENTRE, 2 Pollard Street, Manchester, **LANCASHIRE,** M4 7AN
(T) 0161 274 3272

BOLTON GOLF SHOP & ACADEMY, 169-173 Bradshawgate, Bolton, **LANCASHIRE,** BL2 1BH
(T) 01204 366591

DAVID CLARKE, Shaw Hill Golf & Country Club, Shaw Hill Drive, Whittle-le-Woods, Chorley, **LANCASHIRE,** PR6 7PN
(T) 01257 279222

DIRECT GOLF UK, Unit 1 Moorgate, Bury, **LANCASHIRE,** BL9 7AF
(T) 0161 764 7764

ESCLAPEZ GOLF, Southport Road, Scarisbrick, Ormskirk, **LANCASHIRE,** L40 9RF
(T) 01704 841149

FULL SWING, Suite 17/Glenfield Pk/Lomeshaye Business Village, Turner Road, Nelson, **LANCASHIRE,** BB9 7DR
(T) 01282 617757

GOLF FACTORY RETURNS, 620 Manchester Road, Westhoughton, Bolton, **LANCASHIRE,** BL5 3JD
(T) 01942 841008

GOLF GALLERY, 8 Wigan Gallery, The Galleries, Wigan, **LANCASHIRE,** WN1 1AR
(T) 01942 491101

GOLF INTERNATIONAL, Lomeshaye Industrial Estate, 17 Kenyon Road, Brierfield, Nelson, **LANCASHIRE,** BB9 5SP
(T) 01282 606000

GOLFGEAR (UK) LTD, Palmer House/4 Plantation Road, Burscough Industrial Estate, Ormskirk, **LANCASHIRE,** L40 8JT
(T) 01704 894688

GOLFLAND, Unit 4, Capitol Centre, Walton-le-Dale, Preston, **LANCASHIRE,** PR5 4AW
(T) 01772 555833

INTERGOLF, Three Arches Services Station, 654 Preston Old Road, Blackburn, **LANCASHIRE,** BB2 4EP
(T) 01254 200404

J & G GOLF, Euxton Lane, Euxton, Chorley, **LANCASHIRE,** PR7 6DL
(T) 01257 233500

MIKE GREENOUGH, Tudor Avenue, Lea, Preston, **LANCASHIRE,** PR4 0XA
(T) 01772 720374

NEVADA BOB'S, Great Birchwood, Lytham Road, Warton, Preston, **LANCASHIRE,** PR4 1TE
(T) 01772 631521

NEVADA BOB'S, The Palace, Westgate, Burnley, **LANCASHIRE,** BB11 1RZ
(T) 01282 456556

ORMSKIRK GOLF CENTRE, 78 New Court Way, Ormskirk, **LANCASHIRE,** L39 2YT
(T) 01695 580300

PLEASINGTON GOLF SHOP, Pleasington Lane, Pleasington, Blackburn, **LANCASHIRE,** BB2 5JF
(T) 01254 201630

PROFESSIONAL SHOP, Ladcastle Road, Uppermill, Oldham, **LANCASHIRE,** OL3 6LT
(T) 01457 810412

REGAL GOLF CORPORATION, Leeds Street, Wigan, **LANCASHIRE,** WN3 4BW
(T) 01942 826827

STEPHEN NICHOLLS, Ewood Lane, Haslingden, Rossendale, **LANCASHIRE,** BB4 6LH
(T) 01706 213616

TOWNELEY GOLF SHOP & BOOKINGS, Todmorden Road, Burnley, **LANCASHIRE,** BB11 3ED
(T) 01282 438473

TROLLEY CARE, Riverside Industrial Estate, Hermitage Street, Rishton, Blackburn, **LANCASHIRE,** BB1 4NF
(T) 01254 876007

UK LAKE BALLS, Unit 12 Adlington South Business Village, Coppull, Chorley, **LANCASHIRE,** PR7 4PD
(T) 01257 474083

LEICESTERSHIRE

AMERICAN GOLF DISCOUNT CENTRE, 349 Welford Road, Leicester, **LEICESTERSHIRE,** LE2 6BJ
(T) 0116 244 8866

CHRIS HALL, Stocking Lane, East Leake, Loughborough, **LEICESTERSHIRE,** LE12 5RL
(T) 01509 852701

ENDERBY GOLF SHOP, Mill Lane, Enderby, Leicester, **LEICESTERSHIRE,** LE9 5LH
(T) 0116 284 9388

EUROPEAN DISCOUNT GOLF, 77 Southfields Drive, Leicester, **LEICESTERSHIRE,** LE2 6QT
(T) 0116 244 0297

ROBIN HOOD GOLF CENTRE, 1309 Melton Road, Syston, Leicester, **LEICESTERSHIRE,** LE7 2EN
(T) 0116 260 2653

Golf Shops — Golf Shops

Useful Addresses

Useful Addresses

Golf Shops — Golf Shops

LINCOLNSHIRE

CANWICK PARK GOLF SHOP,
Washingborough Road, Lincoln,
LINCOLNSHIRE, LN4 1EF
(T) 01522 536870

EUROPEAN DISCOUNT GOLF, Boston
West Golf Centre, Hubberts Bridge, Boston,
LINCOLNSHIRE, PE20 3QX
(T) 01205 290540

GARY LESLIE, Carholme Road, Lincoln,
LINCOLNSHIRE, LN1 1SE
(T) 01522 536811

GOLFER'S WORLD WAREHOUSE, Unit
6 Moorland Way, Tritton Road, Lincoln,
LINCOLNSHIRE, LN6 7JW
(T) 01522 695556

**IMMINGHAM GOLF PROFESSIONAL
SHOP,** Church Lane, Immingham,
LINCOLNSHIRE, DN40 2HB
(T) 01469 575493

LINCOLNSHIRE (NORTH)

FOREMOST GOLF, 15 Dunstall Street,
Scunthorpe, **LINCOLNSHIRE (NORTH),**
DN15 6LD
(T) 01724 844811

LONDON

CAPITAL GOLF, 13-14 Woodstock Street,
London, **LONDON,** W1C 2AG
(T) 0207 495 4295

GOLFLIVE 99, 30 Foley Street, London,
LONDON, W1W 7TH
(T) 0207 636 8806

NEVADA BOB'S, The Rotunda, Broadgate
Circle, London, **LONDON,** EC2M 2QS
(T) 0207 628 2333

LONDON (GREATER)

**AMERICAN GOLF DISCOUNT
CENTRE,** 12-14 Ashbourne Parade,
Finchley Road, London, **LONDON
(GREATER),** NW11 0AD
(T) 0208 458 9212

**AMERICAN GOLF DISCOUNT
CENTRE,** Southend Road, London,
LONDON (GREATER), E4 8TA
(T) 0208 503 2777

CHINGFORD GOLF CENTRE LTD, Bury
Road, London, **LONDON (GREATER),** E4
7QJ
(T) 0208 529 5708

CLUBGOLF, 112 Brompton Road, London,
LONDON (GREATER), SW3 1JJ
(T) 0207 581 8877

COMPLETE GOLFER, 1-2 Clive Parade,
Northwood, **LONDON (GREATER),** HA6
2QF
(T) 01923 836059

D BEAL, 100 Barnet Way, London,
LONDON (GREATER), NW7 3AL
(T) 0208 959 7261

DUELLIST SPORTS, 256 Twickenham
Road, Isleworth, **LONDON (GREATER),**
TW7 7DT
(T) 0208 747 9628

DULWICH & SYDENHAM GOLF SHOP,
Grange Lane, London, **LONDON
(GREATER),** SE21 7LH
(T) 0208 693 8491

GOFF & CO, Flat 54/Whitworth House,
Falmouth Road, London, **LONDON
(GREATER),** SE1 6RW
(T) 0207 378 9474

GOLF CENTRE, 19 Aylmer Parade,
Aylmer Road, London, **LONDON
(GREATER),** N2 0PE
(T) 0208 341 6685

GOLF FACTORY LTD, Unit 7/Delta
Business Pk, 10 Smugglers Way, London,
LONDON (GREATER), SW18 1EG
(T) 0208 875 1118

GOLF SHOP, Harefield Place, The Drive,
Uxbridge, **LONDON (GREATER),** UB10 8AQ
(T) 01895 237287

GRIMSDYKE PROFESSIONAL SHOP,
Oxhey Lane, Pinner, **LONDON (GREATER),**
HA5 4AL
(T) 0208 428 7484

**LEA VALLEY LEISURE CENTRE GOLF
SHOP,** Picketts Lock Lane, London,
LONDON (GREATER), N9 0AS
(T) 0208 803 3611

MASHIE NIBLICKS, 310 Worple Road,
London, **LONDON (GREATER),** SW20 8QU
(T) 0208 946 7500

MATCHPLAY GOLF LTD, 51 Ashbourne
Parade, London, **LONDON (GREATER),** W5
3QS
(T) 0208 810 8166

NEVADA BOB'S, 11-13 Temple Fortune
Parade, London, **LONDON (GREATER),**
NW11 0QS
(T) 0208 458 9488

PINNER HILL GOLF SHOP, South View
Road, Pinner, **LONDON (GREATER),** HA5
3YA
(T) 0208 866 2109

RUISLIP GOLF SHOP, Ickenham Road,
Ruislip, **LONDON (GREATER),** HA4 7DQ
(T) 01895 638835

**SANDYLODGE GOLF PROFESSIONAL
SHOP,** Sandy Lodge Lane, Northwood,
LONDON (GREATER), HA6 2JD
(T) 01923 825321

**SHOOTERS HILL PROFESSIONAL
GOLF SHOP,** Eaglesfield Road, London,
LONDON (GREATER), SE18 3DA
(T) 0208 854 0073

SOUTH HERTS SHOP, Links Drive,
London, **LONDON (GREATER),** N20 8QU
(T) 0208 445 4633

SOUTHGATE GOLF SHOP, 5 The
Broadway, Winchmore Hill Road, London,
LONDON (GREATER), N14 6PH
(T) 0208 882 0999

SUDBURY PROFESSIONAL SHOP,
Bridgewater Road, Wembley, **LONDON
(GREATER),** HA0 1AL
(T) 0208 902 7910

V R LAW, 29 Gordon Avenue, Stanmore,
LONDON (GREATER), HA7 2RL
(T) 0208 954 2646

MANCHESTER (GREATER)

COUNTY GOLF CENTRE, 599 Eccles
New Road, Salford, **MANCHESTER
(GREATER),** M5 2EP
(T) 0161 745 7055

COUNTY GOLF DIRECT, Unit 4 Missouri
Avenue, Salford, **MANCHESTER
(GREATER),** M5 2NP
(T) 0161 745 8680

DAVYHULME PARK GOLF SHOP,
Gleneagles Road, Urmston, Manchester,
MANCHESTER (GREATER), M41 8SA
(T) 0161 748 3931

GOLF DIRECT LTD, 243 Barlow Moor
Road, Manchester, **MANCHESTER
(GREATER),** M21 7QL
(T) 0161 881 1777

GOLF FACTORY RETURNS, 153 Bury
New Road, Whitefield, Manchester,
MANCHESTER (GREATER), M45 6AA
(T) 0161 796 3640

GREG NICHOLSON GOLF & LEISURE,
Flixton Road, Urmston, Manchester,
MANCHESTER (GREATER), M41 5AW
(T) 0161 748 2912

NEVADA BOB'S, Heaton Pk Road,
Manchester, **MANCHESTER (GREATER),**
M9 0QS
(T) 0161 740 5629

NORTH MANCHESTER GOLF, Rhodes
House, Manchester Old Road, Middleton,
Manchester, **MANCHESTER (GREATER),**
M24 4PE
(T) 0161 643 7094

PAUL REEVES CLUBHOUSE GOLF,
Higher Lane, Whitefield, Manchester,
MANCHESTER (GREATER), M45 7EZ
(T) 0161 766 3096

TERRY MORLEY GOLF SHOPS, Old
Clough Lane, Worsley, Manchester,
MANCHESTER (GREATER), M28 3HZ
(T) 0161 790 8591

MERSEYSIDE

**AMERICAN GOLF DISCOUNT
CENTRE,** 355b Edge Lane, Fairfield,
Liverpool, **MERSEYSIDE,** L7 9LG
(T) 0151 230 0369

B SEDDON, Hastings Road, Southport,
MERSEYSIDE, PR8 2LU
(T) 01704 564395

CREST SPORTSWEAR INTERNATIONAL LTD, 25a Shakespeare Street, Southport, **MERSEYSIDE,** PR8 5AB
(T) 01704 531308

DISCOUNT GOLF FACTORY, 818 Queens Drive, Stoneycroft, Liverpool, **MERSEYSIDE,** L13 4BT
(T) 0151 228 9061

FLYGHT GOLF LTD, 17b School Lane, Knowsley, Prescot, **MERSEYSIDE,** L34 9ER
(T) 0151 548 7200

FORE THE LADY GOLFER, 58 Lord Street, Southport, **MERSEYSIDE,** PR8 1QB
(T) 01704 531458

GOLF CO, Unit 18 Britannia Pavilion, Albert Dock, Liverpool, **MERSEYSIDE,** L3 4AD
(T) 0151 709 3327

GOLF SHOP, 13-15 Stanley Street, Southport, **MERSEYSIDE,** PR9 0BY
(T) 01704 540260

HOLE IN ONE GOLF SHOP, Unit 9 Columbus Way, Liverpool, **MERSEYSIDE,** L21 2QG
(T) 0151 949 1576

JOHN HEGGARTY, Meols Drive, Hoylake, Wirral, **MERSEYSIDE,** CH47 4AL
(T) 0151 632 6757

KEVIN JONES, Links Hey Road, Wirral, **MERSEYSIDE,** CH48 1NB
(T) 0151 625 1818

MIKE ADAMS, Bayswater Road, Wallasey, **MERSEYSIDE,** CH45 8LA
(T) 0151 638 3888

NEVADA BOB'S, 125 Liverpool Road, St. Helens, **MERSEYSIDE,** WA10 1PQ
(T) 01744 616000

PARKINSONS GOLF, Y M C A Building, College Street, St. Helens, **MERSEYSIDE,** WA10 1TF
(T) 01744 733878

PAUL ROBERTS, Prescot Road, St. Helens, **MERSEYSIDE,** WA10 3AD
(T) 01744 28785

R N BRADBEER, Waterloo Road, Southport, **MERSEYSIDE,** PR8 2LX
(T) 01704 568857

SOUTHPORT GOLF COMPLEX, 64 Sandon Road, Southport, **MERSEYSIDE,** PR8 4QD
(T) 01704 569999

MIDLANDS (WEST)

ALAN QUARTERMAN, 40 Tennal Road, Birmingham, **MIDLANDS (WEST),** B32 2JE
(T) 0121 427 3512

AMERICAN GOLF DISCOUNT CENTRE, Queslett Park Golf Centre, Booths Lane, Birmingham, **MIDLANDS (WEST),** B42 2RG
(T) 0121 366 7000

AMERICAN GOLF DISCOUNT CENTRE, 321-323 Stratford Road, Shirley, Solihull, **MIDLANDS (WEST),** B90 3BL
(T) 0121 745 1999

AMERICAN GOLF DISCOUNT CENTRE, Central Six Retail Pk, Warwick Road, Coventry, **MIDLANDS (WEST),** CV3 6TA
(T) 02476 252111

BIRMINGHAM GOLF CENTRE LTD, 698 Yardley Wood Road, Birmingham, **MIDLANDS (WEST),** B13 0HY
(T) 0121 441 1482

BIRMINGHAM PROFESSIONAL GOLF SHOP LTD, 526 Hagley Road West, Oldbury, **MIDLANDS (WEST),** B68 0BZ
(T) 0121 421 7311

DRESSED TO A TEE, 121 Worcester Road, Hagley, Stourbridge, **MIDLANDS (WEST),** DY9 0NG
(T) 01562 885269

EUROPEAN DISCOUNT GOLF, 127 Stratford Road, Shirley, Solihull, **MIDLANDS (WEST),** B90 3AY
(T) 0121 733 6272

EUROPRO GOLF CENTRE COVENTRY, Care Of John Reay Golf Centre, Sandpits Lane, Coventry, **MIDLANDS (WEST),** CV6 2FR
(T) 02476 338611

GREAT BARR PROFESSIONALS SHOP, Chapel Lane, Great Barr, Birmingham, **MIDLANDS (WEST),** B43 7BA
(T) 0121 357 5270

LEA MARSTON GOLF SHOP, Lea Marston Hotel & Leisure Complex, Haunch Lane, Lea Marston, Sutton Coldfield, **MIDLANDS (WEST),** B76 0BY
(T) 01675 470707

NEVADA BOB'S, 87 Queens Cross, Dudley, **MIDLANDS (WEST),** DY1 1QZ
(T) 01384 242427

NEVADA BOB'S, 15 Mere Green Road, Sutton Coldfield, **MIDLANDS (WEST),** B75 5BL
(T) 0121 308 0123

PROFESSIONAL SHOP, Patshull Pk, Burnhill Green, Wolverhampton, **MIDLANDS (WEST),** WV6 7HR
(T) 01902 700342

RICHARD LAMBERT, Broadway, Walsall, **MIDLANDS (WEST),** WS1 3EY
(T) 01922 626766

ROBIN HOOD GOLF CENTRE, 200 Robin Hood Lane, Birmingham, **MIDLANDS (WEST),** B28 0LG
(T) 0121 778 4161

TERRY MATTHEWS GOLF SHOP LTD, Four Ashes Road, Dorridge, Solihull, **MIDLANDS (WEST),** B93 8NQ
(T) 01564 778072

THREEWAY GOLF, Unit 3, Malthouse Road, Tipton, **MIDLANDS (WEST),** DY4 9AE
(T) 0121 520 7068

U S A GOLF, 7 Mere Green Road, Sutton Coldfield, **MIDLANDS (WEST),** B75 5BL
(T) 0121 308 3417

NORFOLK

AMERICAN GOLF DISCOUNT CENTRE, 5 Guardian Road, Norwich, **NORFOLK,** NR5 8PF
(T) 01603 625262

BROWSTON HALL GOLF SHOP, Browston Green, Browston, Great Yarmouth, **NORFOLK,** NR31 9DW
(T) 01493 651002

DEAN FOOTER PROFESSIONAL, Drayton High Road, Norwich, **NORFOLK,** NR6 5AH
(T) 01603 408459

NEVADA BOB'S, 119-121 Magdalen Street, Norwich, **NORFOLK,** NR3 1LN
(T) 01603 660036

PAOLO GOLF, Sainsburys Shopping Centre, Unit 5 Pound Lane, Norwich, **NORFOLK,** NR7 0SR
(T) 01603 702222

PROFESSIONAL SHOP, Golf Enquiry Line, Hempton Road, Fakenham, **NORFOLK,** NR21 7LA
(T) 01328 863534

NORTHAMPTONSHIRE

AMERICAN GOLF DISCOUNT CENTRE, The Golf Lodge, Kettering Road, Pytchley, Kettering, **NORTHAMPTONSHIRE,** NN14 1EY
(T) 01536 512000

DESIGNER GOLF LTD, 63 Kettering Road, Rothwell, Kettering, **NORTHAMPTONSHIRE,** NN14 6JR
(T) 01536 712220

GOLF 2000, Care Of John White Golf Complex, Bedford Road, Rushden, **NORTHAMPTONSHIRE,** NN10 0SQ
(T) 01933 410411

GOLFERS CHOICE, 47 Barrack Road, Northampton, **NORTHAMPTONSHIRE,** NN1 3RL
(T) 01604 620808

PROSTARGOLF, Balfour Road, Kingsthorpe Hollow, Northampton, **NORTHAMPTONSHIRE,** NN2 6JR
(T) 01604 721999

Golf Shops — Golf Shops

Useful Addresses

Golf Shops — Golf Shops

NORTHUMBERLAND

ARCOT HALL PROFESSIONAL SHOP,
Arcot Lane, Dudley, Cramlington,
NORTHUMBERLAND, NE23 7QP
(T) 0191 236 2147

NOTTINGHAMSHIRE

**AMERICAN GOLF DISCOUNT
CENTRE,** Riverside Retail Park, Queens
Drive, Nottingham, **NOTTINGHAMSHIRE,**
NG2 1RU
(T) 0115 986 7447

EUROPEAN DISCOUNT GOLF, 700-708
Woodborough Road, Nottingham,
NOTTINGHAMSHIRE, NG3 5GJ
(T) 0115 985 7111

FOREMOST GOLF STORE, Hucknall
Road, Nottingham, **NOTTINGHAMSHIRE,**
NG6 9LQ
(T) 0115 976 3172

LADY ON THE GREEN, 40 Earlswood
Drive, Edwalton, Nottingham,
NOTTINGHAMSHIRE, NG12 4AZ
(T) 0115 937 2329

PAOLO GOLF, 15 Outram Street, Sutton-
in-Ashfield, **NOTTINGHAMSHIRE,** NG17
4BA
(T) 01623 555183

OXFORDSHIRE

ABINGDON GOLF STORE, Dunmore
Court, Wootton Road, Abingdon,
OXFORDSHIRE, OX13 6BH
(T) 01235 532900

FORE GOLF, 10 Buttermarket, Thame,
OXFORDSHIRE, OX9 3EW
(T) 01844 217566

**FRILFORD HEATH PROFESSIONAL'S
SHOP,** Frilford Heath, Abingdon,
OXFORDSHIRE, OX13 5NW
(T) 01865 390887

GOLF CAR (UK) LTD, Wootton Road,
Abingdon, **OXFORDSHIRE,** OX13 6BH
(T) 01235 868204

OXFORD GOLF CENTRE, Binsey Lane,
Oxford, **OXFORDSHIRE,** OX2 0EX
(T) 01865 721592

PAOLO GOLF, 10 Fairfax Centre,
Kidlington, **OXFORDSHIRE,** OX5 2PA
(T) 01865 370594

ULTIMATE GOLF, 58 Between Towns
Road, Oxford, **OXFORDSHIRE,** OX4 3LR
(T) 01865 437272

SHROPSHIRE

GOLF SERVICES, 6 Broadway, Shifnal,
SHROPSHIRE, TF11 8AZ
(T) 01952 462162

LINKS LEISURE LTD, Unit 21B Waymills
Industrial Estate, Waymills, Whitchurch,
SHROPSHIRE, SY13 1TT
(T) 01948 663002

TELFORD GOLF CENTRE LTD, Unit E &
F Halesfield 22, Telford, **SHROPSHIRE,** TF7
4QX
(T) 01952 581099

SOMERSET

GEOFF KITE, Sherborne Road, Yeovil,
SOMERSET, BA21 5BW
(T) 01935 473763

**TAUNTON & PICKERIDGE
PROFESSIONAL SHOP,** Corfe, Taunton,
SOMERSET, TA3 7BY
(T) 01823 421790

TIGGERS WOODS, 3 Stony Street,
Frome, **SOMERSET,** BA11 1BU
(T) 01373 455577

WORLEBURY PROFESSIONAL SHOP,
Worlebury Hill Road, Weston-super-Mare,
SOMERSET, BS22 9SX
(T) 01934 623932

STAFFORDSHIRE

ALSAGER GOLF SHOP, Alsager Golf &
Country Club, Audley Road, Alsager, Stoke-
on-Trent, **STAFFORDSHIRE,** ST7 2UR
(T) 01270 877432

**AMERICAN GOLF DISCOUNT
CENTRE,** 75-81 Newcastle Road, Stoke-
on-Trent, **STAFFORDSHIRE,** ST4 6QE
(T) 01782 747787

CLUB HOUSE, 87 Princess Drive, Stoke-
on-Trent, **STAFFORDSHIRE,** ST3 6NG
(T) 01782 336339

CRAYTHORNE GOLF SHOP, Craythorne
Road, Stretton, Burton-on-Trent,
STAFFORDSHIRE, DE13 0AZ
(T) 01283 533745

D J'S GOLF FACTORY, 153 Longford
Road, Cannock, **STAFFORDSHIRE,** WS11
3LG
(T) 01543 467551

**EUROPEAN DISCOUNT GOLF
WAREHOUSE,** Astral House, Clough
Street, Stoke-on-Trent, **STAFFORDSHIRE,**
ST1 4AS
(T) 01782 260701

PAR 4 BUGGIES, Rear Of The Laurels,
Otherton, Penkridge, Stafford,
STAFFORDSHIRE, ST19 5NX
(T) 01785 715993

RUGELEY GOLF DISCOUNT CENTRE,
7 Market Square, Rugeley,
STAFFORDSHIRE, WS15 2BL
(T) 01889 575675

ST THOMAS'S PRIORY GOLF SHOP,
Armitage Lane, Rugeley,
STAFFORDSHIRE, WS15 1ED
(T) 01543 492096

TOTAL GOLF LTD, 45 Scalpcliffe Road,
Burton-on-Trent, **STAFFORDSHIRE,** DE15
9AA
(T) 01283 845789

SUFFOLK

EUROPEAN GOLF MACHINERY, Street
Garage, Main Road, Bucklesham, Ipswich,
SUFFOLK, IP10 0DN
(T) 01473 659815

GLOBAL GOLF DISCOUNT, Rushbrooke
Lane, Bury St. Edmunds, **SUFFOLK,** IP33
2RR
(T) 01284 723440

**GOLF GALORE IPSWICH GOLF
STORE,** 25 Gloster Road, Martlesham
Heath, Ipswich, **SUFFOLK,** IP5 3RD
(T) 01473 614444

LEES TEES, St Andrews House, Boldero
Road, Bury St. Edmunds, **SUFFOLK,** IP32
7BS
(T) 01284 754569

NEVADA BOB'S, 255-257 Felixstowe
Road, Ipswich, **SUFFOLK,** IP3 9HG
(T) 01473 725678

PIN HIGH GOLF & LEISURE WEAR,
Unit 1/Nelson House, 2 Bixley Road,
Ipswich, **SUFFOLK,** IP3 8PL
(T) 01473 718332

TOPS GOLF SHOP, Coupals Road,
Sturmer, Haverhill, **SUFFOLK,** CB9 7UW
(T) 01440 712628

TRIANGLE GOLF SHOPS, Tut Hill,
Fornham All Saints, Bury St. Edmunds,
SUFFOLK, IP28 6LG
(T) 01284 755978

SURREY

459 GOLF, 447 London Road, Camberley,
SURREY, GU15 3JA
(T) 01276 670443

ACE GOLF SUPERSTORE, Hook Rise
North, Surbiton, **SURREY,** KT6 5AT
(T) 0208 288 0149

AMAZING GOLF, 50 High Street, Staines,
SURREY, TW18 4DY
(T) 01784 491438

**AMERICAN GOLF DISCOUNT
CENTRE,** Sunbury Cross Park & Shop,
Staines Rd West, Sunbury-on-Thames,
SURREY, TW16 7AZ
(T) 01932 765777

**BRAMLEY PROFESSIONAL GOLF
SHOP,** Links Road, Bramley, Guildford,
SURREY, GU5 0AL
(T) 01483 893685

BRITISH GOLF DISCOUNT, 132 Hook
Road, Surbiton, **SURREY,** KT6 5BZ
(T) 0208 391 0099

CANON GOLF, 6 Junction Place,
Haslemere, **SURREY,** GU27 1LE
(T) 01428 641108

DOUG MCCLELLAND GOLF STORE,
Redhill Road, Cobham, **SURREY,** KT11 1EF
(T) 01932 867275

DWELLCOURT LTD, Downs Farm, Reigate Road, Epsom, **SURREY,** KT17 3BY
(T) 0208 786 8333

FARNHAM GOLF SUPERSTORE, 47 Wrecclesham Road, Farnham, **SURREY,** GU9 8TY
(T) 01252 728400

GOLF DIRECT UK COM, Kings Yard, Burrows Lane, Gomshall, Guildford, **SURREY,** GU5 9QP
(T) 01483 203023

GOLF MART, 118 Feltham Hill Road, Ashford, **SURREY,** TW15 2BX
(T) 01784 257234

GOLFTEK (UK) LTD, Curtis Road, Dorking, **SURREY,** RH4 1XD
(T) 01306 741888

GRAHAM WILSON, 106 Purley Downs Road, South Croydon, **SURREY,** CR2 0RB
(T) 0208 651 0819

GUILDFORD GOLF SUPERSTORE, 12-14 Madrid Road, Guildford, **SURREY,** GU2 7NT
(T) 01483 576010

HINDHEAD PROFESSIONAL SHOP, Churt Road, Hindhead, **SURREY,** GU26 6HX
(T) 01428 604458

LAMKIN INTERNATIONAL, Unit 5 Bentley Industrial Centre, Bentley, Farnham, **SURREY,** GU10 5NJ
(T) 01420 23768

LONDON PRO GOLF, 145 London Road, Camberley, **SURREY,** GU15 3JY
(T) 01276 691978

N D SPORTS, Unit 4 Epsom Business Park, Kiln Lane, Epsom, **SURREY,** KT17 1JF
(T) 01372 723416

NEVADA BOB'S, 2-5 Royal Oak Centre, Brighton Road, Purley, **SURREY,** CR8 2PG
(T) 0208 668 9393

PETRON MADE TO MEASURE GOLF CLUBS, Packersham Golf Centre, Oak Lawn Road, Leatherhead, **SURREY,** KT22 0BT
(T) 01372 843255

PROFESSIONAL SHOP, Croham Road, South Croydon, **SURREY,** CR2 7HJ
(T) 0208 657 7705

WEST BYFLEET PRO SHOP, Sheerwater Road, West Byfleet, **SURREY,** KT14 6AA
(T) 01932 346584

SUSSEX (EAST)

CITY GOLF, 34 Preston Road, Brighton, **SUSSEX (EAST),** BN1 4QF
(T) 01273 609248

DALE HILL PRO SHOP, Dale Hill, Ticehurst, Wadhurst, **SUSSEX (EAST),** TN5 7DQ
(T) 01580 201800

GOLF ACADEMIES, 2 Marine Road, Eastbourne, **SUSSEX (EAST),** BN22 7AU
(T) 01323 649698

GOLF GALORE, 26 Boundary Road, Hove, **SUSSEX (EAST),** BN3 4EF
(T) 01273 412909

GOLF SHOP, 6 Pelham Ter, Lewes Road, Brighton, **SUSSEX (EAST),** BN2 4AF
(T) 01273 603885

JUST GOLF, Vulcan House Farm, Coopers Green, Uckfield, **SUSSEX (EAST),** TN22 4AT
(T) 01825 733855

P DOBSON, Chapel Hill, Lewes, **SUSSEX (EAST),** BN7 2BB
(T) 01273 483823

ROUNDS OF GOLF, 112 South Street, Eastbourne, **SUSSEX (EAST),** BN21 4LZ
(T) 01323 639553

SUSSEX GOLF DISCOUNTS, 21a Prince Albert Street, Brighton, **SUSSEX (EAST),** BN1 1HF
(T) 01273 206593

TEARDROP GOLF, Bell Lane, Bellbrook Industrial Estate, Uckfield, **SUSSEX (EAST),** TN22 1QL
(T) 01825 761266

TERRY MARSHALL, East Dean Road, Eastbourne, **SUSSEX (EAST),** BN20 8ES
(T) 01323 732264

SUSSEX (WEST)

AIR-EZE LTD, 21 Patchings, Horsham, **SUSSEX (WEST),** RH13 5HJ
(T) 01403 274284

AMERICAN GOLF DISCOUNT CENTRE, 3a Royal George Parade, Shoreham-by-Sea, **SUSSEX (WEST),** BN43 6TB
(T) 01273 870860

CANNON GOLF, Brighton Road, Pease Pottage, Crawley, **SUSSEX (WEST),** RH11 9AD
(T) 01444 400219

GOLF SHOP, 25 Broadwater Street West, Worthing, **SUSSEX (WEST),** BN14 9BT
(T) 01903 204608

GOLFEE PRODUCTS, P O Box 3055, Littlehampton, **SUSSEX (WEST),** BN16 2NU
(T) 01903 787326

PENFOLD GOLF, Unit 1/Independent Business Pk, Imberhorne Lane, East Grinstead, **SUSSEX (WEST),** RH19 1TU
(T) 01342 324404

SQUARE DEALS, Horsham Road, Pease Pottage, Crawley, **SUSSEX (WEST),** RH11 9SG
(T) 01293 521706

SWANSEA

AMERICAN GOLF DISCOUNT CENTRE, 1 Kingsway, Fforestfach, Swansea, **SWANSEA,** SA5 4DL
(T) 01792 580808

GOLF DISCOUNT WAREHOUSE, Unit 1 Gilsea Business Park, Valley Way Enterprise Park, Morriston, Swansea, **SWANSEA,** SA6 8RJ
(T) 01792 700203

GOLF KING, Unit 6-7/Worcester Court, Mannesman Cl, Llansamlet, Swansea, **SWANSEA,** SA7 9AH
(T) 01792 700364

NEVADA BOB'S, 304 Carmarthen Road, Cwmbwrla, Swansea, **SWANSEA,** SA5 8NJ
(T) 01792 521521

TYNE AND WEAR

AMERICAN GOLF DISCOUNT CENTRE, Great North Road, Grange Park, Newcastle upon Tyne, **TYNE AND WEAR,** NE3 2HH
(T) 0191 285 3333

AMERICAN GOLF DISCOUNT CENTRE, Newcastle Road, Sunderland, **TYNE AND WEAR,** SR5 1JT
(T) 0191 549 9111

HOBSON DISCOUNT GOLF CENTRE, Hobson, Newcastle upon Tyne, **TYNE AND WEAR,** NE16 6BZ
(T) 01207 271605

PROFESSIONALS GOLF SHOP, Cleadon Hill, South Shields, **TYNE AND WEAR,** NE34 8EG
(T) 0191 456 0110

TEAM GOLF DISCOUNT, Unit 383a Jedburgh Court, Team Valley Trading Estate, Gateshead, **TYNE AND WEAR,** NE11 0BQ
(T) 0191 491 3702

ZEVOSITZ LTD, 181 Whitley Road, Whitley Bay, **TYNE AND WEAR,** NE26 2DN
(T) 0191 251 2830

ZFL GOLF, King Edward Road, North Shields, **TYNE AND WEAR,** NE30 2ER
(T) 0191 296 2500

WARWICKSHIRE

HARRY'S GOLF STORES LTD, Somers Road, Meriden, Coventry, **WARWICKSHIRE,** CV7 7PL
(T) 01676 522680

HARWAY GOLF, Tracy Farm, Redditch Road, Ullenhall, Solihull, **WARWICKSHIRE,** B95 5NY
(T) 01564 793222

Golf Shops — Golf Shops

Useful Addresses

⅃ **NEVADA BOB'S,** Weddington Road, Nuneaton, **WARWICKSHIRE,** CV10 0AD
(T) 02476 744440

⅃ **PERFECTION PUTTING,** Cherry Tree Cottage, Windmill Lane, Baxterley, Atherstone, **WARWICKSHIRE,** CV9 2HN
(T) 01827 720214

⅃ **STONEBRIDGE PROFESSIONAL SHOP,** Somers Road, Meriden, Coventry, **WARWICKSHIRE,** CV7 7PL
(T) 01676 522334

⅃ **USA GOLF LTD,** 9 Bards Walk, Stratford-upon-Avon, **WARWICKSHIRE,** CV37 6EY
(T) 01789 299556

⅃ **WARWICK GOLF SHOP,** Hampton Street, Warwick, **WARWICKSHIRE,** CV34 6HW
(T) 01926 491284

WILTSHIRE

⅃ **BILL CREAMER GOLF SHOP,** Malmesbury Road, Langley Burrell, Chippenham, **WILTSHIRE,** SN15 5LT
(T) 01249 655519

⅃ **CARDIN GOLF,** Pipers Way, Swindon, **WILTSHIRE,** SN3 1RG
(T) 01793 532403

⅃ **GOLF & GIFTS DIRECT,** 38-40 Silver Street, Salisbury, **WILTSHIRE,** SP1 2NE
(T) 01722 414407

⅃ **GOLF FORE ALL,** 52 Fleet Street, Swindon, **WILTSHIRE,** SN1 1RE
(T) 01793 432456

⅃ **NEVADA BOB'S,** Unit 5 Great Western Way, Swindon, **WILTSHIRE,** SN2 2DJ
(T) 01793 644448

⅃ **OPEN GOLF SHOP LTD,** 41-43 High Street, Westbury, **WILTSHIRE,** BA13 3BN
(T) 01373 858370

⅃ **PROFESSIONAL SHOP,** Thoulstone, Chapmanslade, Westbury, **WILTSHIRE,** BA13 4AQ
(T) 01373 832808

⅃ **RUSHMORE PARK GOLF SHOP,** Rushmore Pk, Tollard Royal, Salisbury, **WILTSHIRE,** SP5 5QB
(T) 01725 516326

⅃ **TONY VALENTINE,** Unit 2/Priory Business Pk, Bradford Road, Corsham, **WILTSHIRE,** SN13 0RB
(T) 01249 714466

WORCESTERSHIRE

⅃ **DEAN'S WHOLE IN ONE GOLF SHOP,** Hindlip Lane, Hindlip, Worcester, **WORCESTERSHIRE,** WR3 8SA
(T) 01905 755408

⅃ **MARK DOVE,** Worcester Golf Range, Weir Lane, Worcester, **WORCESTERSHIRE,** WR2 4AY
(T) 01905 748788

⅃ **MODERNCROSS LTD,** Weights Lane, Redditch, **WORCESTERSHIRE,** B97 6RG
(T) 01527 69100

⅃ **TERRY MATTHEWS,** Stratford Road, Bromsgrove, **WORCESTERSHIRE,** B60 1LD
(T) 01527 575885

⅃ **U S A GOLF LTD,** 2 The Trinity, Worcester, **WORCESTERSHIRE,** WR1 2PN
(T) 01905 26216

⅃ **UK GOLF LTD,** Hill Furze Road, Bishampton, Pershore, **WORCESTERSHIRE,** WR10 2LZ
(T) 01386 462520

YORKSHIRE (EAST)

⅃ **C J GOLF,** 155 Newland Avenue, Hull, **YORKSHIRE (EAST),** HU5 2ER
(T) 01482 342993

⅃ **GOLF 4'S DISCOUNT,** 738-740 Spring Bank West, Hull, **YORKSHIRE (EAST),** HU5 5AA
(T) 01482 574400

⅃ **HORNSEA GOLF SHOP,** Rolston Road, Hornsea, **YORKSHIRE (EAST),** HU18 1XG
(T) 01964 534989

⅃ **HULL GOLF CENTRE,** National Avenue, Hull, **YORKSHIRE (EAST),** HU5 4JB
(T) 01482 492720

YORKSHIRE (NORTH)

⅃ **FIRST TEE,** 1-5 Omega Street, Harrogate, **YORKSHIRE (NORTH),** HG1 2BZ
(T) 01423 504477

⅃ **GOLF CO,** 95 Low Petergate, York, **YORKSHIRE (NORTH),** YO1 7HY
(T) 01904 610591

⅃ **GOLFER,** 3 Cheltenham Parade, Harrogate, **YORKSHIRE (NORTH),** HG1 1DD
(T) 01423 520633

YORKSHIRE (SOUTH)

⅃ **AMERICAN GOLF DISCOUNT CENTRE,** Plumpers Road, Sheffield, **YORKSHIRE (SOUTH),** S9 1UP
(T) 0114 261 0333

⅃ **AMERICAN GOLF DISCOUNT CENTRE,** Penistone Road North, Sheffield, **YORKSHIRE (SOUTH),** S6 1LT
(T) 0114 285 5633

⅃ **CADDY SHACK,** Armthorpe Lane, Barnby Dun, Doncaster, **YORKSHIRE (SOUTH),** DN3 1LZ
(T) 01302 882777

⅃ **GOLF FORE LADIES,** 17b Langsett Rd South, Oughtibridge, Sheffield, **YORKSHIRE (SOUTH),** S35 0GY
(T) 0114 286 2552

⅃ **GOLFERS PARADISE,** 41 Beckett Road, Doncaster, **YORKSHIRE (SOUTH),** DN2 4AD
(T) 01302 328420

⅃ **GREGG ROBERTS,** Bradway Road, Sheffield, **YORKSHIRE (SOUTH),** S17 4QR
(T) 0114 236 6844

⅃ **INDOOR GOLF,** 18 Alexandra Centre, Rail Mill Way, Parkgate, Rotherham, **YORKSHIRE (SOUTH),** S62 6JE
(T) 01709 780222

⅃ **KEVIN M PEARCE,** Holme Lane, Holme, Doncaster, **YORKSHIRE (SOUTH),** DN5 0LR
(T) 01302 722495

⅃ **SHEFFIELD PROFESSIONAL GOLF SHOP,** 605 Queens Road, Sheffield, **YORKSHIRE (SOUTH),** S2 4DX
(T) 0114 255 1969

⅃ **SIMON BERRY,** Lees Hall Club Ltd, Hemsworth Road, Sheffield, **YORKSHIRE (SOUTH),** S8 8LL
(T) 0114 250 7868

⅃ **TARGET GOLF,** Unit 2 Woodburn Court, Park Street, Rotherham, **YORKSHIRE (SOUTH),** S61 1RL
(T) 01709 557866

⅃ **YORKSHIRE GOLF LTD,** 1 Elm Lane, Sheffield, **YORKSHIRE (SOUTH),** S5 7TR
(T) 0114 240 2048

YORKSHIRE (WEST)

⅃ **A1 DISCOUNT GOLF,** Long Lane, Garforth, Leeds, **YORKSHIRE (WEST),** LS25 2DS
(T) 0113 287 5500

⅃ **AITKEN'S SPORTSTURF LTD,** Aviation Road, Sherburn in Elmet, Leeds, **YORKSHIRE (WEST),** LS25 6NB
(T) 01977 681155

⅃ **ALAN SWAINE,** Temple Newsam Road, Leeds, **YORKSHIRE (WEST),** LS15 0NB
(T) 0113 264 7362

⅃ **ALL SQUARE GOLF CO,** Globe Mills, White Abbey Road, Bradford, **YORKSHIRE (WEST),** BD8 8JL
(T) 01274 731375

⅃ **ALWOODLEY GOLF PRO SHOP,** Wigton Lane, Leeds, **YORKSHIRE (WEST),** LS17 8SA
(T) 0113 268 9603

⅃ **ALWOODLEY GOLF SERVICES,** The Halfway House, 2 North Hill, Scarcroft, Leeds, **YORKSHIRE (WEST),** LS14 3BA
(T) 0113 289 2538

⅃ **AMERICAN GOLF DISCOUNT CENTRE,** 139 Street Lane, Leeds, **YORKSHIRE (WEST),** LS8 1AA
(T) 0113 237 1878

⅃ **AMERICAN GOLF DISCOUNT CENTRE,** 6 Queensgate, Huddersfield, **YORKSHIRE (WEST),** HD1 2HG
(T) 01484 421300

AMERICAN GOLF DISCOUNT CENTRE, 112 Bradford Road, Menston, Ilkley, **YORKSHIRE (WEST),** LS29 6BX
(T) 01943 870377

BRADLEY HALL GOLF SHOP, Holywell Green, Halifax, **YORKSHIRE (WEST),** HX4 9AN
(T) 01422 370231

BRONTY GOLF, 3 Musgrave Mount, Bradford, **YORKSHIRE (WEST),** BD2 3LA
(T) 01274 773585

C J SPORTS LTD, 34 Bull Green, Halifax, **YORKSHIRE (WEST),** HX1 5AB
(T) 01422 343941

DAUPHIN GOLF LTD, Unit 27 Chickenley Mills, Short Street, Dewsbury, **YORKSHIRE (WEST),** WF12 8NF
(T) 01924 488499

DIRECT GOLF UK, Unit 10 Mini Market, Leeds Road, Huddersfield, **YORKSHIRE (WEST),** HD1 6PA
(T) 01484 427338

FIRST TEE, 103-105 Otley Road, Leeds, **YORKSHIRE (WEST),** LS6 3PX
(T) 0113 275 8432

FOCUS LEISURE, Russell Works, Old Lane, Birkenshaw, Bradford, **YORKSHIRE (WEST),** BD11 2JL
(T) 01274 652228

FOREMOST GOLF LTD, Audby House, Audby Lane, Wetherby, **YORKSHIRE (WEST),** LS22 7FD
(T) 01937 581210

HOLE IN ONE GOLF SUPERSTORE, Garden Street, Wakefield, **YORKSHIRE (WEST),** WF1 1DX
(T) 01924 299944

KIRKSTALL VALLEY GOLF CENTRE, Redcote Lane, Leeds, **YORKSHIRE (WEST),** LS4 2AW
(T) 0113 263 3030

LEEDS GOLF CAR CO LTD, Thornes Road, Wakefield, **YORKSHIRE (WEST),** WF2 8PL
(T) 01924 201555

LIGHTCLIFFE PROFESSIONAL GOLF SHOP, Knowle Top Road, Halifax, **YORKSHIRE (WEST),** HX3 8SW
(T) 01422 204081

LOW LAITHES GOLF SHOP, Lowlaithes Golf House, Park Mill Lane, Ossett, **YORKSHIRE (WEST),** WF5 9AP
(T) 01924 274667

NEVADA BOB'S, Unit 9-1b Thorp Arch Trading Estate, Thorp Arch, Wetherby, **YORKSHIRE (WEST),** LS23 7BJ
(T) 01937 841440

NICK KRZYWICKI, Hammerstones Leach Lane, Elland, **YORKSHIRE (WEST),** HX5 0TA
(T) 01422 374886

NIGEL HIRST, The Pinnacles, Sands Lane, Mirfield, **YORKSHIRE (WEST),** WF14 8HJ
(T) 01924 496030

OTLEY GOLF SCHOOL, West Busk Lane, Otley, **YORKSHIRE (WEST),** LS21 3NG
(T) 01943 463403

PAR 4 LADIES, 7 Crossley Street, Wetherby, **YORKSHIRE (WEST),** LS22 6RT
(T) 01937 587535

PROFESSIONALS SHOP, Fixby Hall, Fixby, Huddersfield, **YORKSHIRE (WEST),** HD2 2EP
(T) 01484 426463

QUALITY BAG CO, Stross House, Broad Street, Dewsbury, **YORKSHIRE (WEST),** WF13 3SA
(T) 01924 469157

RICHARD LANE PRO-SHOP, Coal Road, Wike, Leeds, **YORKSHIRE (WEST),** LS17 9NH
(T) 0113 266 5209

ROUNDHAY PRO GOLF SHOP, Park Lane, Roundhay, Leeds, **YORKSHIRE (WEST),** LS8 2EJ
(T) 0113 266 1686

TEST DRIVE GOLF, 75c Bradford Road, Riddlesden, Keighley, **YORKSHIRE (WEST),** BD21 4EZ
(T) 01535 663033

YORKSHIRE GOLF ACADEMY, 15 Market Hall, Pontefract, **YORKSHIRE (WEST),** WF8 1AU
(T) 01977 600747

IRELAND
COUNTY CAVAN

CADDYMATIC GOLF EQUIPMENT, Swellan, **COUNTY CAVAN,**
(T) 049 4331476

COUNTY CLARE

GOLFERS, Main St, Lahinch, **COUNTY CLARE,**
(T) 065 7081966

COUNTY CORK

GOLF ADDICT, 6 Emmet Pl, **COUNTY CORK,**
(T) 021 4273393

GOLF GLIDER TROLLEYS, Fennells Bay Myrtleville, **COUNTY CORK,**
(T) 021 4831584

GOLF PLAYER, Doughcloyne, **COUNTY CORK,**
(T) 021 4543495

GOLFWORLD, Frankfield Driving Range Grange, Douglas, **COUNTY CORK,**
(T) 021 4899672

MAHER'S GOLF EMPORIUM, Penrose Quay, **COUNTY CORK,**
(T) 021 4502725

TOUR GOLF IRELAND, Glengarriff Co, **COUNTY CORK,**
(T) 027 62381

COUNTY DUBLIN

AMERICAN GOLF DISCOUNT CENTRE, Unit 2 Belgard Rd, Dublin, **COUNTY DUBLIN,**
(T) 01 4590422

GOLF CARS IRELAND, Rock Rd, Blackrock, **COUNTY DUBLIN,**
(T) 01 2888850

GOLF CRAZEE, Dublin, **COUNTY DUBLIN,**
(T) 01 4781630

GOLF PLUS, Dublin Rd, Skerries, **COUNTY DUBLIN,**
(T) 01 8492654

GOLF WORKS, Lucan Retail Pk, Dundrum, **COUNTY DUBLIN,**
(T) 01 2984130

MARSHALL GOLF AWARDS, 132 North Rd, Finglas, Dublin, **COUNTY DUBLIN,**
(T) 01 8345156

MCGUIRKS GOLF, Harbour Rd, Howth, **COUNTY DUBLIN,**
(T) 01 8393895

NEVADA BOB'S, 50a Kcr Ind Est, Dublin, **COUNTY DUBLIN,**
(T) 01 4929144

OPEN GOLF CENTRE, Newtown Hse, St Margarets, Dublin, **COUNTY DUBLIN,**
(T) 01 8640324

PRO FIT GOLF, Unit 6 Newpark Ctr, Blackrock, **COUNTY DUBLIN,**
(T) 01 2783334

PRO GOLF OF AMERICA, Unit 5 Lucan Retail Park Bally Lucan, Dublin, **COUNTY DUBLIN,**
(T) 01 6210555

RED CORNER GOLF SHOP, 89 Lr Dorset St, Dublin, **COUNTY DUBLIN,**
(T) 01 8304117

COUNTY GALWAY

GOLF STYLE, U5 Liosban Ind Est Tuam Rd, **COUNTY GALWAY,**
(T) 091 758962

COUNTY KERRY

GOLF ANTIQUES LTD, Main St, Ballybunion, **COUNTY KERRY,**
(T) 068 27588

COUNTY KILDARE

CADDYSHACK GOLF, Main St, Maynooth, **COUNTY KILDARE,**
(T) 01 6289572

FORE GOLF, Millbrook Naas, Kildare, **COUNTY KILDARE,**
(T) 045 874961

Golf Shops — Golf Shops

Useful Addresses

GOLF MOBILITY, Barrowhouse, Athy, **COUNTY KILDARE,**
(T) 0507 33003

KIRWAN'S TONY GOLF SHOP, Lr Main St, Newbridge, **COUNTY KILDARE,**
(T) 045 436777

PRO GOLF, Fairt Rd, Naas Co, **COUNTY KILDARE,**
(T) 045 896607

COUNTY KILKENNY

P.J.'S GOLF SHOP, 71 Upr John St, **COUNTY KILKENNY,**
(T) 056 52944

COUNTY LIMERICK

COYLE'S JOHN WORLD OF GOLF, 17 Catherine St, **COUNTY LIMERICK,**
(T) 061 312288

TIGER GOLF, Barnaklye Patrickswell, **COUNTY LIMERICK,**
(T) 061 355745

COUNTY LOUTH

GIMME GOLF LTD, 146 Ard Easmuinn, Dundalk, **COUNTY LOUTH,**
(T) 042 9328729

GIMME GOLF PRODUCTS, 146 Ard Easmuinn, Dundalk, **COUNTY LOUTH,**
(T) 042 9328729

GOLF BAG, Abbey S.c, Drogheda, **COUNTY LOUTH,**
(T) 041 9839955

GOLF CENTRE, U 7 Mayoralty St, Drogheda, **COUNTY LOUTH,**
(T) 041 9830888

COUNTY MONAGHAN

BRENNAN DECLAN GOLF BUGGY'S, Lismeenan Castleshane, **COUNTY MONAGHAN,**
(T) 047 85470

COUNTY OFFALY

BIRR GOLF SHOP & DRIVING RANGE, Golf Links The Glens, Birr, **COUNTY OFFALY,**
(T) 0509 21606

COUNTY SLIGO

GRAYS GOLF SHOP, Strandhill, Sligo, **COUNTY SLIGO,**
(T) 071 68725

COUNTY TIPPERARY

DISCOUNT GOLF, Bank Place, **COUNTY TIPPERARY,**
(T) 062 51183

COUNTY WESTMEATH

GOLF WORKS, Golden Island, Athlone, **COUNTY WESTMEATH,**
(T) 0902 72218

COUNTY WEXFORD

GOLF RANGE, Weafer St, Enniscorthy, **COUNTY WEXFORD,**
(T) 054 37211

COUNTY WICKLOW

GOLF CRAZEE, 8 Goldsmith Tce, Quinsboro Rd, Bray, **COUNTY WICKLOW,**
(T) 01 2863528

GOLFING MEMORIES, 4 Dublin Rd, Bray, **COUNTY WICKLOW,**
(T) 01 2827297

HOME T GOLF MATS, 15 Loreto Grange, Bray, **COUNTY WICKLOW,**
(T) 01 2760469

NORTHERN IRELAND

COUNTY ANTRIM

AMERICAN GOLF DISCOUNT CENTRE, Unit 5 Connswater Retail Park, Albertbridge Road, Belfast, **COUNTY ANTRIM,** BT5 4GX
(T) 02890 466688

BALLYEARL PROFESSIONAL SHOP, 585 Doagh Road, Newtownabbey, **COUNTY ANTRIM,** BT36 5RZ
(T) 02890 840899

GOLF CENTRE, 2 Young Street, Lisburn, **COUNTY ANTRIM,** BT27 5EA
(T) 02892 605999

GOLF FIRST, 24 Ballymaconaghy Road, Belfast, **COUNTY ANTRIM,** BT8 6SB
(T) 02890 799279

NEVADA BOB'S, Unit 3 Boucher Cresent, Belfast, **COUNTY ANTRIM,** BT12 6HU
(T) 02890 382668

PARK GOLF, 84 Dargan Road, Belfast, **COUNTY ANTRIM,** BT3 9JU
(T) 02890 779292

R WILSON, 50 Park Road, Belfast, **COUNTY ANTRIM,** BT7 2FX
(T) 02890 640700

COUNTY DOWN

BULLET GOLF, 14 Banbridge Enterprise Centre, Scarva Road, Banbridge, **COUNTY DOWN,** BT32 3QD
(T) 02840 625300

EPIC GOLF IRELAND, 35 Killyleagh Road, Crossgar, Downpatrick, **COUNTY DOWN,** BT30 9EZ
(T) 02844 832855

GOLF SPOT LTD, Unit 72 1 Balloo Link, Bangor, **COUNTY DOWN,** BT19 7HJ
(T) 02891 272899

GREENGRASS GOLF, 39 Carrickree, Warrenpoint, Newry, **COUNTY DOWN,** BT34 3FA
(T) 02841 754567

ROVAL PRODUCTS, 7 Maze Park, Bangor, **COUNTY DOWN,** BT20 4RL
(T) 02891 270617

COUNTY FERMANAGH

FLETCHER GOLF, Unit B2 Tempo Road, Business Park, Enniskillen, **COUNTY FERMANAGH,** BT74 6HR
(T) 02866 320009

ROSLEA GOLF CENTRE, 59 Rellan Road, Rosslea, Enniskillen, **COUNTY FERMANAGH,** BT92 7QU
(T) 02867 751225

COUNTY LONDONDERRY

BOSTON GOLF, Unit E Balliniska Business Pk/Springtown Industria, Springtown, Londonderry, **COUNTY LONDONDERRY,** BT48 0LY
(T) 02871 262296

COUNTY TYRONE

DUNGANNON GOLF SHOP LTD, 34 Springfield Lane, Dungannon, **COUNTY TYRONE,** BT70 1QX
(T) 02887 727485

OMAGOLF LTD, The Retreat, Derry Road, Omagh, **COUNTY TYRONE,** BT78 5DY
(T) 02882 244440

SCOTLAND

ABERDEEN (CITY OF)

DEESIDE GOLF SHOP, Golf Road, Bieldside, Aberdeen, **ABERDEEN (CITY OF),** AB15 9DL
(T) 01224 861041

NEVADA BOB'S, Springfield Road, Aberdeen, **ABERDEEN (CITY OF),** AB15 7SE
(T) 01224 313880

ABERDEENSHIRE

AMERICAN GOLF DISCOUNT CENTRE, Unit 1/Haudagain Retail Pk, Great Northern Road, Woodside, Aberdeen, **ABERDEENSHIRE,** AB24 2BQ
(T) 01224 789789

BALLATER GOLF SHOP, Victoria Road, Ballater, **ABERDEENSHIRE,** AB35 5QX
(T) 01339 755658

GOLF SHOP, Philorth Road, Fraserburgh, **ABERDEENSHIRE,** AB43 8TL
(T) 01346 517898

GOLF TODAY, 5 Blackhouse Terrace, Peterhead, **ABERDEENSHIRE,** AB42 1LR
(T) 01779 475867

HUMMINGBIRD GOLF & LEISURE LTD, 4-6 Bath Street, Aberdeen, **ABERDEENSHIRE,** AB11 6HY
(T) 01224 586456

INVERURIE GOLF SHOP, Blackhall Road, Inverurie, **ABERDEENSHIRE,** AB51 5JB
(T) 01467 620193

MURCAR GOLF SHOP, Ellon Road, Murcar, Bridge of Don, Aberdeen, **ABERDEENSHIRE,** AB23 8BD
(T) 01224 704370

NEWMACHAR GOLF SHOP, Swailend, Newmachar, Aberdeen, **ABERDEENSHIRE,** AB21 7UU
(T) 01651 862127

ANGUS

BALLUMBIE CASTLE GOLF SHOP, Old Quarry Road, Dundee, **ANGUS,** DD4 0SY
(T) 01382 770028

BRECHIN GOLF & SQUASH CLUB, Trinity, Brechin, **ANGUS,** DD9 7PD
(T) 01356 625270

FORFAR PROFESSIONAL GOLF SHOP, Cunninghill, Forfar, **ANGUS,** DD8 2RL
(T) 01307 465683

HILLTOWN GOLF, 293 Hilltown, Dundee, **ANGUS,** DD3 7AQ
(T) 01382 221970

LETHAM GRANGE RESORT, Letham Grange, Arbroath, **ANGUS,** DD11 4RL
(T) 01241 890377

MONTROSE LINKS TRUST PROFESSIONAL SHOP, Traill Drive, Montrose, **ANGUS,** DD10 8SW
(T) 01674 672634

NEVADA BOB'S, Fairmuir Road, Dundee, **ANGUS,** DD3 8JE
(T) 01382 818062

RON MCLEOD, Golf Shop, 10 Princes Street, Monifieth, Dundee, **ANGUS,** DD5 4AN
(T) 01382 532945

SIMPSONS GOLF SHOP, 6 Links Parade, Carnoustie, **ANGUS,** DD7 7JE
(T) 01241 854477

ARGYLL AND BUTE

EAST END GOLF & TROPHY CENTRE, 141 Glasgow Road, Dumbarton, **ARGYLL AND BUTE,** G82 1RQ
(T) 01389 767247

AYRSHIRE (NORTH)

FAIRWAYS, 42 Bridgegate, Irvine, **AYRSHIRE (NORTH),** KA12 8BQ
(T) 01294 276020

FAIRWAYS, 9 Countess Street, Saltcoats, **AYRSHIRE (NORTH),** KA21 5HW
(T) 01294 466241

KENNETH DOCHERTY, Irvine Road, Largs, **AYRSHIRE (NORTH),** KA30 8EU
(T) 01475 686192

NORTH GAILES GOLF CENTRE, Marine Drive, Gailes, Irvine, **AYRSHIRE (NORTH),** KA11 5AE
(T) 01294 204201

AYRSHIRE (SOUTH)

CROWN GOLF, 2 Crown Street, Ayr, **AYRSHIRE (SOUTH),** KA8 8BY
(T) 01292 610400

DAVID GEMMELL, Belleisle, Ayr, **AYRSHIRE (SOUTH),** KA7 4DU
(T) 01292 441314

NEWSTIX, Ayr Road, Caprington, Kilmarnock, **AYRSHIRE (SOUTH),** KA1 4UW
(T) 01563 551599

PRESTWICK GOLF CENTRE, Monkton Road, Prestwick, **AYRSHIRE (SOUTH),** KA9 2PA
(T) 01292 479849

DUMFRIES AND GALLOWAY

GOLF STORE, 182 St. Michael Street, Dumfries, **DUMFRIES AND GALLOWAY,** DG1 2PR
(T) 01387 251349

EDINBURGH (CITY OF)

AMERICAN GOLF DISCOUNT CENTRE, 16 Meadow Place Road, Edinburgh, **EDINBURGH (CITY OF),** EH12 7UQ
(T) 0131 334 9992

BRUNTSFIELD LINKS PROFESSIONAL SHOP, 32 Barnton Avenue, Edinburgh, **EDINBURGH (CITY OF),** EH4 6JH
(T) 0131 336 4050

CAPITAL GOLF, 3-5 Hanover Street, Edinburgh, **EDINBURGH (CITY OF),** EH2 2DL
(T) 0131 226 6601

GOLF SHOP, Unit 54 Gyle Avenue, South Gyle Broadway, Edinburgh, **EDINBURGH (CITY OF),** EH12 9JX
(T) 0131 538 7733

LADIES GOLF CENTRE, 18 Haymarket Terrace, Edinburgh, **EDINBURGH (CITY OF),** EH12 5JZ
(T) 0131 538 7064

NEVADA BOB'S, 1a Seafield Way, Edinburgh, **EDINBURGH (CITY OF),** EH15 1TB
(T) 0131 669 0891

PROFESSIONAL SHOP, 50 Baberton Avenue, Juniper Green, **EDINBURGH (CITY OF),** EH14 5DU
(T) 0131 453 3555

RANGE MASTER GOLF SERVICES LTD, 91 Liberton Drive, Edinburgh, **EDINBURGH (CITY OF),** EH16 6NS
(T) 0131 664 2333

RATHO PARK PROFESSIONAL SHOP, Newbridge, **EDINBURGH (CITY OF),** EH28 8NX
(T) 0131 333 1406

SCOTSMAN GOLF CLUB, Caledon House, 73 Kirk Brae, Edinburgh, **EDINBURGH (CITY OF),** EH16 6JN
(T) 0131 4682800

TARTAN GOLF LTD, 31 Woodhall Road, Edinburgh, **EDINBURGH (CITY OF),** EH13 0DT
(T) 0131 441 3590

FALKIRK

ACCESSIBLE GOLF SHOP, Princes Street, Falkirk, **FALKIRK,** FK1 1LS
(T) 01324 622686

FIFE

APPLIED GOLF TECHNOLOGY, 3 Main Street, Ceres, Cupar, **FIFE,** KY15 5NA
(T) 01334 828090

AUCHTERLONIE GOLF SHOP, 2 Golf Place, St. Andrews, **FIFE,** KY16 9JA
(T) 01334 473253

EURO GOLF, 242 High Street, Cowdenbeath, **FIFE,** KY4 9NP
(T) 01383 513355

FAIRWAYS GOLF & LEISURE, 21 Tolbooth Street, Kirkcaldy, **FIFE,** KY1 1RW
(T) 01592 644022

GOLF RANGE, 91 Dunnikier Road, Kirkcaldy, **FIFE,** KY2 5AN
(T) 01592 597152

GOLF SHOP OF ST ANDREWS, 4 Ellice Place, St. Andrews, **FIFE,** KY16 9HU
(T) 01334 476996

GOLFINO SHOP, St. Andrews, **FIFE,** KY16 9SP
(T) 01334 478889

GOLFSTOCK.CO.UK, 11 Pilmuir Street, Dunfermline, **FIFE,** KY12 7AJ
(T) 01383 626314

JIM BENNETT, 17 Bridge Street, Dunfermline, **FIFE,** KY12 8AQ
(T) 01383 623581

JIM FARMER, 1, St. Marys Place, St. Andrews, **FIFE,** KY16 9UY
(T) 01334 476796

NINETEENTH HOLE GOLF SHOP, 148 North Street, St. Andrews, **FIFE,** KY16 9AF
(T) 01334 477959

PRO SHOP, 1 Ellice Place, St. Andrews, **FIFE,** KY16 9HU
(T) 01334 476611

TOM MORRIS, 8 The Links, St. Andrews, **FIFE,** KY16 9JB
(T) 01334 473499

GLASGOW (CITY OF)

AMERICAN GOLF DISCOUNT CENTRE, 6 Fenwick Road, Giffnock, Glasgow, **GLASGOW (CITY OF),** G46 6AN
(T) 0141 633 0560

AMERICAN GOLF DISCOUNT CENTRE, 190 Milngavie Road, Bearsden, Glasgow, **GLASGOW (CITY OF),** G61 3DU
(T) 0141 943 2111

Golf Shops — Golf Shops

Useful Addresses

- **BEARSDEN GOLF RANGE,** Milngavie Road, Bearsden, Glasgow, **GLASGOW (CITY OF),** G61 3DH
  (T) 0141 942 2828

- **BOTHWELL CASTLE GOLF PROFESSIONAL SHOP,** Blantyre Road, Bothwell, Glasgow, **GLASGOW (CITY OF),** G71 8PJ
  (T) 01698 852052

- **CRAIG EVERETT,** Strathblane Road, Milngavie, Glasgow, **GLASGOW (CITY OF),** G62 8HJ
  (T) 0141 955 0989

- **GLASGOW GOLF DISCOUNT CENTRE,** 521 Great Western Road, Glasgow, **GLASGOW (CITY OF),** G12 8HN
  (T) 0141 334 4504

- **GOLF FACTORY DIRECT LTD,** 1619 Great Western Road, Glasgow, **GLASGOW (CITY OF),** G13 1LT
  (T) 0141 959 3161

- **GOLF SHOP LTD,** Unit 53/St. Enoch Centre, 55 St. Enoch Square, Glasgow, **GLASGOW (CITY OF),** G1 4BW
  (T) 0141 221 5240

- **HAGGS CASTLE PROFESSIONAL GOLF SHOP,** 70 Dumbreck Road, Glasgow, **GLASGOW (CITY OF),** G41 4SN
  (T) 0141 427 3355

- **HIGHLAND CONNECTION,** 38 Watt Road, Glasgow, **GLASGOW (CITY OF),** G52 4RW
  (T) 0141 882 8340

- **KANE GOLF PRODUCTS,** Unit 13 Dalziel Road, Hillington Industrial Estate, Glasgow, **GLASGOW (CITY OF),** G52 4NN
  (T) 0141 810 2923

- **PROFESSIONAL SHOP,** Killermont, Bearsden, Glasgow, **GLASGOW (CITY OF),** G61 2TW
  (T) 0141 942 8507

- **USA GOLF WAREHOUSE,** 42-66 New City Road, Glasgow, **GLASGOW (CITY OF),** G4 9JT
  (T) 0141 331 0991

HIGHLAND

- **ALISTAIR THOMSON,** Fairways Leisure Centre, Inverness, **HIGHLAND,** IV2 6AA
  (T) 01463 713334

- **INVERNESS GOLF CENTRE,** 5 Longman Road, Inverness, **HIGHLAND,** IV1 1RY
  (T) 01463 711572

INVERCLYDE

- **GREENOCK PROFESSIONAL SHOP,** Forsyth Street, Greenock, **INVERCLYDE,** PA16 8RE
  (T) 01475 787236

LANARKSHIRE (NORTH)

- **WESTERWOOD GOLF & PROFESSIONAL SHOP,** 1 St Andrews Drive, Cumbernauld, Glasgow, **LANARKSHIRE (NORTH),** G68 0EW
  (T) 01236 725281

LANARKSHIRE (SOUTH)

- **CARLUKE PROFESSIONAL GOLF SHOP,** Mauldslie Road, Carluke, **LANARKSHIRE (SOUTH),** ML8 5HG
  (T) 01555 751053

- **D W GOLF,** 32 Burnbank Road, Hamilton, **LANARKSHIRE (SOUTH),** ML3 9AQ
  (T) 01698 423355

LOTHIAN (EAST)

- **AFFLECKS SPORTS & LEISURE,** 126 High Street, North Berwick, **LOTHIAN (EAST),** EH39 4HA
  (T) 01620 892301

- **GLEN GOLF SHOP,** North Berwick Municipal Gold, Tantallon Terrace, North Berwick, **LOTHIAN (EAST),** EH39 4LE
  (T) 01620 894596

- **GOLF TROUSER CO,** 1 Tantallon Road, North Berwick, **LOTHIAN (EAST),** EH39 5NF
  (T) 01620 895795

- **JOHN HENDERSON,** Preston Grange House, Prestonpans, **LOTHIAN (EAST),** EH32 9RP
  (T) 01875 810139

LOTHIAN (WEST)

- **SANDY DAVIDSON,** Brocks Way, East Mains Industrial Estate, Broxburn, **LOTHIAN (WEST),** EH52 5NB
  (T) 01506 858081

PERTH AND KINROSS

- **AUCHTERARDER GOLF SHOP,** Orchil Road, Auchterarder, **PERTH AND KINROSS,** PH3 1LS
  (T) 01764 663711

- **FRANK SMITH,** Unit 3/Highland House, St. Catherines Road, Perth, **PERTH AND KINROSS,** PH1 5YA
  (T) 01738 628459

- **GOLF CO,** 29-31 James Square, Crieff, **PERTH AND KINROSS,** PH7 3EY
  (T) 01764 652095

- **GOLF CO,** 38 Main Street, Callander, **PERTH AND KINROSS,** FK17 8BD
  (T) 01877 330921

- **GOLF CO,** 85 Atholl Road, Pitlochry, **PERTH AND KINROSS,** PH16 5AB
  (T) 01796 473271

- **MURRAYSHALL PROFESSIONAL SHOP,** Murrayshall, Perth, **PERTH AND KINROSS,** PH2 7PH
  (T) 01738 552784

- **USA GOLF WAREHOUSE,** 61 South Street, Perth, **PERTH AND KINROSS,** PH2 8PD
  (T) 01738 633311

RENFREWSHIRE

- **DRIVING RANGES LTD,** Strathmore Avenue, Paisley, **RENFREWSHIRE,** PA1 3DT
  (T) 0141 810 4925

- **PETE THOMSON,** Golf Road, Bishopton, **RENFREWSHIRE,** PA7 5PH
  (T) 01505 862108

SCOTTISH BORDERS

- **BORDER GOLF,** 100 High Street, Galashiels, **SCOTTISH BORDERS,** TD1 1SQ
  (T) 01896 754575

STIRLING

- **CUSTOM GOLF,** Unit 33/John Player Building, Stirling Enterprise Pk, Stirling, **STIRLING,** FK7 7RP
  (T) 01786 449297

- **ONLY GOLF,** 15 Arcade, Stirling, **STIRLING,** FK8 1AX
  (T) 01786 473257

WALES

BLAENAU GWENT

- **GOLF CO,** Unit 4-5 Festival Park, Victoria, Ebbw Vale, **BLAENAU GWENT,** NP23 8DN
  (T) 01495 302920

CAERPHILLY

- **KEVIN DAVIES,** Bargoed Gold Club, Moorlands Road, Bargoed, **CAERPHILLY,** CF81 9GF
  (T) 01443 836411

CARMARTHENSHIRE

- **ASHBURNHAM PROFESSIONAL GOLF SHOP,** Cliffe Ter, Burry Port, **CARMARTHENSHIRE,** SA16 0HN
  (T) 01554 833846

- **GLYNHIR GOLF SHOP,** Glynhir Road, Llandybie, Ammanford, **CARMARTHENSHIRE,** SA18 2TF
  (T) 01269 851010

CONWY

- **GOLF STORE,** 30 Madoc Street, Llandudno, **CONWY,** LL30 2TL
  (T) 01492 860011

- **LOGAN GOLF INTERNATIONAL,** 3 Clonmel Street, Llandudno, **CONWY,** LL30 2LE
  (T) 01492 874315

DENBIGHSHIRE

- **LOGAN GOLF INTERNATIONAL,** 8 Russell Road, Rhyl, **DENBIGHSHIRE,** LL18 3BU
  (T) 01745 344999

GLAMORGAN (VALE OF)

AMERICAN GOLF DISCOUNT CENTRE, 501 Cowbridge Road West, Cardiff, **GLAMORGAN (VALE OF),** CF5 5TG
(T) 02920 598811

CREIGIAU GOLF SHOP, Cardiff Road, Creigiau, Cardiff, **GLAMORGAN (VALE OF),** CF15 9NN
(T) 02920 891909

GOLFBRANDS, Unit 2 Gripoly Mills, Sloper Road, Cardiff, **GLAMORGAN (VALE OF),** CF11 8AA
(T) 02920 399449

ST MARY'S GOLF SHOP, St. Mary Hill, Bridgend, **GLAMORGAN (VALE OF),** CF35 5EA
(T) 01656 868900

SWANSEA BAY GOLF SHOP, Jersey Marine, Neath, **GLAMORGAN (VALE OF),** SA10 6JP
(T) 01792 816159

TOP TEE LTD, 261 Gladstone Road, Barry, **GLAMORGAN (VALE OF),** CF63 1NJ
(T) 01446 744092

MONMOUTHSHIRE

PRODEAL LTD, Unit 2 Mayhill Industrial Estate, Mayhill, Monmouth, **MONMOUTHSHIRE,** NP25 3LX
(T) 01600 714131

POWYS

GOLF SHOP, Severn Road, Welshpool, **POWYS,** SY21 7AY
(T) 01938 556622

RHONDDA CYNON TAFF

B BEBB, The Golf Shop, Rhondda Golf Club, Pontygwaith, Ferndale, **RHONDDA CYNON TAFF,** CF43 3PW
(T) 01443 441385

GOLF DISCOUNT CENTRE, Canal Road, Aberdare, **RHONDDA CYNON TAFF,** CF44 0AG
(T) 01685 870966

PONTYPRIDD GOLF WAREHOUSE, 128 Broadway, Pontypridd, **RHONDDA CYNON TAFF,** CF37 1BH
(T) 01443 405102

TORFAEN

GREENMEADOW GOLF SHOP, Treherbert Road, Croesyceiliog, Cwmbran, **TORFAEN,** NP44 2BZ
(T) 01633 862626

JIM HOWARD GOLF ENTERPRISES, Lasgarn Lane, Trevethin, Pontypool, **TORFAEN,** NP4 8TR
(T) 01495 755544

GOLF WAREHOUSES

ENGLAND

BEDFORDSHIRE

B & W GOLFQUIP CONFIDENCE GOLF, Unit 1 Bedford Business Centre, Mile Road, Bedford, **BEDFORDSHIRE,** MK42 9TW
(T) 01234 341244

CADDYRACK UK LTD, 10 Dane Lane, Wilstead, Bedford, **BEDFORDSHIRE,** MK45 3HT
(T) 01234 740001

CAPE CREST RAINWEAR, Unit 12 Fenlake Road Industrial Estate, Fenlake Road, Bedford, **BEDFORDSHIRE,** MK42 0HB
(T) 01234 211707

SKY GOLF LTD, Unit 9/Heron Trading Estate, Whitefield Avenue, Luton, **BEDFORDSHIRE,** LU3 3BB
(T) 01582 570094

BERKSHIRE

KASCO (EUROPE) LTD, Unit 2 Sterling Centre, Bracknell, **BERKSHIRE,** RG12 2PW
(T) 01344 484080

CAMBRIDGESHIRE

ACUSHNET LTD, Caxton Road, St. Ives, **CAMBRIDGESHIRE,** PE27 3LU
(T) 01480 301114

CHESHIRE

GLENSCOT GOLF LTD, Osbourne Court, Thelwall New Road, Grappenhall, Warrington, **CHESHIRE,** WA4 2LS
(T) 01925 861740

DERBYSHIRE

FIRST GOLF LTD, 1 The Old Stable Block, Coldwell Street, Wirksworth, Matlock, **DERBYSHIRE,** DE4 4FB
(T) 01629 826250

GLOUCESTERSHIRE

COTSWOLD GOLF LTD, 1 Alvin Street, Gloucester, **GLOUCESTERSHIRE,** GL1 3EH
(T) 01452 422009

KENT

MALIBU SPORTS INTERNATIONAL LTD, Vicarage Lane, Hoo, Rochester, **KENT,** ME3 9LW
(T) 01634 250901

LONDON (GREATER)

CHIP 'N' CHUB LTD, 3 Drayton Avenue, London, **LONDON (GREATER),** W13 0LE
(T) 0208 997 4885

J S INTERNATIONAL LTD, 4 Crystal Way, Harrow, **LONDON (GREATER),** HA1 2HG
(T) 0208 901 2870

MANCHESTER (GREATER)

COUNTY GOLF CENTRE, Houston House, Houston Park, Salford, **MANCHESTER (GREATER),** M5 2RP
(T) 0161 745 8085

MIDLANDS (WEST)

EUROPEAN GOLF DISCOUNT WAREHOUSE, Aldridge Road, Walsall, **MIDLANDS (WEST),** WS4 2JS
(T) 01922 613675

SHROPSHIRE

PAOLO GOLF, 33 Market Street, Oakengates, Telford, **SHROPSHIRE,** TF2 6EL
(T) 01952 615588

STAFFORDSHIRE

GOLFING WAREHOUSE LTD, Imex Business Park, Shobnall Road, Burton-on-Trent, **STAFFORDSHIRE,** DE14 2AU
(T) 01283 741144

SURREY

ADAMS GOLF UK LTD, 6/Corium House, Douglas Drive, Godalming, **SURREY,** GU7 1JX
(T) 01483 239333

WHOLE IN ONE GOLF, Unit 4/Epsom Business Pk, Kiln Lane, Epsom, **SURREY,** KT17 1JF
(T) 01372 721279

WORLD CLEARANCE (UK) LTD, 145 London Road, Camberley, **SURREY,** GU15 3JY
(T) 01276 27677

SUSSEX (WEST)

DIAMOND GOLF WORKS INTERNATIONAL, Unit U4 Rudford Industrial Estate, Ford Road, Ford, Arundel, **SUSSEX (WEST),** BN18 0BF
(T) 01903 726999

TYNE AND WEAR

HYMAX PRODUCTS (UK) LTD, Unit 19 Earlsway, Team Valley Trading Estate, Gateshead, **TYNE AND WEAR,** NE11 0RQ
(T) 0191 491 1138

YORKSHIRE (SOUTH)

IZZO (UK) LTD, 32 Queen Victoria Road, Sheffield, **YORKSHIRE (SOUTH),** S17 4HT
(T) 0114 236 4410

YORKSHIRE (WEST)

REGAL GOLF CORPORATION, Bowling Back Lane, Bradford, **YORKSHIRE (WEST),** BD4 8SF
(T) 01274 208080

SCOTLAND

FIFE

BRUCE CLARK DISTRIBUTION LTD, 6 Cromarty Campus, Rosyth, Dunfermline, **FIFE,** KY11 2YB
(T) 01383 420061

Golf Shops — Golf Warehouses

Useful Addresses

Useful Addresses · Golf Warehouses — Pitch & Putt Courses

GOLF WAREHOUSE (SCOTLAND) LTD,
2 Carberry Place, Mitchelston Industrial
Estate, Kirkcaldy, **FIFE,** KY1 3NQ
(T) 01592 654714

GLASGOW (CITY OF)

GOLF TRADITIONS LTD, Unit 8 3
Campsie Road, Kirkintilloch, Glasgow,
GLASGOW (CITY OF), G66 1SL
(T) 0141 776 8111

PITCH & PUTT COURSES
ENGLAND
CORNWALL

FALMOUTH PITCH & PUTT,
Goldenbank, Falmouth, **CORNWALL,** TR11
5BQ
(T) 01637 878198

GWINEAR PITCH & PUTT, 15 Relistian
Lane, Gwinear, Hayle, **CORNWALL,** TR27
5HE
(T) 01736 850938

PENWITH PITCH & PUTT, Greenacres
Shortgolf, Chenhalls Road, St. Erth, Hayle,
CORNWALL, TR27 6HJ
(T) 01736 754343

DERBYSHIRE

MARKEATON PARK PITCH & PUTT,
Ashbourne Rd, Derby, **DERBYSHIRE,** DE22
3AG
(T) 01332 384494

DORSET

SWANAGE PITCH & PUTT, Kirkwood
Park, Victoria Avenue, Swanage, **DORSET,**
BH19 1AR
(T) 01929 426809

ESSEX

WEST PARK PITCH & PUTT,
Waterhouse Lane, Chelmsford, **ESSEX,**
CM1 2RY
(T) 01245 257682

HERTFORDSHIRE

BROXBOURNE PITCH & PUTT, Church
Lane, Broxbourne, **HERTFORDSHIRE,**
EN10 7QG
(T) 01992 442244

**WILLIAN WAY PITCH & PUTT GOLF
COURSE,** Willian Way, Letchworth,
HERTFORDSHIRE, SG6 2HJ
(T) 01462 483863

ISLE OF WIGHT

NEEDLES VIEW PITCH & PUTT, Alum
Bay Tea Rooms, Alum Bay, Totland Bay,
ISLE OF WIGHT, PO39 0JD
(T) 01983 752123

LINCOLNSHIRE (NORTH EAST)

**SOMETHING TO DO MINIATURE
GOLF COURSE,** Kings Rd, Cleethorpes,
LINCOLNSHIRE (NORTH EAST), DN35
0AG
(T) 01472 698131

LONDON (GREATER)

CROYDON PITCH & PUTT COURSE,
Croydon Sports Arena, South Norwood,
Albert Rd, London, **LONDON (GREATER),**
SE25 4QL
(T) 020 86543462

GROVELANDS PITCH & PUTT,
Grovelands Pk, London, **LONDON
(GREATER),** N14 6RS
(T) 020 88826879

JUBILEE PITCH & PUTT, Galliard Road,
London, **LONDON (GREATER),** N9 7PB
(T) 0208 805 9451

OAKWOOD PITCH & PUTT COURSE,
Prince George Avenue, London, **LONDON
(GREATER),** N14 4TL
(T) 0208 364 2530

PALEWELL GOLF & TENNIS LTD,
Recreation Ground, Palewell Common,
Hertford Avenue, London, **LONDON
(GREATER),** SW14 8JJ
(T) 020 88763357

MANCHESTER (GREATER)

HEATON PARK PITCH & PUTT, Heaton
Park, Prestwich, Manchester,
MANCHESTER (GREATER), M25 2SW
(T) 0161 773 7897

NORFOLK

**SILFIELD VILLAGE PITCH & PUTT
GOLF,** Sunnyside, Silfield St, Silfield,
Wymondham, **NORFOLK,** NR18 9NL
(T) 01953 603508

SHROPSHIRE

ELM LODGE GOLF CLUB, Fishmore,
Ludlow, **SHROPSHIRE,** SY8 3DP
(T) 01584 872308

SOMERSET (NORTH)

PARK HOUSE PUTTING COURSE, 34
Knightstone Rd, Weston-Super-Mare,
SOMERSET (NORTH), BS23 2AW
(T) 01934 621170

SUSSEX (EAST)

**ROTTINGDEAN MINIATURE GOLF &
PUTTING COURSE,** Nevill Rd,
Rottingdean, Brighton, **SUSSEX (EAST),**
BN2 7HH
(T) 01273 302127

YORKSHIRE (NORTH)

SNAINTON GOLF CENTRE, Snainton,
Scarborough, **YORKSHIRE (NORTH),**
YO13 9BE
(T) 01723 850014

NORTHERN IRELAND
COUNTY DOWN

CRANFIELD PITCH & PUTT,
Lurganconary Road, Kilkeel, Newry,
COUNTY DOWN, BT34 4LL
(T) 02841 764602

SCOTLAND
LOTHIAN (WEST)

PITCH & PUTT, Almondvale Park,
Livingston, **LOTHIAN (WEST),** EH54 6TG
(T) 01506 412232